SOLUTIONS MANUAL

Merrill

Algebra 2

With Trigonometry

Applications and Connections

GLENCOE
McGraw-Hill

New York, New York
Columbus, Ohio
Mission Hills, California
Peoria, Illinois

The copy in this text was word processed using ChiWriter Software from Horstmann
Software, P.O. Box 5039 San Jose, California 95192

1995 Impression
Copyright © 1992 by Glencoe/McGraw-Hill.

Send all inquires to:
Glencoe/McGraw-Hill
936 Eastwind Drive
Westerville, Oh 43081

ISBN 0-02-824242-4

2 3 4 5 6 7 8 9 10 POH 03 02 01 00 99 98 97 96 95

Contents

Chapter 1
Equations and Inequalities

1-1 | Expressions and Formulas

PAGES 10-11   CHECKING FOR UNDERSTANDING

1. Subtract 4 from 15.

2. A sample answer is to add the length and width and double the sum.

3. $(7 \cdot 4 + 2) \cdot 8$ 4. $7 - 8 \div 2 = 7 - 4 = 3$

5. $9 - 4(3) = 9 - 12 = -3$

6. $4(7 + 3) = 4(10) = 40$

7. $9(4 + 2) = 9(6) = 54$

8. $5 - 4 \div 2 = 5 - 2 = 3$

9. $7 - (3 + 2) = 7 - 5 = 2$

10. $a + b - c = 2 + (-3) - 4 = -5$

11. $a + 2b - c = 2 + 2(-3) - 4$
$$= 2 + (-6) - 4$$
$$= -8$$

12. $a(b + c) = 2(-3 + 4)$
$$= 2(1)$$
$$= 2$$

13. $C = \dfrac{(5F - 160)}{9}$
$$= \dfrac{5(98.6) - 160}{9}$$
$$= \dfrac{(493 - 160)}{9}$$
$$= \dfrac{333}{9}$$
$$= 37$$

14.
$$F = \dfrac{9}{5}C + 32$$
$$98.6 = \dfrac{9}{5}C + 32$$
$$98.6 - 32 = \dfrac{9}{5}C$$
$$66.6 = \dfrac{9}{5}C$$
$$\dfrac{5}{9}(66.6) = \dfrac{5}{9}\left(\dfrac{9}{5}\right)C$$
$$37 = C$$

15. $A = \ell \cdot w = (y + 5)(y - 5) \text{ cm}^2$

16. $A = 0.5(b)(h) = 0.5(a + 6)(a + 2) \text{ ft}^2$

PAGES 11-12   EXERCISES

17. $3(2^2 + 3) = 3(4 + 3)$
$$= 3(7)$$
$$= 21$$

18. $2(3 + 8) - 3 = 2(11) - 3$
$$= 22 - 3$$
$$= 19$$

19. $(6 + 5)4 - 3 = (11)4 - 3$
$$= 44 - 3$$
$$= 41$$

20. $5 + 3^2 - 16 \div 4 = 5 + 9 - 16 \div 4$
$$= 2$$

21. $(5 + 3) - 16 \div 4 = 8 - 16 \div 4$
$$= 8 - 4$$
$$= 4$$

22. $12 + 18 \div 6 + 7 = 12 + 3 + 7$
$$= 22$$

23. $4 + 8(4) \div 2 - 10 = 4 + 32 \div 2 - 10$
$$= 4 + 16 - 10$$
$$= 10$$

24. $[19 - (8 - 1)] \div 3 = [19 - 7] \div 3$
$$= 12 \div 3$$
$$= 4$$

25. $3 + [8 \div (9 - 2(4))] = 3 + [8 \div (9 - 8)]$
$$= 3 + [8 \div 1]$$
$$= 3 + 8$$
$$= 11$$

26. $[(-8 + 3) \times 4 - 2] \div 6 = [(-5) \times 4 - 2] \div 6$
$$= [-20 - 2] \div 6$$
$$= -22 \div 6$$
$$= -\dfrac{11}{3} \text{ or } -3.667$$

27. $15 \div 3 \times 5 + 1 = 5 \times 5 + 1$
$$= 25 + 1$$
$$= 26$$

28. $3 + (21 \div 7) \times 8 \div 4 = 3 + 3 \times 8 \div 4$
$$= 3 + 24 \div 4$$
$$= 3 + 6$$
$$= 9$$

29. $0.2(0.5 + 2.2) \div 6 = 0.2(2.7) \div 6$
$$= 0.54 \div 6$$
$$= 0.09$$

30. $\dfrac{1}{3} - \dfrac{12(77 \div 11)}{9} = \dfrac{1}{3} - \dfrac{12(7)}{9}$
$$= \dfrac{1}{3} - \dfrac{84}{9}$$
$$= \dfrac{1}{3} - 9\dfrac{1}{3}$$
$$= -9$$

31. $\dfrac{3ab}{cd} = \dfrac{3(3)(7)}{(-2)(0.5)}$
$$= \dfrac{(9)(7)}{-1}$$
$$= \dfrac{63}{-1}$$
$$= -63$$

32. $\dfrac{5a + 3c}{3b} = \dfrac{5(3) + 3(-2)}{3(7)}$
$$= \dfrac{15 + (-16)}{21}$$
$$= \dfrac{9}{21}$$
$$= \dfrac{3}{7} \text{ or } 0.429$$

33. $(5a + 3d)^2 - e^2 = [5(3) + 3(0.5)]^2 - (0.3)^2$
$$= [15 + 1.5]^2 - (0.3)^2$$
$$= (16.5)^2 - (0.3)^2$$
$$= 272.25 - 0.09$$
$$= 272.16$$

34. $(3b - 21d)^2 = [3(7) - 21(0.5)]^2$
$$= [21 - 10.5]^2$$
$$= (10.5)^2$$
$$= \dfrac{441}{4} \text{ or } 110.25$$

35. $a(b - 7)^3 = 3(7 - 7)^3$
$= 3(0)^3$
$= 3(0)$
$= 0$

36. $(a + c)^2 - de = [3 + (-2)]^2 - (0.5)(0.3)$
$= [1]^2 - (0.5)(0.3)$
$= 1 - 0.15$
$= 0.85$

37. $\dfrac{4a - 6d}{2b + c} = \dfrac{4(3) - 6(0.5)}{2(7) + (-2)}$
$= \dfrac{12 - 3}{14 - 2}$
$= \dfrac{9}{12}$
$= \dfrac{3}{4}$ or 0.75

38. $c + de^2 = (-2) + (0.5)(0.3)^2$
$= -2 + (0.5)(0.09)$
$= -2 + 0.045$
$= -1.955$

39. $I = prt$
$= (2500)(.0737)(4)$
$= \$737$

40. $I = prt$
$= (5280)(.082)\left(\dfrac{30}{12}\right)$
$= \$1082.40$

41. $I = prt$
$= (65,283.21)(.0932)\left(\dfrac{78}{12}\right)$
$= \$39,548.57$

42. $I = prt$
$= (20,005)(.079)(2.25)$
$= \$3555.89$

43. $A = \dfrac{h}{2}(b_1 + b_2) = \dfrac{8}{2}(8.6 + 14.8)$
$= 4(23.4) = 93.6$ sq. units

44. $A = \dfrac{h}{2}(b_1 + b_2) = \dfrac{7}{2}(4 + 11) = \dfrac{7}{2}(15)$
$= 52.5$ sq. units

45. $A = \dfrac{h}{2}(b_1 + b_2) = \dfrac{9}{2}\left(4\dfrac{1}{6} + 7\dfrac{2}{3}\right) = \dfrac{9}{2}\left(11\dfrac{5}{6}\right) = \dfrac{9}{2}\left(\dfrac{71}{6}\right)$
$= \dfrac{639}{12} = \dfrac{213}{4} = 53\dfrac{1}{4}$ sq. units

46. $A = \dfrac{h}{2}(b_1 + b_2) = \dfrac{12}{2}(6.2 + 9.7) = 6(15.9)$
$= 95.4$ sq. units

47. $S = 2[(\text{area of face 1}) + (\text{area of face 2})$
$+ (\text{area of face 3})]$
$= 2[(a)(2a) + (3a + 4)(2a) + (3a + 4)(a)]$
$= 2[2a^2 + (6a^2 + 8a) + (3a^2 + 4a)]$
$= 2[11a^2 + 12a]$
$= 22a^2 + 24a$ sq. units
$S = 22(4)^2 + 24(4)$
$= 22(16) + 24(4)$
$= 352 + 96$
$= 448$ sq. units
$S = 22(6.2)^2 + 24(6.2)$
$= 22(38.44) + 24(6.2)$
$= 845.68 + 148.8$
$= 994.48$ sq. units

48. $I = prt$
$= (7500)(.072)(3)$
$= \$1620.00$

49. total area = floor area + wall area
$$A = \pi r^2 + 2\pi rh$$
$A = \pi(300)^2 + 2\pi(300)(20)$
$= \pi(90,000) + 2\pi(300)(20)$
$= 90,000\pi + 12,000\pi$
$= 282,743.34 + 37,699.11$
$= 320,442.45$ ft^2

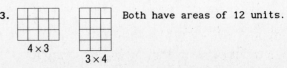

gallons needed $= 320,442.45$ ft$^2 \times \dfrac{1 \text{ gallon}}{425 \text{ ft}^2}$
$= 753.98$
$= 754$ gallons

50.
```
10  PRINT "B", "H", "A"
20  READ B, H
30  IF B=0 THEN 90
40  DATA 6.7, 13.8, 127.2, 82.6
50  DATA 0, 0
60  LET A = B/2 * H
70  PRINT B, H, A
80  GOTO 20
90  END
```
a. $A = \dfrac{1}{2}bh = \dfrac{1}{2}(6.7)(13.8) = 46.23$ cm^2
b. $A = \dfrac{1}{2}bh = \dfrac{1}{2}(127.2)(82.6) = 5253.36$ cm^2

51.
```
10  PRINT "B", "H", "A"
20  READ B, H
30  IF B=0 THEN 90
40  DATA 7.1, 3.5, 97.2, 26.9
50  DATA 0, 0
60  LET A = B * H
70  PRINT B, H, A
80  GOTO 20
90  END
```
a. $A = bh = (7.1)(3.5) = 24.85$ ft^2
b. $A = bh = (97.2)(26.9) = 2614.68$ ft^2

1-2 Properties of Real Numbers

PAGE 16   CHECKING FOR UNDERSTANDING

1. distributive property

2. $a - b \neq b - a$ and $a \div b \neq b \div a$

3. Both have areas of 12 units.
   4×3 3×4

4. Answers may vary. Sample answers are π, $\sqrt{2}$, 1.121231234..., $\sqrt{7}$, 0.10010001... .

5. Answer may vary. Sample answers are 0.111 ..., 0, -6, $\dfrac{2}{7}$, -0.3434... .

6. Z, Q, R   7. Q, R   8. Q, R   9. I, R   10. Q, R

11. N, W, Z, Q, R   12. I, R   13. Q, R

14. W, Z, Q, R   15. Z, Q, R   16. Z, Q, R

17. N, W, Z, Q, R   18. associative +

19. commutative ×   20. distributive

21. commutative +   22. additive inverse

PAGES 16-17   EXERCISES

23. $8 - 7 = 1$ N, W, Z, Q, R

24. $7 - 8 = -1$ Z, Q, R

25. $-54 \div 6 = -9$ Z, Q, R

26. $68 \div 100 = 0.68$ Q, R

27. $-2.4 \times 10 = -24$ Z, Q, R

28. $3.9 + 2.6 = 6.5$ Q, R

29. $6 \div 2^2 = 6 \div 4 = 1.5$, $\frac{3}{2}$ Q, R

30. $\sqrt{36 + 5} = \sqrt{41}$, 6.403 I, R

31. True   32. False; -1 33. False; $\frac{3}{2}$, 1.5

34. False; $\frac{3}{2}$, 1.5   35. True   36. True   37. True

38. distributive   39. additive inverse

40. commutative +   41. commutative +

42. commutative +   43. multiplicative inverse

44. commutative ×   45. additive identity

46. $3(5a + 6b) + 8(2a - b)$

    $= 3(5a) + 3(6b) + 8(2a) + 8(-b)$

    $= 15a + 18b + 16a + (-8b)$

    $= 31a + 10b$

47. $3a + 5b + 7a - 3b = 10a + 2b$

48. $2(7c - 5d) - 3(d + 2c)$

    $= 2(7c) + 2(-5d) + (-3)(d) + (-3)(2c)$

    $= 14c + (-10d) + (-3d) + (-6c)$

    $= 8c - 13d$

49. $\frac{1}{4}(12 + 20a) + \frac{3}{4}(12 + 20a)$

    $= \left(\frac{1}{4}\right)(12) + \left(\frac{1}{4}\right)(20a) + \left(\frac{3}{4}\right)(12) + \left(\frac{3}{4}\right)(20a)$

    $= 3 + 5a + 9 + 15a$

    $= 12 + 20a$

50. $\frac{1}{2}(17 - 4x) - \frac{3}{4}(6 - 16x)$

    $= \left(\frac{1}{2}\right)(17) + \left(\frac{1}{2}\right)(-4x) + \left(-\frac{3}{4}\right)(6) + \left(-\frac{3}{4}\right)(-16x)$

    $= 8.5 + (-2x) + (-4.5) + 12x$

    $= 4 + 10x$

51. $\frac{2}{3}\left(\frac{1}{2}a + 3b\right) + \frac{1}{2}\left(\frac{2}{3}a + b\right)$

    $= \left(\frac{2}{3}\right)\left(\frac{1}{2}a\right) + \left(\frac{2}{3}\right)(3b) + \left(\frac{1}{2}\right)\left(\frac{2}{3}a\right) + \left(\frac{1}{2}\right)(b)$

    $= \frac{1}{3}a + 2b + \frac{1}{3}a + \frac{1}{2}b$

    $= \frac{2}{3}a + \frac{5}{2}b$

52. $\frac{3}{4}(2x - 5y) + \frac{1}{2}\left(\frac{2}{3}x + 4y\right)$

    $= \left(\frac{3}{4}\right)(2x) + \left(\frac{3}{4}\right)(-5y) + \left(\frac{1}{2}\right)\left(\frac{2}{3}x\right) + \left(\frac{1}{2}\right)(4y)$

    $= \frac{3}{2}x + \left(-\frac{15}{4}y\right) + \frac{1}{3}x + 2y$

    $= \frac{9}{6}x - \frac{15}{4}y + \frac{2}{6}x + \frac{8}{4}y$

    $= \frac{11}{6}x - \frac{7}{4}y$

53. $7(0.20m + 0.3n) + 5(0.6m - n)$

    $= (7)(0.2m) + (7)(0.3n) + (5)(0.6m) + (5)(-n)$

    $= 1.4m + 2.1n + 3.0m + (-5n)$

    $= 4.4m - 2.9n$

54. 0   55. $\frac{1}{a}$; multiplicative inverse of a 56. 1

57. a. No; $638 - 577 = 61$, which is not divisible by 9.

    b. Yes; $1095 - 1050 = 45$, which is divisible by 9.

    c. The difference of two such numbers is always divisible by 9.

58. $3 + (3 - 3)^3 - 3 = 3 + (0)^3 - 3$

    $= 3 + 0 - 3$

    $= 0$

59. $-8 \div [20 \div (16 - 11)] = -8 \div [20 \div 5]$

    $= -8 \div 4$

    $= -2$

60. $12(3)^2 + (7)(-2) = (12)(9) + (7)(-2)$

    $= 108 + (-14)$

    $= 94$

61. $I = prt$

    $= (20,000)(0.145)(6)$

    $= \$17,400$

1-3   Solving Equations

PAGES 20-21   CHECKING FOR UNDERSTANDING

1. See students' work.   2. yes

3. See students' work.

4. subtraction property of equality

5. reflexive property of equality

6. symmetric property of equality

7. addition property of equality

8. transitive property of equality

9. multiplication property of equality

10. $\frac{1}{3}q = 872$

    $(3)\left(\frac{1}{3}\right)q = (3)(872)$

    $q = 2616$

11. $7x + 2 = 23$

    $7x + 2 + (-2) = 23 + (-2)$

    $7x = 21$

    $\left(\frac{1}{7}\right)(7)x = \left(\frac{1}{7}\right)(21)$

    $x = 3$

12. $2x + 7 = 8x - 11$

    $2x + 7 + (-7) = 8x - 11 + (-7)$

    $2x = 8x - 18$

    $2x + (-8x) = 8x - 18 + (-8x)$

    $-6x = -18$

    $\left(-\frac{1}{6}\right)(-6)x = \left(-\frac{1}{6}\right)(-18)$

    $x = 3$

13.
$$\frac{3}{8} - \frac{1}{4}x = \frac{1}{16}$$
$$\frac{3}{8} - \frac{1}{4}x + \left(-\frac{3}{8}\right) = \frac{1}{16} + \left(-\frac{3}{8}\right)$$
$$-\frac{1}{4}x = -\frac{5}{16}$$
$$(-4)\left(-\frac{1}{4}\right)x = (-4)\left(-\frac{5}{16}\right)$$
$$x = \frac{5}{4}$$

14.
$$1.2x + 3.7 = 13.3$$
$$1.2x + 3.7 + (-3.7) = 13.3 + (-3.7)$$
$$\frac{1.2x}{1.2} = \frac{9.6}{1.2}$$
$$x = 8$$

15.
$$4.5 - 3.9m = 20.1$$
$$4.5 - 3.9m + (-4.5) = 20.1 + (-4.5)$$
$$\frac{-3.9m}{-3.9} = \frac{15.6}{-3.9}$$
$$m = -4$$

16.
$$1.1x - 0.09 = 2.22$$
$$1.1x - 0.09 + 0.09 = 2.22 + 0.09$$
$$\frac{1.1x}{1.1} = \frac{2.31}{1.1}$$
$$x = 2.1$$

17.
$$9 = 16d + 51$$
$$9 + (-51) = 16d + 51 + (-51)$$
$$\frac{-42}{16} = \frac{16d}{16}$$
$$-\frac{21}{8} \text{ or } -2.625 = d$$

18.
$$5t + 4 = 2t + 13$$
$$5t + 4 + (-4) = 2t + 13 + (-4)$$
$$5t = 2t + 9$$
$$5t + (-2t) = 2t + 9 + (-2t)$$
$$\frac{3t}{3} = \frac{9}{3}$$
$$t = 3$$

19.
$$2y - 8 = 14 - 9y$$
$$2y - 8 + 8 = 14 - 9y + 8$$
$$2y = 22 - 9y$$
$$2y + 9y = 22 - 9y + 9y$$
$$\frac{11y}{11} = \frac{22}{11}$$
$$y = 2$$

20.
$$3x + 5 = 9x + 2$$
$$3x + 5 + (-5) = 9x + 2 + (-5)$$
$$3x = 9x - 3$$
$$3x + (-9x) = 9x - 3 + (-9x)$$
$$\frac{-6x}{-6} = \frac{-3}{-6}$$
$$x = \frac{1}{2} \text{ or } 0.5$$

21.
$$3x - 4 = 7x - 11$$
$$3x - 4 + 4 = 7x - 11 + 4$$
$$3x = 7x - 7$$
$$3x + (-7x) = 7x - 7 + (-7x)$$
$$\frac{-4x}{-4} = \frac{-7}{-4}$$
$$x = \frac{7}{4} \text{ or } 1.75$$

22.
$$\frac{3}{4}s - \frac{1}{2} = \frac{1}{4}s + 5$$
$$\frac{3}{4}s - \frac{1}{2} + \frac{1}{2} = \frac{1}{4}s + 5 + \frac{1}{2}$$
$$\frac{3}{4}s = \frac{1}{4}s + 5\frac{1}{2}$$
$$\frac{3}{4}s + \left(-\frac{1}{4}s\right) = \frac{1}{4}s + 5\frac{1}{2} + \left(-\frac{1}{4}s\right)$$
$$\frac{1}{2}s = 5\frac{1}{2}$$
$$(2)\left(\frac{1}{2}\right)s = (2)\left(5\frac{1}{2}\right)$$
$$s = 11$$

23.
$$\frac{2}{3} - \frac{3}{5}x = \frac{2}{5}x + \frac{4}{3}$$
$$\frac{2}{3} - \frac{3}{5}x + \frac{3}{5}x = \frac{2}{5}x + \frac{4}{3} + \frac{3}{5}x$$
$$\frac{2}{3} = x + \frac{4}{3}$$
$$\frac{2}{3} + \left(-\frac{4}{3}\right) = x + \frac{4}{3} + \left(-\frac{4}{3}\right)$$
$$-0.667 \text{ or } -\frac{2}{3} = x$$

24.
$$8 - x = 5x + 32$$
$$8 - x + x = 5x + 32 + x$$
$$8 = 6x + 32$$
$$8 + (-32) = 6x + 32 + (-32)$$
$$\frac{-24}{6} = \frac{6x}{6}$$
$$-4 = x$$

25.
$$3 = -3(y + 5)$$
$$3 = -3y - 15$$
$$3 + 15 = -3y - 15 + 15$$
$$\frac{18}{-3} = \frac{-3y}{-3}$$
$$-6 = y$$

26.
$$5(3x + 5) = 4x - 8$$
$$15x + 25 = 4x - 8$$
$$15x + 25 + (-25) = 4x - 8 + (-25)$$
$$15x = 4x - 33$$
$$15x + (-4x) = 4x - 33 + (-4x)$$
$$\frac{11x}{11} = \frac{-33}{11}$$
$$x = -3$$

27.
$$2x - 4(x + 2) = -2x - 8$$
$$2x - 4x - 8 = -2x - 8$$
$$-2x - 8 = -2x - 8$$
$$-2x - 8 + 8 = -2x - 8 + 8$$
$$-2x = -2x$$
$$-2x + 2x = -2x + 2x$$
$$0 = 0$$

The solution is all real numbers.

28.
$$285 - 38x = 2033$$
$$285 - 38x + (-285) = 2033 + (-285)$$
$$\frac{-38x}{-38} = \frac{1748}{-38}$$
$$x = -46$$

29.
$$2(6 - 7k) = 2k - 4$$
$$12 - 14k = 2k - 4$$
$$12 - 14k + 14k = 2k - 4 + 14k$$
$$12 = 16k - 4$$
$$12 + 4 = 16k - 4 + 4$$
$$\frac{16}{16} = \frac{16k}{16}$$
$$1 = k$$

30.
$$8x - 3 = 5(2x + 1)$$
$$8x - 3 = 10x + 5$$
$$8x - 3 + 3 = 10x + 5 + 3$$
$$8x = 10x + 8$$
$$8x + (-10x) = 10x + 8 + (-10x)$$
$$\frac{-2x}{-2} = \frac{8}{-2}$$
$$x = -4$$

31. Answers may vary. A sample answer is $x = x + 1$.

32. Answers may vary. A sample answer is
$$4x - 2 = -2(1 - 2x).$$

33.
$$A = p + prt$$
$$A + (-p) = p + prt + (-p)$$
$$\frac{A - p}{pr} = \frac{prt}{pr}$$
$$\frac{A - p}{pr} = t$$

34.

$$V = \frac{1}{3}\pi r^2 h$$
$$40 = \frac{1}{3}\pi(2.5)^2 h$$
$$40 = \frac{1}{3}\pi(6.25)h$$
$$(3)(40) = (3)\left(\frac{1}{3}\right)(\pi)(6.25)h$$
$$\frac{120}{6.25\pi} = \frac{6.25\pi h}{6.25\pi}$$
$$6.11 = h$$

Yes, the pile is only 6.11 meters tall.

35. $\sqrt{9 \div 3} = \sqrt{3}$; I, R

36. Commutative +

37.
$$8a - 3bc = 8(0.3) - 3(7)(-z)$$
$$= 2.4 - (21)(-2)$$
$$= 2.4 - (-42)$$
$$= 2.4 + 42$$
$$= 44.4$$

Graphing Calculator Exploration: Evaluating Expressions

PAGE 23   EXERCISES

1. $2\left[\dfrac{5 + \dfrac{4(3 + 7)}{5}}{4}\right] + 13 = 19.5$

$2(5 + (4(3 + 7) \div 5)) \div 4 + 13$ EXE

2. $(42 \times 5)^3 + \dfrac{89}{12} = 9261007.4167$

CASIO

(42×5) x^y 3 + 89 ÷ 12 EXE

TI-81

(42×5) ∧ 3 + 89 ÷ 12 ENTER

3. $\left(6.23 \times 10^{-7}\right)\left(4.23 \times 10^3\right) = 0.00263529$

CASIO

6.23 $\left(10 \; x^y \; (-) \; 7\right)$ × 4.23 $\left(10 \; x^y \; 3\right)$ EXE

TI-81

6.23 (10 ∧ (−) 7) × 4.23 (10 ∧ 3) ENTER

4. $543.2^4 = 8.706408599E10$ or
$8.706408599E+10$

CASIO

543.2 x^y 4 EXE

TI-81

543.2 ∧ 4 ENTER

1-4 Applications of Equations

PAGE 26   CHECKING FOR UNDERSTANDING

1. The first represents $2n + 2$, the second represents $2(n + 2)$.

2. $8s = 3000$ **3.** $3n + 2(n + 3)$

4. $2(n + 7)$ **5.** $5x - 4$ **6.** $2n + 7$

7. $3 - 2n$ **8.** $12 - x^2$ **9.** $6x^2$

10. $\frac{1}{5}(4 + x)$ **11.** $4(8 + x)$ **12.** $8\left(x + x^2\right)$

13. $8 + 4n$ **14.** $(x + 11)^2$

PAGES 27-28   EXERCISES

15. Let p = cost of one plant (assume both plants cost the same amount).
$$32 = 2p + 18$$
$$14 = 2p$$
$$\$7 = p$$

16. Let x = pastries to be prepared.
$$x = 2(3)(12) + 1(3)(12)$$
$$x = 108 \text{ items}$$

17. Let n = the number.
$$n - 89 = 29$$
$$n = 118$$

18. Let p = the percentage of the dealer's price.
$$7800 = 9750(p)$$
$$0.8 = p$$
$$p = 0.8 \text{ or } 80\%$$

19. Let d = Darian's age.
Thus, $d + 28$ = Darian's dad's age.
$$d + (d + 28) = 64$$
$$2d + 28 = 64$$
$$2d = 36$$
$$d = 18 \text{ years old}$$

20. Let n = first odd integer.
Thus, $n + 2$ = next odd integer.
$$n + (n + 2) = 124$$
$$2n + 2 = 124$$
$$2n = 122$$
$$n = 61, \text{ the first odd integer}$$
$$n + 2 = 63, \text{ the second odd integer}$$

21. Let b = Brittany's age.

Thus, $b + 24$ = Mrs. Gampp's age,

$b + 3$ = Brittany's age in three years, and

$b + 27$ = Mrs. Gampp's age in three years.

$$(b + 3) + (b + 27) = 68$$
$$2b + 30 = 68$$
$$2b = 38$$
$$b = 19, \text{ Brittany's age}$$
$$b + 24 = 43, \text{ Mrs. Gampp's age}$$

22. Let s = Julie's score on the fifth test.
$$\frac{78 + 98 + 67 + 90 + s}{5} = 85$$
$$333 + s = 425$$
$$s = 92$$

23. Let p = the original price.
$$274 = \frac{p}{2} + 60$$
$$214 = \frac{p}{2}$$
$$\$428 = p$$

24. Let r = the pounds of raisins purchased.

Thus, $2r$ = the pounds of peanuts purchased.
$$r(0.99) + 2r(1.29) = 24.99$$
$$0.99r + 2.58r = 24.99$$
$$3.57r = 24.99$$
$$r = 7$$
$$2r = 14 \text{ pounds}$$

25. Let a = the number of adult tickets.

Thus, $5a$ = the number of student tickets.
$$10.50(a) + 7.50(5a) = 192$$
$$10.50a + 37.50a = 192$$
$$48a = 192$$
$$a = 4 \text{ adult tickets}$$
$$5a = 20 \text{ student tickets}$$

26. Let s = price of a student ticket.

Thus, $s + 0.75$ = price of an adult ticket.
$$320(s + 0.75) + 153(s) = 949.50$$
$$320s + 240 + 153s = 949.50$$
$$473s + 240 = 949.50$$
$$473s = 709.50$$
$$s = \$1.50, \text{ student price}$$
$$s + 0.75 = \$2.25, \text{ adult price}$$

27. Let t = time travelling 55 mph.
$$360 = 65(3) + 55(t)$$
$$360 = 195 + 55t$$
$$165 = 55t$$
$$3 = t$$
$$t = 3 \text{ hours}$$

28.

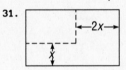

Let ℓ = length of the rectangle.

Thus, $\ell - 12$ = width of the rectangle.

Perimeter = $2[\ell + (\ell - 12)]$
$$2\{(\ell + 30) + [(\ell - 12) + 30]\} = 2\{2[\ell + (\ell - 12)]\}$$
$$2\{2\ell + 48\} = 2\{4\ell - 24\}$$
$$4\ell + 96 = 8\ell - 48$$
$$144 = 4\ell$$
$$36 = \ell$$
$$\ell = 36 \text{ inches, length}$$
$$\ell - 12 = 24 \text{ inches, width}$$

29. The sum of twice a number times the sum of the number and 4 and twice the sum of the number and 6.

30. Let p = price of the ticket.
$$379(p) + 532(p) = 5238.25$$
$$911p = 5238.25$$
$$p = \$5.75$$

31.

Let x = amount added to width.

Thus, $2x$ = amount added to length.

(Equation is based on perimeter change.)
$$2(x + 2x) = 42 - 24$$
$$2(3x) = 18$$
$$6x = 18$$
$$x = 3 \text{ inches added to width}$$
$$2x = 6 \text{ inches added to length}$$

32. Reflexive property of equality

33. Substitution property

34. $3(2x + 2) - 2(x - 1) = 6x + 6 - 2x + 2$
$$= 4x + 8$$

35. $\dfrac{3a + 4c}{b} = \dfrac{3(-3) + 4(0.5)}{2}$
$$= \frac{-9 + 2}{2}$$
$$= \frac{-7}{2} \text{ or } -3.5$$

PAGE 28   MID-CHAPTER REVIEW

1. $(6 + 3)5 - 6 = (9)5 - 6$
$$= 45 - 6$$
$$= 39$$

2. $4 + (3 + 6)9 - 2 = 4 + (9)9 - 2$
$$= 4 + 81 - 2$$
$$= 83$$

3. $ab - cb + a = 6(-2) - 0.5(-2) + 6$
$$= -12 + 1 + 6$$
$$= -5$$

4. $(ab)a + cb + abc$

$= [6(-2)]6 + 0.5(-2) + 6(-2)(0.5)$

$= [-12]6 - 1 + (-12)(0.5)$

$= -72 - 1 - 6$

$= -79$

5. $\quad I = prt$

$23.45 = p(.08)(3)$

$23.45 = 0.24p$

$\$97.71 = p$

6. I, R **7.** Q, R

8. N, W, Z, Q, R **9.** distributive

10. associative   **11.** $1.2x + 3.7 = 34.6$

$1.2x = 30.9$

$x = 25.75$

12. $2x - (3x - 6) + 4x = 3x + 45$

$2x - 3x + 6 + 4x = 3x + 45$

$3x + 6 = 3x + 45$

$6 = 45$

This is a false statement for all real numbers; thus there is no solution.

13. $3n + 9$ **14.** $(n + 2)^2$

15. Let n = the number.   **16.** Let x = the number.

$n + 45 = 213$ $3x + 7 = 46$

$n = 168$ $3x = 39$

$x = 13$

1-5 **Problem-Solving Strategy: List the Possibilities**

PAGE 30   **CHECKING FOR UNDERSTANDING**

1. The strategy is useful when we are asked to find several answers or the number of answers that satisfy the conditions of the problem.

2. Keeping the list organized makes it easier to be sure that all possible answers have been found.

3. Answers may vary.

4. 32 patterns:

TTTTT	TTTFF	TFFTT	FTFFT
TTTTF	TTFTF	FTFTT	FTFTF
TTTFT	TFTTF	FFTTT	FTTFF
TTFTT	FTTTF	FFFTT	FFFFT
TFTTT	TTFFT	FFTFT	FFFTF
FTTTT	TFTFT	FFTTF	FFTFF
FFFFF	FTTFT	TFFFF	FTFFF
TFFFT	TFFTF	TFTFF	TTFFF

5.

WWWWLL	WWWLLW	WLWLWW
WWWLWL	WWLWLW	LWWLWW
WWLWWL	WLWWLW	WLLWWW
WLWWWL	LWWWLW	LWLWWW
LWWWWL	WWLLWW	LLWWWW

---

6. A sample answer is: 765

                        +765

                        1530

7. Assume that your monthly salary is $1000 to start and the first cut or raise will occur in January. Your final salary will be $990 a month with either option. However, if you take the cut first, your salary for January will be $900. If you take the raise first, your salary for January will be $1100. So, if you take the cut first, your total income for the year will be $900 + 11($990) or $11,790. If you take the raise first, your total income for the year will be $1100 + 11($990) or $11,990. Taking the raise first gives more total income for the year.

8.

TAW	UAW	VAW
TAX	UAX	VAX
TAY	UAY	VAY
TBW	UBW	VBW
TBX	UBX	VBX
TBY	UBY	VBY
TCW	UCW	VCW
TCX	UCX	VCX
TCY	UCY	VCY

9. $23 - 5 = 18$ students form half the circle, thus 36 students form all the circle.

10. A sample answer is

$7 \times 7 - 7 + 7 \div 7 \times 7 \div 7 = 43$

PAGE 30   **COOPERATIVE LEARNING ACTIVITY**

1, 3, 9, 27, and 81 grams.

1-6 **Solving Absolute Value Equations**

PAGES 33-34   **CHECKING FOR UNDERSTANDING**

1. To be a solution, the absolute value of the expression would have to be -2, but an absolute value cannot be negative.

2. The absolute value of $3x + 7$ must be non-negative, so it can never be equal to -4.

3. a is a negative number, so $-a$ is a positive number.

4. Sometimes true. If $x < 0$, then $-x > x$. If $x > 0$, then $-x < x$. If $x = 0$, then $-x = x$.

5. $|4x| = |4(-4)|$ **6.** $|-2x| = |-2(-4)|$

$= |-16|$ $= |8|$

$= 16$ $= 8$

7. $-|3x - 4| = -|3(-4) - 4|$
$= -|-12 - 4|$
$= -|-16|$
$= -16$

8. $|-2x - 5| = |-2(-4) - 5|$
$= |8 - 5|$
$= |3|$
$= 3$

9. $7 - |3x + 10| = 7 - |3(-4) + 10|$
$= 7 - |-12 + 10|$
$= 7 - |-2|$
$= 7 - 2$
$= 5$

10. $2|x + 4| + |2x| = 2|(-4) + 4| + |2(-4)|$
$= 2|0| + |-8|$
$= 2(0) + 8$
$= 8$

11. $|-x| = 2$
$-x = 2$ or $-x = -2$
$x = -2$ $x = 2$
$-2, 2$

12. $|x - 2| = 1$
$x - 2 = 1$ or $x - 2 = -1$
$x = 3$ $x = 1$
1 (3 is not in the set.)

13. $|x| = -x$
For $x \geq 0$: $x = -x$ For $x < 0$: $x = -(-x)$
$2x = 0$ $0 = 0,$
$x = 0$ all $x < 0$
Thus, $-2, -1, 0$ are solutions.

14. $|x| = x$
For $x \geq 0$: $x = x$ For $x < 0$: $-x = x$
$0 = 0$, all $x \geq 0$ $-2x = 0$
$x = 0$
Thus, $0, 1, 2$ are solutions.

15. $-x = |x - 2|$
For $x - 2 \geq 0$: $x - 2 = -x$
$2x = 2$
$x = 1$
For $x - 2 < 0$: $x - 2 = x$
$-2 = 0$
no solution
Since 1 does not check, no solution exists.

16. $|x| = |x - 4|$
For both $x = x - 4$ For one $x = -(x - 4)$
positive $0 = -4$ positive $x = -x + 4$
or both no solution and one $2x = 4$
negative: negative: $x = 2$
Thus, 2 is the solution.

PAGE 34-35 EXERCISES

17. $|x + 6| = 19$
$x + 6 = 19$ or $x + 6 = -19$
$x = 13$ $x = -25$

18. $|x + 11| = 42$
$x + 1 = 42$ or $x + 11 = -42$
$x = 31$ $x = -53$

19. $|x - 4| = 11$
$x - 4 = 11$ or $x - 4 = -11$
$x = 15$ $x = -7$

20. $|x - 3| = 17$
$x - 3 = 17$ or $x - 3 = -17$
$x = 20$ $x = -14$

21. $3|x + 6| = 36$
$3(x + 6) = 36$ or $3(x + 6) = -36$
$x + 6 = 12$ $x + 6 = -12$
$x = 6$ $x = -18$

22. $8|x - 3| = 88$
$8(x - 3) = 88$ or $8(x - 3) = -88$
$x - 3 = 11$ $x - 3 = -11$
$x = 14$ $x = -8$

23. $5|x + 4| = 45$
$5(x + 4) = 45$ or $5(x + 4) = -45$
$x + 4 = 9$ $x + 4 = -9$
$x = 5$ $x = -13$

24. $11|x - 9| = 121$
$11(x - 9) = 121$ or $11(x - 9) = -121$
$x - 9 = 11$ $x - 9 = -11$
$x = 20$ $x = -2$

25. $|2x + 9| = 30$
$2x + 9 = 30$ or $2x + 9 = -30$
$2x = 21$ $2x = -39$
$x = \dfrac{21}{2}$ or 10.5 $x = \dfrac{-39}{2}$ or -19.5

26. $|2x - 37| = 15$
$2x - 37 = 15$ or $2x - 37 = -15$
$2x = 52$ $2x = 22$
$x = 26$ $x = 11$

27. $|2x + 7| = 0$
$2x + 7 = 0$
$2x = -7$
$x = -\dfrac{7}{2}$ or -3.5

28. $|4x - 3| = -27$
No solution

29. $3|3x + 2| = 51$
$3(3x + 2) = 51$ or $3(3x + 2) = -51$
$3x + 2 = 17$ $3x + 2 = -17$
$3x = 15$ $3x = -19$
$x = 5$ $x = -\dfrac{19}{3}$ or -6.333

30. $8|4x - 3| = 64$
$8(4x - 3) = 64$ or $8(4x - 3) = -64$
$4x - 3 = 8$ $4x - 3 = -8$
$4x = 11$ $4x = -5$
$x = \dfrac{11}{4}$ or 2.75 $x = -\dfrac{5}{4}$ or -1.25

31. $\quad -6|2x - 14| = -42$

$-6(2x - 14) = -42 \quad$ or $\quad -6(2x - 14) = 42$

$2x - 14 = 7 \qquad\qquad\qquad 2x - 14 = -7$

$2x = 21 \qquad\qquad\qquad\quad 2x = 7$

$x = \dfrac{21}{2}$ or 10.5 $\qquad\quad x = \dfrac{7}{2}$ or 3.5

32. $\quad 4|6x - 1| = 29$

$4(6x - 1) = 29 \quad$ or $\quad 4(6x - 1) = -29$

$24x - 4 = 29 \qquad\qquad\quad 24x - 4 = -29$

$24x = 33 \qquad\qquad\qquad 24x = -25$

$x = \dfrac{33}{24} = \dfrac{11}{8} \qquad\qquad x = -\dfrac{25}{24}$

33. $\quad 7|3x + 5| = 35$

$7(3x + 5) = 35 \quad$ or $\quad 7(3x + 5) = -35$

$3x + 5 = 5 \qquad\qquad\quad 3x + 5 = -5$

$3x = 0 \qquad\qquad\qquad\; 3x = -10$

$x = 0 \qquad\qquad\qquad x = -\dfrac{10}{3}$ or -3.333

34. $\quad |2a + 7| = a - 4$

$2a + 7 = a - 4 \quad$ or $\quad 2a + 7 = -(a - 4)$

$a = -11 \qquad\qquad\qquad 2a + 7 = -a + 4$

$\qquad\qquad\qquad\qquad\qquad 3a = -3$

$\qquad\qquad\qquad\qquad\qquad a = -1$

Neither checks; no solution.

35. $\quad |x - 3| = 2x$

$x - 3 = 2x \quad$ or $\quad x - 3 = -2x$

$-3 = x \qquad\qquad\qquad 3x = 3$

$\qquad\qquad\qquad\qquad\quad x = 1$

-3 doesn't check; 1 is the solution.

36. $\quad 3|x + 6| = 9x - 6$

$3(x + 6) = 9x - 6 \quad$ or $\quad 3(x + 6) = -(9x - 6)$

$x + 6 = 3x - 2 \qquad\qquad 3x + 18 = -9x + 6$

$8 = 2x \qquad\qquad\qquad\quad 12x = -12$

$4 = x \qquad\qquad\qquad\qquad x = -1$

-1 doesn't check; 4 is the solution.

37. $\quad |7 + 3a| = 11 - a$

$7 + 3a = 11 - a \quad$ or $\quad 7 + 3a = -(11 - a)$

$4a = 4 \qquad\qquad\qquad\quad 7 + 3a = -11 + a$

$a = 1 \qquad\qquad\qquad\qquad 2a = -18$

$\qquad\qquad\qquad\qquad\qquad a = -9$

38. $\quad |3t - 5| = 2t$

$3t - 5 = 2t \quad$ or $\quad 3t - 5 = -2t$

$t = 5 \qquad\qquad\qquad 5t = 5$

$\qquad\qquad\qquad\qquad\; t = 1$

39. $|x - 3| + 7 = 2$

$\quad |x - 3| = -5$

$\quad$ no solution

40. $\quad 5|3x - 4| = x + 1$

$5(3x - 4) = x + 1 \quad$ or $\quad 5(3x - 4) = -(x + 1)$

$15x - 20 = x + 1 \qquad\qquad 15x - 20 = -x - 1$

$14x = 21 \qquad\qquad\qquad\quad 16x = 19$

$x = \dfrac{21}{14} = \dfrac{3}{2} \qquad\qquad\qquad x = \dfrac{19}{16}$

41. $\quad |x + 2| = |2x - 4|$

$x + 2 = 2x - 4 \quad$ or $\quad x + 2 = -(2x - 4)$

$6 = x \qquad\qquad\qquad\quad x + 2 = -2x + 4$

$\qquad\qquad\qquad\qquad\qquad 3x = 2$

$\qquad\qquad\qquad\qquad\qquad x = \dfrac{2}{3}$

See students' work.

42.

108 mi	140 mi

Cincinnati $\qquad$ Columbus $\qquad\qquad$ Cleveland

Distance from Cincinnati to Cleveland along Interstate 71 is $108 + 140 = 248$ miles.

43. Let x = weight limit.

$|x - 1| = 0.05$

$x - 1 = 0.05 \quad$ or $\quad x - 1 = -0.05$

$x = 1.05$ lbs, $\qquad\quad x = 0.95$ lbs,

largest amount $\qquad\quad$ smallest amount

44. a. Change line 10 to DEFFNF$(X) = X \wedge 2 - 2 - 4$.

$-2.4,\ 2.4$

b. Change line 10 to DEFFNF$(X) = X \wedge 3 - 3*X$.

$-1.7,\ 0,\ 1.7$

c. Change line 10 to DEFFNF$(X) = $ ABS$(3*X - 2) - 4$.

$-0.7,\ 2$

d. Change line 10 to DEFFNF$(X) =$

$5*X \wedge 3 + 3*X \wedge 2 - 25*X - 15$.

$-2.2,\ -0.6,\ 2.2$

45. 139 319 913

193 391 931

46.

E $\quad$ A $\quad$ AH

E $\quad$ AH $\quad$ A

A $\quad$ E $\quad$ AH

A $\quad$ AH $\quad$ E

AH $\quad$ E $\quad$ A

AH $\quad$ A $\quad$ E

47. $x + x^2$

48. $\sqrt{16} + \sqrt{9} = 4 + 3 = 7$

N, W, Z, Q, R

1-7 | Solving Inequalities

PAGE 39 $\quad$ CHECKING FOR UNDERSTANDING

1. Reverse the order of the inequality.

2. $2(x + 3) < 6$ $\qquad\qquad$ **3.** $18 \geq 3(5x)$

4. $\{x | x > -2\}$ $\qquad\qquad$ **5.** $x \leq 0 \longrightarrow \{x | x \leq 0\}$

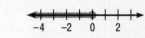

6. $x > -3 \to \{x | x > -3\}$ $\qquad$ **7.** $x > 4.5 \to \{x | x > 4.5\}$

8. $\qquad 0.75x < 4$

$\left(\dfrac{1}{0.75}\right) 0.75x < \left(\dfrac{1}{0.75}\right) 4$

$x < \dfrac{16}{3}$ or 5.333

$\left\{ x \,\middle|\, x < \dfrac{16}{3} \right\}$

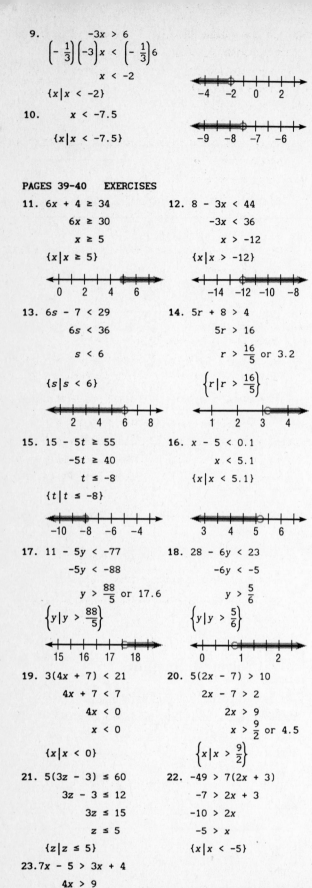

9. $-3x > 6$

$\left(-\frac{1}{3}\right)\left(-3\right)x < \left(-\frac{1}{3}\right)6$

$x < -2$

$\{x \mid x < -2\}$

10. $x < -7.5$

$\{x \mid x < -7.5\}$

PAGES 39-40   EXERCISES

11. $6x + 4 \geq 34$

$6x \geq 30$

$x \geq 5$

$\{x \mid x \geq 5\}$

12. $8 - 3x < 44$

$-3x < 36$

$x > -12$

$\{x \mid x > -12\}$

13. $6s - 7 < 29$

$6s < 36$

$s < 6$

$\{s \mid s < 6\}$

14. $5r + 8 > 4$

$5r > 16$

$r > \frac{16}{5}$ or 3.2

$\left\{r \mid r > \frac{16}{5}\right\}$

15. $15 - 5t \geq 55$

$-5t \geq 40$

$t \leq -8$

$\{t \mid t \leq -8\}$

16. $x - 5 < 0.1$

$x < 5.1$

$\{x \mid x < 5.1\}$

17. $11 - 5y < -77$

$-5y < -88$

$y > \frac{88}{5}$ or 17.6

$\left\{y \mid y > \frac{88}{5}\right\}$

18. $28 - 6y < 23$

$-6y < -5$

$y > \frac{5}{6}$

$\left\{y \mid y > \frac{5}{6}\right\}$

19. $3(4x + 7) < 21$

$4x + 7 < 7$

$4x < 0$

$x < 0$

$\{x \mid x < 0\}$

20. $5(2x - 7) > 10$

$2x - 7 > 2$

$2x > 9$

$x > \frac{9}{2}$ or 4.5

$\left\{x \mid x > \frac{9}{2}\right\}$

21. $5(3z - 3) \leq 60$

$3z - 3 \leq 12$

$3z \leq 15$

$z \leq 5$

$\{z \mid z \leq 5\}$

22. $-49 > 7(2x + 3)$

$-7 > 2x + 3$

$-10 > 2x$

$-5 > x$

$\{x \mid x < -5\}$

23. $7x - 5 > 3x + 4$

$4x > 9$

$x > \frac{9}{4}$ or 2.25

$\left\{x \mid x > \frac{9}{4}\right\}$

24. $40 \leq -6(5r - 7)$

$40 \leq -30r + 42$

$-2 \leq -30r$

$\frac{1}{15} \geq r$

$\left\{r \mid r \leq \frac{1}{15}\right\}$

25. $7 - 2x \geq 0$

$-2x \geq -7$

$x \leq \frac{7}{2}$ or 3.5

$\left\{x \mid x \leq \frac{7}{2}\right\}$

26. $2(r - 4) + 5 \geq 9$

$2r - 8 + 5 \geq 9$

$2r \geq 12$

$r \geq 6$

$\{r \mid r \geq 6\}$

27. $2(3m + 4) - 2 \leq 3(1 + 3m)$

$6m + 8 - 2 \leq 3 + 9m$

$-3m \leq -3$

$m \geq 1$

$\{m \mid m \geq 1\}$

28. $2(m - 5) - 3(2m - 5) < 5m + 1$

$2m - 10 - 6m + 15 < 5m + 1$

$-4m + 5 < 5m + 1$

$4 < 9m$

$\frac{4}{9} < m$

$\left\{m \mid m > \frac{4}{9}\right\}$

29. $7 + 3y > 2(y + 3) -2(-1 - y)$

$7 + 3y > 2y + 6 + 2 + 2y$

$7 + 3y > 4y + 8$

$-1 > y$

$\{y \mid y < -1\}$

30. $3b - 2(b - 5) < 2(b + 4)$

$3b - 2b + 10 < 2b + 8$

$b + 10 < 2b + 8$

$2 < b$

$\{b \mid b > 2\}$

31. $0.01x - 4.23 \geq 0$

$0.01x \geq 4.23$

$x \geq 423$

$\{x \mid x \geq 423\}$

32. $0.75x - 0.5 < 0$

$0.75x < 0.5$

$x < \frac{2}{3}$ or 0.667

$\left\{x \mid x < \frac{2}{3}\right\}$

33. $2.55x - 4.25 \leq 0$

$2.55x \leq 4.25$

$x \leq \frac{5}{3}$ or 1.667

$\left\{x \mid x \leq \frac{5}{3}\right\}$

34. $\frac{4x + 2}{5} \geq -0.04$

$4x + 2 \geq -0.2$

$4x \geq 2.2$

$x \geq -\frac{11}{20}$ or -0.55

$\left\{x \mid x \geq -\frac{11}{20}\right\}$

35. $\frac{2x + 3}{5} \le 0.03$

$2x + 3 \le 0.15$

$2x \le -2.85$

$x \le -1.425$

$\{x \mid x \le -1.425\}$

36. $20\left(\frac{1}{5} - \frac{w}{4}\right) \ge -2w$

$4 - 5w \ge -2w$

$-3w \ge -4$

$w \le \frac{4}{3}$ or 1.333

$\left\{w \mid w \le \frac{4}{3}\right\}$

37. $\frac{3x - 3}{5} < \frac{6(x - 1)}{10}$

$2(3x - 3) < 6(x - 1)$

$6x - 6 < 6x - 6$

$0 < 0$

This is a false statement for all real numbers; no solution or $\{\}$ or $\emptyset$.

38. $\frac{x + 8}{4} - 1 > \frac{x}{3}$

$12\left(\frac{x + 8}{4} - 1\right) > 12\left(\frac{x}{3}\right)$

$3(x + 8) - 12 > 4x$

$3x + 24 > 4x$

$12 > x$

$\{x \mid x < 12\}$

39. Let x = the amount of the greatest check.

$110.37 - x \ge 50$

$-x \ge -60.37$

$x \le 60.37$

Thus, the largest amount is $60.37.

40. Let n = the number of hours parked.

$4.50 \ge 1.50(1) + 0.50(n - 1)$

$4.5 \ge 1.5 + 0.5n - 0.5$

$3.5 \ge 0.5n$

$7 \ge n$

Thus, you can park for 7 hours or less.

41. Let g = games needed to win.

$\frac{30 + g}{84} \ge \frac{3}{5}$

$5(30 + g) = 84(3)$

$150 + 5g = 252$

$5g \ge 102$

$g \ge \frac{102}{5}$ or 20.4

Thus, at least 20 of the last 42 games need to be won.

42. Let d = amount invested in stock.

Thus, $8000 - d$ = amount not in stock.

$400 \le (d)(-0.02) + (8000 - d)(0.08)$

$400 \le -0.02d + 640 - 0.08d$

$-240 \le -0.1d$

$2400 \ge d$

Thus, Karl could have invested at most $2400 in stock.

43. Let s = score on the fifth test.

$89 + 87 + 95 + 98 + s \ge 450$

$369 + s \ge 450$

$s \ge 81$

Thus, you need at least an 81 on the last test.

44. Let m = the most miles paid for.

$90 \ge 12.95 + 0.15m$

$77.05 \ge 0.15\,m$

$513\frac{2}{3} \ge m$

Thus, $513\frac{2}{3}$ miles are paid for.

45. Let x = the amount left to the church

$\frac{1}{4}(300,000) \ge 2x$

$75,000 \ge x$

Thus, $75,000 is the most the church will receive.

Then let y = the amount left to each child

$\frac{1}{4}(300,000 - 75,000 \ge y$

$\frac{1}{4}(225,000) \ge y$

$56,250 \ge y$

$56,250 is the most each child will receive.

46. $3x - 2 \ge 0$ and $5x - 1 \le 0$

$3x \ge 2$ $\qquad$ $5x \le 1$

$x \ge \frac{2}{3}$ $\qquad$ $x \le \frac{1}{5}$

$\left\{x \mid x \ge \frac{2}{3}\right\}$ and $\left\{x \mid x \le \frac{1}{5}\right\}$

No solution or $\emptyset$ or $\{\}$ since no number is a member of both solution sets.

47. Let d = the piston's diameter.

$10 - 0.001 \le d \le 10 + 0.001$

$9.999 \le d \le 10.001$

48. Let s = the number of sets.

$8(60) = 480 \ge s[30 + 4(12)]$

$480 \ge s[30 + 48]$

$480 \ge s[78]$

$6.154 \ge s$

Thus, at most 6 sets can be produced.

49. $|7(-3) + 10| = |-21 + 10|$

$= |-11|$

$= 11$

50. $3|2x - 5| = -1$

no solution

51. $3 - 2x = 18$

$-2x = 15$

$x = -\frac{15}{2}$ or -7.5

52. $7x + 8y + 9y - x(7 - 2) = 7x + 8y + 9y - x(5)$
$$= 7x + 8y + 9y - 5x$$
$$= 2x + 17y$$

53. $\sqrt{9} + \sqrt{4} = 3 + 2$
$$= \frac{3}{2} \text{ or } 1.5$$

Technology: Solving Equations and Inequalities

PAGE 41 EXERCISES

1. $2 - 5x = -8x + 4$

add $8x$ $8x + (2 - 5x) = 8x + (-8x + 4)$

simp $3x + 2 = 4$

sub 2 $3x + 2 - 2 = 4 - 2$

simp
div 3 $\frac{3x}{3} = \frac{2}{3}$

simp $x = \frac{2}{3}$

2. $\frac{x}{4} = \frac{x}{6} + \frac{1}{3}$

mult 12 $12 \cdot \left(\frac{x}{4}\right) = 12 \cdot \left(\frac{x}{6} + \frac{1}{3}\right)$

simp $3x = 2x + 4$

sub $2x$ $3x - 2x = 2x + 4 - 2x$

simp $x = 4$

3. $\frac{2}{5}x + 1 < -7$

mult 5 $5 \cdot \left(\frac{2}{5}x + 1\right) < 5 \cdot (-7)$

simp $2x + 5 < -35$

sub 5 $2x + 5 - 5 < -35 - 5$

simp
div 2 $\frac{2x}{2} < \frac{-40}{2}$

simp $x < -20$

4. $2x - 3(1 - 6x) = 3(2x + 1) - 8$

simp $20x - 3 = 6x - 5$

sub $6x$ $20x - 3 - 6x = 6x - 5 - 6x$

simp $14x - 3 = -5$

add 3 $3 + (14x - 3) = 3 + (-5)$

simp
div 14 $\frac{14x}{14} = \frac{-2}{14}$

simp $x = -\frac{1}{7}$

5. $1 - [2 - (3x - 1)] > 4x - 2(6 + 2x)$

simp $3x - 2 > -12$

add 2 $2 + (3x - 2) > 2 + (-12)$

simp
div 3 $\frac{3x}{3} > \frac{-10}{3}$

simp $x > -\frac{10}{3} \text{ or } -3.333$

1-8	**Solving Compound Sentences and Absolute Value Inequalities**

PAGE 44   CHECKING FOR UNDERSTANDING

1. The absolute value of $x + 2$ is not negative and zero is greater than -4.

2. The absolute value of an expression is always non-negative.

3. A compound sentence containing *and* is true only if both parts of it are true.

4. A compound sentence containing *or* is true if at least one part of it is true.

5. $|x| < 7$ **6.** $|x| < 3$

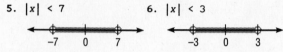

7. $|x| > 11$ **8.** $|x| \le 5$

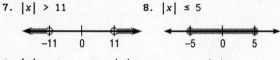

9. $|x| < 6$ **10.** $|x| > 3$ **11.** $|x| \le 9$

12. $|x| \ge 7$ **13.** $|x| \le 6$ **14.** $|x| < 3$

PAGES 44-45   EXERCISES

15. $|x + 2| > 3$ **16.** $2 < x + 4 < 11$

$x + 2 > 3$ or $x + 2 < -3$ $-2 < x < 7$

    $x > 1$ $x < -5$ $\{x| \ -2 < x < 7\}$

$\{x|x < -5$ or $x > 1\}$

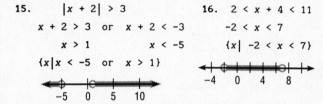

17. $|x| < 9$ **18.** $-2 \le x - 10 \le 6$

$-9 < x < 9$ $8 \le x \le 16$

$\{x| \ -9 < x < 9\}$ $\{x| \ 8 \le x \le 16\}$

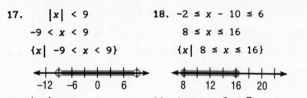

19. $|2x| < 6$ **20.** $1 < x - 2 < 7$

$-6 < 2x < 6$ $3 < x < 9$

$-3 < x < 3$ $\{x|3 < x < 9\}$

$\{x| \ -3 < x < 3\}$

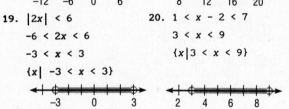

21. $|7x| \ge 21$

$7x \ge 21$ or $7x \le -21$

$x \ge 3$ $x \le -3$

$\{x|x \le -3$ or $x \ge 3\}$

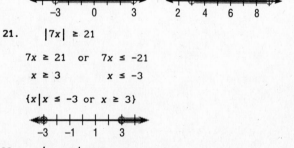

22. $|x - 9| > 5$

$x - 9 > 5$ or $x - 9 < -5$

    $x > 14$ $x < 4$

$\{x|x < 4$ or $x > 14\}$

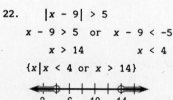

23. $|x| > 5$
$x > 5$ or $x < -5$
$\{x|x < -5 \text{ or } x > 5\}$
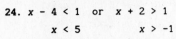

24. $x - 4 < 1$ or $x + 2 > 1$
$x < 5 \qquad x > -1$
$\{x|x > -1 \text{ or } x < 5\}$
all reals
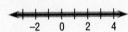

25. $|2x| \geq 28$
$2x \geq 28$ or $2x \leq -28$
$x \geq 14 \qquad x \leq -14$
$\{x|x \leq -14 \text{ or } x \geq 14\}$
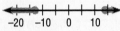

26. $|2x| \geq -64$
all reals
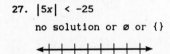

27. $|5x| < -25$
no solution or ø or {}
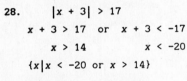

28. $|x + 3| > 17$
$x + 3 > 17$ or $x + 3 < -17$
$x > 14 \qquad x < -20$
$\{x|x < -20 \text{ or } x > 14\}$
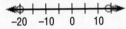

29. $4 < 2x - 2 < 10$
$6 < 2x < 12$
$3 < x < 6$
$\{x|\ 3 < x < 6\}$

30. $|x - 6| \leq -12$
no solution or ø or {}

31. $|x - 15| < 45$
$-45 < x - 15 < 45$
$-30 < x < 60$
$\{x|\ -30 < x < 60\}$

32. $x + 6 \geq -1$ or $x - 2 \leq 4$
$x \geq -7 \qquad x \leq 6$
$\{x|x \geq -7 \text{ or } x \leq 6\}$
all reals

33. $|2x - 9| \leq 27$
$-27 \leq 2x - 9 \leq 27$
$-18 \leq 2x \leq 36$
$-9 \leq x \leq 18$
$\{x|\ -9 \leq x \leq 18\}$

34. $|3x + 12| > 42$
$3x + 12 > 42$ or $3x + 12 < -42$
$3x > 30 \qquad 3x < -54$
$x > 10 \qquad x < -18$
$\{x|x < -18 \text{ or } x > 10\}$

35. $-1 < 3x + 2 < 14$
$-3 < 3x < 12$
$-1 < x < 4$
$\{x|\ -1 < x < 4\}$

36. $5x < 9 + 2x$ or $9 - 2x > 11$
$3x < 9 \qquad -2x > 2$
$x < 3 \qquad x < -1$
$\{x|x < -1 \text{ or } x < 3\}$
$\{x|x < 3\}$

37. $|5x - 7| < 81$
$-81 < 5x - 7 < 81$
$-74 < 5x < 88$
-14.8 or $-\dfrac{74}{5} < x < \dfrac{88}{5}$ or 17.6
$\left\{x|\ -\dfrac{74}{5} < x < \dfrac{88}{5}\right\}$
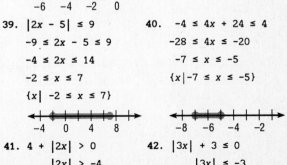

38. $|3x + 11| > 1$
$3x + 11 > 1$ or $3x + 11 < -1$
$3x > -10 \qquad 3x < -12$
$x > -\dfrac{10}{3} \qquad x < -4$
$\left\{x|x < -4 \text{ or } x > -\dfrac{10}{3}\right\}$

39. $|2x - 5| \leq 9$
$-9 \leq 2x - 5 \leq 9$
$-4 \leq 2x \leq 14$
$-2 \leq x \leq 7$
$\{x|\ -2 \leq x \leq 7\}$

40. $-4 \leq 4x + 24 \leq 4$
$-28 \leq 4x \leq -20$
$-7 \leq x \leq -5$
$\{x|-7 \leq x \leq -5\}$

41. $4 + |2x| > 0$
$|2x| > -4$
all reals
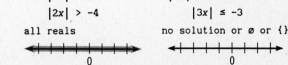

42. $|3x| + 3 \leq 0$
$|3x| \leq -3$
no solution or ø or {}

43. $|x| \leq x$

$-x \leq x \leq x$

$-2x \leq 0 \leq 0$

$-2x \leq 0$

$x \geq 0$

$\{x \mid x \geq 0\}$

44. $|x| > x$

$x > x$ or $x < -x$

$0 > 0 \qquad 2x < 0$

no solution $\quad x < 0$

$\{x \mid x < 0\}$

45. $2x - 1 < -5$ or $3x + 2 \geq 5$

$\qquad 2x < -4 \qquad\qquad 3x \geq 3$

$\qquad\quad x < -2 \qquad\qquad\quad x \geq 1$

$\{x \mid x < -2 \text{ or } x \geq 1\}$

$\qquad -4 \quad -2 \quad 0 \quad 2$

46. $|x + 2| - x \geq 0$

$\qquad |x + 2| \geq x$

$x + 2 \geq x$ or $x + 2 \leq -x$

$2 \geq 0 \qquad\qquad 2x + 2 \leq 0$

All reals $\qquad\qquad 2x \leq -2$

when $x + 2 \geq 0 \qquad x \leq -1$

$\qquad\qquad x \geq -2$

$\{x \mid x \geq -2 \text{ or } x \leq -1\}$

All reals

47. $|x + 1| + |x - 1| \leq 2$

$\qquad\qquad |x + 1| \leq 2 - |x - 1|$

$x + 1 \leq 2 - |x - 1|$ and $\quad x + 1 \geq -(2 - |x - 1|)$

$|x - 1| \leq 1 - x \qquad\qquad\quad x + 1 \geq -2 + |x - 1|$

$-(1 - x) \leq x - 1 \leq 1 - x \qquad x + 3 \geq |x - 1|$

$-1 + x \leq x - 1 \leq 1 - x \quad -(x + 3) \leq x - 1 \leq x + 3$

$x \leq x \leq 2 - x \qquad\qquad -x - 3 \leq x - 1 \leq x + 3$

$0 \leq 0 \leq 2 - 2x \qquad\qquad -2x - 2 \leq 0 \leq 4$

$0 \leq 2 - 2x \qquad\qquad -2x - 2 \leq 0$

$2x \leq 2 \qquad\qquad\qquad -2x \leq 2$

$x \leq 1 \qquad\qquad\qquad\quad x \geq -1$

$\{x \mid x \geq -1 \text{ and } x \leq 1\}$

$\{x \mid -1 \leq x \leq 1\}$

48. a. Let s = car's speed.

$45 \leq s \leq 65$

b. Let s = truck's speed.

$45 \leq s \leq 55$

49. a. Let d = dimension of the part.

$|d - 7.32| \leq 0.002$

$-0.002 \leq d - 7.32 \leq 0.002$

$7.318 \leq \quad d \quad \leq 7.322$

minimum = 7.318 cm, maximum = 7.322 cm

b. $5.18 \leq w \leq 5.24$

$0 \leq w - 5.18 \leq 0.06$

$-0.03 \leq w - 5.21 \leq 0.03$

tolerance = 0.03 cm

50. My best friend is taller than I am; my best friend and I are the same height; my best friend is shorter than I am.

51. Let x = one number.

Then $2x$ = the other number.

If both positive: $\qquad$ If both negative:

$2(x) + 2x \geq 85 \qquad\qquad 2(2x) + x \geq 85$

$4x \geq 85 \qquad\qquad\qquad 5x \geq 85$

$x \geq \dfrac{85}{4}$ or $21.25 \qquad\quad x \geq 17$

$\qquad\qquad\qquad\qquad$ No solution; both are

$\qquad\qquad\qquad\qquad$ negative.

Thus, the last possible value for the lesser number is 21.25.

52. $48|7k - 30|$ for $k = 14$

$7 \times 14 - 30 = 68 \times 48 = 3264$

53.

$\qquad\qquad\qquad\qquad$ 470 mi

SF $\qquad\qquad\qquad\qquad\qquad\qquad\qquad$ LA

	r	$\cdot$ t	$=$ d
passenger SF - LA	x	2.5	$2.5x$
express LA - SF	$x + 10$	2.5	$2.5(x + 10)$

$2.5(x) + 2.5(x + 10) = 470$

$2.5x + 2.5x + 25 = 470$

$5x = 445$

$x = 89$ mph, passenger train

$x + 10 = 99$ mph, express train

54. additive identity

55. $I = prt$

$1200 = (5000)(r)(3)$

$0.08 = r$ The interest rate is 8%.

Chapter 1 Summary and Review

PAGES 46-48 SKILLS AND CONCEPTS

1. $(3 + 7)^2 - 16 \div 2 = (10)^2 - 16 \div 2$

$\qquad\qquad\qquad\qquad = 100 - 8$

$\qquad\qquad\qquad\qquad = 92$

2. $3 + 7^2 - 16 \div 2 = 3 + 49 - 8$

$\qquad\qquad\qquad\qquad = 44$

3. $\dfrac{4a + 3c}{3b} = \dfrac{4(-0.5) + 3(5)}{3(4)}$

$\qquad\qquad = \dfrac{-2 + 15}{12}$

$\qquad\qquad = \dfrac{13}{12}$

4. $\dfrac{3ab^2 - d^3}{a} = \dfrac{3(-0.5)(4)^2 - (-3)^3}{-0.5}$

$\qquad\qquad = \dfrac{3(-0.5)(16) - (-27)}{-0.5}$

$\qquad\qquad = \dfrac{-24 + 27}{-0.5}$

$\qquad\qquad = \dfrac{3}{-0.5} = -6$

14

5. $d = 16t^2$

$= 16(20)^2$

$= 16(400)$

$= 6400$ ft

6. Q,R   7. Q,R

8. Z,Q,R   9. I,R

10. associative +

11. additive identity

12. $(8 + 49)\ 7 + 3 = (57)\ 7 + 3$

$= 399 + 3$

$= 402$

13. $7a + 2b - 5a - 6b = 2a - 4b$

14. $3(a + 4b) - 2(4a + 2b) = 3a + 12b - 8a - 4b$

$= -5a + 8b$

15. $15x + 25 = 2(x - 4)$ 16. $2(3x - 1) = 3(x + 2)$

$15x + 25 = 2x - 8$ $6x - 2 = 3x + 6$

$13x = -33$ $3x = 8$

$x = \dfrac{-33}{13}$ $x = \dfrac{8}{3}$

17. $6 = \dfrac{3x - 6}{3}$ 18. $\dfrac{3a + 3}{4} = \dfrac{5}{2}$

$6 = x - 2$ $2(3a + 3) = 4(5)$

$8 = x$ $6a + 6 = 20$

$6a = 14$

$a = \dfrac{14}{6} = \dfrac{7}{3}$

19. Let ℓ = length of the rectangle, and
$\dfrac{1}{3}\ell + 4$ = width of the rectangle.

$2\left[\ell + \left(\dfrac{1}{3}\ell + 4\right)\right] = 64$

$\ell + \dfrac{1}{3}\ell + 4 = 32$

$\dfrac{4}{3}\ell = 28$

$\ell = 21$ ft, length

$\dfrac{1}{3}(21) + 4 = 7 + 4$

$= 11$ ft, width

20. $|2x - 36| = 14$

$2x - 36 = 14$ or $2x - 36 = -14$

$2x = 50$ $2x = 22$

$x = 25$ $x = 11$

21. $|q - 3| + 7 = 2$

$|q - 3| = 5$

no solution

22. $8|2b - 3| = 64$

$|2b - 3| = 8$

$2b - 3 = 8$ or $2b - 3 = -8$

$2b = 11$ $2b = -5$

$b = \dfrac{11}{2}$ or 5.5 $b = -\dfrac{5}{2}$ or -2.5

23. $9(x + 2) < 72$ 24. $3(3x + 2) > 7x - 2$

$x + 2 < 8$ $9x + 6 > 7x - 2$

$x < 6$ $2x > -8$

$\{x \mid x < 6\}$ $x > -4$

$\{x \mid x > -4\}$

25. $8(2x - 1) > 11x + 31$

$16x - 8 > 11x + 31$

$5x > 39$

$x > \dfrac{39}{5}$ or 7.8

$\left\{x \mid x > \dfrac{39}{5}\right\}$

26. $-1 < 3(y - 2) \le 9$

$-1 < 3y - 6 \le 9$

$5 < 3y \le 15$

$\dfrac{5}{3} < y \le 5$

$\left\{y \mid \dfrac{5}{3} < y \le 5\right\}$

27. $4x - 10 < -10$ or $6x + 4 \ge 10$

$4x < 0$ $6x \ge 6$

$x < 0$ $x \ge 1$

$\{x \mid x < 0 \text{ or } x \ge 1\}$

28. $|2x + 6| \le 4$

$-4 \le 2x + 6 \le 4$

$-10 \le 2x \le -2$

$-5 \le x \le -1$

$\{x \mid -5 \le x \le -1\}$

29. $7 + |9 - 5x| > 1$

$|9 - 5x| > -6$

all reals

30. $|4x| + 3 \le 0$

$|4x| \le -3$

no solution or ø or {}

PAGE 48   APPLICATIONS AND CONNECTIONS

31. There are 64 possible patterns.

TTTTTT	TFFFTT	FTTTTT	FFFFTT
TTTTTF	TFFTFT	FTTTTF	FFFTFT
TTTTFT	TFFTTF	FTTTFT	FFFTTF
TTTFTT	TFTFFT	FTTFTT	FFTFFT
TTFTTT	TFTFTF	FTFTTT	FFTFTF
TFTTTT	TFTTFF	FFTTTT	FFTTFF
TFFTTT	TTFFFT	FFFTTT	FTFFFT
TFTFTT	TTFFTF	FFTFTT	FTFFTF
TFTTFT	TTFTFF	FFTTFT	FTFTFF
TFTTTF	TTTFFF	FFTTTF	FTTFFF
TTFFTT	TFFFFT	FTFFTT	FFFFFT
TTFTFT	TFFFTF	FTFTFT	FFFFTF
TTFTTF	TFFTFF	FTFTTF	FFFTFF
TTTFFT	TFTFFF	FTTFFT	FFTFFF
TTTFTF	TTFFFF	FTTFTF	FTFFFF
TTTTFF	TFFFFF	FTTTFF	FFFFFF

15

32.

	Amt.	%	Solution
50%	10	0.50	(10)(0.50)
Pure	x	1.00	x
80%	10 + x	0.80	(10 + x)(0.80)

Let x = gallons of pure ammonia.

$(10)(0.50) + x = (10 + x)(0.80)$

$5 + x = 8 + 0.8x$

$0.2x = 3$

$x = \dfrac{3}{0.2} = 15$ gallons

33. Let x = gallons able to purchase.

$8.40 \geq 1.40x$ or $8.40 \geq 1.60x$

$6 \geq x$ $\qquad\qquad 5.25 \geq x$

He can buy from 5.25 to 6 gallons.

Chapter 1 Test

PAGE 49

1. associative $\times$

2. commutative $\times$

3. reflexive $=$

4. substitution $=$

5. symmetric $=$

6. transitive $=$

7. $[2 + 3^3 - 4] \div 2 = [2 + 27 - 4] \div 2$

$\qquad\qquad = [25] \div 2$

$\qquad\qquad = \dfrac{25}{2}$ or 12.5

8. $(2 + 3)^3 - 4 \div 2 = (5)^3 - 4 \div 2$

$\qquad\qquad = 125 - 2$

$\qquad\qquad = 123$

9. $(4^5 - 4^2) + 4^3 = (1024 - 16) + 64$

$\qquad\qquad = 1072$

10. $[5(17 - 2) \div 3] - 2^4 = [5(15) \div 3] - 2^4$

$\qquad\qquad = [75 \div 3] - 16$

$\qquad\qquad = 25 - 16$

$\qquad\qquad = 9$

11. $\dfrac{db + 4c}{a}$

$= \dfrac{(-6)\left(\frac{2}{3}\right) + (4)(8)}{(-9)}$

$= \dfrac{-4 + 32}{-9}$

$= \dfrac{28}{-9}$

12. $\dfrac{a}{b^2} + c = \dfrac{-9}{\left(\frac{2}{3}\right)^2} + 8$

$= \dfrac{-9}{\frac{4}{9}} + 8$

$= \dfrac{-81}{4} + 8$

$= -\dfrac{49}{4}$ or -12.25

13. $2b(4a + a^2)$

$= 2\left(\dfrac{2}{3}\right)[4(-9) + (-9)^2]$

$= \dfrac{4}{3}[-36 + 81]$

$= \dfrac{4}{3}[45]$

$= 60$

14. $\dfrac{4a + 3c}{3b} = \dfrac{4(-9) + 3(8)}{3\left(\frac{2}{3}\right)}$

$= \dfrac{-36 + 24}{2}$

$= -18 + 12$

$= -6$

15. I,R

16. Q,R

17. Z,Q,R

18. N,W,Z,Q,R

19. $2x - 7 - (x - 5) = 0$

$2x - 7 - x + 5 = 0$

$x - 2 = 0$

$x = 2$

20. $5t - 3 = -2t + 10$

$7t = 13$

$t = \dfrac{13}{7}$

21. $5r + 7 = 5r - 9$

$7 = -9$

No solution

22. $5m - (5 + 4m) = (3 + m) - 8$

$5m - 5 - 4m = 3 + m - 8$

$m - 5 = m - 5$

$0 = 0$

All reals

23. $|8w + 2| + 2 = 0$

$|8w + 2| = -2$

No solution

24. $|4y - 5| + 4 = 7y + 8$

$|4y - 5| = 7y + 4$

$4y - 5 = 7y + 4$ or $4y - 5 = -(7y + 4)$

$-9 = 3y$ $\qquad\qquad 4y - 5 = -7y - 4$

$-3 = y$ $\qquad\qquad 11y = 1$

$\qquad\qquad\qquad y = \dfrac{1}{11}$

-3 doesn't check; solution is $\dfrac{1}{11}$.

25. $4 > b + 1$

$3 > b$

$\{b \mid b < 3\}$

26. $3q + 7 \geq 13$

$3q \geq 6$

$q \geq 2$

$\{q \mid q \geq 2\}$

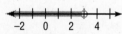

27. $5(3x - 5) + x < 2(4x - 1) + 1$

$15x - 25 + x < 8x - 2 + 1$

$16x - 25 < 8x - 1$

$8x < 24$

$x < 3$

$\{x \mid x < 3\}$

28. $-12 < 7s - 5 \leq 9$

$-7 < 7s \leq 14$

$-1 < s \leq 2$

$\{s \mid -1 < s \leq 2\}$

29. $|9y - 4| + 8 > 4$

$|9y - 4| > -4$

All reals

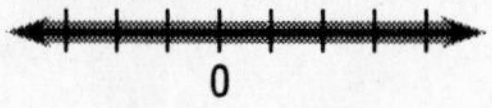

30. $|5 + k| \leq 8$

$-8 \leq 5 + k \leq 8$

$-13 \leq k \leq 3$

$\{k \mid -13 \leq k \leq 3\}$

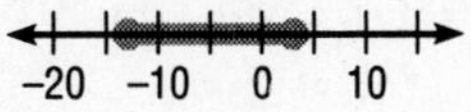

31. Let s = score on last test.

$87 + 89 + 76 + 77 + s \geq 400$

$329 + s \geq 400$

$s \geq 71$

Thus, a score of 71 is needed to earn a "B."

32. There are 10 possible patterns. They are:

WWWLL

WWLWL

WLWWL

WLLWW

WLWLW

WWLLW

LLWWW

LWLWW

LWWLW

LWWWL

33.

$$A = \frac{180(n - 2)}{n}$$

$$150 = \frac{180(n - 2)}{n}$$

$$150n = 180(n - 2)$$

$$150n = 180n - 360$$

$$360 = 30n$$

$$12 = n$$

PAGE 49 BONUS

$3x - 2 \geq 0$ and $5x - 1 \leq 0$

$3x \geq 2 \qquad\qquad 5x \leq 1$

$x \geq \dfrac{3}{2} \qquad\qquad x \leq \dfrac{1}{5}$

No solution or ∅ or { }, because a real number cannot be both larger than $\dfrac{3}{2}$ and smaller than $\dfrac{1}{5}$ at the same time.

Chapter 2
Linear Relations and Functions

2-1 Relations and Functions

1. The domain is {1965, 1970, 1975, 1980, 1985, 1990}. The range is {17, 21, 23, 32, 35, 37}.

2. A relation is any set of ordered pairs. A function is a relation in which no member of the domain is paired with more than one member of the range.

3. Consider the vertical line $x = a$. The value of x is always the same across all values of y and therefore x is paired with more than one y.

4. Substitute 7 for x and evaluate the equation.

5. Answers may vary for points, not locations.

Some points:

x-axis: (1, 0)

y-axis: (0, 1)

origin: (0, 0)

quadrant I: (2, 1)

quadrant II: (-2, 1)

quadrant III: (-2, -1)

quadrant IV: (2, -1)

6. quadrant IV

7. quadrant III

8. quadrant II

9. no quadrant, y-axis

10. function

11. relation

12. function

13. $D = \{-10, 4, 8\}$
    $R = \{-2, 3, 4, 8\}$
    Not a function

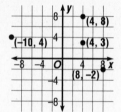

14. $D = \{-3, -2, 2, 4\}$
    $R = \{-3, -2, 2, 4\}$
    Is a function

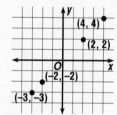

15. $D = \{-3, -2, 2\}$
    $R = \{3, 2, -2, -4\}$
    Not a function

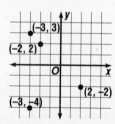

16. $D = \{-3, -2, 2, 4\}$
    $R = \{3\}$
    Is a function

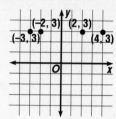

17. $f(4) = 4^2 - 3 \cdot 4$
    $= 16 - 12$
    $= 4$

18. $D = \{3, 2, 1, 0, -1, -2, -3\}$
    $R = \{9, 4, 1, 0\}$
    Is a function

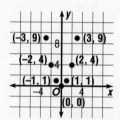

19. $D = \{0, 5, 12\}$
    $R = \{-20, -15, -1, 12\}$
    Not a function

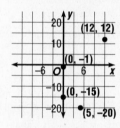

20. $D = \left\{-2, -1, 0, 1\frac{1}{2}\right\}$
    $R = \left\{\frac{1}{2}, \frac{3}{4}, 1\frac{1}{2}, -2\right\}$
    Is a function

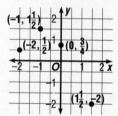

21. $g(12) = \dfrac{7}{12 - 2}$
    $= \dfrac{7}{10}$

22. $g(5.5) = \dfrac{7}{5.5 - 2}$
    $= \dfrac{7}{3.5}$
    $= 2$

23. $g(-5) = \dfrac{7}{(-5) - 2}$
    $= \dfrac{7}{-7}$
    $= -1$

24. $g(0) = \dfrac{7}{0 - 2}$
    $= \dfrac{7}{-2}$

25. $g(2) = \dfrac{7}{2 - 2}$
    $= \dfrac{7}{0}$
    undefined

26. $g(u + 1) = \dfrac{7}{(u + 2) - 2}$
    $= \dfrac{7}{u - 0}$
    $= \dfrac{7}{u}$

27. not a function

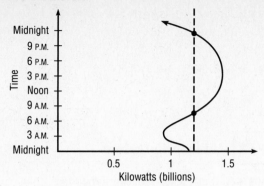

28. function

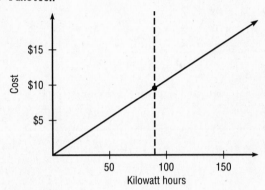

29. not a function

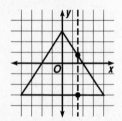

30. function

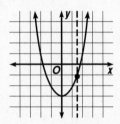

31. function

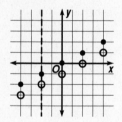

32. ENTER 5 $\boxed{y^x}$ 4 $\boxed{-}$ 3 $\boxed{\times}$ 5 $\boxed{+}$ 1 $\boxed{=}$ 611

33. ENTER $\boxed{(}$ 7 $\boxed{(-)}$ $\boxed{)}$ $\boxed{y^x}$ 4 $\boxed{-}$ 3 $\boxed{\times}$ 7 $\boxed{(-)}$ $\boxed{+}$ 1 $\boxed{=}$ 2423

34. ENTER 0.25 $\boxed{y^x}$ 4 $\boxed{-}$ 3 $\boxed{\times}$ 0.25 $\boxed{+}$ 1 $\boxed{=}$ 0.25390625

35. ENTER $\boxed{(}$ 12 $\boxed{\div}$ 5 $\boxed{(-)}$ $\boxed{)}$ $\boxed{y^x}$ 4 $\boxed{-}$ 3 $\boxed{\times}$ 12 $\boxed{\div}$ 5 $\boxed{(-)}$ $\boxed{+}$ 1 $\boxed{=}$ 41.3776

36. $(-5, 1)$

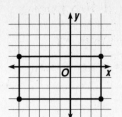

37. $(-3, -3)$

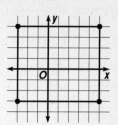

38. $h(3) = \dfrac{3^2 + 5 \cdot 3 - 6}{3 + 3}$

$= \dfrac{9 + 15 - 6}{6}$

$= \dfrac{18}{6}$

$= 3$

39. $h(-2) = \dfrac{(-2)^2 + 5 \cdot (-2) - 6}{(-2) + 3}$

$= \dfrac{4 + (-10) - 6}{1}$

$= \dfrac{-12}{1}$

$= -12$

40. $h\left(\dfrac{1}{2}\right) = \dfrac{\left(\dfrac{1}{2}\right)^2 + 5 \cdot \left(\dfrac{1}{2}\right) - 6}{\left(\dfrac{1}{2}\right) + 3}$

$= \dfrac{\dfrac{1}{4} + \dfrac{5}{2} - 6}{\dfrac{1}{2} + \dfrac{6}{2}}$

$= \dfrac{\dfrac{1}{4} + \dfrac{10}{4} - \dfrac{24}{4}}{\dfrac{7}{2}}$

$= \dfrac{\dfrac{-13}{4}}{\dfrac{7}{2}}$

$= \dfrac{-13}{4} \times \dfrac{2}{7}$

$= \dfrac{-26}{28}$

$= \dfrac{-13}{14}$

41. $h(a - 1) = \dfrac{(a - 1)^2 + 5 \cdot (a - 1) - 6}{(a - 1) + 3}$

$= \dfrac{a^2 - 2a + 1 + 5a - 5 - 6}{a + 2}$

$= \dfrac{a^2 + 3a - 10}{a + 2}$

42. The fraction is undefined whenever the denominator is equal to zero, and $(x^2 - 4) = 0$ whenever $x = 2$ or $x = -2$. Therefore x can be any number except 2 and -2. The domain is all real numbers except 2 and -2.

43.

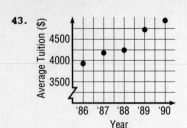

The points do not form a straight line.

44. Answers will vary.

At 60,000 feet the air pressure should be approximately 0.5 lb/in^2.

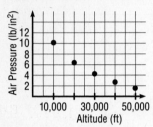

45. $4x + 3 < -9$ or $7 < 2x - 11$

$\quad\quad 4x < -12 \quad\quad 18 < 2x$

$\quad\quad\quad x < -3 \quad\quad\quad 9 < x$

$\{x | x < -3 \text{ or } x > 9\}$

46. $|y + 1| < 7$

$y + 1 < 7$ and $-(y + 1) < 7$

$\quad\quad y < 6 \quad\quad\quad -y - 1 < 7$

$\quad\quad\quad\quad\quad\quad\quad -y < 8$

$\quad\quad\quad\quad\quad\quad\quad\quad y > -8$

$\{y | -8 < y < 6\}$

47. $3x + 7 < 43$ \qquad\qquad **48.** N, W, Z, Q, R

$\quad\quad 3x < 36$

$\quad\quad\quad x < 12$

Maximum posters produced will be 11.

49. $(-4.8)^2 - 144 + 36 = 23.04 - 108$

$\quad\quad\quad\quad\quad\quad\quad\quad\quad\quad = -84.96$

50. $[-2 + (-18)]^3 - (\sqrt{10,000})(16 + 2)$

$= (-20)^3 - (100)(18)$

$= -8000 - 1800$

$= -9800$

Graphing Calculator Exploration: Graphing Linear Equations

PAGE 59 EXERCISES

Answers may vary. Sample answers are given.

1. [-10, 10] by [-10, 10]

2. [-10, 10] by [-10, 10]

3. [-10, 10] by [-10, 20]

4. [-10, 10] by [-10, 25]

5. [-10, 10] by [-40, 10]

6. [-10, 10] by [-10, 40]

7. [-2, 15] by [-10, 10]

8. [-10, 10] by [-10, 10]

9. [-30, 5] by [-5, 15]

10. [-10, 10] by [-0.5, 0.5]

11. [0, 60] by [-60, 0]

12. [-2, 2] by [-150, 10]

2-2 Linear Functions

PAGE 62 CHECKING FOR UNDERSTANDING

1. linear equation \qquad 2. standard

3. $3x + 5y = -2$ \qquad $3x + 5y = -2$

$\quad 3x = -5y - 2 \quad\quad 5y = -3x - 2$

$\quad\quad x = -\frac{5}{3}y - \frac{2}{3} \quad\quad y = -\frac{3}{5}x - \frac{2}{5}$

4. d

5. no; contains exponent greater than 1

6. yes \qquad\qquad 7. yes

8. no; contains exponent greater than 1

9. yes; $m = 0$, $b = 7$ \qquad 10. yes, $m = -3.7$, $b = 1.2$

PAGES 62-63 EXERCISES

11. $\quad\quad y = 3x - 2$ \qquad 12. $\quad\quad y = -5x + 1$

$\quad -3x + y = -2 \quad\quad\quad 5x + y = 1$

$\quad\quad 3x - y = 2$

13. $x = 10$ \qquad\qquad 14. $\quad\quad y = \frac{5}{8}x + 1$

$\quad\quad\quad\quad\quad\quad\quad\quad\quad\quad 8y = 5x + 8$

$\quad\quad\quad\quad\quad\quad\quad\quad -5x + 8y = 8$

$\quad\quad\quad\quad\quad\quad\quad\quad 5x - 8y = -8$

15. $\quad\quad x = \frac{1}{3}y - 4$ \qquad 16. $\quad\quad y = 14x$

$\quad\quad 3x = y - 12 \quad\quad -14x + y = 0$

$\quad\quad 3x - y = -12 \quad\quad 14x - y = 0$

17. $4x + 2y = 9$ \qquad 18. $5a + 3b = 7$

$\quad\quad 2y = 9 - 4x \quad\quad\quad 3b = 7 - 5a$

$\quad\quad\quad y = \frac{9}{2} - 2x \quad\quad\quad b = \frac{7 - 5a}{3}$

19. $y = x$ \qquad\qquad A-2-18

x	$y = x$	y	(x,y)
0	$y = 0$	0	(0,0)
3	$y = 3$	3	(3,3)

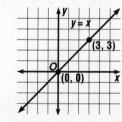

20. $y = 5x - 4$

x	$y = 5x - 4$	y	(x, y)
1	$y = 5(1) - 4$	1	$(1, 1)$
0	$y = 5(0) - 4$	-4	$(0, -4)$

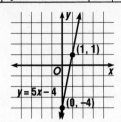

21. $-5m - 3 = n$

$$-5m = n + 3$$
$$m = \frac{n + 3}{-5}$$

22. $x - y = 3$

$$-y = -x + 3$$
$$y = x - 3$$

23. $\frac{3}{4}t + \frac{2}{3}r = 12$

$$\frac{2}{3}r = 12 - \frac{3}{4}t$$
$$r = \frac{36}{2} - \frac{9}{8}t$$
$$r = \frac{144}{8} - \frac{9}{8}t$$
$$r = \frac{144 - 9t}{8}$$

24. $2a = 3b - 4$

$$2a - 3b = -4$$
$$-3b = -2a - 4$$
$$3b = 2a + 4$$
$$b = \frac{2a + 4}{3}$$

25. $b = 2a - 3$

a	$b = 2a - 3$	b	(a, b)
2	$b = 2(2) - 3$	1	$(2, 1)$
0	$b = 2(0) - 3$	-3	$(0, -3)$

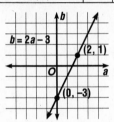

26. $x - y = 4$

$$y = x - 4$$

x	$y = x - 4$	y	(x, y)
4	$y = 4 - 4$	0	$(4, 0)$
2	$y = 2 - 4$	-2	$(2, -2)$

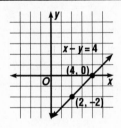

27. $2a + 3b = 6$

$$3b = -2a + 6$$
$$b = -\frac{2}{3}a + 2$$

a	$b = \frac{-2}{3}a + 2$	b	(a, b)
0	$b = \frac{-2}{3}(0) + 2$	2	$(0, 2)$
3	$b = \frac{-2}{3}(3) + 2$	0	$(3, 0)$

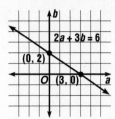

28. $5 = 5x$

$$x = 1$$

y can be any real

x	$x = 1$	y	(x, y)
1		4	$(1, 4)$
1		-1	$(1, -1)$

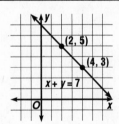

29. $x + y = 7$

$$y = -x + 7$$

x	$y = -x + 7$	y	(x, y)
2	$y = -2 + 7$	5	$(2, 5)$
4	$y = -4 + 7$	3	$(4, 3)$

30. $4x + 3y = 12$

$$3y = -4x + 12$$
$$y = \frac{-4}{3}x + 4$$

x	$y = \frac{-4}{3}x + 4$	y	(x, y)
0	$y = \frac{-4}{3}(0) + 4$	4	$(0, 4)$
3	$y = \frac{-4}{3}(3) + 4$	0	$(3, 0)$

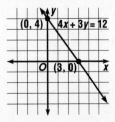

31. $f(x) = 2x + 1$

$y = 2x + 1$

x	$y = 2x + 1$	y	(x, y)
0	$y = 2(0) + 1$	1	$(0, 1)$
1	$y = 2(1) + 1$	3	$(1, 3)$

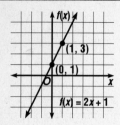

32. $3y + 7 = 12$

$3y = 5$

$y = \dfrac{5}{3}$

x can be any real.

x	$y = \dfrac{5}{3}$	y	(x, y)
0		$\dfrac{5}{3}$	$\left(0, \dfrac{5}{3}\right)$
3		$\dfrac{5}{3}$	$\left(3, \dfrac{5}{3}\right)$

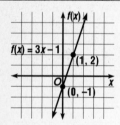

33. $f(x) = 3x - 1$

$y = 3x - 1$

x	$y = 3x - 1$	y	(x, y)
0	$y = 3(0) - 1$	-1	$(0, -1)$
1	$y = 3(1) - 1$	2	$(1, 2)$

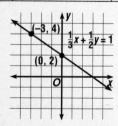

34. $\dfrac{1}{3}x + \dfrac{1}{2}y = 1$

$\dfrac{1}{2}y = -\dfrac{1}{3}x + 1$

$y = -\dfrac{2}{3}x + 2$

x	$y = -\dfrac{2}{3} + 2$	y	(x, y)
0	$y = -\dfrac{2}{3}(0) + 2$	2	$(0, 2)$
-3	$y = -\dfrac{2}{3}(-3) + 2$	4	$(-3, 4)$

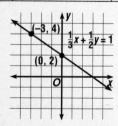

35. $\dfrac{x}{4} - \dfrac{y}{3} = 2$

$-\dfrac{y}{3} = -\dfrac{x}{4} + 2$

$y = \dfrac{3}{4}x - 6$

x	$y = \dfrac{3}{4}x - 6$	y	(x, y)
0	$y = \dfrac{3}{4}(0) - 6$	-6	$(0, -6)$
4	$y = \dfrac{3}{4}(4) - 6$	-3	$(4, -3)$

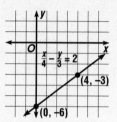

36. $\dfrac{x}{3} + \dfrac{y}{2} = \dfrac{15}{2}$

$\dfrac{y}{2} = -\dfrac{x}{3} + \dfrac{15}{2}$

$y = -\dfrac{2}{3}x + 15$

x	$y = -\dfrac{2}{3}x + 15$	y	(x, y)
0	$y = -\dfrac{2}{3}(0) + 15$	15	$(0, 15)$
-3	$y = -\dfrac{2}{3}(-3) + 15$	17	$(-3, 17)$

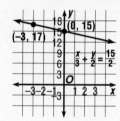

37. If you subtract 50 from the total number of magazines Emilio sells, you will arrive at the number of magazines over 50 that he sells. Multiply that number by 30¢ and add \$150 to get the total salary.

$s = 150 + 0.30(n - 50);\ n > 50$

n = number of magazines

38. The linear equation $x = c$ is not a linear function because the same x value is paired with an infinite number of y values.

39. $t = 4.5$ so $c = 12 + 20(4.5)$

$c = 12 + 90$

$c = 102$ Total charge = \$102.

22

40. b = total bill

c = amount charged

$b = c + 0.02c + 5$

$b = 1.02c + 5$

$c = 110$ so $b = 1.02(110) + 5$

$b = 112.20 + 5$

$b = 117.20$ The bill is \$117.20

41.
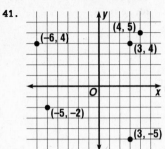

It is not a function because one x value (3) is paired with two y values (4 and -5).

42. $f(-3) = (-3)^2 - 3(-3) - 9$

$= 9 + 9 - 9$

$= 9$

43. MATH MAHT MHAT MHTA MTAH MTHA

ATHM ATMH AMTH AMHT AHMT AHTM

THMA THAM TAHM TAMH TMAH TMHA

HMAT HMTA HTMA HTAM HATM HAMT

24 ways

44. The perimeter is the sum of all the sides. All the sides of a square are equal in length so $4\ell = p$, where ℓ is the length of one side and p is the perimeter. If $p = 42$, $4\ell = 42$.

$$\ell = \frac{42}{4} = 10.5$$

The length of one side is 10.5 inches.

45. Let p = the number of gorillas at the zoo now. If the 5 that were removed are now returned, there would be $p + 5$ gorillas. Therefore $p + 5$ is the original number of gorillas at the zoo.

2-3 Problem-Solving Strategy: Look for a Pattern

1. A diagonal is a segment that connects two nonconsecutive vertices of a polygon.

2. Continuing the table from page 64:

Number of sides	7	8	9	10	11	12
Number of diagonals	14	20	27	35	44	54

+6 +7 +8 +9 +10

12 sides = 54 diagonals

3. $2^7 = 128$, $2^8 = 256$, $2^9 = 512$

4. 6, 10, 15, 21, 28, $\boxed{36}$

+4 +5 +6 +7 +8

5. 1, 4, 9, 16, 25, $\boxed{36}$

1^2 2^2 3^2 4^2 5^2 6^2

6.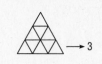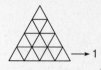

$16 + 6 + 1 + 3 + 1 = 27$

7.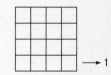

$16 + 9 + 4 + 1 = 30$

8. yes

Finish

Start

9. \$1 + \$5 + \$10 + \$20 + \$50 + \$100 + \$500 = \$686

10. The pyramid has to be 10 cans tall, so start at the one (the top) and add $(n + 1)$ where n is the previous number until you reach 10 numbers.

$1 + 2 + 3 + 4 + 5 + 6 + 7 + 8 + 9 + 10 = 55$

Locker numbers

Number of students

	1	2	3	4	5	6	7	8	9	10	11	12	13	14	15	16
1	O	O	O	O	O	O	O	O	O	O	O	O	O	O	O	O
2		C	O	C	O	C	O	C	O	C	O	C	O	C	O	C
3			C	C	O	O	O	C	C	O	O	O	C	C	O
4				O	O	O	O	C	C	O	C	O	C	O	C	O
5					C	O	O	O	C	O	O	O	O	C	O
6						C	O	O	C	O	O	O	C	O	O
7							C	O	C	O	O	O	O	C	O
8								C	C	O	O	O	O	O	C
9									O	O	O	O	O	O	C
10										C	O	O	O	O	C
11											C	O	O	O	C
12												C	O	O	C
13													C	O	O	C
14														C	O	C
15															C	C
16	O	C	C	O	C	C	C	C	O	C	C	C	C	C	O

The first student opens all the lockers. The second skips the first and changes every second locker. The third student skips the first two and changes every third locker. With this pattern, the lockers whose numbers are perfect squares; that is 1, 4, 9, 16, 25, and so on, remain open.

2-4 Slopes and Intercepts

1. Answers will vary.

2. Slope of vertical line = undefined

   Slope of horizontal line = 0

   Slope of nonvertical, nonhorizontal lines

   = all real numbers except 0

3. In a plane, lines with the same slopes are parallel.

4. In a plane, two nonvertical lines are perpendicular if the product of their slopes is −1.

5. Answers will vary.

6. The slopes are negative reciprocals of each other.

7. The slopes are equal.

8. y-intercept = −2 (where the line crosses the y-axis)

   x-intercept = −3 (where the line crosses the x-axis)

   slope $= \dfrac{-2 - 0}{0 - (-3)} = \dfrac{-2}{3}$

9. y-intercept = 2

   x-intercept = −2

   slope $= \dfrac{3 - 0}{1 - (-2)} = \dfrac{3}{3} = 1$

10. y-intercept = none

    x-intercept = −5

    slope = undefined (vertical line)

11. y-intercept = 2

    x-intercept = none

    slope = 0 (horizontal line)

12. y-intercept = −4

    x-intercept = 2

    slope $= \dfrac{-4 - (-2)}{0 - 1} = \dfrac{-2}{-1} = 2$

13. y-intercept = 2

    x-intercept = 3

    slope $= \dfrac{4 - 2}{-3 - 0} = \dfrac{2}{-3} = -\dfrac{2}{3}$

14. parallel: 8 and 13 (same slope)

    perpendicular: 10 and 11 (slopes are negative reciprocals)

15. $m = \dfrac{-4 - 1}{8 - 6}$

    $= \dfrac{-5}{2}$

    $= -\dfrac{5}{2}$

16. $m = \dfrac{7 - (-6)}{5 - 4}$

    $= \dfrac{13}{1}$

    $= 13$

17. $m = \dfrac{-4 - 2}{-5 - 5}$

    $= \dfrac{-6}{-10}$

    $= \dfrac{6}{10}$

    $= \dfrac{3}{5}$

18. $m = \dfrac{8 - 8}{1 - 7}$

    $= \dfrac{0}{-6}$

    $= 0$

19. $m = \dfrac{3 - (-9)}{2.5 - 1}$

    $= \dfrac{12}{1.5}$

    $= 8$

20. $m = \dfrac{2 - (-2)}{b - b}$

    $= \dfrac{4}{0}$

    $=$ undefined

For problems 21-26, pick two points and find the slope of the line.

21. (0,3), (3,0)

    $m = \dfrac{3 - 0}{0 - 3}$

    $= \dfrac{3}{-3}$

    $= -1$

    falls

22. (−6,0), (−6,2)

    $m = \dfrac{0 - 2}{-6 - (-6)}$

    $= \dfrac{-2}{0}$

    $=$ undefined

    vertical

23. (0,−6), (3,0)

    $m = \dfrac{-6 - 0}{0 - 3}$

    $= \dfrac{-6}{-3}$

    $= 2$

    rises

24. (−1,−10), (−16,0)

    $m = \dfrac{-10 - 0}{-1 - (-16)}$

    $= \dfrac{-10}{15}$

    $= -\dfrac{2}{3}$

    falls

25. (0,0), (3,2)

    $m = \dfrac{0 - 2}{0 - 3}$

    $= \dfrac{-2}{-3}$

    $= \dfrac{2}{3}$

    rises

26. (5,3.5), (0, 3.5)

    $m = \dfrac{3.5 - 3.5}{5 - 0}$

    $= \dfrac{0}{5}$

    $= 0$

    horizontal

27. $y = 6(0) + 9$ $0 = 6x + 9$ y-intercept: 9

    $y = 0 + 9$ $-9 = 6x$ x-intercept: $-\dfrac{3}{2}$

    $y = 9$ $\dfrac{9}{6} = x$

    $-\dfrac{3}{2} = x$

28. $y = -3(0) - 5$ $0 = -3x - 5$ y-intercept: −5

    $y = -5$ $5 = -3x$ x-intercept: $-\dfrac{5}{3}$

    $-\dfrac{5}{3} = x$

29. y-intercept: −2

    x-intercept: none

30. y-intercept: none

    x-intercept: 8

31. $y + 6 = 5(0)$ $0 + 6 = 5x$ y-intercept: −6

    $y + 6 = 0$ $6 = 5x$ x-intercept: $\dfrac{6}{5}$

    $y = -6$ $\dfrac{6}{5} = x$

32. $3(0) = y$ $3x = 0$ y-intercept: 0

    $0 = y$ $x = 0$ x-intercept: 0

33. $f(0) = 0 - 2$ $0 = x - 2$ y-intercept: −2

    $= -2$ $2 = x$ x-intercept: 2

34. $g(0) = 4(0) - 1$ $0 = 4x - 1$ y-intercept: -1

$\qquad = 0 - 1$ $1 = 4x$ x-intercept: $\frac{1}{4}$

$\qquad = -1$ $\frac{1}{4} = x$

35. $5(0) + 3y = 15$ $5x + 3(0) = 15$ y-intercept: 5

$\qquad 3y = 15$ $\qquad 5x = 15$ x-intercept: 3

$\qquad y = 5$ $\qquad x = 3$

36. $(0,0)$, $m = 3$ **37.** $(-1,1)$, $m = \frac{1}{4}$

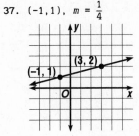

38. $(-4,1)$ $m = \frac{3}{5}$ **39.** $(2,2)$, no slope

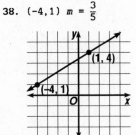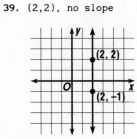

40. Find the slope of $x + y = 12$. Pick 2 points, for example $(4,8)$ and $(6,6)$, and calculate m.

$m = \frac{8 - 6}{4 - 6}$

$\quad = \frac{2}{-2}$

$\quad = -1$

Since parallel lines have the same slope, $m = -1$ for the line to be graphed. Graph a line through $(0,0)$, $m = -1$.

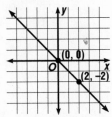

41. $(-3,-1)$, no slope   **42.** $(1,1)$, no slope and $m = 0$

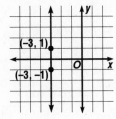

43. First, find the x-intercept.

$\qquad 3x - 2(0) = 24$

$\qquad\qquad 3x = 24$

$\qquad\qquad x = 8$

The point $(8,0)$ is at the x-intercept. Find another point, say when $x = 0$.

$\qquad 3(0) - 2y = 24$

$\qquad\qquad -2y = 24$

$\qquad\qquad y = -12$

Now use these two points $(8,0)$ and $(0,-12)$ to find the slope.

$m = \frac{0 - (-12)}{8 - 0}$

$\quad = \frac{12}{8}$ or $\frac{3}{2}$

The slope of the perpendicular line is the negative reciprocal of $m = \frac{3}{2}$, or $m = -\frac{2}{3}$.

The graph is through the point $(8,0)$ with slope $= -\frac{2}{3}$.

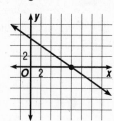

44. First, find two points on each line.

$2y + x = 6$	$y = 2x + 3$
$2y = 6 - x$	If $x = 0$, $y = 2(0) + 3$
$y = 3 - \frac{1}{2}x$	$= 3$
	$(0,3)$
$x = 0$, $y = 3 - \frac{1}{2}(0)$	If $y = 0$, $0 = 2x + 3$
$= 3$	$-3 = 2x$
$(0,3)$	$-\frac{3}{2} = x$
If $y = 0$, $0 = 3 - \frac{1}{2}x$	$\left(-\frac{3}{2}, 0\right)$
$-3 = -\frac{1}{2}x$	
$6 = x$	
$(6,0)$	

Now find the slope of each line and graph.

$2y + x = 6$	$y = 2x + 3$
$m = \dfrac{3 - 0}{0 - 6}$	$m = \dfrac{3 - 0}{0 - \left(-\frac{3}{2}\right)}$
$= \dfrac{3}{-6}$	$m = \dfrac{3}{\frac{3}{2}}$
$= -\dfrac{1}{2}$	$m = \dfrac{2}{3} \cdot 3$
	$m = 2$

The line containing $(8,4)$ must be parallel to $y = 2x + 3$, so its slope is 2. Graph this line.

The other line containing $(8,4)$ must be parallel to $2y + x = 6$, so its slope is $-\frac{1}{2}$. Graph this line.

The vertices are $(8,4)$, $(6,0)$, $(0,3)$, $(2,7)$.

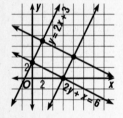

45.

$y = x$	$y = 2x$
If $x = 0$, $y = 0$ $(0,0)$	If $x = 0$, $y = 0$ $(0,0)$
If $x = 1$, $y = 1$ $(1,1)$	If $x = 1$, $y = 2$ $(1,2)$
$m = \dfrac{0 - 1}{0 - 1}$	$m = \dfrac{0 - 2}{0 - 1}$
$= \dfrac{-1}{-1}$ or 1	$= \dfrac{-2}{-1}$ or 2
$y = 5x$	$y = \frac{1}{2}x$
If $x = 0$, $y = 0$ $(0,0)$	If $x = 0$, $y = 0$ $(0,0)$
If $x = 1$, $y = 5$ $(1,5)$	If $x = 2$, $y = 1$ $(2,1)$
$m = \dfrac{0 - 5}{0 - 1}$	$m = \dfrac{0 - 1}{0 - 2}$
$= \dfrac{-5}{-1}$ or 5	$= \dfrac{-1}{-2}$ or $\dfrac{1}{2}$

$y = \frac{1}{5}x$

If $x = 0$, $y = 0$ $(0,0)$

If $x = 5$, $y = 1$ $(5,1)$

$m = \dfrac{0 - 1}{0 - 5}$

$= \dfrac{-1}{-5}$ or $\dfrac{1}{5}$

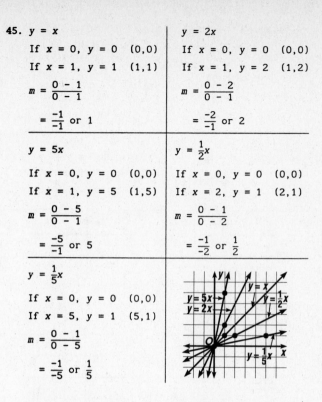

The greater the absolute value of the slope, the steeper the line is.

46. The rate of increase would be the change in population (y) divided by the change in years (x).

rate of increase $= \dfrac{183{,}000 - 172{,}000}{1991 - 1988}$

$= \dfrac{11{,}000}{3}$

$\approx 3{,}667$ people per year

47. rate of travel $= \dfrac{\text{change in miles}}{\text{change in time}}$

$= \dfrac{455 - 195}{14 - 10}$ (must change 2:00 to 14:00)

$= \dfrac{260}{4}$

$= 65$ mph

48. 100, 95, 85, 70, $\boxed{50}$

-5 -10 -15 -20

49.

2	2	2	2	2	2

↑ ↑ ↑ ↑ ↑

cuts = 5

50. $|x - 6| = 3x + 4$

$x - 6 = 3x + 4$ or $x - 6 = -(3x + 4)$

$-6 = 2x + 4$ $\qquad x - 6 = -3x - 4$

$-10 = 2x$ $\qquad\qquad 4x - 6 = -4$

$-5 = x$ $\qquad\qquad\quad 4x = 2$

$\qquad\qquad\qquad\qquad x = \dfrac{2}{4}$ or $\dfrac{1}{2}$

Check:

$|-5 - 6| = 3(-5) + 4$ $\qquad \left|\dfrac{1}{2} - 6\right| = 3\left(\dfrac{1}{2}\right) + 4$

$|-11| = -15 + 4$ $\qquad\qquad \left|\dfrac{1}{2} - \dfrac{12}{2}\right| = \dfrac{3}{2} + \dfrac{8}{2}$

$11 \neq -11$ $\qquad\qquad\qquad \left|-\dfrac{11}{2}\right| = \dfrac{11}{2}$

does not check $\qquad\qquad\qquad\quad \dfrac{11}{2} = \dfrac{11}{2}$

The only solution is $x = \dfrac{1}{2}$.

51. Distributive property

PAGE 72   MID-CHAPTER REVIEW

1. $D = \{0, 5, 10, 15, 20, 25, 30, 35, 40\}$

$R = \{30, 27, 16, 9, 4, 1, -2, -4, -5\}$

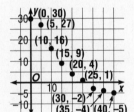

Is a function

2. $g(7) = \dfrac{7^2 - 2(7) + 3}{7 - 5}$

$= \dfrac{49 - 14 + 3}{2}$

$= \dfrac{35 + 3}{2}$

$= \dfrac{38}{2}$

$= 19$

3. $2x + 4y = 7$

$4y = 7 - 2x$

$y = \dfrac{7 - 2x}{4}$

4. $\dfrac{3}{2}t + \dfrac{4}{7}s = 12$

$\dfrac{4}{7}s = 12 - \dfrac{3}{2}t$

$s = \dfrac{7}{4}(12) - \dfrac{7}{4}\left(\dfrac{3}{2}\right)t$

$s = 21 - \dfrac{21}{8}t$

5. $3a + 2b - 4c = 24$

$2b - 4c = 24 - 3a$

$-4c = 24 - 3a - 2b$

$c = \dfrac{24}{-4} - \dfrac{3a}{-4} - \dfrac{2b}{-4}$

$c = -6 + \dfrac{3}{4}a + \dfrac{1}{2}b$

$c = \dfrac{3}{4}a + \dfrac{1}{2}b - 6$

6. $g(x) = x(2 - x)$

$= 2x - x^2$

Not linear because of x^2.

7. $2x - 5y = 10$

$-5y = 10 - 2x$

$y = \dfrac{10}{-5} - \dfrac{2}{-5}x$

$y = -2 + \dfrac{2}{5}x$

$y = \dfrac{2}{5}x - 2$

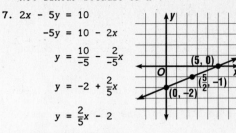

x	0	5	$\dfrac{5}{2}$
y	-2	0	-1

8. $\quad 3 \times 60 = 180 \quad = 9 \times 20$

$4 \times 90 = 360 \quad = 9 \times 40$

$5 \times 108 = 540 \quad = 9 \times 60$

$6 \times 120 = 720 \quad = 9 \times 80$

$7 \times 128\dfrac{4}{7} = 900 \quad = 9 \times 100$

$8 \times \boxed{135} = 1080 \quad = 9 \times 120$

9. x-intercept: 3 $\qquad$ y-intercept: -2

$2x - 3(0) = 6 \qquad\quad 2(0) - 3y = 6$

$2x - 0 = 6 \qquad\qquad\quad 0 - 3y = 6$

$2x = 6 \qquad\qquad\qquad -3y = 6$

$x = \dfrac{6}{2} \qquad\qquad\qquad y = \dfrac{6}{-3}$

$x = 3 \qquad\qquad\qquad\quad y = -2$

$(3, 0) \qquad\qquad\qquad\quad (0, -2)$

$m = \dfrac{0 - t - (-2)}{3 - 0}$

$= \dfrac{2}{3}$

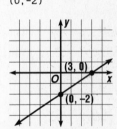

10. x-intercept: $\dfrac{9}{2}$ $\qquad$ y-intercept: 3

$2x + 3(0) = 9 \qquad\quad 2(0) + 3y = 9$

$2x = 9 \qquad\qquad\qquad 3y = 9$

$x = \dfrac{9}{2} \qquad\qquad\qquad y = 3$

$\left(\dfrac{9}{2}, 0\right) \qquad\qquad\qquad (0, 3)$

$m = \dfrac{0 - 3}{\dfrac{9}{2} - 0}$

$= \dfrac{-3}{\dfrac{9}{2}}$

$= -3 \cdot \dfrac{2}{9}$

$= -\dfrac{6}{9}$ or $-\dfrac{2}{3}$

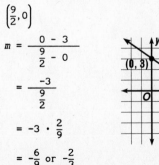

Writing Linear Equations

1. $y = mx + b$; m is the slope and b is the y-intercept.

2. x is on the horizontal axis and y is on the vertical axis.

3. Find the slope; this is the same as $-\frac{A}{B}$. Use A and B to substitute the values into the standard form $Ax + By = C$. Substitute the value for one of the points in place of x and y to find C. Now you know A, B, and C and can put these into the form $Ax + By = C$.

4. A line parallel to the line has the same slope, $\frac{1}{2}$. A line perpendicular to the line has a slope that is the negative reciprocal of $\frac{1}{2}$, $-\frac{2}{1}$ or -2.

5. $\frac{c}{d}$

6. $m = -3$, $b = -4$

7. $y = -3x - 4$
   $3x + y = -4$

8. $y = 5x + 6$

9. $y = 2.5x + 0$
   $y = 2.5x$

10. $y = -\frac{1}{4}x - 9$

11. $y = 0x + 0$
   $y = 0 + 0$
   $y = 0$

12. $m = 4$, $b = 5$
   $y = 4x + 5$

13. $m = -\frac{3}{4}$, $b = -3$

14. $m = \frac{1}{3}$, $b = 0$

15. $-y = 0.2x + 6$
   $y = -0.2x - 6$
   $m = -0.2$, $b = -6$

16. $6y = 3x - 12$
   $y = \frac{3}{6}x - \frac{12}{6}$
   $y = \frac{1}{2}x - 2$
   $m = \frac{1}{2}$, $b = -2$

17. $-5y = 3x - 30$
   $y = \frac{3}{-5}x - \frac{30}{-5}$
   $y = -\frac{3}{5} + 6$
   $m = -\frac{3}{5}$, $b = 6$

18. $y = cx + t$
   $m = c$, $b = t$

19. The slope of $\overleftrightarrow{FG} = -\frac{2}{3}$, $b = 4$.

   $y = -\frac{2}{3}x + 4$

   $\frac{2}{3}x + y = 4$

   $2x + 3y = 12$

20. $2x - 5y = 10$
   $-5y = -2x + 10$
   $y = \frac{2}{5}x - 2$

21. $3x - y = 6$
   $-y = -3x + 6$
   $y = 3x - 6$

22. $2x - 2y = 4$
   $-2y = -2x + 4$
   $y = x - 2$

23. $2x = 11$
   $x = \frac{11}{2}$
   no slope-intercept form

24. $m = \frac{1}{2}$, $(6,4)$
   $y = \frac{1}{2}x + b$
   $4 = \frac{1}{2}(6) + b$
   $4 = 3 + b$
   $1 = b$
   $\boxed{y = \frac{1}{2}x + 1}$
   $-\frac{1}{2}x + y = 1$
   $\boxed{x - 2y = -2}$

25. $m = -\frac{4}{5}$, $(2,-3)$
   $y = -\frac{4}{5}x + b$
   $-3 = -\frac{4}{5}(2) + b$
   $-\frac{15}{5} + \frac{8}{5} = b$
   $-\frac{7}{5} = b$
   $\boxed{y = -\frac{4}{5}x - \frac{7}{5}}$
   $\frac{4}{5}x + y = -\frac{7}{5}$
   $\boxed{4x + 5y = -7}$

26. $m = 5$, $(0,0)$
   $y = 5x + b$
   $y = 5x + 0$
   $\boxed{y = 5x}$
   $-5x + y = 0$
   $\boxed{5x - y = 0}$

27. $(6,1)$, $(8,-4)$
   $m = \frac{1 - (-4)}{6 - 8}$
   $= \frac{1 + 4}{-2}$
   $= \frac{-5}{2}$ or $-\frac{5}{2}$
   $y = -\frac{5}{2}x + b$
   $1 = -\frac{5}{2}(6) + b$
   $1 = -15 + b$
   $16 = b$
   $\boxed{y = -\frac{5}{2}x + 16}$
   $\frac{5}{2}x + y = 16$
   $\boxed{5x + 2y = 32}$

28. $(6,1)$, $(6,7)$ The slope is undefined, so there is no slope-intercept form. It is a vertical line, $x = 6$.
   $m = \frac{1 - 7}{6 - 6}$
   $= \frac{-6}{0}$

29. $(4,6)$, $(0,0)$
   $m = \frac{6 - 0}{4 - 0}$ $b = 0$
   $= \frac{6}{4}$ or $\frac{3}{2}$
   $y = \frac{3}{2}x + 0$
   $\boxed{y = \frac{3}{2}x}$
   $-\frac{3}{2}x + y = 0$
   $\boxed{3x - 2y = 0}$

30. $(-3,0)$, $(0,6)$

$m = \dfrac{0 - 6}{-3 - 0}$, $b = 6$

$\quad = \dfrac{-6}{-3}$ or 2

$\boxed{y = 2x + 6}$

$-2x + y = 6$

$\boxed{2x - y = -6}$

31. $\left(\dfrac{1}{3}, 0\right)$, $\left(0, -\dfrac{1}{4}\right)$

$m = \dfrac{0 - \left(-\dfrac{1}{4}\right)}{\dfrac{1}{3} - 0}$, $b = -\dfrac{1}{4}$

$\quad = \dfrac{\dfrac{1}{4}}{\dfrac{1}{3}}$

$\quad = \dfrac{3}{4}$

$\boxed{y = \dfrac{3}{4}x - \dfrac{1}{4}}$

$-\dfrac{3}{4}x + y = -\dfrac{1}{4}$

$\boxed{3x - 4y = 1}$

32. $(0,0)$, $(0,2)$

$m = \dfrac{0 - 2}{0 - 0}$

$m = \dfrac{-2}{0}$

no slope-intercept
form; is a vertical
line, $x = 0$

33. $(-1,-1)$, $(8,-1)$

$m = \dfrac{-1 - (-1)}{-1 - 8}$

$m = \dfrac{0}{-9}$

$m = 0$

$y = 0x + b$

$-1 = 0(-1) + b$

$-1 = b$

$y = 0(x) - 1$

$\boxed{y = -1}$

Standard form is also
$y = -1$.

34. $y = 2x - 4$

$m = 2$, $(4,2)$

$y = 2x + b$

$2 = 2(4) + b$

$2 = 8 + b$

$-6 = b$

$\boxed{y = 2x - 6}$

35. $y = -3x + 7$

$m = -3$

perpendicular: $m = \dfrac{1}{3}$, $(-2,0)$

$y = \dfrac{1}{3}x + b$

$0 = \dfrac{1}{3}(-2) + b$

$0 = -\dfrac{2}{3} + b$

$\dfrac{2}{3} = b$

$\boxed{y = \dfrac{1}{3}x + \dfrac{2}{3}}$

36. $m = \dfrac{3 - 6}{3 - 0} = \dfrac{-3}{3}$ or -1

parallel: $m = -1$, $(-3,-1)$

$y = -1x + b$

$-1 = -1(-3) + b$

$-1 = 3 + b$

$-4 = b$

$y = -1x - 4$ or $y = -x - 4$

37. $3x - \dfrac{1}{5}y = 3 \quad A = 3$, $B = -\dfrac{1}{5}$

$m = -\dfrac{A}{B} = -\dfrac{3}{\left(-\dfrac{1}{5}\right)} = 15$

perpendicular: $m = -\dfrac{1}{15}$

$A = 1$, $B = 15$, $(6,-5)$

$Ax + By = C$

$1(6) + 15(-5) = C$

$6 + -75 = C$

$-69 = C$

$Ax + By = C$

$\boxed{x + 15y = -69}$

or $m = -\dfrac{1}{15}$, $(6,-5)$

$-5 = -\dfrac{1}{15}(6) + b$

$-5 = -\dfrac{6}{15} + b$

$b = -\dfrac{69}{15}$ or $-\dfrac{23}{5}$

$\boxed{y = -\dfrac{1}{15}x - \dfrac{23}{5}}$

38. $5(3) + k(-1) = 8$

$15 - k = 8$

$-k = -7$

$k = 7$

39. $4(4) - k(3) = 7$

$16 - 3k = 7$

$-3k = -9$

$k = 3$

40. $3(0) + 8(0.5) = k$

$0 + 4 = k$

$4 = k$

41. $k(7) + 3(2) = 11$

$7k + 6 = 11$

$7k = 5$

$k = \dfrac{5}{7}$

42. The parallelogram may be formed three ways with
three different points.

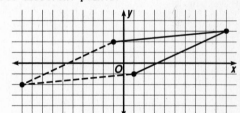

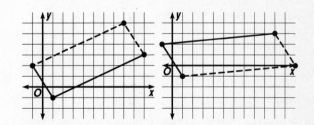

43. Use $y = 0.445x + 14.7$ from Example 3.

$y = 0.445(35,840) + 14.7$

$y = 15948.8 + 14.7$

$y = 15963.5$

Approximate pressure is $15{,}963.5$ lb/in^2.

44. $m = \dfrac{\text{change in temperature } (t)}{\text{change in number of chirps } (n)}$

$m = \dfrac{18 - 16}{60 - 50}$

$m = \dfrac{2}{10}$ or $\dfrac{1}{5}$

$t = mn + b$ If $n = 130$,

$16 = \dfrac{1}{5}(50) + b$ $t = \dfrac{1}{5}(130) + 6$

$16 = 10 + b$ $t = 26 + 6$

$6 = b$ $t = 32$

$\boxed{t = \dfrac{1}{5}n + 6}$ Temperature when number of chirps equals 130 is $32°$C.

45. Let d = number of deer.

Start with 6000 and subtract 75 times the number of years (x).

$d = 6000 - 75x$

46. Let x = number of miles.

Let y = cost.

a) $y = 0.25x + 20$

   $y = 0.25x + 35$

b) $m = 0.25$; have the same slope so they are parallel

c) Compact: Luxury:

   $y = 0.25(750) + 20$ $y = 0.25(750) + 35$

   $y = 187.50 + 20$ $y = 187.50 + 35$

   $y = 207.50$ $y = 222.50$

Difference = $222.50 - 207.50 = \$15.00$

47. a. $m = -2$, y: 2   b. $m = \dfrac{4}{3}$, y: $5\dfrac{2}{3}$

    $y = -2x + 2$

                        $y = \dfrac{4}{3}x + 5\dfrac{2}{3}$

  c. $m = \dfrac{4}{3}$, y: $-\dfrac{2}{3}$ d. $m = \dfrac{1}{2}$, y: $-3\dfrac{1}{2}$

    $y = \dfrac{4}{3}x - \dfrac{2}{3}$ $y = \dfrac{1}{2}x - 3\dfrac{1}{2}$

48. $m = \dfrac{4 - 2}{5 - 2} = \dfrac{2}{3}$

49. $3(0) - 2y = 12$ $3x - 2(0) = 12$

         $-2y = 12$ $3x = 12$

            $y = -6$ $x = 4$

y-intercept $= -6$ x-intercept $= 4$

50. $f(-2) = (-2)^2 - 4$ **51.** $3x - 5 > -26$

          $= 4 - 4$ $3x > -21$

          $= 0$ $x > -7$

                          $\{x \mid x > -7\}$

52.

RGBW	GRBW	BWRG	WBRG
RGWB	GRWB	BWGR	WBGR
RBWG	GBRW	BGWR	WRBG
RBGW	GBWR	BGRW	WRGB
RWBG	GWBR	BRGW	WGRB
RWGB	GWRB	BRWG	WGBR

      24 ways

PAGES 82-83   **CHECKING FOR UNDERSTANDING**

1. to provide an equation that can be used for predictions when only an estimate is needed

2. scatter plots

3. because weight might be affected by height, but height is not determined by weight

4. $h = 0.5(2) + 0.5$ **5.** $h = 0.5(5) + 0.5$

     $= 1.0 + 0.5$ $= 2.5 + 0.5$

     $= 1.5$ cm $= 3.0$ cm

6. $h = 0.5(12) + 0.5$

     $= 6.0 + 0.5$

     $= 6.5$ cm

7. a. $m = \dfrac{22,000,000 - 10,000,000}{50,000 - 20,000}$

         $= \dfrac{12,000,000}{30,000}$

         $= 400$

b. $S = Ax + B$

  $10,000,000 = 400(20,000) + B$

  $10,000,000 = 8,000,000 + B$

    $2,000,000 = B$

c. $S = 400A + 2,000,000$

d. $S = 400(10,000) + 2,000,000$

     $= 4,000,000 + 2,000,000$

     $= 6,000,000$ \$6,000,000

e. $16,000,000 = 400A + 2,000,000$

  $14,000,000 = 400A$

  $\dfrac{14,000,000}{400} = A$

    $35,000 = A$ \$35,000

PAGES 83-84   **EXERCISES**

8. a. slope $= \dfrac{72 - 60}{24 - 20}$ b. As the person's height *increases*, their head size *increases*.

            $= \dfrac{12}{4}$ or 3

  c. $h = 3m + b$ d. $66 = 3m$

    $60 = 3(20) + b$ $\dfrac{66}{3} = m$

    $60 = 60 + b$ $22 = m$

      $0 = b$ 22 inches

    $h = 3m + 0$

    $h = 3m$

  e. $76 = 3m$ f. $h = 3(18)$

    $25\dfrac{1}{3} = m$ $h = 54$

                     54 inches

    $25\dfrac{1}{3}$ inches

9. a.

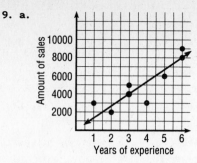

Years of experience

b. Draw a line.
Pick two points on the line, for example (2,2666) and (5,6665).

$m = \dfrac{6665 - 2666}{5 - 2}$

$= \dfrac{3999}{3}$

$= 1333$

$y = 1333x + b$

$2666 = 1333(2) + b$

$2666 = 2666 + b$

$0 = b$

$y = 1333x + 0$

$y = 1333x$

c. $y = 1333(8)$

$y = 10,664$

$\$10,644$

d. $y = 1333(0)$

$y = 0$

$\$0$

e. $7300 = 1333x$

$\dfrac{7300}{1333} = x$

$5.5 \approx x$

about 5.5 years

10. a. (66,143), (68,153)

$m = \dfrac{153 - 143}{68 - 66}$

$= \dfrac{10}{2}$ or 5

$y = mx + b$

$143 = 5(66) + b$

$143 = 330 + b$

$-187 = b$

$y = 5x - 187$

b. $y = 5(71) - 187$

$= 355 - 187$

$= 168$

168 lb

c. $190 = 5x - 187$

$377 = 5x$

$75.4 = x$

75.4 inches

d. They are very similar and when graphed almost define the same line.

11. Answers will vary. Make a table showing the x-coordinates and y-coordinates for the data. Add a column to the table for the y-coordinates that result using the x values from the data and the prediction equation. If the two sets of y-coordinates vary greatly, the prediction equation is probably not a good one.

12. No, eventually there is a maximum speed one can obtain regardless of how much experience they have. The graph would climb and then level off at that point.

13. a.

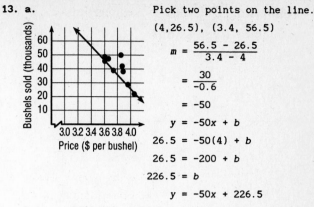

Price ($ per bushel)

Pick two points on the line. (4,26.5), (3.4, 56.5)

$m = \dfrac{56.5 - 26.5}{3.4 - 4}$

$= \dfrac{30}{-0.6}$

$= -50$

$y = -50x + b$

$26.5 = -50(4) + b$

$26.5 = -200 + b$

$226.5 = b$

$y = -50x + 226.5$

b. $y = -50(3.90) + 226.5$

$y = -195 + 226.5$

$= 31.5$

31,500 bushels

c. $25.5 = -50x + 226.5$

$-201 = -50x$

$4.02 = x$

$\$4.02$

14. Let $c - 20$ be the items over 20 she sells.
If $c > 20$, $p = 240 + 0.40(c - 20)$
If $c \leq 20$, $p = 240$.

15. $m = \dfrac{-2 - 1}{8 - 5}$

$= \dfrac{-3}{3}$ or -1

$m = -\dfrac{A}{B} = -1$

$A = 1\ B = 1$

$Ax + By = C$

$1(5) + 1(1) = C$

$5 + 1 = C$

$6 = C$

$Ax + By = C$

$x + y = 6$

16. $m = \dfrac{-2 - 0}{-4 - 0}$

$= \dfrac{-2}{-4}$ or $\dfrac{1}{2}$

perpendicular line:

$m = \dfrac{-2}{1} = -2$

17. $y - 3x = 2$

$y - 3(0) = 2$

$y = 2$

y-intercept: 2

x	0	1
y	2	5

$m = \dfrac{5 - 2}{1 - 0}$

$= \dfrac{3}{1}$ or 3

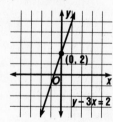

18. $|30(-2) - 20| + 72 = |-60 - 20| + 72$

$= |-80| + 72$

$= 80 + 72$

$= 152$

19. $3(x + 2y) - 4(3x - 2y) = 3x + 6y - 12x + 8y$

$= -9x + 14y$

Graphing Calculator Exploration: Lines of Regression

1.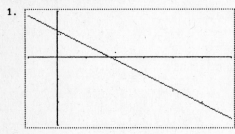

2.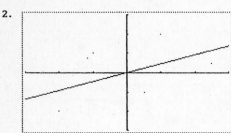

3. a.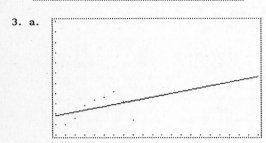

b. about 492 thousand

c.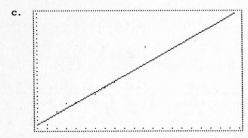

d. about 596 thousand

2-7 | Special Functions

1. $d = \frac{1}{3} \cdot 5$

   $= \frac{5}{3}$

   $= 1.67$ km

2. constant function: $m = 0$; a and c are examples

3. Both form congruent angles but $y = |x - 5|$ has its vertex at $(5,0)$ while $y = |x|$ has its vertex at $(0,0)$.

4. the function that identifies the greatest integer not greater than the given number

5. $[-4.1] = -5$ instead of -4 because $-4 > -4.1$.

6. A   7. G   8. D, $b = 0$

9. A   10. C, $m = 0$ 11. D, $b = 0$

12. $g(3) = [3 - 4]$

    $= [-1]$

    $= -1$

13. $m = 1$, $b = 0$ identity

14. $m = 0$ constant

15. greatest integer function

16. $h(2) = [2(2) + 1]$

    $= [4 + 1]$

    $= [5]$

    $= 5$

17. $h(-3) = [2(-3) + 1]$

    $= [-6 + 1]$

    $= [-5]$

    $= -5$

18. $h(1.4) = [2(1.4) + 1]$

    $= [2.8 + 1]$

    $= 3.8$

    $= 3$

19. $h\left(\frac{2}{3}\right) = \left[2\left(\frac{2}{3}\right) + 1\right]$

    $= \left[\frac{4}{3} + 1\right]$

    $= \left[2\frac{1}{3}\right]$

    $= 2$

20. $h\left(-\frac{9}{7}\right) = \left[2\left(-\frac{9}{7}\right) + 1\right]$

    $= \left[-\frac{18}{7} + 1\right]$

    $= \left[-1\frac{2}{7}\right]$

    $= -2$

21. $f(x) = x + 2$

x	x + 2	f(x)
-2	-2 + 2	0
-1	-1 + 2	1
0	0 + 2	2
1	1 + 2	3

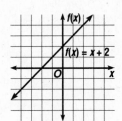

22. $f(x) = |x + 2|$

x	|x + 2|	f(x)
-4	|-4 + 2|	2
-3	|-3 + 2|	1
-2	|-2 + 2|	0
-1	|-1 + 2|	1
0	|0 + 2|	2

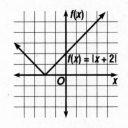

23. $f(x) = [x + 2]$

x	[x + 2]	f(x)
-4	[-4 + 2]	-2
-3	[-3 + 2]	-1
-2	[-2 + 2]	0
-1	[-1 + 2]	1
0	[0 + 2]	2

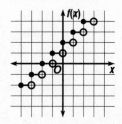

24. $g(x) = |x| + 2$

x	$|x| + 2$	g(x)
-2	$|-2| + 2$	4
-1	$|-1| + 2$	3
0	$|0| + 2$	2
1	$|1| + 2$	3
2	$|2| + 2$	4

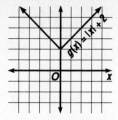

25. $g(x) = [x] + 2$

x	$[x] + 2$	g(x)
-4	$[-4] + 2$	-2
-3	$[-3] + 2$	-1
-2	$[-2] + 2$	0
-1	$[-1] + 2$	1
0	$[0] + 2$	2

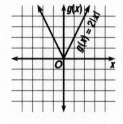

26. $g(x) = 2|x|$

x	$2|x|$	g(x)
-2	$2|-2|$	4
-1	$2|-1|$	2
0	$2|0|$	0
1	$2|1|$	2
2	$2|2|$	4

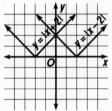

27. $y = |x + 2|$

x	$|x + 2|$	y
-4	$|-4 + 2|$	2
-3	$|-3 + 2|$	1
-2	$|-2 + 2|$	0
-1	$|-1 + 2|$	1
0	$|0 + 2|$	2

$y = |x - 2|$

x	$|x - 2|$	y
-1	$|-1 - 2|$	3
0	$|0 - 2|$	2
1	$|1 - 2|$	1
2	$|2 - 2|$	0
3	$|3 - 2|$	1

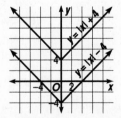

Same graph translated 4 units to the right.

28. $y = |x| + 4$

x	$|x| + 4$	y
-2	$|-2| + 4$	6
-1	$|-1| + 4$	5
0	$|0| + 4$	4
1	$|1| + 4$	5
2	$|2| + 4$	6

$y = |x| - 4$

x	$|x| - 4$	y
-2	$|-2| - 4$	-2
-1	$|-1| - 4$	-3
0	$|0| - 4$	-4
1	$|1| - 4$	-3
2	$|2| - 4$	-2

Same graph translated 8 units down.

29. $y = |x + 2|$

x	$|x + 2|$	y
-4	$|-4 + 2|$	2
-3	$|-3 + 2|$	1
-2	$|-2 + 2|$	0
-1	$|-1 + 2|$	1
0	$|0 + 2|$	2

$y = |x + 2| - 1$

x	$|x + 2| - 1$	y
-4	$|-4 + 2| - 1$	1
-3	$|-3 + 2| - 1$	0
-2	$|-2 + 2| - 1$	-1
-1	$|-1 + 2| - 1$	0
0	$|0 + 2| - 1$	1

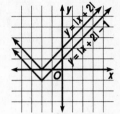

Same graph translated 1 unit down.

30. $y = 2[x]$

x	$2[x]$	y
-1	$2[-1]$	-2
0	$2[0]$	0
1	$2[1]$	2
2	$2[2]$	4

$y = [2x]$

x	$[2x]$	y
-1	$[2 \cdot -1]$	-2
0	$[2 \cdot 0]$	0
0.5	$[2 \cdot 0.5]$	1
1	$[2 \cdot 1]$	2

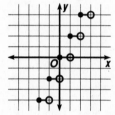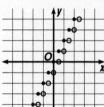

$2[x]$ steps 2 units vertically at intervals of 1 unit, $[2x]$ steps 1 unit vertically at intervals of $\frac{1}{2}$ unit.

31. $y = [x + 5]$

x	$[x + 5]$	y
-2	$[-2 + 5]$	3
-1	$[-1 + 5]$	4
0	$[0 + 5]$	5
1	$[1 + 5]$	6

$y = [x] + 5$

x	$[x] + 5$	y
-2	$[-2] + 5$	3
-1	$[-1] + 5$	4
0	$[0] + 5$	5
1	$[1] + 5$	6

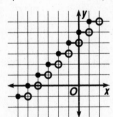

Graphs are the same.

33

32. $y = |3x|$ $y = 3|x|$

x	|3x|	y
-1	|3 · -1|	3
0	|3 · 0|	0
1	|3 · 1|	3
2	|3 · 2|	6

x	3|x|	y
-1	3|-1|	3
0	3	0		0
1	3	1		3
2	3	2		6

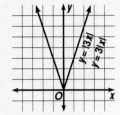

Graphs are the same.

33. $y = -2|4x|$ $y = 4|-2x|$

x	-2|4x|	y
-1	-2|4 · -1|	-8
0	-2|4 · 0|	0
.5	-2|4 · .5|	-4
1	-2|4 · 1|	-8

x	4|-2x|	y
-1	4|-2 · -1|	8
0	4|-2 · 0|	0
.5	4|-2 · .5|	4
1	4|-2 · 1|	8

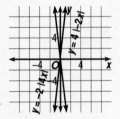

Same shape graph reflected over the x-axis.

34. $y = -3[x]$ $y = [-3x]$

x	-3[x]	y
-1	-3[-1]	3
0	-3[0]	0
1	-3[1]	-3
2	-3[2]	-6

x	[-3x]	y
-1	[-3 · -1]	3
0	[-3 · 0]	0
$\frac{1}{3}$	$\left[-3 \cdot \frac{1}{3}\right]$	-1
$\frac{2}{3}$	$\left[-3 \cdot \frac{2}{3}\right]$	-2

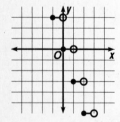 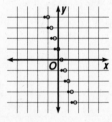

-3[x] steps 3 units vertically at intervals of 1 unit, [-3x] steps 1 unit vertically at intervals of $\frac{1}{3}$ unit.

35. If $a \geq 0$, the two graphs are the same. If $a < 0$, the graphs are reflected images over the x-axis.

36. $y = |x + b|$ is the graph of $y = |x|$ translated b units along the x-axis or horizontally.

$y = |x| + b$ translates $y = |x|$ vertically by b units.

37. $y = [|x|]$

x	[|x|]	y
0	[|0|]	0
0.5	[|0.5|]	0
1	[|1|]	1
2	[|2|]	2
-0.5	[|-0.5|]	0
-1	[|-1|]	1
-2	[|-2|]	2

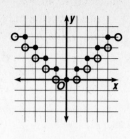

38. $y = |[x]|$

x	|[x]|	y
0	|[0]|	0
1	|[1]|	1
2	|[2]|	2
3	|[3]|	3
-1	|[-1]|	1
-2	|[-2]|	2
-3	|[-3]|	3

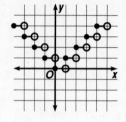

39. $y = x - [x]$

x	x - [x]	y
0	0 - [0]	0
0.5	0.5 - [0.5]	0.5
1	1 - [1]	0
1.5	1.5 - [1.5]	0.5
-0.5	-0.5 - [-0.5]	0.5
-1	-1 - [-1]	0
-2	-2 - [-2]	0

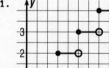 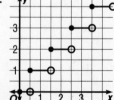

40. $y = x + |x|$

x	x + |x|	y
0	0 + |0|	0
1	1 + |1|	2
2	2 + |2|	4
3	3 + |3|	6
-1	-1 + |-1|	0
-2	-2 + |-2|	0
-3	-3 + |-3|	0

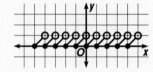

41.

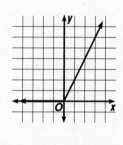

This is a step function that increases one unit vertically with a one unit increase horizontally at each $\frac{1}{2}$ unit.

$\left(\text{i.e. } \frac{1}{2},\ 1\frac{1}{2},\ 2\frac{1}{2},\ \text{etc.}\right)$

42. $y = 12.79t$; constant function since speed remains the same

43. Step function; if they work any time up to an hour it costs \$35, after an hour and up until two hours it costs \$70.

44. a.

Choose two points on the line, for example (35,4250) and (40,2250).

$$m = \frac{4250 - 2250}{35 - 40}$$

$$= \frac{2000}{-5} \text{ or } -400$$

$$y = -400x + b$$

$$4250 = -400(35) + b$$

$$4250 = -14,000 + b$$

$$b = 18,250$$

prediction equation: $y = -400x + 18,125$

b. $y = -400x + 18,125$

$$3000 = -400x + 18,125$$

$$-15,125 = -400x$$

$$37.8125 = x$$

about 37.8%

c. $y = -400x + 18,125$

$$= -400(41) + 18,125$$

$$= -16,400 + 18,125$$

$$= 1725$$

about \$1725

45. $3x - 4y = -10$ $3(0) - 4y = -10$

x	y
2	4
-2	1

$$-4y = -10$$

$$y = \frac{10}{4} \text{ or } \frac{5}{2}$$

$$m = \frac{1 - 4}{-2 - 2}$$

y-intercept: $\frac{5}{2}$

$$= \frac{-3}{-4} \text{ or } \frac{3}{4}$$

slope $= \frac{3}{4}$

46.
$$\frac{3(1)^2 + 2(2)}{(3)^2} = \frac{3 + 4}{9}$$

$$= \frac{7}{9}$$

Technology: Median-Fit Lines

1. a. ENTER: 0.42333 $\boxed{\times}$ 1922 $\boxed{-}$ 796.93359

   $\boxed{=}$ 16.70667 about 16.7 million.

b. ENTER: 0.42333 $\boxed{\times}$ 1955 $\boxed{-}$ 796.93359

   $\boxed{=}$ 30.67656 about 30.7 million.

c. ENTER: 0.42333 $\boxed{\times}$ 1978 $\boxed{-}$ 796.93359

   $\boxed{=}$ 40.41315 about 40.4 million.

d. ENTER: 0.42333 $\boxed{\times}$ 1991 $\boxed{-}$ 796.93359

   $\boxed{=}$ 45.91644 about 45.9 million.

e. ENTER: 0.42333 $\boxed{\times}$ 2005 $\boxed{-}$ 796.93359

   $\boxed{=}$ 51.84306 about 51.8 million.

2. $y = -0.12963x + 37.84569$

2-8   Graphing Linear Inequalities

1. The boundary line separates two regions. The boundary line is the graph of the line that would be graphed if the inequality symbol were replaced by an equal sign.

2. This is the daily rental rate of the Reasonable Car Rental.

3. It is easily substituted into an equation to check the solution.

4. If the inequality contains an equal sign ($\leq$ or $\geq$), then the line is solid. If the inequality does not contain an equal sign ($<$ or $>$), then the line is dashed.

5. Substitute (0,2) in equation.

$$2 \leq -8(0) + 2$$

$$2 \leq 0 + 2$$

$$2 \leq 2 \text{ This is true.}$$

6. (0,0): $0 + 2(0) < 7$

              $0 < 7$ yes

   (2,-3): $2 + 2(-3) < 7$

              $-4 < 7$ yes

   (-1,2): $-1 + 2(2) < 7$

              $3 < 7$ yes

   (0,0), (2,-3), (-1,2)

7. (0,0): $3(0) + 2(0) \leq 0$

              $0 \leq 0$ yes

   (2,-3): $3(2) + 2(-3) \leq 0$

              $0 \leq 0$ yes

   (-1,2): $3(-1) + 2(2) \leq 0$

              $1 \leq 0$ no

   (0,0), (2,-3)

8. $(0,0)$: $4(0) + 2(0) \geq 7$

$0 \geq 7$ no

$(2,-3)$: $4(2) + 2(-3) \geq 7$

$2 \geq 7$ no

$(-1,2)$: $4(-1) + 2(2) \geq 7$

$0 \geq 7$ no

None

9. $(0,0)$: $0 > 0$ no

$(2,-3)$: $-3 > 0$ no

$(-1,2)$: $2 > 0$ yes

$(-1,2)$

10. $y < 3$

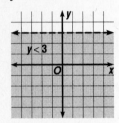

11. $x > -1$

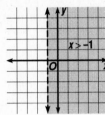

12. $x - y \geq 0$

$x \geq y$

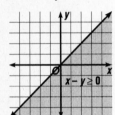

PAGES 94-95   EXERCISES

13. $y + 1 < 5$

$y < 4$

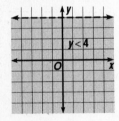

14. $x - 3 < -5$

$x < -2$

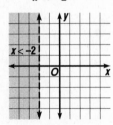

15. $y > 5x - 3$

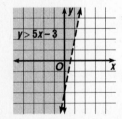

16. $x - 7 \leq y$

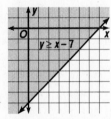

17. $y \geq -3x + 1$

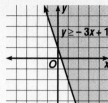

18. $y - 3 < 2x$

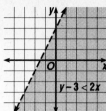

19. $x > 4$

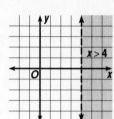

20. $y > \frac{1}{3}x + 7$

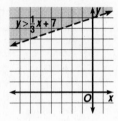

21. $y > \frac{1}{2}x - 3$

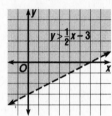

22. $2 \geq x - 2y$

$2 - x \geq -2y$

$x - 2 \leq 2y$

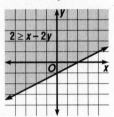

23. $-2x + 5 \leq 3y$

$3y \geq -2x + 5$

$y \geq -\frac{2}{3}x + \frac{5}{3}$

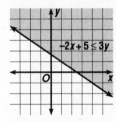

24. $y \geq |x|$

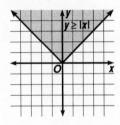

25. $|x| - 3 \leq y$

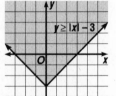

26. $|x| + y \geq 3$

$y \geq -|x| + 3$

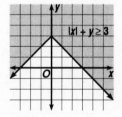

27. $y + |x| < 2$

$y < -|x| + 2$

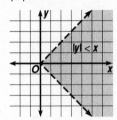

28. $y \geq |3x|$

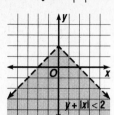

29. $|y| < x$

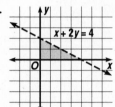

30.

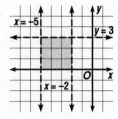

31.

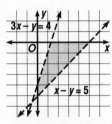

32.

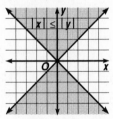

33. $|x| \leq |y|$

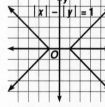

34. $|x| - |y| = 1$

$|y| = |x| - 1$

$y = x + 1$

$y = -x - 1$

$y = x + 1$

$y = -x + 1$

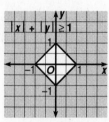

35. $|x| + |y| \geq 1$

$|y| \geq -|x| + 1$

$y \geq x + 1$

$y \geq x - 1$

$y \geq -x - 1$

$y \geq -x + 1$

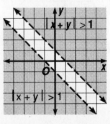

36. $|x + y| > 1$

37.

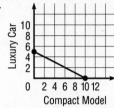

38.

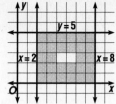

a. $10{,}000(5) + 20{,}000(2) = 50{,}000 + 40{,}000$

$= 90{,}000$

$90{,}000 < 100{,}000$

below, $10{,}000C + 20{,}000\mathcal{L} < 100{,}000$

b. $10{,}000(6) + 20{,}000(2) = 60{,}000 + 40{,}000$

$= 100{,}000$

$10{,}000C + 20{,}000\mathcal{L} = 100{,}000$

c. $10{,}000(9) + 20{,}000(1) = 90{,}000 + 20{,}000$

$= 110{,}000$

$110{,}000 > 100{,}000$

$10{,}000C + 20{,}000\mathcal{L} > 100{,}000$

39. $y = 2|x| + 7$

x	$2|x| + 7$	y
-1	$2|-1| + 7$	9
0	$2|0| + 7$	7
1	$2|1| + 7$	9
2	$2|2| + 7$	11

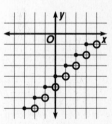

40. $y = [x] - 4$

x	$[x] - 4$	y
0	$[0] - 4$	-4
-1	$[-1] - 4$	-5
2	$[2] - 4$	-2
1	$[1] - 4$	-3

41. $h(a - 3) = (a - 3)^2 + 5$

$= (a - 3)(a - 3) + 5$

$= a^2 - 3a - 3a + 9 + 5$

$= a^2 - 6a + 14$

42. $|4x + 2| \geq -10$

$4x + 2 \geq -10$ or $-(4x + 2) \geq -10$

$4x \geq -12$ $-4x - 2 \geq -10$

$x \geq -3$ $-4x \geq -8$

$x \leq 2$

All real numbers

43. $000, 001, 002, 003, \ldots\ldots, 999$

1000 numbers

Chapter 2
Summary and Review

1. $D = \{-3, 3, 4, 6\}$

   $R = \{-6, -3, -2, 2\}$

   Is a function

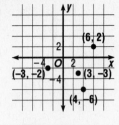

2. $D = \{-4.5, -3.5, 4.5\}$

   $R = \{1, 2, 3, 4\}$

   Not a function

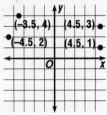

3. $D = \{-3.5, 1, 2, 3,\}$

   $R = \{-4.5, 4, 4.5\}$

   Is a function

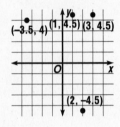

4. $f(-3) = 2(-3)^3 + 4(-3)^2 + 4(-3) + 1$

   $= 2(-27) + 4(9) + -12 + 1$

   $= -54 + 36 - 12 + 1$

   $= -29$

5. $f(2a) = 3(2a)^2 - 2(2a) - 1$

   $= 3(4a^2) - 4a - 1$

   $= 12a^2 - 4a - 1$

6. Not linear

7. Linear

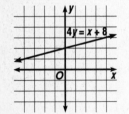

$4y = x + 8$

$y = \dfrac{x}{4} + 2$

x	y
0	2
4	3
-4	1

8. Not linear

9. Linear

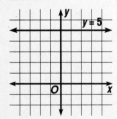

10. $m = \dfrac{7 - 1}{3 - 5}$

    $= \dfrac{6}{-2}$ or -3

11. $m = \dfrac{-1 - 2}{5 - (-3)}$

    $= \dfrac{-3}{8}$ or $-\dfrac{3}{8}$

12. $m = \dfrac{-5 - (-1)}{-7 - 2}$

    $= \dfrac{-4}{-9}$ or $\dfrac{4}{9}$

13. $x + 4y = 8$

$4y = 8 - x$

$y = 2 - \dfrac{x}{4}$

x	y
0	2
4	1

$4x - y = -2$

$-y = -2 - 4x$

$y = 4x + 2$

x	y
0	2
-1	-2

perpendicular

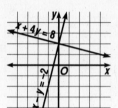

14. $2x - 4y = 8$

$-4y = 8 - 2x$

$y = -2 + \dfrac{1}{2}x$

x	y
-2	-3
0	-2

$2x - y = 4$

$-y = 4 - 2x$

$y = 2x - 4$

x	y
-2	-8
0	-4

neither

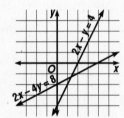

15. $2y = -4x - 5$

$y = -2x - \dfrac{5}{2}$

x	y
0	$-\dfrac{5}{2}$
$\dfrac{1}{2}$	$-\dfrac{7}{2}$

$2x + y = 10$

$y = 10 - 2x$

x	y
0	10
$\dfrac{1}{2}$	9

parallel

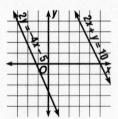

16. $m = 5 \quad b = -7$

$\boxed{y = 5x - 7}$

$-5x + y = -7$

$\boxed{5x - y = 7}$

17. $m = -3 \quad (1, -4)$

$y = -3x + b$

$-4 = -3(1) + b$

$-4 = -3 + b$

$-1 = b$

$\boxed{y = -3x - 1}$

$\boxed{3x + y = -1}$

18. $m = \dfrac{-4 - 0}{1 - (-3)}$

$\quad\quad = \dfrac{-4}{4}$ or -1

$y = -1x + b$

$0 = -1(-3) + b$

$0 = 3 + b$

$-3 = b$

$\boxed{y = -x - 3}$

$\boxed{x + y = -3}$

19. $y = mx + 5$

$0 = m(-2) + 5$

$0 = -2m + 5$

$-5 = -2m$

$\dfrac{5}{2} = m$

$\boxed{y = \dfrac{5}{2}x + 5}$

$-\dfrac{5}{2}x + y = 5$

$\boxed{5x - 2y = -10}$

20. $y = 3x + 5;\ m = 3$

Since parallel, $m = 3$.

$y = 3x + b,\ (2,4)$

$4 = 3(2) + b$

$4 = 6 + b$

$-2 = b$

$\boxed{y = 3x - 2}$

$-3x + y = -2$

$\boxed{3x - y = 2}$

21. $2y + 3x = 10$

$2y = -3x + 10$

$y = -\dfrac{3}{2}x + 5$

$m = -\dfrac{3}{2}$

perpendicular: $m = \dfrac{2}{3}$

$y = \dfrac{2}{3}x + b,\ (-1,-1)$

$-1 = \dfrac{2}{3}(-1) + b$

$-1 = -\dfrac{2}{3} + b$

$-\dfrac{1}{3} = b$

$\boxed{y = \dfrac{2}{3}x - \dfrac{1}{3}}$

$-\dfrac{2}{3}x + y = -\dfrac{1}{3}$

$\boxed{2x - 3y = 1}$

22. $(180,76),\ (160,57)$

$m = \dfrac{76 - 57}{180 - 160}$

$\quad = \dfrac{19}{20}$

$w = \dfrac{19}{20}h + b$

$76 = \dfrac{19}{20}(180) + b$

$76 = 171 + b$

$-95 = b$

$\boxed{w = \dfrac{19}{20}h - 95}$

23. $w = \dfrac{19}{20}(174) - 95$

$w = 165.3 - 95$

$w = 70.3$

70.3 kilograms

24. $\quad 88 = \dfrac{19}{20}h - 95$

$\quad 183 = \dfrac{19}{20}h$

$\dfrac{20}{19}(183) = h$

$192.6 \approx h$

about 193 centimeters

25. $f(x) = |x + 4|$

x	$|x + 4|$	$f(x)$
-5	$|-5 + 4|$	1
-4	$|-4 + 4|$	0
-3	$|-3 + 4|$	1
-2	$|-2 + 4|$	2

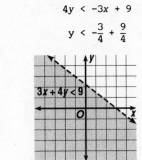

26. $f(x) = 0.5|x|$

x	$0.5|x|$	$f(x)$
-1	$0.5|-1|$	0.5
0	$0.5|0|$	0
1	$0.5|1|$	0.5

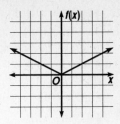

27. $f(x) = [x] - 1$

x	$[x] - 1$	$f(x)$
-1	$[-1] - 1$	-2
0	$[0] - 1$	-1
1	$[1] - 1$	0
2	$[2] - 1$	1

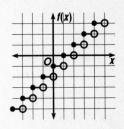

28. $g(x) = 2[x]$

x	$2[x]$	$g(x)$
0	$2[0]$	0
0.5	$2[0.5]$	0
1.0	$2[1.0]$	2
1.5	$2[1.5]$	2
-0.5	$2[-0.5]$	-2
-1.0	$2[-1.0]$	-2

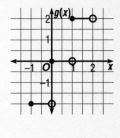

29. $y - 3 > -2x$

$\quad y > -2x + 3$

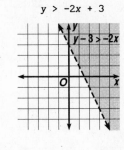

30. $2x - 5y \geq 4$

$\quad -5y \geq -2x + 4$

$\quad y \leq \dfrac{2}{5}x - \dfrac{4}{5}$

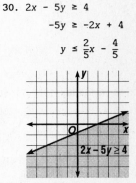

31. $3x + 4y < 9$

$\quad 4y < -3x + 9$

$\quad y < -\dfrac{3}{4} + \dfrac{9}{4}$

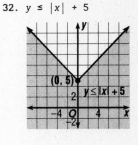

32. $y \leq |x| + 5$

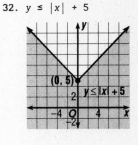

PAGE 98   APPLICATIONS AND CONNECTIONS

33. $c = 10 + 0.15x$

Is linear

34. Find the number of paths to each E.

1 + 4 + 6 + 4 + 1 + 4 +   *1*
6 + 4 + 1 + 4 + 6 + 4 +   *4 E 4*
1 + 4 + 6 + 4   *6 E P E 6*
= 60 ways   *E P O P E*
                             4 E P O L O P E 4
                           1 E P O L S L O P E 1
                             4 E P O L O P E 4
                                E P O P E
                              6 E P E 6
                                 4 E 4
                                   1

35. $s = 5.5h - 10$

$s = 5.5(32) - 10$

$s = 176 - 10$

$s = 166$

$166.00

Chapter 2 Test

PAGE 99

1. $D = \{-8, -4, 3, 8\}$

$R = \{-5, 0, 1, 8\}$

Not a function

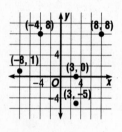

2. $D = \{1988, 1989, 1990, 1991, 1992\}$

$R = \{4000, 4100, 4200, 4300\}$

Is a function

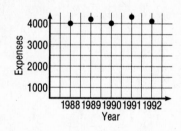

3. no

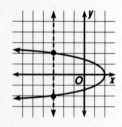

4. yes

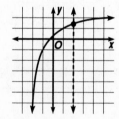

5. yes

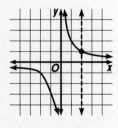

6. $f(4) = 3(4)^2 - 5(4) - 4$

$= 48 - 20 - 4$

$= 24$

$f(c + 2) = 3(c + 2)^2 - 5(c + 2) - 4$

$= 3(c^2 + 4c + 4) - 5c - 10 - 4$

$= 3c^2 + 12c + 12 - 5c - 14$

$= 3c^2 + 7c - 2$

7. $y = \frac{8}{7}x$

x	$\frac{8}{7}x$	y
-7	$\frac{8}{7}(-7)$	-8
0	$\frac{8}{7}(0)$	0
7	$\frac{8}{7}(7)$	8

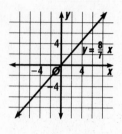

8. $y = -7$

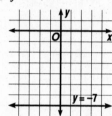

9. $x = 6$

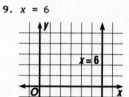

10. $y = -3x + 4$

x	$-3x + 4$	y
-1	$-3(-1) + 4$	7
0	$-3(0) + 4$	4
1	$-3(1) + 4$	1

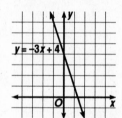

11. $5x - 2y = 12$

$-2y = -5x + 12$

$y = \frac{5}{2}x - 6$

x	$\frac{5}{2}x - 6$	y
-2	$\frac{5}{2}(-2) - 6$	-11
0	$\frac{5}{2}(0) - 6$	-6
2	$\frac{5}{2}(2) - 6$	-1

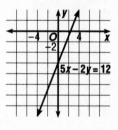

12. $2x + 3y > 9$

$3y > 9 - 2x$

$y > 3 - \frac{2}{3}x$

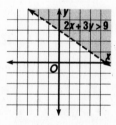

13. $2x + 6y \geq 18$

$6y \geq 18 - 2x$

$y \geq 3 - \frac{1}{3}x$

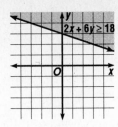

14. $f(x) = |x - 2|$

x	$|x - 2|$	$f(x)$
-2	$|-2 - 2|$	4
0	$|0 - 2|$	2
2	$|2 - 2|$	0
3	$|3 - 2|$	1

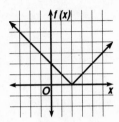

15. $y = 2[x] - 1$

x	$2[x] - 1$	y
-1	$2[-1] - 1$	-3
0	$2[0] - 1$	-1
1	$2[1] - 1$	1

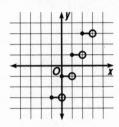

16. $m = \frac{1}{3}$, $b = -7$

$\boxed{y = \frac{1}{3}x - 7}$

$3y = x - 21$

$-x + 3y = -21$

$\boxed{x - 3y = 21}$

17. $m = 4$, $(-3, 3)$

$y = 4x + b$

$3 = 4(-3) + b$

$3 = -12 + b$

$15 = b$

$\boxed{y = 4x + 15}$

$-4x + y = 15$

$\boxed{4x - y = -15}$

18. $(-6,0)$ $b = -6$

$y = mx - 6$

$0 = m(-6) - 6$

$0 = -6m - 6$

$6 = -6m$

$-1 = m$

$\boxed{y = -x - 6}$

$\boxed{x + y = -6}$

19. $(0,7)$ $(5,2)$

$m = \frac{7 - 2}{0 - 5}$

$= \frac{5}{-5}$

$= -1$

$y = -1x + b$

$7 = -1(0) + b$

$7 = b$

$\boxed{y = -x + 7}$

$\boxed{x + y = 7}$

20. $2x + 3y = 6$

$3y = -2x + 6$

$y = -\frac{2}{3}x + 2$

$m = -\frac{2}{3}$ parallel: $m = -\frac{2}{3}$

$y = -\frac{2}{3}x + b$, $(7,7)$

$7 = -\frac{2}{3}(7) + b$

$7 = -\frac{14}{3} + b$

$\frac{35}{3} = b$

$\boxed{y = -\frac{2}{3}x + \frac{35}{3}}$

$3y = -2x + 35$

$\boxed{2x + 3y = 35}$

21.

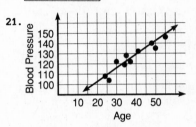

22. $(30,116)$, $(60,156)$

$m = \frac{156 - 116}{60 - 30}$

$= \frac{40}{30}$ or $\frac{4}{3}$

$y = \frac{4}{3}x + b$

$116 = \frac{4}{3}(30) + b$

$116 = 40 + b$

$76 = b$

$y = \frac{4}{3}x + 76$

23. $y = \frac{4}{3}(45) + 76$

$= 60 + 76$

$= 136$

24. $(120) = \frac{4}{3}x + 76$

$44 = \frac{4}{3}x$

$\frac{3}{4} \cdot 44 = x$

$33 = x$

33 years old

25. 2, 5, 9, 14, 20, $\boxed{27}$

+3 +4 +5 +6 +7

PAGE 99   BONUS

Let $p - 60 =$ the number of shoes over 60.

If $p > 60$, $d = 275 + 0.40(p - 60)$.

If $p \leq 60$, $d = 275$.

41

Chapter 2
College Entrance Exam Preview

1. The numbers, in order from least to greatest are

   $\frac{1}{3}$, $\frac{5}{6}$, 1, $\frac{6}{5}$, $\frac{3}{2}$.

   So $\frac{5}{6}$ corresponds to B on the number line.

   The correct choice is B.

2. Let p = perimeter, ℓ = length, and w = width.

   $$p = 2\ell + 2w$$
   $$8x + 10y = 2\ell + 2(x + 3y)$$
   $$8x + 10y = 2\ell + 2x + 6y$$
   $$6x + 4y = 2\ell$$
   $$3x + 2y = \ell$$

   The correct choice is A.

3. 2 ⌣ 6 ⌣ 11 ⌣ 17 ⌣ 24 ⌣ 32 ⌣ 41 ⌣ 51

     +4   +5   +6   +7   +8   +9   +10

   The eighth term will be 51.

   The correct choice is C.

4. Let x = the number.

   $$-4x - 9 > 7$$
   $$-4x > 16$$
   $$x < -4$$

   The correct choice is A.

5. $(4 + 3)2^2 - 5 = (7)2^2 - 5$

                    $= (7)4 - 5$

                    $= 28 - 5$

                    $= 23$

   The correct choice is C.

6. The correct choice is D.

7. The least common denominator of $\frac{1}{2}$, $\frac{7}{13}$, $\frac{4}{9}$, and

   $\frac{8}{15}$ is 1170.

   $$\frac{1}{2}\left(\frac{585}{585}\right) = \frac{585}{1170}$$
   $$\frac{7}{13}\left(\frac{90}{90}\right) = \frac{630}{1170}$$
   $$\frac{4}{9}\left(\frac{130}{130}\right) = \frac{520}{1170}$$
   $$\frac{8}{15}\left(\frac{78}{78}\right) = \frac{624}{1170}$$

   The least number is $\frac{520}{1170}$ or $\frac{4}{9}$.

   The correct choice is C.

8. Let r = the original radius.

   Area of original circle = πr^2

   Area of circle with radius tripled = $\pi(3r)^2$

                                  $= 9\pi r^2$

   The correct choice is C.

9. a. (4, 4)

   $$4 + 3(4) \overset{?}{=} 13$$
   $$4 + 12 \overset{?}{=} 13$$
   $$16 \neq 13$$

   This point is not on the graph.

   b. (-5, 6)

   $$-5 + 3(6) \overset{?}{=} 13$$
   $$-5 + 18 \overset{?}{=} 13$$
   $$13 = 13$$

   This point is on the graph.

   c. (-2, 3)

   $$-2 + 4(3) \overset{?}{=} 13$$
   $$-2 + 12 \overset{?}{=} 13$$
   $$10 \neq 13$$

   This point is not on the graph.

   d. (4, -3)

   $$4 + 4(-3) \overset{?}{=} 13$$
   $$4 - 12 \overset{?}{=} 13$$
   $$-8 \neq 13$$

   This point is not on the graph.

   The correct choice is B.

10. $\frac{-2}{3}$, $\sqrt{4}$ or 2, and 0 are rational numbers, π is not.

    The correct choice is C.

11. $$2y - 4 = 2y + 6$$
    $$-4 = 6$$

    no solution

    The correct choice is D.

12. $$\frac{7 + 5 + 9 + 3 + 2x}{5} = x$$
    $$24 + 2x = 5x$$
    $$24 = 3x$$
    $$8 = x$$

    The correct choice is D.

13. Let x = the number.

    $$8(x + 5) = 168$$
    $$8x + 40 = 168$$
    $$8x = 128$$
    $$x = 16$$

    The correct choice is A.

14. Let r = the number of revolutions.

    distance = circumference × revolutions

    $$400\pi = (2\pi(4))r$$
    $$400\pi = 8\pi r$$
    $$400 = 8r$$
    $$50 = r$$

    The correct choice is C.

15. 2 and 3 are two consecutive prime numbers less than 40. Their difference is 1.

    The correct choice is A.

16. The numbers divisible by 4 are:

    200, 204, 208...300 There are 26 of them.

    The numbers divisible by 10 are:

    200, 210, 220...300 There are 11 of them.

    The numbers divisible by 4 and 10 are:

    200, 220, 240...300 There are 6 of them.

    There are 26 + 11 - 6 or 31 nunmbers between 199 and 301 that are divisible by 4 or 10.

    The correct choice is B.

17. The patient will receive medication at:

+ 7 hours 〈 7 AM MONDAY
+ 7 hours 〈 2 PM MONDAY
+ 7 hours 〈 9 PM MONDAY
+ 7 hours 〈 4 AM TUESDAY
+ 7 hours 〈 11 AM TUESDAY
+ 7 hours 〈 6 PM TUESDAY

The correct choice is B.

18. a. $a + b = b + a$ according to the commutative property of equality.

b. $a - b = b - a$

$2a = 2b$ This statement is true

$a = b$ only if $a = b$.

c. $a - b = a + (-b)$ by the definition of subtraction.

d. $a - b = (-b) + a$ by the definition of subtraction and the commutative property.

The correct choice is B.

19. According to the definition of absolute value, $|a| = a$ if $a \geq 0$ and $|a| = -a$ if $a < 0$. Therefore, $|a| > a$ if $a < 0$.

The correct choice is B.

20. $|x + 3| > 5$

$x + 3 < -5$ or $x + 3 > 5$

$x < -8$ or $\quad x > 2$

The correct choice is D.

21. $\dfrac{\frac{1}{a} + \frac{1}{b}}{ab} = \dfrac{\frac{1}{3} + \frac{1}{5}}{3(5)}$

$\quad = \dfrac{\frac{5}{15} + \frac{3}{15}}{15}$

$\quad = \dfrac{\frac{8}{15}}{15}$

$\quad = \dfrac{8}{225}$

The correct choice is B.

22. If a number is divisible by 3, then it can be written in the form $3k$, where k is an integer. If k is an even nunmber, then it is divisible by 2, and $3k$ will be divisible by 6. The remainder of $3k \div 6$ would be 0. If k is odd, then $k - 1$ is even and would be divisible by 6. So $3k = 3(k - 1) + 3$, and the remainder of $3k \div 6$ is 3.

The correct choice is C.

23. a. $(-2, 11)$

$2(-2) - 11 \overset{?}{<} 5$

$-4 - 11 \overset{?}{<} 5$

$-15 < 5$

This point is on the graph.

b. $(1, 7)$

$2(1) - 7 \overset{?}{<} 5$

$2 - 7 \overset{?}{<} 5$

$-5 < 5$

This point is on the graph.

c. $(2, 6)$

$2(2) - 6 \overset{?}{<} 5$

$4 - 6 \overset{?}{<} 5$

$-2 < 5$

This point is on the graph.

d. $(3, -11)$

$2(3) - (-11) \overset{?}{<} 5$

$6 + 11 \overset{?}{<} 5$

$17 \not< 5$

This point is not on the graph.

The correct choice is D.

Chapter 3
Systems of Equations and Inequalities

Graphing Calculator Exploration:
Graphing Systems of Equations

1. CASIO: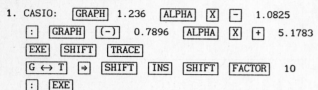

   $x = 3.0908373$

   $y = 2.7377749$

   TI-81 :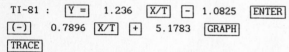

   $x = 3.0908373$

   $y = 2.7377749$

   Key sequences similar to those given for exercise 1 are used to solve exercises 2-6.

2. $x = 1.1627907$

   $y = -0.0930232$

3. $2.1x + 3.2y = 4.3$ $\qquad$ $1.4x - 1.8y = 1.6$

   $3.2y = -2.1x + 4.3$ $\qquad$ $-1.8y = -1.4x + 1.6$

   $y = \frac{21}{32}x + \frac{43}{32}$ $\qquad$ $y = \frac{7}{9}x - \frac{8}{9}$

   $x = 1.5569007$
   $y = 0.3220339$

4. $3.12x + 4.68y = 5$ $\qquad$ $-4.38x + 9.21y = 1.6$

   $4.68y = -3.12x + 5$ $\qquad$ $9.21y = 4.38x + 1.6$

   $y = \frac{-312}{468}x + \frac{500}{468}$ $\qquad$ $y = \frac{438}{921}x + \frac{160}{921}$

   $x = 0.7832456$

   $y = 0.5462123$

5. $x = -0.3753846$

   $y = -1.7330769$

6. $x = -2.7238679$

   $y = -5.3874702$

7. $y \geq x$, $y \leq 3$

   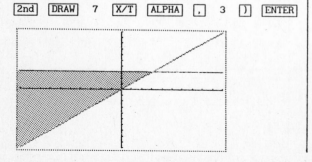

8. $y \geq 5x$, $y \leq 8x$

   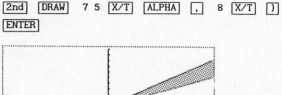

   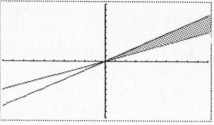

9. $y \geq 0.5x$, $y \leq 4x - 2$

   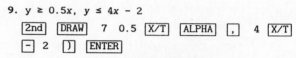

   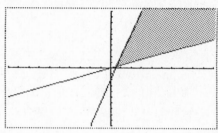

10. $y \geq 0.2x - 5$, $y \leq -0.1x - 5$

    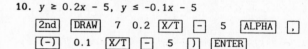

    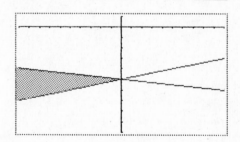

11. $y \geq 5 - x$, $y \leq 0.8x - 7$

    $y \geq -x + 5$

    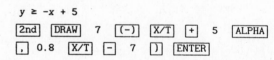

    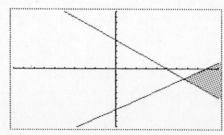

12. $y \geq 12 - 4x$, $y \leq -3x + 9$

$y \geq -4x + 12$

2nd DRAW 7 (−) 4 X/T + 12 ALPHA
, (−) 3 X/T + 9) ENTER

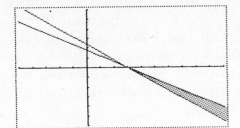

13. $y \geq 3x + 0.5$, $y \leq -6x - 2.8$

2nd DRAW 7 3 X/T + 0.5 ALPHA , (−)
6 X/T − 2.8) ENTER

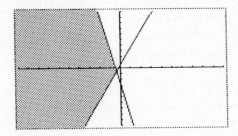

14. $12x + 6y \geq 12$, $y \leq x$

$6y \geq -12x + 12$

$y \geq -2x + 2$

2nd DRAW 7 (−) 2 X/T + 2 ALPHA
, X/T) ENTER

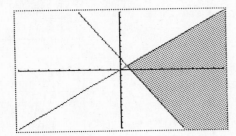

3-1 Graphing Systems of Equations

PAGE 110   CHECKING FOR UNDERSTANDING

1. inconsistent   2. same slope, different
                      y-intercepts

3. Independent systems have exactly one solution.
   Dependent systems have infinitely many.

4. Answers may vary. A sample answer is $y = 3x + 2$
   and $y = 3x + 7$.

5. $y = 2x - 3$ consistent and independent, $\left(\frac{11}{7}, \frac{1}{7}\right)$
   $4x + 5y = 7$

6. $y = -\frac{1}{2}x + 1$ consistent and dependent
   $2x + 4y = 4$

7.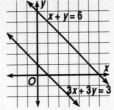

no solutions;
inconsistent

8.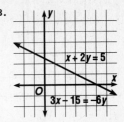

$\{(x, y) \mid x + 2y = 5\}$;
consistent and
dependent

9.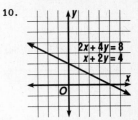

no solutions;
inconsistent

10.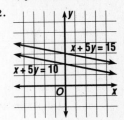

$\{(x,y) \mid x + 2y = 4\}$;
consistent and
dependent

11.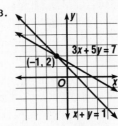

$(2, -6)$; consistent
and independent

12.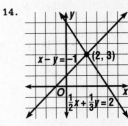

no solutions;
inconsistent

13.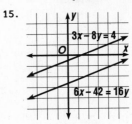

$(-1, 2)$; consistent
and independent

14.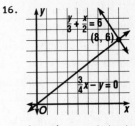

$(2, 3)$; consistent
and independent

15.

no solutions;
inconsistent

16.

$(8, 6)$; consistent and
independent

45

17.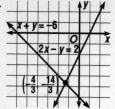

$-\frac{4}{3}$, $-\frac{14}{3}$; consistent and independent

18.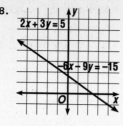

$\{(x,y) \mid 2x + 3y = 5\}$; consistent and dependent

19.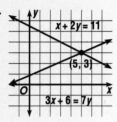

(5, 3); consistent and independent

20.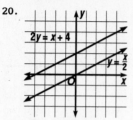

no solutions; inconsistent

21.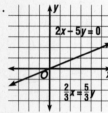

$\{(x,y) \mid 2x - 5y = 0\}$; consistent and dependent

22.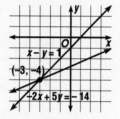

(-3, -4); consistent and independent

23.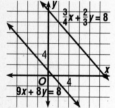

no solutions; inconsistent

24.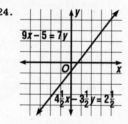

$\{(x,y) \mid 9x - 5 = 7y\}$; consistent and dependent

25. $ax + 5y = b$

$6x + 10y = 16$

Since the two lines are the same, one equation is a multiple of the other. For y, $\frac{10}{5} = 2$. Thus the second equation is double the first.

$2a = 6 \qquad 2b = 16$

$a = 3 \qquad b = 8$

26. $\qquad ax + by = -10$

$\quad a(2) + b(1) = -10$

$\qquad 2a + b = -10$

Answers may vary. A sample answer is $a = -6$, $b = 2$.

27. No solution means lines with same slopes but different intercepts. Answers may vary. A sample answer is $a = -4$, $b = 5$.

28. Let x = boys in the family, and

$\qquad y$ = girls in the family.

$x + y > 10$ and $x^2 + y^2 = 100$

We know x and y are nonnegative integers (whole numbers) and since $10^2 = 100$, we know that neither x nor y may be greater than 10. Thus we have three line boundaries: $x + y > 10$, $y \leq 10$ and $x \leq 10$.

We can see by graphing what integer pairs satisfy all three conditions. By listing integers and their squares, we find out by trial and error that when $x = 6$ and $y = 8$ or $x = 8$ and $y = 6$, then $x^2 + y^2 = 6^2 + 8^2 = 36 + 64 = 100$. Thus the Leshins have $6 + 8 = 14$ children.

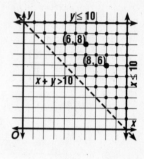

29. Let x = drums of the first fluid at \$30 each.

Let y = drums of the second fluid at \$20 each.

$x + y = 7$

$30x + 20y = 160$

Thus, Mr. George purchased 2 of the \$30 drums and 5 of the \$20 drums.

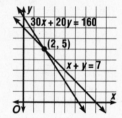

30. Let x = film price.

Let y = battery price.

$8x + 2y = 23.00$

$6x + 2y = 18.00$

Thus, film is \$2.50 and batteries \$1.50.

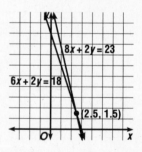

31. $\qquad\qquad 4x - |y| \leq 12$

$4(0) - |0| \leq 12 \quad 4(-1) - |-3| \leq 12 \quad 4(4) - |0| \leq 12$

$\quad 0 - 0 \leq 12 \qquad -4 - (3) \leq 12 \qquad 16 - 0 \leq 12$

$\qquad 0 \leq 12 \qquad\qquad -7 \leq 12 \qquad\qquad 16 \leq 12$

$\qquad$ True $\qquad\qquad\quad$ True $\qquad\qquad\quad$ False

(0,0) and (-1,-3) satisfy the inequality.

32.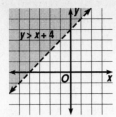

$y > x + 4$

33. $m = \dfrac{y_2 - y_1}{x_2 - x_1}$

$= \dfrac{5 - 0}{-3 - 2}$

$= \dfrac{5}{-5} = -1$

34. $D = \{9, 2, 1\}$

$R = \{3, -7, 1\}$ Yes, it is a function.

35. $3x + 7 > 43$

$3x > 36$

$x > 12$

$\{x \mid x > 12\}$

3-2 Solving Systems of Equations Algebraically

PAGE 114   CHECKING FOR UNDERSTANDING

1. Answers may vary. A sample answer is that the second equation could be multiplied by 2 and then the two equations could be added together to eliminate the w's. After solving for ℓ, you could substitute the value of ℓ in one of the original equations and solve for w.

2. Answers may vary. A sample answer is that the substitution method would be used when one of the equations can be easily solved for one of the variables.

3. Use elimination, since x is easily eliminated by adding the two equations.

4. Multiply first equation by -1.

$x - y = 1$	$\Rightarrow$	$-x + y = -1$	$-1 + y = -1$
$3x - y = 3$		$\underline{3x - y = 3}$	$y = 0$
		$2x\quad = 2$	
		$x = 1$	$(1, 0)$

5. Multiply first equation by 3, second by -2.

$2x + 3y = 7 \Rightarrow 6x + 9y = 21$

$3x - 4y = 2 \qquad \underline{-6x + 8y = -4}$

$\qquad\qquad\qquad\qquad 17y = 17$

$\qquad\qquad\qquad\qquad\quad y = 1$

$2x + 3(1) = 7$

$\quad 2x = 4$

$\quad\; x = 2 \qquad (2, 1)$

---

6. Multiply second equation by 2.

$3x - 2y = 10 \Rightarrow 3x - 2y = 10$

$4x + y = 6 \qquad \underline{8x + 2y = 12}$

$\qquad\qquad\qquad 11x \quad = 22$

$\qquad\qquad\qquad\quad x = 2$

$4(2) + y = 6$

$\quad 8 + y = 6$

$\qquad\; y = -2 \qquad (2, -2)$

7. Multiply first equation by 2, second by -3.

$3x + 4y = 6 \Rightarrow 6x + 8y = 12$

$2x + 5y = 11 \qquad \underline{-6x + 15y = -33}$

$\qquad\qquad\qquad\qquad -7y = -21$

$\qquad\qquad\qquad\qquad\quad y = 3$

$2x + 5(3) = 11$

$\qquad 2x = -4$

$\qquad\; x = -2 \qquad (-2, 3)$

8. Multiply first equation by 3, second by 4.

$2x + 4y = 6 \Rightarrow 6x + 12y = 18$

$5x - 3y = 2 \qquad \underline{20x - 12y = 8}$

$\qquad\qquad\qquad\qquad 26x = 26$

$\qquad\qquad\qquad\qquad\; x = 1$

$2(1) + 4y = 6$

$\qquad 4y = 4$

$\qquad\; y = 1 \qquad (1, 1)$

9. Multiply first equation by -3.

$x + 8y = 12 \Rightarrow -3x - 24y = -36$

$3x - 7y = 5 \qquad \underline{3x - 7y = 5}$

$\qquad\qquad\qquad\qquad -31y = -31$

$\qquad\qquad\qquad\qquad\quad y = 1$

$x + 8(1) = 12$

$\quad x + 8 = 12$

$\qquad\; x = 4 \qquad (4, 1)$

PAGES 115-116   EXERCISES

10. $y = 3x \qquad\quad x + 21 = -2(3x) \quad y = 3(-3)$

$x + 21 = -2y \quad x + 21 = -6x \qquad y = -9$

$\qquad\qquad\qquad\qquad 7x = -21 \qquad (-3, -9)$

$\qquad\qquad\qquad\qquad\; x = -3$

11. $x + y = 2 \qquad 2y + y = 2 \qquad x = 2\left(\dfrac{2}{3}\right) = \dfrac{4}{3}$

$x - 2y = 0 \qquad\quad 3y = 2$

$\qquad x = 2y \qquad\quad y = \dfrac{2}{3} \qquad \left(\dfrac{4}{3}, \dfrac{2}{3}\right)$

12. $3x - 2y = -3 \qquad 3x - 2(-3x + 3) = -3$

$3x + y = 3 \qquad\qquad 3x + 6x - 6 = -3$

$\qquad y = -3x + 3 \qquad\qquad 9x - 6 = -3$

$\qquad\qquad\qquad\qquad\qquad\qquad 9x = 3$

$\qquad\qquad\qquad\qquad\qquad\qquad\; x = \dfrac{1}{3}$

$y = -3\left(\dfrac{1}{3}\right) + 3$

$y = -1 + 3$

$y = 2 \qquad\qquad \left(\dfrac{1}{3}, 2\right)$

13. $2r + s = 1$ $2(s + 8) + s = 1$ $r = (-5) + 8$
    $r - s = 8$ $2x + 16 + s = 1$ $r = 3$
        $r = s + 8$ $3s + 16 = 1$ $(3, -5)$
                     $3s = -15$
                     $s = -5$

14. $5s - 2t = 16$ $5(-3t + 10) - 2t = 16$
    $s + 3t = 10$ $-15t + 50 - 2t = 16$
        $s = -3t + 10$ $-17t + 50 = 16$
                        $-17t = -34$
                        $t = 2$

    $s = -3(s) + 10$
    $s = -6 + 10$
    $s = 4$ $(4, 2)$

15. $2.5x - y = 11$ $3.25x + (2.5x - 11) = 12$
    $3.25x + y = 12$ $5.75x - 11 = 12$
    $2.5x - 11 = y$ $5.75x = 23$
                       $x = 4$

    $y = 2.5(4) - 11$
    $y = 10 - 11$
    $y = -1$ $(4, -1)$

16. $m + n = 6$ $3 + n = 6$
    $\underline{2m - n = 3}$ $n = 3$
    $3m\ \ \ \ = 9$ $(3, 3)$
    $m\ \ \ \ = 3$

17. $3x - 6y = 15$ $-3x + 5(-7) = -8$
    $\underline{-3x + 5y = -8}$ $-3x - 35 = -8$
    $-y = 7$ $-3x = 27$
    $y = -7$ $x = -9$
                       $(-9, -7)$

18. $4s + t = 9$ $\Rightarrow$ $8s + 2t = 18$ $4(2) + t = 9$
    $3s - 2t = 4$ $\underline{3s - 2t = 4}$ $8 + t = 9$
                    $11s = 22$ $t = 1$
                    $s = 2$ $(2, 1)$

19. $4a + 3b = -2$ $\Rightarrow$ $20a + 15b = -10$ $4a + 3(6) = -2$
    $5a + 7b = 17$ $\underline{-20a - 28b = -68}$ $4a + 18 = -2$
                     $-13b = -78$ $4a = -20$
                     $b = 6$ $a = -5$
                                            $(-5, 6)$

20. $4x - 6y = 12$ $\Rightarrow$ $4x - 6y = 12$ $x - 7(-2) = 14$
    $x - 7y = 14$ $\underline{-4x + 28y = -56}$ $x + 14 = 14$
                    $22y = -44$ $x = 0$
                    $y = -2$ $(0, -2)$

21. $8x + 3y = 4$ $\Rightarrow$ $24x + 9y = 12$ $4\left(\dfrac{1}{4}\right) - 9y = -5$
    $4x - 9y = -5$ $\underline{4x - 9y = -5}$ $1 - 9y = -5$
                     $28x = 7$ $-9y = -6$
                     $x = \dfrac{1}{4}$ $y = \dfrac{2}{3}$

                                        $\left(\dfrac{1}{4}, \dfrac{2}{3}\right)$

22. $6x + 4y = 80$ $\Rightarrow$ $6x + 4y = 80$ $x - 7(2) = -2$
    $x - 7y = -2$ $\underline{-6x + 42y = 12}$ $x - 14 = -2$
                    $46y = 92$ $x = 12$
                    $y = 2$ $(12, 2)$

23. $m + n = 6$ $5.25 + n = 6$
    $\underline{m - n = 4.5}$ $n = 0.75$
    $2m = 10.5$ $(5.25, 0.75)$
    $m = 5.25$

24. $3x + 2y = 8$ $\Rightarrow$ $3x + 2y = 8$ $-x + \left(\dfrac{14}{5}\right) = 2$
    $y - x = 2$ $\underline{-3x + 3y = 6}$ $-x = -\dfrac{4}{5}$
    $-x + y = 2$ $5y = 14$ $x = \dfrac{4}{5}$
                  $y = \dfrac{14}{5}$
                                        $\left(\dfrac{4}{5}, \dfrac{14}{5}\right)$

25. $9x + y = 30$ $9x + (6x - 15) = 30$ $6(3) + 15 = y$
    $6x - 15 = y$ $15x = 45$ $18 - 15 = y$
                      $x = 3$ $3 = y$
                                        $(3, 3)$

26. $2x - y = 36$ $\Rightarrow$ $2x - y = 26$ $2(4) - y = 36$
    $3x - \dfrac{1}{2}y = 26$ $\underline{-6x + y = -52}$ $8 - y = 36$
                    $-4x = -16$ $-y = 28$
                    $x = 4$ $y = -28$
                                        $(4, -28)$

27. $3y - 2x = 4$ $\Rightarrow$ $3y - 2x = 4$ $3y - 2(-1) = 4$
    $\dfrac{1}{6}(3y - 4x) = 1$ $\underline{-3y + 4x = -6}$ $3y + 2 = 4$
                    $2x = -2$ $3y = 2$
                    $x = -1$ $y = \dfrac{2}{3}$
                                        $\left(-1, \dfrac{2}{3}\right)$

28. $5a + 2b = -8$ $\Rightarrow$ $15a + 6b = -24$ $4(-4) + 3b = 2$
    $4a + 3b = 2$ $\underline{-8a - 6b = -4}$ $-16 + 3b = 2$
                    $7a = -28$ $3b = 18$
                    $a = -4$ $b = 6$
                                        $(-4, 6)$

29. $4x + 4y = -6$ $\Rightarrow$ $12x + 12y = -18$
    $5x + 3y = 6$ $\underline{-20x - 12y = -24}$
                    $-8x = -42$
                    $x = \dfrac{21}{4}$

    $4\left(\dfrac{21}{4}\right) + 4y = -6$
    $21 + 4y = -6$
    $4y = -27$
    $y = \dfrac{-27}{4}$ $\left(\dfrac{21}{4}, -\dfrac{27}{4}\right)$

30. $a - b = 0$ $\Rightarrow$ $2a - 2b = 0$ $(-3) - b = 0$
    $3a + 2b = -15$ $\underline{3a + 2b = -15}$ $-3 = b$
                      $5a = -15$ $(-3, -3)$
                      $a = -3$

48

31. $\frac{1}{4}x + y = \frac{7}{2}$ $2\left(\frac{10}{3}\right) - y = 4$

$\underline{2x - y = 4}$ $\frac{20}{3} - y = 4$

$\frac{9}{4}x = \frac{15}{2}$ $-y = \frac{-8}{3}$

$x = \frac{10}{3}$ $y = \frac{8}{3}$

$\left(\frac{10}{3}, \frac{8}{3}\right)$

32. $\frac{s + 3t}{7} = 3$ $33s - 3t = -21$ $(0) + 3t = 21$

$11s - t = -7$ $\underline{s + 3t = 21}$ $3t = 21$

$s + 3t = 21$ $34s = 0$ $t = 7$

$s = 0$ $(0, 7)$

33. $\frac{2x + y}{3} = 15$ $2(10) + y = 45$

$3x - y = 5$ $20 + y = 45$

$\underline{2x + y = 45}$ $y = 25$

$5x = 50$ $(10, 25)$

$x = 10$

34. Vertex 1:

$x - y = 7$ $-3x + 3y = -21$ $x - (4) = 7$

$3x - 11y = -11$ $\underline{3x - 11y = -11}$ $x - 4 = 7$

$-8y = -32$ $x = 11$

$y = 4$ $(11, 4)$

Vertex 2:

$x - y = 7$ $x - y = 7$ $(3) - y = 7$

$x + y + 1 = 0$ $\underline{x + y = -1}$ $-y = 4$

$2x = 6$ $y = -4$

$x = 3$ $(3, -4)$

Vertex 3:

$3x - 11y = -11$ $3x - 11y = -11$

$x + y + 1 = 0$ $\underline{11x + 11y + 11 = 0}$

$14x + 11 = -11$

$14x = -22$

$x = -\frac{11}{7}$

$\left(-\frac{11}{7}\right) + y + 1 = 0$

$y = \frac{4}{7}$ $\left(-\frac{11}{7}, \frac{4}{7}\right)$

35. Vertex 1:

$2x + y = -12$ $2(-5) + y = -12$

$\underline{2x - y = -8}$ $-10 + y = -12$

$4x = -20$ $y = -2$

$x = -5$ $(-5, -2)$

Vertex 2:

$2x + y = -12$ $2x + y = -12$

$2x - y - 4 = 0$ $\underline{2x - y = 4}$

$4x = -8$

$x = -2$

$2(-2) + y = -12$

$-4 + y = -12$

$y = -8$ $(-2, -8)$

Vertex 3:

$4x + 2y = 24$ $4x + 2y = 24$

$2x - y = -8$ $\underline{4x - 2y = -16}$

$8x = 8$

$x = 1$

$2(1) - y = -8$

$2 - y = -8$

$-y = -10$

$y = 10$ $(1, 10)$

Vertex 4:

$4x + 2y = 24$ $4x + 2y = 24$

$2x - y - 4 = 0$ $\underline{4x - 2y - 8 = 0}$

$8x - 8 = 24$

$8x = 32$

$x = 4$

$2(4) - y - 4 = 0$

$8 - y - 4 = 0$

$4 = y$ $(4, 4)$

36. $\frac{1}{x} - \frac{1}{y} = \frac{5}{8}$

$\frac{3}{x} + \frac{2}{y} = \frac{-5}{8}$

Let $m = \frac{1}{x}$ and $n = \frac{1}{y}$.

$m - n = \frac{5}{8}$ $\frac{1}{8} - n = \frac{5}{8}$

$3m + 2n = \frac{-5}{8}$ $-n = \frac{4}{8}$

$n = -\frac{1}{2}$

$2m - 2n = \frac{10}{8}$

$\underline{3m + 2n = \frac{-5}{8}}$ Thus, $\frac{1}{8} = \frac{1}{x}$ and $-\frac{1}{2} = \frac{1}{y}$

$5m = \frac{5}{8}$ $x = 8$ $y = -2$

$m = \frac{1}{8}$ $(8, -2)$

37. Let w = width of the picture,

and ℓ = length of the picture.

$2\ell + 2w = 86$

$2w - \ell = 2$

$2w - 2 = \ell$

$2(2w - 2) + 2w = 86$

$4w - 4 + 2w = 86$

$6w - 4 = 86$

$6w = 90$

$w = 15$

$\ell = 2(15) - 2$

$\ell = 30 - 2$

$\ell = 28$

Thus, the picture is 15 inches wide and 28 inches long.

38. Let x = the length of one leg,
and y = the length of the other leg.

$$x = 4\left(\frac{1}{3}\right)(y)$$

$$x^2 + y^2 = 75$$

$$x = \frac{4}{3}y$$

$$\left(\frac{4}{3}y\right)^2 + y^2 = 75^2$$

$$\frac{16}{9}y^2 + y^2 = 5625$$

$$\frac{25}{9}y^2 = 5625 \qquad x = \frac{4}{3}(45)$$

$$y^2 = 2025 \qquad x = 60$$

$$y = \sqrt{2025}$$

$$y = 45$$

Thus, the legs are 45 meters and 60 meters long.

39. a. $a_1 = 16$ $\qquad x_2 = \dfrac{a_1 - a_2}{f - 1}$

$\quad a_2 = 12$ $\qquad x_2 = \dfrac{16 - 12}{5 - 1}$

$\quad f = 5$ $\qquad x_2 = \dfrac{4}{4}$

$\qquad\qquad\qquad x_2 = 1$

$x_1 = x_2 + a_1 - a_2$

$x_1 = 1 + 16 - 12$

$x_1 = 5$ Thus, when Maggie was 1, Dwayne was 5, and that was 16-5 = 11 years ago.

b. $a_1 = 27$ $\qquad x_2 = \dfrac{a_1 - a_2}{f - 1}$

$\quad a_2 = 9$ $\qquad x_2 = \dfrac{27 - 9}{10 - 1}$

$\quad f = 10$ $\qquad x_2 = \dfrac{18}{9}$

$\qquad\qquad\qquad x_2 = 2$

$x_1 = x_1 + a_1 - a_2$

$x_1 = 2 + 27 - 9$

$x_1 = 20$

Thus, when Barry was 2, Karen was 20, and that was 27 - 20 = 7 years ago.

c. $a_1 = 45$ $\qquad x_2 = \dfrac{a_1 - a_2}{f - 1}$

$\quad a_2 = 17$ $\qquad x_2 = \dfrac{45 - 17}{2 - 1}$

$\quad f = 2$ $\qquad x_2 = 28$

$x_1 = x_2 + a_1 - a_2$

$x_1 = 28 + 45 - 17$

$x_1 = 56$

Thus, when Tiffany is 28, her mother will be 56, and that will be 56 - 45 = 11 years from now.

40. $(-2, -4)$

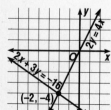

41. $(0, 2)$

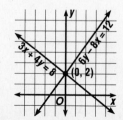

42. $y = mx + b$

$1 = -2(3) + b$

$1 = -6 + b$

$7 = b$

$y = -2x + 7$

43. $\quad y = ax + 9$ $\qquad$ slope$_1$ = a

$\quad x + 3y = 14$ $\qquad$ slope$_2$ = $-\dfrac{1}{3}$

Perpendicular slopes are negative inverses, so $a = 3$.

Technology: Solving Systems of Equations

PAGE 117   EXERCISES

1. $x - 3y = 6$

   $2x + 6y = 24$

   $A = 1, B = -3, C = 6$

   $D = 2, E = 6, F = 24$

   $(9, 1)$

2. $3x - y = 1$

   $-6x + 2y = -2$

   $A = 3, B = -1, C = 1$

   $D = -6, E = 2, F = -2$

   infinite

3. $x - 5y = 2$

   $-2x + 10y = 4$

   $A = 1, B = -5, C = 2$

   $D = -2, E = 10, F = 4$

   no solution or $\emptyset$

4. $x + 4y = 2$

   $-x + y = -7$

   $A = 1, B = 4, C = 2$

   $D = -1, E = 1, F = -7$

   $(6, -1)$

5. $3x - 6y = 12$

   $2x + 3y = 1$

   $A = 3, B = -6, C = 12$

   $D = 2, E = 3, F = 1$

   $(2, -1)$

6. $9x + 3y = 9$

   $3x + y = 3$

   $A = 9, B = 3, C = 9$

   $D = 3, E = 1, F = 3$

   infinite

3-3 | Cramer's Rule

PAGE 120   CHECKING FOR UNDERSTANDING

1. $\begin{vmatrix} 0 & a \\ 0 & b \end{vmatrix} = 0 \cdot b - a \cdot 0$

   $= 0$

   $\begin{vmatrix} 0 & 0 \\ a & b \end{vmatrix} = 0 \cdot b - 0 \cdot a$

   $= 0$

2. $\begin{vmatrix} a & b \\ c & d \end{vmatrix} = ad - bc = 0$

   Thus when $ad = bc$, the determinant would be 0.

3. Cramer's rule is best. Since there are fewer calculations, there is less chance of making an error. A calculator would be very helpful.

4. $\begin{vmatrix} 6 & 1 \\ 4 & 3 \end{vmatrix} = 6(3) - 1(4)$

   $= 14$

5. $\begin{vmatrix} 1 & 0 \\ 1 & 0 \end{vmatrix} = 1(0) - 0(1)$

   $= 0$

6. $\begin{vmatrix} 7 & -3 \\ 0 & 1 \end{vmatrix} = 7(1) - (-3)(0)$

   $= 7$

7. $\begin{vmatrix} 1 & 0 \\ 0 & 1 \end{vmatrix} = 1(1) - 0(0)$

$\qquad = 1$

8. $\begin{vmatrix} -5 & -2 \\ -3 & 11 \end{vmatrix} = -5(11) - (-2)(-3)$

$\qquad = -61$

9. $\begin{vmatrix} -8 & -7 \\ -4 & -6 \end{vmatrix} = -8(-6) - (-7)(-4)$

$\qquad = 20$

10. $\begin{vmatrix} 4 & 2 \\ 1 & -3 \end{vmatrix} = 4(-3) - 2(1)$

$\qquad = -14$

11. $\begin{vmatrix} 5 & -3 \\ -1 & -2 \end{vmatrix} = 5(-2) - (-3)(-1)$

$\qquad = -13$

12. $\begin{vmatrix} 4 & -11 \\ 0 & -9 \end{vmatrix} = 4(-9) - (-11)(0)$

$\qquad = -36$

13. $x = \dfrac{\begin{vmatrix} 3 & -1 \\ 5 & 2 \end{vmatrix}}{\begin{vmatrix} 4 & -1 \\ 3 & 2 \end{vmatrix}} \qquad\qquad y = \dfrac{\begin{vmatrix} 4 & 3 \\ 3 & 5 \end{vmatrix}}{\begin{vmatrix} 4 & -1 \\ 3 & 2 \end{vmatrix}}$

$\quad = \dfrac{3(2) - (-1)(5)}{4(2) - (-1)(3)} \qquad = \dfrac{4(5) - 3(3)}{4(2) - (-1)(3)}$

$\quad = \dfrac{11}{11} \qquad\qquad\qquad = \dfrac{11}{11}$

$\quad = 1 \qquad\qquad\qquad\quad = 1 \qquad\qquad (1,\ 1)$

14. $m = \dfrac{\begin{vmatrix} 8 & 2 \\ 0 & -3 \end{vmatrix}}{\begin{vmatrix} 4 & 2 \\ 6 & -3 \end{vmatrix}} \qquad\qquad n = \dfrac{\begin{vmatrix} 4 & 8 \\ 6 & 0 \end{vmatrix}}{\begin{vmatrix} 4 & 2 \\ 6 & -3 \end{vmatrix}}$

$\quad = \dfrac{8(-3) - 2(0)}{4(-3) - 2(6)} \qquad = \dfrac{4(0) - 8(6)}{4(-3) - 2(6)}$

$\quad = \dfrac{-24}{-24} \qquad\qquad\quad = \dfrac{-48}{-24}$

$\quad = 1 \qquad\qquad\qquad = 2 \qquad (1,\ 2)$

15. $x = \dfrac{\begin{vmatrix} 8 & -2 \\ 21 & -5 \end{vmatrix}}{\begin{vmatrix} 1 & -2 \\ 3 & -5 \end{vmatrix}} \qquad\qquad y = \dfrac{\begin{vmatrix} 1 & 8 \\ 3 & 21 \end{vmatrix}}{\begin{vmatrix} 1 & -2 \\ 3 & -5 \end{vmatrix}}$

$\quad = \dfrac{8(-5) - (-2)(21)}{1(-5) - (-2)(3)} \qquad = \dfrac{1(21) - 8(3)}{1(-5) - (-2)(3)}$

$\quad = \dfrac{2}{1} \qquad\qquad\qquad = \dfrac{-3}{1}$

$\quad = 2 \qquad\qquad\qquad = -3 \qquad (2,\ -3)$

16. $a = \dfrac{\begin{vmatrix} 0 & -1 \\ -6 & 10 \end{vmatrix}}{\begin{vmatrix} 1 & -1 \\ 4 & 10 \end{vmatrix}} \qquad\qquad b = \dfrac{\begin{vmatrix} 1 & 0 \\ 4 & -6 \end{vmatrix}}{\begin{vmatrix} 1 & -1 \\ 4 & 10 \end{vmatrix}}$

$\quad = \dfrac{0(10) - (-1)(-6)}{1(10) - (-1)(4)} \qquad = \dfrac{1(-6) - 0(4)}{1(10) - (-1)(4)}$

$\quad = \dfrac{-6}{14} \qquad\qquad\qquad = \dfrac{-6}{14}$

$\quad = \dfrac{-3}{7} \qquad\qquad\qquad = \dfrac{-3}{7} \qquad \left(\dfrac{-3}{7},\ \dfrac{-3}{7}\right)$

17. $s = \dfrac{\begin{vmatrix} 6 & 1 \\ 2 & -1 \end{vmatrix}}{\begin{vmatrix} 1 & 1 \\ 1 & -1 \end{vmatrix}} \qquad\qquad t = \dfrac{\begin{vmatrix} 1 & 6 \\ 1 & 2 \end{vmatrix}}{\begin{vmatrix} 1 & 1 \\ 1 & -1 \end{vmatrix}}$

$\quad = \dfrac{6(-1) - 1(2)}{1(-1) - 1(1)} \qquad = \dfrac{1(2) - 6(1)}{1(-1) - 1(1)}$

$\quad = \dfrac{-8}{-2} \qquad\qquad\qquad = \dfrac{-4}{-2}$

$\quad = 4 \qquad\qquad\qquad = 2 \qquad (4,\ 2)$

18. $x = \dfrac{\begin{vmatrix} -7 & -5 \\ 16 & 2 \end{vmatrix}}{\begin{vmatrix} 3 & -5 \\ 1 & 2 \end{vmatrix}} \qquad\qquad y = \dfrac{\begin{vmatrix} 3 & -7 \\ 1 & 16 \end{vmatrix}}{\begin{vmatrix} 3 & -5 \\ 1 & 2 \end{vmatrix}}$

$\quad = \dfrac{-7(2) - (-5)(16)}{3(2) - (-5)(1)} \qquad = \dfrac{3(16) - (-7)(1)}{3(2) - (-5)(1)}$

$\quad = \dfrac{66}{11} \qquad\qquad\qquad = \dfrac{55}{11}$

$\quad = 6 \qquad\qquad\qquad = 5 \qquad (6,\ 5)$

PAGE 121   EXERCISES

19. $\begin{vmatrix} -4 & 6 \\ -13 & 24 \end{vmatrix} = -4(24) - 6(-13) = -18$

20. $\begin{vmatrix} -6 & 7 \\ -9 & 10 \end{vmatrix} = -6(10) - 7(-9) = 3$

21. $\begin{vmatrix} 2 & -5 \\ -1 & 11 \end{vmatrix} = 2(11) - (-5)(-1) = 17$

22. $\begin{vmatrix} -13 & -11 \\ 17 & -12 \end{vmatrix} = -13(-12) - (-11)(17) = 343$

23. $\begin{vmatrix} 0.9 & 0.12 \\ 89 & -23 \end{vmatrix} = 0.9(-23) - 0.12(89) = -31.38$

24. $\begin{vmatrix} 0.007 & 0.873 \\ 0.063 & 7.857 \end{vmatrix} = 0.007(7.857) - 0.873(0.063) = 0$

25. $x = \dfrac{\begin{vmatrix} 1 & -4 \\ 13 & 3 \end{vmatrix}}{\begin{vmatrix} 1 & -4 \\ 2 & 3 \end{vmatrix}} \qquad\qquad y = \dfrac{\begin{vmatrix} 1 & 1 \\ 2 & 13 \end{vmatrix}}{\begin{vmatrix} 1 & -4 \\ 2 & 3 \end{vmatrix}}$

$\quad = \dfrac{1(3) - (-4)(13)}{1(3) - (-4)(2)} \qquad = \dfrac{1(13) - 1(2)}{1(3) - (-4)(2)}$

$\quad = \dfrac{55}{11} \qquad\qquad\qquad = \dfrac{11}{11}$

$\quad = 5 \qquad\qquad\qquad = 1 \qquad (5,\ 1)$

26. $s = \dfrac{\begin{vmatrix} 5 & 1 \\ 3 & -1 \end{vmatrix}}{\begin{vmatrix} 1 & 1 \\ 3 & -1 \end{vmatrix}} \qquad\qquad t = \dfrac{\begin{vmatrix} 1 & 5 \\ 3 & 3 \end{vmatrix}}{\begin{vmatrix} 1 & 1 \\ 3 & -1 \end{vmatrix}}$

$\quad = \dfrac{5(-1) - 1(3)}{1(-1) - 1(3)} \qquad = \dfrac{1(3) - 5(3)}{1(-1) - 1(3)}$

$\quad = \dfrac{-8}{-4} \qquad\qquad\qquad = \dfrac{-12}{-4}$

$\quad = 2 \qquad\qquad\qquad = 3 \qquad (2,\ 3)$

27. $m = \dfrac{\begin{vmatrix} 4 & -1 \\ 1 & 2 \end{vmatrix}}{\begin{vmatrix} 1 & -1 \\ 1 & 2 \end{vmatrix}}$ $\qquad n = \dfrac{\begin{vmatrix} 1 & 4 \\ 1 & 1 \end{vmatrix}}{\begin{vmatrix} 1 & -1 \\ 1 & 2 \end{vmatrix}}$

$= \dfrac{4(2) - (-1)(1)}{1(2) - (-1)(1)}$ $\qquad = \dfrac{1(1) - 4(1)}{1(2) - (-1)(1)}$

$= \dfrac{9}{3}$ $\qquad\qquad = \dfrac{-3}{3}$

$= 3$ $\qquad\qquad\quad = -1 \qquad (3, -1)$

28. $x = \dfrac{\begin{vmatrix} 9 & 2 \\ 19 & -3 \end{vmatrix}}{\begin{vmatrix} 3 & 2 \\ 2 & -3 \end{vmatrix}}$ $\qquad y = \dfrac{\begin{vmatrix} 3 & 9 \\ 2 & 19 \end{vmatrix}}{\begin{vmatrix} 3 & 2 \\ 2 & -3 \end{vmatrix}}$

$= \dfrac{9(-3) - 2(19)}{3(-3) - 2(2)}$ $\qquad = \dfrac{3(19) - 9(2)}{3(-3) - 2(2)}$

$= \dfrac{-65}{-13}$ $\qquad\qquad = \dfrac{39}{-13}$

$= 5$ $\qquad\qquad\quad = -3 \qquad (5, -3)$

29. $r + 11 = 8s \;\Rightarrow\; r - 8s = -11$

$\quad 8(r - s) = 3 \qquad 8r - 8s = 3$

$r = \dfrac{\begin{vmatrix} -11 & -8 \\ 3 & -8 \end{vmatrix}}{\begin{vmatrix} 1 & -8 \\ 8 & -8 \end{vmatrix}}$ $\qquad s = \dfrac{\begin{vmatrix} 1 & 11 \\ 8 & 3 \end{vmatrix}}{\begin{vmatrix} 1 & -8 \\ 8 & -8 \end{vmatrix}}$

$= \dfrac{-11(-8) - (-8)(3)}{1(-8) - (-8)(8)}$ $\qquad = \dfrac{1(3) - (-11)(8)}{1(-8) - (-8)(8)}$

$= \dfrac{112}{56}$ $\qquad\qquad = \dfrac{91}{56}$

$= 2$ $\qquad\qquad\quad = \dfrac{13}{8} \qquad \left(2, \dfrac{13}{8}\right)$

30. $x = \dfrac{\begin{vmatrix} 7 & -1 \\ 7 & 3 \end{vmatrix}}{\begin{vmatrix} 2 & -1 \\ 1 & 3 \end{vmatrix}}$ $\qquad y = \dfrac{\begin{vmatrix} 2 & 7 \\ 1 & 7 \end{vmatrix}}{\begin{vmatrix} 2 & -1 \\ 1 & 3 \end{vmatrix}}$

$= \dfrac{7(3) - (-1)(7)}{2(3) - (-1)(1)}$ $\qquad = \dfrac{2(7) - 7(1)}{2(3) - (-1)(1)}$

$= \dfrac{28}{7}$ $\qquad\qquad = \dfrac{7}{7}$

$= 4$ $\qquad\qquad\quad = 1 \qquad (4, 1)$

31. $3x + 8 = -y \;\Rightarrow\; 3x + y = -8$

$\quad 4x - 2y = -14 \qquad 4x - 2y = -14$

$x = \dfrac{\begin{vmatrix} -8 & 1 \\ -14 & -2 \end{vmatrix}}{\begin{vmatrix} 3 & 1 \\ 4 & -2 \end{vmatrix}}$ $\qquad y = \dfrac{\begin{vmatrix} 3 & -8 \\ 4 & -14 \end{vmatrix}}{\begin{vmatrix} 3 & 1 \\ 4 & -2 \end{vmatrix}}$

$= \dfrac{-8(-2) - 1(-14)}{3(-2) - 1(4)}$ $\qquad = \dfrac{3(-14) - (-8)(4)}{3(-2) - 1(4)}$

$= \dfrac{30}{-10}$ $\qquad\qquad = \dfrac{-10}{-10}$

$= -3$ $\qquad\qquad\quad = 1 \qquad (-3, 1)$

32. $a = \dfrac{\begin{vmatrix} -1 & 4 \\ 10 & -1 \end{vmatrix}}{\begin{vmatrix} 5 & 4 \\ 2 & -1 \end{vmatrix}}$ $\qquad b = \dfrac{\begin{vmatrix} 5 & -1 \\ 2 & 10 \end{vmatrix}}{\begin{vmatrix} 5 & 4 \\ 2 & -1 \end{vmatrix}}$

$= \dfrac{-1(-1) - 4(10)}{5(-1) - 4(2)}$ $\qquad = \dfrac{5(10) - (-1)(2)}{5(-1) - 4(2)}$

$= \dfrac{-39}{-13}$ $\qquad\qquad = \dfrac{52}{-13}$

$= 3$ $\qquad\qquad\quad = -4 \qquad (3, -4)$

33. $x = \dfrac{\begin{vmatrix} 2 & -7 \\ 4 & -13 \end{vmatrix}}{\begin{vmatrix} 3 & -7 \\ 6 & -13 \end{vmatrix}}$ $\qquad y = \dfrac{\begin{vmatrix} 3 & 2 \\ 6 & 4 \end{vmatrix}}{\begin{vmatrix} 3 & -7 \\ 6 & -13 \end{vmatrix}}$

$= \dfrac{2(-13) - (-7)(4)}{3(-13) - (-7)(6)}$ $\qquad = \dfrac{3(4) - 2(6)}{3(-13) - (-7)(6)}$

$= \dfrac{2}{3}$ $\qquad\qquad = \dfrac{0}{3} \qquad \left(\dfrac{2}{3}, 0\right)$

34. $x = \dfrac{\begin{vmatrix} -7 & 5 \\ 7 & -3 \end{vmatrix}}{\begin{vmatrix} 6 & 5 \\ 2 & -3 \end{vmatrix}}$ $\qquad y = \dfrac{\begin{vmatrix} 6 & -7 \\ 2 & 7 \end{vmatrix}}{\begin{vmatrix} 6 & 5 \\ 2 & -3 \end{vmatrix}}$

$= \dfrac{-7(-3) - 5(7)}{6(-3) - 5(2)}$ $\qquad = \dfrac{6(7) - (-7)(2)}{6(-3) - 5(2)}$

$= \dfrac{-14}{-28}$ $\qquad\qquad = \dfrac{56}{-28}$

$= \dfrac{1}{2}$ $\qquad\qquad\quad = -2 \qquad \left(\dfrac{1}{2}, -2\right)$

35. $\qquad 0.2a = 0.3b \;\Rightarrow\; 0.2a - 0.3b = 0$

$\quad 0.4a - 0.2b = 0.2 \qquad 0.4a - 0.2b = 0.2$

$a = \dfrac{\begin{vmatrix} 0 & -0.3 \\ 0.2 & -0.2 \end{vmatrix}}{\begin{vmatrix} 0.2 & -0.3 \\ 0.4 & -0.2 \end{vmatrix}}$

$= \dfrac{0(-0.2) - (-0.3)(0.2)}{0.2(-0.2) - (-0.3)(0.4)}$

$= \dfrac{0.06}{0.08}$

$= \dfrac{3}{4} \text{ or } 0.75$

$b = \dfrac{\begin{vmatrix} 0.2 & 0 \\ 0.4 & 0.2 \end{vmatrix}}{\begin{vmatrix} 0.2 & -0.3 \\ 0.4 & -0.2 \end{vmatrix}}$

$= \dfrac{0.2(0.2) - 0(0.4)}{0.2(-0.2) - (-0.3)(0.4)}$

$= \dfrac{0.04}{0.08}$

$= \dfrac{1}{2} \text{ or } 0.5 \quad (0.75, 0.5)$

36. $3.5x + 4y = -5 \quad \Rightarrow \quad 3.5x + 4y = -5$

$\; 2(x - y) = 10 \qquad\qquad 2x - 2y = 10$

$$x = \frac{\begin{vmatrix} -5 & 4 \\ 10 & -2 \end{vmatrix}}{\begin{vmatrix} 3.5 & 4 \\ 2 & -2 \end{vmatrix}} \qquad\qquad y = \frac{\begin{vmatrix} 3.5 & -5 \\ 2 & 10 \end{vmatrix}}{\begin{vmatrix} 3.5 & 4 \\ 2 & -2 \end{vmatrix}}$$

$$= \frac{-5(-2) - 4(10)}{3.5(-2) - 4(2)} \qquad = \frac{3.5(10) - (-5)(2)}{3.5(-2) - 4(2)}$$

$$= \frac{-30}{-15} \qquad\qquad = \frac{45}{-15}$$

$$= 2 \qquad\qquad = -3 \quad (2, -3)$$

37. $x = \dfrac{\begin{vmatrix} 0 & -\frac{1}{9} \\ 15 & 1 \end{vmatrix}}{\begin{vmatrix} \frac{1}{6} & -\frac{1}{9} \\ 1 & 1 \end{vmatrix}} \qquad\qquad y = \dfrac{\begin{vmatrix} \frac{1}{6} & 0 \\ 1 & 15 \end{vmatrix}}{\begin{vmatrix} \frac{1}{6} & -\frac{1}{9} \\ 1 & 1 \end{vmatrix}}$

$$= \frac{0(1) - \left(-\frac{1}{9}\right)(15)}{\frac{1}{6}(1) - \left(-\frac{1}{9}\right)(1)} \qquad = \frac{\frac{1}{6}(15) - 0\,(1)}{\frac{1}{6}(1) - \left(-\frac{1}{9}\right)(1)}$$

$$= \frac{\frac{5}{3}}{\frac{5}{18}} \qquad\qquad = \frac{\frac{5}{2}}{\frac{5}{18}}$$

$$= 6 \qquad\qquad = 9 \quad (6, 9)$$

38. $\dfrac{x}{2} - \dfrac{2y}{3} = 2\dfrac{1}{3} \quad \Rightarrow \quad \dfrac{1}{2}x - \dfrac{2}{3}y = \dfrac{7}{3}$

$\; 3x + 4y = -50 \qquad\qquad 3x + 4y = -50$

$$x = \dfrac{\begin{vmatrix} \frac{7}{3} & -\frac{2}{3} \\ -50 & 4 \end{vmatrix}}{\begin{vmatrix} \frac{1}{2} & -\frac{2}{3} \\ 3 & 4 \end{vmatrix}} \qquad\qquad y = \dfrac{\begin{vmatrix} \frac{1}{2} & \frac{7}{3} \\ 3 & -50 \end{vmatrix}}{\begin{vmatrix} \frac{1}{2} & -\frac{2}{3} \\ 3 & 4 \end{vmatrix}}$$

$$= \frac{\frac{7}{3}(4) - \left(-\frac{2}{3}\right)(-50)}{\frac{1}{2}(4) - \left(-\frac{2}{3}\right)(3)} \qquad = \frac{\frac{1}{2}(-50) - \frac{7}{3}(3)}{\frac{1}{2}(4) - \left(-\frac{2}{3}\right)(3)}$$

$$= \frac{-24}{4} \qquad\qquad = \frac{-32}{4}$$

$$= -6 \qquad\qquad = -8 \quad (-6, -8)$$

39. $7y + 4x = 22 \quad \Rightarrow \quad 4x + 7y = 22$

$\; 8x - 2y = -5 \qquad\qquad 8x - 2y = -5$

$$x = \dfrac{\begin{vmatrix} 22 & 7 \\ -5 & -2 \end{vmatrix}}{\begin{vmatrix} 4 & 7 \\ 8 & -2 \end{vmatrix}} \qquad\qquad y = \dfrac{\begin{vmatrix} 4 & 22 \\ 8 & -5 \end{vmatrix}}{\begin{vmatrix} 4 & 7 \\ 8 & -2 \end{vmatrix}}$$

$$= \frac{22(-2) - 7(-5)}{4(-2) - 7(8)} \qquad = \frac{4(-5) - 22(8)}{4(-2) - 7(8)}$$

$$= \frac{-9}{-64} \qquad\qquad = \frac{-196}{-64}$$

$$= \frac{9}{64} \qquad\qquad = \frac{49}{16} \quad \left(\frac{9}{64}, \frac{49}{16}\right)$$

40. Dependent or inconsistent equations have the same slope. For example, if the two equations are: $ax + by = c$

$\qquad\qquad\quad dx + ey = f$,

the slopes of the two lines are $-\dfrac{a}{b}$ and $-\dfrac{d}{e}$, and we know that $-\dfrac{a}{b} = -\dfrac{d}{e}$ or $-ae = -bd$.

Using Cramer's rule, $x = \dfrac{\begin{vmatrix} c & b \\ f & e \end{vmatrix}}{\begin{vmatrix} a & b \\ d & e \end{vmatrix}} \qquad y = \dfrac{\begin{vmatrix} a & c \\ d & f \end{vmatrix}}{\begin{vmatrix} a & b \\ d & e \end{vmatrix}}$

$$= \frac{ce - bf}{ae - bd} \qquad = \frac{af - cd}{ae - bd}.$$

Since $-ae = -bd$

$\quad 0 = ae - bd$. Thus the denominator will be zero, and division by zero is undefined.

41. Let $h = $ cost of half-inch screws, and

$\quad q = $ cost of quarter-inch screws.

$5h + 12q = 56$

$8h + 15q = 77$

$$h = \dfrac{\begin{vmatrix} 56 & 12 \\ 77 & 15 \end{vmatrix}}{\begin{vmatrix} 5 & 12 \\ 8 & 15 \end{vmatrix}} \qquad\qquad q = \dfrac{\begin{vmatrix} 5 & 56 \\ 8 & 77 \end{vmatrix}}{\begin{vmatrix} 5 & 12 \\ 8 & 15 \end{vmatrix}}$$

$$= \frac{56(15) - 12(77)}{5(15) - 12(8)} \qquad = \frac{5(77) - 56(8)}{5(15) - 12(8)}$$

$$= \frac{-84}{-21} \qquad\qquad = \frac{-63}{-21}$$

$$= 4 \qquad\qquad = 3$$

Thus, half-inch screws cost 4¢, quarter-inch 3¢.

42. Let $s = $ savings investment, and

$\quad c = $ certificate of deposite investment.

$s + c = 4000$

$0.065s + 0.08c = 297.500$

$$s = \dfrac{\begin{vmatrix} 4000 & 1 \\ 297.50 & 0.08 \end{vmatrix}}{\begin{vmatrix} 1 & 1 \\ 0.065 & 0.08 \end{vmatrix}}$$

$$s = \frac{4000(0.08) - 1(297.50)}{1(0.08) - 1(0.065)}$$

$$= \frac{22.50}{0.015}$$

$$= 1500$$

$$c = \dfrac{\begin{vmatrix} 1 & 4000 \\ 0.065 & 297.50 \end{vmatrix}}{\begin{vmatrix} 1 & 1 \\ 0.065 & 0.08 \end{vmatrix}}$$

$$= \frac{1(297.50) - 4000(0.065)}{1(0.08) - 1(0.065)}$$

$$= \frac{37.50}{0.015}$$

$$= 2500$$

Thus, she invested $2500 in certificates of deposit and $1500 in savings.

43.
$$2x + y = 0$$
$$5x + 3y = 0 \rightarrow$$

$$-6x - 3y = 0$$
$$\underline{5x + 3y = 1}$$
$$-x = 1$$
$$x = -1$$

$$2(-1) + y = 0$$
$$-2 + y = 0$$
$$y = 2 \qquad (-1, 2)$$

44.
$$4a - 3b = -4$$
$$3a - 2b = -4 \rightarrow$$

$$12a - 9b = -12$$
$$\underline{-12a + 8b = 16}$$
$$-b = 4$$
$$b = -4$$

$$3a - 2(-4) = -4$$
$$3a + 8 = -4$$
$$3a = -12$$
$$a = -4 \qquad (-4, -4)$$

45.
$$x = 4y + 7$$
$$\frac{1}{4}x - \frac{7}{4} = y$$
$$\text{Slope} = \frac{1}{4}$$

Perpendicular line slope is negative reciprocal of $\frac{1}{4}$ or -4.

46. $D = \{-11, 0, 1, 3, 9, 12\}$

$R = \{-6, -4, -3, 0, 1, 7, 8\}$

No, because when $x = 12$, $y = 7$ and 8.

47. $|x - 8| = 9$

$$x - 8 = 9 \quad \text{or} \quad x - 8 = -9$$
$$x = 17 \qquad\qquad x = -1$$

3-4 Graphing Systems of Inequalities

PAGE 124   CHECKING FOR UNDERSTANDING

1. See if it is a solution to all of the inequalities in the system.

2. Choose a point on one side of the line and test it. If it makes the inequality true, shade that side of the line. If it does not make the inequality true, then shade the other side of the line.

3. Answers may vary. The TI-81 graphing calculator can graph inequalities.

4. $y > -3x$ (2, 5) is a solution.

5. $y < x - 2$ $y > -x$
   $1 < 0 - 2$ $1 > 0$
   $1 < -2$
   　　　　no

6. $y < 2x + 4$ 　　　 $y > 3x - 2$
   $0 < 2(0) + 4$ 　　 $0 > 3(0) - 2$
   $0 < 4$ 　　　　　 $0 > -2$
   　　　　yes

7. $y < 3$ 　　 $x \geq -1$
   $4 < 3$ 　　 $4 \geq -1$
   　　　no

8. $x \leq 1$ 　　 $y > -2$
   $1 \leq 1$ 　　 $1 > -2$
   　　　yes

9. $|y| \leq 2$
   $-2 \leq y \leq 2$
   $\{(3, 1), (-3, -1), (2, 1), (1, 2), (-1, -2)\}$

10. $|x| > 3$
   $x > 3$ 　　 or 　　 $x < -3$
   　　　　　∅

11. $|y| \leq 2x + 2$
   For (3, 1): $|1| \leq 2(3) + 2$
   　　　　　 $1 \leq 8$ 　 yes
   For (1, 2): $|2| \leq 2(1) + 2$
   　　　　　 $2 \leq 4$ 　 yes
   For (-3, -1): $|-1| \leq 2(-3) + 2$
   　　　　　 $1 \leq -6 + 2$
   　　　　　 $1 \leq -4$ 　 no
   For (-1, -2): $|-2| \leq 2(-1) + 2$
   　　　　　 $2 \leq -2 + 2$
   　　　　　 $2 \leq 0$ 　 no
   For (2, 1): $|1| \leq 2(2) + 2$
   　　　　　 $1 \leq 6$ 　 yes 　 $\{(3,1), (2,1), (1,2)\}$

12. $y < 2x - 1$
   $y > 3x + 2$
   For (2,1): $1 < 2(2) - 1$
   　　　　 $1 < 3$
   　　　　 $1 > 3(2) + 2$
   　　　　 $1 > 8$ 　 no
   For (3,1): $1 < 2(3) - 1$
   　　　　 $1 < 5$
   　　　　 $1 > 3(3) + 2$
   　　　　 $1 > 11$ 　 no
   For (1,2): $2 < 2(1) - 1$
   　　　　 $2 < 1$ 　 no
   For (-3,-1): $-1 < 2(-3) - 1$
   　　　　 $-1 < -7$ 　 no
   For (-1, -2): $-2 < 2(-1) - 1$
   　　　　 $-2 < -3$ 　 no
   　　　　　∅

13. $y \geq 3x - 7$
   $y \leq 2x + 4$
   For (2, 1): $1 \geq 3(2) - 7$
   　　　　 $1 \geq -1$
   　　　　 $1 \leq 2(2) + 4$
   　　　　 $1 \leq 8$
   For (3, 1): $1 \geq 3(3) - 7$
   　　　　 $1 \geq 2$ no
   For (1, 2): $2 \geq 3(1) - 7$
   　　　　 $2 \geq -4$
   　　　　 $2 \leq 2(1) + 4$
   　　　　 $2 \leq 6$

For (-3, -1): -1 ≥ 3(-3) - 7

-1 ≥ -16

-1 ≤ 2(-3) + 4

-1 ≤ -2 no

For (-1, -2): -2 ≥ 3(-1) - 7

-2 ≥ -10

-2 ≤ 2(-1) + 4

-2 ≤ 2

{(2, 1), (1, 2), (-1, -2)}

14. $|x| ≥ 1 → \{x | x ≤ -1$ or $x ≥ 1\}$: true for all
$|x| ≤ 2 → \{x | -2 ≤ x ≤ 2\}$: true for (2, 1),
(1, 2), (-1, -2)

{(2, 1), (1, 2), (-1, -2)}

PAGES 124-125   EXERCISES

15.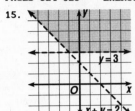

16.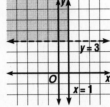

17.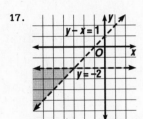

18.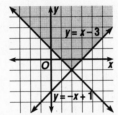

19.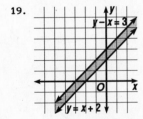

20.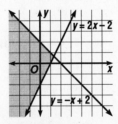

21.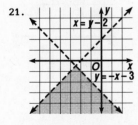

22.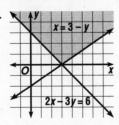

23.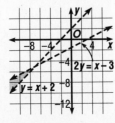

24.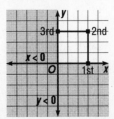

25.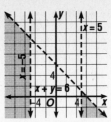

26.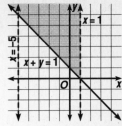

27.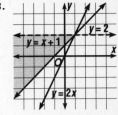

28.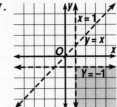

29.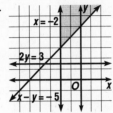

30.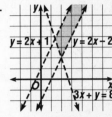

31.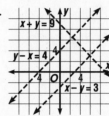

32.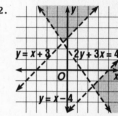

33. Answers may vary. A sample answer is:

$y > 2$, $y < -2$, $y ≥ x$.

To get an intersection, change the sign of the
second inequality to read $y > -2$.

34. $|x| + |y| ≤ 2$

$|y| ≤ 2 - |x|$

If $x ≥ 0$, $|y| ≤ 2 - x$

$-(2 - x) ≤ y ≤ 2 - x$

$-2 + x ≤ y ≤ 2 - x$

$y ≥ -2 + x$ and $y ≤ 2 - x$

If $x < 0$, $|y| ≤ 2 + x$

$-(2 + x) ≤ y ≤ 2 + x$

$-2 - x ≤ y ≤ 2 + x$

$y ≥ -2 - x$ and $y ≤ 2 + x$

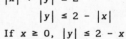

35. Foul ball if $y < 0$ or $x < 0$

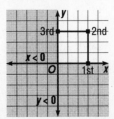

36. $2x + 3y - 8 = 0 \Rightarrow 2x + 3y = 8$

    $3x - 2y - 17 = 0 \qquad 3x + 2y = 17$

$$x = \frac{\begin{vmatrix} 8 & 3 \\ 17 & 2 \end{vmatrix}}{\begin{vmatrix} 2 & 3 \\ 3 & 2 \end{vmatrix}} \qquad\qquad y = \frac{\begin{vmatrix} 2 & 8 \\ 3 & 17 \end{vmatrix}}{\begin{vmatrix} 2 & 3 \\ 3 & 2 \end{vmatrix}}$$

$$= \frac{8(2) - 3(17)}{2(2) - 3(3)} \qquad = \frac{2(17) - 8(3)}{2(2) - 3(3)}$$

$$= \frac{-35}{-5} \qquad\qquad\quad = \frac{10}{-5}$$

$$= 7 \qquad\qquad\qquad = -2 \qquad (7, -2)$$

37. $a = \dfrac{\begin{vmatrix} -10.15 & 7 \\ 69.944 & -6 \end{vmatrix}}{\begin{vmatrix} 6 & 7 \\ 9.2 & -6 \end{vmatrix}}$

$$= \frac{-10.15(-6) - 7(69.944)}{6(-6) - 7(9.2)}$$

$$= \frac{-428.708}{-100.4}$$

$$= 4.27$$

    $b = \dfrac{\begin{vmatrix} 6 & -10.15 \\ 9.2 & 69.944 \end{vmatrix}}{\begin{vmatrix} 6 & 7 \\ 9.2 & -6 \end{vmatrix}}$

$$= \frac{6(69.944) - (-10.15)(9.2)}{6(-6) - 7(9.2)}$$

$$= \frac{513.044}{-100.4}$$

$$= -5.11$$

    $(4.27, -5.11)$

38. $t = 0.36s + 61.4; \ s = 60$

    $t = 0.36(60) + 61.4$

    $t = 83$

39. $\qquad y = -\dfrac{1}{3}x - 18$

    $\qquad 3y = -x - 54$

    $x + 3y = -54$

40. $p \le 400$

PAGE 125   MID-CHAPTER REVIEW

1.

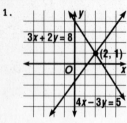

2. $4x + y = 7 \quad \Rightarrow \quad 12x + 3y = 21$

    $2x - 3y = -7 \qquad \dfrac{2x - 3y = -7}{14x \qquad\quad = 14}$

    $\qquad\qquad\qquad\qquad x = 1$

    $4(1) + y = 7$

    $\quad 4 + y = 7$

    $\qquad\quad y = 3 \qquad (1, 3)$

3. $4r - 2s = 13 \qquad 2\left(\dfrac{10}{3}\right) + 2s = 7$

    $\dfrac{2r + 2s = 7}{6r \qquad = 20} \qquad \dfrac{20}{3} + 2s = 7$

    $\qquad r = \dfrac{10}{3} \qquad\qquad 2s = \dfrac{1}{3}$

    $\qquad\qquad\qquad\qquad\quad s = \dfrac{1}{6}$

    $\left(\dfrac{10}{3}, \dfrac{1}{6}\right)$

4. $x + y = 6 \Rightarrow 2x + 2y = 12 \quad x + (3) = 6$

    $-2x + y = -3 \quad \dfrac{-2x + y = -3}{3y = 9} \qquad\quad x = 3$

    $\qquad\qquad\qquad\quad y = 3 \qquad\qquad (3, 3)$

5. $6x - y = 20 \qquad 4\left(\dfrac{13}{5}\right) + y = 6$

    $\dfrac{4x + y = 6}{10x \qquad = 26} \qquad \dfrac{52}{5} + y = 6$

    $\qquad x = \dfrac{13}{5} \qquad\qquad y = \dfrac{-22}{5} \quad \left(\dfrac{13}{5}, -\dfrac{22}{5}\right)$

6. $\begin{vmatrix} 3 & 4 \\ -7 & 2 \end{vmatrix} = 3(2) - 4(-7)$

    $\qquad\qquad = 34$

7. $x = \dfrac{\begin{vmatrix} 13 & -2 \\ 10 & 4 \end{vmatrix}}{\begin{vmatrix} 5 & -2 \\ 2 & 4 \end{vmatrix}} \qquad\qquad y = \dfrac{\begin{vmatrix} 5 & 13 \\ 2 & 10 \end{vmatrix}}{\begin{vmatrix} 5 & -2 \\ 2 & 4 \end{vmatrix}}$

$$= \frac{13(4) - (-2)(10)}{5(4) - (-2)(2)} \qquad = \frac{5(10) - 13(2)}{5(4) - (-2)(2)}$$

$$= \frac{72}{24} = 3 \qquad\qquad\quad = \frac{24}{24} = 1 \qquad (3, 1)$$

8. $x = \dfrac{\begin{vmatrix} 7 & -3 \\ 2 & -1 \end{vmatrix}}{\begin{vmatrix} 2 & -3 \\ 3 & -1 \end{vmatrix}} \qquad\qquad y = \dfrac{\begin{vmatrix} 2 & 7 \\ 3 & 2 \end{vmatrix}}{\begin{vmatrix} 2 & -3 \\ 3 & -1 \end{vmatrix}}$

$$= \frac{7(-1) - (-3)(2)}{2(-1) - (-3)(3)} \qquad = \frac{2(2) - 7(3)}{2(-1) - (-3)(3)}$$

$$= \frac{-1}{7} \qquad\qquad\qquad = \frac{-17}{7} \quad \left(-\dfrac{1}{7}, -\dfrac{17}{7}\right)$$

9.

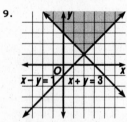

10.

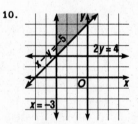

1. when a method for solution of a difficult problem is not obvious

2. Let n = number of stations.

   Number of lines = $\dfrac{n(n-1)}{2}$

   For $n = 20$, $\dfrac{20(20-1)}{2} = \dfrac{20(19)}{2} = 190$.

3. $s = 1 + 2 + \ldots + 2000$
   $s = 2000 + 1999 + . + 1$

   $\overline{2s = 2001 + 2001 + \ldots + 2001}$

   $2s = 2000 \cdot 2001$

   $s = 1000 \cdot 2001 s = 2,001,000$

   $s = 2,001,000$

4.

Number of Teams	2	3	4	. . .	n
Number of Games	1	2	3	. . .	$n-1$

   Thus, for 30 teams, 29 games need to be played.

5.

Date	1	2	3	. . .	n
Day	+100	+100	+100	. . .	+100
Night	-80	-80	-80	. . .	-80
Gain	+20	+40	+60	. . .	20n

   The spider will reach the top the day it is
   750 - 100 = 650 inches or more up the pipe.

   $\dfrac{650}{20} = 32.5$ full days

   After full day 32, it will have traveled 640 inches. On the 33rd day, it will go as high as 640 + 100 = 740 inches, then fall back down to 660 inches. On day 34 it will reach the top (660 + 100 ≥ 750).

6. Neither X nor Y can be 0. If $YYZZ$ is a 4-digit number, 1111 is the smallest possibility. Thus, $XX \geq \sqrt{1111}$, $XX \geq 33.33$. Thus X must be at least 4. The most XX can be is 99 and $99^2 = 9801$ which does not fit the pattern. By trial and error, $44^2 = 1936$, $55^2 = 3025$, $66^2 = 4356$, $77^2 = 5929$, and $88^2 = 7744$. Thus $X = 8$, $Y = 7$, and $Z = 4$.

7.

Digits	Pages	Total Numbers	× Digits	= Total Digits	Cum. Total
Single	1-9	9	× 1	= 9	9
Double	10-99	90	× 2	= 180	189
Triple	100-999	900	× 3	= 2700	2889

   3001 - 2889 = 112

   $\dfrac{112 \text{ digits left}}{4 \text{ digits/page}}$ = 28 four-digit pages

   So, there are 999 + 28 or 1027 pages in the yearbook.

8.

Cuts	1	2	3	. . .	n
Names	25,000	12,500	6,250	...	$\dfrac{50,000}{2^n}$

   Powers of 2:

$2^1 = 2$	$2^7 = 128$	$2^{12} = 4096$
$2^2 = 4$	$2^8 = 256$	$2^{13} = 8192$
$2^3 = 8$	$2^9 = 512$	$2^{14} = 16,384$
$2^4 = 16$	$2^{10} = 1024$	$2^{15} = 32,768$
$2^5 = 32$	$2^{11} = 2048$	$2^{16} = 65,536$
$2^6 = 64$		

   Two names might be on the saved list after the 15th cut $\left(\dfrac{50,000}{32,768} > 1\right)$, but after the 16th cut, at most one name will be left $\left(\dfrac{50,000}{65,536} < 1\right)$.

9.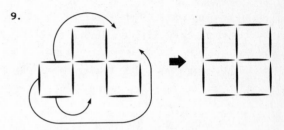

10. Let x = the smallest number of cans

    "one short of. . ." 2   2 and 3   2, 3,...n

    x 1   5 $(2 \times 3 x \ldots \times n) - 1$?

    Try 2, 3, 4: $2 \times 3 \times 4 = 24$, 24 - 1 = 23

    Is 23 the smallest value "one short of" 2, 3, and 4? No, 11 is. Note that 4 = 2 × 2 and the least common multiple of 2, 3, and 4 is 12 = 2 × 2 × 3.

    Try 2, 3, 4, 5   and   2, 3, 4, 5, 6

    LCM = 60   LCM = 60

    $x = 59$ $x = 59$

    These work, and thus "one short of" 2, 3, 4, 5, 6, 7, 8, 9, and 10 yields

    LMC(2, 3, 4, 5, 6, 7, 8, 9, 10)

    = 2 × 3 × 2 × 5 × 7 × 2 × 3 = 2520 - 1 = 2519.

11. (99 - 9)(99 - 19)(99 - 29) . . . (99 - 199) = (90)(80)(70) . . . (-100) = 0 because in the progression there will be a (99 - 99) = 0.

12. One billion numbers = one billion seconds =

    1,000,000,000 sec × $\dfrac{1 \text{ min}}{60 \text{ sec}}$ × $\dfrac{1 \text{ hr}}{60 \text{ min}}$ × $\dfrac{1 \text{ day}}{24 \text{ hr}}$ = 11,574.07 days

    11,575 days × $\dfrac{1 \text{ year}}{365 \text{ days}}$ = 31 years and 9 months

    It would take 11,575 days or about 31 years and 9 months.

13.

	Days Before			After + Before Next
Jan	1-12	13	14-31	18 + 12 = 30
Feb	1-12	13	14-28	15 or 16 + 12 = 27
			or 29	or 28
Mar	1-12	13	14-31	18 + 12 = 30
Apr	1-12	13	14-31	17 + 12 = 29
May	1-12	13	14-31	18 + 12 = 30
Jun	1-12	13	14-30	17 + 12 = 29
Jul	1-12	13	14-31	18 + 12 = 30
Aug	1-12	13	14-31	18 + 12 = 30
Sept	1-12	13	14-30	17 + 12 = 29
Oct	1-12	13	14-31	18 + 12 = 30
Nov	1-12	13	14-30	17 + 12 = 29
Dec	1-12	13	14-31	18 + 12 = 30

Start keeping track of where each "13" ends up by day of the week. Start with Jan 1 = Monday.

	M	T	W	TH	F	S	SU
No Leap:	Aug	Feb	Jun	Sept	Apr	Jan	May
		Mar		Dec	Jul	Oct	
		Nov					

	M	T	W	TH	F	S	SU
Leap:	May	Feb	Mar	Jun	Sept	Jan	Oct
		Aug	Nov		Dec	Apr	
						Jul	

Counting days between the "13's", we find that in any given year, each day will have at least one "13" and the most number of "13's" possible is three.

14.

Outer Cubes:

   9 top

 + 9 bottom

 + 8 middle

  26   Thus, 1 not colored.

3 colored sides	=	8	corners
2 colored sides	=	12	middle edge
1 colored side	=	6	center face
0 colored sides	=	1	inner cube
		27	

PAGE 128   COOPERATIVE LEARNING ACTIVITY

Make a table. Notice the pattern. Each entry is the sum of the entry to the left and the entry above the entry to the left. The entries on the diagonal are 1.

Number of Vertices

Number of n-gons	3	4	5	6	7	8	9	10
3	1	4	10	20	35	56	84	120
4	–	4	5	15	35	70	126	210
5	–	–	1	6	21	56	126	252
6	–	–	–	1	7	28	84	210
7	–	–	–	–	1	8	36	120
8	–	–	–	–	–	1	9	45
9	–	–	–	–	–	–	1	10
10	–	–	–	–	–	–	–	1
total	1	5	16	42	99	219	466	968

There are 968 distinct polygons possible.

3-6 Linear Programming

PAGE 132   CHECKING FOR UNDERSTANDING

1. Answers will vary. Linear programming is the process used to find maximum and minimum values of a function under certain constraints.

2. The real-life situation requires positive values for both x and y. These are located in quadrant I.

3. Yes, although the maximum profit may change each day due to different constraints.

4. (0,0), (5, 0), (0, 6), (3, 4)

5. $f(4, 1) = 3(4) + 2(1)$
   $= 14$

6. $f(3, 3) = 3(3) + 2(3)$
   $= 15$

7. $f(-2, 1) = 3(-2) + 2(1)$
   $= -4$

8. $f(6, 0) = 3(6) + 2(0)$
   $= 18$

9. $f(x,y) = x + 3y$
   min. $f(0, 0) = 0 + 3(0) = 0$
   $f(4, 0) = 4 + 3(0) = 4$
   $f(5, 5) = 5 + 3(5) = 20$
   max. $f(0, 8) = 0 + 3(8) = 24$

10. $f(x, y) = -x - 3y$
    max. $f(0, 0) = -0 - 3(0) = 0$
    $f(4, 0) = -4 - 3(0) = -4$
    $f(5, 5) = -5 - 3(5) = -20$
    min. $f(0, 8) = -0 - 3(8) = -24$

11. $f(x, y) = 0.5x - 1.5y$
    $f(0, 0) = 0.5(0) - 1.5(0) = 0$
    max. $f(4, 0) = 0.5(4) - 1.5(0) = 2$
    $f(5, 5) = 0.5(5) - 1.5(5) = -5$
    min. $f(0, 8) = 0.5(0) - 1.5(8) = -12$

12. $f(0, 0) = 5(0) - 2(0) = 0$

13. $f(4, 1) = 5(4) - 2(1) = 18$

14. $f(-2, -6) = 5(-2) - 2(-6) = 2$

15. $f(5, 4) = 5(5) - 2(4) = 17$

16. $f(3, 1.5) = 5(3) - 2(1.5) = 12$

17. $f(-0.2, -1) = 5(-0.2) - 2(-1) = 1$

18. $y \geq 1$

$y \leq 2x + 1$

$x \leq 6$

vertices:

(0, 1), (6, 1),

(6, 13)

maximum value:

$6 + 13 = 19$

minimum value:

$0 + 1 = 1$

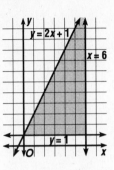

19. $y \geq 2$

$1 \leq x \leq 5$

$y \leq x + 3$

vertices (1, 2)

(1, 4), (5, 8), (5, 2)

maximum value:

$3(5) - 2(2) = 11$

minimum value:

$3(1) - 2(4) = -5$

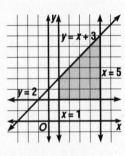

20. $x + y \geq 2$

$4y \leq x + 8$

$y \geq 2x - 5$

vertices:

$(0, 2), (4, 3), \left(\frac{7}{3}, -\frac{1}{3}\right)$

maximum value:

$4(4) + 3(3) = 25$

minimum value:

$4(0) + 3(2) = 6$

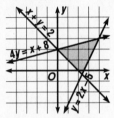

21. $x + y \geq 2$

$4y \leq x + 8$

$2y \geq 3x - 6$

vertices:

(0, 2), (4, 3), (2, 0)

maximum value:

$3(3) + 4 = 13$

minimum value:

$3(0) + 2 = 2$

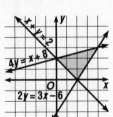

22. $y \leq x + 6$

$y + 2x \geq 6$

$2 \leq x \leq 6$

vertices: (6, 12),

(2, 8), (2, 2), (6, -6)

maximum value:

$-6 + 3(12) = 30$

minimum value:

$-6 + 3(-6) = -24$

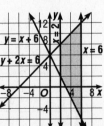

23. $1 \leq y \leq 3$

$y \leq 2x + 1$

$y \leq -\frac{1}{2}x + 6$

vertices: (0, 1),

(1, 3), (6, 3), (10, 1)

maximum value:

$3(10) + 1 = 31$

minimum value:

$3(0) + 1 = 1$

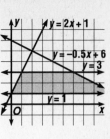

24. $y \leq 7$

$y \leq x + 4$

$y \geq -x + 6$

$x \leq 5$

vertices: (3, 7),

(5, 7), (5, 1), (1, 5)

maximum value:

$2(5) - 3(1) = 7$

minimum value:

$2(3) - 3(7) = -15$

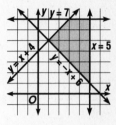

25. $y \leq x + 5$

$y \geq x$

$x \geq -3$

$y + 2x \leq 5$

vertices: $\left(\frac{5}{3}, \frac{5}{3}\right)$, (0, 5),

(-3, 2), (-3, -3)

maximum value:

$-3 - 2(-3) = 3$

minimum value:

$0 - 2(5) = -10$

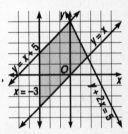

26. $y \geq 0$

$0 \leq x \leq 5$

$-x + y \leq 2$

$x + y \leq 6$

vertices (5, 0),

(0, 0), (0, 2), (2, 4),

(5, 1)

maximum value:

$5(5) - 3(0) = 25$

minimum value:

$5(0) - 3(2) = -6$

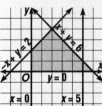

27. $y \leq 1$

$y \geq -2$

$5x \leq -2$

$1.2x - y \geq -2.9$

vertices: (-4.08, -2),

(-1.58, 1), (-0.4, 1),

(-0.4, -2)

maximum value:

$4(-0.4) + 2(1) = 0.4$

minimum value:

$4(-4.08) + 2(-2) = -20.32$

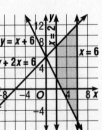

28. $x \geq 0$

$y \geq 0$

$x + 2y \leq 6$

$2y - x \leq 2$

$x + y \leq 5$

vertices: (0, 0),

(0, 1), (2, 2), (4, 1),

(5, 0)

maximum value:

$3(5) - 0 = 15$

minimum value:

$3(0) - 5(1) = -5$

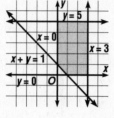

29. $x \geq 0$

$y \leq 5$

$x \leq 3$

$y \geq 0$

$x + y \geq 1$

vertices (0, 1), (1, 0),

(3, 0), (3, 5), (0, 5)

maximum value:

$2(3) + 8(5) + 10 = 56$

minimum value:

$2(1) + 8(0) + 10 = 12$

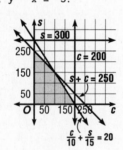

30. Answers may vary. A sample answer is:

$y \leq 4, \ y \geq 0, \ y - x \leq 4, \ y - x \leq -5$.

31. Let c = corn acres and

s = soybean acres.

$s + c \leq 250$

$0 \leq s \leq 300$

$0 \leq c \leq 200$

$\dfrac{c}{10} + \dfrac{s}{15} \leq 20$

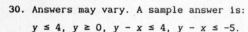

vertices: (0, 250), (100, 150), (200, 0), (0, 0)

max.　　$f(c, s) = 30c + 25s$

$f(100, 150) = 30(100) + 25(150)$

$= 3000 + 3750$

$= \$6750$

Thus, the farmer should plant 100 acres of corn

and 150 acres of soybeans.

32. Let a = adults and

s = students.

$a + s \leq 150$

$a \geq 0$

$s \geq 0$

$2s \geq a$

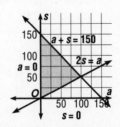

vertices: (0, 0), (0, 150), (100, 50)

max.　　$f(a, s) = 2a + s$

$f(100, 50) = 2(100) + 50$

$= 250$

Thus, 100 adults and 50 students should attend.

33.

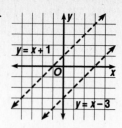

34.

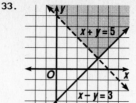

35.

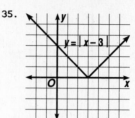

36.　　$3x - 12y = 24$

$3x - 12(0) = 24$

$3x = 24$

$x = 8 \quad (8, 0)$

$3(0) - 12y = 24$

$-12y = 24$

$y = -2 \quad (0, -2)$

37. Let s = score on 4th test.

$87 + 92 + 81 + s \geq 350$

$260 + s \geq 350$

$s \geq 90$

You need to score at least a 90.

3–7 **Applications of Linear Programming**

PAGE 136　　CHECKING FOR UNDERSTANDING

1. They are the maximum and minimum values.

2. Yes. there will be more than one value if the profit function passes through two of the vertices or if the profit function represents a line that is a boundary of the region.

3. Yes. If the region is not bounded, there may be no maximum.

4. $P(A, B) = 10A + 20B$　　5. $0 \leq A \leq 9; \ B \geq 18$

6. $4A + 12B \leq 300$

7.

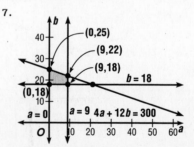

8. (0, 18), (0, 25), (9, 18), (9, 22)

60

9. $P(0, 18) = 10(0) + 20(18) = 360$

   $P(0, 25) = 10(0) + 20(25) = 500$

   $P(9, 18) = 10(9) + 20(18) = 450$

   $P(9, 22) = 10(9) + 20(22) = 530$

10. 9 units of A, 22 units of B

11. 530 pounds

PAGES 136-138   EXERCISES

12. **a.** $6c + 30b \leq 600$

   $c + b \leq 60$

   $c \geq 0$

   $b \geq 0$

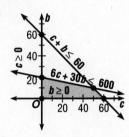

   b. vertices: $(0, 0)$, $(0, 20)$, $(50, 10)$, $(60, 0)$

   $f(0, 0) = 2.5(0) + 7.5(0) = 0$

   $f(0, 20) = 2.5(0) + 7.5(20) = 150$

max. $f(50, 10) = 2.5(50) + 7.5(10) = 200$

   $f(60, 0) = 2.5(60) + 7.5(0) = 150$

   50 cars, 10 buses; income of $200

   c. $f(0, 0) = 4(0) + 8(0) = 0$

   $f(0, 20) = 4(0) + 8(20) = 160$

max. $f(50, 10) = 4(50) + 8(10) = 280$

   $f(60, 0) = 4(60) + 8(0) = 240$

   50 cars, 10 buses; income of $280

13. $A \leq 120$, $B \leq 72$, $C \leq 10$

   1 football: $4A + 2B$

   1 basketball: $6A + 6B + 1C$

   Let f = football and b = basketball

   $4f + 6b \leq 120$

   $2f + 6b \leq 72$

   $0 \leq b \leq 10$

   $f \geq 0$

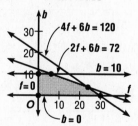

   vertices: $(0, 0)$, $(0, 10)$, $(6, 10)$, $(24, 4)$, $(30, 0)$

   $f(0, 0) = 3(0) + 2(0) = 0$

   $f(0, 10) = 3(0) + 2(10) = 20$

   $f(6, 10) = 3(6) + 2(10) = 38$

   $f(24, 4) = 3(24) + 2(4) = 80$

   $f(30, 0) = 3(30) + 2(0) = 90$

   30 footballs, 0 basketballs; $90

14. **a.** Let x = pounds of type X and

   y = pounds of type Y.

   $40 \leq x + y \leq 100$

   $x + \frac{1}{3}y \geq 20$

   $\frac{1}{2}x + y \geq 30$

   $x \geq 0$

   $y \geq 0$

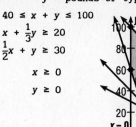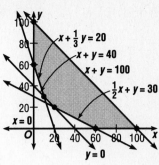

   vertices: $(0, 60)$, $(0, 100)$, $(100, 0)$

   $(60, 0)$, $(20, 20)$, $(10, 30)$

   $f(0, 60) = 0.8(0) + 0.4(60) = 24$

   $f(0, 100) = 0.8(0) + 0.4(100) = 40$

   $f(100, 0) = 0.8(100) + 0.4(0) = 80$

   $f(60, 0) = 0.8(60) + 0.4(0) = 48$

   $f(20, 20) = 0.8(20) + 0.4(20) = 24$

min. $f(10, 30) = 0.8(10) + 0.4(30) = 20$

   10 pounds of X, 30 pounds of Y; $20

   b. $f(0, 60) = (0) + 0.4(60) = 24$

   $f(0, 100) = (0) + 0.4(100) = 40$

   $f(100, 0) = (100) + 0.4(0) = 100$

   $f(60, 0) = (60) + 0.4(0) = 60$

   $f(20, 20) = (20 + 0.4(20) = 28$

min. $f(10, 30) = (10) + 0.4(30) = 22$

   10 pounds X, 30 pounds Y; $22

   same vertex; no

15. **a.**   32 blue

      54 red

   A = 4 blue + 1 red

   B = 1 blue + 6 red

   $a \geq 0$

   $b \geq 0$

   $4a + b \leq 32$

   $a + 6b \leq 54$

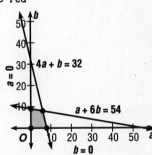

   vertices: $(0, 0)$, $(0, 8)$, $(6, 8)$, $(8, 0)$

   b. $f(0, 0) = 0 + 0 = 0$

   $f(0, 8) = 0 + 8 = 8$

max. $f(6, 8) = 6 + 8 = 14$

   $f(8, 0) = 8 + 10 = 8$

   6 gallons A + 8 gallons B = 14 gallons

16. Let r = rocker and
   s = swivel.

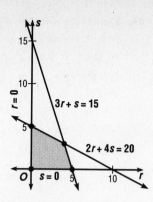

$0 \le A \le 20$

$0 \le B \le 15$

rocker: $2A + 3B$

swivel: $4A + B$

$2r + 4s \le 20$

$3r + s \le 15$

$r \ge 0$

$s \ge 0$

vertices: $(0, 0)$, $(0, 5)$, $(4, 3)$, $(5, 0)$

   $f(0, 0) = 12(0) + 10(0) = 0$

   $f(0, 5) = 12(0) + 10(5) = 50$

max. $f(4, 3) = 12(4) + 10(3) = 78$

   $f(5, 0) = 12(5) + 10(0) = 60$

4 rockers, 3 swivels; $78

17. 1 jean: 10 hrs

   1 leather: 20 hrs

   Let j = jean jackets

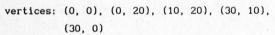

   ℓ = leather jackets

   $0 \le$ hours ≤ 500

   $0 \le j \le 30$

   $0 \le \ell \le 20$

   $10j + 20\ell \le 500$

   vertices: $(0, 0)$, $(0, 20)$, $(10, 20)$, $(30, 10)$,
   $(30, 0)$

a. $f(0, 0) = 0 + 0 = 0$

   $f(0, 20) = 0 + 20 = 20$

   $f(10, 20) = 10 + 20 = 30$

max. $f(30, 10) = 30 + 10 = 40$

   $f(30, 0) = 30 + 0 = 30$

   30 jean, 10 leather jackets maximize profit

b. $f(0, 0) = 0 + 3(0) = 0$

   $f(0, 20) = 0 + 3(20) = 60$

max. $f(10, 20) = 10 + 3(20) = 70$

   $f(30, 10) = 30 + 3(10) = 60$

   $f(30, 0) = 30 + 3(0) = 30$

   10 jean, 20 leather jackets

18. Let s = short answer and
   e = essay.

	Worth	Time
Short Answer	5 pts	2 min
Essay	15 pts	12 min

$s \ge 0$

$e \ge 0$

$s + e \le 20$

a. $2s + 12e \le 60$

   vertices $(0, 0)$,

   $(0, 5)$, $(18, 2)$,

   $(20, 0)$

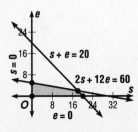

   $f(0, 0)$

   $= 5(0) + 15(0) = 0$

   $f(0, 5)$

   $= 5(0) + 15(5) = 75$

max. $f(18, 2) = 5(18) + 15(2) = 120$

   $f(20, 0) = 5(20) + 15(0) = 100$

   18 short answer, 2 essay for a score of 120 pts

b. $2s + 12e \le 120$

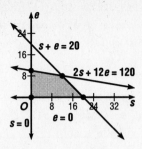

   vertices: $(0, 0)$, $(0, 10)$, $(12, 8)$, $(20, 0)$

   $f(0, 0) = 5(0) + 15(0) = 0$

   $f(0, 10) = 5(0) + 15(10) = 150$

max. $f(12, 8) = 5(12) + 15(8) = 180$

   $f(20, 0) = 5(20) + 15(0) = 100$

   12 short answer, 8 essay for a score of 180 pts.

19. Answers may vary.

   Recall for a regular hexagon:

a. Each side is the same length.

b. The exterior angle of one side measures
   $\dfrac{360}{6} = 60°$

   If you "box in" the hexagon with one corner on
   the origin and one side resting on the x-axis,
   you can easily find the vertices. The corners
   of the box form 30-60-90 triangles. Let the
   length of one of the short sides be 1; the
   other leg will be $\sqrt{3}$ and the hypotenuse 2. With
   these lengths known you can describe the
   coordinates of the six vertices.

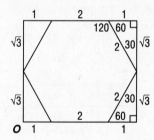

   In this example, the inequalities are:

   $y \ge 0$, $y \ge \sqrt{3}x - 3\sqrt{3}$; $y \le -\sqrt{3}x + 5\sqrt{3}$; $y \le 2\sqrt{3}$;
   $y \le \sqrt{3}x + \sqrt{3}$; $y \ge -\sqrt{3}x + \sqrt{3}$

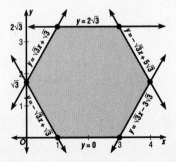

20. $x \geq 0$
$y \geq 3$
$y \geq 2x + 1$
$y \leq -0.5x + 6$

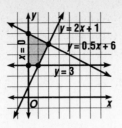

vertices: $(0, 3)$, $(0, 6)$, $(2, 5)$, $(1, 3)$

maximum value: $3(1) - 2(3) = -3$

minimum value: $3(0) - 2(6) = -12$

21. $0 \leq x \leq 50$
$0 \leq y \leq 70$
$60 \leq x + y \leq 80$

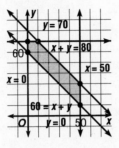

vertices: $(0, 60)$, $(0, 70)$, $(10, 70)$, $(50, 10)$, $(50, 30)$

maximum value: $4(50) + 3(30) = 290$

minimum value: $4(0) + 3(60) = 180$

22. No, because x is squared.

23. $|a + 5| + 5 = 3$
$|a + 5| = -2$
false; no solution

24. Reflexive property of equality

3-8 **Graphing Equations in Three Variables**

PAGE 142   CHECKING FOR UNDERSTANDING

1. An equation of a plane can be written in the form $Ax + By + Cz = D$, such that A, B, and C are nonzero real numbers. An equation of a line can be written in the form $Ax + By = C$, where both A and B cannot be 0.

2. Answers may vary. A sample answer is: $(2, 1, 2)$ and $(1, 1, 5)$.

3. $3x + 4y = 12$

4. $(+, +, +)$: octant 1   **5.** $(+, +, -)$: octant 4

6. $(+, 0, +)$ none   **7.** $(+, -, +)$: octant 2

8. $2x + 0 - 0 = 12$
$2x = 12$
$x = 6$ x-intercept: 6
$2(0) + y - 0 = 12$
$y = 12$ y-intercept: 12
$2(0) + 0 - z = 12$
$-z = 12$
$z = -12$ z-intercept: -12

9. $20x - 4(0) + 10(0) = 20$
$20x = 20$
$x = 1$ x-intercept: 1
$20(0) - 4y + 10(0) = 20$
$-4y = 20$
$y = -5$ y-intercept: -5
$20(0) - 4(0) + 10z = 20$
$10z = 20$
$z = 2$ z-intercept: 2

10. $2x + 0 - 3(0) = 10$
$2x = 10$
$x = 5$ x-intercept: 5
$2(0) + y - 3(0) = 10$
$y = 10$ y-intercept: 10
$2(0) + 0 - 3z = 10$
$-3z = 10$
$z = -\frac{10}{3}$ z-intercept: $-\frac{10}{3}$

11. $3x + 5(0) + 2(0) = 30$
$3x = 30$
$x = 10$ x-intercept: 10
$3(0) + 5y + 2(0) = 30$
$5y = 30$
$y = 6$ y-intercept: 6
$3(0) + 5(0) + 2z = 30$
$2z = 30$
$z = 15$ z-intercept: 15

PAGES 142-143   EXERCISES

12. $(-, +, +)$: octant 5   **13.** $(+, +, -)$: octant 4

14. $(+, +, +)$: octant 1   **15.** $(-, -, -)$: octant 7

16. $(+, -, +)$: octant 2   **17.** $(+, -, -)$: octant 3

18. x-intercept: 3
y-intercept: $\frac{3}{2}$
z-intercept: $\frac{9}{2}$
xy-trace:
$3x + 6y + 2(0) = 9$
$3x + 6y = 9$
$x + 2y = 3$
yz-trace:
$3(0) + 6y + 2z = 9$
$6y + 2z = 9$
xz-trace:
$3x + 6(0) + 2z = 9$
$3x + 2z = 9$

19. x-intercept: $\frac{5}{2}$

    y-intercept: -10

    z-intercept: 5

    xy-trace:

    $4x - y + 2(0) = 10$

        $4x - y = 10$

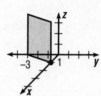

    yz-trace:

    $4(0) - y + 2z = 10$

        $-y + 2z = 10$

    xz-trace:

    $4x - 0 + 2z = 10$

        $4x + 2z = 10$

        $2x + z = 5$

20. x-intercept: 1

    y-intercept: -3

    z-intercept: none

    xy-trace:

    $3x - y = 3$

    yz-trace:

    $3(0) - y = 3$

        $-y = 3$

        $y = -3$

    xz-trace:

    $3x - 0 = 3$

        $3x = 3$

        $x = 1$

21. x-intercept: none

    y-intercept: 4

    z-intercept: 10

    xy-trace:

    $5y + 2(0) = 20$

        $5y = 20$

        $y = 4$

    yz-trace:

    $5y + 2z = 20$

    xz-trace:

    $5(0) + 2z = 20$

        $2z = 20$

        $z = 10$

22. x-intercept: $\frac{-5}{2}$

    y-intercept: none

    z-intercept: $\frac{5}{3}$

    xy-trace:

    $3(0) - 2x = 5$

        $-2x = 5$

        $2x = -5$

    yz-trace:

    $3z - 2(0) = 5$

        $3z = 5$

    xz-trace:

    $3z - 2x = 5$

23. x-intercept: $\frac{-12}{5}$

    y-intercept: $\frac{3}{2}$

    z-intercept: none

    yx-trace:

    $5x - 8y = -12$

    yz-trace:

    $5(0) - 8y = -12$

        $-8y = -12$

        $2y = 3$

    xz-trace:

    $5x - 8(0) = -12$

        $5x = -12$

24. x-intercept: 2

    y-intercept: -2

    z-intercept: 5

    LCM $(2, -2, 5) = 10$

    $\frac{10x}{2} + \frac{10y}{-2} + \frac{10z}{5} = 5x - 5y + 2z = 10$

25. x-intercept: $\frac{1}{2}$

    y-intercept: 3

    z-intercept: -2

    $\text{LCM}\left(\frac{1}{2}, 3, -2\right) = 6$

    $\frac{6x}{\frac{1}{2}} + \frac{6y}{3} + \frac{6z}{-2} = 12x + 2y - 3z = 6$

26. x-intercept: 3

    y-intercept: 5

    z-intercept: 5

    LCM$(3, 5, 5) = 15$

    $\frac{15x}{3} + \frac{15y}{5} + \frac{15z}{5} = 15$

    $5x + 3y + 3z = 15$

27. x-intercept: 1

    y-intercept: $-\frac{1}{4}$

    z-intercept: -2

    $\text{LCM}\left(1, -\frac{1}{4}, -2\right) = 2$

    $\frac{2x}{1} + \frac{2y}{-\frac{1}{4}} + \frac{2z}{-2} = 2$

        $2x - 8y - z = 2$

28. x-intercept: none

    y-intercept: -2

    z-intercept: $-\frac{3}{2}$

    $\text{LCM}\left(2, -\frac{3}{2}\right) = 6$

    $\frac{6y}{2} + \frac{6z}{-\frac{3}{2}} = 6$

    $3y - 4z = 6$

29. x-intercept: -2

    y-intercept: none

    z-intercept 5

    LCM $(-2, 5) = 10$

    $\frac{10x}{-2} + \frac{10z}{5} = 10$

    $-5x + 2z = 10$ or

    $5x - 2z = -10$

30. The coefficients of each variable are the same, but the constant term is different. A sample answer is: $x + y + z = 5$

                    $x + y + z = 10$

31.

a. $12 \times 10 \times 10 = 1200$ cubic inches

b. surface area = sum of all six face areas

        $= (12 \times 10) + (12 \times 10) + (12 \times 10)$

           $+ (12 \times 10) + (10 \times 10)$

           $+ (10 \times 10)$

        $= 480 + 200$

        $= 680$ square inches

c. $(24, 20, 20)$ $24 \times 20 \times 20 = 9600$ cubic inches

    $\frac{9600}{1200} = 8$ times greater

32.

a. $\sqrt{(3-0)^2 + (0-4)^2 + (0-0)^2} = \sqrt{9 + 16 + 0}$
$= \sqrt{25} = 5.00$

b. $\sqrt{(0-1)^2 + (0-2)^2 + (0-3)^2} = \sqrt{1 + 4 + 9}$
$= \sqrt{14} = 3.74$

c. $\sqrt{(5-3)^2 + [1-(-2)]^2 + (3-6)^2} = \sqrt{4 + 9 + 9}$
$= \sqrt{22} = 4.69$

d. $\sqrt{[-1-(-2)]^2 + [7-(-1)]^2 + [1-(-3)]^2}$
$= \sqrt{1 + 64 + 16}$
$= \sqrt{81} = 9.00$

e. Answers may vary. Through trial and error, a sample answer is $a = 4$, $b = 4$, $c = 2$, $d = 6$.

33. 25 days total
275 acres

	Rate	Profit
Cotton	9 acres/day	$25/acre
Corn	12 acres/day	$18/acre

a. $c \geq 0$, $r \geq 0$; $c + r \leq 275$;
$\frac{c}{9} + \frac{r}{12} \leq 25$

b.
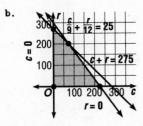

vertices: $(0, 0)$, $(0, 275)$,
$(75, 200)$, $(225, 0)$
maximum value: $25(225) +$
$18(0) = 5625$
To maximize profit, plant 225 acres of cotton and 0 acres of corn, for a profit of $5625.

34. $0 + 2(0) \leq 7$ $1 + 2(-2) \leq 7$
$0 \leq 7$, yes $-3 \leq 7$, yes
$-3 + 2(1) \leq 7$
$-1 \leq 7$, yes
$(0, 0)$, $(1, -2)$, $(-3, 1)$ satisfy the inequality.

35. $\frac{1}{2}$, $\frac{2}{3}$, $\frac{4}{4}$, $\frac{8}{5}$, $\frac{16}{6}$, $\frac{32}{7}$

36. $|m - 4| + 2 \geq 0$
$|m - 4| \geq -2$
all reals

PAGE 147   CHECKING FOR UNDERSTANDING

1. Substitution or Cramer's Rule

2. z is easy to find.

3. Answers may vary. A sample answer is that you might find a false statement after eliminating variables. For example, $0 = 5$.

4. Answers may vary. A sample answer is that you might find a true statement after eliminating variables. For example, $0 = 0$.

5. $0 + 2(0) + 0 = 0$
$0 = 0$
$0 - 0 + 0 = 0$
$0 = 0$
$2(0) + 3(0) - 0 = 0$
$0 = 0$
Yes

6. $2 - 3(2) + 2(2) = 1$
$2 - 6 + 4 = 1$
$0 = 1$
No

7. $4(3) + 0 - 2(6) = 0$
$0 = 0$
$3 - 2(0) = 0$
$3 = 0$
No

8. $2(8) + (-11) - 3 = 2$
$2 = 2$
$3(8) + 2(-11) + 3 = 5$
$5 = 5$
$8 - 11 + 3 = 0$
$0 = 0$
Yes

9. $3 - 2 = 1$
$1 = 1$
$3 + (-2) + 2 = 3$
$2 - (-2) = 4$
$4 = 4$
Yes

10. $-4 + (-2) = -6$
$-6 = -6$
$-4 + 2 = -2$
$-2 = -2$
$-2 + 2 = 2$
$0 = 2$
No

PAGES 147-149   EXERCISES

11. $x - 2y + z = -9$
$2y + 3z = 16$
$2y = 4$
$y = 2$
$2(2) + 3z = 16$
$3z = 12$
$z = 4$
$x - 2(2) + 4 = -9$
$x - 4 + 4 = -9$
$x = -9$
$(-9, 2, 4)$

12. $2a + b = 2$
$5a = 15$
$a + b + c = -1$
$5a = 15$
$a = 3$
$2(3) + b = 2$
$6 + b = 2$
$b = -4$
$3 + (-4) + c = -1$
$-1 + c = -1$
$c = 0$
$(3, -4, 0)$

13.
$$x + y - z = -1$$
$$\underline{x + y + z = 3}$$
$$2x + 2y = 2$$
$$x + y = 1$$

$$x + y + z = 3$$
$$\underline{3x - 2y - z = -4}$$
$$4x - y \quad = -1$$

$$x + y = 1$$
$$\underline{4x - y = -1}$$
$$5x = 0$$
$$x = 0$$

$$0 + y = 1$$
$$y = 1$$
$$0 + 1 + z = 3$$
$$z = 2$$
$$(0, 1, 2)$$

14.
$$b + c = 4$$
$$2a + 4b - c = -3$$
$$3b = -3 \longrightarrow b = -1$$

$$-1 + c = 4$$
$$c = 5$$
$$2a + 4(-1) - 5 = -3$$
$$2a - 4 - 5 = -3$$
$$2a = 6$$
$$a = 3$$
$$(3, -1, 5)$$

15.
$$r + s + t = 15$$
$$r + t = 12$$
$$s + t = 10$$

$$r + s + t = 15$$
$$\underline{-r \quad - t = -12}$$
$$s = 3$$
$$3 + t = 10$$
$$t = 7$$

$$r + 3 + 7 = 15$$
$$r = 5$$
$$(5, 3, 7)$$

16.
$$4x + 2y - 4z = 62$$
$$\underline{x - 2y - 3z = 23}$$
$$5x - 7z = 85$$

$$4x + 2y - 4z = 62$$
$$\underline{x - 2y + z = 3}$$
$$5x - 3z = 65$$

$$5x - 7z = 85$$
$$\underline{-5x + 3z = -65}$$
$$-4z = 20$$
$$z = -5$$

$$5x - 3(-5) = 65$$
$$5x = 50$$
$$x = 10$$
$$10 - 2y + (-5) = 3$$
$$-2y = -2$$
$$y = 1$$
$$(10, 1, -5)$$

17.
$$a + b + c = 0$$
$$\underline{2a + b - c = 2}$$
$$3a + 2b = 2$$

$$2a + 2b + c = 5$$
$$\underline{2a + b - c = 2}$$
$$4a + 3b = 7$$

$$12a + 8b = 8$$
$$\underline{-12a - 9b = -21}$$
$$-b = -13$$
$$b = 13$$

$$3a + 2(13) = 2$$
$$3a = -24$$
$$a = -8$$
$$-8 + 13 + c = 0$$
$$c = -5$$
$$(-8, 13, -5)$$

18.
$$x + y + z = 4$$
$$\underline{x - y - z = -2}$$
$$2x = 2$$
$$x = 1$$

$$x + y + z = 4$$
$$\underline{x - y + z = 0}$$
$$2x + 2z = 4$$

$$2(1) + 2z = 4$$
$$2z = 2$$
$$z = 1$$
$$1 + y + 1 = 4$$
$$y = 2$$
$$(1, 2, 1)$$

19.
$$r + s - 2t = 4$$
$$\underline{2r + s + 2t = 0}$$
$$3r + 2s = 4$$

$$r - 3s - 4t = -2$$
$$\underline{4r + 2s + 4t = 0}$$
$$5r - s \quad = -2$$

$$3r + 2s = 4$$
$$\underline{10r - 2s = -4}$$
$$13r = 0$$
$$r = 0$$

$$5(0) - s = -2$$
$$-s = -2$$
$$s = 2$$

$$0 + 2 - 2t = 4$$
$$-2t = 2$$
$$t = -1$$
$$(0, 2, -1)$$

20.
$$2x + 3y + z = 28$$
$$\underline{-x - y - z = -16}$$
$$x + 2y = 12$$

$$3x + 4y - 2z = 24$$
$$\underline{2x + 2y + 2z = 32}$$
$$5x + 6y = 56$$

$$-3x - 6y = -36$$
$$\underline{5x + 6y = 56}$$
$$2x = 20$$
$$x = 10$$

$$10 + 2y = 12$$
$$2y = 2$$
$$y = 1$$

$$10 + 1 + z = 16$$
$$z = 5$$
$$(10, 1, 5)$$

21.
$$3x - 2y + 2z = -2$$
$$\underline{-3x + 9y - 3z = 6}$$
$$7y - z = 4$$

$$-2x + 6y - 2z = 4$$
$$\underline{2x - y + 4z = 7}$$
$$5y + 2z = 11$$

$$14y - 2z = 8$$
$$\underline{5y + 2z = 11}$$
$$19y = 19$$
$$y = 1$$

$$7(1) - z = 4$$
$$-z = -3$$
$$z = 3$$
$$x - 3(1) + 3 = -2$$
$$x = -2$$
$$(-2, 1, 3)$$

22.
$$-3a - 24b - 6c = 72$$
$$\underline{3a + b + 7c = -3}$$
$$-23b + c = 69$$

$$-4a - 32b - 8c = 96$$
$$\underline{4a - 3b + 6c = 9}$$
$$-35b - 2c = 105$$

$$-46b + 2c = 138$$
$$\underline{-35b - 2c = 105}$$
$$-81b = 243$$
$$b = -3$$

$$-23(-3) + c = 69$$
$$69 + c = 69$$
$$c = 0$$

$$a + 8(-3) + 2(0) = -24$$
$$a - 24 = -24$$
$$a = 0$$
$$(0, -3, 0)$$

23.
$$2x + 2y + 2z = -2$$
$$\underline{3x - 2y - 4z = 16}$$
$$5x - 2z = 14$$

$$x + y + z = -1$$
$$\underline{2x - y + z = 19}$$
$$3x + 2z = 18$$

$$5x - 2z = 14$$
$$\underline{3x + 2z = 18}$$
$$8x = 32$$
$$x = 4$$

$$3(4) + 2z = 18$$
$$2z = 6$$
$$z = 3$$
$$4 + y + 3 = -1$$
$$y = -8$$
$$(4, -8, 3)$$

24.

$$4x + 3y + 2z = 34$$
$$\underline{-4x - 8y - 6z = -90}$$
$$-5y - 4z = -56$$

$$6x + 12y + 9z = 135$$
$$\underline{-6x - 4y - 8z = -94}$$
$$8y + z = 41$$

$$-5y - 4z = -56$$
$$\underline{32y + 4z = 164}$$
$$27y = 108$$
$$y = 4$$

$$8(4) + z = 41$$
$$z = 9$$

$$2x + 4(4) + 3(9) = 45$$
$$2x + 16 + 27 = 45$$
$$2x = 2$$
$$x = 1$$
$$(1, 4, 9)$$

25.

$$3a + b + 2c = 6$$
$$\underline{3a + b - 2c = 0}$$
$$6a + 2b = 6$$

$$6a - 2b = 2$$
$$\underline{6a + 2b = 6}$$
$$12a = 8$$
$$a = \frac{2}{3}$$

$$6\left(\frac{2}{3}\right) + 2b = 6$$
$$4 + 2b = 6$$
$$2b = 2$$
$$b = 1$$

$$3\left(\frac{2}{3}\right) + 1 + 2c = 6$$
$$2 + 1 + 2c = 6$$
$$2c = 3$$
$$c = \frac{3}{2}$$
$$\left(\frac{2}{3}, 1, \frac{3}{2}\right)$$

26.

$$x + y + z = 1$$
$$\underline{2x - y = 0}$$
$$3x + z = 1$$

$$3x + z = 1$$
$$\underline{-3x + z = 0}$$
$$2z = 1$$
$$z = \frac{1}{2}$$

$$3x + \frac{1}{2} = 1$$
$$3x = \frac{1}{2}$$
$$x = \frac{1}{6}$$

$$\frac{1}{6} + y + \frac{1}{2} = 1$$
$$y = \frac{1}{3}$$
$$\left(\frac{1}{6}, \frac{1}{3}, \frac{1}{2}\right)$$

27.

$$2r - 3s + 4t = 1$$
$$\underline{2r + 3s + 4t = 3}$$
$$4r + 8t = 4$$

$$6r + 9s + 12t = 9$$
$$\underline{5r - 9s + 6t = 1}$$
$$11r + 18t = 10$$

$$-36r - 72t = -36$$
$$\underline{44r + 72t = 40}$$
$$8r = 4$$
$$r = \frac{1}{2}$$

$$4\left(\frac{1}{2}\right) + 8t = 4$$
$$8t = 2$$
$$t = \frac{1}{4}$$

$$2\left(\frac{1}{2}\right) + 3s + 4\left(\frac{1}{4}\right) = 3$$
$$1 + 3s + 1 = 3$$
$$3s = 1$$
$$s = \frac{1}{3}$$
$$\left(\frac{1}{2}, \frac{1}{3}, \frac{1}{4}\right)$$

28.

$$2x - 3y + z = -1$$
$$\underline{-2x - y - z = -7}$$
$$-4y = -8$$
$$y = 2$$

$$2x + 2 + z = 7$$
$$2x + z = 5$$

$$12x - 2(2) - 2z = 2$$
$$12x - 4 - 2z = 2$$
$$12x - 2z = 6$$

$$4x + 2z = 10$$
$$\underline{12x - 2z = 6}$$
$$16x = 16$$
$$x = 1$$

$$2(1) + z = 5$$
$$z = 3$$
$$(1, 2, 3)$$

29. Let x = 1st number

$$y = \text{2nd number}$$
$$z = \text{3rd number}$$
$$x + y + z = 6$$
$$x = 2y$$
$$z = 3y$$
$$2y + y + 3y = 6$$
$$6y = 6$$
$$y = 1$$
$$x = 2(1) = 2$$
$$z = 3(1) = 3$$
$$(2, 1, 3)$$

30. Let x = 1st number

$$y = \text{2nd number}$$
$$z = \text{3rd number}$$
$$x + y + z = 20$$
$$x = y + z$$
$$z = 3x$$
$$x + x = 20$$
$$2x = 20$$
$$x = 10$$
$$z = 3(10) = 30$$
$$y = x - z$$
$$= 10 - 30$$
$$= -20$$
$$(10, -20, 30)$$

31.

$$w + x + y + z = 2$$
$$\underline{2w - x - y + 2z = 7}$$
$$3w + 3z = 9$$

$$w + x + y + z = 2$$
$$\underline{3w - 2x - y - 3z = -2}$$
$$4w - x - 2z = 0$$

$$4w - 2x - 2y + 4z = 14$$
$$\underline{2w + 3x + 2y - z = -2}$$
$$6w + x + 3z = 12$$

$$4w - x - 2z = 0$$
$$\underline{6w + x + 3z = 12}$$
$$10w + z = 12$$

$$3w + 3z = 9$$
$$\underline{-30w - 3z = -36}$$
$$-27w = -27$$
$$w = 1$$

$$3(1) + 3z = 9$$
$$3z = 6$$
$$z = 2$$

$$4(1) - x - 2(2) = 0$$
$$4 - x - 4 = 0$$
$$-x = 0$$
$$x = 0$$

$$1 + 0 + y + 2 = 2$$
$$y + 3 = 2$$
$$y = -1$$

$$(1, 0, -1, 2)$$

32. Let x = longest side

      y = remaining side

      z = shortest side

$$x + y + z = 180$$
$$x = 2z$$
$$y = \frac{1}{2}(x + z)$$
$$y = \frac{3}{2}z$$
$$2z + \frac{3}{2}z + z = 180$$
$$\frac{9}{2}z = 180$$
$$z = 40$$
$$x = 2(40) = 80$$
$$y = \frac{3}{2}(40) = 60$$

    80, 60, 40 meters

33. Let p = cost of a pizza slice

      s = cost of a salad

      d = cost of a soda

$$5p + 2s + 2d = 9.75$$
$$3p + 2s + d = 7.15$$
$$2p + s + d = 4.35$$

$$5p + 2s + 2d = 9.75 \qquad 5p + 2s + 2d = 9.75$$
$$\underline{-3p - 2s - d = -7.15} \qquad \underline{-4p - 2s - 2d = -8.70}$$
$$2p + d = 2.60 \qquad\qquad p = 1.05$$

$$2(1.05) + d = 2.60 \qquad 2(1.05) + s + 0.50 = 4.35$$
$$2.10 + d = 2.60 \qquad 2.10 + s + 0.50 = 4.35$$
$$d = 0.50 \qquad\qquad\qquad s = 1.75$$

pizza: \$1.05, salad: \$1.75, soda: \$0.50

34. Let c = interest rate of certificate of deposit

      s = interest rate of stocks

      b = interest rate of bonds

$$s = c + 0.015$$
$$5000c = 400$$
$$2000c + 2000b + 1000s = 385$$

$$5000c = 400 \qquad\qquad s = c + 0.015$$
$$c = 0.08 \qquad\qquad = 0.08 + 0.015$$
$$= 0.095$$

$$2000(0.08) + 2000b + 1000(0.095) = 385$$
$$160 \qquad + 2000b + 95 \qquad\quad = 385$$
$$2000b = 130$$
$$b = 0.065$$

CD at 8%, stocks at 9.5%, bonds at 6.5%

35. $-3x + 6(0) - 4(0) = 24$

$$-3x = 24$$
$$x = -8 \qquad x\text{-intercept: } -8$$
$$-3(0) + 6y - 4(0) = 24$$
$$6y = 24$$
$$y = 4 \qquad y\text{-intercept: } 4$$
$$-3(0) + 6(0) - 4z = 24$$
$$-4z = 24$$
$$z = -6 \qquad z\text{-intercept: } -6$$

36. $9x + 6(0) - 3(0) = 36$

$$9x = 36$$
$$x = 4 \qquad x\text{-intercept: } 4$$
$$9(0) + 6y - 3(0) = 36$$
$$6y = 36$$
$$y = 6 \qquad y\text{-intercept: } 6$$
$$9(0) + 6(0) - 3z = 36$$
$$-3z = 36$$
$$z = -12 \qquad z\text{-intercept: } -12$$

37. $-3x + y = -5$

$$y = 3x - 5$$
$$2x + 3(3x - 5) = -4$$
$$2x + 9x - 15 = -4$$
$$11x = 11$$
$$x = 1$$
$$y = 3(1) - 5$$
$$= 3 - 5$$
$$= -2$$
$$(1, -2)$$

38. $\text{Cost} = c = 25\left(t - \frac{1}{2}\right) + 35$

39. Perpendicular line to $3y = 2x + 3$ will have a negative reciprocal slope.

$$3y = 2x + 3$$
$$y = \frac{2}{3}x + 1 \quad \text{New Line: } y = -\frac{3}{2}x + b$$
$$\text{At } (-3, 4), \ 4 = -\frac{3}{2}(-3) + b$$
$$4 = \frac{9}{2} + b$$
$$-\frac{1}{2} = b$$
$$y = -\frac{3}{2}x - \frac{1}{2}$$

Chapter 3 Summary and Review

PAGES 150-152   SKILLS AND CONCEPTS

1.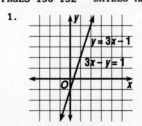

2.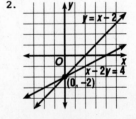

$\{(x, y) \mid y = 3x - 1\}$ $(0, -2)$

consistent   consistent

and dependent   and independent

3.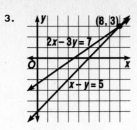

(8, 3)

consistent and

independent

4.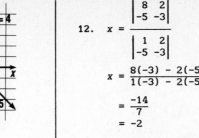

(3, 2)

consistent and

independent

5. $x + y = 8$

$\underline{x - y = 4.5}$

$\quad 2x = 12.5$

$\quad\quad x = 6.25$

$6.25 + y = 8$

$\quad\quad y = 1.75$

$(6.25, 1.75)$

6. $3x - 5y = -13$

$4x + 3y = 2$

$12x - 20y = -52$

$\underline{-12x - 9y = -6}$

$\quad -29y = -58$

$\quad\quad y = 2$

$4x + 3(2) = 2$

$4x + 6 = 2$

$4x = -4$

$x = -1$

$(-1, 2)$

7. $2x + 3y = 8$

$\underline{3x - 3y = 6}$

$\quad 5x = 14$

$\quad\ x = \dfrac{14}{5}$

$\dfrac{14}{5} - y = 2$

$\quad -y = -\dfrac{4}{5}$

$\quad\ y = \dfrac{4}{5}$

$\left(\dfrac{14}{5}, \dfrac{4}{5}\right)$

8. $\dfrac{1}{6}x - \dfrac{1}{9}y = 0$

$\dfrac{1}{3}x + \dfrac{1}{3}y = 5$

$-2\left(\dfrac{1}{6}x - \dfrac{1}{9}y = 0\right)$

$\dfrac{1}{3}x + \dfrac{1}{3}y = 5$

$\overline{\qquad\dfrac{5}{9}y = 5}$

$\quad y = 9$

$\dfrac{1}{6}x - \dfrac{1}{9}(9) = 0$

$\dfrac{1}{6}x - 1 = 0$

$\dfrac{1}{6}x = 1$

$x = 6$

$(6, 9)$

9. $\begin{vmatrix} 2 & 4 \\ 3 & 5 \end{vmatrix} = 2(5) - 4(3)$

$\qquad\qquad = -2$

10. $\begin{vmatrix} 8 & -1 \\ 3 & -2 \end{vmatrix} = 8(-2) - (-1)(3)$

$\qquad\qquad\quad = -13$

11. $x = \dfrac{\begin{vmatrix} 12 & -8 \\ 23 & 1 \end{vmatrix}}{\begin{vmatrix} 4 & -8 \\ 3 & 1 \end{vmatrix}}$ $\qquad y = \dfrac{\begin{vmatrix} 4 & 12 \\ 3 & 23 \end{vmatrix}}{\begin{vmatrix} 4 & -8 \\ 3 & 1 \end{vmatrix}}$

$x = \dfrac{12(1) - (-8)(23)}{4(1) - (-8)(3)}$ $\quad y = \dfrac{4(23) - 12(3)}{4(1) - (-8)(3)}$

$\quad = \dfrac{196}{28}$ $\qquad\qquad = \dfrac{56}{28}$

$\quad = 7$ $\qquad\qquad = 2 \quad (7, 2)$

12. $x = \dfrac{\begin{vmatrix} 8 & 2 \\ -5 & -3 \end{vmatrix}}{\begin{vmatrix} 1 & 2 \\ -5 & -3 \end{vmatrix}}$ $\qquad y = \dfrac{\begin{vmatrix} 1 & 8 \\ -5 & -5 \end{vmatrix}}{\begin{vmatrix} 1 & 2 \\ -5 & -3 \end{vmatrix}}$

$x = \dfrac{8(-3) - 2(-5)}{1(-3) - 2(-5)}$ $\quad y = \dfrac{1(-5) - 8(-5)}{1(-3) - 2(-5)}$

$\quad = \dfrac{-14}{7}$ $\qquad\qquad = \dfrac{35}{7}$

$\quad = -2$ $\qquad\qquad = 5 \quad (-2, 5)$

13.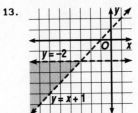

14.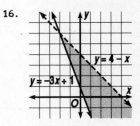

15.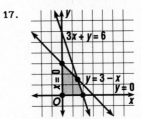

16.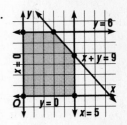

17.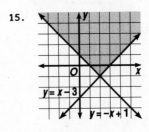

18.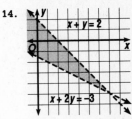

vertices: (0, 0),

(0, 3), (1.5, 1.5),

(2, 0)

maximum value

$2(0) + (3) = 12$

minimum value:

$2(0) + 4(0) = 0$

vertices: (0, 0),

(0, 6), (3, 6), (5, 4),

(5, 0)

maximum value:

$2(3) + 3(6) = 24$

minimum value:

$2(0) + 3(0) = 0$

19. (+, −, +): octant 2

20. (−, −, −): octant 7

21. (0, +, 0): none

22. (+, +, −): octant 4

23. (+, +, +): octant 1

24. (−, −, +): octant 6

25. (+, −, −): octant 3

26. (−, −, +): octant 6

27. x-intercept: 4

y-intercept: 4

z-intercept: −2

xy-trace:

$x + y - 2(0) = 4$

$x + y = 4$

yz-trace:

$0 + y - 2z = 4$

$y - 2z = 4$

xz-trace:

$x + 0 - 2z = 4$

$x - 2z = 4$

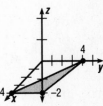

28. x-intercept: $\frac{6}{5}$

y-intercept: -3

z-intercept: 2

xy-trace:

$5x - 2y + 3(0) = 6$

$5x - 2y = 6$

yz-trace:

$5(0) - 2y + 3z = 6$

$-2y + 3z = 6$

xz-trace:

$5x - 2(0) + 3z = 6$

$5x + 3z = 6$

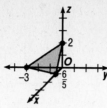

29. $2x + 4y - 6z = -6$

$\underline{-2x - 4y - z = -1}$

$-7z = -7$

$z = 1$

$x + 2y - 3z = -3$

$\underline{-x - y - z = 1}$

$y - 4z = -2$

$y - 4(1) = -2$

$y - 4 = -2$

$y = 2$

$x + 2 + 1 = -1$

$x + 3 = -1$

$x = -4$

$(-4, 2, 1)$

30. $a + b + 3c = 7$

$\underline{3a - b - 2c = 1}$

$4a + c = 8$

$2a + 2b + 6c = 14$

$\underline{2a - 2b - 3c = 2}$

$4a + 3c = 16$

$-4a - c = -8$

$\underline{4a + 3c = 16}$

$2c = 8$

$c = 4$

$4a + 4 = 8$

$4a = 4$

$a = 1$

$1 + b + 3(4) = 7$

$b + 13 = 7$

$b = -6$

$(1, -6, 4)$

PAGE 152   APPLICATIONS AND CONNECTIONS

31. 2-digit: XX 11, 22, ..., 99 ⇒ $\boxed{9}$

3-digit: YXY or YYY Ends 1-9 ⇒ 9

Middle 0-9 ⇒ ×10

⇒ $\boxed{90}$

4-digit: $ZZZZ$ ⇒ $\boxed{0}$

There are a total of 99.

32. Let k = jackets

n = jeans

$n \geq 0$

$k \geq 0$

$k + 2n \leq 40$

$4k + 2n \leq 52$

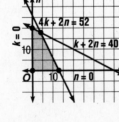

vertices: $(0, 0)$,

$(0, 20)$, $(4, 18)$,

$(13, 0)$

maximum value:

$14(4) + 8(18) = 200$

Make 4 jackets and 18 jeans to make a profit of \$200.

33. Let m = multiple choice

e = essay

	Time	Points
m	1 min	5
e	12 min	20

$m + e \leq 30$

$m + 12e \leq 96$

$m \geq 0$

$e \geq 0$

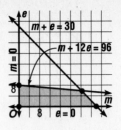

vertices: $(0, 0)$, $(0, 8)$, $(24, 6)$, $(30, 0)$

maximum value:

$5(24) + 20(6) = 240$

24 multiple choice and 6 essay questions for 240 points

Chapter 3 Test

PAGE 153

1. $(4, 3)$

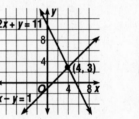

2. $(-5, -2)$

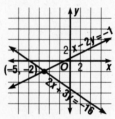

3. $4x + 6y = 10$

$\underline{3x - 6y = -12}$

$7x = -2$

$x = \frac{-2}{7}$

$2\left(-\frac{2}{7}\right) + 3y = 5$

$-\frac{4}{7} + 3y = 5$

$3y = \frac{39}{7}$

$y = \frac{13}{7}$

$\left(-\frac{2}{7}, \frac{13}{7}\right)$

4. $2x + y - 5z = 4$

$\underline{3x - y - 4z = -11}$

$5x - 9z = -7$

$x + 3y + z = 5$

$\underline{9x - 3y - 12z = -33}$

$10x - 11z = -28$

$-10x + 18z = 14$

$\underline{10x - 11z = -28}$

$7z = -14$

$z = -2$

$5x - 9(-2) = -7$

$5x = -25$

$x = -5$

$-5 + 3y - 2 = 5$

$3y = 12$

$y = 4$

$(-5, 4, -2)$

5. $\begin{vmatrix} -3 & 1 \\ -2 & -4 \end{vmatrix} = -3(-4) - 1(-2)$

$= 14$

6. $\begin{vmatrix} 6 & 5 \\ 0 & -9 \end{vmatrix} = 6(-9) - 5(0)$
$= -54$

7. $x = \dfrac{\begin{vmatrix} -1 & 7 \\ 7 & 1 \end{vmatrix}}{\begin{vmatrix} 4 & 7 \\ 2 & 1 \end{vmatrix}}$ $\qquad$ $y = \dfrac{\begin{vmatrix} 4 & -1 \\ 2 & 7 \end{vmatrix}}{\begin{vmatrix} 4 & 7 \\ 2 & 1 \end{vmatrix}}$

$\quad = \dfrac{-1(1) - 7(7)}{4(1) - 7(2)}$ $\qquad = \dfrac{4(7) - (-1)(2)}{4(1) - 7(2)}$

$\quad = \dfrac{-50}{-10} = 5$ $\qquad\quad = \dfrac{30}{-10} = -3 \quad (5, -3)$

8. $x = \dfrac{\begin{vmatrix} -10 & -3 \\ 5 & 1 \end{vmatrix}}{\begin{vmatrix} 8 & -3 \\ 4 & 1 \end{vmatrix}}$ $\qquad$ $y = \dfrac{\begin{vmatrix} 8 & -10 \\ 4 & 5 \end{vmatrix}}{\begin{vmatrix} 8 & -3 \\ 4 & 1 \end{vmatrix}}$

$\quad = \dfrac{-10(1) - (-3)(5)}{8(1) - (-3)(4)}$ $\qquad = \dfrac{8(5) - (-10)(4)}{8(1) - (-3)(4)}$

$\quad = \dfrac{5}{20} = \dfrac{1}{4}$ $\qquad\quad = \dfrac{80}{20} = 4 \qquad \left(\dfrac{1}{4}, 4\right)$

9.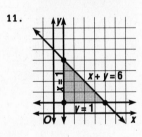

10.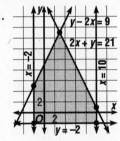

11.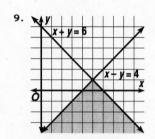

12.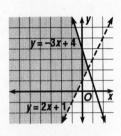

vertices: (1, 1) $\qquad$ vertices: (-2, -2),

(1, 5), (5, 1) $\qquad$ (-2, 5), (3, 15),

maximum value: $\qquad$ (10, 1), (10, -2)

1 + 3(5) = 16 $\qquad$ maximum value:

minimum value: $\qquad$ 3(10) - 2(-2) = 34

1 + 3(1) = 4 $\qquad$ minimum value:

$\qquad\qquad\qquad\qquad$ 3(3) - 2(15) = -21

13. Let x = the number of yoyo's to be produced, and
$\qquad$ y = the number of tops to be produced.

$\quad 3x + 4y \le 450$

$\quad 5x + 2y \le 400$

$\quad x \ge 0$

$\quad y \ge 0$

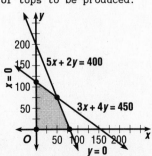

The vertices of the convex polygon are

A(0, 0); B(0, 112.5); C(50, 75); and D(80, 0).

If P is the profit function, then

$P(x, y) = 3x + 3y.$

$P(0, 0) = 3(0) + 3(0) = 0$

$P(0, 112.5) = 3(0) + 3(112.5) = 337.5$

$P(50, 75) = 3(50) + 3(75) = 375$

$P(80, 0) = 3(80) + 3(0) = 240$

The maximum profit is obtained by producing 5000
yoyo's and 7500 tops.

14. The maximum profit is $37,500.

15. (-, -, +): octant 6 $\quad$ **16.** (+, -, +): octant 2

17. x-intercept: 10

$\quad$ y-intercept: -6

$\quad$ z-intercept: 5

$\quad$ xy-trace:

$\quad$ $3x - 5y + 6(0) = 30$

$\qquad$ $3x + 5y = 30$

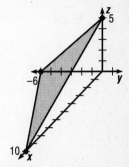

$\quad$ yz-trace: $\qquad\qquad$ xz-trace:

$\quad$ $3(0) - 5y + 6z = 30 \quad$ $3x - 5(0) + 6z = 30$

$\qquad$ $-5y + 6z = 30 \qquad\quad$ $3x + 6z = 30$

$\qquad\qquad\qquad\qquad\qquad\qquad$ $x + 2z = 10$

18. x-intercept: $\dfrac{3}{2}$

$\quad$ y-intercept: -3

$\quad$ z-intercept: 2

$\quad$ xy-trace:

$\quad$ $4x - 2y + 3(0) = 6$

$\qquad$ $4x - 2y = 6$

$\qquad$ $2x - y = 3$

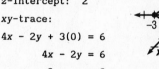

$\quad$ yz-trace: $\qquad\qquad$ xz-trace:

$\quad$ $4(0) - 2y + 3z = 6 \quad$ $4x - 2(0) + 3z = 6$

$\qquad$ $-2y + 3z = 6 \qquad\quad$ $4x + 3z = 6$

19. Let c = colonial, and

$\qquad$ r = ranch.

$\quad c \ge 0$

$\quad r \ge 0$

$\quad 3c \le r$

$\quad r + c \le 60$

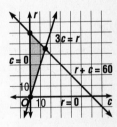

vertices: (0, 0), (0, 60), (15, 45)

maximum profit: 5000(15) + 4500(45) = 277,500

15 colonial and 45 ranch would be best.

20. $f(0, 0) = 3500(0) + 4000(0) = 0$

$\quad f(0, 60) = 3500(0) + 4000(60) = 240,000$

$\quad f(15, 45) = 3500(15) + 4000(45) = 232,500$

$\quad$ 0 colonial and 60 ranch would be best.

$|x| + |y| \leq 5$

$\qquad |y| \leq 5 - |x|$

If $x \geq 0$,

$|y| \leq 5 - x$

$-(5 - x) \leq y \leq 5 - x$

$-5 + x \leq y \leq 5 - x$

$-5 + x \leq y$ and $y \leq 5 - x$

If $x \leq 0$,

$|y| \leq 5 - (-x)$

$|y| \leq 5 + x$

$-(5 + x) \leq y \leq 5 + x$

$\quad -5 - x \leq y \leq 5 + x$

$\quad -5 - x \leq y$ and $y \leq 5 + x$

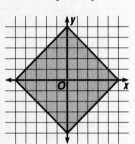

Chapter 4   Matrices

4-1   **Problem-Solving Strategy: Using Matrix Logic**

PAGE 157   CHECKING FOR UNDERSTANDING

1. because you use a matrix to make decisions in solving the problem

2. Use X for matchings you are eliminating and √ for matchings you conclude are correct.

3.

	sculpt.	cars	garden	doctor	teacher	lawyer
Rae	X	X	✔	✔	X	X
Carol	✔	X	X	X	✔	X
Dena	X	✔	X	X	X	✔
doctor	X	X	✔			
teacher	✔	X	X			
lawyer	X	✔	X			

Carol is a teacher and does sculpture. Dena is a lawyer and fixes cars. Rae is a doctor and likes gardening.

PAGES 157–158   EXERCISES

4. Let x = tens digit and y = ones digit.

$$x + y = 10 \quad \rightarrow \quad 2x + 2y = 20$$
$$3x = 2y \quad \rightarrow \quad \underline{3x - 2y = 0}$$
$$5x \quad\quad\quad = 20$$
$$x \quad\quad\quad = 4$$

$$x + y = 10$$
$$4 + y = 10$$
$$y = 6 \quad \text{The two-digit number is 46.}$$

5. 16 : A, B, C, D, E, H, I, K, M, O, T, U, V, W, X, Y

6.

hours	minutes	number of times
1	00	1
2	00,01	2
3	00,01,02	3
4	00,01,02,03	4
5	00,01,02,03,04	5
6	.	6
7	.	7
8	.	8
9	.	9
10	.	10
11	.	11
12	00,01,02,03,04,05, 06,07,08,09,10,11	12

total = 1 + 2 + 3 + 4 + 5 + 6 + 7 + 8 + 9 + 10 + 11 + 12 = 78

7. a. Yes; it will form a cube.
   b. Yes; it will form a cube.
   c. No; the side pieces are too long.
   d. Yes; it will form a rectangular prism.

8. a small block sitting in a corner; a small block cut out of a large block

9. rabbit, duck

10. $2 \cdot (1 + 2 \cdot 3) - 2 \div (2 - 1) = 12$

PAGE 158   COOPERATIVE LEARNING ACTIVITY

	Cassady	Casto	Coffman	Crosby	Cortez	red	blue	black	white	tan
Bobbie	✔	X	X	X	X	✔	X	X	X	X
Bebe	X	X	X	✔	X	X	✔	X	X	X
Bruno	X	X	X	X	✔	X	X	✔	X	X
Bart	X	✔	X	X	X	X	X	X	X	✔
Benito	X	X	✔	X	X	X	X	X	✔	X
red	✔	X	X	X	X					
blue	X	X	X	✔	X					
black	X	X	X	X	✔					
white	X	X	✔	X	X					
tan	X	✔	X	X	X					

Bobbie Cassady, red; Bebe Crosby, blue; Bruno Cortez, black; Bart Casto, tan; Benito Coffman, white

Graphing Calculator Exploration: Matrices

PAGE 160   EXERCISES

1. $\begin{bmatrix} -1 & 5 \\ -4 & 3 \\ -7 & 6 \end{bmatrix}$

2. $\begin{bmatrix} 25 & -10 & 30 \\ 20 & 35 & -5 \end{bmatrix}$

3. -28

4. $\begin{bmatrix} -2 & 10 \\ -8 & 6 \\ -14 & 12 \end{bmatrix}$

5. $\begin{bmatrix} -.1428571429 & .4285714286 & .2857142857 \\ .2142857143 & .1071428571 & -.1785714286 \\ -.1428571429 & -.5714285714 & .2857142857 \end{bmatrix}$

6. $\begin{bmatrix} -15 & -37 & 11 \\ 8 & -29 & 27 \\ 11 & -56 & 48 \end{bmatrix}$

7. $\begin{bmatrix} 39 & -55 \\ 25 & -35 \end{bmatrix}$

8. 10

9. $\begin{bmatrix} 26 & 64 & 35 \\ 12 & 28 & 2 \end{bmatrix}$

10. $\begin{bmatrix} -17 & -45 & 8 \\ 7 & -29 & 28 \\ 8 & -60 & 45 \end{bmatrix}$ **11.** 0

12. $\begin{bmatrix} -13 & -29 & 14 \\ 9 & -29 & 26 \\ 14 & -52 & 51 \end{bmatrix}$ **13.** $\begin{bmatrix} -3.5 & 5.5 \\ -2.5 & 3.9 \end{bmatrix}$

14. $\begin{bmatrix} 21 & 28 & 7 \\ -1 & 4 & 0 \\ 19 & 36 & 14 \end{bmatrix}$ **15.** $\begin{bmatrix} 146 & -220 \\ 100 & -150 \end{bmatrix}$

16. $\begin{bmatrix} 31 & 62 & 41 \\ 16 & 35 & 1 \end{bmatrix}$ **17.** $\begin{bmatrix} 527 & -532 \\ 138 & -156 \end{bmatrix}$

18. $\begin{bmatrix} -34 & -76 & 25 \\ 68 & 172 & 134 \\ 110 & 280 & 233 \end{bmatrix}$

4-2 An Introduction to Matrices

PAGE 164   CHECKING FOR UNDERSTANDING

1. an array of numbers in columns and rows
2. a matrix that has 3 rows and 2 columns
3. The two matrices must have the same dimensions and corresponding elements are equal.
4. They must have the same dimensions.
5. A dilation changes the size but not the shape of a figure. A translation moves a figure, but does not change its orientation, size, or shape.

6. $A_{4\times 3}$;

$$-2\begin{bmatrix} 7 & -2 & -4 \\ -8 & 9 & 10 \\ 1 & 17 & 10 \\ 21 & -3 & 6 \end{bmatrix} = \begin{bmatrix} -2(7) & -2(-2) & -2(-4) \\ -2(-8) & -2(9) & -2(10) \\ -2(1) & -2(17) & -2(10) \\ -2(21) & -2(-3) & -2(6) \end{bmatrix}$$

$$= \begin{bmatrix} -14 & 4 & 8 \\ 16 & -18 & -20 \\ -2 & -34 & -20 \\ -42 & 6 & -12 \end{bmatrix}$$

7. $V_{1\times 3}$;

$-2[-7 \quad 5 \quad 26] = [-2(-7) \quad -2(5) \quad -2(26)]$
$\qquad\qquad\qquad\qquad = [14 \qquad -10 \qquad -52]$

8. $\begin{bmatrix} 2 & x \\ y & 5 \end{bmatrix} = \begin{bmatrix} 2 & 1 \\ 3 & z \end{bmatrix}$

$x = 1,\ y = 3,\ z = 5$

9. $[2x \quad 3 \quad 3z] = [5 \quad 3y \quad 9]$

$\quad 2x = 5 \qquad\qquad 3 = 3y \qquad 3z = 9$

$\quad x = \dfrac{5}{2} \qquad\qquad 1 = y \qquad\quad z = 3$

$\quad x = 2\dfrac{1}{2} \qquad\qquad y = 1$

10. $\begin{bmatrix} 7 & 4 & -3 \\ -2 & 5 & 4 \end{bmatrix} + \begin{bmatrix} -5 & -5 & -5 \\ 1 & 1 & 1 \end{bmatrix}$

$= \begin{bmatrix} 7 + (-5) & 4 + (-5) & -3 + (-5) \\ -2 + 1 & 5 + 1 & 4 + 1 \end{bmatrix}$

$= \begin{bmatrix} 2 & -1 & -8 \\ -1 & 6 & 5 \end{bmatrix}$

$D'(2, -1)$
$E'(-1, 6)$
$F'(-8, 5)$

PAGES 165-166   EXERCISES

11. $4\begin{bmatrix} 2 & -3 \\ 4 & 1 \\ 0 & 3 \end{bmatrix} = \begin{bmatrix} 4(2) & 4(-3) \\ 4(4) & 4(1) \\ 4(0) & 4(3) \end{bmatrix} = \begin{bmatrix} 8 & -12 \\ 16 & 4 \\ 0 & 12 \end{bmatrix}$; $A_{3\times 2}$

12. $\begin{bmatrix} 3 & 7 \\ -2 & 1 \end{bmatrix} - \begin{bmatrix} 2 & -3 \\ 5 & -4 \end{bmatrix} = \begin{bmatrix} 3 - 2 & 7 - (-3) \\ -2 - 5 & 1 - (-4) \end{bmatrix}$

$\qquad\qquad = \begin{bmatrix} 1 & 10 \\ -7 & 5 \end{bmatrix}$; $B_{2\times 2}$

13. $[4 \quad 1 \quad -3] + [6 \quad -5 \quad 8]$

$= [4 + 6 \quad 1 + (-5) \quad -3 + 8]$

$= [10 \quad -4 \quad 5]$; $C_{1\times 3}$

14. $\begin{bmatrix} 2x & 3y \\ 40 & 50 \end{bmatrix} = \begin{bmatrix} -12 & 36 \\ 8z & 2.5w \end{bmatrix}$

$2x = -12 \quad 3y = 36 \quad 40 = 8z \quad 50 = 2.5w$

$x = -6 \qquad y = 12 \qquad 5 = z \qquad 20 = w$

15. $\begin{bmatrix} 2x \\ y + 1 \end{bmatrix} = \begin{bmatrix} y \\ 3 \end{bmatrix}$

$2x = y \quad y + 1 = 3$

$\qquad\qquad\quad y = 2$

Substitute: $2x = y$

$\qquad\qquad\quad 2x = 2$

$\qquad\qquad\qquad x = 1 \quad x = 1,\ y = 2$

16. $y\begin{bmatrix} 3 & -4 \\ 2 & x \end{bmatrix} = \begin{bmatrix} 15 & -20 \\ z & 5 \end{bmatrix}$

$\begin{bmatrix} 3y & -4y \\ 2y & xy \end{bmatrix} = \begin{bmatrix} 15 & -20 \\ z & 5 \end{bmatrix}$

$3y = 15 \quad -4y = -20 \quad 2y = z \quad xy = 5$

$y = 5 \qquad y = 5 \qquad 2(5) = z \quad x(5) = 5$

$\qquad\qquad\qquad\qquad\qquad\quad 10 = z \qquad x = 1$

$x = 1,\ y = 5,\ z = 10$

17.

$$4\begin{bmatrix} x & y-1 \\ 3 & z \end{bmatrix} = \begin{bmatrix} 20 & 8 \\ 6z & x+y \end{bmatrix}$$

$$\begin{bmatrix} 4x & 4(y-1) \\ 12 & 4z \end{bmatrix} = \begin{bmatrix} 20 & 8 \\ 6z & x+y \end{bmatrix}$$

$4x = 20$	$4(y-1) = 8$	$12 = 6z$	$4z = x + y$
$x = 5$	$y - 1 = 2$	$2 = z$	$4(2) \overset{?}{=} 5 + 3$
	$y = 3$		$8 = 8$

$x = 5,\ y = 3,\ z = 2$

18.

$$\begin{bmatrix} x^2 & 7 & 9 \\ 5 & 12 & 6 \end{bmatrix} = \begin{bmatrix} 25 & 7 & y \\ 5 & 2z & 6 \end{bmatrix}$$

$x^2 = 25$	$y = 9$	$12 = 2z$
$x = \pm 5$		$6 = z$

$x = \pm 5,\ y = 9,\ z = 6$

19.

$$\begin{bmatrix} x + 3y \\ 3x + y \end{bmatrix} = \begin{bmatrix} -13 \\ 1 \end{bmatrix}$$

$$\begin{array}{l} x + 3y = -13 \\ 3x + y = 1 \end{array} \rightarrow \begin{array}{l} x + 3y = -13 \\ \underline{-9x - 3y = -3} \\ -8x \qquad = -16 \\ \qquad\quad x = 2 \end{array} \qquad \begin{array}{l} 3x + y = 1 \\ 3(2) + y = 1 \\ 6 + y = 1 \\ \qquad y = -5 \end{array}$$

20. translation of x-coordinates: $5 + x = 3$

$$x = -2$$

translation of y-coordinates: $-2 + y = 4$

$$y = 6$$

$$\begin{bmatrix} 5 & 8 & -3 \\ -2 & 4 & -1 \end{bmatrix} + \begin{bmatrix} -2 & -2 & -2 \\ 6 & 6 & 6 \end{bmatrix} = \begin{bmatrix} 3 & 6 & -5 \\ 4 & 10 & 5 \end{bmatrix}$$

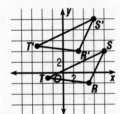

$S'(6, 10)$

$T'(-5, 5)$

21.

$$3\begin{bmatrix} 3 & -2 & 5 \\ 2 & 7 & -5 \end{bmatrix} + 2\begin{bmatrix} -1 & 3 & 4 \\ 2 & -3 & 0 \end{bmatrix}$$

$$= \begin{bmatrix} 9 & -6 & 15 \\ 6 & 21 & -15 \end{bmatrix} + \begin{bmatrix} -2 & 6 & 8 \\ 4 & -6 & 0 \end{bmatrix}$$

$$= \begin{bmatrix} 7 & 0 & 23 \\ 10 & 15 & -15 \end{bmatrix}$$

22.

$$\frac{1}{2}\begin{bmatrix} 4 & 12 & 9 \\ 3 & 6 & 0 \end{bmatrix} - \frac{2}{3}\begin{bmatrix} 9 & 27 & 6 \\ 0 & 3 & 4 \end{bmatrix}$$

$$= \begin{bmatrix} 2 & 6 & \frac{9}{2} \\ \frac{3}{2} & 3 & 0 \end{bmatrix} - \begin{bmatrix} 6 & 18 & 4 \\ 0 & 2 & \frac{8}{3} \end{bmatrix}$$

$$= \begin{bmatrix} 4 & -12 & \frac{1}{2} \\ \frac{3}{2} & 1 & -\frac{8}{3} \end{bmatrix}$$

23.

$$3\begin{bmatrix} 4 \\ 1 \\ 7 \end{bmatrix} + 2\begin{bmatrix} 3 \\ -2 \\ 6 \end{bmatrix} - 5\begin{bmatrix} -2 \\ 3 \\ 6 \end{bmatrix} = \begin{bmatrix} 12 \\ 3 \\ 21 \end{bmatrix} + \begin{bmatrix} 6 \\ -4 \\ 12 \end{bmatrix} - \begin{bmatrix} -10 \\ 15 \\ 30 \end{bmatrix}$$

$$= \begin{bmatrix} 12 + 6 - (-10) \\ 3 + (-4) - 15 \\ 21 + 12 - 30 \end{bmatrix}$$

$$= \begin{bmatrix} 28 \\ -16 \\ 3 \end{bmatrix}$$

24.

$$5\begin{bmatrix} -2 & 4 \\ 1 & -1 \\ 3 & 0 \end{bmatrix} - 2\begin{bmatrix} 5 & 3 \\ -3 & 2 \\ 8 & -9 \end{bmatrix} + \begin{bmatrix} 0 & -5 \\ 9 & -3 \\ -2 & 7 \end{bmatrix}$$

$$= \begin{bmatrix} -10 & 20 \\ 5 & -5 \\ 15 & 0 \end{bmatrix} - \begin{bmatrix} 10 & 6 \\ -6 & 4 \\ 16 & -18 \end{bmatrix} + \begin{bmatrix} 0 & -5 \\ 9 & -3 \\ -2 & 7 \end{bmatrix}$$

$$= \begin{bmatrix} -10 - 10 + 0 & 20 - 6 + (-5) \\ 5 - (-6) + 9 & -5 - 4 + (-3) \\ 15 - 16 + (-2) & 0 - (-18) + 7 \end{bmatrix}$$

$$= \begin{bmatrix} -20 & 9 \\ 20 & -12 \\ -3 & 25 \end{bmatrix}$$

25. a. translation of x-coordinates: $-1 + x = 3$

$$x = 4$$

translation of y-coordinates: $4 + y = 2$

$$y = -2$$

translation matrix: $\begin{bmatrix} 4 & 4 & 4 & 4 \\ -2 & -2 & -2 & -2 \end{bmatrix}$

b.

$$\begin{bmatrix} 6 & 3 & -1 & -3 \\ 1 & 5 & 4 & -5 \end{bmatrix} + \begin{bmatrix} 4 & 4 & 4 & 4 \\ -2 & -2 & -2 & -2 \end{bmatrix}$$

$$= \begin{bmatrix} 10 & 7 & 3 & 1 \\ -1 & 3 & 2 & -7 \end{bmatrix}$$

$B'(10, -1),\ T'(1, -7),\ U'(7, 3)$

26.
$$4\begin{bmatrix} 0 & 5 & 0 \\ 12 & 0 & 0 \end{bmatrix} = \begin{bmatrix} 0 & 20 & 0 \\ 48 & 0 & 0 \end{bmatrix}$$

$(0, 48), (20, 0), (0, 0)$

27.
$$\begin{bmatrix} x \\ 7z \\ 2y \end{bmatrix} - \begin{bmatrix} 4z \\ -3y \\ 3x \end{bmatrix} + \begin{bmatrix} -2y \\ 2x \\ -5z \end{bmatrix} = \begin{bmatrix} -4 \\ 11 \\ 18 \end{bmatrix}$$

$$\begin{cases} x - 4z + (-2y) = -4 \\ 7z - (-3y) + 2x = 11 \\ 2y - 3x + (-5z) = 18 \end{cases}$$

$x - 2y - 4z = -4$

$-3x + 2y - 5z = 18$

$-2x \quad\quad - 9z = 14$

$\begin{aligned} 3x - 6y - 12z &= -12 \\ 4x + 6y + 14z &= 22 \\ \hline 7x \quad\quad + 2z &= 10 \end{aligned}$

$\begin{aligned} -14x - 63z &= 98 \\ 14x + 4z &= 20 \\ \hline - 59z &= 118 \\ z &= -2 \end{aligned}$

$\begin{aligned} 7x + 2(-2) &= 10 \\ 7x &= 14 \\ x &= 2 \end{aligned}$

$\begin{aligned} 2 - 4(-2) + (-2y) &= -4 \\ 10 - 2y &= -4 \\ -2y &= -14 \\ y &= 7 \end{aligned}$

28.
$$\begin{bmatrix} r^2 - 24 & 17 \\ 7 & t^3 \end{bmatrix} = \begin{bmatrix} 1 & 2y + 3 \\ z^2 - 12 & 27 \end{bmatrix}$$

$\begin{aligned} r^2 - 24 &= 1 \\ r^2 &= 25 \\ r &= \pm 5 \end{aligned}$
$\begin{aligned} 2y + 3 &= 17 \\ 2y &= 14 \\ y &= 7 \end{aligned}$

$\begin{aligned} z^2 - 12 &= 7 \\ z^2 &= 19 \\ z &= \pm\sqrt{19} \end{aligned}$
$\begin{aligned} t^3 &= 27 \\ t &= 3 \end{aligned}$

29.
$$\begin{bmatrix} 5x - 7 & 11 \\ 5 & 23 \end{bmatrix} \quad \begin{bmatrix} 8 & 21 - m \\ r^3 - 3 & 4y + x \end{bmatrix}$$

$\begin{aligned} 5x - 7 &= 8 \\ 5x &= 15 \\ x &= 3 \end{aligned}$
$\begin{aligned} 21 - m &= 11 \\ -m &= -10 \\ m &= 10 \end{aligned}$

$\begin{aligned} r^3 - 3 &= 5 \\ r^3 &= 8 \\ r &= 2 \end{aligned}$
$\begin{aligned} 4y + x &= 23 \\ 4y + 3 &= 23 \\ 4y &= 20 \\ y &= 5 \end{aligned}$

30.
$$\begin{bmatrix} 13 - 7y & a \\ 1 & 2b - 38 \end{bmatrix} = \begin{bmatrix} 5x & 2 - 6b \\ 2x + 3y & 5a \end{bmatrix}$$

$\begin{cases} 13 - 7y = 5x \;\to\; 5x + 7y = 13 \;\to\; 10x + 14y = 26 \\ 2x + 3y = 1 \;\to\; 2x + 3y = 1 \;\to\; \underline{-10x - 15y = -5} \end{cases}$

$\begin{aligned} -1y &= 21 \\ y &= -21 \end{aligned}$

$\begin{aligned} 2x + 3(-21) &= 1 \\ 2x - 63 &= 1 \\ 2x &= 64 \\ x &= 32 \end{aligned}$

$\begin{cases} a = 2 - 6b \;\to\; a - 6b = 2 \;\to\; -5a - 30b = -10 \\ 2b - 38 = 5a \;\to\; 5a - 2b = -38 \;\to\; \underline{5a - 2b = -38} \end{cases}$

$\begin{aligned} -32b &= -48 \\ b &= \frac{48}{32} \text{ or } \frac{3}{2} \end{aligned}$

$\begin{aligned} a &= 2 - 6\left(\frac{3}{2}\right) \\ &= 2 - 9 \\ &= -7 \end{aligned}$

$x = 32, \; y = -21, \; a = -7, \; b = \dfrac{3}{2}$

31. translation of x-coordinates: $5 + x = 0$

$\qquad\qquad\qquad\qquad\qquad\qquad x = -5$

translation of y-coordinates: $-3 + y = 0$

$\qquad\qquad\qquad\qquad\qquad\qquad y = 3$

$$\begin{bmatrix} 5 & 2 & -3 & -5 \\ -3 & 7 & 3 & 1 \end{bmatrix} + \begin{bmatrix} -5 & -5 & -5 & -5 \\ 3 & 3 & 3 & 3 \end{bmatrix}$$

$$= \begin{bmatrix} 0 & -3 & -8 & -10 \\ 0 & 10 & 6 & 4 \end{bmatrix}$$

$M(0, 0), \; N(-3, 10), \; P(-8, 6), \; Q(-10, 4)$

32.
$$-\frac{1}{2}\begin{bmatrix} -2 & 4 & -1 \\ -1 & 2 & 3 \end{bmatrix} = \begin{bmatrix} 1 & -2 & \frac{1}{2} \\ \frac{1}{2} & -1 & -\frac{3}{2} \end{bmatrix}$$

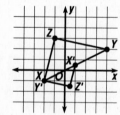

The triangle perimeter is half and the triangle is rotated 180°.

76

33. a.

$$M = \begin{bmatrix} 120 & 97 & 64 & 75 \\ 80 & 59 & 36 & 60 \\ 72 & 84 & 29 & 48 \end{bmatrix}$$

$$T = \begin{bmatrix} 112 & 87 & 56 & 74 \\ 84 & 65 & 39 & 70 \\ 88 & 98 & 43 & 60 \end{bmatrix}$$

$$\begin{bmatrix} 120 & 97 & 64 & 75 \\ 80 & 59 & 36 & 60 \\ 72 & 84 & 29 & 48 \end{bmatrix} + \begin{bmatrix} 112 & 87 & 56 & 74 \\ 84 & 65 & 39 & 70 \\ 88 & 98 & 43 & 60 \end{bmatrix}$$

$$= \begin{bmatrix} 232 & 184 & 120 & 149 \\ 164 & 124 & 75 & 130 \\ 160 & 182 & 72 & 108 \end{bmatrix}$$

b. total donuts = 232 + 184 + 120 + 149 + 164

+ 124 + 75 + 130 + 160 + 182

+ 72 + 108

= 1700

total cups of flour = $\frac{1}{4}$(1700)

= 425

total pounds of flour = $\frac{425}{4}$

= 106.25

106.25 pounds of flour

34. $2x - 7y = 11$

$-7y = 2x + 11$

$y = \frac{2}{7}x - \frac{11}{7}$

slope: $\frac{2}{7}$

$y = mx + b$

$2 = \frac{2}{7}(-1) + b$

$2 = -\frac{2}{7} + b$

$\frac{16}{7} = b$

$y = \frac{2}{7}x + \frac{16}{7}$

$7y = 2x + 16$

$2x - 7y = -16$

35. $f(x) = 2x^2 + 5x - 3$

$f\left(\frac{2}{3}\right) = 2\left(\frac{2}{3}\right)^2 + 5\left(\frac{2}{3}\right) - 3$

$= 2\left(\frac{4}{9}\right) + \frac{10}{3} - 3$

$= \frac{8}{9} + \frac{10}{3} - 3$

$= \frac{8 + 30 - 27}{9}$

$= \frac{11}{9}$ or $1\frac{2}{9}$

36. $5a + 1 \leq 8a - 3$

$1 \leq 3a - 3$

$4 \leq 3a$

$\frac{4}{3} \leq a$

$\left\{a \mid a \geq \frac{4}{3}\right\}$

37. $\frac{3}{4}(x - 5) = \frac{4}{5}(x + 4)$

$15(x - 5) = 16(x + 4)$

$15x - 75 = 16x + 64$

$-139 = x$

PAGE 170   CHECKING FOR UNDERSTANDING

1. when it is a square matrix

2. Cross out the row containing 6. Cross out the column containing 6. The four remaining elements are the minor of 6.

3. finding the area of a triangle

4. Substitute -4 for n and re-evaluate the determinant.

5. yes, because it is a square matrix

$$\begin{vmatrix} 2 & 5 \\ -3 & 8 \end{vmatrix} = 2(8) - (-3)(5)$$

$$= 16 + 15$$

$$= 31$$

6. no determinant because it is not a square matrix

7. no determinant because it is not a square matrix

8. yes, because it is a square matrix

$$\begin{vmatrix} 6 & 9 \\ 2 & 3 \end{vmatrix} = 6(3) - 2(9)$$

$$= 18 - 18$$

$$= 0$$

9. $\begin{vmatrix} 5 & x \\ 2x & 7 \end{vmatrix} = -63$

$5(7) - 2x(x) = -63$

$35 - 2x^2 = -63$

$-2x^2 = -98$

$x^2 = 49$

$x = \pm 7$

10. $\begin{vmatrix} 3 & -2 & x \\ x & 1 & -5 \\ 2 & 0 & -1 \end{vmatrix} = 1$

$3\begin{vmatrix} 1 & -5 \\ 0 & -1 \end{vmatrix} - (-2)\begin{vmatrix} x & -5 \\ 2 & -1 \end{vmatrix} + x\begin{vmatrix} x & 1 \\ 2 & 0 \end{vmatrix} = 1$

$3(-1 - 0) + 2[-x - (-10)] + x(0 - 2) = 1$

$3(-1) + 2(-x + 10) + x(-2) = 1$

$-3 - 2x + 20 - 2x = 1$

$-4x + 17 = 1$

$-4x = -16$

$x = 4$

11. $A = \frac{1}{2}\begin{vmatrix} 4 & -5 & 1 \\ 3 & 8 & 1 \\ -2 & 3 & 1 \end{vmatrix}$

12. no determinant

13. $\begin{vmatrix} 9 & -3 \\ 17 & 4 \end{vmatrix} = 9(4) - 17(-3)$

$$= 36 + 51$$
$$= 87$$

14. no determinant   **15.** no determinant

16. $\begin{vmatrix} 5 & 7 \\ -2 & 2x \end{vmatrix} = 54$

$$5(2x) - (-2)(7) = 54$$
$$10x + 14 = 54$$
$$10x = 40$$
$$x = 4$$

17. $\begin{vmatrix} x & 7 & 5 \\ 0 & 3 & 4 \\ 3 & 2 & -x \end{vmatrix} = 11$

$$x\begin{vmatrix} 3 & 4 \\ 2 & -x \end{vmatrix} - 7\begin{vmatrix} 0 & 4 \\ 3 & -x \end{vmatrix} + 5\begin{vmatrix} 0 & 3 \\ 3 & 2 \end{vmatrix} = 11$$
$$x(-3x - 8) - 7(0 - 12) + 5(0 - 9) = 11$$
$$3x^2 - 8x + 84 - 45 = 11$$
$$-3x^2 - 8x + 39 = 11$$
$$-3x^2 - 8x + 28 = 0$$

$$x = \frac{8 \pm \sqrt{(-8)^2 - 4(-3)(28)}}{2(-3)}$$

$$= \frac{8 \pm \sqrt{400}}{-6}$$

$$x = \frac{28}{6} \text{ or } x = \frac{-12}{-6}$$
$$= -\frac{14}{3} \qquad = 2$$

18. $A = \frac{1}{2}\begin{vmatrix} 0 & 0 & 1 \\ 5 & -6 & 1 \\ 3 & 7 & 1 \end{vmatrix}$

$$= \frac{1}{2}[0(-6)(1) + 0(1)(3) + 1(7)(5) - 3(-6)(1)$$
$$- 0(1)(7) - 0(5)(1)]$$
$$= \frac{1}{2}[0 + 0 + 35 + 18 - 0 - 0]$$
$$= \frac{1}{2}(53)$$
$$= 26.5 \qquad\qquad 26.5 \text{ units}^2$$

19. $\begin{vmatrix} 6 & 4 \\ -3 & 2 \end{vmatrix} = 6(2) - (-3)4$

$$= 12 + 12$$
$$= 24$$

20. $\begin{vmatrix} 2 & -3 & 4 \\ -2 & 1 & 5 \\ 5 & 3 & -2 \end{vmatrix}$

$$= 2\begin{vmatrix} 1 & 5 \\ 3 & -2 \end{vmatrix} - (-3)\begin{vmatrix} -2 & 5 \\ 5 & -2 \end{vmatrix} + 4\begin{vmatrix} -2 & 1 \\ 5 & 3 \end{vmatrix}$$
$$= 2(-2 - 15) + 3(4 - 25) + 4(-6 - 5)$$
$$= 2(-17) + 3(-21) + 4(-11)$$
$$= -34 - 63 - 44$$
$$= -141$$

21. $\begin{vmatrix} 6 & 5 & -2 \\ -3 & 0 & 6 \\ 1 & 4 & 2 \end{vmatrix} = 6 \cdot 0 \cdot 2 + 5 \cdot 6 \cdot 1 +$

$$(-2)(-3)4 - 1 \cdot 0 \cdot (-2)$$
$$- 4 \cdot 6 \cdot 6 - 2(-3)5$$
$$= 0 + 30 + 24 - 0 - 144 + 30$$
$$= -60$$

22. $\begin{vmatrix} 5a & 3 \\ a & 5 \end{vmatrix} = 7$

$$25a - 3a = 7$$
$$22a = 7$$
$$a = \frac{7}{22}$$

23. $\begin{vmatrix} x^2 & x \\ 3 & 1 \end{vmatrix} = 4$

$$x^2 - 3x = 4$$
$$x^2 - 3x - 4 = 0$$
$$(x - 4)(x + 1) = 0$$
$$x = 4 \text{ or } \quad x = -1$$

24. $\frac{1}{2}\begin{vmatrix} 6 & 5 & 1 \\ 8 & 2 & 1 \\ x & 11 & 1 \end{vmatrix} = 30$

$$\frac{1}{2}(12 + 5x + 88 - 2x - 66 - 40) = 30$$
$$\frac{1}{2}(3x - 6) = 30$$
$$\frac{3}{2}x - 3 = 30$$
$$\frac{3}{2}x = 33$$
$$x = 22$$

25. $\begin{vmatrix} x & 5 & 2 \\ -6 & 4 & 1 \\ 3 & 1 & x \end{vmatrix} = x^2 + 22x - 1$

$$4x^2 + 15 + (-12) - 24 - x - (-30x) = x^2 + 22x - 1$$
$$4x^2 + 29x - 21 = x^2 + 22x - 1$$
$$3x^2 + 7x - 20 = 0$$

$$x = \frac{-7 \pm \sqrt{49 - 4(3)(-20)}}{2(3)}$$

$$= \frac{-7 \pm \sqrt{289}}{6}$$

$$= \frac{-7 \pm 17}{6}$$

$$x = \frac{10}{6} \text{ or } x = -4$$
$$= \frac{5}{3}$$

26. $\begin{vmatrix} 2x & 4 & 1 \\ 2 & 3 & -1 \\ 0 & -2 & x \end{vmatrix} = 6x^2 - 10$

$$6x^2 + 0 + (-4) - 0 - 4x - 8x = 6x^2 - 10$$
$$6x^2 - 12x - 4 = 6x^2 - 10$$
$$-12x + 6 = 0$$
$$-12x = -6$$
$$x = \frac{1}{2}$$

27. If the area = 0, the points are collinear.

28. Answers may vary. One matrix is

$\begin{vmatrix} 1 & 1 & 1 \\ 1 & 1 & 1 \\ 1 & 1 & 1 \end{vmatrix}$.

29. original matrix:

$\begin{vmatrix} 8 & 3 \\ -3 & 5 \end{vmatrix} = 40 - (-9) = 49$

Multiply each row or column by 6.

$\begin{vmatrix} 48 & 18 \\ -3 & 5 \end{vmatrix} = 48(5) - (-3)(18)$
$$= 240 + 54$$
$$= 294$$

$\begin{vmatrix} 8 & 3 \\ -18 & 30 \end{vmatrix} = 8(30) - (-18)(3)$
$$= 240 + 54$$
$$= 294$$

$\begin{vmatrix} 48 & 3 \\ -18 & 5 \end{vmatrix} = 48(5) - (-18)(3)$
$$= 240 + 54$$
$$= 294$$

$\begin{vmatrix} 8 & 18 \\ -3 & 30 \end{vmatrix} = 8(30) - (-3)(18)$
$$= 240 + 54$$
$$= 294$$

294 is six times 49.

30. a. Draw a line to make the quadrilateral into two triangles. Then use the formula.

b.
$A_1 = \frac{1}{2} \begin{vmatrix} -5 & 2 & 1 \\ -3 & 7 & 1 \\ 3 & 8 & 1 \end{vmatrix}$

$= \frac{1}{2}\Big[(-5) \cdot 7 \cdot 1 + 2 \cdot 1 \cdot 3 + 1 \cdot (-3) \cdot 8$
$\quad - 3 \cdot 7 \cdot 1 - 8 \cdot 1 \cdot (-5) - 1 \cdot (-3) \cdot 2\Big]$
$= \frac{1}{2}\Big(-35 + 6 - 24 - 21 + 40 + 6\Big)$
$= \frac{1}{2}\Big(-28\Big)$
$= -14$

Since A_1 must be positive, $A = \begin{vmatrix} -14 \end{vmatrix} = 14.$

$A_2 = \frac{1}{2} \begin{vmatrix} -5 & 2 & 1 \\ 4 & -1 & 1 \\ 3 & 8 & 1 \end{vmatrix}$

$= \frac{1}{2}\Big[(-5) \cdot (-1) \cdot 1 + 2 \cdot 1 \cdot 3 + 1 \cdot 4 \cdot 8$
$\quad - 3 \cdot (-1) \cdot 1 - 8 \cdot 1 \cdot (-5) - 1 \cdot 4 \cdot 2\Big]$
$= \frac{1}{2}\Big(5 + 6 + 32 + 3 + 40 - 8\Big)$
$= \frac{1}{2}\Big(78\Big)$
$= 39$

$A_1 + A_2 = 14 + 39 = 53$

53 units^2

31. $\frac{1}{2} \begin{vmatrix} -2 & 4 & 1 \\ 3 & -5 & 1 \\ 3 & f & 1 \end{vmatrix} = 25$

$\frac{1}{2}\Big[(-2) \cdot (-5) \cdot 1 + 4 \cdot 1 \cdot 3 + 1 \cdot 3 \cdot f$
$\quad - 3 \cdot [-5 \cdot 1 - f \cdot 1 \cdot (-2) - 1 \cdot 3 \cdot 4] = 25$
$\frac{1}{2}\Big(10 + 12 + 3f + 15 + 2f - 12\Big) = 25$
$\frac{1}{2}\Big(5f + 25\Big) = 25$
$5f + 25 = 50$
$5f = 25$
$f = 5$

32. $\begin{vmatrix} -3 & 14 & 12 \\ -2 & -1 & 7 \end{vmatrix} + \begin{vmatrix} 1 & -5 & 10 \\ 22 & 13 & -8 \end{vmatrix}$

$= \begin{vmatrix} -3 + 1 & 14 + (-5) & 12 + 10 \\ -2 + 22 & -1 + 13 & 7 + (-8) \end{vmatrix}$

$= \begin{vmatrix} -2 & 9 & 22 \\ 20 & 12 & -1 \end{vmatrix}$

33. $4 \begin{vmatrix} -7 & 5 & -11 \\ 2 & -4 & 9 \end{vmatrix} = \begin{vmatrix} 4(-7) & 4(5) & 4(-11) \\ 4(2) & 4(-4) & 4(9) \end{vmatrix}$

$= \begin{vmatrix} -28 & 20 & -44 \\ 8 & -16 & 36 \end{vmatrix}$

34. x-intercept:
$$15x + 10(0) + 6(0) = 30$$
$$15x = 30$$
$$x = 2$$

y-intercept:
$$15((0) + 10y + 6(0) = 30$$
$$10y = 30$$
$$y = 3$$

z-intercept:
$$15(0) + 10(0) + 6z = 30$$
$$6z = 30$$
$$z = 5$$

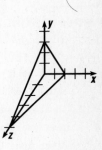

79

35. $(0.19)r + (0.29)t = 5.46$

$r = 24 - t$

Substitute: $(0.19)(24 - t) + (0.29)t = 5.46$

$$4.56 - 0.19t + 0.29t = 5.46$$
$$0.1t = 0.9$$
$$t = 9$$

$r = 24 - t$

$= 24 - 9$ or 15

36. Slope: $\dfrac{0 - (-5)}{6 - 0} = \dfrac{5}{6}$

$y = mx + b$

$y = \dfrac{5}{6}x + (-5)$

$6y = 5x - 30$

$-5x + 6y = -30$

$5x - 6y = 30$

PAGE 172   CHALLENGE

The area of the triangle is the area of the rectangle minus the areas of the right triangles ADB, BEC, and CFA.

Area ABC

$=$ Area $ADEF$ $-$ Area ADB $-$ Area BEC $-$ Area CFA

$= (c - a)(f - b) - \dfrac{1}{2}(c - a)(d - b)$

$\quad - \dfrac{1}{2}(c - e)(f - d) - \dfrac{1}{2}(f - b)(e - a)$

$= ab + cf - af - bc - \dfrac{1}{2}(cd - bc - ad + ab)$

$\quad - \dfrac{1}{2}(cf - cd - ef + de) - \dfrac{1}{2}(ef - af - be + ab)$

$= \dfrac{1}{2}cf - \dfrac{1}{2}af - \dfrac{1}{2}bc + \dfrac{1}{2}ad + \dfrac{1}{2}be - \dfrac{1}{2}de$

$= \dfrac{1}{2}(ad + be + cf - af - bc - de)$

In the formula, $A = \dfrac{1}{2}\begin{vmatrix} a & b & 1 \\ c & d & 1 \\ e & f & 1 \end{vmatrix}$.

If the determinant is expanded and multiplied by $\dfrac{1}{2}$, you get the six terms listed above.

4-4   Multiplication of Matrices

PAGE 175   CHECKING FOR UNDERSTANDING

1. The number of columns in the first matrix must equal the number of rows in the second.

2. In adding matrices, the two matrices must have the same dimensions. In multiplying, the dimensions are frequently different, so long as the number of columns in the first matrix equals the number of rows in the second.

3. The product of an $m \times y$ matrix and an $n \times r$ matrix is an $m \times r$ matrix. So

$A_{3\times 2} \cdot B_{2\times 4} = M_{3\times 4}$.

---

4. Answers will vary. A sample answer is

$$\begin{bmatrix} a & b \\ c & d \end{bmatrix} \cdot \begin{bmatrix} e & f & g \\ h & i & j \end{bmatrix} =$$

$$\begin{bmatrix} (ae + bh) & (af + bi) & (ag + bj) \\ (ce + dh) & (cf + di) & (cg + dj) \end{bmatrix}.$$

5. $\begin{bmatrix} 0 & -1 \\ 1 & 0 \end{bmatrix}$

6. 3×5 **7.** 4×2

8. $N = \begin{bmatrix} 3 & -1 \\ 2 & 4 \end{bmatrix} \cdot \begin{bmatrix} 4 & 0 & -3 \\ 7 & -5 & 9 \end{bmatrix}$

$= \begin{bmatrix} 3(4)+(-1)(7) & 3(0)+(-1)(-5) & 3(-3)+(-1)9 \\ 2(4)+4(7) & 2(0)+4(-5) & 2(-3)+4(9) \end{bmatrix}$

$= \begin{bmatrix} 5 & 5 & -18 \\ 36 & -20 & 30 \end{bmatrix}$

9. not defined because the number of columns in the first matrix does not equal the number of rows in the second matrix

10. $N = \begin{bmatrix} 2 & 3 & 4 \\ 1 & 0 & -1 \end{bmatrix} \cdot \begin{bmatrix} 1 & 2 \\ 0 & 0 \\ 1 & -1 \end{bmatrix}$

$= \begin{bmatrix} 2(1)+3(0)+4(1) & 2(2)+3(0)+4(-1) \\ 1(1)+0(0)+(-1)(1) & 1(2)+0(0)+(-1)(-1) \end{bmatrix}$

$= \begin{bmatrix} 6 & 0 \\ 0 & 3 \end{bmatrix}$

11. $N = \begin{bmatrix} 2 & -1 \\ 0 & 1 \end{bmatrix} \cdot \begin{bmatrix} 3 & 0 \\ 1 & 2 \end{bmatrix}$

$= \begin{bmatrix} 2(3) + (-1)(1) & 2(0) + (-1)(2) \\ 0(3) + 1(1) & 0(0) + 1(2) \end{bmatrix}$

$= \begin{bmatrix} 5 & -2 \\ 1 & 2 \end{bmatrix}$

PAGES 176-178   EXERCISES

12. 4×3 **13.** 1×2

14. 3×1 **15.** not defined

16. $3\begin{bmatrix} 4 & -2 \\ 5 & 7 \end{bmatrix} + 2\begin{bmatrix} -3 & 5 \\ -4 & 3 \end{bmatrix} = \begin{bmatrix} 12 & -6 \\ 15 & 21 \end{bmatrix} + \begin{bmatrix} -6 & 10 \\ -8 & 6 \end{bmatrix}$

$= \begin{bmatrix} 12 + (-6) & -6 + 10 \\ 5 + (-8) & 21 + 6 \end{bmatrix}$

$= \begin{bmatrix} 6 & 4 \\ 7 & 27 \end{bmatrix}$

17. $\begin{bmatrix} 3 & -1 \\ 2 & 5 \end{bmatrix} \cdot \begin{bmatrix} 4 & -1 & -2 \\ -3 & 5 & 4 \end{bmatrix}$

$= \begin{bmatrix} 3(4)+(-1)(-3) & 3(-1)+(-1)(5) & 3(-2)+(-1)(4) \\ 2(4)+5(-3) & 2(-1)+5(5) & 2(-2)+5(4) \end{bmatrix}$

$= \begin{bmatrix} 15 & -8 & -10 \\ -7 & 23 & 16 \end{bmatrix}$

18. not possible to evaluate

19.
$\begin{bmatrix} 6 & 4 & 1 \end{bmatrix} \cdot \begin{bmatrix} 2 & 5 \\ -3 & 0 \\ -1 & 3 \end{bmatrix} = \begin{bmatrix} 6(2) + 4(-3) + 1(-1) & 6(5) + 4(0) + 1(3) \end{bmatrix}$

$= \begin{bmatrix} 12 - 12 - 1 & 30 + 0 + 3 \end{bmatrix}$

$= \begin{bmatrix} -1 & 33 \end{bmatrix}$

20. $\begin{bmatrix} -6 & 3 \\ 4 & 7 \end{bmatrix} \cdot \begin{bmatrix} 2 & -5 \\ -3 & 6 \end{bmatrix} = \begin{bmatrix} -6(2)+3(-3) & -6(-5)+3(6) \\ 4(2)+7(-3) & 4(-5)+7(6) \end{bmatrix}$

$= \begin{bmatrix} -21 & 48 \\ -13 & 22 \end{bmatrix}$

21.
$\begin{bmatrix} 2 & 7 \end{bmatrix} \cdot \begin{bmatrix} 5 \\ -4 \end{bmatrix} = \begin{bmatrix} 2(5) + 7(-4) \end{bmatrix}$
$= \begin{bmatrix} -18 \end{bmatrix}$

22. $\begin{bmatrix} 0 & 8 \\ 3 & 1 \\ -1 & 5 \end{bmatrix} \cdot \begin{bmatrix} 3 & 1 & -2 \\ 0 & 8 & -5 \end{bmatrix}$

$= \begin{bmatrix} 0(3) + 8(0) & 0(1) + 8(8) & 0(-2) + 8(-5) \\ 3(3) + 1(0) & 3(1) + 1(8) & 3(-2) + 1(-5) \\ -1(3) + 5(0) & -1(1) + 5(8) & -1(-2) + 5(-5) \end{bmatrix}$

$= \begin{bmatrix} 0 & 64 & -40 \\ 9 & 11 & -11 \\ -3 & 39 & -23 \end{bmatrix}$

23. not possible to evaluate

24. $\begin{bmatrix} 0 & -1 \\ 1 & 0 \end{bmatrix} \cdot \begin{bmatrix} 3 & 6 & 0 \\ 4 & 5 & 0 \end{bmatrix}$

$= \begin{bmatrix} 0(3)+(-1)(4) & 0(6)+(-1)(5) & 0(0)+(-1)(0) \\ 1(3)+0(4) & 1(6)+0(5) & 1(0)+0(0) \end{bmatrix}$

$= \begin{bmatrix} -4 & -5 & 0 \\ 3 & 6 & 0 \end{bmatrix}$

$A'(-4, 3)$, $B'(-5, 6)$, $C'(0, 0)$

25. $\begin{bmatrix} 0 & -1 \\ 1 & 0 \end{bmatrix} \cdot \begin{bmatrix} -1 & -4 & -4 & -1 \\ -1 & -1 & -3 & -3 \end{bmatrix}$

$= \begin{bmatrix} 0(-1) + (-1)(-1) & 0(-4) + (-1)(-1) \\ 1(-1) + 0(-1) & 1(-4) + 0(-1) \end{bmatrix}$

$\qquad \begin{matrix} 0(-4) + (-1)(-3) & 0(-1) + (-1)(-3) \\ 1(-4) + 0(-3) & 1(-1) + 0(-3) \end{matrix}$

$= \begin{bmatrix} 1 & 1 & 3 & 3 \\ -1 & -4 & -4 & -1 \end{bmatrix}$

$D'(1, -1)$, $E'(1, -4)$, $F'(3, -4)$, $G'(3, -1)$

26. $\begin{bmatrix} 3 & -1 \\ 2 & 4 \end{bmatrix}\begin{bmatrix} 4 & 0 & -3 \\ 7 & -5 & 9 \end{bmatrix} + \begin{bmatrix} 4 & 0 & -3 \\ 7 & -5 & 9 \end{bmatrix}$

$= \begin{bmatrix} 5 & 5 & -18 \\ 36 & -20 & 30 \end{bmatrix} + \begin{bmatrix} 4 & 0 & -3 \\ 7 & -5 & 9 \end{bmatrix}$

$= \begin{bmatrix} 9 & 5 & -21 \\ 43 & -25 & 39 \end{bmatrix}$

27. not defined   **28.** not defined

29. $\begin{bmatrix} 3 & -1 \\ 2 & 4 \end{bmatrix}\begin{bmatrix} -1 & 0 \\ 3 & 7 \end{bmatrix} + \begin{bmatrix} 4 & 0 & -3 \\ 7 & -5 & 9 \end{bmatrix}\begin{bmatrix} -6 & 4 \\ -2 & 8 \\ 3 & 0 \end{bmatrix}$

$= \begin{bmatrix} -6 & -7 \\ 10 & 28 \end{bmatrix} + \begin{bmatrix} 33 & 16 \\ -5 & -12 \end{bmatrix}$

$= \begin{bmatrix} -39 & 9 \\ 5 & 16 \end{bmatrix}$

30. $\begin{bmatrix} 0 & -1 \\ 1 & 0 \end{bmatrix} \cdot \begin{bmatrix} -2 & 2 & 2 & -2 \\ -2 & -2 & 2 & 2 \end{bmatrix} = \begin{bmatrix} 2 & 2 & -2 & -2 \\ -2 & 2 & 2 & -2 \end{bmatrix}$

$M'(2, -2)$, $O'(2, 2)$, $B'(-2, 2)$, $Y'(-2, -2)$

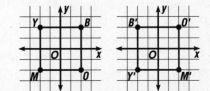

They are the same square in the same position.

31. $\begin{bmatrix} 0 & -1 \\ 1 & 0 \end{bmatrix} \cdot \begin{bmatrix} a & b & c \\ d & e & f \end{bmatrix} = \begin{bmatrix} -3 & -2 & 1 \\ -5 & 7 & 4 \end{bmatrix}$

$0(a) + (-1)d = -3$ $\quad 0(b) + (-1)e = -2$

$\quad\quad\quad -d = -3$ $\quad\quad\quad\quad -e = -2$

$\quad\quad\quad\quad d = 3$ $\quad\quad\quad\quad\quad e = 2$

$0(c) + (01)f = 1$ $\quad 1(a) + 0(d) = -5$

$\quad\quad\quad -f = 1$ $\quad\quad\quad\quad a = -5$

$\quad\quad\quad\quad f = -1$

$1(b) + 0(e) = 7$ $\quad\quad 1(c) + 0(f) = 4$

$\quad\quad\quad b = 7$ $\quad\quad\quad\quad c = 4$

$\begin{bmatrix} -5 & 7 & 4 \\ 3 & 2 & -1 \end{bmatrix} \rightarrow (-5, 3), (7, 2), (4, -1)$

32. $\begin{bmatrix} 0 & -1 \\ 1 & 0 \end{bmatrix} \cdot \begin{bmatrix} -2 & 3 & 2 & -1 \\ -1 & 0 & 2 & 2 \end{bmatrix} = \begin{bmatrix} 1 & 0 & -2 & -2 \\ -2 & 3 & 2 & -1 \end{bmatrix}$

$\begin{bmatrix} 0 & -1 \\ 1 & 0 \end{bmatrix} \cdot \begin{bmatrix} 1 & 0 & -2 & -2 \\ -2 & 3 & 2 & -1 \end{bmatrix} = \begin{bmatrix} 2 & -3 & -2 & 1 \\ 1 & 0 & -2 & -2 \end{bmatrix}$

The coordinates (a, b) become $(-a, -b)$.

33. $\begin{bmatrix} 1 & 2 \\ 3 & 4 \end{bmatrix} \cdot \begin{bmatrix} w & y \\ x & z \end{bmatrix} = \begin{bmatrix} 1 & 2 \\ 3 & 4 \end{bmatrix}$

$\begin{bmatrix} w + 2x & y + 2z \\ 3w + 4x & 3y + 4z \end{bmatrix} = \begin{bmatrix} 1 & 2 \\ 3 & 4 \end{bmatrix}$

$w + 2x = 1 \rightarrow -2w - 4x = -2 \quad\quad w + 2x = 1$

$3w + 4x = 3 \rightarrow \underline{3w + 4x = 3} \quad\quad\quad 1 + 2x = 1$

$\quad\quad\quad\quad\quad w\quad\quad = 1 \quad\quad\quad\quad\quad 2x = 0$

$\quad\quad\quad\quad\quad\quad\quad\quad\quad\quad\quad\quad\quad x = 0$

$y + 2z = 2 \rightarrow -2y - 4z = -4 \quad\quad y + 2z = 2$

$3y + 4z = 4 \rightarrow \underline{3y + 4z = 4} \quad\quad\quad 0 + 2z = 2$

$\quad\quad\quad\quad\quad y\quad\quad = 0 \quad\quad\quad\quad\quad z = 1$

$w = 1, x = 0, y = 0, z = 1$; the result would be
the same matrix you began with.

34. $\begin{bmatrix} 4 & 10 & 6 \\ 7 & 6 & 9 \\ 8 & 3 & 4 \end{bmatrix} \cdot \begin{bmatrix} 5 \\ 3 \\ 1 \end{bmatrix} = \begin{bmatrix} 20 + 30 + 6 \\ 35 + 18 + 9 \\ 40 + 9 + 4 \end{bmatrix} = \begin{bmatrix} 56 \\ 62 \\ 53 \end{bmatrix}$

Birmingham = 56

Chatsworth = 62

Monroe = 53

35.

$[64 \quad 37 \quad 73] \cdot \begin{bmatrix} 3.80 \\ 5.40 \\ 7.15 \end{bmatrix} = 243.20 + 199.80 + 521.95$

$= 964.95$

nickels: $243.20

dimes: $199.80

quarters: $521.95

total: $964.95

36. See answers to Exercises 17-23.

37. $\begin{vmatrix} 2 & -3 & 1 \\ 3 & 5 & 2 \\ 1 & 0 & -3 \end{vmatrix} = 2(5)(-3) + (-3)(2)(1) +$

$\quad\quad\quad\quad\quad\quad\quad (1)(3)(0) - 1(5)(1) -$

$\quad\quad\quad\quad\quad\quad\quad 0(2)(2) - (-3)(3)(-3)$

$\quad\quad\quad\quad = -30 - 6 + 0 - 5 - 0 - 27$

$\quad\quad\quad\quad = -68$

38. $2x - 3y = -9 \rightarrow 2x - 3y = -9$

$\quad x + 7y = -13 \rightarrow \underline{-2x - 14y = 26}$

$\quad\quad\quad\quad\quad\quad\quad\quad - 17y = 17$

$\quad\quad\quad\quad\quad\quad\quad\quad\quad y = -1$

$\quad\quad x + 7y = -13$

$\quad\quad x + 7(-1) = -13$

$\quad\quad\quad\quad x = -6 \quad\quad (-6, -1)$

39. 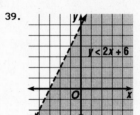 **40.**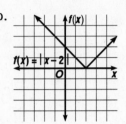

41. Let x = original price of bicycle.

$\quad 0.75x = x - 41$

$\quad -0.25x = -41$

$\quad\quad\quad x = 164$

original price: $164

sale price: $x - 41 = 164 - 41 = 123$; $123

4-5 Identity and Inverse Matrices

PAGES 181-182   CHECKING FOR UNDERSTANDING

1. matrix A **2.** I **3.** Z^{-1}

4. $\begin{bmatrix} 1 & 0 & 0 & 0 \\ 0 & 1 & 0 & 0 \\ 0 & 0 & 1 & 0 \\ 0 & 0 & 0 & 1 \end{bmatrix}$ **5.** yes

6. no, det = 0

7. no, det = 0

8. yes

9. $\begin{vmatrix} 1 & 2 \\ 2 & 1 \end{vmatrix} = 1 - 4 = -3$

$A^{-1} = -\dfrac{1}{3} \begin{bmatrix} 1 & -2 \\ -2 & 1 \end{bmatrix}$

PAGES 182-183   EXERCISES

10. $\dfrac{1}{4(8) - (-3)(3)} \begin{bmatrix} 8 & 3 \\ -3 & 4 \end{bmatrix} = \dfrac{1}{41} \begin{bmatrix} 8 & 3 \\ -3 & 4 \end{bmatrix}$

11. $\dfrac{1}{2(1) - 6(-5)} \begin{bmatrix} 1 & 5 \\ -6 & 2 \end{bmatrix} = \dfrac{1}{32} \begin{bmatrix} 1 & 5 \\ -6 & 2 \end{bmatrix}$

12. No inverse exists because det = 0.

13. $\dfrac{1}{3(1) - (-4)(1)} \begin{bmatrix} 1 & -1 \\ 4 & 3 \end{bmatrix} = \dfrac{1}{7} \begin{bmatrix} 1 & -1 \\ 4 & 3 \end{bmatrix}$

14. $\dfrac{1}{4(1) - 0(0)} \begin{bmatrix} 1 & 0 \\ 0 & 4 \end{bmatrix} = \dfrac{1}{4} \begin{bmatrix} 1 & 0 \\ 0 & 4 \end{bmatrix}$

15. No inverse exists because det = 0.

16. $\begin{bmatrix} 0 & 1 \\ 1 & 1 \end{bmatrix} \cdot \begin{bmatrix} -1 & 1 \\ 1 & 0 \end{bmatrix} \overset{?}{=} I$

$\begin{bmatrix} 1 & 0 \\ 0 & 1 \end{bmatrix} = \begin{bmatrix} 1 & 0 \\ 0 & 1 \end{bmatrix}$

true

17. $\begin{bmatrix} 2 & 1 & -4 \\ -3 & 6 & 5 \end{bmatrix} \cdot \begin{bmatrix} 1 & 0 & 0 \\ 0 & 1 & 0 \\ 0 & 0 & 1 \end{bmatrix} \overset{?}{=} \begin{bmatrix} 2 & 1 & -4 \\ -3 & 6 & 5 \end{bmatrix}$

$\begin{bmatrix} 2 & 1 & -4 \\ -3 & 6 & 5 \end{bmatrix} = \begin{bmatrix} 2 & 1 & -4 \\ -3 & 6 & 5 \end{bmatrix}$

true

18. $\begin{bmatrix} 1 & 5 \\ 1 & -2 \end{bmatrix} \cdot \begin{bmatrix} \frac{2}{7} & \frac{5}{7} \\ \frac{1}{7} & -\frac{1}{7} \end{bmatrix} \overset{?}{=} I$

$\begin{bmatrix} \frac{2}{7} + \frac{5}{7} & \frac{5}{7} - \frac{5}{7} \\ \frac{2}{7} - \frac{2}{7} & \frac{5}{7} + \frac{2}{7} \end{bmatrix} \overset{?}{=} \begin{bmatrix} 1 & 0 \\ 0 & 1 \end{bmatrix}$

$\begin{bmatrix} 1 & 0 \\ 0 & 1 \end{bmatrix} = \begin{bmatrix} 1 & 0 \\ 0 & 1 \end{bmatrix}$ true

19. $\begin{bmatrix} \frac{1}{3} & -\frac{2}{3} \\ \frac{2}{3} & -\frac{1}{3} \end{bmatrix} \cdot \begin{bmatrix} 1 & 2 \\ 2 & 1 \end{bmatrix} \overset{?}{=} I$

$\begin{bmatrix} \frac{1}{3} + \left(-\frac{4}{3}\right) & \frac{2}{3} + \left(-\frac{2}{3}\right) \\ \frac{2}{3} + \left(-\frac{2}{3}\right) & \frac{4}{3} + \left(-\frac{1}{3}\right) \end{bmatrix} \overset{?}{=} \begin{bmatrix} 1 & 0 \\ 0 & 1 \end{bmatrix}$

$\begin{bmatrix} -1 & 0 \\ 0 & 1 \end{bmatrix} \neq \begin{bmatrix} 1 & 0 \\ 0 & 1 \end{bmatrix}$

false

20. $-\dfrac{1}{64} \begin{bmatrix} -20 & 8 & 4 \\ 16 & 0 & -16 \\ -10 & -12 & 2 \end{bmatrix} = \begin{bmatrix} \frac{5}{16} & -\frac{1}{8} & -\frac{1}{16} \\ -\frac{1}{4} & 0 & \frac{1}{4} \\ \frac{5}{32} & \frac{3}{16} & -\frac{1}{32} \end{bmatrix}$

$\begin{bmatrix} \frac{5}{16} & -\frac{1}{8} & -\frac{1}{16} \\ -\frac{1}{4} & 0 & \frac{1}{4} \\ \frac{5}{32} & \frac{3}{16} & -\frac{1}{32} \end{bmatrix} \cdot \begin{bmatrix} 3 & 1 & 2 \\ -2 & 0 & 4 \\ 3 & 5 & 2 \end{bmatrix}$

$= \begin{bmatrix} \frac{15}{16} + \frac{1}{4} - \frac{3}{16} & \frac{5}{16} + 0 - \frac{5}{16} & \frac{10}{16} - \frac{4}{8} - \frac{2}{16} \\ -\frac{3}{4} + 0 + \frac{3}{4} & -\frac{1}{4} + 0 + \frac{5}{4} & -\frac{2}{4} + 0 + \frac{2}{4} \\ \frac{15}{32} - \frac{6}{16} - \frac{3}{32} & \frac{5}{32} + 0 - \frac{5}{32} & \frac{10}{32} + \frac{12}{16} - \frac{2}{32} \end{bmatrix}$

$= \begin{bmatrix} 1 & 0 & 0 \\ 0 & 1 & 0 \\ 0 & 0 & 1 \end{bmatrix}$ It is the inverse.

21. rotation matrix: $\begin{bmatrix} 0 & -1 \\ 1 & 0 \end{bmatrix}$

inverse: $\dfrac{1}{0 - (1)(-1)} \begin{bmatrix} 0 & 1 \\ -1 & 0 \end{bmatrix} = \dfrac{1}{1} \begin{bmatrix} 0 & 1 \\ -1 & 0 \end{bmatrix} = \begin{bmatrix} 0 & 1 \\ -1 & 0 \end{bmatrix}$

Drawings will vary; sample given.

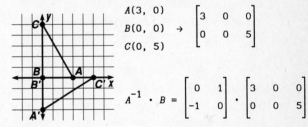

$\begin{matrix} A(3, 0) \\ B(0, 0) \\ C(0, 5) \end{matrix} \rightarrow \begin{bmatrix} 3 & 0 & 0 \\ 0 & 0 & 5 \end{bmatrix}$

$A^{-1} \cdot B = \begin{bmatrix} 0 & 1 \\ -1 & 0 \end{bmatrix} \cdot \begin{bmatrix} 3 & 0 & 0 \\ 0 & 0 & 5 \end{bmatrix}$

$= \begin{bmatrix} 0 & 0 & 5 \\ -3 & 0 & 0 \end{bmatrix}$

90° clockwise turn

22.

	A	B	C
A	1	1	1
B	0	0	2
C	1	1	0

23. $\begin{bmatrix} -2 & 1 \\ 3 & -6 \\ 4 & 5 \end{bmatrix} \cdot \begin{bmatrix} 1 & 2 & -3 & 7 \\ -3 & 2 & 9 & -1 \end{bmatrix} = \begin{bmatrix} -5 & -2 & 15 & -15 \\ 21 & -6 & -63 & 27 \\ -11 & 18 & 33 & 23 \end{bmatrix}$

24. $5x - 3y = 6$

$-3y = -5x + 6$

$y = \dfrac{5}{3}x - 2$

x	y
3	3
0	-2

25. $9x - 2y = 4$ x-intercept:

$-2y = -9x + 4$ $9x - 2(0) = 4$

$y = \frac{9}{2}x - 2$ $9x = 4$

                           $x = \frac{4}{9}$

Slope: $\frac{9}{2}$

x-intercept: $\frac{4}{9}$

y-intercept: -2

26. List the possibilities:

BCDA BDCA BACD BADC BCAD BDAC

CBDA CDBA CABD CADB CBAD CDAB

DBCA DCBA DABC DACB DBAC DCAB

18 arrangements

Page 183   MID-CHAPTER REVIEW

1. Let S = Sue, J = Jane, L = Liz

$S = J + 200$

$L = S + 200 = J + 400$

                 $S + J + L = 2400$

$(J + 200) + J + (J + 400) = 2400$

                    $3J + 600 = 2400$

                        $3J = 1800$

                  $J = 600,\ S = 800,$

                      $L = 1000$

Since the total money is \$5400 and the wives received \$2400, the husbands must have 5400 - 2400 or \$3000.

Use guess-and-check to match husbands with wives.

Lou: $\frac{1}{2}(800)$ $\rightarrow$ Sue

Bob: 600 $\rightarrow$ Jane

Matt: 2(1000) $\rightarrow$ Liz

total: 3000

Sue/Lou, Liz/Matt, Jane/Bob

2. $\begin{bmatrix} 3 & 2 & -3 & -7 \\ 5 & -6 & -1 & 5 \end{bmatrix} + \begin{bmatrix} -4 & -4 & -4 & -4 \\ 3 & 3 & 3 & 3 \end{bmatrix}$

$= \begin{bmatrix} -1 & -2 & -7 & -11 \\ 8 & -3 & 2 & 8 \end{bmatrix}$

$M'(-1, 8),\ A'(-2, -3),\ T'(-7, 2),\ H'(-11, 8)$

3. $\begin{bmatrix} -2 & 1.5 \\ 3 & -0.25 \end{bmatrix} - \begin{bmatrix} -6 & 2 \\ 3 & 1.25 \end{bmatrix}$

$= \begin{bmatrix} -2 - (-6) & 1.5 - 2 \\ 3 - 3 & -0.25 - 1.25 \end{bmatrix} = \begin{bmatrix} 4 & -0.5 \\ 0 & -1.5 \end{bmatrix}$

4. $-4 \begin{bmatrix} -1 & -\frac{1}{4} \\ 0 & 2 \\ \frac{1}{2} & 4 \end{bmatrix} = \begin{bmatrix} -4(-1) & -4\left(-\frac{1}{4}\right) \\ -4(0) & -4(2) \\ -4\left(\frac{1}{2}\right) & -4(4) \end{bmatrix} = \begin{bmatrix} 4 & 1 \\ 0 & -8 \\ -2 & -16 \end{bmatrix}$

5. $\begin{vmatrix} -1 & 3 & 4 \\ 0 & 5 & 1 \\ 6 & -2 & 3 \end{vmatrix}$ = $(-1)(5)(3) + (3)(1)(6)$

                        $+ (4)(0)(-2) - (6)(5)(4)$

                        $- (-2)(1)(-1) - (3)(0)(3)$

                 $= -15 + 18 - 0 - 120 - 2 - 0$

                 $= -119$

6. $A = \frac{1}{2} \begin{vmatrix} 0 & 0 & 1 \\ 12 & 0 & 1 \\ 0 & 5 & 1 \end{vmatrix}$

$= \frac{1}{2}\Big[0(0)(1) + (0)(1)(0) + (1)(12)(5) - (0)(0)(1)$

           $- (5)(1)(0) - (1)(12)(0) \Big]$

$= \frac{1}{2}\Big[0 + 0 + 60 - 0 - 0 - 0 \Big]$

$= \frac{1}{2}\Big[60 \Big]$

$= 30$ 30 square units

7. $\begin{bmatrix} -2 & 3 \\ 1 & 10 \\ 0 & -6 \end{bmatrix} \cdot \begin{bmatrix} 9 & 3 \\ 1 & 4 \end{bmatrix} = \begin{bmatrix} -2(9)+3(1) & -2(3)+3(4) \\ 1(9)+10(1) & 1(3)+10(4) \\ 0(1)+(-6)(1) & 0(1)+(-6)(4) \end{bmatrix}$

$= \begin{bmatrix} -15 & 6 \\ 19 & 43 \\ -6 & -24 \end{bmatrix}$

8. cannot be evaluated

9. $\dfrac{1}{(-2)(1) - (3)(5)} \begin{bmatrix} 1 & -5 \\ -3 & -2 \end{bmatrix} = -\dfrac{1}{17} \begin{bmatrix} 1 & -5 \\ -3 & -2 \end{bmatrix}$

4-6   Using Inverse Matrices

PAGE 188   CHECKING FOR UNDERSTANDING

1. $\begin{bmatrix} 2 & -3 \\ 7 & -3 \end{bmatrix} \cdot \begin{bmatrix} x \\ y \end{bmatrix} = \begin{bmatrix} 8 \\ 5 \end{bmatrix}$

2. the identity matrix

3. $\begin{bmatrix} 5 & 2 \\ 2 & 9 \end{bmatrix} \cdot \begin{bmatrix} a \\ b \end{bmatrix} = \begin{bmatrix} -49 \\ 5 \end{bmatrix}$

4. $\begin{bmatrix} 2 & -3 & 1 \\ 1 & 4 & 2 \\ 3 & 1 & -2 \end{bmatrix} \cdot \begin{bmatrix} x \\ y \\ z \end{bmatrix} = \begin{bmatrix} 29 \\ 3 \\ -3 \end{bmatrix}$

5. $5x + y = 26$ **6.** $2m + n - p = -7$

     $2x - 3y = 41$ $m - 4n + 3p = 5$

                                $6m - 2n + 5p = 9$

7. $\frac{1}{6}\begin{bmatrix} 3 & -1 \\ -9 & 5 \end{bmatrix} \cdot \begin{bmatrix} 5 & 1 \\ 9 & 3 \end{bmatrix} \cdot \begin{bmatrix} x \\ y \end{bmatrix} = \frac{1}{6}\begin{bmatrix} 3 & -1 \\ -9 & 5 \end{bmatrix} \cdot \begin{bmatrix} 1 \\ 1 \end{bmatrix}$

$\begin{bmatrix} 1 & 0 \\ 0 & 1 \end{bmatrix} \cdot \begin{bmatrix} x \\ y \end{bmatrix} = \frac{1}{6}\begin{bmatrix} 2 \\ -4 \end{bmatrix}$

$\begin{bmatrix} x \\ y \end{bmatrix} = \begin{bmatrix} \frac{1}{3} \\ -\frac{2}{3} \end{bmatrix} \quad \left(\frac{1}{3}, -\frac{2}{3}\right)$

PAGE 188-189   EXERCISES

8. $5x + 4y = -3$
   $3x - 5y = -24$

9. $3x + y = 13$
   $4x - 2y = 24$

10. $2x + 5z = 1$
    $x + 8y + 2z = 2$
    $3x - 5y + 7z = 3$

11. $x - 2y = -8$
    $3x + y + 2z = 9$
    $4x - 3y + 3z = 1$

12. $\begin{bmatrix} 3 & -1 \\ 2 & 3 \end{bmatrix}\begin{bmatrix} x \\ y \end{bmatrix} = \begin{bmatrix} 5 \\ 29 \end{bmatrix}$

13. $\begin{bmatrix} 2 & 5 \\ 3 & 4 \end{bmatrix}\begin{bmatrix} x \\ y \end{bmatrix} = \begin{bmatrix} 1 \\ 12 \end{bmatrix}$

14. $\begin{bmatrix} 6 & 9 \\ 4 & 6 \end{bmatrix}\begin{bmatrix} a \\ b \end{bmatrix} = \begin{bmatrix} 6 \\ 8 \end{bmatrix}$

15. $-\frac{1}{28}\begin{bmatrix} -3 & -8 \\ -2 & 4 \end{bmatrix}\begin{bmatrix} 4 & 8 \\ 2 & -3 \end{bmatrix}\begin{bmatrix} x \\ y \end{bmatrix} = -\frac{1}{28}\begin{bmatrix} -3 & -8 \\ -2 & 4 \end{bmatrix}\begin{bmatrix} 7 \\ 0 \end{bmatrix}$

$\begin{bmatrix} x \\ y \end{bmatrix} = -\frac{1}{28}\begin{bmatrix} -21 \\ -14 \end{bmatrix} \quad \left(\frac{3}{4}, \frac{1}{2}\right)$

16. $-\frac{1}{9}\begin{bmatrix} 1 & -1 & -2 \\ 21 & -12 & -15 \\ -33 & 15 & 21 \end{bmatrix}\begin{bmatrix} 3 & 1 & 1 \\ -6 & 5 & 3 \\ 9 & -2 & -1 \end{bmatrix}\begin{bmatrix} x \\ y \\ z \end{bmatrix}$

$= -\frac{1}{9}\begin{bmatrix} 1 & -1 & -2 \\ 21 & -12 & -15 \\ -33 & 15 & 21 \end{bmatrix}\begin{bmatrix} -1 \\ -9 \\ 5 \end{bmatrix}$

$\begin{bmatrix} x \\ y \\ z \end{bmatrix} = -\frac{1}{9}\begin{bmatrix} -2 \\ 12 \\ 3 \end{bmatrix} \quad \left(\frac{2}{9}, -\frac{4}{3}, -\frac{1}{3}\right)$

17. $-\frac{1}{9}\begin{bmatrix} -1 & -10 & 4 \\ -3 & -3 & 3 \\ -1 & 8 & -5 \end{bmatrix}\begin{bmatrix} 1 & 2 & 2 \\ 2 & -1 & 1 \\ 3 & -2 & 3 \end{bmatrix}\begin{bmatrix} a \\ b \\ c \end{bmatrix}$

$= -\frac{1}{9}\begin{bmatrix} -1 & -10 & 4 \\ -3 & -3 & 3 \\ -1 & 8 & -5 \end{bmatrix}\begin{bmatrix} 0 \\ -1 \\ -4 \end{bmatrix}$

$\begin{bmatrix} a \\ b \\ c \end{bmatrix} = -\frac{1}{9}\begin{bmatrix} -6 \\ -9 \\ 12 \end{bmatrix} \quad \left(\frac{2}{3}, 1, -\frac{4}{3}\right)$

18. $-\frac{1}{54}\begin{bmatrix} -8 & -2 \\ -3 & 6 \end{bmatrix}\begin{bmatrix} 6 & 2 \\ 3 & -8 \end{bmatrix}\begin{bmatrix} a \\ b \end{bmatrix} = -\frac{1}{54}\begin{bmatrix} -8 & -2 \\ -3 & 6 \end{bmatrix}\begin{bmatrix} 11 \\ 1 \end{bmatrix}$

$\begin{bmatrix} a \\ b \end{bmatrix} = -\frac{1}{54}\begin{bmatrix} -90 \\ -27 \end{bmatrix} \quad \left(\frac{5}{3}, \frac{1}{2}\right)$

19. $-\frac{1}{60}\begin{bmatrix} -9 & -3 \\ -8 & 4 \end{bmatrix}\begin{bmatrix} 4 & 3 \\ 8 & -9 \end{bmatrix}\begin{bmatrix} x \\ y \end{bmatrix} = -\frac{1}{60}\begin{bmatrix} -9 & -3 \\ -8 & 4 \end{bmatrix}\begin{bmatrix} 5 \\ 0 \end{bmatrix}$

$\begin{bmatrix} x \\ y \end{bmatrix} = -\frac{1}{60}\begin{bmatrix} -45 \\ -40 \end{bmatrix} \quad \left(\frac{3}{4}, \frac{2}{3}\right)$

20. No, because you can't find an inverse for a matrix whose determinant is 0. The graphs of the equations would be parallel lines, or the same line.

21. Let x = the number of round trips of the 10-ton truck,

    y = the number of round trips of the 12-ton truck.

$\begin{cases} x + y = 20 \\ 10x + 12y = 226 \end{cases} \rightarrow \begin{bmatrix} 1 & 1 \\ 10 & 12 \end{bmatrix} \cdot \begin{bmatrix} x \\ y \end{bmatrix} = \begin{bmatrix} 20 \\ 226 \end{bmatrix}$

$\frac{1}{2}\begin{bmatrix} 12 & -1 \\ -10 & 1 \end{bmatrix} \cdot \begin{bmatrix} 1 & 1 \\ 10 & 12 \end{bmatrix} \cdot \begin{bmatrix} x \\ y \end{bmatrix} = \frac{1}{2}\begin{bmatrix} 12 & -1 \\ -10 & 1 \end{bmatrix}\begin{bmatrix} 20 \\ 226 \end{bmatrix}$

$\begin{bmatrix} x \\ y \end{bmatrix} = \begin{bmatrix} 7 \\ 13 \end{bmatrix}$

7 trips for the 10-ton truck and 13 trips for the 12-ton truck

22. Let x = amount of metal with 55% aluminum content, y = amount of metal with 80% aluminum content.

$(0.55)x + (0.80)y = 0.70(x + y)$

$55x + 80y = 70x + 70y$

$-15x + 10y = 0$

$\begin{cases} x + y = 20 \\ -15x + 10y = 0 \end{cases} \rightarrow \begin{bmatrix} 1 & 1 \\ -15 & 10 \end{bmatrix} \cdot \begin{bmatrix} x \\ y \end{bmatrix} = \begin{bmatrix} 20 \\ 0 \end{bmatrix}$

$\frac{1}{25}\begin{bmatrix} 10 & -1 \\ 15 & 1 \end{bmatrix} \cdot \begin{bmatrix} 1 & 1 \\ -15 & 10 \end{bmatrix} \cdot \begin{bmatrix} x \\ y \end{bmatrix} = \frac{1}{25}\begin{bmatrix} 10 & -1 \\ 15 & 1 \end{bmatrix} \cdot \begin{bmatrix} 20 \\ 0 \end{bmatrix}$

$\begin{bmatrix} x \\ y \end{bmatrix} = \begin{bmatrix} 8 \\ 12 \end{bmatrix}$

8 kg of 55% and 12 kg of 80%

23. $\frac{1}{4(6) - (-3)(-2)}\begin{bmatrix} 6 & 2 \\ 3 & 4 \end{bmatrix} = \frac{1}{18}\begin{bmatrix} 6 & 2 \\ 3 & 4 \end{bmatrix}$

24. If you multiply a 2 × 3 matrix by another matrix, m, and get the same 2 × 3 matrix, m must be the 3 × 3 identity matrix: $\begin{bmatrix} 1 & 0 & 0 \\ 0 & 1 & 0 \\ 0 & 0 & 1 \end{bmatrix}$

25.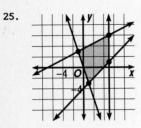

vertices:

(1, −3), (−1, 3),

(5, 6), (5, 1)

maximum value:

$4(5) - 3(1) = 17$

minimum value:

$4(-1) - 3(3) = -13$

26. $-6x + 11y = 4$

$$11y = 6x + 4$$

$$y = \frac{6}{11}x + \frac{4}{11}$$

Slope: $-\frac{6}{11}$

Slope of perpendicular line: $-\frac{11}{6}$

So, $a = -\frac{11}{6}$.

27. Slope: $\frac{-1 - 2}{4 - (-3)} = -\frac{3}{7}$

$y = -\frac{3}{7}x + b$ $y = -\frac{3}{7}x + \frac{5}{7}$

$(-1) = -\frac{3}{7}(4) + b$ $7y = -3x + 5$

$-1 = -\frac{12}{7} + b$ $3x + 7y = 5$

$\frac{5}{7} = b$

28. $5 < 2x - 9$ and $2x - 9 < 11$

$14 < 2x$ $2x < 20$

$7 < x$ $x < 10$ $\{x \mid 7 < x < 10\}$

29. $9 - 3t > 5$ or $9 - 3t < -5$

$-3t > -4$ $-3t < -14$

$t < \frac{-4}{-3}$ $t > \frac{-14}{-3}$

$t < \frac{4}{3}$ $t > \frac{14}{3}$

$\left\{ t \mid t < \frac{4}{3} \text{ or } t > \frac{14}{3} \right\}$

4-7 Using Cramer's Rule

PAGE 192   CHECKING FOR UNDERSTANDING

1. No; it only works for systems with unique solutions.

2. 0

3. At least one of the coefficients must be a fraction.

4. $3a = 5b + 6$ $3a - 5b = 6$ $\begin{vmatrix} 3 & -5 \\ 1 & -1 \end{vmatrix}$

$a - b = 4$ → $a - b = 4$

5. $\begin{vmatrix} 6 & 1 \\ 5 & -8 \end{vmatrix}$

6. $3x + 2y = 0$ $\begin{vmatrix} 3 & 2 & 0 \\ 4 & 0 & -1 \\ 5 & 0 & 3 \end{vmatrix}$

$4x - z = 3$

$5x + 3z = 0$

7. $x = \dfrac{\begin{vmatrix} -6 & 4 & -1 \\ 2 & -2 & 3 \\ -10 & 2 & -4 \end{vmatrix}}{\begin{vmatrix} 2 & 4 & -1 \\ 1 & -2 & 3 \\ 1 & 2 & -4 \end{vmatrix}}$

$= \dfrac{-48 + (-120) + (-4) - (-20) - (-36) - (-32)}{16 + 12 + (-2) - 2 - 12 - (-16)}$

$= \dfrac{-84}{29}$ or -3

$y = \dfrac{\begin{vmatrix} 2 & -6 & -1 \\ 1 & 2 & 3 \\ 1 & -10 & -4 \end{vmatrix}}{\begin{vmatrix} 2 & 4 & -1 \\ 1 & -2 & 3 \\ 1 & 2 & -4 \end{vmatrix}}$

$= \dfrac{(-16) + (-18) + 10 - (-2) - (-60) - 24}{28}$

$= \dfrac{14}{28}$ or $\dfrac{1}{2}$

$z = \dfrac{\begin{vmatrix} 2 & 4 & -6 \\ 1 & -2 & 2 \\ 1 & 2 & -10 \end{vmatrix}}{\begin{vmatrix} 2 & 4 & -1 \\ 1 & -2 & 3 \\ 1 & 2 & -4 \end{vmatrix}}$

$= \dfrac{40 + 8 + (-12) - 12 - 8 - (-40)}{28}$

$= \dfrac{56}{28}$ or 2 $\left(-3, \dfrac{1}{2}, 2\right)$

8. $a = \dfrac{\begin{vmatrix} -4 & -2 & 3 \\ -1 & -1 & 4 \\ 1 & 3 & 5 \end{vmatrix}}{\begin{vmatrix} 1 & -2 & 3 \\ 2 & -1 & 4 \\ 2 & 3 & 5 \end{vmatrix}}$

$= \dfrac{20 + (-8) + (-9) - (-3) - (-48) - 10}{-5 + (-16) + 18 - (-6) - 12 - (-20)}$

$= \dfrac{44}{11}$ or 4

$$b = \frac{\begin{vmatrix} 1 & -4 & 3 \\ 2 & -1 & 4 \\ 2 & 1 & 5 \end{vmatrix}}{\begin{vmatrix} 1 & -2 & 3 \\ 2 & -1 & 4 \\ 2 & 3 & 5 \end{vmatrix}}$$

$$= \frac{-5 + (-32) + 6 - (-6) - 4 - (-40)}{11}$$

$$= \frac{11}{11} \text{ or } 1$$

$$c = \frac{\begin{vmatrix} 1 & -2 & -4 \\ 2 & -1 & -1 \\ 2 & 3 & 1 \end{vmatrix}}{\begin{vmatrix} 1 & -2 & 3 \\ 2 & -1 & 4 \\ 2 & 3 & 5 \end{vmatrix}}$$

$$= \frac{-1 + 4 + (-24) - 8 - (-3) - (-4)}{11}$$

$$= -\frac{22}{11} \text{ or } -2 \qquad (4, 1, -2)$$

PAGES 192-193   EXERCISES

9. $2(-2)(-4) + 4(3)(1) + (-4)(1)(2) - 1(-2)(-1)$
$- (2)(3)(2) - (-4)(1)(4)$

$= 16 + 12 - 8 - 2 - 12 + 16 = 22;$ yes

10. $2(3)(0) + 0(-3)(-3) + 0(2)(3) - (-3)(3)(2)$
$- (-2)(-3)(2) - 0(0)(0)$

$= 0 + 0 + 0 + 18 - 12 - 0 = 6;$ yes

11. $(-1)(1)(-2) + (7)(0)(3) + (2)(2)(-6) - (3)(1)(2)$
$- (-6)(0)(-1) - (-2)(2)(7)$

$= 2 + 0 - 24 - 6 - 0 + 28 = 0;$ no

12. $\begin{vmatrix} 4 & 1 & 3 \\ 2 & 0 & 1 \\ 4 & -6 & 0 \end{vmatrix} = -8$

$$a = \frac{\begin{vmatrix} 1 & 1 & 3 \\ 3 & 0 & 1 \\ 8 & -6 & 0 \end{vmatrix}}{-8} = \frac{-40}{-8} = 5$$

$$b = \frac{\begin{vmatrix} 4 & 1 & 3 \\ 2 & 3 & 1 \\ 4 & 8 & 0 \end{vmatrix}}{-8} = \frac{-16}{-8} = 2$$

$$c = \frac{\begin{vmatrix} 4 & 1 & 1 \\ 2 & 0 & 3 \\ 4 & -6 & 8 \end{vmatrix}}{-8} = \frac{56}{-8} = -7$$

The solution is $(5, 2, -7)$.

13. $\begin{vmatrix} 2 & -1 & 3 \\ 3 & 2 & -5 \\ 1 & -4 & 11 \end{vmatrix} = 0$; no unique solution

14. $\begin{vmatrix} 1 & 2 & -3 \\ 2 & -1 & 3 \\ 3 & 1 & -3 \end{vmatrix} = 15$

$$a = \frac{\begin{vmatrix} -13 & 2 & -3 \\ 23 & -1 & 3 \\ -8 & 1 & -3 \end{vmatrix}}{15} = \frac{45}{15} = 3$$

$$b = \frac{\begin{vmatrix} 1 & -13 & -3 \\ 2 & 23 & 3 \\ 3 & -8 & -3 \end{vmatrix}}{15} = \frac{15}{15} = 1$$

$$c = \frac{\begin{vmatrix} 1 & 2 & -13 \\ 2 & -1 & 23 \\ 3 & 1 & -8 \end{vmatrix}}{15} = \frac{90}{15} = 6$$

The solution is $(3, 1, 6)$.

15.

$$\begin{vmatrix} 3 & -1 & 2 \\ 6 & -3 & 1 \\ -3 & -2 & 2 \end{vmatrix} = -39$$

$$x = \frac{\begin{vmatrix} 11 & -1 & 11 \\ -1 & -3 & -1 \\ 11 & -2 & 2 \end{vmatrix}}{-39} = \frac{13}{-39} = -\frac{1}{3}$$

$$y = \frac{\begin{vmatrix} 3 & 11 & 2 \\ 6 & -1 & 1 \\ -3 & -3 & 11 \end{vmatrix}}{-39} = \frac{-78}{-39} = 2$$

$$z = \frac{\begin{vmatrix} 3 & -1 & 11 \\ 6 & -3 & -1 \\ -3 & -2 & 11 \end{vmatrix}}{-39} = \frac{-273}{-39} = 7$$

The solution is $\left(-\frac{1}{3}, 2, 7\right)$.

16. $\begin{vmatrix} 1 & 9 & -2 \\ -1 & -3 & 4 \\ 2 & 3 & -6 \end{vmatrix} = 18$

$$x = \dfrac{\begin{vmatrix} 2 & 9 & -2 \\ 1 & -3 & 4 \\ -5 & 3 & -6 \end{vmatrix}}{18} = \dfrac{-90}{18} = -5$$

$$y = \dfrac{\begin{vmatrix} 1 & 2 & -2 \\ -1 & 1 & 4 \\ 2 & -5 & -6 \end{vmatrix}}{18} = \dfrac{12}{18} = \dfrac{2}{3}$$

$$z = \dfrac{\begin{vmatrix} 1 & 9 & 2 \\ -1 & -3 & 1 \\ 2 & 3 & -5 \end{vmatrix}}{18} = \dfrac{-9}{18} = -\dfrac{1}{2}$$

The solution is $\left(-5, \dfrac{2}{3}, -\dfrac{1}{2}\right)$.

17. $\begin{vmatrix} 1 & 4 & 3 \\ 2 & -2 & 1 \\ 1 & 2 & -3 \end{vmatrix} = 50$

$$x = \dfrac{\begin{vmatrix} 10 & 4 & 3 \\ 15 & -2 & 1 \\ -1 & 2 & -3 \end{vmatrix}}{50} = \dfrac{300}{50} = 6$$

$$y = \dfrac{\begin{vmatrix} 1 & 10 & 3 \\ 2 & 15 & 1 \\ 1 & -1 & -3 \end{vmatrix}}{50} = \dfrac{-25}{50} = -\dfrac{1}{2}$$

$$z = \dfrac{\begin{vmatrix} 1 & 4 & 10 \\ 2 & -2 & 15 \\ 1 & 2 & -1 \end{vmatrix}}{50} = \dfrac{100}{50} = 2$$

The solution is $\left(6, -\dfrac{1}{2}, 2\right)$.

18. Let p = number of pennies.

Let n = number of nickels.

Let d = number of dimes.

$\begin{array}{ll} p + n + d = 16 & p + n + d = 16 \\ \quad\quad d = p + n \;\rightarrow & p + n - d = 0 \\ p + 5n + 10d = 108 & p + 5n + 10d = 108 \end{array}$

19. Let c = cost of a cheeseburger.

Let f = cost of fries.

Let m = cost of a milkshake.

$$2c + 3f = 3.65$$
$$c + 2m = 2.47$$
$$c + 2f + m = 3.01$$

20. Let s = number of T-60 tapes.

Let n = number of T-90 tapes.

Let t = number of T-120 tapes.

$$s + n + t = 10$$
$$3.19s + 3.89n + 4.59t = 40.30$$
$$n - 2t = 0$$

21. possible equations: $0.05n + 0.10d + 0.25q = 1.35$
$$0.05n = 0.10d$$

There are two equations and three variables. You cannot find the determinant unless there is a third equation. However, there is a unique solution.

$0.05n + 0.10d + 0.25q = 1.35$

$0.10d + 0.10d + 0.25q = 1.35$ Substitute $0.10d$ for $0.05n$.

$0.20d + 0.25q = 1.35$ Multiply by 20.

$4d + 5q = 27$

Since n, d, and q must be whole numbers, the only solution to this equation is $d = 3$ and $q = 3$. So the answer is 6 nickels, 3 dimes, and 3 quarters.

22. Let w = number of points scored by Mrs. Winters.

Let g = number of points scored by Mrs. Gordon.

Let s = number of points scored by Mr. Gossell.

$\begin{array}{ll} w + g + s = 63 & \quad w + g + s = 63 \\ \quad\quad w = 2s & \rightarrow \quad w - 2s = 0 \\ \quad g = s + w + 3 & \quad -w + g - s = 3 \end{array}$

$$\begin{vmatrix} 1 & 1 & 1 \\ 1 & 0 & -2 \\ -1 & 1 & -1 \end{vmatrix} = 0 + 2 + 1 - 0 - (-2) - (-1) = 6$$

$$w = \dfrac{\begin{vmatrix} 63 & 1 & 1 \\ 0 & 0 & -2 \\ 3 & 1 & -1 \end{vmatrix}}{6}$$

$$= \dfrac{0 + (-6) + 0 - 0 - (-126) - 0}{6} = 20$$

$$g = \dfrac{\begin{vmatrix} 1 & 63 & 1 \\ 1 & 0 & -2 \\ -1 & 3 & -1 \end{vmatrix}}{6}$$

$$= \dfrac{0 + 126 + 3 - 0 - (-6) - (-63)}{6} = 33$$

$$s = \dfrac{\begin{vmatrix} 1 & 1 & 63 \\ 1 & 0 & 0 \\ -1 & 1 & 3 \end{vmatrix}}{6}$$

$$= \dfrac{0 + 0 + 63 - 0 - 0 - 3}{6} = 10$$

Winters: 20, Gordon: 33, Gossell: 10

23. Let s = number of small cones sold.

Let m = number of medium cones sold.

Let l = number of large cones sold.

$s + m + l = 52$

$m - 2l = 2$

$89s + 119m + 139l = 5898$

$$\begin{vmatrix} 1 & 1 & 1 \\ 0 & 1 & -2 \\ 89 & 119 & 139 \end{vmatrix} = 139 + (-178) + 0 - 89 - (-238) - 0$$

$$= 110$$

$$s = \frac{\begin{vmatrix} 52 & 1 & 1 \\ 2 & 1 & -2 \\ 5898 & 119 & 139 \end{vmatrix}}{110}$$

$$= \frac{7228 + (-11{,}796) + 238 - 5898 - (-12{,}376) - 278}{110}$$

$$= \frac{1870}{110} \text{ or } 17$$

$$m = \frac{\begin{vmatrix} 1 & 52 & 1 \\ 0 & 2 & -2 \\ 89 & 5898 & 139 \end{vmatrix}}{110}$$

$$= \frac{278 + (-9256) + 0 - 178 - (-11{,}796) - 0}{110}$$

$$= \frac{2640}{110} \text{ or } 24$$

$$l = \frac{\begin{vmatrix} 1 & 1 & 52 \\ 0 & 1 & 2 \\ 89 & 119 & 5898 \end{vmatrix}}{110}$$

$$= \frac{5898 + 178 + 0 - 4628 - 238 - 0}{110}$$

$$= \frac{1210}{110} \text{ or } 11$$

17 small cones, 24 medium cones, and 11 large cones

24. a matrix with 2 rows and 4 columns

25. $y \geq |3x|$

when $x < 0$, when $x \geq 0$,

$y > -3x$ $y \geq 3x$

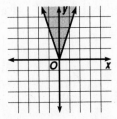

26.

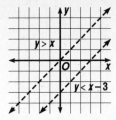

The solution is the empty set, ø.

27. Let c = cost of telephone call.

Let m = number of minutes.

$c = 3.38 + (0.96)(m - 3)$

$= 3.38 + (0.96)(12 - 3)$ Substitute 12 for m.

$= 3.38 + 8.64$

$= 12.02$ $12.02

Technology: Cramer's Rule

PAGE 194 EXERCISES

1. 55 DATA 2, 3, 4, 4, 2, 0, -8, -1, 4, -6, 4, -1

$\left(\frac{1}{2}, \frac{2}{3}, \frac{1}{4}\right)$

2. 55 DATA 5, -1, 2, 5, 2, -3, 5, 1, 3, 2, -3, 4

ø

4-8 ## Using Augmented Matrices

PAGES 198-199 CHECKING FOR UNDERSTANDING

1. An augmented matrix is a matrix containing the coefficients of the variables along with a column containing the constant terms.

2. The system is dependent, and the solution is a line.

3. The system has no solutions.

4. Interchange any two rows.

Replace any row with a nonzero multiple of that row.

Replace any row with the sum of that row and a multiple of another row.

5. Variables used may vary.

$x + 3z = -2$

$3x + 9y - 2z = -5$

$-4x + y - 7z = 3$

6. Answers may vary. Sample answer:

Multiply row 1 by -2 and add to row 2. Multiply row 2 by $-\frac{1}{5}$. Multiply row 2 by -3 and add to row 1.

7. $\begin{bmatrix} 5 & -3 & 7 \\ 3 & 9 & -3 \end{bmatrix} = \begin{bmatrix} 5 & -3 & 7 \\ 18 & 0 & 18 \end{bmatrix} = \begin{bmatrix} 18 & 0 & 18 \\ 5 & -3 & 7 \end{bmatrix}$

$= \begin{bmatrix} 1 & 0 & 1 \\ 5 & -3 & 7 \end{bmatrix} = \begin{bmatrix} 1 & 0 & 1 \\ 0 & -3 & 2 \end{bmatrix} = \begin{bmatrix} 1 & 0 & 1 \\ 0 & 1 & -\frac{2}{3} \end{bmatrix}$

$\left(1, -\frac{2}{3}\right)$

8. $\begin{bmatrix} 6 & 0 & -7 & 13 \\ 0 & 8 & 2 & 14 \\ 7 & 0 & 1 & 6 \end{bmatrix} = \begin{bmatrix} 6 & 0 & -7 & 13 \\ 0 & 4 & 1 & 7 \\ 7 & 0 & 1 & 6 \end{bmatrix}$

$= \begin{bmatrix} 55 & 0 & 0 & 55 \\ 0 & 4 & 1 & 7 \\ 7 & 0 & 1 & 6 \end{bmatrix} = \begin{bmatrix} 1 & 0 & 0 & 1 \\ 0 & 4 & 1 & 7 \\ 7 & 0 & 1 & 6 \end{bmatrix}$

$= \begin{bmatrix} 1 & 0 & 0 & 1 \\ 0 & 4 & 1 & 7 \\ 0 & 0 & 1 & -1 \end{bmatrix} = \begin{bmatrix} 1 & 0 & 0 & 1 \\ 0 & 4 & 0 & 8 \\ 0 & 0 & 1 & -1 \end{bmatrix}$

$= \begin{bmatrix} 1 & 0 & 0 & 1 \\ 0 & 1 & 0 & 2 \\ 0 & 0 & 1 & -1 \end{bmatrix}$ $(1, 2, -1)$

PAGES 199-200   EXERCISES

9. Answers will vary. Sample answer:

Add row 1 to row 2. Multiply row 2 by -4 and add to row 1. Multiply row 1 by $\frac{1}{2}$.

10. $\begin{bmatrix} 4 & 3 & 10 \\ 5 & -1 & 3 \end{bmatrix} = \begin{bmatrix} 19 & 0 & 19 \\ 5 & -1 & 3 \end{bmatrix} = \begin{bmatrix} 1 & 0 & 1 \\ 5 & -1 & 3 \end{bmatrix}$

$= \begin{bmatrix} 1 & 0 & 1 \\ 0 & -1 & -2 \end{bmatrix} = \begin{bmatrix} 1 & 0 & 1 \\ 0 & 1 & 2 \end{bmatrix}$ $(1, 2)$

11. $\begin{bmatrix} 7 & -3 & 41 \\ 2 & 5 & 0 \end{bmatrix} = \begin{bmatrix} 7 & -3 & 41 \\ 14 & 35 & 0 \end{bmatrix} = \begin{bmatrix} 7 & -3 & 41 \\ 0 & 41 & -82 \end{bmatrix}$

$= \begin{bmatrix} 7 & -3 & 41 \\ 0 & 1 & -2 \end{bmatrix} = \begin{bmatrix} 7 & 0 & 35 \\ 0 & 1 & -2 \end{bmatrix} = \begin{bmatrix} 1 & 0 & 5 \\ 0 & 1 & -2 \end{bmatrix}$

$(5, -2)$

12. $\begin{bmatrix} 3 & -5 & 2 & 22 \\ 2 & 3 & -1 & -9 \\ 4 & 3 & 3 & 1 \end{bmatrix} = \begin{bmatrix} 7 & 1 & 0 & 4 \\ 2 & 3 & -1 & -9 \\ 4 & 3 & 3 & 1 \end{bmatrix}$

$= \begin{bmatrix} 7 & 1 & 0 & 4 \\ 2 & 3 & -1 & -9 \\ -17 & 0 & 3 & -11 \end{bmatrix} = \begin{bmatrix} 7 & 1 & 0 & 4 \\ 6 & 9 & -3 & -27 \\ -17 & 0 & 3 & -11 \end{bmatrix}$

$= \begin{bmatrix} 7 & 1 & 0 & 4 \\ -11 & 9 & 0 & -38 \\ -17 & 0 & 3 & -11 \end{bmatrix} = \begin{bmatrix} 7 & 1 & 0 & 4 \\ -74 & 0 & 0 & -74 \\ -17 & 0 & 3 & -11 \end{bmatrix}$

$= \begin{bmatrix} 7 & 1 & 0 & 4 \\ 1 & 0 & 0 & 1 \\ -17 & 0 & 3 & -11 \end{bmatrix} = \begin{bmatrix} 1 & 0 & 0 & 1 \\ 7 & 1 & 0 & 4 \\ -17 & 0 & 3 & -11 \end{bmatrix}$

$= \begin{bmatrix} 1 & 0 & 0 & 1 \\ 0 & 1 & 0 & -3 \\ -17 & 0 & 3 & -11 \end{bmatrix} = \begin{bmatrix} 1 & 0 & 0 & 1 \\ 0 & 1 & 0 & -3 \\ 0 & 0 & 3 & 6 \end{bmatrix}$

$= \begin{bmatrix} 1 & 0 & 0 & 1 \\ 0 & 1 & 0 & -3 \\ 0 & 0 & 1 & 2 \end{bmatrix}$ $(1, -3, 2)$

13. unique: $(3, 5)$ **14.** $\varnothing$

15. an equation in two variables: a line

16. $\begin{bmatrix} 6 & 1 & 9 \\ 3 & 2 & 0 \end{bmatrix} = \begin{bmatrix} -12 & -2 & -18 \\ 3 & 2 & 0 \end{bmatrix} = \begin{bmatrix} -9 & 0 & -18 \\ 3 & 2 & 0 \end{bmatrix}$

$= \begin{bmatrix} 1 & 0 & 2 \\ 3 & 2 & 0 \end{bmatrix} = \begin{bmatrix} 1 & 0 & 2 \\ 0 & 2 & -6 \end{bmatrix} = \begin{bmatrix} 1 & 0 & 2 \\ 0 & 1 & -3 \end{bmatrix}$

$(2, -3)$

17. $\begin{bmatrix} 1 & 1 & 1 & -2 \\ 2 & -3 & 1 & -11 \\ -1 & 2 & -1 & 8 \end{bmatrix} = \begin{bmatrix} -1 & -1 & -1 & 2 \\ 2 & -3 & 1 & -11 \\ -1 & 2 & -1 & 8 \end{bmatrix}$

$= \begin{bmatrix} 1 & -4 & 0 & -9 \\ 1 & -1 & 0 & -3 \\ -1 & 2 & -1 & 8 \end{bmatrix} = \begin{bmatrix} -1 & 4 & 0 & 9 \\ 4 & -4 & 0 & -12 \\ -1 & 2 & -1 & 8 \end{bmatrix}$

$= \begin{bmatrix} 3 & 0 & 0 & -3 \\ 4 & -4 & 0 & -12 \\ -1 & 2 & -1 & 8 \end{bmatrix} = \begin{bmatrix} 1 & 0 & 0 & -1 \\ 1 & -1 & 0 & -3 \\ -1 & 2 & -1 & 8 \end{bmatrix}$

$= \begin{bmatrix} 1 & 0 & 0 & -1 \\ 0 & -1 & 0 & -2 \\ 0 & 2 & -1 & 7 \end{bmatrix} = \begin{bmatrix} 1 & 0 & 0 & -1 \\ 0 & 1 & 0 & 2 \\ 0 & 2 & -1 & 7 \end{bmatrix}$

$= \begin{bmatrix} 1 & 0 & 0 & -1 \\ 0 & 1 & 0 & 2 \\ 0 & 0 & -1 & 3 \end{bmatrix} = \begin{bmatrix} 1 & 0 & 0 & -1 \\ 0 & 1 & 0 & 2 \\ 0 & 0 & 1 & -3 \end{bmatrix}$

$(-1, 2, -3)$

18.

$$\begin{bmatrix} 2 & 1 & 1 & 0 \\ 3 & -2 & -3 & -21 \\ 4 & 5 & 3 & -2 \end{bmatrix} = \begin{bmatrix} 6 & 3 & 3 & 0 \\ 3 & -2 & -3 & -21 \\ 7 & 3 & 0 & -23 \end{bmatrix}$$

$$= \begin{bmatrix} 9 & 1 & 0 & -21 \\ 3 & -2 & -3 & -21 \\ 7 & 3 & 0 & -23 \end{bmatrix} = \begin{bmatrix} -27 & -3 & 0 & 63 \\ 3 & -2 & -3 & -21 \\ 7 & 3 & 0 & -23 \end{bmatrix}$$

$$= \begin{bmatrix} -20 & 0 & 0 & 40 \\ 3 & -2 & -3 & -21 \\ 7 & 3 & 0 & -23 \end{bmatrix} = \begin{bmatrix} 1 & 0 & 0 & -2 \\ 3 & -2 & -3 & -21 \\ 7 & 3 & 0 & -23 \end{bmatrix}$$

$$= \begin{bmatrix} 1 & 0 & 0 & -2 \\ 0 & -2 & -3 & -15 \\ 0 & 3 & 0 & -9 \end{bmatrix} = \begin{bmatrix} 1 & 0 & 0 & -2 \\ 0 & -2 & -3 & -15 \\ 0 & 1 & 0 & -3 \end{bmatrix}$$

$$= \begin{bmatrix} 1 & 0 & 0 & -2 \\ 0 & 1 & 0 & -3 \\ 0 & -2 & -3 & -15 \end{bmatrix} = \begin{bmatrix} 1 & 0 & 0 & -2 \\ 0 & 1 & 0 & -3 \\ 0 & 0 & -3 & -21 \end{bmatrix}$$

$$= \begin{bmatrix} 1 & 0 & 0 & -2 \\ 0 & 1 & 0 & -3 \\ 0 & 0 & 1 & 7 \end{bmatrix} \quad (-2, -3, 7)$$

19.

$m\angle A + m\angle B + m\angle c = 180°$ $m\angle A + m\angle B + m\angle c = 180°$

$m\angle A = 2(m\angle B)$ $\rightarrow$ $m\angle A - 2(m\angle B) = 0$

$m\angle C - 4(m\angle B) + 12°$ $-4(m\angle B) + m\angle C = 12°$

$$\begin{bmatrix} 1 & 1 & 1 & 180 \\ 1 & -2 & 0 & 0 \\ 0 & -4 & 1 & 12 \end{bmatrix} = \begin{bmatrix} 1 & 1 & 1 & 180 \\ 0 & -3 & -1 & -180 \\ 0 & -4 & 1 & 12 \end{bmatrix}$$

$$= \begin{bmatrix} 1 & 1 & 1 & 180 \\ 0 & -7 & 0 & -168 \\ 0 & -4 & 1 & 12 \end{bmatrix} = \begin{bmatrix} 1 & 5 & 0 & 168 \\ 0 & 1 & 0 & 24 \\ 0 & -4 & 1 & 12 \end{bmatrix}$$

$$= \begin{bmatrix} 1 & 0 & 0 & 48 \\ 0 & 1 & 0 & 24 \\ 0 & 0 & 1 & 108 \end{bmatrix} \quad 48°, 24°, 108°$$

20.

$$\begin{bmatrix} 8 & -3 & -4 & 6 \\ 4 & 9 & -2 & -4 \\ 6 & 12 & 5 & -1 \end{bmatrix} = \begin{bmatrix} 0 & -21 & 0 & 14 \\ 4 & 9 & -2 & -4 \\ 6 & 12 & 5 & -1 \end{bmatrix}$$

$$= \begin{bmatrix} 0 & 1 & 0 & -\frac{2}{3} \\ 4 & 0 & -2 & 2 \\ 6 & 0 & 5 & 7 \end{bmatrix} = \begin{bmatrix} 4 & 0 & -2 & 2 \\ 0 & 1 & 0 & -\frac{2}{3} \\ 6 & 0 & 5 & 7 \end{bmatrix}$$

$$= \begin{bmatrix} 20 & 0 & -10 & 10 \\ 0 & 1 & 0 & -\frac{2}{3} \\ 6 & 0 & 5 & 7 \end{bmatrix} = \begin{bmatrix} 32 & 0 & 0 & 24 \\ 0 & 1 & 0 & -\frac{2}{3} \\ 6 & 0 & 5 & 7 \end{bmatrix}$$

$$= \begin{bmatrix} 1 & 0 & 0 & \frac{3}{4} \\ 0 & 1 & 0 & -\frac{2}{3} \\ 0 & 0 & 5 & \frac{5}{2} \end{bmatrix} = \begin{bmatrix} 1 & 0 & 0 & \frac{3}{4} \\ 0 & 1 & 0 & -\frac{2}{3} \\ 0 & 0 & 1 & \frac{1}{2} \end{bmatrix}$$

$$\left(\frac{3}{4}, -\frac{2}{3}, \frac{1}{2}\right)$$

21. Two rows of zeros mean that all 3 equations were forms of the same equation. The solution would be the plane the equation describes.

22. Let b = cost of a battery.

Let s = cost of a case of spark plugs.

Let w = cost of a dozen wiper blades.

$6b + 5s + 2w = 830$

$3b + 7s + 4w = 820$

$b = 2w - 22 \quad \rightarrow \quad b - 2w = -22$

$$\begin{bmatrix} 6 & 5 & 2 & 830 \\ 3 & 7 & 4 & 820 \\ 1 & 0 & -2 & -22 \end{bmatrix} = \begin{bmatrix} 0 & 5 & 14 & 962 \\ 0 & 7 & 10 & 886 \\ 1 & 0 & -2 & -22 \end{bmatrix}$$

$$= \begin{bmatrix} 1 & 0 & -2 & -22 \\ 0 & 5 & 14 & 962 \\ 0 & 7 & 10 & 886 \end{bmatrix} = \begin{bmatrix} 1 & 0 & -2 & -22 \\ 0 & 5 & 14 & 962 \\ 0 & -35 & -50 & -4430 \end{bmatrix}$$

$$= \begin{bmatrix} 1 & 0 & -2 & -22 \\ 0 & 5 & 14 & 962 \\ 0 & 0 & 48 & 2304 \end{bmatrix} = \begin{bmatrix} 1 & 0 & -2 & -22 \\ 0 & 5 & 14 & 962 \\ 0 & 0 & 1 & 48 \end{bmatrix}$$

$$= \begin{bmatrix} 1 & 0 & 0 & 74 \\ 0 & 5 & 0 & 290 \\ 0 & 0 & 1 & 48 \end{bmatrix} = \begin{bmatrix} 1 & 0 & 0 & 74 \\ 0 & 1 & 0 & 58 \\ 0 & 0 & 1 & 48 \end{bmatrix}$$

batteries, \$74; spark plugs, \$58 per case; wiper blades, \$48 per dozen

23. Let s = cost of a salad.

Let r = cost of a roll.

Let c = cost of a piece of chicken.

$$s + 2r + 2c = 3.65$$
$$r + 3c = 3.20$$
$$s = 3r \rightarrow s - 3r = 0$$

$$\begin{bmatrix} 1 & 2 & 2 & 3.65 \\ 0 & 1 & 3 & 3.20 \\ 1 & -3 & 0 & 0 \end{bmatrix} = \begin{bmatrix} 1 & 0 & -4 & -2.75 \\ 0 & 1 & 3 & 3.20 \\ 1 & -3 & 0 & 0 \end{bmatrix}$$

$$= \begin{bmatrix} 1 & 0 & -4 & -2.75 \\ 0 & 1 & 3 & 3.20 \\ 0 & -3 & 4 & 2.75 \end{bmatrix} = \begin{bmatrix} 1 & 0 & -4 & -2.75 \\ 0 & 1 & 3 & 3.20 \\ 0 & 0 & 13 & 12.35 \end{bmatrix}$$

$$= \begin{bmatrix} 1 & 0 & -4 & -2.75 \\ 0 & 1 & 3 & 3.20 \\ 0 & 0 & 1 & 0.95 \end{bmatrix} = \begin{bmatrix} 1 & 0 & 0 & 1.05 \\ 0 & 1 & 0 & 0.35 \\ 0 & 0 & 1 & 0.95 \end{bmatrix}$$

chicken, $0.95 per piece; salad, $1.05;
roll, $0.35

24. $\begin{bmatrix} 1 & 5 & 2 \\ 3 & -3 & 2 \\ 2 & 4 & -1 \end{bmatrix} \cdot \begin{bmatrix} x \\ y \\ z \end{bmatrix} = \begin{bmatrix} 10 \\ 2 \\ -15 \end{bmatrix}$

25. $\begin{vmatrix} 4 & -2 \\ 3 & 7 \end{vmatrix} = 4(7) - (3)(-2) = 28 + 6 = 34$

26. $\begin{vmatrix} 9 & -1 \\ 3 & 2 \end{vmatrix} = 21$

$a = \dfrac{\begin{vmatrix} 1 & -1 \\ 12 & 2 \end{vmatrix}}{21} \qquad b = \dfrac{\begin{vmatrix} 9 & 1 \\ 3 & 12 \end{vmatrix}}{21}$

$= \dfrac{14}{21} \text{ or } \dfrac{2}{3} \qquad\quad = \dfrac{105}{21} \text{ or } 5 \quad \left(\dfrac{2}{3},\ 5\right)$

27.

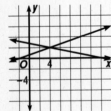

$(4, 2)$

28. Distributive property

PAGE 200   LANGUAGE CONNECTION

first: e_{11}, last: e_{mn}

Chapter 4 Summary and Review

PAGES 202-204   SKILLS AND CONCEPTS

1. $P_{2\times3}$ **2.** $Q_{3\times1}$

3. $3\begin{bmatrix} 8 & -3 & 2 \\ 4 & 1 & 7 \end{bmatrix} = \begin{bmatrix} 24 & -9 & 6 \\ 12 & 3 & 21 \end{bmatrix}$

4. $2\begin{bmatrix} 8 & -1 \\ 3 & 4 \end{bmatrix} - 3\begin{bmatrix} 1 & 6 \\ -2 & -3 \end{bmatrix}$

$= \begin{bmatrix} 16 & -2 \\ 6 & 8 \end{bmatrix} - \begin{bmatrix} 3 & 18 \\ -6 & -9 \end{bmatrix} = \begin{bmatrix} 13 & -20 \\ 12 & 17 \end{bmatrix}$

5.
$$\begin{array}{ll} 7x = 5 + 2y & 7x - 2y = 5 \\ x + y = 11 \rightarrow & \underline{-7x - 7y = -77} \\ & -9y = -72 \\ & y = 8 \end{array}$$

$$x + y = 11$$
$$x + 8 = 11$$
$$x = 3 \qquad (3, 8)$$

6. $\begin{vmatrix} 5 & -1 & 2 \\ -6 & -7 & 3 \\ 7 & 0 & 4 \end{vmatrix} = 5(-7)(4) + (-1)(3)(7) +$
$\qquad (2)(-6)(0) - (7)(-7)(2) -$
$\qquad (0)(3)(5) - (4)(-6)(-1)$

$= -140 + (-21) + 0 - (-98) - 0 - 24$

$= -87$

7. $\begin{vmatrix} 2 & -3 & 1 \\ 0 & 7 & 8 \\ 2 & 1 & 3 \end{vmatrix} = 2(7)(3) + (-3)(8)(2) + (1)(0)(1)$
$\qquad - (2)(7)(1) - (1)(8)(2)$
$\qquad - (3)(0)(-3)$

$= 42 + (-48) + 0 - 14 - 16 - 0$

$= -36$

8. $\begin{bmatrix} 2 & -3 \\ 6 & 4 \end{bmatrix} \cdot \begin{bmatrix} 1 & -3 & 4 \\ 3 & 1 & 1 \end{bmatrix} = \begin{bmatrix} -7 & -9 & 5 \\ 18 & -14 & 28 \end{bmatrix}$

9. $\begin{bmatrix} 5 & -2 & 3 \end{bmatrix} \cdot \begin{bmatrix} 2 & 5 \\ -1 & 3 \\ 6 & 4 \end{bmatrix} = \begin{bmatrix} 30 & 31 \end{bmatrix}$

10. not defined

11. $\begin{bmatrix} 1 & 0 & 0 & 0 \\ 0 & 1 & 0 & 0 \\ 0 & 0 & 1 & 0 \\ 0 & 0 & 0 & 1 \end{bmatrix}$ **12.** $\begin{bmatrix} 1 & 0 & 0 & 0 & 0 & 0 \\ 0 & 1 & 0 & 0 & 0 & 0 \\ 0 & 0 & 1 & 0 & 0 & 0 \\ 0 & 0 & 0 & 1 & 0 & 0 \\ 0 & 0 & 0 & 0 & 1 & 0 \\ 0 & 0 & 0 & 0 & 0 & 1 \end{bmatrix}$

13. $\dfrac{1}{(8)(7) - (9)(6)}\begin{bmatrix} 7 & -6 \\ -9 & 8 \end{bmatrix} = \dfrac{1}{2}\begin{bmatrix} 7 & -6 \\ -9 & 8 \end{bmatrix}$

14.

$$\frac{1}{(3)(-2) - (4)(2)} \begin{bmatrix} -2 & -2 \\ -4 & 3 \end{bmatrix} = -\frac{1}{14} \begin{bmatrix} -2 & -2 \\ -4 & 3 \end{bmatrix}$$

15. $-\frac{1}{8} \begin{bmatrix} -2 & -2 \\ -1 & 3 \end{bmatrix} \cdot \begin{bmatrix} 3 & 2 \\ 1 & -2 \end{bmatrix} \cdot \begin{bmatrix} x \\ y \end{bmatrix} = -\frac{1}{8} \begin{bmatrix} -2 & -2 \\ -1 & 3 \end{bmatrix} \cdot \begin{bmatrix} 9 \\ 11 \end{bmatrix}$

$$\begin{bmatrix} x \\ y \end{bmatrix} = -\frac{1}{8} \begin{bmatrix} -40 \\ 24 \end{bmatrix}$$

$$\begin{bmatrix} x \\ y \end{bmatrix} = \begin{bmatrix} 5 \\ -3 \end{bmatrix} \quad (5, -3)$$

16. $\frac{1}{14} \begin{bmatrix} 5 & 1 & -3 \\ -3 & 5 & -1 \\ 2 & -8 & 10 \end{bmatrix} \cdot \begin{bmatrix} 3 & 1 & 1 \\ 2 & 4 & 1 \\ 1 & 3 & 2 \end{bmatrix} \cdot \begin{bmatrix} a \\ b \\ c \end{bmatrix}$

$$= \frac{1}{14} \begin{bmatrix} 5 & 1 & -3 \\ -3 & 5 & -1 \\ 2 & -8 & 10 \end{bmatrix} \cdot \begin{bmatrix} -2 \\ 4 \\ 12 \end{bmatrix}$$

$$\begin{bmatrix} a \\ b \\ c \end{bmatrix} = \frac{1}{14} \begin{bmatrix} -42 \\ 14 \\ 84 \end{bmatrix}$$

$$\begin{bmatrix} a \\ b \\ c \end{bmatrix} = \begin{bmatrix} -3 \\ 1 \\ 6 \end{bmatrix} \quad (-3, 1, 6)$$

17. $\begin{vmatrix} 2 & -1 & -3 \\ 4 & 2 & 1 \\ 2 & 1 & -1 \end{vmatrix} = -4 + (-2) + (-12) - (-12)$
$$- 2 - 4$$
$$= -12$$

$$a = \frac{\begin{vmatrix} -20 & -1 & -3 \\ 6 & 2 & 1 \\ -6 & 1 & -1 \end{vmatrix}}{-12}$$

$$= \frac{40 + 6 (-18) - 36 - (-20) - 6}{-12} = -\frac{1}{2}$$

$$b = \frac{\begin{vmatrix} 2 & -20 & -3 \\ 4 & 6 & 1 \\ 2 & -6 & -1 \end{vmatrix}}{-12}$$

$$= \frac{-12 + (-40) + 72 - (-36) - (-12) - 80}{-12} = 1$$

$$c = \frac{\begin{vmatrix} 2 & -1 & -20 \\ 4 & 2 & 6 \\ 2 & 1 & -6 \end{vmatrix}}{-12}$$

$$= \frac{-24 + (-12) + (-80) - (-80) - 12 - 24}{-12} = 6$$

$$\left(-\frac{1}{2}, 1, 6\right)$$

18. $\begin{vmatrix} 2 & -1 & 3 \\ 1 & -1 & 4 \\ 3 & -2 & 1 \end{vmatrix} = -2 + (-12) + (-6) - (-9)$
$$- (-16) - (-1) = 6$$

$$x = \frac{\begin{vmatrix} 1 & -1 & 3 \\ 0 & -1 & 4 \\ -5 & -2 & 1 \end{vmatrix}}{6}$$

$$= \frac{-1 + 20 + 0 - 15 - (-8) - 0}{6}$$

$$= 2$$

$$y = \frac{\begin{vmatrix} 2 & 1 & 3 \\ 1 & 0 & 4 \\ 3 & -5 & 1 \end{vmatrix}}{6}$$

$$= \frac{0 + 12 + (-15) - 0 - (-40) - 1}{6}$$

$$= 6$$

$$z = \frac{\begin{vmatrix} 2 & -1 & 1 \\ 1 & -1 & 0 \\ 3 & -2 & -5 \end{vmatrix}}{6}$$

$$= \frac{10 + 0 + (-2) - (-3) - 0 - 5}{6}$$

$$= 1$$

$$(2, 6, 1)$$

19. $\begin{bmatrix} 1 & 5 & 1 \\ 2 & -3 & 15 \end{bmatrix} = \begin{bmatrix} 1 & 5 & 1 \\ 0 & -13 & 13 \end{bmatrix} = \begin{bmatrix} 1 & 5 & 1 \\ 0 & 1 & -1 \end{bmatrix}$

$$= \begin{bmatrix} 1 & 0 & 6 \\ 0 & 1 & -1 \end{bmatrix} \quad (6, -1)$$

20. $\begin{bmatrix} 1 & -2 & 1 & 6 \\ 3 & 2 & -1 & 0 \\ 2 & 1 & -6 & -2 \end{bmatrix} = \begin{bmatrix} 1 & -2 & 1 & 6 \\ 0 & 8 & -4 & -18 \\ 0 & 5 & -8 & -14 \end{bmatrix}$

$$= \begin{bmatrix} 1 & -2 & 1 & 6 \\ 0 & -16 & 8 & 36 \\ 0 & 5 & -8 & -14 \end{bmatrix} = \begin{bmatrix} 1 & -2 & 1 & 6 \\ 0 & -11 & 0 & 22 \\ 0 & 5 & -8 & -14 \end{bmatrix}$$

$$= \begin{bmatrix} 1 & -2 & 1 & 6 \\ 0 & 1 & 0 & -2 \\ 0 & 5 & -8 & -14 \end{bmatrix} = \begin{bmatrix} 1 & 0 & 1 & 2 \\ 0 & 1 & 0 & -2 \\ 0 & 0 & -8 & -4 \end{bmatrix}$$

$$= \begin{bmatrix} 1 & 0 & 1 & 2 \\ 0 & 1 & 0 & -2 \\ 0 & 0 & 1 & \frac{1}{2} \end{bmatrix} = \begin{bmatrix} 1 & 0 & 0 & \frac{3}{2} \\ 0 & 1 & 0 & -2 \\ 0 & 0 & 1 & \frac{1}{2} \end{bmatrix}$$

$$\left(\frac{3}{2}, -2, \frac{1}{2}\right)$$

21.

	Alan	Bill	Cathy
Soup	✔	X	X
Sandwich	X	X	✔
Salad	X	✔	X

Alan: soup, Bill: salad, Cathy: sandwich

22. $3\begin{bmatrix} 5 & -3 & -2 \\ -2 & 4 & -3 \end{bmatrix} = \begin{bmatrix} 15 & -9 & -6 \\ -6 & 12 & -9 \end{bmatrix}$

$A'(15, -6)$, $B'(-9, 12)$, $C'(-6, -9)$

23. $3\begin{bmatrix} 5 & -3 & -2 \\ -2 & 4 & -3 \end{bmatrix} + \begin{bmatrix} 4 & 4 & 4 \\ -1 & -1 & -1 \end{bmatrix} = \begin{bmatrix} 9 & 1 & 2 \\ -3 & 3 & -4 \end{bmatrix}$

$A'(9, -3)$, $B'(1, 3)$, $C'(2, -4)$

24. $A = \frac{1}{2}\begin{vmatrix} -2 & 6 & 1 \\ -3 & -2 & 1 \\ 3 & 5 & 1 \end{vmatrix} = \frac{1}{2}[4 + 18 + (-15) - (-6)$
$- (-10) - (-18)]$

$= \frac{1}{2}(41)$

$= 20.5 \quad 20.5 \text{ units}^2$

25. $\begin{bmatrix} 0 & -1 \\ 1 & 0 \end{bmatrix} \cdot \begin{bmatrix} 5 & -2 & 3 \\ 0 & 6 & -4 \end{bmatrix} = \begin{bmatrix} 0 & -6 & 4 \\ 5 & -2 & 3 \end{bmatrix}$

$M'(0, 5)$, $P'(-6, -2)$, $Q'(4, 3)$

26. Let s = amount in stocks.

Let b = amount in bonds.

Let t = amount in a term account.

$s + b + t = 29{,}000$

$s = b + t \quad \rightarrow \quad s - b - t = 0$

$(0.04)s + (0.06)b + (0.055)t = 1414$

$\begin{bmatrix} 1 & 1 & 1 & 29{,}000 \\ 1 & -1 & -1 & 0 \\ .04 & .06 & .055 & 1414 \end{bmatrix} = \begin{bmatrix} 2 & 0 & 0 & 29{,}000 \\ 1 & -1 & -1 & 0 \\ 0 & .1 & .095 & 1414 \end{bmatrix}$

$= \begin{bmatrix} 1 & 0 & 0 & 14{,}500 \\ 0 & -1 & 01 & -14{,}500 \\ 0 & .1 & .095 & 1414 \end{bmatrix} = \begin{bmatrix} 1 & 0 & 0 & 14{,}500 \\ 1 & 1 & -1 & 0 \\ 0 & 0 & -.005 & -36 \end{bmatrix}$

$= \begin{bmatrix} 1 & 0 & 0 & 14{,}500 \\ 0 & 1 & 1 & 14{,}500 \\ 0 & 0 & 1 & 7200 \end{bmatrix} = \begin{bmatrix} 1 & 0 & 0 & 14{,}500 \\ 0 & 1 & 0 & 7300 \\ 0 & 0 & 1 & 7200 \end{bmatrix}$

Stocks: $14,500; bonds: $7300;

term account: $7200

Chapter 4 Test

1. 3×3;

$\begin{vmatrix} 2 & -3 & 1 \\ 3 & -1 & 2 \\ 1 & 2 & -3 \end{vmatrix} = 6 - 6 + 6 + 1 - 8 - 27 = -28$

2. 2×4; no determinant

3. 3×3;

$\begin{vmatrix} 1 & 3 & 1 \\ 2 & 1 & -5 \\ 3 & -1 & -4 \end{vmatrix} = -4 - 45 - 2 - 3 - 5 + 24 = -35$

4. $\begin{bmatrix} 1 & 2 \\ -4 & 3 \\ 5 & 2 \end{bmatrix} \begin{bmatrix} 5 \\ 4 \end{bmatrix} = \begin{bmatrix} 13 \\ -8 \\ 33 \end{bmatrix}$

5. $\begin{bmatrix} 2 & -4 & 1 \\ 3 & 8 & -2 \end{bmatrix} - 2\begin{bmatrix} 1 & 2 & -4 \\ -2 & 3 & 7 \end{bmatrix}$

$= \begin{bmatrix} 2 & -4 & 1 \\ 3 & 8 & -2 \end{bmatrix} - \begin{bmatrix} 2 & 4 & -8 \\ -4 & 6 & 14 \end{bmatrix}$

$= \begin{bmatrix} 0 & -8 & 9 \\ 7 & 2 & -16 \end{bmatrix}$

6. $\begin{bmatrix} x \\ 2y \end{bmatrix} - 3\begin{bmatrix} y + 1 \\ 2x \end{bmatrix} = \begin{bmatrix} 5 \\ -16 \end{bmatrix}$

$\begin{array}{ll} x - 3(y + 1) = 5 & \rightarrow \quad x - 3y = 8 \\ \quad 2y - 6x = -16 & \qquad 3x - y = 8 \\ -3x + 9y = -24 & \qquad x - 3y = 8 \\ \underline{\quad 3x - y = 8} & \qquad x - 3(-2) = 8 \\ \qquad 8y = -16 & \qquad\qquad x = 2 \\ \qquad y = -2 & \end{array}$

7. $\det M = (5)(3) - (-2)(6) = 27$
$M^{-1} = \frac{1}{27}\begin{bmatrix} 3 & 2 \\ -6 & 5 \end{bmatrix}$

8. $\det M = 1(-7)(3) + 1(2)(-9) + 1(3)(21)$
$- (-9)(-7)(1)$
$= 21(2)(1) - 3(3)(1)$
$= -90$

$r = \dfrac{\begin{vmatrix} 7 & 1 & 1 \\ 11 & -7 & 2 \\ -3 & 21 & -3 \end{vmatrix}}{-90} = \dfrac{-270}{-90} = 3$

$s = \dfrac{\begin{vmatrix} 1 & 7 & 1 \\ 3 & 11 & 2 \\ -9 & -3 & 3 \end{vmatrix}}{-90} = \dfrac{-60}{-90} = \dfrac{2}{3}$

$$t = \frac{\begin{vmatrix} 1 & 1 & 7 \\ 3 & -7 & 11 \\ -9 & 21 & -3 \end{vmatrix}}{-90} = \frac{-300}{-90} = \frac{10}{3}$$

The solution is $\left(3,\ \dfrac{2}{3},\ \dfrac{10}{3}\right)$.

9. $\begin{bmatrix} 1 & 8 \\ 2 & -6 \end{bmatrix} \begin{bmatrix} x \\ y \end{bmatrix} = \begin{bmatrix} -3 \\ -17 \end{bmatrix}$;

$\dfrac{-1}{22} \begin{bmatrix} -6 & -8 \\ -2 & 1 \end{bmatrix} \begin{bmatrix} 1 & 8 \\ 2 & -6 \end{bmatrix} \begin{bmatrix} x \\ y \end{bmatrix} = \dfrac{-1}{22} \begin{bmatrix} -6 & -8 \\ -2 & 1 \end{bmatrix} \begin{bmatrix} -3 \\ -17 \end{bmatrix}$

$\begin{bmatrix} x \\ y \end{bmatrix} = \dfrac{-1}{22} \begin{bmatrix} 154 \\ -11 \end{bmatrix} \qquad \left(-7,\ \dfrac{1}{2}\right)$

10. $\begin{bmatrix} 6 & -1 & -15 \\ 5 & 2 & -4 \end{bmatrix} = \begin{bmatrix} 12 & -2 & -30 \\ 5 & 2 & -4 \end{bmatrix} = \begin{bmatrix} 17 & 0 & -34 \\ 5 & 2 & -4 \end{bmatrix}$

$= \begin{bmatrix} 1 & 0 & -2 \\ 5 & 2 & -4 \end{bmatrix} = \begin{bmatrix} 1 & 0 & -2 \\ 0 & 2 & 6 \end{bmatrix} = \begin{bmatrix} 1 & 0 & -2 \\ 0 & 1 & 3 \end{bmatrix}$

$(-2,\ 3)$

11. $\begin{bmatrix} 2 & -3 & 1 & 7 \\ 3 & -1 & 2 & 1 \\ 1 & 2 & -3 & -14 \end{bmatrix} = \begin{bmatrix} 1 & 2 & -3 & -14 \\ 2 & -3 & 1 & 7 \\ 3 & -1 & 2 & 1 \end{bmatrix}$

$= \begin{bmatrix} 1 & 2 & -3 & -14 \\ 0 & -7 & 7 & 35 \\ 0 & -7 & 11 & 43 \end{bmatrix} = \begin{bmatrix} 1 & 2 & -3 & -14 \\ 0 & -7 & 7 & 35 \\ 0 & 0 & 4 & 8 \end{bmatrix}$

$= \begin{bmatrix} 1 & 2 & -3 & -14 \\ 0 & 1 & -1 & -5 \\ 0 & 0 & 1 & 2 \end{bmatrix} = \begin{bmatrix} 1 & 2 & -3 & -14 \\ 0 & 1 & 0 & -3 \\ 0 & 0 & 1 & 2 \end{bmatrix}$

$= \begin{bmatrix} 1 & 0 & -3 & -8 \\ 0 & 1 & 0 & -3 \\ 0 & 0 & 1 & 2 \end{bmatrix} = \begin{bmatrix} 1 & 0 & 0 & -2 \\ 0 & 1 & 0 & -3 \\ 0 & 0 & 1 & 2 \end{bmatrix}$

$(-2,\ -3,\ 2)$

12. translation of x-coordinate: $1 + x = 3$

$x = 2$

translation of y-coordinate: $5 + y = 1$

$y = -4$

$\begin{bmatrix} 6 & 1 & -1 \\ 3 & 5 & 4 \end{bmatrix} + \begin{bmatrix} 2 & 2 & 2 \\ -4 & -4 & -4 \end{bmatrix} = \begin{bmatrix} 8 & 3 & 1 \\ -1 & 1 & 0 \end{bmatrix}$

$A'(8,\ -1),\ C'(1,\ 0)$

13. $5\begin{bmatrix} 6 & 1 & -1 \\ 3 & 5 & 4 \end{bmatrix} = \begin{bmatrix} 30 & 5 & -5 \\ 15 & 25 & 20 \end{bmatrix}$

$A'(30,\ 15),\ B'(5,\ 25),\ C'(-5,\ 20)$

14. $\begin{bmatrix} 0 & -1 \\ 1 & 0 \end{bmatrix} \cdot \begin{bmatrix} 6 & 1 & -1 \\ 3 & 5 & 4 \end{bmatrix} = \begin{bmatrix} -3 & -5 & -4 \\ 6 & 1 & -1 \end{bmatrix}$

$A'(-3,\ 6),\ B'(-5,\ 1),\ C'(-4,\ -1)$

PAGE 205   BONUS

inverse of the rotation matrix: $\begin{bmatrix} 0 & 1 \\ -1 & 0 \end{bmatrix}$

$\dfrac{1}{2} \cdot \begin{bmatrix} 0 & 1 \\ -1 & 0 \end{bmatrix} \cdot \begin{bmatrix} 6 & 1 & -1 \\ 3 & 5 & 4 \end{bmatrix} = \dfrac{1}{2}\begin{bmatrix} 3 & 5 & 4 \\ -6 & -1 & 1 \end{bmatrix}$

$= \begin{bmatrix} \frac{3}{2} & \frac{5}{2} & 2 \\ -3 & -\frac{1}{2} & \frac{1}{2} \end{bmatrix}$

$A'\left(1\frac{1}{2},\ -3\right),\ B'\left(2\frac{1}{2},\ -\frac{1}{2}\right),\ C'\left(2,\ \frac{1}{2}\right)$

Chapter 4
College Entrance Exam Preview

PAGES 206-207

1. 40% of 10 inches = 4 inches. There are 24 inches in 2 feet. $\dfrac{4}{24} = \dfrac{1}{6}$. 40% of 10 inches is one-sixth of 2 feet.

The correct choice is B.

2. Choice A is not possible since $\dfrac{a}{b} = \dfrac{c}{d}$.

Choice B is not possible since $\dfrac{a + b}{b} = \dfrac{a}{b} + 1 = \dfrac{c}{d} + 1 = \dfrac{c + d}{d} \neq \dfrac{c + b}{d}$.

Choice C implies $ad = bc$ which implies $\dfrac{a}{b} = \dfrac{c}{d}$ which was given.

Choice D implies $ab + b^2 = ad + d^2$ which does not follow from what was given.

The correct choice is C.

3. Let x = percent increase.

$250x + 250 = 300$

$250x = 50$

$x = 0.20$ or 20%

The correct choice is B.

4. Let x = percent decrease.

$90 - 90x = 75$

$90x = 15$

$x = 0.16\overline{6}$ or $16\frac{2}{3}\%$

The correct choice is A.

5. Let x = the number.

$0.06x = 9$

$x = 150$

The correct choice is D.

6. $\dfrac{x}{y} = \dfrac{5}{6} \;\rightarrow\;$
$\quad\quad\quad\; 6x = 5y$
$\quad\quad\quad 3(6x) = 3(5y)$
$\quad\quad\quad\; 18x = 15y$

The correct choice is C.

7. Let x = original price.

The price after the first reduction is $x - 0.20x$. The price after the second reduction is $(x - 0.20x) - 0.05(x - 0.20x) = x - 0.24x$. So, the two reductions are equivalent to a reduction of 24%.

The correct choice is B.

8. Let x = number of gallons the tank will hold.

$\dfrac{1}{4}x + 10 = \dfrac{7}{8}x$

$\quad\quad\;\; \dfrac{5}{8}x = 10$

$\quad\quad\quad\;\; x = 16$

The correct choice is A.

9. Let x = Jean's weight and y = Jim's weight.

$\dfrac{x}{y} = \dfrac{3}{4} \quad\rightarrow\quad\quad\quad\quad x = \dfrac{3}{4}y$

$\dfrac{x + 30}{y} = \dfrac{7}{8} \quad\quad\quad \dfrac{\frac{3}{4}y + 30}{y} = \dfrac{7}{8}$

$\quad\quad\quad\quad\quad\quad\quad\quad 6y + 240 = 7y$

$\quad\quad\quad\quad\quad\quad\quad\quad\;\; 240 = y$

The correct choice is D.

10. Work backward to find the solution. Jan attended 3 times as many events as George did, or 24 events. Joe attended $\dfrac{1}{2}$ as many as Jan, or 12 events.

The correct choice is D.

11. $\dfrac{1}{9} = \dfrac{x}{0.45}$

$0.45 = 9x$

$0.05 = x$

The correct choice is A.

12. The number of students who are not honor students is 54 - 12 or 42 students.

$\dfrac{42}{54} = \dfrac{7}{9}.$

The correct choice is B.

13. Let x = the number.

$0.22\,(440) = 0.044x$

$\quad\quad\; 2200 = x$

The correct choice is D.

14. Let x = the percent.

$0.75(10a) = b \quad\quad x[2(7.5a)] = a$

$\quad\; x(2b) = a \quad\quad\quad\quad x = 0.066\overline{6} \text{ or } 6\dfrac{2}{3}\%$

The correct choice is B.

15. Consider the amounts remaining after each transaction; he has $\dfrac{3}{5}$ of $\dfrac{3}{4}$ of the original, or $\dfrac{9}{20}$.

The correct choice is C.

16. $\dfrac{0.4}{100} = \dfrac{4}{1000} = \dfrac{1}{250}$

The correct choice is A.

17. $\dfrac{\frac{1}{2}}{100}\,(500) = \dfrac{1}{2}(5) = 2.5$

The correct choice is D.

18. $\quad 3n = m$

$\dfrac{2}{3}(3n) = \dfrac{2}{3}m$

$\quad\; 2n = \dfrac{2}{3}m$

The correct choice is A.

19. Let x = Ms. Kwan's sales.

$300 + 0.06x = 345$

$\quad\quad\; 0.06x = 45$

$\quad\quad\quad\quad x = 750$

The correct choice is C.

20. $A_1 = 3^2 = 9$

$A_2 = \left(1\dfrac{1}{4}\right)^2 = \dfrac{25}{16}$

$\dfrac{A_1}{A_2} = \dfrac{9}{\frac{25}{16}}$

$\quad\;\; = \dfrac{144}{25}$

144:25

The correct choice is D.

21. $\dfrac{t}{100}(8) = \dfrac{2t}{25}$

The correct choice is A.

Chapter 5 Polynomials

5-1 Monomials

CHECKING FOR UNDERSTANDING

1. No, $(4x)^2 = (4x)(4x) = 16x^2 \neq 4x^2$
2. Negative; a negative number raised to an odd power is negative.
3. $4g$
4. yes, 3, 1
5. yes, 1, 2
6. no
7. yes, -5, 2
8. yes, $\frac{11}{7}$, 2
9. no
10. yes, 5, 9
11. yes, 0, none
12. no
13. 8.104×10^2
14. 2.1×10^3
15. 9×10^9
16. 7.865×10^8
17. 7.21×10^7
18. 5.28×10^5
19. 42,000
20. 254.1
21. 57
22. 42.7
23. 3,210,000
24. 72,000

PAGES 213-214   **EXERCISES**

25. $3x + 2x + (-4x)$
$= 5x + (-4x)$
$= x$

26. $4d^3 - d^3 + 2d^3$
$= 3d^3 + 2d^3$
$= 5d^3$

27. $4ab^2 - 3ab^2 = ab^2$

28. $3x^2 + 4 - 3x^2$
$= 3x^2 - 3x^2 + 4$
$= 4$

29. $y^5 \cdot y^7 = y^{5+7}$
$= y^{12}$

30. $b^4 \cdot b^3 \cdot b^2 = b^{4+3+2}$
$= b^9$

31. $8^6 \cdot 8^4 \cdot (8^2)^2$
$= 8^{6+4} \cdot 8^{2 \cdot 2}$
$= 8^{10} \cdot 8^4$
$= 8^{10+4}$
$= 8^{14}$

32. $(y^5)^2 = y^{5 \cdot 2}$
$= y^{10}$

33. $(3a)^4$
$= (3a)(3a)(3a)(3a)$
$= 3^4 a^4$
$= 81a^4$

34. $(x^2 y^2)^2 x^3 y^3$
$= x^{2 \cdot 2} y^{2 \cdot 2} x^3 y^3$
$= x^4 y^4 x^3 y^3$
$= x^{4+3} y^{4+3}$
$= x^7 y^7$

35. $\left(-\frac{3}{4}x^2 y^3\right)^2 \left(\frac{8}{9}xy^4\right)$
$= \left(-\frac{3}{4}\right)^2 (x^{2 \cdot 2})(y^{3 \cdot 2})\left(\frac{8}{9}xy^4\right)$
$= \frac{9}{16}x^4 y^6 \cdot \frac{8}{9}xy^4$
$= \frac{9}{16} \cdot \frac{8}{9}x^{4+1} y^{6+4}$
$= \frac{1}{2}x^5 y^{10}$

36. $\left(\frac{3}{5}c^2 f\right)\left(\frac{4}{3}cd\right)^2$
$= \left(\frac{3}{5}c^2 f\right)\left(\frac{4}{3}\right)^2 c^2 d^2$
$= \frac{3}{5}c^2 f\frac{16}{9}c^2 d^2$
$= \frac{3}{5} \cdot \frac{16}{9} \cdot c^{2+2}d^2 f$
$= \frac{16}{15}c^4 d^2 f$

37. $(-4a)(a^2)(-a^3) + 3a^2(a^4)$
$= (-4)a \cdot a^2 \cdot (-1)a^3 + 3a^2 \cdot a^4$
$= 4a^{1+2+3} + 3a^{2+4}$
$= 4a^6 + 3a^6$
$= 7a^6$

38. $2(rk)^2 5(rt^2) - k(2rk)(2rt)^2$
$= 2 \cdot 5 \cdot r^2 k^2 \cdot rt^2 - 2rk^{1+1}(2)^2 r^2 t^2$
$= 10r^{2+1}k^2 t^2 - 2 \cdot 4r \cdot r^2 \cdot k^2 \cdot t^2$
$= 10r^3 k^2 t^2 - 8r^{1+2}k^2 \cdot t^2$
$= 10r^3 k^2 t^2 - 8r^3 k^2 t^2$
$= 2r^3 k^2 t^2$

39. $(5a)(6a^2 b)(3ab^3) + (4a^2)(3b^3)(2a^2 b)$
$= 5 \cdot 6 \cdot 3 \cdot a \cdot a^2 \cdot a \cdot b \cdot b^3 +$
$\quad 4 \cdot 3 \cdot 2 \cdot a^2 \cdot a^2 \cdot b^3 \cdot b$
$= 90a^{1+2+1}b^{1+3} + 24a^{2+2}b^{3+1}$
$= 90a^4 b^4 + 24a^4 b^4$
$= 114a^4 b^4$

40. $(5mn^2)(m^3 n)(-3p^2) + (8np)(3mp)(m^3 n^2)$
$= 5(-3) \cdot m \cdot m^3 \cdot n^2 \cdot n \cdot p^2 +$
$\quad 8 \cdot 3 \cdot m \cdot m^3 \cdot n \cdot n^2 \cdot p \cdot p$
$= (-15)m^{1+3}n^{2+1}p^2 + 24m^{1+3}n^{1+2} + p^{1+1}$
$= (-15)m^4 n^3 p^2 + 24m^4 n^3 p^2$
$= 9m^4 n^3 p^2$

41. $(9.5 \times 10^3)(9.5 \times 10^3)$

    $= (9.5 \times 9.5)(10^3 \times 10^3)$

    $= 90.25 \times 10^{3+3}$

    $= 90.25 \times 10^6$

    $= 9.025 \times 10^7$

    $= 90,250,000$

42. $(7.2 \times 10^5)(8.1 \times 10^3)$

    $= (7.2 \times 8.1)(10^5 \times 10^3)$

    $= 58.32 \times 10^{5+3}$

    $= 58.32 \times 10^8$

    $= 5.832 \times 10^9$

    $= 5,832,000,000$

43. $(4.5 \times 10^3)(7.0 \times 10^2)$

    $= (4.5 \times 7.0)(10^3 \times 10^2)$

    $= 31.5 \times 10^{3+2}$

    $= 31.5 \times 10^5$

    $= 3.15 \times 10^6$

    $= 3,150,000$

44. $(2.5 \times 10^2)(1.1 \times 10^2)$

    $= (2.5 \times 1.1)(10^2 \times 10^2)$

    $= 2.75 \times 10^{2+2}$

    $= 2.75 \times 10^4$

    $= 27,500$

45. $(34,000)(0.0056)$

    $= (3.4 \times 10^4)(5.6 \times 10^{-3})$

    $= (3.4 \times 5.6)(10^4 \times 10^{-3})$

    $= 19.04 \times 10^{4+(-3)}$

    $= 19.04 \times 10^1$

    $= 1.904 \times 10^2$

    $= 190.4$

46. $(4,300)(0.02)$

    $= (4.3 \times 10^3)(2 \times 10^{-2})$

    $= (4.3 \times 2)(10^3 \times 10^{-2})$

    $= 8.6 \times 10^{3+(-2)}$

    $= 8.6 \times 10^1$

    $= 86$

47. $(3,000)(82,500)$

    $= (3 \times 10^3)(8.25 \times 10^4)$

    $= (3 \times 8.25)(10^3 \times 10^4)$

    $= 24.75 \times 10^{3+4}$

    $= 24.75 \times 10^7$

    $= 2.475 \times 10^8$

    $= 247,500,000$

48. $(45,000)(0.0025)$

    $= (4.5 \times 10^4)(2.5 \times 10^{-3})$

    $= (4.5 \times 2.5)(10^4 \times 10^{-3})$

    $= 11.25 \times 10^{4+(-3)}$

    $= 11.25 \times 10^1$

    $= 1.125 \times 10^2$

    $= 112.5$

49. $(4.4 \times 10^5) - (3.2 \times 10^5)$

    $= (4.4 - 3.2)10^5$

    $= 1.2 \times 10^5$

    $= 120,000$

50. $1.2 \times 10^3 - 1.2 \times 10^2$

    $= 1.2 \times 10^3 - 0.12 \times 10^3$

    $= (1.2 - 0.12)10^3$

    $= 1.08 \times 10^3$

    $= 1,080$

51. What is the least integer that has factors of 2, 3, 6, and 9? 18.

    So, 2^{18} is the least integer greater than one that contains these powers.

    $262,144 = 512^2 = 64^3 = 8^6 = 4^9 = 2^{18}$

52. 10^{100} is greater.

    $100^{10} = (10^2)^{10} = 10^{20} < 10^{100}$

53. rate $\times$ time = distance

    $3.00 \times 10^5 \times 1.25 = d$

    $(3.00 \times 1.25)(10^5) = d$

        $3.75 \times 10^5 = d$ 3.75×10^5 kilometers

54. (number of molecules)

    = (number of moles) $\times 6.02 \times 10^{23}$

    $= 19.9 \times 6.02 \times 10^{23}$

    $= 119.798 \times 10^{23}$

    $= 1.19798 \times 10^{25}$

    about 1.20×10^{25} molecules

55. Multiply row 3 by −1 and add to row 1.
Multiply row 1 by −2 and add to row 2.
Multiply row 1 by −3 and add to row 3.
Multiply row 2 by −5 and add to row 3.
Multiply row 2 by −1.

$$\begin{bmatrix} 4 & -1 & 1 & 6 \\ 2 & 1 & 2 & 3 \\ 3 & -2 & 1 & 3 \end{bmatrix} = \begin{bmatrix} 1 & 1 & 0 & 3 \\ 2 & 1 & 2 & 3 \\ 3 & -2 & 1 & 3 \end{bmatrix} = \begin{bmatrix} 1 & 1 & 0 & 3 \\ 0 & -1 & 2 & -3 \\ 3 & -2 & 1 & 3 \end{bmatrix} =$$

$$\begin{bmatrix} 1 & 1 & 0 & 3 \\ 0 & -1 & 2 & -3 \\ 0 & -5 & 1 & -6 \end{bmatrix} = \begin{bmatrix} 1 & 1 & 0 & 3 \\ 0 & -1 & 2 & -3 \\ 0 & 0 & -9 & 9 \end{bmatrix} = \begin{bmatrix} 1 & 1 & 0 & 3 \\ 0 & 1 & -2 & 3 \\ 0 & 0 & -9 & 9 \end{bmatrix}$$

$-9z = 9$ $y - 2(-1) = 3$ $x + 1 = 3$

$z = -1$ $y + 2 = 3$ $x = 2$

$y = 1$

The solution is (2, 1, −1).

56. Add row 1 to row 2. Multiply row 1 by −2 and add to row 3. Multiply row 2 by $\frac{1}{8}$. Multiply row 2 by 6 and add to row 3.

$$\begin{bmatrix} 1 & 3 & -2 & 9 \\ -1 & 5 & 2 & 31 \\ 2 & 0 & -9 & -32 \end{bmatrix} = \begin{bmatrix} 1 & 3 & -2 & 9 \\ 0 & 8 & 0 & 40 \\ 2 & 0 & -9 & -32 \end{bmatrix} = \begin{bmatrix} 1 & 3 & -2 & 9 \\ 0 & 8 & 0 & 40 \\ 0 & -6 & -5 & -50 \end{bmatrix} =$$

$$\begin{bmatrix} 1 & 3 & -2 & 9 \\ 0 & 1 & 0 & 5 \\ 0 & -6 & -5 & -50 \end{bmatrix} = \begin{bmatrix} 1 & 3 & -2 & 9 \\ 0 & 1 & 0 & 5 \\ 0 & 0 & -5 & -20 \end{bmatrix}$$

$y = 5$ $-5z = -20$ $x + 3(5) - 2(4) = 9$

$z = 4$ $x + 7 = 9$

$x = 2$

The solution is (2, 5, 4).

57. $x + y = 42$ and $x - y = 12$. Solve by first adding the equations to eliminate a variable.

$x + y = 42$ $27 + y = 42$

$x - y = 12$ $y = 15$

$2x = 54$

$x = 27$

The numbers are 27 and 15.

58. $3x + 4y = 16$

$4y = 16 - 3x$

$y = 4 - \frac{3}{4}x$

59. $x + 1 \le 3$ $x + 1 \ge -3$

$x \le 2$ $x \ge -4$

$\{x | -4 \le x \le 2\}$

60. Yes; you can't get a total score of 1.

5-2 Dividing Monomials

PAGE 218   CHECKING FOR UNDERSTANDING

1. 0^n for $n > 0 = 0$, 0^n for $n \le 0$ is undefined. No factor of 0 can produce a 1.

2. $\frac{1}{7^3}$ 3. No, $2(x^2y)^3 = 2x^6y^3$.

4. rate × time = distance

$3.00 \times 10^5 \times t = 4.58 \times 10^9$

$t = \dfrac{4.58 \times 10^9}{3.00 \times 10^5}$

$= \left(\dfrac{4.58}{3.00}\right)\left(\dfrac{10^9}{10^5}\right)$

$= 1.5267(10^{9-5})$

$= 1.5267 \times 10^4$

1.53×10^4 seconds or about 4 hours, 15 minutes

5. $\dfrac{x^5}{x^3} = x^{5-3}$ 6. $\dfrac{n^4}{n^4} = n^{4-4}$

$= x^2$ $= n^0$

$= 1$

7. $\dfrac{r^4}{r} = r^{4-1}$ 8. $\dfrac{t^6}{t^8} = t^{6-8}$

$= r^3$ $= t^{-2}$ or $\dfrac{1}{t^2}$

9. $\dfrac{5y^{10}}{y^{13}} = 5(y^{10-13})$ 10. $\dfrac{1}{m^{-2}} = m^2$

$= 5y^{-3}$ or $\dfrac{5}{y^3}$

11. $\dfrac{3^{-3}}{3^{-2}} = 3^{-3+2}$ 12. $\left(\dfrac{1}{2}\right)^{-2} = 2^2$ or 4

$= 3^{-1}$ or $\dfrac{1}{3}$

13. $\left(\dfrac{2}{3}\right)^0 = \dfrac{2^0}{3^0}$ 14. $\left(\dfrac{3}{b}\right)^6 = \dfrac{3^6}{b^6}$

$= \dfrac{1}{1}$ or 1 $= \dfrac{729}{b^6}$

15. $\left(\dfrac{1}{10}\right)^{-4} = 10^4$ 16. $\left(\dfrac{k}{4}\right)^{-3} = \left(\dfrac{4}{k}\right)^3$

$= 10{,}000$ $= \dfrac{4^3}{k^3}$

$= \dfrac{64}{k^3}$

PAGES 218-219   EXERCISES

17. $t^{-2}t^4 = t^{-2+4}$ 18. $m^{-8}m^3 = m^{-8+3}$

$= t^2$ $= m^{-5}$ or $\dfrac{1}{m^5}$

19. $\dfrac{12x^8}{4x^3} = \left(\dfrac{12}{4}\right)\left(\dfrac{x^8}{x^3}\right)$ 20. $\dfrac{an^6}{n^5} = a\left(\dfrac{n^6}{n^5}\right)$

$= 3(x^{8-3})$ $= a(n^{6-5})$

$= 3x^5$ $= an^1$ or an

21. $\dfrac{-24s^8}{2s^5} = \left(\dfrac{-24}{2}\right)\left(\dfrac{s^8}{s^5}\right)$

$= -12(s^{8-5})$

$= -12s^3$

22. $\dfrac{6mn^2}{3m} = \left(\dfrac{6}{3}\right)\left(\dfrac{m}{m}\right)n^2$

$= 2 \cdot 1 \cdot n^2$

$= 2n^2$

23. $\dfrac{xy^7}{x^4} = \left(\dfrac{x}{x^4}\right)y^7$

$= x^{-3}y^7$ or $\dfrac{y^7}{x^3}$

24. $\dfrac{48a^8}{12a^{11}} = \left(\dfrac{48}{12}\right)\left(\dfrac{a^8}{a^{11}}\right)$

$= 4a^{-3}$ or $\dfrac{4}{a^3}$

25. $\dfrac{4z^3}{28z^5} = \left(\dfrac{4}{28}\right)\left(\dfrac{z^3}{z^5}\right)$

$= \dfrac{1}{7}z^{-2}$ or $\dfrac{1}{7z^2}$

26. $\dfrac{-15r^4}{30r^3} = \left(\dfrac{-15}{30}\right)\left(\dfrac{r^4}{r^3}\right)$

$= \left(-\dfrac{1}{2}\right)r$ or $-\dfrac{r}{2}$

27. $\dfrac{12b^4}{60b^6} = \left(\dfrac{12}{60}\right)\left(\dfrac{b^4}{b^6}\right)$

$= \dfrac{1}{5}b^{-2}$ or $\dfrac{1}{5b^2}$

28. $\dfrac{2x^{-3}}{6(x^2)^2} = \left(\dfrac{2}{6}\right)\left(\dfrac{x^{-3}}{x^{2\cdot2}}\right)$

$= \dfrac{1}{3}x^{-7}$ or $\dfrac{1}{3x^7}$

29. $\dfrac{16b^6c^5}{4b^4c^2}$

$= \left(\dfrac{16}{4}\right)\left(\dfrac{b^6}{b^4}\right)\left(\dfrac{c^5}{c^2}\right)$

$= 4b^2c^3$

30. $\dfrac{8(k^{-2})^2}{4k^{-2}} = \left(\dfrac{8}{4}\right)\left(\dfrac{k^{(-2)\cdot2}}{k^{-2}}\right)$

$= 2(k^{-4-(-2)})$

$= 2k^{-2}$ or $\dfrac{2}{k^2}$

31. $\dfrac{1}{x^0 + y^0} = \dfrac{1}{1 + 1}$

$= \dfrac{1}{2}$

32. $\dfrac{-27w^3t^7}{-3w^3t^{12}}$

$= \left(\dfrac{-27}{-3}\right)\left(\dfrac{w^3}{w^3}\right)\left(\dfrac{t^7}{t^{12}}\right)$

$= 9(1)(t^{-5})$

$= 9t^{-5}$ or $\dfrac{9}{t^5}$

33. $\dfrac{-15r^5s^2}{5r^5s^{-4}}$

$= \left(\dfrac{-15}{5}\right)\left(\dfrac{r^5}{r^5}\right)\left(\dfrac{s^2}{s^{-4}}\right)$

$= -3r^0s^6$

$= -3s^6$

34. $\dfrac{8}{m^0 + n^0} = \dfrac{8}{1 + 1}$

$= \dfrac{8}{2}$ or 4

35. $\dfrac{-2c^3d^6}{24c^2d^2}$

$= \left(\dfrac{-2}{24}\right)\left(\dfrac{c^3}{c^2}\right)\left(\dfrac{d^6}{d^2}\right)$

$= -\dfrac{1}{12}cd^4$ or $-\dfrac{cd^4}{12}$

36. $\dfrac{(3c^2)^2(-d^5)}{-45c^7d^3}$

$= \left(\dfrac{3^2}{-45}\right)\left(\dfrac{c^4}{c^7}\right)\left(\dfrac{-d^5}{d^3}\right)$

$= \left(-\dfrac{1}{5}\right)(c^{-3})(-1)(d^2)$

$= \dfrac{1}{5}c^{-3}d^2$ or $\dfrac{d^2}{5c^3}$

37. $\dfrac{20a^5b^9}{20ab^7}$

$= \left(\dfrac{20}{20}\right)\left(\dfrac{a^5}{a}\right)\left(\dfrac{b^9}{b^7}\right)$

$= a^4b^2$

38. $\dfrac{16s^6t^5}{(2s^2t)^2} = \dfrac{16s^6t^5}{2^2s^4t^2}$

$= \left(\dfrac{16}{4}\right)\left(\dfrac{s^6}{s^4}\right)\left(\dfrac{t^5}{t^2}\right)$

$= 4s^2t^3$

39. $\dfrac{3^{xy+5}}{3^{xy}} = 3^{(xy+5-xy)}$

$= 3^5 = 243$

40. $\dfrac{s^{3x}}{s^{3x-2}} = s^{3x-(3x-2)}$

$= s^2$

41. $\dfrac{5^{2x}}{5^{2x+2}} = 5^{2x-(2x+2)}$

$= 5^{-2}$

$= \dfrac{1}{5^2}$ or $\dfrac{1}{25}$

42. $(m^4n^5)^{-2} = (m^4)^{-2}(n^5)^{-2}$

$= m^{-8}n^{-10}$ or

$\dfrac{1}{m^8n^{10}}$

43. $36a^3b^5(12a^2b^2)^{-1}$

$= \dfrac{36a^3b^5}{12a^2b^2}$

$= \left(\dfrac{36}{12}\right)\left(\dfrac{a^3}{a^2}\right)\left(\dfrac{b^5}{b^2}\right)$

$= 3ab^3$

44. $3^3x^3y^3(3x)^{-2} = \dfrac{27x^3y^3}{3^2x^2}$

$= \left(\dfrac{27}{9}\right)\left(\dfrac{x^3}{x^2}\right)y^3$

$= 3xy^3$

45. $\left(\dfrac{a}{b^{-1}}\right)^{-1} = (ab)^{-1}$

$= \dfrac{1}{ab}$

46. $\left(\dfrac{x}{y^{-1}z^2}\right)^{-1} = \left(\dfrac{xy}{z^2}\right)^{-1}$

$= \dfrac{z^2}{xy}$

47. $\left(\dfrac{1}{5}\right)^{-2} + \left(\dfrac{1}{4}\right)^{-1}$

$= 5^2 + 4$

$= 25 + 4$

$= 29$

48. $\dfrac{-15m^5n^8(m^3n^2)}{45m^4n}$

$= \dfrac{-15m^8n^{10}}{45m^4n}$

$= \left(-\dfrac{15}{45}\right)\left(\dfrac{m^8}{m^4}\right)\left(\dfrac{n^{10}}{n}\right)$

$= -\dfrac{1}{3}m^4n^9$ or $-\dfrac{m^4n^9}{3}$

49. $\dfrac{(-2t^3)^2(t^{-2})^{-1}}{(t^2)^{-3}}$

$= \dfrac{4t^6t^2}{t^{-6}}$

$= 4\left(\dfrac{t^8}{t^{-6}}\right)$

$= 4t^{14}$

50. $\dfrac{(4x^3y)(4^2x^{-1}y)}{4^3xy^2}$

$= \dfrac{(4 \cdot 16)(x^3x^{-1})(y \cdot y)}{64xy^2}$

$= \left(\dfrac{64}{64}\right)\left(\dfrac{x^2}{x}\right)\left(\dfrac{y^2}{y^2}\right)$

$= x^1y^0$

$= x$

51. $\left(\dfrac{-3y^4}{2y^2}\right)^{-2} = \left(\dfrac{2y^2}{-3y^4}\right)^2$

$= \dfrac{4y^4}{9y^8}$

$= \left(\dfrac{4}{9}\right)\left(\dfrac{y^4}{y^8}\right)$

$= \dfrac{4}{9}y^{-4}$ or $\dfrac{4}{9y^4}$

52. $\left(\dfrac{1}{2}\right)^{-2} + \left(\dfrac{1}{3}\right)^2 = 2^2 + \dfrac{1}{9}$

$= 4\dfrac{1}{9}$

53. $\dfrac{8 \times 10^{-1}}{16 \times 10^{-2}}$

$= \left(\dfrac{8}{16}\right)\left(\dfrac{10^{-1}}{10^{-2}}\right)$

$= 0.5 \times 10$

$= 5 \times 10^0$

$= 5$

54. $\dfrac{15 \times 10^4}{6 \times 10^{-2}} = \left(\dfrac{15}{6}\right)\left(\dfrac{10^4}{10^{-2}}\right)$

$= \dfrac{5}{2}(10^6)$

$= 2.5 \times 10^6$

$= 2,500,000$

55. $(4.5 \times 10^3)(7.5 \times 10^2)^{-1}$

$= \dfrac{4.5 \times 10^3}{7.5 \times 10^2}$

$= 0.6 \times 10^1$

$= 6 \times 10^0$

$= 6$

56. $(6.9 \times 10^3)(1.4 \times 10^3)^{-1}$

$= \dfrac{6.9 \times 10^3}{1.4 \times 10^3}$

$= 4.93 \times 10^0$

$= 4.93$

57. $\dfrac{0.000000036}{0.00011}$

$= \dfrac{3.6 \times 10^{-8}}{1.1 \times 10^{-4}}$

$= 3.\overline{27} \times 10^{-4}$

$= 0.0003\overline{27}$

58. $\dfrac{5,600,000,000}{60,000}$

$= \dfrac{5.6 \times 10^9}{6.0 \times 10^4}$

$= 0.9\overline{3} \times 10^5$

$= 9.\overline{3} \times 10^4$

$= 93,333.\overline{3}$

59. $\dfrac{(84,000,000)(0.00004)}{0.0016}$

$= \dfrac{(8.4 \times 10^7)(4.0 \times 10^{-5})}{1.6 \times 10^{-3}}$

$= \dfrac{33.6 \times 10^2}{1.6 \times 10^{-3}}$

$= 21 \times 10^5$

$= 2.1 \times 10^6$

$= 2,100,000$

60. $\dfrac{(93,000,000)(0.0005)}{0.0015}$

$= \dfrac{(9.3 \times 10^7)(5.0 \times 10^{-4})}{1.5 \times 10^{-3}}$

$= \dfrac{46.5 \times 10^3}{1.5 \times 10^{-3}}$

$= 31 \times 10^6$

$= 3.1 \times 10^7$

$= 31,000,000$

61. $\dfrac{x + x^2 + x^3 + x^4 + x^5 + x^6 + x^7}{x^{-3} + x^{-4} + x^{-5} + x^{-6} + x^{-7} + x^{-8} + x^{-9}}$

Simplifying the denominator: divide by x^{-10}

Denominator $= \left(\dfrac{x^{-3}}{x^{-10}} + \dfrac{x^{-4}}{x^{-10}} + \dfrac{x^{-5}}{x^{-10}} + \dfrac{x^{-6}}{x^{-10}} + \dfrac{x^{-7}}{x^{-10}} \right.$

$\left. + \dfrac{x^{-8}}{x^{-10}} + \dfrac{x^{-9}}{x^{-10}}\right)(x^{-10})$

$= (x^{-10})(x^7 + x^6 + x^5 + x^4 + x^3 + x^2 + x)$

Substitute into the equation:

$\dfrac{x + x^2 + x^3 + x^4 + x^5 + x^6 + x^7}{(x^{-10})(x + x^2 + x^3 + x^4 + x^5 + x^6 + x^7)} = \dfrac{1}{x^{-10}}$

$= x^{10}$

62. $r \times t = d$

$(3.00 \times 10^5) \times t = 1.496 \times 10^8$

$t = \dfrac{1.496 \times 10^8}{3.00 \times 10^5}$

$= 0.498\overline{6} \times 10^3$

$= 4.98\overline{6} \times 10^2$

$4.98\overline{6} \times 10^2$ seconds or about 8 minutes 19 seconds

63. $r \times t = d$

$(3.00 \times 10^5) \times t = 36$

$t = \dfrac{36}{3.00 \times 10^5}$

$= \dfrac{3.6 \times 10^1}{3.00 \times 10^5}$

$= 1.2 \times 10^{-4}$

0.00012 seconds

64. $(5 \times 10^6)(9 \times 10^2)$

$= (5 \times 9)(10^6 \times 10^2)$

$= 45 \times 10^8$

$= 4.5 \times 10^9$

$= 4,500,000,000$

65. $(1.5 \times 10^3)^4$

$= (1.5)^4(10^3)^4$

$= 5.0625 \times 10^{12}$

$= 5,062,500,000,000$

66. $AB = \begin{bmatrix} 2 & -3 \\ 1 & 4 \end{bmatrix}\begin{bmatrix} -4 & 0 \\ 2 & 5 \end{bmatrix}$

$= \begin{bmatrix} 2(-4) + (-3)2 & 2(0) + (-3)5 \\ 1(-4) + 4(2) & 1(0) + 4(5) \end{bmatrix}$

$= \begin{bmatrix} -14 & -15 \\ 4 & 20 \end{bmatrix}$

67. octant 2

68. Multiply equation 1 by 3 and equation 2 by 4 OR multiply equation 1 by 4 and equation 2 by -3.

69. $\frac{1}{4}x = 2y - 1$

$x = 8y - 4$

$x - 8y = -4$

70. $2|-3(5)| - 9 = 2(15) - 9$

$= 30 - 9 = 21$

5-3 Problem-Solving Strategy: Draw a Diagram

PAGE 221   CHECKING FOR UNDERSTANDING

1. $w + 5w + w + 5w = 42$

$12w = 42$

$w = 3.5$

$4(5w) = 4(5 \times 3.5) = 4 \times 17.5 = 70$

70 meters

2. the length of a side of the original square

3. one fourth

4.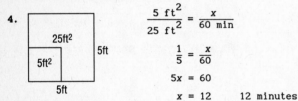

$\frac{5 \text{ ft}^2}{25 \text{ ft}^2} = \frac{x}{60 \text{ min}}$

$\frac{1}{5} = \frac{x}{60}$

$5x = 60$

$x = 12$ 12 minutes

5.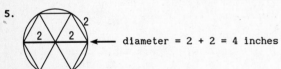

diameter = 2 + 2 = 4 inches

6.

Asheville ———————|———————————— Indianapolis
            Fell asleep

Let d = total distance from Asheville to Indianapolis.

Let t = distance traveled while asleep.

$d = 1$ for whole distance

$d = \frac{1}{2} + t + \frac{1}{2}t$

$1 = \frac{1}{2} + \frac{3}{2}t$

$\frac{1}{2} = \frac{3}{2}t$

$\frac{1}{3} = t$ Carole was asleep $\frac{1}{3}$ of the trip.

PAGE 222   EXERCISES

7.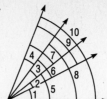

10 acute angles

8. Let c = number correct.

Let w = number wrong.

$c + w = 15 \Rightarrow 2c + 2w = 30$

$5c - 2w = 61$ $\underline{5c - 2w = 61}$

$7c = 91$

$c = 13$

13 correct

9.

10. By trial and error, $A = 1$, $B = 4$, $C = 8$.

11. Any line in the plane of a square that passes through the point of intersection of the diagonals of the square separates the square into two congruent parts, so there are infinitely many ways.

12. The sum of the squares of the sides of a parallelogram is equal to the sum of the squares of its diagonals.

Let c = the length of one diagonal and d = the length of the other diagonal.

$9^2 + 7^2 + 9^2 + 7^2 = c^2 + d^2$

$260 = c^2 + d^2$

The two integral pairs whose squares equal 260 are (16, 2) and (14, 8). The triangle inequality rules out (16, 2). So the lengths of the diagonals are 14 and 8.

13. $96 = 100 - 4 = 10^2 - 2^2$

$96 = 121 - 25 = 11^2 - 5^2$

$96 = 196 - 100 = 14^2 - 10^2$

$96 = 625 - 529 = 25^2 - 23^2$

14. $13^2 = (5)^2 + h^2$

$169 = 25 + h^2$

$169 - 25 = h^2$

$144 = h^2$

$\pm 12 = h$

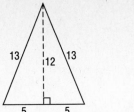

$A = \frac{1}{2}bh$

$A = \frac{1}{2}(10)(12)$

$A = 60$

Let $2x$ = the length of the base of the second triangle and y = the length of the height.

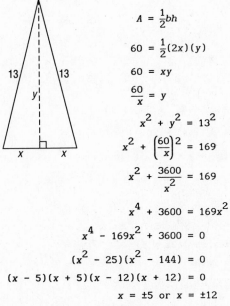

$A = \frac{1}{2}bh$

$60 = \frac{1}{2}(2x)(y)$

$60 = xy$

$\frac{60}{x} = y$

$x^2 + y^2 = 13^2$

$x^2 + \left(\frac{60}{x}\right)^2 = 169$

$x^2 + \frac{3600}{x^2} = 169$

$x^4 + 3600 = 169x^2$

$x^4 - 169x^2 + 3600 = 0$

$(x^2 - 25)(x^2 - 144) = 0$

$(x - 5)(x + 5)(x - 12)(x + 12) = 0$

$x = \pm5 \text{ or } x = \pm12$

$2x = 10$ or 24. Since 10 was the base of the first triangle, 24 is the base of the second triangle.

15.

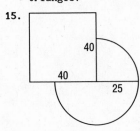

The radius of the circle is $r = 25$.

The area is $\pi r^2 - \frac{1}{4}\pi r^2$.

$A = 625\pi - 156.25\pi$

$= \pi(625 - 156.25)$

$= \pi(468.75)$

$= 1472.62$

about 1473 square feet

PAGE 222   COOPERATIVE LEARNING ACTIVITY

Solve a simpler problem, where you know the values of m and n. Then look for a pattern.

Size of "board"   1 × 1   1 × 2   2 × 2   2 × 3
Number of toothpicks   4   7   12   17

By guess-and-check, $(1 + 1) + (1 + 1) = 4$

$2(1 + 1) + (2 + 1) = 7$

$2(2 + 1) + 2(2 + 1) = 12$

$3(2 + 1) + 2(3 + 1) = 17$

Substituting m and n gives the expression

$n(m + 1) + m(n + 1)$.

5-4 Polynomials

PAGE 225   CHECKING FOR UNDERSTANDING

1. The FOIL method is two applications of the distributive property.

2. $(2x + 3)(5x - 8)$

$= 2x \cdot 5x + 2x(-8) + 3 \cdot 5x + 3(-8)$

$= 10x^2 + (-16x) + 15x + (-24)$

$= 10x^2 - x - 24$

3. Yes, rewrite the trinomial as the sum of a binomial and a monomial. Then use FOIL, treating the binomial as a term.

4. 2   5. 2   6. 8   7. 6

8. 5   9. 3   10. 2   11. 9

12. $(4a + 2) + (2a + 6) = (4a + 2a) + (2 + 6)$
$= 6a + 8$

13. $(5x + 6y) - (3x + 8y) = (5x - 3x) + (6y - 8y)$
$= 2x - 2y$

14. $(12n^2 - 4n + 8) - (4n^2 - 1)$

$= (12n^2 - 4n^2) + (-4n) + [8 - (-1)]$

$= 8n^2 - 4n + 9$

15. $3p(p^2 - 2p + 3) = 3p(p^2) - 3p(2p) + 3p(3)$
$= 3p^3 - 6p^2 + 9p$

PAGES 226-228   EXERCISES

16. $A = \frac{1}{2}b \cdot h$

$= \frac{1}{2}(2a + b)(3a)$

$= \frac{1}{2}(6a^2 + 3ab)$

$= 3a^2 + 1.5ab$

17. $A = \frac{1}{2}bh$

$= \frac{1}{2}(5y + 3)(4y)$

$= \frac{1}{2}(20y^2 + 12y)$

$= 10y^2 + 6y$

18. $(9x + 4y) + (7x - 2y)$

$= (9x + 7x) + (4y - 2y)$

$= 16x + 2y$

19. $(-3a + 5b) + (-6a + 8b)$

$= (-3a + -6a) + (5b + 8b)$

$= -9a + 13b$

20. $(m^2 + 9m + 3) - (3m^2 + m + 2)$

$= m^2 - 3m^2 + 9m - m + 3 - 2$

$= -2m^2 + 8m + 1$

21. $(3a^2 - 5d + 17) - (-a^2 + 5d - 3)$

$= 3a^2 + a^2 - 5d - 5d + 17 + 3$

$= 4a^2 - 10d + 20$

22. $(3y^2 + 5y - 7) + (2y^2 - 7y + 10)$

$= 3y^2 + 2y^2 + 5y - 7y - 7 + 10$

$= 5y^2 + (-2y) + 3$

$= 5y^2 - 2y + 3$

23. $(8r^2 + 5r + 14) - (7r^2 + 6r + 8)$

$= 8r^2 - 7r^2 + 5r - 6r + 14 - 8$

$= r^2 - r + 6$

24. $(10n^2 - 3nt + 4t^2) - (3n^2 + 5nt)$

$= 10n^2 - 3n^2 - 3nt - 5nt + 4t^2$

$= 7n^2 - 8nt + 4t^2$

25. $(-12y - 6y^2) + (-7y + 6y^2)$

$= -12y - 7y - 6y^2 + 6y^2$

$= -19y$

26. $(x^3 - 3x^2y + 4xy^2 + y^3)$

$\quad - (7x^3 + x^2y - 9xy^2 + y^3)$

$= x^3 - 7x^3 - 3x^2y - x^2y + 4xy^2 + 9xy^2 + y^3 - y^3$

$= -6x^3 - 4x^2y + 13xy^2$

27. $4f(gf - bh) = 4f(gf) - 4f(bh)$

$\quad\quad\quad\quad = 4f^2g - 4fbh$

28. $-5mn^2(-3m^2n + 6m^3n - 3m^4n^4)$

$= (-5mn^2)(-3m^2n) + (-5mn^2)6m^3n - (-5mn^2)3m^4n^4$

$= 15m^3n^3 - 30m^4n^3 + 15m^5n^6$

29. $x^{-4}(x^2 + x - 3)$

$= x^{-4}(x^2) + x^{-4}(x) - x^{-4}(3)$

$= x^{-2} + x^{-3} - 3x^{-4}$

$= \dfrac{1}{x^2} + \dfrac{1}{x^3} - \dfrac{3}{x^4}$

30. $r^{-3}(r^5 - 2r^3 + r^{-1})$

$= r^{-3}(r^5) - r^{-3}(2r^3) + r^{-3}(r^{-1})$

$= r^2 - 2r^0 + r^{-4}$

$= r^2 - 2 + \dfrac{1}{r^4}$

31. $4a^{-1}b^2(a^2b^{-1} + 3a^3b^{-2} + 4^{-2}ab^{-1})$

$= 4a^{-1}b^2(a^2b^{-1}) + 4a^{-1}b^2(3a^3b^{-2})$

$\quad + 4a^{-1}b^2(4^{-2}ab^{-1})$

$= 4a^1b^1 + 12a^2b^0 + 4^{-1}a^0b^1$

$= 4ab + 12a^2 + \dfrac{b}{4}$

$= 12a^2 + 4ab + \dfrac{b}{4}$

32. $y^2x^{-3}(yx^4 + y^{-1}x^3 + y^{-2}x^2)$

$= y^2x^{-3}(yx^4) + y^2x^{-3}(y^{-1}x^3) + y^2x^{-3}(y^{-2}x^2)$

$= y^3x^1 + y^1x^0 + y^0x^{-1}$

$= xy^3 + y + \dfrac{1}{x}$

33. $(x + 7)(x + 2) = x \cdot x + x \cdot 2 + 7 \cdot x + 7 \cdot 2$

$\quad\quad\quad\quad\quad = x^2 + 2x + 7x + 14$

$\quad\quad\quad\quad\quad = x^2 + 9x + 14$

34. $(a + 5)(a - 7) = a \cdot a + (-7)a + 5a + (-7)5$

$\quad\quad\quad\quad\quad = a^2 - 7a + 5a - 35$

$\quad\quad\quad\quad\quad = a^2 - 2a - 35$

35. $(s^2 + 5)(s^2 - 4)$

$= s^2 \cdot s^2 + (-4)s^2 + 5s^2 + (-4)5$

$= s^4 - 4s^2 + 5s^2 - 20$

$= s^4 + s^2 - 20$

36. $(y^2 + y)(y^2 + 5)$

$= y^2 \cdot y^2 + y^2 \cdot 5 + y \cdot y^2 + 5 \cdot y$

$= y^4 + 5y^2 + y^3 + 5y$

$= y^4 + y^3 + 5y^2 + 5y$

37. $(2x + 7)(3x + 5)$

$= 2x(3x) + 2x \cdot 5 + 3x \cdot 7 + 7 \cdot 5$

$= 6x^2 + 10x + 21x + 35$

$= 6x^2 + 31x + 35$

38. $(3t - 8)(2t + 7)$

$= 3t(2t) + 3t \cdot 7 + (-8)2t + (-8)7$

$= 6t^2 + 21t + (-16)t - 56$

$= 6t^2 + 5t - 56$

39. $(w^2 - 5)(2w^2 + 3)$

$= w^2 \cdot 2w^2 + 3w^2 - 5(2w^2) + (-5)3$

$= 2w^4 + 3w^2 - 10w^2 - 15$

$= 2w^4 - 7w^2 - 15$

40. $(2x + 3y)(3x - 5y)$

$= 2x(3x) + 2x(-5y) + 3y(3x) + 3y(-5y)$

$= 6x^2 - 10xy + 9xy - 15y^2$

$= 6x^2 - xy - 15y^2$

41. $(6p - 5)(7p - 9)$

$= 6p(7p) + 6p(-9) + (-5)7p + (-5)(-9)$

$= 42p^2 - 54p - 35p + 45$

$= 42p^2 - 89p + 45$

42. $(9y^2 - 1)(y + 2)$

$= 9y^2(y) + 9y^2(2) + (-1)y + (-1)2$

$= 9y^3 + 18y^2 - y - 2$

43. $(a - b)^2 = (a - b)(a - b)$

$\qquad = a^2 - ab - ab + b^2$

$\qquad = a^2 - 2ab + b^2$

44. $(a - b)(a + b) = a^2 + ab - ab - b^2$

$\qquad\qquad\quad = a^2 - b^2$

45. $(d + 3)^2 = (d + 3)(d + 3)$

$\qquad = d^2 + 3d + 3d + 9$

$\qquad = d^2 + 6d + 9$

46. $(r - 8)^2 = (r - 8)(r - 8)$

$\qquad = r^2 - 8r - 8r + 64$

$\qquad = r^2 - 16r + 64$

47. $(y - 2)^2 = (y - 2)(y - 2)$

$\qquad = y^2 - 2y - 2y + 4$

$\qquad = y^2 - 4y + 4$

48. $(y - 5)(y + 5) = y^2 + 5y - 5y + (-25)$

$\qquad\qquad\quad = y^2 - 25$

49. $(2p + q^3)^2 = (2p + q^3)(2p + q^3)$

$\qquad = 4p^2 + 4pq^3 + q^6$

50. $(x - 3y)^2 = (x - 3y)(x - 3y)$

$\qquad = x^2 - 3xy - 3xy + 9y^2$

$\qquad = x^2 - 6xy + 9y^2$

51. $(4m - 3n)^2 = (4m - 3n)(4m - 3n)$

$\qquad = 16m^2 - 12mn - 12mn + 9n^2$

$\qquad = 16m^2 - 24mn + 9n^2$

52. $(5r - 2)^2 = (5r - 2)(5r - 2)$

$\qquad = 25r^2 - 10r - 10r + 4$

$\qquad = 25r^2 - 20r + 4$

53. $(1 + 4r)^2 = (1 + 4r)(1 + 4r)$

$\qquad = 1 + 4r + 4r + 16r^2$

$\qquad = 1 + 8r + 16r^2$

54. $(x^3 - y)(x^3 + y) = x^6 + x^3y - x^3y - y^2$

$\qquad\qquad\qquad = x^6 - y^2$

55. $A = (3x + 6y)(x + y)$

$\qquad = 3x^2 + 3xy + 6xy + 6y^2$

$\qquad = 3x^2 + 9xy + 6y^2$

56. $A = (a - 2b)^2$

$\qquad = (a - 2b)(a - 2b)$

$\qquad = a^2 - 2ab - 2ab + 4b^2$

$\qquad = a^2 - 4ab + 4b^2$

57. $A = (8x - 2y)(8x + 2y)$

$\qquad = 64x^2 + 16xy - 16xy - 4y^2$

$\qquad = 64x^2 - 4y^2$

58. $(a + b)(a^2 - ab + b^2)$

$\qquad = a(a^2 - ab + b^2) + b(a^2 - ab + b^2)$

$\qquad = a^3 - a^2b + ab^2 + a^2b - ab^2 + b^3$

$\qquad = a^3 + b^3$

59. $(2x - 3)(x^2 - 3x - 8)$

$\qquad = 2x(x^2 - 3x - 8) - 3(x^2 - 3x - 8)$

$\qquad = 2x^3 - 6x^2 - 16x - 3x^2 + 9x + 24$

$\qquad = 2x^3 - 9x^2 - 7x + 24$

60. $(x - y)(x^2 + xy + y^3)$

$\qquad = x(x^2 + xy + y^3) - y(x^2 + xy + y^3)$

$\qquad = x^3 + x^2y + xy^3 - x^2y - xy^2 - y^4$

$\qquad = x^3 - xy^2 + xy^3 - y^4$

61. $(m - 4)(3m^2 + 5m - 4)$

$\qquad = m(3m^2 + 5m - 4) - 4(3m^2 + 5m - 4)$

$\qquad = 3m^3 + 5m^2 - 4m - 12m^2 - 20m + 16$

$\qquad = 3m^3 - 7m^2 - 24m + 16$

62. $r(r - 2)(r - 3) = (r^2 - 2r)(r - 3)$

$\qquad\qquad\qquad = r^3 - 3r^2 - 2r^2 + 6r$

$\qquad\qquad\qquad = r^3 - 5r^2 + 6r$

63. $(b + 1)(b - 2)(b + 3) = (b^2 - 2b + b - 2)(b + 3)$

$\qquad = (b^2 - b - 2)(b + 3)$

$\qquad = (b^2 - b - 2)b + (b^2 - b - 2)3$

$\qquad = b^3 - b^2 - 2b + 3b^2 - 3b - 6$

$\qquad = b^3 + 2b^2 - 5b - 6$

64. $(2x - 3)(x + 1)(3x - 2)$

$\qquad = (2x^2 + 2x - 3x - 3)(3x - 2)$

$\qquad = (2x^2 - x - 3)(3x - 2)$

$\qquad = (2x^2 - x - 3)3x - (2x^2 - x - 3)(2)$

$\qquad = 6x^3 - 3x^2 - 9x - 4x^2 + 2x + 6$

$\qquad = 6x^3 - 7x^2 - 7x + 6$

65. $(2a + 1)(a - 2)^2$

$\qquad = (2a + 1)(a - 2)(a - 2)$

$\qquad = (2a^2 - 4a + a - 2)(a - 2)$

$\qquad = (2a^2 - 3a - 2)(a - 2)$

$\qquad = (2a^2 - 3a - 2)a - (2a^2 - 3a - 2)(2)$

$\qquad = 2a^3 - 3a^2 - 2a - 4a^2 + 6a + 4$

$\qquad = 2a^3 - 7a^2 + 4a + 4$

66. $(a - b)(a^2 + ab + b^2)$

$= a(a^2 + ab + b^2) - b(a^2 + ab + b^2)$

$= a^3 + a^2b + ab^2 - a^2b - ab^2 - b^3$

$= a^3 - b^3$

67. $(2k + 3)(k^2 - 7k + 21)$

$= 2k(k^2 - 7k + 21) + 3(k^2 - 7k + 21)$

$= 2k^3 - 14k^2 + 42k + 3k^2 - 21k + 63$

$= 2k^3 - 11k^2 + 21k + 63$

68. $(a + b + c)^2 = (a + b + c)(a + b + c)$

$= a(a + b + c) + b(a + b + c) + c(a + b + c)$

$= a^2 + ab + ac + ab + b^2 + bc + ac + bc + c^2$

$= a^2 + 2ab + 2ac + b^2 + 2bc + c^2$

69. $m\angle B = \frac{1}{2}[(3x - 8) + (6x + 6)]$

$= \frac{1}{2}(9x - 2)$

$m\angle A = \frac{1}{2}[(4x + 8) + (6x + 6)]$

$= \frac{1}{2}(10x + 14)$

$\dfrac{m\angle A}{m\angle B} = \dfrac{\frac{1}{2}(10x + 14)}{\frac{1}{2}(9x - 2)} = \dfrac{10x + 14}{9x - 2}$

70. $23,450 + 23,450p = 23,450(1 + p)$

After 3 years, $23,450(1 + p)^3$.

71. Let $m - 50$ = the number of miles over 50.

cost = $19.95 + 0.25(m - 50)$

72.

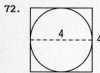

Leftover = Area of Square - Area of Circle

$= s^2 - \pi r^2$

$= 4^2 - \pi 4$

$= 16 - 4\pi$

about 3.4 square inches

73. Let w = width.

$w + 2w + w + 2w = 48$

$6w = 48$

$w = 8$

The length is $2w = 16$.

Find the area of one of the four triangles.

$A = \frac{1}{2}(8)(4)$

$= 16$

Since there are 4 triangles, the area of the parallelogram is $16 \times 4 = 64$ square meters.

74. $\begin{bmatrix} 3 & 0 \\ -1 & 5 \end{bmatrix}$

Inverse: $\dfrac{1}{3(5) - 0(-1)} \begin{bmatrix} 5 & 0 \\ 1 & 3 \end{bmatrix} = \dfrac{1}{15} \begin{bmatrix} 5 & 0 \\ 1 & 3 \end{bmatrix}$

$= \begin{bmatrix} \frac{1}{3} & 0 \\ \frac{1}{15} & \frac{1}{5} \end{bmatrix}$

75. $x = \dfrac{\begin{vmatrix} 0 & -3 \\ 7 & 5 \end{vmatrix}}{\begin{vmatrix} 2 & -3 \\ 6 & 5 \end{vmatrix}} = \dfrac{0(5) - 7(-3)}{2(5) - 6(-3)} = \dfrac{0 - (-21)}{10 - (-18)} = \dfrac{21}{10 + 18}$

$= \dfrac{21}{28} = \dfrac{3}{4}$

$y = \dfrac{\begin{vmatrix} 2 & 0 \\ 6 & 7 \end{vmatrix}}{\begin{vmatrix} 2 & -3 \\ 6 & 5 \end{vmatrix}} = \dfrac{2(7) - 6(0)}{2(5) - 6(-3)} = \dfrac{14 - 0}{10 - (-18)} = \dfrac{14}{10 + 18}$

$= \dfrac{14}{28} = \dfrac{1}{2}$

The solution is $\left(\dfrac{3}{4}, \dfrac{1}{2}\right)$.

76. The graph of $y = 3[x]$ jumps by threes at intervals of one unit. The graph at $y = [3x]$ jumps by ones at intervals of $\frac{1}{3}$ unit.

77. $\dfrac{3(3)(7)^2 - (-2)^3}{3 + (-2)} = \dfrac{9(7)^2 - (-8)}{1} = 9(49) + 8$

$= 441 + 8 = 449$

PAGE 228   MID-CHAPTER REVIEW

1. $5c^2 + 8d^2 - 10c^2 = 8d^2 - 5c^2$

2. $3d^3 - 4d^3 + d^3 = -1d^3 + d^3$

$= 0$

3. $(4x^2y)^2(3x^2y) = (4)^2(x^4)(y^2)(3x^2y)$

$= (16 \cdot 3)(x^4 \cdot x^2)(y^2 \cdot y)$

$= 48x^6y^3$

4. $\left(\frac{1}{3}x^2y\right)^3\left(\frac{2}{3}xy\right)^2 = \left(\frac{1}{27}\right)(x^6)(y^3)\left(\frac{4}{9}\right)(x^2)(y^2)$

$= \left(\frac{1}{27} \cdot \frac{4}{9}\right)(x^6 \cdot x^2)(y^3 \cdot y^2)$

$= \dfrac{4}{243}x^8y^5$

5. $(32,000,000)(48,000) = (3.2 \times 10^7)(4.8 \times 10^4)$

$= 15.36 \times 10^{11}$

$= 1.536 \times 10^{12}$

$= 1,536,000,000,000$

6. $\dfrac{18b^4}{6b^2} = \left(\dfrac{18}{6}\right)\left(\dfrac{b^4}{b^2}\right)$

$= 3b^2$

7. $\dfrac{20m^5n^4}{10mn^2} = \left(\dfrac{20}{10}\right)\left(\dfrac{m^5}{m}\right)\left(\dfrac{n^4}{n^2}\right)$

$= 2m^4n^2$

8. $\left(\dfrac{1}{4y}\right)^{-1} = 4y$

9. $\dfrac{-3w^2t^3}{(4w^2)(6w^3t^4)}$

$= \dfrac{-3w^2t^3}{24w^5t^4}$

$= \left(-\dfrac{3}{24}\right)\left(\dfrac{w^2}{w^5}\right)\left(\dfrac{t^3}{t^4}\right)$

$= \left(-\dfrac{1}{8}\right)(w^{-3})(t^{-1})$

$= -\dfrac{1}{8w^3t}$

10. $\dfrac{42 \times 10^5}{14 \times 10^{-2}}$

$= \left(\dfrac{42}{14}\right)\left(\dfrac{10^5}{10^{-2}}\right)$

$= 3 \times 10^7$

$= 30{,}000{,}000$

11. $\dfrac{682{,}000}{480} = \dfrac{6.82 \times 10^5}{4.80 \times 10^2}$

$= 1.4208\overline{3} \times 10^3$

$= 1420.8\overline{3}$

12.

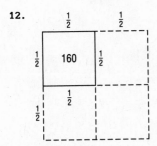

For 2 miles: For 4 miles:

$4y = 2$ $4y = 4$

$y = \dfrac{1}{2}$ $y = 1$

From the drawing, adding $\dfrac{1}{2}$ to all sides increases the size of the field 4 times, thus the field is $160(4) = 640$ acres.

13. $(3x - 2y) - (4x + 7y)$

$= 3x - 4x - 2y - 7y$

$= -x - 9y$

14. $(4d^2 - 2d + 8) - (6d^2 - 7d + 2)$

$= 4d^2 - 6d^2 - 2d + 7d + 8 - 2$

$= -2d^2 + 5d + 6$

15. $(3y - 8)(2y + 9)$

$= 6y^2 + 27y - 16y - 72$

$= 6y^2 + 11y - 72$

16. $(x + 7)(x - 3)$

$= x^2 - 3x + 7x - 21$

$= x^2 + 4x - 21$

17. $(m + 2)^2$

$= (m + 2)(m + 2)$

$= m^2 + 2m + 2m + 4$

$= m^2 + 4m + 4$

18. $(2x - 3)^2$

$= (2x - 3)(2x - 3)$

$= 4x^2 - 6x - 6x + 9$

$= 4x^2 - 12x + 9$

19. $(x + 2)(x - 3)^2$

$= (x + 2)(x - 3)(x - 3)$

$= (x + 2)(x^2 - 6x + 9)$

$= x(x^2 - 6x + 9) + 2(x^2 - 6x + 9)$

$= x^3 - 6x^2 + 9x + 2x^2 - 12x + 18$

$= x^3 - 4x^2 - 3x + 18$

20. $(2y - 4)(y^2 + 2y - 7)$

$= 2y(y^2 + 2y - 7) - 4(y^2 + 2y - 7)$

$= 2y^3 + 4y^2 - 14y - 4y^2 - 8y + 28$

$= 2y^3 - 22y + 28$

$\boxed{5\text{-}5}$ **Factoring**

PAGES 232–233   CHECKING FOR UNDERSTANDING

1. $2x^2 + 7x + 3$

$= (2x + 1)(x + 3)$

2.

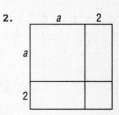

3. Squares: 1, 4, 9, 16, 25, 36, 49, 64, 81, 100, 121, 144, 169, 196, 225, 256, 289, 324, 361, 400

Cubes: 1, 8, 27, 64, 125, 216, 343, 512, 729, 1000

4. $3x^3 + 6x^2 - 3x - 6 = (3x^3 + 6x^2) - (3x + 6)$

$= 3x^2(x + 2) - 3(x + 2)$

$= (3x^2 - 3)(x + 2)$

$= 3(x^2 - 1)(x + 2)$

$= 3(x - 1)(x + 1)(x + 2)$

same prime factorization

5. $3s + 3t = 3(s + t)$ **6.** $8a - 2b = 2(4a - b)$

7. $ab + ac = a(b + c)$ **8.** $x^2 - x = x(x - 1)$

9. $r^2 - 9$ **10.** $x^2 - 25$

$= (r + 3)(r - 3)$ $= (x + 5)(x - 5)$

11. $100 - m^2$ **12.** $y^2 - 81z^2$

$= (10 + m)(10 - m)$ $= (y + 9z)(y - 9z)$

13. $y(3y - 2) + 4k(3y - 2) = (3y - 2)(y + 4k)$

14. $2x^2 + 6y + 8b = 2(x^2 + 3y + 4b)$

15. $9p^2 - 3pq = 3p(3p - q)$

16. $3m(m - 7) + k(m - 7) = (m - 7)(3m + k)$

17. $-15x^2 - 5x = -5x(3x + 1)$

18. $s^2 - 6s + 8 = s^2 - (4 + 2)s + 4 \cdot 2$
$$= (s - 4)(s - 2)$$

19. $2ab(c - d) + 10d(c - d) = (2ab + 10d)(c - d)$
$$= 2(ab + 5d)(c - d)$$

20. $a^2 + 5a + 6 = a^2 + (2 + 3)a + 2 \cdot 3$
$$= (a + 2)(a + 3)$$

21. $y^2 + 6y + 9 = y^2 + (3 + 3)y + 3 \cdot 3$
$$= (y + 3)(y + 3) = (y + 3)^2$$

22. $a(y - b) - c(y - b) = (y - b)(a - c)$

23. $r^2 + 16r + 64 = r^2 + (8 + 8)r + 8 \cdot 8$
$$= (r + 8)(r + 8) = (r + 8)^2$$

24. $x^2 + xy + 3x = x(x + y + 3)$

25. $3a^2 + 6a + 9y = 3(a^2 + 2a + 3y)$

26. $a^4 + a^3b + a^2b^2 = a^2(a^2 + ab + b^2)$

27. $5x^2y - 10xy^2 = 5xy(x - 2y)$

28. $49s^2 - 100 = 7 \cdot 7s^2 - 10 \cdot 10$
$$= (7s - 10)(7s + 10)$$

29. $x^3 + 8 = x^3 + 2^3$
$$= (x + 2)(x^2 - 2x + 4)$$

30. $d^3 - 27 = d^3 - 3^3$
$$= (d - 3)(d^2 + 3d + 9)$$

31. $f^2 - 18f + 81 = f^2 - (9 + 9)f + 9 \cdot 9$
$$= (f - 9)(f - 9) = (f - 9)^2$$

32. $t^2 + 12t + 35 = t^2 + (5 + 7)t + 5 \cdot 7$
$$= (t + 5)(t + 7)$$

33. $s^2 + 12s + 36 = s^2 + (6 + 6)s + 6 \cdot 6$
$$= (s + 6)(s + 6) = (s + 6)^2$$

34. $a^2 + 4ab + 4b^2 = a^2 + (2 + 2)ab + 2 \cdot 2b^2$
$$= (a + 2b)(a + 2b) = (a + 2b)^2$$

35. $4x^2 - 9 = (2 \cdot 2)x^2 - 3 \cdot 3$
$$= (2x - 3)(2x + 3)$$

36. $3y^2 + 5y + 2 = (3y + 2)(y + 1)$

37. $4s^2 - 20s + 21 = (2 \cdot 2)s^2 - (14 + 6)s + 7 \cdot 3$
$$= (2s - 7)(2s - 3)$$

38. $3d^2 - 48 = 3(d^2 - 16)$
$$= 3(d^2 - 4^2)$$
$$= 3(d - 4)(d + 4)$$

39. $x^3 + 2x^2 - 35x = x(x^2 + 2x - 35)$
$$= x[x^2 + 2x - (7 \cdot 5)]$$
$$= x(x + 7)(x - 5)$$

40. $4s^2 - 20st + 4t^2 = 4(s^2 - 5st + t^2)$

41. $p^2 - 4bp + 4b^2 = p^2 - (2 + 2)bp + (2 \cdot 2)b^2$
$$= (p - 2b)(p - 2b) = (p - 2b)^2$$

42. $6d^2 + 33d - 63 = 3(2d^2 + 11d - 21)$
$$= 3[2d^2 + (14 - 3)d - (7 \cdot 3)]$$
$$= 3(2d - 3)(d + 7)$$

43. $f^3 - 1 = f^3 - 1^3$
$$= (f - 1)(f^2 + f + 1)$$

44. $x^4 - 13x^2 + 36 = x^4 - (9 + 4)x^2 + (9 \cdot 4)$
$$= (x^2 - 9)(x^2 - 4)$$
$$= (x - 3)(x + 3)(x - 2)(x + 2)$$

45. $(x + y)^2 - \dfrac{1}{4} = (x + y)^2 - \left[\dfrac{1}{2}\right]^2$
$$= \left(x + y - \dfrac{1}{2}\right)\left(x + y + \dfrac{1}{2}\right)$$

46. $2r^3 - 16s^3 = 2(r^3 - 8s^3)$
$$= 2(r^3 - 2^3s^3)$$
$$= 2(r - 2s)(r^2 + 2rs + 4s^2)$$

47. $m^2 - k^2 + 6k - 9 = m^2 - (k^2 - 6k + 9)$
$$= m^2 - (k - 3)^2$$
$$= [m - (k - 3)][m + (k - 3)]$$
$$= (m - k + 3)(m + k - 3)$$

48. $16y^4 - z^4 = (4)^2y^4 - z^4$
$$= (4y^2 - z^2)(4y^2 + z^2)$$
$$= (2y - z)(2y + z)(4y^2 + z^2)$$

49. $a + b + 3a^2 - 3b^2 = (a + b) + 3(a^2 - b^2)$
$$= (a + b) + 3(a - b)(a + b)$$
$$= (a + b)[1 + 3(a - b)]$$
$$= (a + b)(1 + 3a - 3b)$$

50. $a^3b^3 - 27 = a^3b^3 - 3^3$
$$= (ab - 3)(a^2b^2 + 3ab + 9)$$

51. $1 - 8m^6 = 1^3 - 2^3(m^2)^3$
$$= (1 - 2m^2)(1 + 2m^2 + 4m^4)$$

52. $4a^2 + 4ab - y^2 + b^2 = (4a^2 + 4ab + b^2) - y^2$
$$= (2a + b)^2 - y^2$$
$$= (2a + b - y)(2a + b + y)$$

53. $a^{2n} - 64 = a^{n+n} - 8^2$
$$= (a^n - 8)(a^n + 8)$$

54. $x^{3n} - y^{3n} = (x^n - y^n)(x^{2n} + x^ny^n + y^{2n})$

55. $\left(\dfrac{3}{a + b}\right)^2 - \dfrac{6}{a + b} + 1 = 0$

$$\left(\dfrac{3}{a + b} - 1\right)^2 = 0$$

$$\dfrac{3}{a + b} - 1 = 0$$

$$\dfrac{3}{a + b} = 1$$

56.

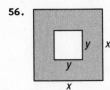

Let x = side of the outer square.

Let y = side of the inner square.

Area of outer square = $x \cdot x = x^2$

Area of inner square = $y \cdot y = y^2$

Area of shaded area = $x^2 - y^2$

$$= (x - y)(x + y)$$

57. Area = length × width

$3x^2 - 2x - 5 = (3x - 5)(x + 1)$

$$\boxed{3x^2 - 2x - 5} \quad x + 1$$
$$3x - 5$$

58. $(s + 3)^2$

$= (s + 3)(s + 3)$

$= s^2 + 3s + 3s + 9$

$= s^2 + 6s + 9$

59. $(2x + 4)(7x - 1)$

$= 14x^2 - 2x + 28x - 4$

$= 14x^2 + 26x - 4$

60. $\begin{bmatrix} 3 & 0 \\ 1 & -2 \end{bmatrix} \begin{bmatrix} x \\ y \end{bmatrix} = \begin{bmatrix} 12 \\ 8 \end{bmatrix}$

$3x + 0y = 12 \qquad 1x - 2y = 8$

$3x = 12 \qquad x - 2y = 8$

61. $M_{3 \times 5}$

62. $f(0.1, -0.3) = 1.2(0.1) - (0.8)(-0.3)$

$ = 0.12 + 0.24$

$ = 0.36$

63. No, there are two y's $(0, 1)$ for one $x(0)$.

64. $\dfrac{3}{4}t + 1 = 10$

$ \dfrac{3}{4}t = 9$

$ t = 12$

Technology: Factoring

PAGE 235   EXERCISES

1. $16ab(6a^2b^2 - 5a + 7)$

2. $5m(26m + 3n^2)$

3. $9(x - 2)(x + 2)(x^2 + 4)$

4. $(x + 1)(x^2 - x + 1)(x^6 - x^3 + 1)$

5-6 ## Dividing Polynomials

PAGE 238   CHECKING FOR UNDERSTANDING

1. $n = \dfrac{170(6)^2}{6^2 + 1} = \dfrac{170(36)}{36 + 1} = \dfrac{6120}{37} = 165.4$

about 165 people

2. If $m = 7$, then we are dividing by 0 and division by zero is undefined.

3. The divisor is a factor of the dividend.

4. when the numerator and denominator are both easily factorable and contain a common factor

5. $\dfrac{5ab^2 - 4ab + 7a^2b}{ab}$

$= \dfrac{5ab^2}{ab} - \dfrac{4ab}{ab} + \dfrac{7a^2b}{ab}$

$= 5a^{1-1}b^{2-1} - 4a^{1-1}b^{1-1} + 7a^{2-1}b^{1-1}$

$= 5b - 4 + 7a$

6. $\dfrac{x^3y^2 - x^2y + 2x}{-xy}$

$= \dfrac{x^3y^2}{-xy} - \dfrac{x^2y}{-xy} + \dfrac{2x}{-xy}$

$= (-1)x^{3-1}y^{2-1} + x^{2-1}y^{1-1} + (-1)2x^{1-1}y^{2-1}$

$= -x^2y + x - \dfrac{2}{y}$

7. $\dfrac{6r^2s^2 + 3rs^2 - 9r^2s}{3rs}$

$= \dfrac{6r^2s^2}{3rs} + \dfrac{3rs^2}{3rs} - \dfrac{9r^2s}{3rs}$

$= \dfrac{6}{3}r^{2-1}s^{2-1} + \dfrac{3}{3}r^{1-1}s^{2-1} - \dfrac{9}{3}r^{2-1}s^{1-1}$

$= 2rs + s - 3r$

8. $\dfrac{3(x - 7)^6}{(x - 7)^{10}} = 3(x - 7)^{6-10}$

$ = 3(x - 7)^{-4} \text{ or } \dfrac{3}{(x - 7)^4}$

9. $\dfrac{2(y^2 - 5)^3}{8(y^2 - 5)^5} = \dfrac{2}{8}(y^2 - 5)^{3-5}$

$ = \dfrac{1}{4}(y^2 - 5)^{-2} \text{ or } \dfrac{1}{4(y^2 - 5)^2}$

10. $\dfrac{2(t + 3)^4}{10(t + 3)^2} = \dfrac{2}{10}(t + 3)^{4-2}$

$\qquad = \dfrac{1}{5}(t + 3)^2$ or $\dfrac{(t + 3)^2}{5}$

11. $\dfrac{c^2 - c - 30}{c - 6} = \dfrac{(c - 6)(c + 5)}{(c - 6)}$

$\qquad = (c + 5)(c - 6)^{1-1}$

$\qquad = c + 5$

12. $\dfrac{m^2 + 8m + 16}{m + 4}$

$\quad = \dfrac{(m + 4)(m + 4)}{(m + 4)}$

$\quad = \dfrac{(m + 4)^2}{(m + 4)}$

$\quad = (m + 4)^{2-1}$

$\quad = (m + 4)^1$ or $m + 4$

13. $(w^2 - w^3)(w^2 - 1)^{-1}$

$\quad = \dfrac{(w^2 - w^3)}{(w^2 - 1)}$

$\quad = \dfrac{-w^2(w - 1)}{(w + 1)(w - 1)}$

$\quad = \dfrac{-w^2}{(w + 1)}(w - 1)^{1-1}$

$\quad = \dfrac{-w^2}{w + 1}$

14. $(a^3 - b^3)(a - b)^{-2}$

$\quad = \dfrac{a^3 - b^3}{(a - b)^2}$

$\quad = \dfrac{(a - b)(a^2 + ab + b^2)}{(a - b)^2}$

$\quad = (a^2 + ab + b^2)(a - b)^{1-2}$

$\quad = (a^2 + ab + b^2)(a - b)^{-1}$

$\quad = \dfrac{a^2 + ab + b^2}{a - b}$

15. $\dfrac{12pq^3 + 9p^2q^2 - 15p^2q}{3pq}$

$\quad = \dfrac{12pq^3}{3pq} + \dfrac{9p^2q^2}{3pq} - \dfrac{15p^2q}{3pq}$

$\quad = 4q^2 + 3pq - 5p$

16. $\dfrac{6m^4n^2 + 4m^2n + 5mn^3}{-mn}$

$\quad = \dfrac{6m^4n^2}{-mn} + \dfrac{4m^2n}{-mn} + \dfrac{5mn^3}{-mn}$

$\quad = -6m^3n - 4m - 5n^2$

17. $\dfrac{28k^3py - 42kp^2y^2 + 56kp^3y^2}{14kpy}$

$\quad = \dfrac{28k^3py}{14kpy} - \dfrac{42kp^2y^2}{14kpy} + \dfrac{56kp^3y^2}{14kpy}$

$\quad = 2k^2 - 3py + 4p^2y$

18. $\dfrac{15r^2s + 23rs^2 + 6s^2}{3rs}$

$\quad = \dfrac{15r^2s}{3rs} + \dfrac{23rs^2}{3rs} + \dfrac{6s^2}{3rs}$

$\quad = 5r + \dfrac{23}{3}s + \dfrac{2s}{r}$

19. $(a^2 - 5a - 84)(a + 7)^{-1}$

$\quad = \dfrac{(a^2 - 5a - 84)}{a + 7}$

$\quad = \dfrac{(a - 12)(a + 7)}{(a + 7)}$

$\quad = (a - 12)(a + 7)^0$

$\quad = a - 12$

20.
$$\begin{array}{r} 2r - 1 \\ r + 3 \overline{\smash{)}2r^2 + 5r - 3} \\ \underline{2r^2 + 6r} \\ -r - 3 \\ \underline{-r - 3} \\ 0 \end{array}$$

21.
$$\begin{array}{r} n - 15 \\ n + 3 \overline{\smash{)}n^2 - 12n - 45} \\ \underline{n^2 + 3n} \\ -15n - 45 \\ \underline{-15n - 45} \\ 0 \end{array}$$

22. $(6y^2 + 7y - 3)(2y + 3)^{-1}$

$\quad = \dfrac{6y^2 + 7y - 3}{2y + 3}$

$\quad = \dfrac{(2y + 3)(3y - 1)}{2y + 3}$

$\quad = (3y - 1)(2y + 3)^0$

$\quad = 3y - 1$

23.
$$\begin{array}{r} 2x + 7 + \dfrac{5}{x - 3} \\ x - 3 \overline{\smash{)}2x^2 + x - 16} \\ \underline{2x^2 - 6x} \\ 7x - 16 \\ \underline{7x - 21} \\ 5 \end{array}$$

24. $(8g^2 - 18g - 9)(g - 3)^{-1}$

$\quad = \dfrac{(8g^2 - 18g - 9)}{(g - 3)}$

$$\begin{array}{r} 8g + 6 + \dfrac{9}{g - 3} \\ g - 3 \overline{\smash{)}8g^2 - 18g - 9} \\ \underline{8g^2 - 24g} \\ 6g - 9 \\ \underline{6g - 18} \\ 9 \end{array}$$

25. $(s^2 + 4s - 16) \div (6 - s)$

$= (s^2 + 4s - 16) \div (-s + 6)$

$$-s + 6 \overline{)\,s^2 + 4s - 16} \quad \frac{-s - 10 + \dfrac{44}{6 - s}}{}$$

$$\underline{s^2 - 6s}$$
$$10s - 16$$
$$\underline{10s - 60}$$
$$44$$

26. $(8x^2 - 4x + 11)(x + 5)^{-1}$

$= \dfrac{(8x^2 - 4x + 11)}{(x + 5)}$

$$x + 5 \overline{)\,8x^2 - 4x + 11} \quad \frac{8x - 44 + \dfrac{231}{x + 5}}{}$$

$$\underline{8x^2 + 40x}$$
$$-44x + 11$$
$$\underline{-44x - 220}$$
$$231$$

27. $3y - 1 \overline{)\,6y^3 + 13y^2 + y - 2} \quad \frac{2y^2 + 5y + 2}{}$

$$\underline{6y^3 - 2y^2}$$
$$15y^2 + y - 2$$
$$\underline{15y^2 - 5y}$$
$$6y - 2$$
$$\underline{6y - 2}$$
$$0$$

28. $8c - 7 \overline{)\,56c^2 - 113c + 59} \quad \frac{7c - 8 + \dfrac{3}{8c - 7}}{}$

$$\underline{56c^2 - 49c}$$
$$-64c + 59$$
$$\underline{-64c + 56}$$
$$3$$

29. $2x + 3 \overline{)\,6x^3 + 5x^2 + 0x + 9} \quad \frac{3x^2 - 2x + 3}{}$

$$\underline{6x^3 + 9x^2}$$
$$-4x^2 + 0x + 9$$
$$\underline{-4x^2 - 6x}$$
$$6x + 9$$
$$\underline{6x + 9}$$
$$0$$

30. $(y^3 - 1) \div (y - 1)$

$= \dfrac{y^3 - 1}{y - 1}$

$= \dfrac{(y - 1)(y^2 + y + 1)}{(y - 1)}$

$= (y^2 + y + 1)(y - 1)^0$

$= y^2 + y + 1$

31. $r - 3 \overline{)\,r^3 - 9r^2 + 27r - 28} \quad \frac{r^2 - 6r + 9 - \dfrac{1}{r - 3}}{}$

$$\underline{r^3 - 3r^2}$$
$$-6r^2 + 27r$$
$$\underline{-6r^2 + 18r}$$
$$9r - 28$$
$$\underline{9r - 27}$$
$$-1$$

32. $m^2 - 7 \overline{)\,m^3 + 3m^2 - 7m - 21} \quad \frac{m + 3}{}$

$$\underline{m^3 - 0m^2 - 7m}$$
$$3m^2 + 0m - 21$$
$$\underline{3m^2 + 0m - 21}$$
$$0$$

33. $3x + 2 \overline{)\,6x^3 - 5x^2 - 12x - 4} \quad \frac{2x^2 - 3x - 2}{}$

$$\underline{6x^3 + 4x^2}$$
$$-9x^2 - 12x$$
$$\underline{-9x^2 - 6x}$$
$$-6x - 4$$
$$\underline{-6x - 4}$$
$$0$$

34. $x + 2 \overline{)\,x^2 + 4x - 4} \quad \frac{x + 2 - \dfrac{8}{x + 2}}{}$

$$\underline{x^2 + 2x}$$
$$2x - 4$$
$$\underline{2x + 4}$$
$$-8$$

35. $t - 1 \overline{)\,2t^3 - 0t^2 - 2t - 3} \quad \frac{2t^2 + 2t - \dfrac{3}{t - 1}}{}$

$$\underline{2t^3 - 2t^2}$$
$$2t^2 - 2t - 3$$
$$\underline{2t^2 - 2t}$$
$$-3$$

36. $v^2 - 2v + 2 \overline{)\,v^4 + 0v^3 + 0v^2 + 0v + 4} \quad \frac{v^2 + 2v + 2}{}$

$$\underline{v^4 - 2v^3 + 2v^2}$$
$$2v^3 - 2v^2 + 0v + 4$$
$$\underline{2v^3 - 4v^2 + 4v}$$
$$2v^2 - 4v + 4$$
$$\underline{2v^2 - 4v + 4}$$
$$0$$

37. $(s^3 - 8) \div (s - 2)$

$$= \frac{s^3 - 8}{s - 2}$$

$$= \frac{(s - 2)(s^2 + 2s + 4)}{(s - 2)}$$

$$= s^2 + 2s + 4$$

38.

$$
\begin{array}{r}
y^2 + 2y + 3 \\
y^2 + 2y + 3 \overline{\smash{\big)}\ y^4 + 4y^3 + 10y^2 + 12y + 9} \\
\underline{y^4 + 2y^3 + 3y^2} \\
2y^3 + 7y^2 + 12y + 9 \\
\underline{2y^3 + 4y^2 + 6y} \\
3y^2 + 6y + 9 \\
\underline{3y^2 + 6y + 9} \\
0
\end{array}
$$

39.

$$
\begin{array}{r}
x^2 - 2x + 3 \\
x^2 + 2x - 3 \overline{\smash{\big)}\ x^4 + 0x^3 - 4x^2 + 12x - 9} \\
\underline{x^4 + 2x^3 - 3x^2} \\
-2x^3 - x^2 + 12x - 9 \\
\underline{-2x^3 - 4x^2 + 6x} \\
3x^2 + 6x - 9 \\
\underline{3x^2 + 6x - 9} \\
0
\end{array}
$$

40.

$$
\begin{array}{r}
2y + y - 1 \\
3y - 2 \overline{\smash{\big)}\ 6y^3 - y^2 - 5y + 2} \\
\underline{6y^3 - 4y^2} \\
3y^2 - 5y + 2 \\
\underline{3y^2 - 2y} \\
-3y + 2 \\
\underline{-3y + 2} \\
0
\end{array}
$$

yes

41.

$$
\begin{array}{r}
a^2 - 1 \\
a - 2 \overline{\smash{\big)}\ a^3 - 2a^2 - a + 2} \\
\underline{a^3 - 2a^2} \\
-a + 2 \\
\underline{-a + 2} \\
0
\end{array}
$$

$$(a^2 - 1) = (a - 1)(a + 1)$$

42.

$$
\begin{array}{r}
x + 5 \\
x - 2 \overline{\smash{\big)}\ x^2 + 3x + 5} \\
\underline{x^2 - 2x} \\
5x + 5 \\
\underline{5x - 10} \\
15
\end{array}
$$

Remainder: 15

$$f(2) = 2^2 + 3(2) + 5$$
$$= 4 + 6 + 5 = 15$$

Both are 15.

43.

$$
\begin{array}{r}
x + 12 \\
x - 4 \overline{\smash{\big)}\ x^2 + 8x + k} \\
\underline{x^2 - 4x} \\
12x + k \\
12x - 48
\end{array}
$$

$$k = -48$$

44. $\left(\dfrac{y^2 + 2y - 15}{y^2 + 3y - 10}\right)\left(\dfrac{y^2 - 9}{y^2 - 9y + 14}\right)^{-1}$

$$= \left(\frac{y^2 + 2y - 15}{y^2 + 3y - 10}\right)\left(\frac{y^2 - 9y + 14}{y^2 - 9}\right)$$

$$= \frac{(y + 5)(y - 3)}{(y + 5)(y - 2)} \cdot \frac{(y - 7)(y - 2)}{(y - 3)(y + 3)}$$

$$= (y + 5)^{1-1}(y - 3)^{1-1}(y - 2)^{1-1}\frac{(y - 7)}{(y + 3)}$$

$$= \frac{y - 7}{y + 3}$$

45. $(x + 4)\left(3x^2 - x + 32 - \dfrac{121}{x + 4}\right)$

$$= (x + 4)(3x^2 - x + 32) - (x + 4)\left(\frac{121}{x + 4}\right)$$

$$= x(3x^2 - x + 32) + 4(3x^2 - x + 23) - \frac{121(x + 4)}{(x + 4)}$$

$$= 3x^3 - x^2 + 32x + 12x^2 - 4x + 128 - 121$$

$$= 3x^3 + 11x^2 + 28x + 7$$

46. Let x = number chosen.

1) Multiply the number by 3 $\Rightarrow$ $3x$

2) Add the sum of your number and 8 $\Rightarrow$

$$3x + (x + 8)$$

3) Divide by the sum of your number and 2 $\Rightarrow$

$$\frac{3x + x + 8}{x + 2}$$

$$\frac{3x + x + 8}{x + 2} = \frac{4x + 8}{x + 2} = \frac{4(x + 2)}{(x + 2)} = 4(x + 2)^0 = 4$$

47.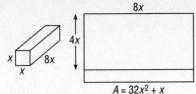

$$A = 32x^2 + x$$

If the area is $32x^2 + x$, divide by the length, $8x$, to find the width of the piece of metal used.

$$\frac{32x^2 + x}{8x} = \frac{32x^2}{8x} + \frac{x}{8x}$$

$$= 4x + \frac{1}{8}$$

Since $4x$ is the perimeter of the pipe, the excess is $\frac{1}{8}$.

The seam is $\frac{1}{8}$ inch.

48. $4a^2 - 16 = 4(a^2 - 4)$

$$= 4(a - 2)(a + 2)$$

49. $d^2 - 11d - 26 = d^2 - (13 - 2)d - (13 \cdot 2)$

$$= (d - 13)(d + 2)$$

50. $\dfrac{1}{2x^0 + y^0} = \dfrac{1}{2 \cdot 1 + 1} = \dfrac{1}{2 + 1} = \dfrac{1}{3}$

51. Let x = number of chairs.
Let y = number of tables.

$4x + 3y \leq 40$

$4x + 2y \leq 36$

	Cutting	Assembly	Profit
Chair	4	4	$28
Table	3	2	$22

Vertices: $(0, 0)$, $(9, 0)$, $(7, 4)$
$(0, 13.\overline{3})$

Maximum Profit $= 28x + 22y$

$$= 28(7) + 22(4)$$

$$= 196 + 88$$

$$= 284$$

7 chairs, 4 tables

52. $|x| + x = 0 \qquad \{-2, -1, 0, 1, 2\}$

$|-2| + (-2) = 0 \quad |-1| + (-1) = 0 \quad |0| + 0 = 0$

$\quad 2 + (-2) = 0 \qquad 1 + (-1) = 0 \qquad 0 + 0 = 0$

$\qquad\qquad 0 = 0 \checkmark \qquad\qquad 0 = 0 \checkmark \qquad\quad 0 = 0 \checkmark$

$|1| + 1 = 0 \qquad |2| + 2 = 0$

$\quad 1 + 1 = 0 \qquad\quad 2 + 2 = 0$

$\qquad 2 \neq 0 \qquad\qquad\quad 4 \neq 0 \qquad \{-2, -1, 0\}$

53. Real Numbers, R

Irrational Numbers, I

5-7 Synthetic Division

1. Synthetic division assumes that the coefficient of x in the divisor is 1, so the 2 was factored out to make that coefficient 1.

2. If the zero coefficients were not included, you would be combining unlike terms when you divide.

3. $14(6.5)^2 + 21(6.5) + 6 = 14(42.25) + 136.5 + 6$

$$= 591.5 + 142.5$$

$$= 734 \text{ in}^2$$

$V = (2w + 3)(w)(2w + 1)$

$$= (2w^2 + 3w)(2w + 1)$$

$$= 4w^3 + 2w^2 + 6w^2 + 3w$$

$$= 4w^3 + 8w^2 + 3w$$

$V = 4(6.5)^3 + 8(6.5)^2 + 3(6.5)$

$$= 1098.5 + 338 + 19.5$$

$$= 1456 \text{ in}^3$$

4.
$$\begin{array}{r|rrr} 4 & 2 & -7 & -4 \\ & & 8 & 4 \\ \hline & 2 & 1 & 0 \end{array}$$
yes

5.
$$\begin{array}{r|rrr} -1 & 2 & -7 & -4 \\ & & -2 & 9 \\ \hline & 2 & -9 & 5 \end{array}$$
no

6. $\dfrac{2x^2 - 7x - 4}{2x - 1}$

$$= \dfrac{2\left(x^2 - \frac{7}{2}x - 2\right)}{2\left(x - \frac{1}{2}\right)}$$

$$= \dfrac{x^2 - \frac{7}{2}x - 2}{x - \frac{1}{2}}$$

$$\begin{array}{r|rrr} \frac{1}{2} & 1 & -\frac{7}{2} & -2 \\ & & \frac{1}{2} & -\frac{3}{2} \\ \hline & 1 & -3 & -\frac{7}{2} \end{array}$$

no

7.
$$\begin{array}{r|rrr} 1 & 2 & -7 & -4 \\ & & 2 & -5 \\ \hline & 2 & -5 & -9 \end{array}$$
no

8. $\dfrac{2x^2 - 7x - 4}{2x + 1} = \dfrac{2\left(x^2 - \frac{7}{2}x - 2\right)}{2\left(x + \frac{1}{2}\right)}$

$$= \dfrac{x^2 - \frac{7}{2}x - 2}{x + \frac{1}{2}}$$

$$\begin{array}{r|rrr} -\frac{1}{2} & 1 & -\frac{7}{2} & -2 \\ & & -\frac{1}{2} & 2 \\ \hline & 1 & -4 & 0 \end{array}$$

yes

9.
$$\frac{2x^2 - 7x - 4}{2x - 3} = \frac{2\left(x^2 - \frac{7}{2}x - 2\right)}{2\left(x - \frac{3}{2}\right)}$$

$$= \frac{x^2 - \frac{7}{2}x - 2}{x - \frac{3}{2}}$$

```
3/2 | 1   -7/2   -2
    |      3/2   -3
    |_____
      1    -2    -5
```

no

PAGES 244–245 EXERCISES

10.
```
3 | 3   2   -32   2
  |     9    33   3
  |_____
    3  11    1 | 5
```
$3y^2 + 11y + 1 + \dfrac{5}{y - 3}$

11.
```
-1 | 2   1   -2   3
   |    -2   1    1
   |_____
     2  -1  -1 | 4
```
$2b^2 - b - 1 + \dfrac{4}{b + 1}$

12.
```
2 | 2   -3   3    -4
  |      4   2    10
  |_____
    2    1   5 | 6
```
$2c^2 + c + 5 + \dfrac{6}{c - 2}$

13.
```
1 | 3   -2   2    -1
  |      3   1     3
  |_____
    3    1   3 | 2
```
$3x^2 + x + 3 + \dfrac{2}{x - 1}$

14.
```
2 | 1   -2   1   -3    2
  |      2   0    2   -2
  |_____
    1    0   1   -1 | 0
```
$t^3 + t - 1$

15.
```
-1 | 3   -6   -2   1    -6
   |     -3    9  -7     6
   |_____
     3   -9    7  -6 | 0
```
$3r^3 - 9r^2 + 7r - 6$

16.
```
4 | 1   -3   -1   -11   -4
  |      4    4    12    4
  |_____
    1    1    3    1 | 0
```
$z^3 + z^2 + 3z + 1$

17.
```
3 | 2   -11   12   9
  |       6  -15  -9
  |_____
    2   -5   -3 | 0
```
$2b^2 - 5b - 3$

18.
```
3 | 6   -19   1    6
  |      18  -3   -6
  |_____
    6   -1   -2 | 0
```
$6s^2 - s - 2$

19.
```
2 | 1   2   -5   -6
  |      2    8    6
  |_____
    1   4    3 | 0
```
$x^2 + 4x + 3$

20.
```
1 | 1   3   -7   1
  |      1    4  -3
  |_____
    1   4   -3 | -2
```
$x^2 + 4x - 3 - \dfrac{2}{x - 1}$

21.
```
5 | 1   -8    0    54   105
  |      5  -15  -75  -105
  |_____
    1   -3  -15  -21 | 0
```
$n^3 - 3n^2 - 15n - 21$

22.
```
1 | 2   -5   0   2   -3
  |      2  -3  -3   -1
  |_____
    2   -3  -3  -1 | -4
```
$2x^3 - 3x^2 - 3x - 1 - \dfrac{4}{x - 1}$

23.
```
2 | 1   0   -6   4   0   -3
  |      2    4  -4   0    0
  |_____
    1   2   -2   0   0 | -3
```
$z^4 + 2z^3 - 2z^2 - \dfrac{3}{z - 2}$

24.
```
-3 | 1    3   0   1   -1
   |     -3   0   0   -3
   |_____
     1    0   0   1 | -4
```
$y^3 + 1 - \dfrac{4}{y + 3}$

25.
$$\frac{4s^4 + 0s^3 - 5s^2 + 2s + 3}{2s - 1}$$

$$= \frac{2s^4 + 0s^3 - \frac{5}{2}s^2 + s + \frac{3}{2}}{s - \frac{1}{2}}$$

```
1/2 | 2   0   -5/2   1    3/2
    |     1    1/2  -1     0
    |_____
      2   1   -2    0 | 3/2
```

$$2s^3 + s^2 - 2s + 0 + \frac{\frac{3}{2}}{s - \frac{1}{2}}$$

$$= 2s^3 + s^2 - 2s + \frac{3}{2s - 1}$$

26.
$$\frac{2x^3 - 3x^2 - 8x + 4}{2x + 1} = \frac{x^3 - \frac{3}{2}x^2 - 4x + 2}{x + \frac{1}{2}}$$

```
-1/2 | 1   -3/2   -4    2
     |     -1/2    1   3/2
     |_____
       1   -2    -3 | 7/2
```

$$x^2 - 2x - 3 + \frac{\frac{7}{2}}{x + \frac{1}{2}} = x^2 - 2x - 3 + \frac{7}{2x + 1}$$

27.
$$\frac{4x^4 + 0x^3 - 5x^2 - 8x - 10}{2x - 3}$$

$$= \frac{2x^4 + 0x^3 - \frac{5}{2}x^2 - 4x - 5}{x - \frac{3}{2}}$$

```
3/2 | 2   0   -5/2   -4     -5
    |     3    9/2    3    -3/2
    |_____
      2   3    2    -1 | -13/2
```

$$2x^3 + 3x^2 + 2x - 1 - \frac{\frac{13}{2}}{x - \frac{3}{2}}$$

$$= 2x^3 + 3x^2 + 2x - 1 - \frac{13}{2x - 3}$$

28. $\dfrac{6j^3 - 28j^2 + 19j + 3}{3j - 2} = \dfrac{2j^3 - \frac{28}{3}j^2 + \frac{19}{3}j + 1}{j - \frac{2}{3}}$

$$\begin{array}{r|rrrr} \frac{2}{3} & 2 & -\frac{28}{3} & \frac{19}{3} & 1 \\ & & \frac{4}{3} & \frac{-16}{3} & \frac{2}{3} \\ \hline & 2 & -8 & 1 & \frac{5}{3} \end{array}$$

$2j^2 - 8j + 1 + \dfrac{\frac{5}{3}}{j - \frac{2}{3}} = 2j^2 - 8j + 1 + \dfrac{5}{3j - 2}$

29.
$$\begin{array}{r|rrrrrr} 2 & 1 & 0 & 0 & -3 & 0 & -20 \\ & & 2 & 4 & 8 & 10 & 20 \\ \hline & 1 & 2 & 4 & 5 & 10 & 0 \end{array}$$

$y^4 + 2y^3 + 4y^2 + 5y + 10$

30.
$$\begin{array}{r|rrrr} 2 & 3 & 0 & -5 & -2 \\ & & 6 & 12 & 14 \\ \hline & 3 & 6 & 7 & 12 \end{array}$$
$f(2) = 3(2)^3 - 5(2) - 2$
$= 3(8) - 10 - 2$
$= 24 - 12$

$3y^2 + 6y + 7 + \dfrac{12}{y - 2}$ $\qquad = 12$

Both are 12.

31.
$$\begin{array}{r|rrrrr} -1 & 2 & 0 & -3 & 0 & 1 \\ & & -2 & 2 & 1 & -1 \\ \hline & 2 & -2 & -1 & 1 & 0 \end{array}$$
$f(-1) = 2(-1)^4 - 3(-1)^2 + 1$
$= 2(1) - 3(1) + 1$
$= 2 - 3 + 1$

$2x^3 - 2x^2 - x + 1$ $\qquad = 0$

Both are 0.

32. $f(r) = $ remainder of division

33. Let $w = $ width; $3w + 4 = $ height.

$6w^3 - 4w^2 - 16w = $ length $(w)(3w + 4)$

$6w^3 - 4w^2 - 16w = $ length $(3w^2 + 4w)$

$\dfrac{6w^3 - 4w^2 - 16w}{3w^2 + 4w} = $ length

$\dfrac{3w\left(2w^2 - \frac{4}{3}w - \frac{16}{3}\right)}{3w\left(w + \frac{4}{3}\right)} = $ length

$\dfrac{2w^2 - \frac{4}{3}w - \frac{16}{3}}{w + \frac{4}{3}} = $ length

$$\begin{array}{r|rrr} -\frac{4}{3} & 2 & -\frac{4}{3} & -\frac{16}{3} \\ & & -\frac{8}{3} & \frac{16}{3} \\ \hline & 2 & -4 & 0 \end{array}$$

$2w - 4 = $ length $\qquad$ $2w - 4$ inches

34.

$4x^3 - 168x^2 + 1728x = (48 - 2x)(\text{width})(x)$

$\dfrac{4x^3 - 168x^2 + 1728x}{48x - 2x^2} = w$

$\dfrac{-2x^2 + 84x - 864}{x - 24} = w$

$$\begin{array}{r|rrr} 24 & -2 & 84 & -864 \\ & & -48 & 864 \\ \hline & -2 & 36 & 0 \end{array}$$

width $= -2x + 36 = 36 - 2x$

The box is $36 - 2x$ inches wide.

The piece of cardboard is 36 inches wide.

35. $x^3 + 5x^2 + 8x + 26 + \dfrac{70}{x - 3}$

36. $x^3 + 7x^2 + 15x + 9$

37. $2x^4 + x^3 - 7x^2 + 13x - 21 + \dfrac{24}{x + 1}$

38. $x^4 + 2x^3 + 4x^2 + 5x + 10$

39. $x^4 - 3x^3 - 6x^2 + 8x + 36 - \dfrac{36}{x + 3}$

40.
$$\begin{array}{r} x - 6 \\ x - 1 \overline{\smash{\big)}\, x^2 - 7x + 6} \\ \underline{x^2 - x} \\ -6x + 6 \\ \underline{-6x + 6} \\ 0 \end{array}$$

41.
$$\begin{array}{r} a^2 + 3a - 2 - \dfrac{1}{a + 4} \\ a + 4 \overline{\smash{\big)}\, a^3 + 7a^2 + 10a - 9} \\ \underline{a^3 + 4a^2} \\ 3a^2 + 10a - 9 \\ \underline{3a^2 + 12a} \\ -2a - 9 \\ \underline{-2a - 8} \\ -1 \end{array}$$

42. $M : (9 \times 1)$

43. $\begin{vmatrix} 3 & -2 \\ 0 & 1 \end{vmatrix}$

det $= 3(1) - 0(-2)$
$= 3 - 0$
$= 3$

44. $y = -11x + 2$

$11x + y = 2$

Chapter 5 Summary and Review

PAGES 246-248   SKILLS AND CONCEPTS

1. $4m + 3m + (-6m)$
   $= 7m - 6m$
   $= m$

2. $4d^3 - 7d^3 + 5d^3$
   $= -3d^3 + 5d^3$
   $= 2d^3$

3. $y^8(y^5) = y^{8+5}$
   $= y^{13}$

4. $x^2(x^4)(x^5) = x^{2+4+5}$
   $= x^{11}$

5. $(3xy^2)^2(4xy)^2$
   $= (9x^2y^4)(16x^2y^2)$
   $= 144x^4y^6$

6. $(-3x^2y)^3(2x)^2$
   $= (-27x^6y^3)(4x^2)$
   $= -108x^8y^3$

7. $(3.2 \times 10^5)(4.2 \times 10^9)$
   $= (3.2)(4.2)(10^5)(10^9)$
   $= 13.44 \times 10^{14}$
   $= 1.344 \times 10^{15}$
   $= 1,344,000,000,000,000$

8. $(4.7 \times 10^2)(11 \times 10^4)$
   $= (4.7)(11)(10^2)(10^4)$
   $= 51.7 \times 10^6$
   $= 5.17 \times 10^7$
   $= 51,700,000$

9. $\dfrac{a^5}{a^3} = a^{5-3} = a^2$

10. $\dfrac{5y^{10}}{y^7} = 5(y^{10-7}) = 5y^3$

11. $\dfrac{4^{-6}}{4^{-3}} = 4^{-6-1-3}$
    $= 4^{-3} = \dfrac{1}{4^3} = \dfrac{1}{64}$

12. $\left(\dfrac{3}{4}\right)^0 = \dfrac{3^0}{4^0} = \dfrac{1}{1} = 1$

13. $(a^3b^2)^{-2}$
    $= (a^3)^{-2}(b^2)^{-2}$
    $= a^{-6}b^{-4}$
    $= \dfrac{1}{a^6b^4}$

14. $\dfrac{25m^2n^3}{5mn}$
    $= \left(\dfrac{25}{5}\right)\left(\dfrac{m^2}{m}\right)\left(\dfrac{n^3}{n}\right)$
    $= 5mn^2$

15. $\dfrac{20 \times 10^5}{10 \times 10^{-2}} = \left(\dfrac{20}{10}\right)\left(\dfrac{10^5}{10^{-2}}\right)$
    $= 2 \times 10^7$
    $= 20,000,000$

16. $\dfrac{(34,000,000)(24,000)}{6800} = \dfrac{(3.4 \times 10^7)(2.4 \times 10^4)}{6.8 \times 10^3}$

    $= \dfrac{(3.4)(2.4)(10^7)(10^4)}{6.8 \times 10^3}$

    $= \dfrac{8.16 \times 10^{11}}{6.8 \times 10^3}$

    $= 1.2 \times 10^8$

    $= 120,000,000$

17. $(9x + 2y) - (7x - 3y) = 9x - 7x + 2y + 3y$
    $= 2x + 5y$

18. $(4y^2 + 2y - 7) + (6y^2 - 3y + 2)$
    $= 4y^2 + 6y^2 + 2y - 3y - 7 + 2$
    $= 10y^2 - y - 5$

19. $(m - 2)(m + 5)$
    $= m^2 + 5m - 2m - 10$
    $= m^2 + 3m - 10$

20. $(2y + 7)(3y - 9)$
    $= 6y^2 - 18y + 21y - 63$
    $= 6y^2 + 3y - 63$

21. $(n + 2)(n^2 - 3n + 1)$
    $= n(n^2 - 3n + 1) + 2(n^2 - 3n + 1)$
    $= n^3 - 3n^2 + n + 2n^2 - 6n + 2$
    $= n^3 - n^2 - 5n + 2$

22. $(r + 4)(r - 1)^2$
    $= (r + 4)(r - 1)(r - 1)$
    $= (r + 4)(r^2 - 2r + 1)$
    $= r(r^2 - 2r + 1) + 4(r^2 - 2r + 1)$
    $= r^3 - 2r^2 + r + 4r^2 - 8r + 4$
    $= r^3 + 2r^2 - 7r + 4$

23. $5a + 5b = 5(a + b)$

24. $-14x^2 - 7x = -7x(2x + 1)$

25. $s^2 + 7s + 6 = s^2 + (6 + 1)s + 6 \cdot 1$
    $= (s + 6)(s + 1)$

26. $a(y + 2) - b(y + 2) = (y + 2)(a - b)$

27. $b^3 - 64 = b^3 - 4^3$
    $= (b - 4)(b^2 + 4b + 16)$

28. $8a^3 + 27 = 2^3a^3 + 3^3$
    $= (2a + 3)(2^2a^2 - 3 \cdot 2a + 3^2)$
    $= (2a + 3)(4a^2 - 6a + 9)$

29. $x^2 + 6x + 9 = x^2 + (3 + 3)x + 3 \cdot 3$
    $= (x + 3)(x + 3)$ or $(x + 3)^2$

30. $4x^2 - 81 = 2^2x^2 - 9^2$
    $= (2x - 9)(2x + 9)$

31. $2y^3 - 98y$

$= 2y(y^2 - 49)$

$= 2y(y^2 - 7^2)$

$= 2y(y - 7)(y + 7)$

32. $y^{2n} - 81$

$= (y^n)^2 - 9^2$

$= (y^n - 9)(y^n + 9)$

33.
$$\begin{array}{r} 6y + 4 \\ y + 2 \overline{\smash{\big)}\, 6y^2 + 16y + 8} \\ \underline{6y^2 + 12y} \\ 4y + 8 \\ \underline{4y + 8} \\ 0 \end{array}$$

34.
$$\begin{array}{r} x^2 + x + 3 + \frac{14}{x-3} \\ x - 3 \overline{\smash{\big)}\, x^3 - 2x^2 + 0x + 5} \\ \underline{x^3 - 3x^2} \\ x^2 + 0x \\ \underline{x^2 - 3x} \\ 3x + 5 \\ \underline{3x - 9} \\ 14 \end{array}$$

35.
$$\begin{array}{r} 4s - 2 \\ 2s + 1 \overline{\smash{\big)}\, 8s^2 + 0s - 2} \\ \underline{8s^2 + 4s} \\ -4s - 2 \\ \underline{-4s - 2} \\ 0 \end{array}$$

36.
$$\begin{array}{r} d^2 + d - 3 \\ 2d^2 - 3 \overline{\smash{\big)}\, 2d^4 + 2d^3 - 9d^2 - 3d + 9} \\ \underline{2d^4 + 0d^3 - 3d^2} \\ 2d^3 - 6d^2 - 3d + 9 \\ \underline{2d^3 + 0d^2 - 3d} \\ -6d^2 + 0d + 9 \\ \underline{-6d^2 + 0d + 9} \\ 0 \end{array}$$

37.
$$\begin{array}{r|rrrr} 4 & 1 & -4 & 3 & -7 \\ & & 4 & 0 & 12 \\ \hline & 1 & 0 & 3 & | \; 5 \end{array}$$

$x^2 + 3 + \dfrac{5}{x - 4}$

38.
$$\begin{array}{r|rrrrr} -2 & 1 & 0 & 0 & 0 & -16 \\ & & -2 & 4 & -8 & 16 \\ \hline & 1 & -2 & 4 & -8 & | \; 0 \end{array}$$

$n^3 - 2n^2 + 4n - 8$

39. $\dfrac{6y^3 + 11y^2 + y - 1}{2y + 3} = \dfrac{3y^3 + \frac{11}{2}y^2 + \frac{1}{2}y - \frac{1}{2}}{y + \frac{3}{2}}$

$$\begin{array}{r|rrrr} -\frac{3}{2} & 3 & \frac{11}{2} & \frac{1}{2} & -\frac{1}{2} \\ & & -\frac{9}{2} & -\frac{3}{2} & \frac{3}{2} \\ \hline & 3 & 1 & -1 & | \; 1 \end{array}$$

$3y^2 + y - 1 + \dfrac{1}{y + \frac{3}{2}} = 3y^2 + y - 1 + \dfrac{2}{2y + 3}$

40. $\dfrac{10a^4 - 11a^3 + a^2 - 3a + 1}{2a - 1}$

$= \dfrac{5a^4 - \frac{11}{2}a^3 + \frac{1}{2}a^2 - \frac{3}{2}a + \frac{1}{2}}{a - \frac{1}{2}}$

$$\begin{array}{r|rrrrr} \frac{1}{2} & 5 & \frac{-11}{2} & \frac{1}{2} & \frac{-3}{2} & \frac{1}{2} \\ & & \frac{5}{2} & \frac{-3}{2} & \frac{-1}{2} & -1 \\ \hline & 5 & -3 & -1 & -2 & | \; \frac{-1}{2} \end{array}$$

$5a^3 - 3a^2 - a - 2 - \dfrac{\frac{1}{2}}{a - \frac{1}{2}}$

$= 5a^3 - 3a^2 - a - 2 - \dfrac{1}{2a - 1}$

PAGE 248   APPLICATIONS AND CONNECTIONS

41. 365 days = 8760 hours = 525,600 minutes

$= 31,536,000$ seconds

$(186,000) \times (31,536,000)$ = miles in a light year

$= (1.86 \times 10^5)(3.1536 \times 10^7)$

$= (1.86)(3.1536)(10^5)(10^7)$

$= 5.865696 \times 10^{12}$ miles

$= 5,865,696,000,000$ miles

42. $908 = \dfrac{6.67 \times 10^{-8} \times M}{(6.37 \times 10^8)^2}$

$908(6.37 \times 10^8)^2 = 6.67 \times 10^{-8} \times M$

$908(40.5769)(10^{16}) = 6.67 \times 10^{-8} \times M$

$3.684382520 \times 10^{20} = 6.67 \times 10^{-8} \times M$

$\dfrac{3.684382520 \times 10^{20}}{6.67 \times 10^{-8}} = M$

$0.552381187 \times 10^{28} = M$

$5.52381187 \times 10^{27} = M$

about 5.5238×10^{27} g

or $5,523,800,000,000,000,000,000,000,000$

43.

Atlanta • ——— lunch ——— • Memphis

Let t = distance traveled while eating.

Let d = total distance. $d = 1$

$d = \frac{1}{3} + t + \frac{1}{2}\left(\frac{1}{3}\right)$

$1 = \frac{1}{3} + t + \frac{1}{6}$

$1 = \frac{1}{2} + t$

$\frac{1}{2} = t$

Troy traveled $\frac{1}{2}$ the trip while he was eating lunch.

117

44. Let p = the original price. Each week the price is 0.9 times the price the previous week. So,

price after 1 week = $0.9p$,

price after 2 weeks = $0.9(0.9p)$, and

price after 3 weeks = $0.9(0.9)(0.9)p$ or $0.729p$.

45. (length)(width) = $2x^2 + x - 6$

$\qquad\qquad\qquad = (2x - 3)(x + 2)$

the length is $2x - 3$; the width is $x + 2$

The perimeter is $2l + 2w$ or $2(2x - 3) + 2(x + 2)$

$\qquad\qquad\qquad\qquad = 4x - 6 + 2x + 4$

$\qquad\qquad\qquad\qquad = 6x - 2$

The baseboard needed is $6x - 2$ yards.

Chapter 5 Test

PAGE 249

1. $4y + 7y - 14y = -3y$

2. $9a^2 + 4a^2 - 2a^2 = 11a^2$

3. $x^4 y^3 (x^8) = x^{4+8} y^3$

$\qquad\qquad = x^{12} y^3$

4. $(4y)^3 (2y)^2 = 64y^3 4y^2$

$\qquad\qquad\qquad = 256y^5$

5. $\dfrac{n^4}{n^4} = n^0 = 1$

6. $\dfrac{y^2 (3x)^3}{4x^{-2}} = \dfrac{y^2 (3)^3 (x^3)}{4x^{-2}}$

$\qquad\qquad = y^2 \left(\dfrac{27}{4}\right) \left(\dfrac{x^3}{x^{-2}}\right)$

$\qquad\qquad = \dfrac{27}{4} x^5 y^2$

7. $\left(\dfrac{4s}{3t}\right)^0 = \dfrac{(4s)^0}{(3t)^0} = \dfrac{1}{1} = 1$

8. $\dfrac{13^{-6}}{13^{-9}} = 13^3 = 2197$

9. $\dfrac{r^2 s^{-3}}{s^{-2} t^4} = r^2 s^{-1} t^{-4} = \dfrac{r^2}{s t^4}$

10. $(7.82 \times 10^3)(934 \times 10^2)$

$\qquad = (7.82)(934)(10^3)(10^2)$

$\qquad = 7303.88 \times 10^5$

$\qquad = 7.30388 \times 10^8$

$\qquad = 730{,}388{,}000$

11. $\dfrac{84{,}000{,}000 \times 0.0013}{0.021}$

$\qquad = \dfrac{(8.4 \times 10^7)(1.3 \times 10^{-3})}{2.1 \times 10^{-2}}$

$\qquad = \dfrac{(8.4)(1.3)(10^7)(10^{-3})}{2.1 \times 10^{-2}}$

$\qquad = \dfrac{10.92 \times 10^4}{2.1 \times 10^{-2}}$

$\qquad = 5.2 \times 10^6$

$\qquad = 5{,}200{,}000$

12.

$10 \times 10 = 100$ sq. ft in 60 minutes

$5 \times 5 = 25$ sq. ft in x minutes

$\dfrac{x}{60} = \dfrac{25}{100}$

$1500 = 100x$

$15 = x$

It would take 15 minutes.

13. $(3x + 2) - (7x - 6) = 3x + 2 - 7x + 6$

$\qquad\qquad\qquad\qquad = -4x + 8$

14. $(m + 2)(m - 8)$

$\quad = m^2 - 8m + 2m - 16$

$\quad = m^2 - 6m - 16$

15. $(4n - 9)(5n + 2)$

$\quad = 20n^2 + 8n - 45n - 18$

$\quad = 20n^2 - 37n - 18$

16. $(s + 2)(s + 1)^2$

$\quad = (s + 2)(s + 1)(s + 1)$

$\quad = (s + 2)(s^2 + 2s + 1)$

$\quad = s(s^2 + 2s + 1) + 2(s^2 + 2s + 1)$

$\quad = s^3 + 2s^2 + s + 2s^2 + 4s + 2$

$\quad = s^3 + 4s^2 + 5s + 2$

17. $(t - 1)(t^2 - 2t - 6)$

$\quad = t(t^2 - 2t - 6) - 1(t^2 - 2t - 6)$

$\quad = t^3 - 2t^2 - 6t - t^2 + 2t + 6$

$\quad = t^3 - 3t^2 - 4t + 6$

18. $(r - 8)(r + 8)$

$\quad = r^2 + 8r - 8r - 64$

$\quad = r^2 - 64$

19. $3ab - 9b^2 = 3b(a - 3b)$

20. $y^2 - 7y + 6$

$\quad = y^2 - (6 + 1)y + (6 \cdot 1)$

$\quad = (y - 6)(y - 1)$

21. $f^2 + 16f + 64$

$= f^2 + (8 + 8)f + (8 \cdot 8)$

$= (f + 8)(f + 8)$ or $(f + 8)^2$

22. $w^2 - 144$

$= w^2 - (12)^2$

$= (w - 12)(w + 12)$

23. $y^3 - 125$

$= y^3 - (5)^3$

$= (y - 5)(y^2 + 5y + 25)$

24. $8x^3 + 1 = (2)^3 x^3 + 1^3$

$= (2x + 1)(4x^2 - 2x + 1)$

25. $x^{2n} - 49 = (x^n)^2 - (7)^2$

$= (x^n - 7)(x^n + 7)$

26. $ay + 2a - by - 2b = a(y + 2) - b(y + 2)$

$= (y + 2)(a - b)$

27. $\dfrac{5(w + 1)^6}{(w + 1)^3} = 5(w + 1)^3$

28. $\dfrac{4r^2 st + 12rst^2 - 10rt}{2rt} = \dfrac{2rt(2rs + 6st - 5)}{2rt}$

$= 2rs + 6st - 5$

29.
$$2s^2 - 5 \overline{\smash{\big)}\,16s^3 - 8s^2 - 40s + 15} \quad \begin{array}{l} 8s - 4 \quad - \dfrac{5}{2s^2 - 5} \end{array}$$

$\underline{16s^3 + 0s^2 - 40s}$

$-8s^2 - 0s + 15$

$\underline{-8s^2 + 0s + 20}$

-5

30.
$$x^2 + 2 \overline{\smash{\big)}\,x^4 - x^3 + x^2 - 2x - 2} \quad \begin{array}{l} x^2 - x - 1 \end{array}$$

$\underline{x^4 + 0x^3 + 2x^2}$

$-x^3 - x^2 - 2x - 2$

$\underline{-x^3 + 0x^2 - 2x}$

$-x^2 + 0x - 2$

$\underline{-x^2 + 0x - 2}$

0

31.
$$\begin{array}{r|rrrr} 1 & 2 & 1 & 4 & -7 \\ & & 2 & 3 & 7 \\ \hline & 2 & 3 & 7 & | \; 0 \end{array}$$

$2x^2 + 3x + 7$

32.
$$\begin{array}{r|rrrr} -4 & 1 & -2 & -17 & 30 \\ & & -4 & 24 & -28 \\ \hline & 1 & -6 & 7 & | \; 2 \end{array}$$

$m^2 - 6m + 7 + \dfrac{2}{m + 4}$

33.
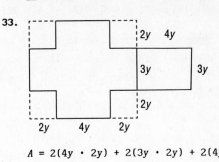

$A = 2(4y \cdot 2y) + 2(3y \cdot 2y) + 2(4y \cdot 3y)$

$= 16y^2 + 12y^2 + 24y^2$

$= 52y^2$

$52y^2 \text{ cm}^2$

PAGE 249   BONUS

$(36x^2 - 84xy + 49y^2 - 16a^2 - 24ab - 9b^2) \div$
$\qquad (-18xz + 21yz + 12az + 9bz)$

$= [6^2 x^2 - (42 + 42)xy + 7^2 y^2 - 4^2 a^2 - (12 + 12)ab -$
$\qquad 3^2 b^2] \div [-3z(6x - 7y) + 3z(4a + 3b)]$

$= \dfrac{[(6x - 7y)^2 - (4a + 3b)^2]}{-3z[(6x - 7y) - (4a + 3b)]}$

$= \dfrac{[(6x - 7y) - (4a + 3b)][(6x - 7y) + (4a + 3b)]}{-3z[(6x - 7y) - (4a + 3b)]}$

$= \dfrac{(6x - 7y) + (4a + 3b)}{-3z}$

Chapter 6
Irrational and Complex Numbers

6-1 Roots of Real Numbers

PAGE 255   CHECKING FOR UNDERSTANDING

1. An absolute value is not necessary if the root is a positive number regardless of the value of the variable.

2. $(-2n^3)^3 = (-2)^3(n^3)^3 = (-8n^9) \neq 8n^9$

3. Taking an nth root and raising to the nth power are inverse operations.

4. Only true for $x > 0$; if $x < 0$ then

$\sqrt[4]{(-x)^4} = -x.$

5. Only true for $x > 0$; if $x < 0$ then $\sqrt[5]{(-x)^5} = -x.$

6. $\sqrt{144} = \sqrt{(12)^2} = 12$

7. $-\sqrt{121} = -\sqrt{(11)^2} = -11$

8. $\sqrt[3]{8} = \sqrt[3]{2^3} = 2$ 9. $\sqrt[3]{y^3} = y$

10. $\sqrt[4]{16} = \sqrt[4]{2^4} = 2$ 11. $-\sqrt[4]{x^4} = -|x|$

12. $\sqrt[4]{t^8} = \sqrt[4]{(t^2)^4} = t^2$

13. $\sqrt[3]{-125} = \sqrt[3]{(-5)^3} = -5$

14. $\sqrt[5]{32n^5} = \sqrt[5]{2^5 n^5} = \sqrt[5]{(2n)^5} = 2n$

15. $\sqrt{16a^2b^4} = \sqrt{4^2 a^2 b^4} = 4|a|b^2$

16. $\sqrt{(y + 1)^2} = |y + 1|$

17. $\sqrt{x^2 + 6x + 9} = \sqrt{(x + 3)^2} = |x + 3|$

18. $\sqrt{3.2} = 1.789$ 19. $\sqrt{55} = 7.416$

20. $\sqrt[3]{9.8} = 2.140$ 21. $-\sqrt[3]{47} = -3.609$

22. $-\sqrt[3]{670} = -8.750$ 23. $\sqrt{64} = 8.000$

PAGES 256-257   EXERCISES

24. $\sqrt{83} = 9.110$ 25. $-\sqrt{99} = -9.950$

26. $\sqrt{9.5} = 3.082$ 27. $\sqrt[3]{23} = 2.844$

28. $\sqrt[3]{8.1} = 2.008$ 29. $-\sqrt[3]{41} = 3.448$

30. $\pm\sqrt{81} = \pm\sqrt{9^2}$ 31. $\sqrt{196} = \sqrt{14^2}$
$ = \pm 9$ $ = 14$

32. $\sqrt{256} = \sqrt{16^2}$ 33. $\sqrt[4]{81} = \sqrt[4]{(3)^4}$
$ = 16$ $ = 3$

34. $-\sqrt[3]{27} = -\sqrt[3]{3^3}$ 35. $\sqrt[3]{-216} = \sqrt[3]{(-6)^3}$
$ = -3$ $ = -6$

36. $\sqrt[5]{-1} = \sqrt[5]{(-1)^5}$ 37. $\sqrt[3]{-1000} = \sqrt[3]{(-10)^3}$
$ = -1$ $ = -10$

38. $\pm\sqrt{0.49} = \pm\sqrt{0.7^2}$ 39. $\sqrt[3]{0.125} = \sqrt[3]{0.5^3}$
$ = \pm 0.7$ $ = 0.5$

40. $\sqrt{121n^2} = \sqrt{(11n)^2}$ 41. $\sqrt{25y^6} = \sqrt{(5y^3)^2}$
$ = 11|n|$ $ = 5|y^3|$

42. $\sqrt{(3s)^4} = \sqrt{[(3s)^2]^2}$ 43. $\pm\sqrt{576} = \pm\sqrt{(24)^2}$
$ = (3s)^2$ or $9s^2$ $ = \pm 24$

44. $\sqrt{676} = \sqrt{(26)^2}$ 45. $\sqrt{64a^2b^4} = \sqrt{(8ab^2)^2}$
$ = 26$ $ = 8|a|b^2$

46. $-\sqrt{144b^2c^6} = -\sqrt{(12bc^3)^2}$
$ = -12|bc^3|$

47. $\sqrt[3]{-8b^3c^3} = \sqrt[3]{(-2bc)^3}$
$ = -2bc$

48. $\pm\sqrt[3]{27r^3s^3} = \pm\sqrt[3]{(3rs)^3}$ 49. $\sqrt[3]{64a^6b^3}$
$ = \pm 3rs$ $ = \sqrt[3]{(4a^2b)^3}$
$ = 4a^2b$

50. $\sqrt[4]{625n^8m^4} = \sqrt[4]{(5n^2m)^4}$ 51. $\sqrt{(3x + y)^2}$
$ = 5n^2|m|$ $ = |3x + y|$

52. $\sqrt{(a + b)^2} = |a + b|$ 53. $\sqrt[3]{(s + t)^3} = s + t$

54. $\sqrt[3]{(2x - y)^3} = 2x - y$ 55. $\sqrt[4]{(r + s)^4}$
$ = |r + s|$

56. $\sqrt[5]{(2m - 3)^5} = 2m - 3$ 57. $\sqrt{x^2 + 10x + 25}$
$ = \sqrt{(x + 5)^2}$
$ = |x + 5|$

58. $\sqrt{x^2 + 6x + 9}$ 59. $\sqrt{9a^2 + 6a + 1}$
$= \sqrt{(x + 3)^2}$ $= \sqrt{(3a + 1)^2}$
$= |x + 3|$ $= |3a + 1|$

60. $\sqrt{4y^2 + 12y + 9}$ 61. $\sqrt{s^2 - 2st + t^2}$
$= \sqrt{(2y + 3)^2}$ $= \sqrt{(s - t)^2}$
$= |2y + 3|$ $= |s - t|$

62. $\sqrt{4x^2 + 12xy + 9y^2}$
$= \sqrt{(2x + 3y)^2}$
$= |2x + 3y|$

63. when n is even and $x > 0$, or when n is any number and $x = 0$

64. $h = 64$, $g = 32$

$$t = \sqrt{\frac{2(64)}{32}} = \sqrt{\frac{128}{32}} = \sqrt{4} = 2$$

It will take 2 seconds for the ball to hit the ground.

65. $a = \frac{1}{2}(9.8) = 4.9$, $r = 25$

$$N = \frac{1}{2\pi}\sqrt{\frac{4.9}{25}} = \frac{1}{2\pi}\sqrt{0.196} = \frac{1}{2\pi}(0.4427) = \frac{0.4427}{2\pi}$$
$$= 0.07$$

0.07 rotations per second × 60 = 4.2 rotations per minute.

66.

$$\begin{array}{r|rrrr} -2 & 1 & 0 & -3 & 2 \\ & & -2 & 4 & -2 \\ \hline & 1 & -2 & 1 & 0 \end{array}$$

$$t^2 - 2t + 1$$

67. $\dfrac{5x^3 - 8x^2 + 38x - 18}{5x - 3}$

$$\frac{x^3 - \frac{8}{5}x^2 + \frac{38}{5}x - \frac{18}{5}}{x - \frac{3}{5}}$$

$$\begin{array}{r|rrrr} \frac{3}{5} & 1 & \frac{-8}{5} & \frac{38}{5} & \frac{-18}{5} \\ & & \frac{3}{5} & \frac{-3}{5} & \frac{21}{5} \\ \hline & 1 & -1 & 7 & \frac{3}{5} \end{array}$$

$$x^2 - x + 7 + \frac{\frac{3}{5}}{x - \frac{3}{5}} = x^2 - x + 7 + \frac{3}{5x - 3}$$

68. $(4.5 \times 10^4)(3.33 \times 10^2)$

$$= (4.5)(3.33)(10^4)(10^2)$$
$$= 14.985 \times 10^6$$
$$= 1.4985 \times 10^7$$
$$= 14{,}985{,}000$$

69. Multiply row 1 by −2 and add to row 2.
Multiply row 1 by −1 and add to row 3.
Multiply row 2 by $\frac{3}{2}$ and add to row 3.
Multiply row 3 by $\frac{2}{7}$. Add row 3 to row 2.
Multiply row 3 by −1 and add to row 1.
Multiply row 2 by $\frac{1}{2}$.
Multiply row 2 by −1 and add to row 1.

$$\begin{bmatrix} 1 & 1 & 1 & 0 \\ 2 & 4 & 1 & -1 \\ 1 & -2 & -1 & -2 \end{bmatrix} = \begin{bmatrix} 1 & 1 & 1 & 0 \\ 0 & 2 & -1 & -1 \\ 1 & -2 & -1 & -2 \end{bmatrix} = \begin{bmatrix} 1 & 1 & 1 & 0 \\ 0 & 2 & -1 & -1 \\ 0 & -3 & -2 & -2 \end{bmatrix} =$$

$$\begin{bmatrix} 1 & 1 & 1 & 0 \\ 0 & 2 & -1 & -1 \\ 0 & 0 & -\frac{7}{2} & -\frac{7}{2} \end{bmatrix} = \begin{bmatrix} 1 & 1 & 1 & 0 \\ 0 & 2 & -1 & -1 \\ 0 & 0 & 1 & 1 \end{bmatrix} = \begin{bmatrix} 1 & 1 & 1 & 0 \\ 0 & 2 & 0 & 0 \\ 0 & 0 & 1 & 1 \end{bmatrix}$$

$$= \begin{bmatrix} 1 & 1 & 0 & -1 \\ 0 & 2 & 0 & 0 \\ 0 & 0 & 1 & 1 \end{bmatrix} = \begin{bmatrix} 1 & 1 & 0 & -1 \\ 0 & 1 & 0 & 0 \\ 0 & 0 & 1 & 1 \end{bmatrix} = \begin{bmatrix} 1 & 0 & 0 & -1 \\ 0 & 1 & 0 & 0 \\ 0 & 0 & 1 & 1 \end{bmatrix}$$

The solution is $(-1, 0, 1)$.

70. 2 × 3, no determinant

71. 4

72. Up to and including one hour → \$1.50
One hour to two hours → \$3.00
Two hours to 3 hours → \$4.50
This is a step function.

PAGE 257   LANGUAGE CONNECTION

Answers will vary. Sample answers are given.

1. Don't be a negative person. The negative of −3 is 3.

2. There is power in learning. Five raised to the 3rd power is 125.

3. A rational person has good sense. A rational number can be written as $\frac{a}{b}$.

4. A suit and a blouse are coordinates. In a graph, the coordinates are numbers paired with points.

5. Darlene earned a degree in mathematics. The degree of a variable is its exponent.

6. That is the absolute truth. The absolute value of −2 is 2.

7. The identity of your secret admirer is unknown. An example of a mathematical identity is $x + 5 = x + 5$.

8. That is a real flower! Real numbers contain no imaginary numbers.

6-2 Products and Quotients of Radicals

PAGES 261-262   CHECKING FOR UNDERSTANDING

1. the product and quotient properties of radicals

2. If a and b were allowed to be negative when n is even, they would have no real roots. a and b may be negative when n is odd because negative radicands can have real roots if n is odd.

3. It meets all criteria for simplified expressions.

4. Multiply by $\dfrac{\sqrt{2}}{\sqrt{2}}$ to get $2\sqrt{2}$.

5. $\sqrt{27} = \sqrt{9 \cdot 3} = 3\sqrt{3}$

6. $\sqrt{32} = \sqrt{16 \cdot 2} = 4\sqrt{2}$

7. $\sqrt{98y^4} = \sqrt{(49 \cdot 2)(y^2)^2}$
$= 7y^2\sqrt{2}$

8. $\sqrt{50x^2} = \sqrt{25 \cdot 2 \cdot x^2}$
$= 5|x|\sqrt{2}$

9. $\sqrt[3]{16} = \sqrt[3]{8 \cdot 2} = 2\sqrt[3]{2}$ 10. $\sqrt[4]{48} = \sqrt[4]{16 \cdot 3} = 2\sqrt[4]{3}$

11. $\sqrt{y^3} = \sqrt{y^2 \cdot y}$ 12. $\sqrt{a^5} = \sqrt{a^4 \cdot a}$

$\quad = y\sqrt{y}$ $\quad = a^2\sqrt{a}$

13. $\sqrt[4]{t^5} = \sqrt[4]{t^4 \cdot t}$ 14. $\dfrac{6}{\sqrt{2}} = \dfrac{6}{\sqrt{2}} \cdot \dfrac{\sqrt{2}}{\sqrt{2}}$

$\quad = t\sqrt[4]{t}$ $\quad = \dfrac{6\sqrt{2}}{2}$

$\quad = 3\sqrt{2}$

15. $\dfrac{1}{\sqrt{3}} = \dfrac{1}{\sqrt{3}} \cdot \dfrac{\sqrt{3}}{\sqrt{3}}$ 16. $\dfrac{1}{\sqrt{x}} = \dfrac{1}{\sqrt{x}} \cdot \dfrac{\sqrt{x}}{\sqrt{x}}$

$\quad = \dfrac{\sqrt{3}}{3}$ $\quad = \dfrac{\sqrt{x}}{x}$

17. $\dfrac{3}{\sqrt{b}} = \dfrac{3}{\sqrt{b}} \cdot \dfrac{\sqrt{b}}{\sqrt{b}}$ 18. $\dfrac{3}{\sqrt[3]{4}} = \dfrac{3}{\sqrt[3]{4}} \cdot \dfrac{\sqrt[3]{2}}{\sqrt[3]{2}}$

$\quad = \dfrac{3\sqrt{b}}{b}$ $\quad = \dfrac{3\sqrt[3]{2}}{\sqrt[3]{8}}$

$\quad = \dfrac{3\sqrt[3]{2}}{2}$

19. $\dfrac{7}{\sqrt[3]{9}} = \dfrac{7}{\sqrt[3]{9}} \cdot \dfrac{\sqrt[3]{3}}{\sqrt[3]{3}}$

$\quad = \dfrac{7\sqrt[3]{3}}{\sqrt[3]{27}}$

$\quad = \dfrac{7\sqrt[3]{3}}{3}$

PAGES 262-263   EXERCISES

20. $5\sqrt{50} = 5\sqrt{25 \cdot 2}$ 21. $4\sqrt{54} = 4\sqrt{9 \cdot 6}$

$\quad = 25\sqrt{2}$ $\quad = 12\sqrt{6}$

22. $\sqrt[3]{32} = \sqrt[3]{8 \cdot 4}$ 23. $\sqrt[3]{56} = \sqrt[3]{8 \cdot 7}$

$\quad = 2\sqrt[3]{4}$ $\quad = 2\sqrt[3]{7}$

24. $\sqrt{162} = \sqrt{81 \cdot 2}$ 25. $\sqrt{675} = \sqrt{225 \cdot 3}$

$\quad = 9\sqrt{2}$ $\quad = 15\sqrt{3}$

26. $\sqrt{8a^2b^3}$ 27. $\sqrt{8x^2y} \cdot \sqrt{2xy}$

$\quad = \sqrt{4 \cdot 2a^2b^2 \cdot b}$ $\quad = \sqrt{16x^3y^2}$

$\quad = 2|a|b\sqrt{2b}$ $\quad = 4xy\sqrt{x}$

28. $\sqrt[4]{81m^4n^5}$ 29. $\dfrac{\sqrt{10}}{\sqrt{5}} = \dfrac{\sqrt{5 \cdot 2}}{\sqrt{5}}$

$\quad = \sqrt[4]{3^4 m^4 n^4 \cdot n}$ $\quad = \sqrt{2}$

$\quad = 3|m|n\sqrt[4]{n}$

30. $\dfrac{\sqrt{12}}{\sqrt{3}} = \dfrac{\sqrt{4 \cdot 3}}{\sqrt{3}}$ 31. $\dfrac{\sqrt{22}}{\sqrt{2}} = \dfrac{\sqrt{2 \cdot 11}}{\sqrt{2}}$

$\quad = \sqrt{4} = 2$ $\quad = \sqrt{11}$

32. $\sqrt[3]{-192} = \sqrt[3]{-64 \cdot 3}$ 33. $6\sqrt{216} = 6\sqrt{36 \cdot 6}$

$\quad = -4\sqrt[3]{3}$ $\quad = 36\sqrt{6}$

34. $3\sqrt{242} = 3\sqrt{121 \cdot 2}$ 35. $\sqrt[4]{112} = \sqrt[4]{16 \cdot 7}$

$\quad = 33\sqrt{2}$ $\quad = 2\sqrt[4]{7}$

36. $(-3\sqrt{24})(5\sqrt{20})$ 37. $(4\sqrt{18})(2\sqrt{14})$

$\quad = (-3\sqrt{4 \cdot 6})(5\sqrt{4 \cdot 5})$ $\quad = (12\sqrt{2})(2\sqrt{14})$

$\quad = (-6\sqrt{6})(10\sqrt{5})$ $\quad = 24\sqrt{28}$

$\quad = -60\sqrt{30}$ $\quad = 48\sqrt{7}$

38. $\sqrt[3]{121} \cdot \sqrt[3]{88}$ 39. $\sqrt{3}(\sqrt{6} - 2)$

$\quad = \sqrt[3]{121} \cdot 2\sqrt[3]{11}$ $\quad = \sqrt{18} - 2\sqrt{3}$

$\quad = 2\sqrt[3]{1331}$ $\quad = 3\sqrt{2} - 2\sqrt{3}$

$\quad = 2\sqrt[3]{11^3}$

$\quad = 22$

40. $\sqrt{3x^2z^3} \cdot \sqrt{15x^2z}$ 41. $\sqrt[4]{a^5b^3} \cdot \sqrt[4]{81a^3b^2}$

$\quad = \sqrt{45x^4z^4}$ $\quad = \sqrt[4]{81a^8b^5}$

$\quad = 3x^2z^2\sqrt{5}$ $\quad = 3a^2b\sqrt[4]{b}$

42. $\sqrt{\dfrac{7}{4}} = \dfrac{\sqrt{7}}{\sqrt{4}} = \dfrac{\sqrt{7}}{2}$ 43. $\dfrac{\sqrt[3]{81}}{\sqrt[3]{9}} = \sqrt[3]{\dfrac{81}{9}} = \sqrt[3]{9}$

44. $\sqrt{\dfrac{1}{3}} = \dfrac{\sqrt{1}}{\sqrt{3}} = \dfrac{\sqrt{3}}{3}$ 45. $\sqrt{\dfrac{5}{12a}} = \dfrac{\sqrt{5}}{\sqrt{12a}}$

$\quad = \dfrac{\sqrt{5}}{2\sqrt{3a}}$

$\quad = \dfrac{\sqrt{5}}{2\sqrt{3a}} \cdot \dfrac{\sqrt{3a}}{\sqrt{3a}}$

$\quad = \dfrac{\sqrt{15a}}{6a}$

46. $\sqrt{7}(\sqrt{14} + \sqrt{21})$ 47. $\sqrt{a}(\sqrt{b} + \sqrt{ab})$

$\quad = \sqrt{98} + \sqrt{147}$ $\quad = \sqrt{ab} + \sqrt{a^2b}$

$\quad = 7\sqrt{2} + 7\sqrt{3}$ $\quad = \sqrt{ab} + a\sqrt{b}$

48. $\sqrt{r}(\sqrt{r} + r\sqrt{s})$ 49. $\sqrt[3]{\dfrac{54}{125}} = \dfrac{\sqrt[3]{54}}{\sqrt[3]{125}} = \dfrac{3\sqrt[3]{2}}{5}$

$\quad = \sqrt{r^2} + r\sqrt{rs}$

$\quad = r + r\sqrt{rs}$

50. $\sqrt[4]{\dfrac{5}{16}} = \dfrac{\sqrt[4]{5}}{\sqrt[4]{16}} = \dfrac{\sqrt[4]{5}}{2}$ 51. $\sqrt{\dfrac{5}{32x}} = \dfrac{\sqrt{5}}{\sqrt{32x}}$

$\quad = \dfrac{\sqrt{5}}{4\sqrt{2x}} \cdot \dfrac{\sqrt{2x}}{\sqrt{2x}}$

$\quad = \dfrac{\sqrt{10x}}{8x}$

52. $\sqrt[4]{\dfrac{2}{3}} = \dfrac{\sqrt[4]{2}}{\sqrt[4]{3}} \cdot \dfrac{\sqrt[4]{3^3}}{\sqrt[4]{3^3}}$

$\quad = \dfrac{\sqrt[4]{2 \cdot 27}}{3}$

$\quad = \dfrac{\sqrt[4]{54}}{3}$

53. $r = \dfrac{1}{2}\sqrt{\dfrac{616}{\pi}}$

$\quad = \dfrac{1}{2}\dfrac{\sqrt{616\pi}}{\pi}$

$\quad = \dfrac{1}{2}\dfrac{2\sqrt{154\pi}}{\pi}$

$\quad = \dfrac{\sqrt{154\pi}}{\pi}$

$\quad = \dfrac{22}{\pi}$

$\quad \sim 7 \text{ inches}$

54. true; Every integer can be written as the square root of a square.

55. $T = 2\pi\sqrt{\dfrac{L}{384}}$

$\quad 1 = 2\pi\sqrt{\dfrac{L}{384}}$

$\quad \dfrac{1}{2\pi} = \dfrac{\sqrt{L}}{\sqrt{384}}$

$\quad \dfrac{1}{2\pi} = \dfrac{\sqrt{L}}{8\sqrt{6}}$

$\quad \dfrac{1}{2\pi} = \dfrac{\sqrt{6L}}{48}$

$\quad \dfrac{48}{2\pi} = \sqrt{6L}$

$\quad \dfrac{24}{\pi} = \sqrt{6L}$

$\quad \dfrac{576}{\pi^2} = 6L$

$\quad \dfrac{96}{\pi^2} = L$

$\quad 9.73 = L \qquad 9.73 \text{ inches}$

56. $t = \dfrac{1}{4}\sqrt{s}$

$\quad t = \dfrac{1}{4}\sqrt{150}$

$\quad t = \dfrac{1}{4} \cdot 5\sqrt{6}$

$\quad t = \dfrac{5\sqrt{6}}{4}$

$\quad = 3.06 \quad \sim 3.06 \text{ seconds}$

57. $\sqrt{(5b)^4} = \sqrt{[(5b)^2]^2}$

$\quad = (5b)^2$

$\quad = 25b^2$

58. $-\sqrt{121b^2c^6}$

$\quad = -\sqrt{11^2 b^2 (c^3)^2}$

$\quad = -11|bc^3|$

59. $(9 \times 10^3)^{-1}(3.5 \times 10^{-2})$

$\quad = \dfrac{3.5 \times 10^{-2}}{9 \times 10^3}$

$\quad = 0.3\overline{8} \times 10^{-5}$

$\quad = 3.\overline{8} \times 10^{-6}$

$\quad = 0.00000 3\overline{8}$

60. No, only square matrices have inverses.

61. $3x + 6(0) - 8(0) = 24 \qquad 3(0) + 6y - 8(0) = 24$

$\qquad\qquad\qquad 3x = 24 \qquad\qquad\qquad\qquad 6y = 24$

$\qquad\qquad\qquad\ x = 8 \qquad\qquad\qquad\qquad\ y = 4$

$\quad 3(0) + 6(0) - 8z = 24$

$\qquad\qquad\qquad -8z = 24$

$\qquad\qquad\qquad\ \ z = -3$

$\qquad\qquad x = 8,\ y = 4,\ z = -3$

62. $h(-2.1) = [3(-2.1) - 1]$

$\qquad\qquad = [-6.3 - 1]$

$\qquad\qquad = [-7.3]$

$\qquad\qquad = -8$

6-3 Computing with Radicals

1. No, they have different indices.

2. $-4 + 2\sqrt{2}$

3. The product is the difference of two squares.

$(a\sqrt{b} + c\sqrt{d})(a\sqrt{b} - c\sqrt{d})$

$\quad = (a\sqrt{b})^2 - (a\sqrt{b})(c\sqrt{d}) + (a\sqrt{b})(c\sqrt{d}) - (c\sqrt{d})^2$

$\quad = (a\sqrt{b})^2 - (c\sqrt{d})^2$

$\quad = a^2 b - c^2 d$

As long as a, b, c and d are rational, the product of the conjugates will also be rational.

4. $\dfrac{5 - 2\sqrt{3}}{5 - 2\sqrt{3}}$

5. $5 + \sqrt{7}$ 　　　　　　 **6.** $1 - \sqrt{3}$

7. $\sqrt{3} - \sqrt{10}$ 　　　 **8.** $\sqrt{3} - 5$

9. $2 + 2\sqrt{3}$ 　　　　 **10.** $7 + 3\sqrt{5}$

11. $5\sqrt{3} - 4\sqrt{3} = \sqrt{3}$ 　　 **12.** $7\sqrt{y} - 4\sqrt{y} = 3\sqrt{y}$

13. $8\sqrt[3]{6} + 3\sqrt[3]{6} = 11\sqrt[3]{6}$ 　 **14.** $\sqrt[5]{3} + 4\sqrt[5]{3} = 5\sqrt[5]{3}$

15. $2\sqrt{2} + \sqrt{8}$ 　　　 **16.** $\sqrt[3]{40} - 2\sqrt{5}$

$\quad = 2\sqrt{2} + \sqrt{4 \cdot 2}$ 　　 $= \sqrt[3]{2^3 \cdot 5} - 2\sqrt{5}$

$\quad = 2\sqrt{2} + 2\sqrt{2}$ 　　　 $= 2\sqrt{5} - 2\sqrt{5}$

$\quad = 4\sqrt{2}$ 　　　　　　 $= 0$

17. $-3\sqrt{5} + 5\sqrt{2} + 4\sqrt{20} - 3\sqrt{50}$

$\quad = -3\sqrt{5} + 5\sqrt{2} + 4\sqrt{2^2 \cdot 5} - 3\sqrt{5^2 \cdot 2}$

$\quad = -3\sqrt{5} + 5\sqrt{2} + 8\sqrt{5} - 15\sqrt{2}$

$\quad = 5\sqrt{5} - 10\sqrt{2}$

18. $5\sqrt{2} + 3\sqrt{2} - 8 = 8\sqrt{2} - 8$

19. $8\sqrt{3} - 3\sqrt{75} = 8\sqrt{3} - 3\sqrt{5^2 \cdot 3}$

$\qquad\qquad\qquad\ = 8\sqrt{3} - 15\sqrt{3}$

$\qquad\qquad\qquad\ = -7\sqrt{3}$

20. $3\sqrt{7} - 5\sqrt{28} = 3\sqrt{7} - 5\sqrt{2^2 \cdot 7}$

$\qquad\qquad\qquad\ = 3\sqrt{7} - 10\sqrt{7}$

$\qquad\qquad\qquad\ = -7\sqrt{7}$

21. $(3 + \sqrt{5})(4 + \sqrt{5}) = 3 \cdot 4 + 3\sqrt{5} + 4\sqrt{5} + (\sqrt{5})^2$

$\qquad\qquad\qquad\qquad = 12 + 7\sqrt{5} + 5$

$\qquad\qquad\qquad\qquad = 17 + 7\sqrt{5}$

22. $(5 + \sqrt{3})(3 - \sqrt{3})$

$= 5 \cdot 3 + 5(-\sqrt{3}) + 3\sqrt{3} + (\sqrt{3})(-\sqrt{3})$

$= 15 - 5\sqrt{3} + 3\sqrt{3} - (\sqrt{3})^2$

$= 15 + -2\sqrt{3} - 3$

$= 12 - 2\sqrt{3}$

23. $(3x + \sqrt{5y})(3x - \sqrt{5y})$

$= 9x^2 - 3x\sqrt{5y} + 3x\sqrt{5y} - (\sqrt{5y})^2$

$= 9x^2 - 5y$

24. $(6 - \sqrt{2})(6 + \sqrt{2}) = 36 + 6\sqrt{2} - 6\sqrt{2} + 2$

$= 34$

25. $(4 + \sqrt{3})^2 = 16 + 4\sqrt{3} + 4\sqrt{3} + 3$

$= 19 + 8\sqrt{3}$

26. $(a + \sqrt{b})^2 = a^2 + a\sqrt{b} + a\sqrt{b} + (\sqrt{b})^2$

$= a^2 + 2a\sqrt{b} + b$

27. $5\sqrt{20} + \sqrt{24} - \sqrt{180} + 7\sqrt{54}$

$= 5\sqrt{2^2 \cdot 5} + \sqrt{2^2 \cdot 6} - \sqrt{6^2 \cdot 5} + 7\sqrt{3^2 \cdot 6}$

$= 10\sqrt{5} + 2\sqrt{6} - 6\sqrt{5} + 21\sqrt{6}$

$= 4\sqrt{5} + 23\sqrt{6}$

28. $7\sqrt[3]{5t} + 4\sqrt[3]{5t} = 11\sqrt[3]{5t}$

29. $\sqrt[3]{54} - \sqrt[3]{128} = \sqrt[3]{27 \cdot 2} - \sqrt[3]{64 \cdot 2}$

$= 3\sqrt[3]{2} - 4\sqrt[3]{2}$

$= -\sqrt[3]{2}$

30. $8\sqrt[3]{2x} + 3\sqrt[3]{2x} - 8\sqrt[3]{2x} = 3\sqrt[3]{2x}$

31. $3\sqrt[3]{48} - \sqrt[3]{6} = \sqrt[3]{8 \cdot 6} - \sqrt[3]{6}$

$= 2\sqrt[3]{6} - \sqrt[3]{6}$

$= \sqrt[3]{6}$

32. $7\sqrt[3]{2} + 6\sqrt[3]{150} = 7\sqrt[3]{2} + 6\sqrt[3]{150}$

33. $5\sqrt[3]{135} - 2\sqrt[3]{81} = 5\sqrt[3]{27 \cdot 5} - 2\sqrt[3]{27 \cdot 3}$

$= 5 \cdot 3\sqrt[3]{5} - 2 \cdot 3\sqrt[3]{3}$

$= 15\sqrt[3]{5} - 6\sqrt[3]{3}$

34. $(5 + \sqrt{2})(3 + \sqrt{2}) = 15 + 5\sqrt{2} + 3\sqrt{2} + 2$

$= 17 + 8\sqrt{2}$

35. $(5 + \sqrt{6})(5 - \sqrt{2}) = 25 - 5\sqrt{2} + 5\sqrt{6} - \sqrt{12}$

$= 25 - 5\sqrt{2} + 5\sqrt{6} - 2\sqrt{3}$

36. $(8 - \sqrt{3})(6 + \sqrt{3}) = 48 + 8\sqrt{3} - 6\sqrt{3} - 3$

$= 45 + 2\sqrt{3}$

37. $(7 + \sqrt{11y})(7 - \sqrt{11y}) = 49 - 7\sqrt{11y} + 7\sqrt{11y} - 11y$

$= 49 - 11y$

38. $(\sqrt{3} + \sqrt{5})(\sqrt{12} - \sqrt{5}) = \sqrt{36} - \sqrt{15} + \sqrt{60} - 5$

$= 6 - \sqrt{15} + \sqrt{4 \cdot 15} - 5$

$= 6 - 5 - \sqrt{15} + 2\sqrt{15}$

$= 1 + \sqrt{15}$

39. $\dfrac{1}{3 + \sqrt{5}} = \dfrac{1}{3 + \sqrt{5}} \cdot \dfrac{3 - \sqrt{5}}{3 - \sqrt{5}}$

$= \dfrac{3 - \sqrt{5}}{3^2 + -(\sqrt{5})^2}$

$= \dfrac{3 - \sqrt{5}}{9 + (-5)}$

$= \dfrac{3 - \sqrt{5}}{4}$

40. $\dfrac{7}{4 - \sqrt{3}} = \dfrac{7}{4 - \sqrt{3}} \cdot \dfrac{4 + \sqrt{3}}{4 + \sqrt{3}}$

$= \dfrac{28 + 7\sqrt{3}}{16 - 3}$

$= \dfrac{28 + 7\sqrt{3}}{13}$

41. $7\sqrt[3]{24} + \sqrt[3]{24} = 7\sqrt[3]{2^2 \cdot 6} + \sqrt[3]{2^3 \cdot 3}$

$= 14\sqrt[3]{6} + 2\sqrt[3]{3}$

42. $\sqrt{98} - \sqrt{72} + \sqrt{32} = \sqrt{7^2 \cdot 2} - \sqrt{6^2 \cdot 2} + \sqrt{4^2 \cdot 2}$

$= 7\sqrt{2} - 6\sqrt{2} + 4\sqrt{2}$

$= 5\sqrt{2}$

43. $7\sqrt[4]{2} + 8\sqrt[4]{2} = 15\sqrt[4]{2}$

44. $\sqrt[4]{x^2} + \sqrt[4]{x^6} = \sqrt[4]{x^2} + \sqrt[4]{x^4 \cdot x^2}$

$= \sqrt[4]{x^2} + |x|\sqrt[4]{x^2}$

$= (1 + |x|)\sqrt[4]{x^2}$

45. $\sqrt[4]{y^4} + \sqrt[3]{y^6} + \sqrt{y^8} = |y| + \sqrt[3]{(y^2)^3} + \sqrt{(y^4)^2}$

$= |y| + y^2 + y^4$

46. $(4\sqrt{5} - 3\sqrt{2})(2\sqrt{5} + 2\sqrt{2})$

$= 8(\sqrt{5})^2 + 8\sqrt{10} - 6\sqrt{10} - 6(\sqrt{2})^2$

$= 40 + 2\sqrt{10} - 12$

$= 28 + 2\sqrt{10}$

47. $\left(m + \sqrt[3]{4}\right)\left(m^2 - m\sqrt[3]{4} + \sqrt[3]{16}\right)$

$= m^3 - m^2\sqrt[3]{4} + m\sqrt[3]{16} + m^2\sqrt[3]{4} - m\sqrt[3]{16} + \sqrt[3]{64}$

$= m^3 + 4$

48. $\left(2 + \sqrt[3]{s}\right)\left(4 - 2\sqrt[3]{s} + \sqrt[3]{s^2}\right)$

$= 8 - 4\sqrt[3]{s} + 2\sqrt[3]{s^2} + 4\sqrt[3]{s} - 2\sqrt[3]{s^2} + \sqrt[3]{s^3}$

$= 8 + s$

49. $\dfrac{\sqrt{x + 1}}{\sqrt{x - 1}} = \dfrac{\sqrt{x + 1}}{\sqrt{x - 1}} \cdot \dfrac{\sqrt{x - 1}}{\sqrt{x - 1}}$

$= \dfrac{\sqrt{x^2 - x + x - 1}}{x - 1}$

$= \dfrac{\sqrt{x^2 - 1}}{x - 1}$

50. $\dfrac{\sqrt{3} + n\sqrt{6}}{4 - \sqrt{n}} = \dfrac{\sqrt{3} + n\sqrt{6}}{4 - \sqrt{n}} \cdot \dfrac{4 + \sqrt{n}}{4 + \sqrt{n}}$

$$= \dfrac{4\sqrt{3} + \sqrt{3}\sqrt{n} + 4n\sqrt{6} + n\sqrt{6}\sqrt{n}}{4^2 - (\sqrt{n})^2}$$

$$= \dfrac{4\sqrt{3} + \sqrt{3n} + 4n\sqrt{6} + n\sqrt{6n}}{16 - n}$$

51. $\sqrt{\dfrac{2}{5}} + \sqrt{40} + \sqrt{10} = \dfrac{\sqrt{2}}{\sqrt{5}} + 2\sqrt{10} + \sqrt{10}$

$$= \dfrac{\sqrt{2}}{\sqrt{5}} + 3\sqrt{10}$$

$$= \dfrac{\sqrt{2}}{\sqrt{5}} \cdot \dfrac{\sqrt{5}}{\sqrt{5}} + 3\sqrt{10}$$

$$= \dfrac{\sqrt{10}}{5} + 3\sqrt{10}$$

$$= \dfrac{\sqrt{10} + 15\sqrt{10}}{5}$$

$$= \dfrac{16\sqrt{10}}{5}$$

52. $\sqrt[3]{\dfrac{2}{3}} + \sqrt[3]{144} - \sqrt[3]{243} = \dfrac{\sqrt[3]{2}}{\sqrt[3]{3}} \cdot \dfrac{\sqrt[3]{3^2}}{\sqrt[3]{3^2}} + 2\sqrt[3]{18} - 3\sqrt[3]{9}$

$$= \dfrac{\sqrt[3]{18}}{3} + \dfrac{2\sqrt[3]{18} \cdot 3}{3} - 3\sqrt[3]{9}$$

$$= \dfrac{7\sqrt[3]{18}}{3} - 3\sqrt[3]{9}$$

53. No, all of these operations can have a rational number as a result.

54. $V = \sqrt{\dfrac{F_c r}{100}}$, $F_c = 2000$, $r = 320$

$$V = \sqrt{\dfrac{2000(320)}{100}} = \sqrt{\dfrac{640,000}{100}} = \sqrt{6400} = 80$$

The car can round the turn at 80 ft/sec, or about 55 mph.

55. $t = 2\sqrt{\dfrac{2h}{g}}$, $h = 112$, $g = 32$

$$t = 2\sqrt{\dfrac{2(112)}{32}} = 2\sqrt{\dfrac{224}{32}} = 2\sqrt{7}$$

The catcher has $2\sqrt{7}$ seconds or 5.3 seconds.

56. $5\sqrt{54} = 5\sqrt{9 \cdot 6}$

$$= 15\sqrt{6}$$

57. $\sqrt[4]{5m^3n^5} \cdot \sqrt[4]{125m^2n^3} = \sqrt[4]{5 \cdot 125m^3 \cdot m^2 \cdot n^5 \cdot n^3}$

$$= \sqrt[4]{5^4 m^5 n^8}$$

$$= 5mn^2\sqrt[4]{m}$$

58. $1 - 8a^3 = 1^3 - 2^3a^3$

$$= 1^3 - (2a)^3$$

$$= (1 - 2a)(1 + 2a + 4a^2)$$

59. $c^3 \cdot c^2 \cdot c^4 = c^9$

60. Dimension: (3×3)

Determinant $= (-1) \cdot 4 \cdot (3) + 1 \cdot 0 \cdot 2 + 7 \cdot 0$
$\cdot 2 - 2 \cdot 4 \cdot 7 - 2 \cdot 0 \cdot (-1) - 3$
$\cdot 0 \cdot 1$

$$= -68$$

61. $f(0, 0) = 0 - 0$ The maximum is 6 at $(6, 0)$
$= 0$ and the minimum is (-5) at
$f(0, 5) = 0 - 5$ $(0, 5)$.
$= -5$
$f(3, 4) = 3 - 4$
$= -1$
$f(6, 0) = 6 - 0$
$= 6$

6-4   Rational Exponents

PAGE 272   CHECKING FOR UNDERSTANDING

1. If the base were negative and the denominator were even, then we would be taking an even root of a negative, which is undefined.

2. $\sqrt[4]{33} = 33^{\frac{1}{4}}$

3. No, because $256 = 2^6 \cdot 4$.

$\sqrt[6]{256} = \sqrt[6]{2^6 \cdot 4} = \sqrt[6]{2^6} \cdot \sqrt[6]{4} = 2\sqrt[6]{2^2} = 2\left(2^{\frac{2}{6}}\right)$

$= 2\left(2^{\frac{1}{3}}\right) = 2\sqrt[3]{2}$

4. $9^{\frac{3}{2}} = \sqrt[2]{9^3}$ **5.** $8^{\frac{2}{3}} = \sqrt[3]{8^2}$ **6.** $4^{\frac{3}{2}} = \sqrt[2]{4^3}$
$= \sqrt{729}$ $= \sqrt[3]{64}$ $= \sqrt{64}$
$= 27$ $= 4$ $= 8$

7. $16^{\frac{3}{4}} = \sqrt[4]{16^3}$ **8.** $64^{\frac{5}{6}} = \left(\sqrt[6]{64}\right)^5$
$= \sqrt[4]{4096}$ $= 2^5$
$= 8$ $= 32$

9. $27^{-\frac{2}{3}} = \left(\sqrt[3]{27}\right)^{-2}$ **10.** $\sqrt[3]{8^2} = \left(\sqrt[3]{8}\right)^2$
$= 3^{-2}$ $= 2^2$
$= \dfrac{1}{3^2}$ or $\dfrac{1}{9}$ $= 4$

11. $343^{\frac{2}{3}} = \left(\sqrt[3]{343}\right)^2$ **12.** $\sqrt[4]{81} = \sqrt[4]{3^4}$
$= 7^2$ $= 3$
$= 49$

13. $9^{\frac{1}{3}} \cdot 9^{\frac{5}{3}} = 9^{\frac{6}{3}}$

$\qquad = 9^2$

$\qquad = 81$

14. $16^{-\frac{3}{2}} = (\sqrt{16})^{-3}$

$\qquad = 4^{-3}$

$\qquad = \frac{1}{4^3}$ or $\frac{1}{64}$

15. $36^{\frac{3}{4}} \div 36^{\frac{1}{4}} = 36^{\frac{1}{2}}$

$\qquad = \sqrt{36}$

$\qquad = 6$

16. $\sqrt[6]{49} = \sqrt[6]{7^2}$

$\qquad = 7^{\frac{2}{6}}$

$\qquad = 7^{\frac{1}{3}}$

$\qquad = \sqrt[3]{7}$

17. $\sqrt[4]{36} = \sqrt[4]{6^2}$

$\qquad = 6^{\frac{2}{4}}$

$\qquad = 6^{\frac{1}{2}}$

$\qquad = \sqrt{6}$

18. $\sqrt[6]{81} = \sqrt[6]{9^2}$

$\qquad = 9^{\frac{2}{6}}$

$\qquad = 9^{\frac{1}{3}}$

$\qquad = \sqrt[3]{9}$

19. $\sqrt[8]{16} = \sqrt[8]{2^4}$

$\qquad = 2^{\frac{4}{8}}$

$\qquad = 2^{\frac{1}{2}}$

$\qquad = \sqrt{2}$

20. $\sqrt[4]{25} = \sqrt[4]{5^2}$

$\qquad = 5^{\frac{2}{4}}$

$\qquad = 5^{\frac{1}{2}}$

$\qquad = \sqrt{5}$

21. $\sqrt[9]{64} = \sqrt[9]{2^6}$

$\qquad = 2^{\frac{6}{9}}$

$\qquad = 2^{\frac{2}{3}}$

$\qquad = \sqrt[3]{2^2}$

$\qquad = \sqrt[3]{4}$

PAGES 272-274 EXERCISES

22. $\sqrt{14} = 14^{\frac{1}{2}}$

23. $\sqrt[3]{17} = 17^{\frac{1}{3}}$

24. $\sqrt[6]{32} = 32^{\frac{1}{6}}$

25. $\sqrt[4]{y} = y^{\frac{1}{4}}$

26. $\sqrt[3]{m} = m^{\frac{1}{3}}$

27. $\sqrt{25a^3b^4}$

$\qquad = 25^{\frac{1}{2}}a^{\frac{3}{2}}b^{\frac{4}{2}}$

$\qquad = 5a^{\frac{3}{2}}b^2$

28. $\sqrt[3]{8x^3y^6}$

$\qquad = 8^{\frac{1}{3}}x^{\frac{3}{3}}y^{\frac{6}{3}}$

$\qquad = 2xy^2$

29. $\sqrt[4]{27} = 27^{\frac{1}{4}}$

30. $\sqrt[4]{8x^3y^5}$

31. $\sqrt[3]{n^2} = n^{\frac{2}{3}}$

$= 8^{\frac{1}{4}}x^{\frac{3}{4}}y^{\frac{5}{4}}$

32. $\sqrt[6]{b^3} = b^{\frac{3}{6}}$

$\qquad = b^{\frac{1}{2}}$

33. $\sqrt[3]{16a^5b^7}$

$\qquad = 16^{\frac{1}{3}}a^{\frac{5}{3}}b^{\frac{7}{3}}$

34. $7^{\frac{1}{2}} = \sqrt{7}$

35. $36^{\frac{1}{4}} = \sqrt{6}$

36. $6^{\frac{1}{3}} = \sqrt[3]{6}$

37. $n^{\frac{3}{4}} = \sqrt[4]{n^3}$

38. $x^{\frac{3}{2}}y^{\frac{5}{2}}$

$\qquad = \sqrt{x^3y^5}$

$\qquad = xy^2\sqrt{xy}$

39. $2^{\frac{5}{3}}a^{\frac{7}{3}}$

$\qquad = \sqrt[3]{2^5a^7}$

$\qquad = 2a^2\sqrt[3]{4a}$

40. $(2m)^{\frac{1}{2}}m^{\frac{1}{2}}$

$\qquad = \sqrt{2m^2}$

$\qquad = m\sqrt{2}$

41. $p^{\frac{5}{2}}q^{\frac{3}{4}}$

$\qquad = p^{\frac{10}{4}}q^{\frac{3}{4}}$

$\qquad = \sqrt[4]{p^{10}q^3}$

$\qquad = p^2\sqrt[4]{p^2q^3}$

42. $4^{\frac{1}{3}}x^{\frac{2}{3}}y^{\frac{4}{3}}$

$\qquad = \sqrt[3]{4x^2y^4}$

$\qquad = y\sqrt[3]{4x^2y}$

43. $(3r)^{\frac{2}{5}}s^{\frac{3}{5}}$

$\qquad = \sqrt[5]{(3r)^2s^3}$

$\qquad = \sqrt[5]{9r^2s^3}$

44. $x^{\frac{4}{7}}y^{\frac{3}{7}}$

$\qquad = \sqrt[7]{x^4y^3}$

45. $5^{\frac{1}{3}}s^{\frac{2}{3}}t^{\frac{1}{3}}$

$\qquad = \sqrt[3]{5s^2t}$

46. $16^{0.25} = 2$

47. $\left(\frac{1}{32}\right)^{\frac{1}{5}} = \frac{1}{2}$

48. $144^{\frac{1}{2}} = 12$

49. $\sqrt[4]{256} = 4$

50. $25^{2.5} = 3125$

51. $27^{\frac{4}{3}} = 81$

52. $\left(\frac{343}{64}\right)^{\frac{1}{3}} = \frac{7}{4}$

53. $(9^{0.75})^{\frac{2}{3}} = 3$

54. $\left(\frac{216}{729}\right)^{\frac{2}{3}} = \frac{4}{9}$

55. $(0.008)^{\frac{1}{3}} = 0.2$

56. $(0.125)^{\frac{2}{3}} = 0.25$

57. $\left(6^{\frac{2}{3}}\right)^3 = 36$

58. $\sqrt[4]{9} = \sqrt[4]{3^2} = 3^{\frac{2}{4}} = 3^{\frac{1}{2}} = \sqrt{3}$

59. $x^{\frac{1}{3}}y^{\frac{1}{2}}$

$\qquad = x^{\frac{2}{6}}y^{\frac{3}{6}}$

$\qquad = \sqrt[6]{x^2y^3}$

60. $a^{\frac{3}{4}}b^{\frac{1}{3}}c^{\frac{5}{6}}$

$\qquad = a^{\frac{9}{12}}b^{\frac{4}{12}}c^{\frac{10}{12}}$

$\qquad = \sqrt[12]{a^9b^4c^{10}}$

61. $\sqrt[6]{8} = \sqrt[6]{2^3}$

$= 2^{\frac{3}{6}}$

$= 2^{\frac{1}{2}}$

$= \sqrt{2}$

62. $5a^{\frac{1}{2}}b^{\frac{1}{4}}$

$= 5a^{\frac{2}{4}}b^{\frac{1}{4}}$

$= 5\sqrt[4]{a^2 b}$

63. $x^{\frac{5}{6}}y^{\frac{3}{2}}z^{\frac{7}{3}}$

$= x^{\frac{5}{6}}y^{\frac{9}{6}}z^{\frac{14}{6}}$

$= \sqrt[6]{x^5 y^9 z^{14}}$

$= yz^2\sqrt[6]{x^5 y^3 z^2}$

64. $\sqrt[3]{2^5} \cdot \sqrt[4]{2}$

$= 2^{\frac{5}{3}} \cdot 2^{\frac{1}{4}}$

$= 2^{\frac{20}{12}}2^{\frac{3}{12}}$

$= \sqrt[12]{2^{20}2^3}$

$= 2\sqrt[12]{2^{11}}$

65. $\sqrt{3} \cdot \sqrt[3]{3^2}$

$= 3^{\frac{1}{2}} \cdot 3^{\frac{2}{3}}$

$= 3^{\frac{3}{6}} \cdot 3^{\frac{4}{6}}$

$= \sqrt[6]{3^3 \cdot 3^4}$

$= \sqrt[6]{3^7}$

$= 3\sqrt[6]{3}$

66. $\sqrt[3]{\sqrt{27}}$

$= \left(27^{\frac{1}{2}}\right)^{\frac{1}{3}}$

$= \left(27^{\frac{1}{3}}\right)^{\frac{1}{2}}$

$= 3^{\frac{1}{2}}$

$= \sqrt{3}$

67. yes; $\sqrt[n]{\dfrac{m}{\sqrt{b}}} = \left(b^{\frac{1}{m}}\right)^{\frac{1}{n}}$

$= b^{\frac{1}{m} \cdot \frac{1}{n}}$

$= b^{\frac{1}{n} \cdot \frac{1}{m}}$

$= \left(b^{\frac{1}{n}}\right)^{\frac{1}{m}}$

$= \sqrt[m]{\dfrac{n}{\sqrt{b}}}$

68. a. $f_n = 440\left(\dfrac{12}{\sqrt{2}}\right)^{12-1}$

$= 440\left(\dfrac{12}{\sqrt{2}}\right)^{11}$

$= 440\left(2^{\frac{11}{12}}\right)$

$= 440(1.89)$

$= 831$

The frequency should be 831 vibrations per second.

b. $f_n = 440\left(\dfrac{12}{\sqrt{2}}\right)^{-9-1}$

$= 440\left(\dfrac{12}{\sqrt{2}}\right)^{-10}$

$= 440(2)^{\frac{-10}{12}}$

$= 440(2)^{\frac{-5}{6}}$

$= \dfrac{440}{2^{\frac{5}{6}}}$

$= \dfrac{440}{1.78}$

$= 247$

The frequency should be 247 vibrations per second.

69. $A = 1500(1 + 0.075)^{2.5}$

$= 1500(1.075)^{2.5}$

$= 1500(1.98)$

$= 1797.27$

Connor has \$1797.27.

70. $A = 500(2.7)^{\frac{-3}{5}}$

$= 500(0.55104)$

$= 275.52$

There are about 276 milligrams left.

71. $5 - 3\sqrt{3}$

72. $\sqrt{108} - \sqrt{48} + (\sqrt{3})^3$

$= \sqrt{6^2 \cdot 3} - \sqrt{4^2 \cdot 3} + (\sqrt{3})^2(\sqrt{3})$

$= 6\sqrt{3} - 4\sqrt{3} + 3\sqrt{3}$

$= 5\sqrt{3}$

73. $\begin{array}{r} a - 2b \\ a - 3b{\overline{\smash{\big)}\,a^2 - 5ab + 6b^2}} \end{array}$

$\underline{a^2 - 3ab}$

$-2ab + 6b^2$

$\underline{-2ab + 6b^2}$

0

74. $\begin{vmatrix} 3 & 1 \\ 2 & -4 \end{vmatrix} = (3)(-4) - (2)1 = -14$

Inverse $= -\dfrac{1}{14}\begin{bmatrix} -4 & -1 \\ -2 & 3 \end{bmatrix} = \dfrac{1}{14}\begin{bmatrix} 4 & 1 \\ 2 & -3 \end{bmatrix}$

75. $14(0.05) = 0.70$

The fine is 70 cents.

76. $4(5x + 2y) + 9(x - 2y)$

$= 20x + 8y + 9x - 18y$

$= 29x - 10y$

1. $-\sqrt{81x^2}$

   $= -\sqrt{9^2x^2}$

   $= -9|x|$

2. $\sqrt{a^2 + 14a + 49}$

   $= \sqrt{(a + 7)^2}$

   $= |a + 7|$

3. $\sqrt[3]{-64x^9}$

   $= \sqrt[3]{-4^3(x^3)^3}$

   $= -4x^3$

4. $\sqrt{48m^2n^3}$

   $= \sqrt{16 \cdot 3 \cdot m^2 \cdot n^2 \cdot n}$

   $= 4|m|n\sqrt{3n}$

5. $\sqrt{6}(\sqrt{3} + 5\sqrt{2})$

   $= \sqrt{18} + 5\sqrt{12}$

   $= \sqrt{9 \cdot 2} + 5\sqrt{4 \cdot 3}$

   $= 3\sqrt{2} + 10\sqrt{3}$

6. $\dfrac{5}{3\sqrt{5}} = \dfrac{5}{3\sqrt{5}} \cdot \dfrac{\sqrt{5}}{\sqrt{5}}$

   $= \dfrac{5\sqrt{5}}{15}$

   $= \dfrac{\sqrt{5}}{3}$

7. $\dfrac{12}{\sqrt[3]{4x}} = \dfrac{12}{\sqrt[3]{4x}} \cdot \dfrac{\sqrt[3]{2x^2}}{\sqrt[3]{2x^2}}$

   $= \dfrac{12\sqrt[3]{2x^2}}{\sqrt[3]{8x^3}}$

   $= \dfrac{12\sqrt[3]{2x^2}}{2x}$

   $= \dfrac{6\sqrt[3]{2x^2}}{x}$

8. $\sqrt[4]{3b^6r^7} \cdot \sqrt[4]{81b^2r^2} = \sqrt[4]{243b^8r^9}$

   $= \sqrt[4]{3^4 \cdot 3 \cdot (b^2)^4 \cdot (r^2)^4 \cdot r}$

   $= 3b^2r^2\sqrt[4]{3r}$

9. $t = \dfrac{1}{4}\sqrt{200}$

   $= \dfrac{1}{4}(14.14)$

   $= 3.53$

   The pebble will reach the ground in 3.53 seconds.

10. $2\sqrt{18} + 3\sqrt{8} - 4\sqrt{50} = 6\sqrt{2} + 6\sqrt{2} - 20\sqrt{2}$

    $= -8\sqrt{2}$

11. $(5 + \sqrt{3})(7 - 2\sqrt{3}) = 35 - 10\sqrt{3} + 7\sqrt{3} - 2(\sqrt{3})^2$

    $= 35 - 3\sqrt{3} - 6$

    $= 29 - 3\sqrt{3}$

12. $(11 - \sqrt{7})(11 + \sqrt{7}) = 121 + 11\sqrt{7} - 11\sqrt{7} - 7$

    $= 114$

13. $\dfrac{1 + \sqrt{3}}{5 - 2\sqrt{3}} = \dfrac{1 + \sqrt{3}}{5 - 2\sqrt{3}} \cdot \dfrac{(5 + 2\sqrt{3})}{(5 + 2\sqrt{3})}$

    $= \dfrac{5 + 2\sqrt{3} + 5\sqrt{3} + 6}{25 - 12}$

    $= \dfrac{11 + 7\sqrt{3}}{13}$

14. $8^{\frac{2}{3}} \cdot 9^{\frac{1}{2}} = \sqrt[3]{8^2}\sqrt{9}$

    $= \sqrt[3]{64}(3)$

    $= 4 \cdot 3$

    $= 12$

15. $5^{\frac{2}{3}}x^{\frac{1}{2}}y^{\frac{3}{4}} = 5^{\frac{8}{12}}x^{\frac{6}{12}}y^{\frac{9}{12}}$

    $= \sqrt[12]{5^8x^6y^9}$

16. $\sqrt[6]{27a^3b^4c^6} = \sqrt[6]{3^3a^3b^4c^6}$

    $= 3^{\frac{3}{6}}a^{\frac{3}{6}}b^{\frac{4}{6}}c^{\frac{6}{6}}$

    $= 3^{\frac{1}{2}}a^{\frac{1}{2}}b^{\frac{2}{3}}|c|$

6-5 Problem-Solving Strategy: Identify Subgoals

1. It breaks the problem down into smaller, simpler steps.

2. The multiples of 36 were subtracted twice—once in the multiples of 4 and once in the multiples of 9. We had to add them back in so that they were subtracted only once.

3. Sum of 1 to 300 $= \dfrac{1}{2}(300)(301)$

   $= 45,150$

   Sum of multiples of 4 $= 4(1 + 2 + 3 + \ldots + 75)$

   $= 4\left(\dfrac{1}{2}(75)(76)\right)$

   $= 11,400$

   Sum of multiples of 9 $= 9(1 + 2 + \ldots + 33)$

   $= 9\left(\dfrac{1}{2}(33)(34)\right)$

   $= 5049$

   Multiples of 36 $= 36 + 72 + 108 + 144 + 180 + 216 + 252 + 288 = 1296$

   Sum $= 45,150 - 11,400 - 5049 + 1296$

   $= 29,997$

4. $\sqrt{\left(\sqrt{\left(\sqrt{\left(\sqrt{2^2}\right)^2}\right)^4}\right)^2} = 2$

   Working from the inside, express this with exponents.

   $\sqrt{2^2} = (2^2)^{\frac{1}{2}} = 2$

   $\sqrt{2^2} = (2^2)^{\frac{1}{2}} = 2$

   $\sqrt{2^4} = (2^4)^{\frac{1}{2}} = 2^2 = 4$

   $\sqrt{4^2} = (4^2)^{\frac{1}{2}} = 4$

   $\sqrt{4} = 2$

5. Factors of 2000:

(2, 1000), (4, 500), (5, 400), (8, 250),

(10, 200), (25, 80), (40, 50), (100, 20),

(125, 16), (2000, 1)

There are 6 perfect squares: 4, 25, 100, 400,

16, 1.

6. $\left(\dfrac{1}{2} + \dfrac{1}{2^2} + \dfrac{1}{2^3} + \ldots + \dfrac{1}{2^{10}}\right)$

Find the denominators: {2, 4, 8, 16, 32, 64,

128, 256, 512, 1024}

The GCF of the denominators is 2^{10} or 1024.

Change all the fractions so they have a

denominator of 1024.

$\dfrac{512}{1024} + \dfrac{256}{1024} + \dfrac{128}{1024} + \dfrac{64}{1024} + \dfrac{32}{1024} + \dfrac{16}{1024} + \dfrac{8}{1024} +$

$\dfrac{4}{1024} + \dfrac{2}{1024} + \dfrac{1}{1024} = \dfrac{1023}{1024}$

7. The number has to have 5 sets of numbers that

when multiplied equal the number. It also must

be a small number with a lot of factors.

(1, 48), (2, 24), (3, 16), (4, 12), (6, 8) are

the factors of 48.

{1, 2, 3, 4, 6, 8, 12, 16, 24} are the 9 proper

divisors.

8. Let $232 + n$ = sum of the ages

Average = $\dfrac{232 + n}{5}$

$58 = \dfrac{232 + n}{5}$

$290 = 232 + n$

$58 = n$

The age of the 5th president was 58.

9. Original area = $14 \times 14 = 196$

Add 60   ⇒   256

Area = s^2

$256 = s^2$

$\sqrt{256} = s$

$16 = s$

The square has dimensions 16 cm by 16 cm.

10. Let n = number

$n = n^2 + (-n)$

$n = n^2 - n$

$n^2 - 2n = 0$

$n(n - 2) = 0$

$n = 0$ or $n - 2 = 0$

$n = 2$

The possible number is 2.

$(1 \times 2 \times 3 \times \ldots \times 100)$

The only numbers that when multiplied to others

result in a number that ends in zero are 5 and 10.

The numbers ending in 5 are 5, 15, 25, 35, 45, 55,

65, 75, 85, and 95. Any even number multiplied by

one of these produces a product ending in zero.

Thus, there are 10 zeros from these factors. The

numbers ending in zero are 10, 20, 30, 40, 50, 60,

70, 80, 90, and 100. This accounts for an

additional 11 zeros. The total number of zeros in

the product $1 \cdot 2 \cdot 3 \cdot 4 \cdot \ldots \cdot 100$ is 21.

6-6 Simplifying Expressions with Rational Exponents

1. when the denominator contains a radical or a

term with a fractional or negative exponent

2. no; the exponent in the denominator should be a

positive integer

3. Choose a fraction equivalent to 1 that will make

the denominator the least possible positive

integer, while the exponents in the numerator

are also positive.

4. $\dfrac{3^{\frac{1}{2}}}{3^{\frac{1}{2}}}$;

$\dfrac{8}{3^{\frac{1}{2}}} \cdot \dfrac{3^{\frac{1}{2}}}{3^{\frac{1}{2}}}$

$= \dfrac{8 \cdot 3^{\frac{1}{2}}}{3}$

5. $\dfrac{4^{\frac{1}{2}}}{4^{\frac{1}{2}}}$;

$\dfrac{16}{4^{\frac{3}{2}}} \cdot \dfrac{4^{\frac{1}{2}}}{4^{\frac{1}{2}}}$

$= \dfrac{16 \cdot 4^{\frac{1}{2}}}{4^{\frac{4}{2}}}$

$= \dfrac{16 \cdot 2}{4^2}$

$= \dfrac{32}{16} = 2$

6. $\dfrac{y^{\frac{1}{3}}}{y^{\frac{1}{3}}}$;

$\dfrac{1}{y^{\frac{2}{3}}} \cdot \dfrac{y^{\frac{1}{3}}}{y^{\frac{1}{3}}}$

$= \dfrac{y^{\frac{1}{3}}}{y}$

7. $\dfrac{a^{\frac{2}{3}}}{a^{\frac{2}{3}}}$;

$\dfrac{1}{a^{\frac{1}{3}}} \cdot \dfrac{a^{\frac{2}{3}}}{a^{\frac{2}{3}}}$

$= \dfrac{a^{\frac{2}{3}}}{a}$

8. $\dfrac{x^{\frac{4}{5}}}{x^{\frac{4}{5}}}$;

$x^{\frac{-1}{5}} = \dfrac{1}{x^{\frac{1}{5}}} \cdot \dfrac{x^{\frac{4}{5}}}{x^{\frac{4}{5}}}$

$= \dfrac{x^{\frac{4}{5}}}{x}$

9. $\dfrac{t^{\frac{1}{2}} - 1}{t^{\frac{1}{2}} - 1}$;

$\dfrac{1}{t^{\frac{1}{2}} + 1} \cdot \dfrac{t^{\frac{1}{2}} - 1}{t^{\frac{1}{2}} - 1}$

$= \dfrac{t^{\frac{1}{2}} - 1}{\left(t^{\frac{1}{2}}\right)^2 - 1^2}$

$= \dfrac{t^{\frac{1}{2}} - 1}{t - 1}$

10. $\dfrac{m^{\frac{1}{2}}}{m^{\frac{1}{2}}}$;

$m^{-\frac{3}{2}} = \dfrac{1}{m^{\frac{3}{2}}} \cdot \dfrac{m^{\frac{1}{2}}}{m^{\frac{1}{2}}}$

$= \dfrac{m^{\frac{1}{2}}}{m^{\frac{4}{2}}}$

$= \dfrac{m^{\frac{1}{2}}}{m^2}$

11. $\dfrac{q^{\frac{1}{2}} + r^{\frac{1}{2}}}{q^{\frac{1}{2}} + r^{\frac{1}{2}}}$;

$\dfrac{q}{q^{\frac{1}{2}} - r^{\frac{1}{2}}} \cdot \dfrac{q^{\frac{1}{2}} + r^{\frac{1}{2}}}{q^{\frac{1}{2}} + r^{\frac{1}{2}}}$

$= \dfrac{q\left(q^{\frac{1}{2}} + r^{\frac{1}{2}}\right)}{\left(q^{\frac{1}{2}}\right)^2 - \left(r^{\frac{1}{2}}\right)^2}$

$= \dfrac{q^{\frac{3}{2}} + qr^{\frac{1}{2}}}{q - r}$

12. $\dfrac{a^{\frac{1}{2}} - b}{a^{\frac{1}{2}} - b}$;

$\dfrac{a + b}{a^{\frac{1}{2}} + b} \cdot \dfrac{a^{\frac{1}{2}} - b}{a^{\frac{1}{2}} - b}$

$= \dfrac{a^{\frac{3}{2}} - ab + a^{\frac{1}{2}}b - b^2}{\left(a^{\frac{1}{2}}\right)^2 - (b)^2}$

$= \dfrac{a^{\frac{3}{2}} - ab + a^{\frac{1}{2}}b - b^2}{a - b^2}$

13. $\dfrac{t^{\frac{3}{2}} - s^{\frac{1}{2}}}{t^{\frac{3}{2}} - s^{\frac{1}{2}}}$;

$\dfrac{2}{t^{\frac{3}{2}} + s^{\frac{1}{2}}} \cdot \dfrac{t^{\frac{3}{2}} - s^{\frac{1}{2}}}{t^{\frac{3}{2}} - s^{\frac{1}{2}}}$

$= \dfrac{2t^{\frac{3}{2}} - 2s^{\frac{1}{2}}}{\left(t^{\frac{3}{2}}\right)^2 - \left(s^{\frac{1}{2}}\right)^2}$

$= \dfrac{2t^{\frac{3}{2}} - 2s^{\frac{1}{2}}}{t^3 - s}$

14. $\dfrac{c^{\frac{3}{2}} - c^{\frac{1}{2}}}{c^{\frac{3}{2}} - c^{\frac{1}{2}}}$;

$\dfrac{3}{c^{\frac{3}{2}} + c^{\frac{1}{2}}} \cdot \dfrac{c^{\frac{3}{2}} - c^{\frac{1}{2}}}{c^{\frac{3}{2}} - c^{\frac{1}{2}}}$

$= \dfrac{3c^{\frac{3}{2}} - 3c^{\frac{1}{2}}}{\left(c^{\frac{3}{2}}\right)^2 - \left(c^{\frac{1}{2}}\right)^2}$

$= \dfrac{3c^{\frac{3}{2}} - 3c^{\frac{1}{2}}}{c^3 - c}$

15. $\dfrac{w + w^{\frac{1}{2}}}{w + w^{\frac{1}{2}}}$;

$\dfrac{w + 1}{w - w^{\frac{1}{2}}} \cdot \dfrac{w + w^{\frac{1}{2}}}{w + w^{\frac{1}{2}}}$

$= \dfrac{w^2 + w^{\frac{3}{2}} + w + w^{\frac{1}{2}}}{w^2 - \left(w^{\frac{1}{2}}\right)^2}$

$= \dfrac{w^2 + w^{\frac{3}{2}} + w + w^{\frac{1}{2}}}{w^2 - w}$

PAGES 279–280   EXERCISES

16. $x^{-\frac{1}{4}} = \dfrac{1}{x^{\frac{1}{4}}} \cdot \dfrac{x^{\frac{3}{4}}}{x^{\frac{3}{4}}}$

$= \dfrac{x^{\frac{3}{4}}}{x}$

17. $\dfrac{1}{s^{\frac{4}{5}}} = \dfrac{1}{s^{\frac{4}{5}}} \cdot \dfrac{s^{\frac{1}{5}}}{s^{\frac{1}{5}}}$

$= \dfrac{s^{\frac{1}{5}}}{s}$

18. $\dfrac{1}{y^{\frac{2}{5}}} = \dfrac{1}{y^{\frac{2}{5}}} \cdot \dfrac{y^{\frac{3}{5}}}{y^{\frac{3}{5}}}$

$= \dfrac{y^{\frac{3}{5}}}{y}$

19. $t^{-\frac{5}{6}} = \dfrac{1}{t^{\frac{5}{6}}} \cdot \dfrac{t^{\frac{1}{6}}}{t^{\frac{1}{6}}}$

$= \dfrac{t^{\frac{1}{6}}}{t}$

20. $n^{-\frac{3}{2}} = \dfrac{1}{n^{\frac{3}{2}}} \cdot \dfrac{n^{\frac{1}{2}}}{n^{\frac{1}{2}}}$

$= \dfrac{n^{\frac{1}{2}}}{n^2}$

21. $\dfrac{1}{x^{\frac{1}{2}} + 1} = \dfrac{1}{x^{\frac{1}{2}} + 1} \cdot \dfrac{x^{\frac{1}{2}} - 1}{x^{\frac{1}{2}} - 1}$

$= \dfrac{x^{\frac{1}{2}} - 1}{\left(x^{\frac{1}{2}}\right)^2 - 1^2}$

$= \dfrac{x^{\frac{1}{2}} - 1}{x - 1}$

22. $\dfrac{p+q}{p^{\frac{1}{2}}+q} \cdot \dfrac{p^{\frac{1}{2}}-q}{p^{\frac{1}{2}}-q} = \dfrac{p^{\frac{3}{2}}-pq+p^{\frac{1}{2}}q-q^2}{\left(p^{\frac{1}{2}}\right)^2-q^2}$

$= \dfrac{p^{\frac{3}{2}}-pq+p^{\frac{1}{2}}q-q^2}{p-q^2}$

23. $\dfrac{1}{t^{\frac{3}{2}}+t^{\frac{1}{2}}} \cdot \dfrac{t^{\frac{3}{2}}-t^{\frac{1}{2}}}{t^{\frac{3}{2}}-t^{\frac{1}{2}}} = \dfrac{t^{\frac{3}{2}}-t^{\frac{1}{2}}}{t^3-t}$

$= \dfrac{t^{\frac{1}{2}}(t-1)}{t(t-1)(t+1)}$

$= \dfrac{t^{\frac{1}{2}}}{t(t+1)}$

24. $\dfrac{rt}{r^{\frac{1}{2}}+t^{\frac{1}{2}}} \cdot \dfrac{r^{\frac{1}{2}}-t^{\frac{1}{2}}}{r^{\frac{1}{2}}-t^{\frac{1}{2}}}$

$= \dfrac{rt\left(r^{\frac{1}{2}}-t^{\frac{1}{2}}\right)}{\left(r^{\frac{1}{2}}\right)^2-\left(t^{\frac{1}{2}}\right)^2}$

$= \dfrac{rt\left(r^{\frac{1}{2}}-t^{\frac{1}{2}}\right)}{r-t}$

25. $\dfrac{24}{6^{\frac{2}{3}}} \cdot \dfrac{6^{\frac{1}{3}}}{6^{\frac{1}{3}}}$

$= \dfrac{24 \cdot 6^{\frac{1}{3}}}{6}$

$= 4 \cdot 6^{\frac{1}{3}}$

26. $\dfrac{15}{5^{\frac{2}{3}}} \cdot \dfrac{5^{\frac{1}{3}}}{5^{\frac{1}{3}}}$

$= \dfrac{15 \cdot 5^{\frac{1}{3}}}{5}$

$= 3 \cdot 5^{\frac{1}{3}}$

27. $\dfrac{ab^{\frac{1}{2}}}{c^{\frac{3}{2}}} \cdot \dfrac{c^{\frac{1}{2}}}{c^{\frac{1}{2}}}$

$= \dfrac{ab^{\frac{1}{2}}c^{\frac{1}{2}}}{c^2}$

28. $\dfrac{xy}{\sqrt[3]{z}}$

$= \dfrac{xy}{z^{\frac{1}{3}}} \cdot \dfrac{z^{\frac{2}{3}}}{z^{\frac{2}{3}}}$

$= \dfrac{xyz^{\frac{2}{3}}}{z}$

29. $\dfrac{n^{\frac{3}{2}}+3n^{-\frac{1}{2}}}{n^{\frac{1}{2}}} \cdot \dfrac{n^{\frac{1}{2}}}{n^{\frac{1}{2}}}$

$= \dfrac{n^2+3n^0}{n}$

$= \dfrac{n^2+3}{n}$

30. $\dfrac{a^{\frac{5}{3}}b+3a^{-\frac{1}{3}}}{a^{\frac{2}{3}}} \cdot \dfrac{a^{\frac{1}{3}}}{a^{\frac{1}{3}}}$

$= \dfrac{a^2b+3a^0}{a}$

$= \dfrac{a^2b+3}{a}$

31. $\dfrac{3x+4x^2}{x^{-\frac{2}{3}}}$

$= (3x+4x^2)x^{\frac{2}{3}}$

$= 3x^{\frac{5}{3}}+4x^{\frac{8}{3}}$

32. $\left(r^{-\frac{1}{6}}\right)^{-\frac{2}{3}}$

$= \left(r^{\frac{2}{18}}\right)$

$= r^{\frac{1}{9}}$

33. $\dfrac{3x}{y^{-\frac{3}{2}} \cdot \sqrt[3]{z}}$

$= \dfrac{3x \cdot y^{\frac{3}{2}}}{z^{\frac{1}{3}}} \cdot \dfrac{z^{\frac{2}{3}}}{z^{\frac{2}{3}}}$

$= \dfrac{3xy^{\frac{3}{2}}z^{\frac{2}{3}}}{z}$

34. $\left(y^{\frac{1}{3}}\right)^{-\frac{3}{4}} = y^{-\frac{1}{4}}$

$= \dfrac{1}{y^{\frac{1}{4}}} \cdot \dfrac{y^{\frac{3}{4}}}{y^{\frac{3}{4}}}$

$= \dfrac{y^{\frac{3}{4}}}{y}$

35. $\dfrac{r^{\frac{3}{2}}}{r^{\frac{1}{2}}+2} \cdot \dfrac{r^{\frac{1}{2}}-2}{r^{\frac{1}{2}}-2}$

$= \dfrac{r^2-2r^{\frac{3}{2}}}{\left(r^{\frac{1}{2}}\right)^2-2^2}$

$= \dfrac{r^2-2r^{\frac{3}{2}}}{r-4}$

36. $\dfrac{s^{\frac{1}{2}}+t^{\frac{1}{2}}}{s^{\frac{1}{2}}-t^{\frac{1}{2}}} \cdot \dfrac{s^{\frac{1}{2}}+t^{\frac{1}{2}}}{s^{\frac{1}{2}}+t^{\frac{1}{2}}} = \dfrac{s+s^{\frac{1}{2}}t^{\frac{1}{2}}+s^{\frac{1}{2}}t^{\frac{1}{2}}+t}{\left(s^{\frac{1}{2}}\right)^2-\left(t^{\frac{1}{2}}\right)^2}$

$= \dfrac{s+2s^{\frac{1}{2}}t^{\frac{1}{2}}+t}{s-t}$

37. $\dfrac{b^{\frac{1}{2}}}{b^{\frac{3}{2}}-b^{\frac{1}{2}}} \cdot \dfrac{b^{\frac{3}{2}}+b^{\frac{1}{2}}}{b^{\frac{3}{2}}+b^{\frac{1}{2}}} = \dfrac{b^2+b}{b^3-b}$

$= \dfrac{b(b+1)}{b(b+1)(b-1)}$

$= \dfrac{1}{b-1}$

38.
$$\frac{s^{\frac{1}{2}}+1}{s^{\frac{1}{2}}-1} \cdot \frac{s^{\frac{1}{2}}+1}{s^{\frac{1}{2}}+1}$$

$$= \frac{s + s^{\frac{1}{2}} + s^{\frac{1}{2}} + 1}{\left(s^{\frac{1}{2}}\right)^2 - 1^2}$$

$$= \frac{s + 2s^{\frac{1}{2}} + 1}{s-1}$$

39. $\left(\dfrac{x^{-2}y^{-6}}{9}\right)^{-\frac{1}{2}}$

$$= \left(\frac{9}{x^{-2}y^{-6}}\right)^{\frac{1}{2}}$$

$$= \frac{3}{x^{-1}y^{-3}}$$

$$= 3xy^3$$

40.
$$\frac{8^{\frac{1}{6}}-9^{\frac{1}{4}}}{\sqrt{3}+\sqrt{2}} = \frac{8^{\frac{1}{6}}-9^{\frac{1}{4}}}{3^{\frac{1}{2}}+2^{\frac{1}{2}}} \cdot \frac{3^{\frac{1}{2}}-2^{\frac{1}{2}}}{3^{\frac{1}{2}}-2^{\frac{1}{2}}}$$

$$= \frac{6^{\frac{1}{2}} - 2 - 3 + 6^{\frac{1}{2}}}{3-2}$$

$$= 2 \cdot 6^{\frac{1}{2}} - 5$$

$$= 2\sqrt{6} - 5$$

41. $\dfrac{a^{-\frac{2}{3}}b^{\frac{1}{2}}}{b^{-\frac{3}{2}}\sqrt{a}}$

$$= \frac{b^{\frac{1}{2}} \cdot b^{\frac{3}{2}}}{a^{\frac{2}{3}} \cdot a^{\frac{1}{3}}}$$

$$= \frac{b^2}{a}$$

42. $\dfrac{x^{\frac{5}{3}}-x^{\frac{1}{3}}y^{\frac{4}{3}}}{x^{\frac{2}{3}}+y^{\frac{2}{3}}} \cdot \dfrac{x^{\frac{2}{3}}-y^{\frac{2}{3}}}{x^{\frac{2}{3}}-y^{\frac{2}{3}}}$

$$= \frac{x^{\frac{1}{3}}\left(x^{\frac{4}{3}}-y^{\frac{4}{3}}\right)\left(x^{\frac{2}{3}}-y^{\frac{2}{3}}\right)}{x^{\frac{4}{3}}-y^{\frac{4}{3}}}$$

$$= x^{\frac{1}{3}}\left(x^{\frac{2}{3}}-y^{\frac{2}{3}}\right)$$

$$= x - x^{\frac{1}{3}}y^{\frac{2}{3}}$$

43. $-\dfrac{4}{9}\left(2^{\frac{1}{6}}\right)^9\left(\dfrac{3}{\left(2^{\frac{1}{6}}\right)^2} - \dfrac{1}{\sqrt[3]{2}}\right)$

$$= -\frac{4}{9}\cdot 2^{\frac{9}{6}}\left(\frac{3}{2^{\frac{1}{3}}} - \frac{1}{2^{\frac{1}{3}}}\right)$$

$$= -\frac{4}{9}\cdot 2^{\frac{3}{2}}\left(\frac{2}{2^{\frac{1}{3}}}\right)$$

$$= -\frac{4}{9}(2)2^{\frac{3}{2}}\cdot 2^{-\frac{1}{3}}$$

$$= -\frac{8}{9}\cdot 2^{\frac{7}{6}}$$

$$= -\frac{8}{9}\cdot 2 \cdot 2^{\frac{1}{6}}$$

$$= -\frac{16}{9}\cdot 2^{\frac{1}{6}}$$

44. $R_t = \left(\dfrac{1}{R_1}+\dfrac{1}{R_2}+\dfrac{1}{R_3}+\dfrac{1}{R_4}\right)^{-1}$

$$= \left(\frac{R_2R_3R_4}{R_1R_2R_3R_4}+\frac{R_1R_3R_4}{R_1R_2R_3R_4}+\frac{R_1R_2R_4}{R_1R_2R_3R_4}+\frac{R_1R_2R_3}{R_1R_2R_3R_4}\right)^{-1}$$

$$= \left(\frac{R_2R_3R_4 + R_1R_3R_4 + R_1R_2R_4 + R_1R_2R_3}{R_1R_2R_3R_4}\right)^{-1}$$

$$= \frac{R_1R_2R_3R_4}{R_2R_3R_4 + R_1R_3R_4 + R_1R_2R_4 + R_1R_2R_3}$$

Let $R_1 = 16$, $R_2 = 12$, $R_3 = 8$, $R_4 = 24$

$$R_t = \frac{16\cdot12\cdot8\cdot24}{12\cdot8\cdot24 + 16\cdot8\cdot24 + 16\cdot12\cdot24 + 16\cdot12\cdot8}$$

$$= \frac{36,864}{2304 + 3072 + 4608 + 1536}$$

$$= \frac{36,864}{11,520} = 3.2 \text{ ohms}$$

45. $20\left(\dfrac{1}{3}\right), \quad t = 1$

$20\left(\dfrac{1}{3}\right)^2, \quad t = 2$

$$\vdots$$

$$20\left(\frac{1}{3}\right)^t = 20\left(\frac{1}{3^t}\right)$$

$$= 20\left(\frac{1}{3^t}\right)$$

$$= \frac{20}{3^t}$$

46. The perfect squares are: {1, 4, 9, 16, 25, 36, 49, 64, 81, 100}.

Every other one is odd, so half of the numbers are odd.

47. $\sqrt[7]{5^3} = 5^{\frac{3}{7}}$

48.
$$\begin{array}{r|rrrr}
-1 & 2 & -2 & 0 & 4 \\
 & & -2 & 4 & -4 \\
\hline
 & 2 & -4 & 4 & 0
\end{array}$$

$$2x^2 - 4x + 4$$

49. A linear equation that is dependent only has the trivial solution (or $x_1 = x_2 = \ldots = x_n = 0$).

Thus, two linearly dependent equations on a graph would be the same line.

50. $m = \dfrac{y_2 - y_1}{x_2 - x_1} = \dfrac{-5 - 0}{4 - 9} = 1$

| **6-7** | **Solving Equations Containing Radicals** |

PAGE 284   CHECKING FOR UNDERSTANDING

1. It is a result found when solving the equation that does not satisfy the equation.

2. In example 2, squaring each side made the negative constant term a positive constant. We could have looked at $\sqrt{x-1} = -8$ and determined

that there was no solution since no real number has a principle square root of -8.

3. You isolate the radical so that it is eliminated when you square.

4. $\sqrt{x} = 3$ Check: $\sqrt{9} \overset{?}{=} 3$
   $x = 9$ $3 = 3$

5. $\sqrt{y} = 5$ Check: $\sqrt{25} \overset{?}{=} 5$
   $y = 25$ $5 = 5$

6. $\sqrt{n} - 8 = 0$ Check: $\sqrt{64} \overset{?}{=} 0$
   $\sqrt{n} = 8$ $8 - 8 \overset{?}{=} 0$
   $n = 64$ $0 = 0$

7. $\sqrt{s} - 4 = 0$ Check: $\sqrt{16} - 4 \overset{?}{=} 0$
   $\sqrt{s} = 4$ $4 - 4 \overset{?}{=} 0$
   $s = 16$ $0 = 0$

8. $\sqrt{2y + 7} = 3$ Check: $\sqrt{2 \cdot 1 + 7} \overset{?}{=} 3$
   $2y + 7 = 9$ $\sqrt{9} \overset{?}{=} 3$
   $2y = 2$ $3 = 3$
   $y = 1$

9. $\sqrt{3m + 7} = 7$ Check: $\sqrt{3 \cdot 14 + 7} \overset{?}{=} 7$
   $3m + 7 = 49$ $\sqrt{42 + 7} \overset{?}{=} 7$
   $3m = 42$ $\sqrt{49} \overset{?}{=} 7$
   $m = 14$ $7 = 7$

10. $\sqrt[3]{x - 2} = 3$ Check: $\sqrt[3]{29 - 2} \overset{?}{=} 3$
    $x - 2 = 27$ $\sqrt[3]{27} \overset{?}{=} 3$
    $x = 29$ $3 = 3$

11. $\sqrt[4]{3w + 7} = 2$ Check: $\sqrt[4]{3 \cdot 3 + 7} \overset{?}{=} 2$
    $3w + 7 = 16$ $\sqrt[4]{9 + 7} \overset{?}{=} 2$
    $3w = 9$ $\sqrt[4]{16} \overset{?}{=} 2$
    $w = 3$ $2 = 2$

12. $y\sqrt{3} - y = 7$
    $y(\sqrt{3} - 1) = 7$
    $y = \dfrac{7}{\sqrt{3} - 1}$
    $y = \dfrac{7}{\sqrt{3} - 1} \cdot \dfrac{\sqrt{3} + 1}{\sqrt{3} + 1}$
    $= \dfrac{7\sqrt{3} + 7}{3 - 1}$
    $= \dfrac{7(\sqrt{3} + 1)}{2}$
    $= \dfrac{7}{2}(\sqrt{3} + 1)$

Check: $\dfrac{1}{2}(\sqrt{3} + 1)\sqrt{3} - \dfrac{7}{2}(\sqrt{3} + 1) \overset{?}{=} 7$

$\dfrac{7\sqrt{3} + 7}{2} \cdot \sqrt{3} - \dfrac{7}{2}(\sqrt{3} + 1) \overset{?}{=} 7$

$\dfrac{7 \cdot 3 + 7\sqrt{3}}{2} - \dfrac{7(\sqrt{3} + 1)}{2} \overset{?}{=} 7$

$\dfrac{21 + 7\sqrt{3} - 7\sqrt{3} - 7}{2} \overset{?}{=} 7$

$\dfrac{14}{2} \overset{?}{=} 7$

$7 = 7$

PAGES 284-286   EXERCISES

13. $1 + x\sqrt{2} = 0$
    $x\sqrt{2} = -1$
    $x = \dfrac{-1}{\sqrt{2}} \cdot \dfrac{\sqrt{2}}{\sqrt{2}}$
    $x = \dfrac{-\sqrt{2}}{2}$

14. $7 + 6n\sqrt{5} = 0$
    $6n\sqrt{5} = -7$
    $n = \dfrac{-7}{6\sqrt{5}} \cdot \dfrac{\sqrt{5}}{\sqrt{5}}$
    $n = \dfrac{-7\sqrt{5}}{30}$

15. $6 + 2x\sqrt{3} = 0$
    $2x\sqrt{3} = -6$
    $x = \dfrac{-6}{2\sqrt{3}} \cdot \dfrac{\sqrt{3}}{\sqrt{3}}$
    $= \dfrac{-6\sqrt{3}}{6}$
    $= -\sqrt{3}$

16. $2 + 5r\sqrt{10} = 0$
    $5r\sqrt{10} = -2$
    $r = \dfrac{-2}{5\sqrt{10}} \cdot \dfrac{\sqrt{10}}{\sqrt{10}}$
    $= \dfrac{-2\sqrt{10}}{50}$
    $= \dfrac{-\sqrt{10}}{25}$

17. $x\sqrt{2} + 3x = 4$
    $x(\sqrt{2} + 3) = 4$
    $x = \dfrac{4}{\sqrt{2} + 3} \cdot \dfrac{\sqrt{2} - 3}{\sqrt{2} - 3}$
    $= \dfrac{4\sqrt{2} - 12}{2 - 9}$
    $= \dfrac{4\sqrt{2} - 12}{-7}$
    $= \dfrac{12 - 4\sqrt{2}}{7}$

18. $3x + 5 = x\sqrt{3}$
    $3x - x\sqrt{3} = -5$
    $x(3 - \sqrt{3}) = -5$
    $x = \dfrac{-5}{3 - \sqrt{3}} \cdot \dfrac{3 + \sqrt{3}}{3 + \sqrt{3}}$
    $= \dfrac{-15 - 5\sqrt{3}}{9 - 3}$
    $= \dfrac{-15 - 5\sqrt{3}}{6}$

19. $x - x\sqrt{5} = 2$
    $x(1 - \sqrt{5}) = 2$
    $x = \dfrac{2}{1 - \sqrt{5}} \cdot \dfrac{1 + \sqrt{5}}{1 + \sqrt{5}}$
    $= \dfrac{2 + 2\sqrt{5}}{1 - 5}$
    $= \dfrac{2(1 + \sqrt{5})}{-4}$
    $= \dfrac{1 + \sqrt{5}}{-2}$

20.
$$13 - 3p = p\sqrt{5}$$
$$13 = p\sqrt{5} + 3p$$
$$13 = p(\sqrt{5} + 3)$$
$$\frac{\sqrt{5} - 3}{\sqrt{5} - 3} \cdot \frac{13}{\sqrt{5} + 3} = p$$
$$\frac{13\sqrt{5} - 39}{5 - 9} = p$$
$$\frac{13\sqrt{5} - 39}{-4} = p$$
$$\frac{39 - 13\sqrt{5}}{4} = p$$

21. $\sqrt{a - 4} - 3 = 0$
$$\sqrt{a - 4} = 3$$
$$a - 4 = 9$$
$$a = 13$$

22. $\sqrt{x - 5} - 7 = 0$
$$\sqrt{x - 5} = 7$$
$$x - 5 = 49$$
$$x = 54$$

23. $\sqrt[3]{s + 1} = 2$
$$s + 1 = 8$$
$$s = 7$$

24. $\sqrt[3]{n - 1} = 3$
$$n - 1 = 27$$
$$n = 28$$

25. $\sqrt[4]{3q} - 2 = 0$
$$\sqrt[4]{3q} = 2$$
$$3q = 16$$
$$q = \frac{16}{3}$$
$$q = 5\frac{1}{3}$$

26. $\sqrt[4]{4b} = 3$
$$4b = 81$$
$$b = \frac{81}{4}$$
$$b = 20\frac{1}{4}$$

27. $\sqrt{2c + 3} - 7 = 0$
$$\sqrt{2c + 3} = 7$$
$$2c + 3 = 49$$
$$2c = 46$$
$$c = 23$$

28. $\sqrt{3z - 5} - 3 = 1$
$$\sqrt{3z - 5} = 4$$
$$3z - 5 = 16$$
$$3z = 21$$
$$z = 7$$

29. $\sqrt{4x + 8} + 9 = 11$
$$\sqrt{4x + 8} = 2$$
$$4x + 8 = 4$$
$$4x = -4$$
$$x = -1$$

30. $\sqrt{1 + 2g} - 6 = -3$
$$\sqrt{1 + 2g} = 3$$
$$1 + 2g = 9$$
$$2g = 8$$
$$g = 4$$

31. $\sqrt{5y + 1} + 6 = 10$
$$\sqrt{5y + 1} = 4$$
$$5y + 1 = 16$$
$$5y = 15$$
$$y = 3$$

32. $\sqrt[4]{2d + 3} + 5 = 4$
$$\sqrt[4]{2d + 3} = -1$$
$$2d + 3 = 1$$
$$2d = -2$$
$$d = -1$$
does not check;
no solution

33. $\sqrt{3f + 1} - 2 = 6$
$$\sqrt{3f + 1} = 8$$
$$3f + 1 = 64$$
$$3f = 63$$
$$f = 21$$

34. $\sqrt[3]{x + 5} + 6 = 4$
$$\sqrt[3]{x + 5} = -2$$
$$x + 5 = -8$$
$$x = -13$$

35. $\sqrt{y + 5} = \sqrt{2y - 3}$
$$y + 5 = 2y - 3$$
$$8 = y$$

36. $\sqrt{x - 4} = \sqrt{2x - 3}$
$$x - 4 = 2x - 3$$
$$-1 = x$$
does not check;
no solution

37. $\sqrt{n + 12} - \sqrt{n} = 2$
$$\sqrt{n + 12} = 2 + \sqrt{n}$$
$$n + 12 = 4 + 4\sqrt{n} + n$$
$$8 = 4\sqrt{n}$$
$$2 = \sqrt{n}$$
$$4 = n$$

38. $\sqrt{x + 6} - \sqrt{x} = \sqrt{2}$
$$\sqrt{x + 6} = \sqrt{2} + \sqrt{x}$$
$$x + 6 = 2 + 2\sqrt{2x} + x$$
$$4 = 2\sqrt{2x}$$
$$2 = \sqrt{2x}$$
$$4 = 2x$$
$$2 = x$$

39. $\sqrt{y - 5} - \sqrt{y} = 1$
$$\sqrt{y - 5} = 1 + \sqrt{y}$$
$$y - 5 = 1 + 2\sqrt{y} + y$$
$$-6 = 2\sqrt{y}$$
$$-3 = \sqrt{y}$$
$$9 = y \quad \text{does not check}$$
no solution

40. $\sqrt{c + 4} = \sqrt{c + 20} - 2$
$$c + 4 = c + 24 - 4\sqrt{c + 20}$$
$$-20 = -4\sqrt{c + 20}$$
$$5 = \sqrt{c + 20}$$
$$25 = c + 20$$
$$5 = c$$

41. $\sqrt{x - 1} + \sqrt{x + 3} = 5$
$$\sqrt{x - 1} = 5 - \sqrt{x + 3}$$
$$x - 1 = 28 - 10\sqrt{x + 3} + x$$
$$-29 = -10\sqrt{x + 3}$$
$$\frac{29}{10} = \sqrt{x + 3}$$
$$8.41 = x + 3$$
$$5.41 = x$$

42. $\sqrt{4y + 1} - \sqrt{4y - 2} = 3$
$$\sqrt{4y + 1} = 3 + \sqrt{4y - 2}$$
$$4y + 1 = 7 + 4y + 6\sqrt{4y - 2}$$
$$-6 = 6\sqrt{4y - 2}$$
$$-1 = \sqrt{4y - 2}$$
$$1 = 4y - 2$$
$$3 = 4y$$
$$\frac{3}{4} = y \quad \text{does not check}$$
no solution

43. $\sqrt{y + 1} + \sqrt{y - 3} = 5$

$\sqrt{y + 1} = 5 - \sqrt{y - 3}$

$y + 1 = 22 + y - 10\sqrt{y - 3}$

$-21 = -10\sqrt{y - 3}$

$\dfrac{21}{10} = \sqrt{y - 3}$

$4.41 = y - 3$

$7.41 = y$

44. $\sqrt{x^2 + 5x} + x + 10 = 0$

$\sqrt{x^2 + 5x} = -x - 10$

$x^2 + 5x = x^2 + 20x + 100$

$0 = 15x + 100$

$-100 = 15x$

$-\dfrac{20}{3} = x$ does not check

no solution

45. $\sqrt{x + 12} + 1 = \sqrt{x + 21}$

$x + 13 + 2\sqrt{x + 12} = x + 21$

$2\sqrt{x + 12} = 8$

$\sqrt{x + 12} = 4$

$x + 12 = 16$

$x = 4$

46. $\sqrt{5y^2 + 7y - 2} - y\sqrt{5} = -4$

$\sqrt{5y^2 + 7y - 2} = -4 + y\sqrt{5}$

$5y^2 + 7y - 2 = 16 - 8y\sqrt{5} + 5y^2$

$7y + 8y\sqrt{5} = 18$

$y(7 + 8\sqrt{5}) = 18$

$y = \dfrac{18}{7 + 8\sqrt{5}} \cdot \dfrac{7 - 8\sqrt{5}}{7 - 8\sqrt{5}}$

$= \dfrac{18(7 - 8\sqrt{5})}{49 - 320}$

$= \dfrac{126 - 144\sqrt{5}}{-271}$

does not check;

no solution

47. $y^2 = r^2 + s^2$

$y^2 - s^2 = r^2$

$\pm\sqrt{y^2 - s^2} = r$

48. $t^2 = \dfrac{2s}{g}$

$t^2 g = 2s$

$\dfrac{t^2 g}{2} = s$

49. $r^3 = \dfrac{2mM}{c}$

$r^3 c = 2mM$

$c = \dfrac{2mM}{r^3}$

50. $m^6 = \dfrac{rp}{g^2}$

$m^6 g^2 = rp$

$\dfrac{m^6 g^2}{r} = p$

51. There will be no solution if the value under the radical sign is negative, or, if the principle root is negative. Thus for $\sqrt{5x - 7} + a = b$, if $5x < 7$ or $a > b$, then there will be no real solution.

52. $7854 = \pi r^2$

$\dfrac{7854}{\pi} = r^2$

$2500 = r^2$

$\sqrt{2500} = r$

$50 = r$

The greatest distance is ~50 miles.

53. Let A = area of cell.

$\dfrac{1}{0.01} = \dfrac{A}{15} \Rightarrow 15 = 0.01A$

$1500 = A$

$s^2 = A \Rightarrow s^2 = 1500$

$s = 10\sqrt{15}$

$s = 38.73$

The cell should be 38.73 cm on each side.

54. $r^3 = \dfrac{GMt^2}{4\pi^2}$

$4\pi^2 r^3 = GMt^2$

$\dfrac{4\pi^2 r^3}{GM} = t^2$

$\sqrt{\dfrac{4\pi^2 r^3}{GM}} = t$

$2\pi r \sqrt{\dfrac{r}{GM}} = t$

$2\pi r \dfrac{\sqrt{rGM}}{GM} = t$

55. $\dfrac{rs}{r^{\frac{1}{2}} + r^{\frac{3}{2}}} \cdot \dfrac{r^{\frac{1}{2}} - r^{\frac{3}{2}}}{r^{\frac{1}{2}} - r^{\frac{3}{2}}}$

$= \dfrac{r^{\frac{3}{2}}s - r^{\frac{5}{2}}s}{r - r^3}$

$= \dfrac{r^{\frac{3}{2}}s(1 - r)}{r(1 - r)(1 + r)}$

$= \dfrac{r^{\frac{1}{2}}s}{1 + r}$

56. $\left(6\sqrt{5a^{\frac{7}{4}}b^{-\frac{2}{3}}} \right)^{12}$

$= \left(5^{\frac{1}{6}}a^{\frac{7}{4}}b^{-\frac{2}{3}} \right)^{12}$

$= 5^2 a^{21} b^{-8}$

$= \dfrac{25a^{21}}{b^8}$

57. 8

58. det $= 3 \cdot 1 \cdot 4 + 4 \cdot 0 \cdot -1 + (-2) \cdot 0 \cdot (-1)$
     $- (-1 \cdot 1 \cdot (-2)) + (-1) \cdot 3 + 4 \cdot 0 \cdot 4)$

$= 12 - 2$

$= 10$

Yes, there is an inverse.

59. Let s = number of student tickets.

Let a = number of adult tickets.

$$s \geq 50$$

$$0 \leq a \leq 100$$

$$a + s \leq 150$$

Vertices $(50, 100)$, $(50, 0)$, $(150, 0)$

Maximize: $s + 2a$

(s, a)	$(50, 100)$	$(50, 0)$	$(150, 0)$
$s + 2a$	350	50	150

50 students and 100 adults

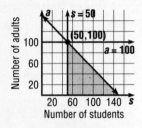

60. The relation is a function; each member of the domain is paired with only one member of the range.

Technology: Solving Radical Equations

PAGE 287   EXERCISES

1. $\frac{1}{25}$, 1 **2.** 21 **3.** no solutions **4.** 2, 6

6-8 Pure Imaginary Numbers

PAGES 289-290   CHECKING FOR UNDERSTANDING

1. An imaginary number is a number that involves the square root of a negative number; it is not a real number.

2. Answers will vary. Some examples: $4i$, $-3i$

3. The values i, -1, $-i$ and 1 repeat in cycles of four.

4. $\sqrt{-49}$

$= \sqrt{49} \cdot \sqrt{-1}$

$= 7i$

5. $\sqrt{-36}$

$= \sqrt{36} \cdot \sqrt{-1}$

$= 6i$

6. $4\sqrt{-3}$

$= 4\sqrt{3} \cdot \sqrt{-1}$

$= 4i\sqrt{3}$

7. $\sqrt{-2} \cdot \sqrt{-2}$

$= i\sqrt{2} \cdot i\sqrt{2}$

$= i^2 \cdot 2$

$= -2$

8. $6\sqrt{-4}$

$= 6\sqrt{4} \cdot \sqrt{-1}$

$= 12i$

9. $\sqrt{-3} \cdot \sqrt{-3}$

$= i\sqrt{3} \cdot i\sqrt{3}$

$= i^2 \cdot 3$

$= -3$

10. $\sqrt{-5} \cdot \sqrt{5}$

$= (\sqrt{5})^2 \cdot \sqrt{-1}$

$= 5i$

11. $4 \cdot 5i$

$= 20i$

12. i^{10}

$= (i^2)^5$

$= (-1)^5$

$= -1$

PAGES 290-291   EXERCISES

13. $\sqrt{-169} = \sqrt{169} \cdot \sqrt{-1}$

$= 13i$

14. $\sqrt{-100} = \sqrt{100} \cdot \sqrt{-1}$

$= 10i$

15. $\sqrt{-50} = \sqrt{25} \cdot \sqrt{2} \cdot \sqrt{-1}$

$= 5i\sqrt{2}$

16. $\sqrt{-98} = \sqrt{49} \cdot \sqrt{2} \cdot \sqrt{-1}$

$= 7i\sqrt{2}$

17. $\sqrt{-\frac{4}{9}} = \sqrt{\frac{4}{9}} \cdot \sqrt{-1}$

$= \frac{2}{3}i$

18. $\sqrt{-\frac{9}{25}} = \sqrt{\frac{9}{25}} \cdot \sqrt{-1}$

$= \frac{3}{5}i$

19. $\sqrt{-\frac{1}{5}} = \frac{\sqrt{1}}{\sqrt{5}} \cdot \sqrt{-1}$

$= \frac{1}{\sqrt{5}}i$

$= \frac{i}{\sqrt{5}} \cdot \frac{\sqrt{5}}{\sqrt{5}}$

$= \frac{i\sqrt{5}}{5}$

20. $\sqrt{-\frac{1}{2}} = \frac{\sqrt{1}}{\sqrt{2}} \cdot \sqrt{-1}$

$= \frac{1}{\sqrt{2}}i$

$= \frac{i}{\sqrt{2}} \cdot \frac{\sqrt{2}}{\sqrt{2}}$

$= \frac{i\sqrt{2}}{2}$

21. i^5

$= i^2 i^2 i$

$= (-1)(-1)i$

$= 1 \cdot i$

$= i$

22. i^{11}

$= (i^2)^5 i$

$= (-1)^5 i$

$= -1 \cdot i$

$= -i$

23. i^{91}

$= (i^2)^{45} i$

$= (-1)^{45} i$

$= -1 \cdot i$

$= -i$

24. i^{244}

$= (i^2)^{122}$

$= (-1)^{122}$

$= 1$

25. $\sqrt{-8} \cdot \sqrt{-2}$

$= i\sqrt{8} \cdot i\sqrt{2}$

$= i^2\sqrt{16}$

$= (-1)4$

$= -4$

26. $\sqrt{-3} \cdot \sqrt{-18}$

$= i\sqrt{3} \cdot i\sqrt{18}$

$= i^2\sqrt{54}$

$= (-1)3\sqrt{6}$

$= -3\sqrt{6}$

27. $\sqrt{-14} \cdot \sqrt{-7}$

$= i\sqrt{14} \cdot i\sqrt{7}$

$= i^2\sqrt{98}$

$= (-1)7\sqrt{2}$

$= -7\sqrt{2}$

28. $(\sqrt{-5})^2$

$= \sqrt{-5} \cdot \sqrt{-5}$

$= i\sqrt{5} \cdot i\sqrt{5}$

$= i^2 \cdot 5$

$= -5$

29. $(\sqrt{-12})^2$

$= \sqrt{-12} \cdot \sqrt{-12}$

$= i\sqrt{12} \cdot i\sqrt{12}$

$= i^2 \cdot 12$

$= -12$

30. $(\sqrt{-3})^3$

$= \sqrt{-3} \cdot \sqrt{-3} \cdot \sqrt{-3}$

$= i\sqrt{3} \cdot i\sqrt{3} \cdot i\sqrt{3}$

$= i^2 \cdot 3 \cdot i\sqrt{3}$

$= -3i\sqrt{3}$

31. $(\sqrt{-4})^3$

$= 2i \cdot 2i \cdot 2i$

$= 8 \cdot i^2 \cdot i$

$= 8(-1)(i)$

$= -8i$

32. $\sqrt{9} \cdot \sqrt{-9}$

$= \sqrt{9} \cdot i\sqrt{9}$

$= i \cdot 9$

$= 9i$

33. $\sqrt{3} \cdot \sqrt{-27}$

$= \sqrt{3} \cdot i\sqrt{9} \cdot \sqrt{3}$

$= i\sqrt{9} \cdot \sqrt{3} \cdot \sqrt{3}$

$= i \cdot 3 \cdot 3$

$= 9i$

34. $\sqrt{-5} \cdot \sqrt{20}$

$= i\sqrt{5} \cdot \sqrt{5} \cdot \sqrt{4}$

$= i \cdot 5 \cdot 2$

$= 10i$

35. $\sqrt{-8} \cdot \sqrt{6}$

$= i\sqrt{8} \cdot \sqrt{6}$

$= i\sqrt{48}$

$= i \cdot 4\sqrt{3}$

$= 4i\sqrt{3}$

36. $(2i)(3i)^2$

$= 2i(9i^2)$

$= 2i(-9)$

$= -18i$

37. $(-2\sqrt{-8})(3\sqrt{-2})$

$= (-2i\sqrt{8})(3i\sqrt{2})$

$= -6i^2\sqrt{16}$

$= -6(-1)4$

$= 24$

38. $(4\sqrt{-12})(-2\sqrt{-3})$

$= 4i\sqrt{12}(-2i\sqrt{3})$

$= -8i^2\sqrt{36}$

$= -8(-1)6$

$= 48$

39. $5i(-2i)^2$

$= 5i(4i^2)$

$= 5i(-4)$

$= -20i$

40. $(3\sqrt{21})(-2\sqrt{-21})$

$= (3\sqrt{21})(-2i\sqrt{21})$

$= -6i \cdot 21$

$= -126i$

41. $a^2 + 16 = 0$

$a^2 = -16$

$a = \pm\sqrt{-16}$

$a = \pm 4i$

42. $x^2 + 64 = 0$

$x^2 = -64$

$x = \pm\sqrt{-64}$

$x = \pm 8i$

43. $m^2 + 121 = 0$

$m^2 = -121$

$m = \pm\sqrt{-121}$

$m = \pm 11i$

44. $n^2 + 169 = 0$

$n^2 = -169$

$n = \pm\sqrt{-169}$

$n = \pm 13i$

45. $3x^2 + 27 = 0$

$3x^2 = -27$

$x^2 = -9$

$x = \pm\sqrt{-9}$

$x = \pm 3i$

46. $6y^2 = -96$

$y^2 = -16$

$y = \pm\sqrt{-16}$

$y = \pm 4i$

47. $t^2 + 12 = 0$

$t^2 = -12$

$t = \pm\sqrt{-12}$

$t = \pm i\sqrt{4}\sqrt{3}$

$t = \pm 2i\sqrt{3}$

48. $3a^2 + 18 = 0$

$3a^2 = -18$

$a^2 = -6$

$a = \pm\sqrt{-6}$

$a = \pm i\sqrt{6}$

49. $4x^2 + 5 = 0$

$4x^2 = -5$

$x^2 = -\dfrac{5}{4}$

$x = \pm\sqrt{-\dfrac{5}{4}}$

$x = \pm i\dfrac{\sqrt{5}}{\sqrt{4}}$

$x = \pm i\dfrac{\sqrt{5}}{2}$

50. $5w^2 = -40$

$w^2 = -8$

$w = \pm\sqrt{-8}$

$w = \pm i\sqrt{4}\sqrt{2}$

$w = \pm 2i\sqrt{2}$

51. $\sqrt{-81} \cdot \sqrt{-8} + \sqrt[3]{256} = i\sqrt{81} \cdot i\sqrt{4}\sqrt{2} + \sqrt[3]{64}\sqrt[3]{4}$

$= 9i(2i\sqrt{2}) + 4\sqrt[3]{4}$

$= 18i^2\sqrt{2} + 4\sqrt[3]{4}$

$= -18\sqrt{2} + 4\sqrt[3]{4}$

52. a. $6i = 14i - X_C$

$X_C = 14i - 6i$

$X_C = 8i$

Total reactance is 8i ohms.

b. $8i = X_L - 7i$

$15i = X_L$

Reactance of the inductions is 15i ohms.

53. a. $i^{17} = i$

b. $i^{34} = -1$

c. $i^{59} = -i$

d. $i^{92} = 1$

e. $i^{103} = -i$

f. $i^{300} = 1$

g. $i^{997} = i$

h. $i^{2002} = -1$

54. $2x + 7 = -x\sqrt{2}$

$2x + x\sqrt{2} = -7$

$x(2 + \sqrt{2}) = -7$

$x = \dfrac{-7}{2 + \sqrt{2}} \cdot \dfrac{2 - \sqrt{2}}{2 - \sqrt{2}}$

$x = \dfrac{7\sqrt{2} - 14}{2}$

55. $\sqrt{3y^2 + 11y - 5} = y\sqrt{3} + 1$

$3y^2 + 11y - 5 = 3y^2 + 2y\sqrt{3} + 1$

$11y - 6 = 2y\sqrt{3}$

$-6 = 2y\sqrt{3} - 11y$

$-6 = y(2\sqrt{3} - 11)$

$\dfrac{-6}{2\sqrt{3} - 11} \cdot \dfrac{2\sqrt{3} + 11}{2\sqrt{3} + 11} = y$

$\dfrac{6(2\sqrt{3} + 11)}{109} = y$

56. $\sqrt{(x - 2)^2} = |x - 2|$

57. $a^3 + 1 = (a + 1)(a^2 - a + 1)$

58. Let p = pizza price.

Let m = milk price.

Let c = cookie price.

$$2p + 2m + c = 205$$

$$m + 3c = 75 \Rightarrow c = \frac{75 - m}{3}$$

$$p + m = 95 \Rightarrow p = 95 - m$$

$$2(95 - m) + 2m + \frac{75 - m}{3} = 205$$

$$190 + \frac{75 - m}{3} = 205$$

$$570 + 75 - m = 615$$

$$645 - m = 615$$

$$30 = m$$

$$p = 95 - 30 \qquad c = \frac{75 - 30}{3}$$

$$= 65 \qquad = \frac{45}{3} = 15$$

Pizza is 65 cents, milk is 30 cents, cookies are 15 cents.

59. det = $18(11) - (-9)(-5) = 153$

60. $r = 0.6(220 - 20)$

$= 0.6(200)$

$= 120$

6-9   Complex Numbers

PAGE 294   CHECKING FOR UNDERSTANDING

1. Complex numbers are equal when their real parts and their imaginary parts are equal.

2. The set of real numbers is a subset of the set of complex numbers.

3. Answers will vary; clouds, mountains, interference on communication lines

4. $4 + 2i$

5. $(4 - i) + (3 + 3i)$
    $= (4 + 3) + (-i + 3i)$
    $= 7 + 2i$

6. $(7 + 2i) + (2 + 8i)$
    $= (7 + 2) + (2i + 8i)$
    $= 9 + 10i$

7. $(5 + 2i) - (2 + 2i)$
    $= (5 - 2) + (2i - 2i)$
    $= 3 + 0i$
    $= 3$

8. $(7 - 6i) - (5 - 6i)$
    $= (7 - 5) + (-6i + 6i)$
    $= 2 + 0i$
    $= 2$

9. $(7 + 3i) + (3 - 3i)$
    $= (7 + 3) + (3i - 3i)$
    $= 10 + 0i$
    $= 10$

10. $(2 - 4i) + (2 + 4i)$
    $= (2 + 2) + (-4i + 4i)$
    $= 4 + 0i$
    $= 4$

11. $4(5 + 3i)$
    $= 20 + 12i$

12. $-6(2 - 3i)$
    $= -12 + 18i$

13. $(2 + 4i)(1 + 3i)$
    $= 2 + 6i + 4i + 12i^2$
    $= 2 + 10i - 12$
    $= -10 + 10i$

14. $(1 - 4i)(2 - 3i)$
    $= 2 - 3i - 8i + 12i^2$
    $= 2 - 11i - 12$
    $= -10 - 11i$

15. $(4 + i)(4 - i)$
    $= 16 - 4i + 4i - i^2$
    $= 16 - 0i + 1$
    $= 17$

16. $(4 - i)(3 + 2i)$
    $= 12 + 8i - 3i - 2i^2$
    $= 12 + 5i + 2$
    $= 14 + 5i$

17. $x = 2,\ y = -3$

18. $x = 5,\ -y = 6$
    $y = -6$

19. $x = 3,\ 2y = 0$
    $y = 0$

20. $x = 4,\ -y = 5$
    $y = -5$

21. $x = 7,\ -y = -2$
    $y = 2$

22. $2x = 0,\ y = 5$
    $x = 0$

PAGES 294-296   EXERCISES

23. $(4 + 2i) + (1 + 3i) = 5 + 5i$

24. $(2 + 6i) + (4 + 3i) = 6 + 9i$

25. $(11 + 5i) - (4 + 2i) = 7 + 3i$

26. $(11 - \sqrt{-3}) - (-4 + \sqrt{-5})$
    $= (11 - i\sqrt{3}) - (-4 + i\sqrt{5})$
    $= 15 - i\sqrt{3} - i\sqrt{5}$

27. $(8 - 7i) + (-5 - i) = 3 - 8i$

28. $(5 + \sqrt{-7}) + (-3 + \sqrt{-2}) = (5 + i\sqrt{7}) + (-3 + i\sqrt{2})$
              $= 2 + i\sqrt{7} + i\sqrt{2}$

29. $(-6 - 2i) - (-8 - 3i) = 2 + i$

30. $(3 - 11i) - (-5 + 4i) = 8 - 15i$

31. $(1 - 5i\sqrt{3}) + (4 + 2i\sqrt{3}) = 5 - 3i\sqrt{3}$

32. $(8 - 3i\sqrt{5}) + (-3 + 2i\sqrt{5}) = 5 - i\sqrt{5}$

33. $3(4 - 5i) - 6(2 - i) = 12 - 15i - 12 + 6i$
                 $= -9i$

34. $3(-5 - 2i) + 2(-3 + 2i) = -15 - 6i - 6 + 4i$
                   $= -21 - 2i$

35. $(5 + 3i)(6 - i) = 30 - 5i + 18i - 3i^2$
               $= 30 + 13i + 3$
               $= 33 + 13i$

36. $(5 + i)(2 - 3i) = 10 - 15i + 2i - 3i^2$
             $= 10 - 13i + 3$
             $= 13 - 13i$

37. $(6 - 2i)(6 - 2i) = 36 - 12i - 12i + 4i^2$
               $= 36 - 24i - 4$
               $= 32 - 24i$

38. $(2 + i\sqrt{3})(2 + i\sqrt{3}) = 4 + 2i\sqrt{3} + 2i\sqrt{3} + i^2 \cdot 3$
                  $= 4 + 4i\sqrt{3} - 3$
                  $= 1 + 4i\sqrt{3}$

39. $(7 - 2i)(4 - 3i) = 28 - 21i - 8i + 6i^2$
              $= 28 - 29i - 6$
              $= 22 - 29i$

40. $(7 - i\sqrt{2})(5 + i\sqrt{2}) = 35 + 7i\sqrt{2} - 5i\sqrt{2} - i^2 \cdot 2$
                 $= 35 + 2i\sqrt{2} + 2$
                 $= 37 + 2i\sqrt{2}$

41. $(3 + 4i)(3 + 4i) = 9 + 12i + 12i + 16i^2$
$$= 9 + 24i - 16$$
$$= -7 + 24i$$

42. $(3 + 2i)(3 + 2i) = 9 + 6i + 6i + 4i^2$
$$= 9 + 12i - 4$$
$$= 5 + 12i$$

43. $(\sqrt{2} + i)(\sqrt{2} - i) = 2 - i\sqrt{2} + i\sqrt{2} - i^2$
$$= 2 + 0 + 1$$
$$= 3$$

44. $(2 - \sqrt{-3})(2 + \sqrt{-3}) = (2 - i\sqrt{3})(2 + i\sqrt{3})$
$$= 4 + 2i\sqrt{3} - 2i\sqrt{3} - i^2 \cdot 3$$
$$= 4 + 0 + 3$$
$$= 7$$

45. $(3 + 2i)(3 - 2i) = 9 - 6i + 6i - 4i^2$
$$= 9 - 0 + 4$$
$$= 13$$

46. $(3 + \sqrt{-2})(3 - \sqrt{-2}) = (3 + i\sqrt{2})(3 - i\sqrt{2})$
$$= 9 - 3i\sqrt{2} + 3i\sqrt{2} - i^2 \cdot 2$$
$$= 9 - 0 + 2$$
$$= 11$$

47. $(-2 + i) + (4 + 4i)$
$$= (-2 + 4) + (i + 4i)$$
$$= 2 + 5i$$

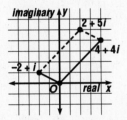

48. $(9 + 4i) + (3 - 2i)$
$$= (9 + 3) + (4i - 2i)$$
$$= 12 + 2i$$

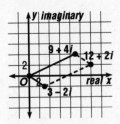

49. $(-1 - 5i) + (4 + 0i)$
$$= (-1 + 4) + (-5i + 0i)$$
$$= 3 - 5i$$

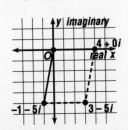

50. $(3 + 2i) + (-11 - 5i)$
$$= (3 - 11) + (2i - 5i)$$
$$= -8 - 3i$$

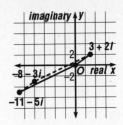

51. $3x = 18$, $2y = 7$ **52.** $3x = 6$, $5y = 20$

   $x = 6$ $y = \dfrac{7}{2}$ $x = 2$ $y = 4$

53. $x - y = 2$, $x + y = -4$

     $x = 2 + y$ $2 + y + y = -4$

     $x = 2 - 3$ $2y = -6$

     $x = -1$ $y = -3$

54. $2x + y = 7$, $x - y = -1$

  $2(-1 + y) + y = 7$ $x = -1 + y$

    $-2 + 2y + y = 7$ $x = -1 + 3$

            $3y = 9$ $x = 2$

             $y = 3$

55. $x + 2y = 5$, $2x - y = 5$

      $x = 5 - 2y$ $2(5 - 2y) - y = 5$

      $x = 5 - 2 \cdot 1$ $10 - 4y - y = 5$

      $x = 5 - 2$ $-5y = -5$

      $x = 3$ $y = 1$

56. $x + 4y = 13$ $2x - 3y = 7$

      $x = 13 - 4y$ $2(13 - 4y) - 3y = 7$

      $x = 13 - 4\left(\dfrac{19}{11}\right)$ $26 - 8y - 3y = 7$

      $x = \dfrac{143}{11} - \dfrac{76}{11}$ $-11y = -19$

      $x = \dfrac{67}{11}$ $y = \dfrac{19}{11}$

57. $(1 + 2i)(3 - 4i)(2 + i)$
$$= (3 - 4i + 6i - 8i^2)(2 + i)$$
$$= (3 + 2i + 8)(2 + i)$$
$$= (11 + 2i)(2 + i)$$
$$= 22 + 11i + 4i + 2i^2$$
$$= 22 + 15i - 2$$
$$= 20 + 15i$$

58. $(3 + 3i)(6 - i)(5 + 2i)$
$$= (18 - 3i + 18i - 3i^2)(5 + 2i)$$
$$= (18 + 15i + 3)(5 + 2i)$$
$$= (21 + 15i)(5 + 2i)$$
$$= 105 + 42i + 75i + 30i^2$$
$$= 105 + 117i - 30$$
$$= 75 + 117i$$

59. $(2 - 3i)(7 + 5i)(7 - 5i)$

$= (2 - 3i)(49 - 35i + 35i - 25i^2)$

$= (2 - 3i)(49 + 25)$

$= (2 - 3i)(74)$

$= 148 - 222i$

60. $(4 + 3i)(3 + i)(2 - 7i)$

$= (12 + 4i + 9i + 3i^2)(2 - 7i)$

$= (9 + 13i)(2 - 7i)$

$= 18 - 63i + 26i - 91i^2$

$= 18 - 37i + 91$

$= 109 - 37i$

61. $(7 - i)(5 + 2i)(4 + 2i)$

$= (35 + 14i - 5i - 2i^2)(4 + 2i)$

$= (37 + 9i)(4 + 2i)$

$= 148 + 74i + 36i + 18i^2$

$= 148 + 110i - 18$

$= 130 + 110i$

62. $(5 + i)(9 + 2i)(9 - 2i)$

$= (5 + i)(81 - 18i + 18i - 4i^2)$

$= (5 + i)(81 + 4)$

$= (5 + i)(85)$

$= 425 + 85i$

63. $-a - bi$

64. $a + bi + 0 + 0i$

$= (a + 0) + (bi + 0i)$

$= (a + 0) + (b + 0)i$

$= a + bi$

65. $(a + bi) \cdot 1$

$= (a \cdot 1) + (bi \cdot 1)$

$= a + bi$

66. The imaginary numbers are not closed under any of these operations:

Addition: $(2 + 3i) + (2 - 3i) = 4$

Subtraction: $(1 + 2i) - (3 + 2i) = -2$

Multiplication: $(3 + 2i)(3 - 2i) = 13$

67. $f(1 + i)^2 = (1 + i)^2 - 1$

$= 1 + i + i + i^2 - 1$

$= 1 + 2i - 1 - 1$

$= -1 + 2i$

$(1 + i, -1 + 2i)$

$f(-1 + 2i) = (-1 + 2i)^2 - 1$

$= 1 - 2i - 2i + 4i^2 - 1$

$= 1 - 4i - 4 - 1$

$= -4 - 4i$

$(-1 + 2i, -4 - 4i)$

$f(-4 - 4i) = (-4 - 4i)^2 - 1$

$= 16 + 16i + 16i + 16i^2 - 1$

$= 16 + 32i - 16 - 1$

$= -1 + 32i$

$(-4 - 4i, -1 + 32i)$

$f(-1 + 32i) = (-1 + 32i)^2 - 1$

$= 1 - 32i - 32i + 1024i^2 - 1$

$= -64i - 1024$

$= -1024 - 64i$

$(-1 + 32i, -1024 - 64i)$

68. $E = (6 - 8j)(14 + 8j)$

$= 84 - 64j + 64$

$= 148 - 64j$

69. $\sqrt{-\dfrac{1}{3}}$

$= i\dfrac{\sqrt{1}}{\sqrt{3}}$

$= i\dfrac{1}{\sqrt{3}} \cdot \dfrac{\sqrt{3}}{\sqrt{3}}$

$= i \cdot \dfrac{\sqrt{3}}{3}$

$= \dfrac{i\sqrt{3}}{3}$

70. $3a^2 + 24 = 0$

$3a^2 = -24$

$a^2 = -8$

$a = \pm i\sqrt{8}$

$a = \pm 2i\sqrt{2}$

71. $\sqrt[4]{5} + 6\sqrt[4]{5} - 2\sqrt[4]{5} = 5\sqrt[4]{5}$

72.
$$
\begin{array}{r|rrrrr}
-3 & 1 & 6 & -7 & 7 & -1 \\
   &   & -3 & -9 & 48 & -165 \\
\hline
   & 1 & 3 & -16 & 55 & -166
\end{array}
$$

$y^3 + 3y^2 - 16y + 55 - \dfrac{166}{y + 3}$

73. $\dfrac{7.35 \times 10^{22}}{1.672 \times 10^{-24}} = \left(\dfrac{7.35}{1.672}\right)\left(\dfrac{10^{22}}{10^{-24}}\right)$

$= 4.39 \times 10^{46}$

$\sim 4.4 \times 10^{46}$ times

74. $\begin{bmatrix} 4 & 5 \\ 2 & -2 \\ 4 & 9 \end{bmatrix} + \begin{bmatrix} -3 & 2 \\ -1 & 4 \\ 4 & 4 \end{bmatrix} = \begin{bmatrix} 1 & 7 \\ 1 & 2 \\ 8 & 13 \end{bmatrix}$

75. $x + y < 8$

$x + y > 5$

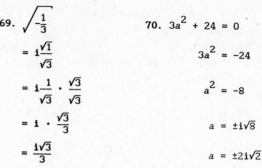

76. $3x - y = 4 \Rightarrow y = 3x - 4$

$9x - 6 = 3y$

$9x - 6 = 3(3x - 4)$

$9x - 6 = 9x - 12$

$-6 \neq -12$

Inconsistent

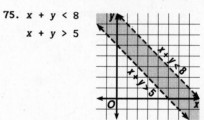

77. No

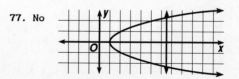

140

PAGE 299   CHECKING FOR UNDERSTANDING

1. $3 + 2i$

2. $(a + bi)(a - bi) = a^2 + b^2$

3. It is the conjugate divided by the product of the number and its conjugate.

4. No, all have inverses except 0.

5. $4 - i$ 6. $1 - 6i$ 7. $5 + 4i$

8. $3 + 3i$ 9. $-5i$ 10. $-6i$

11. $10i$ 12. 9 13. $12 + i$

14. $(2 + 3i)\left(\dfrac{2 - 3i}{13}\right) = \dfrac{4 + 9}{13} = 1$

15. $(5 - 4i)\left(\dfrac{5 + 4i}{41}\right) = \dfrac{25 + 16}{41} = 1$

16. $(6 + 8i)\left(\dfrac{3 - 4i}{50}\right) = 2(3 + 4i)\left(\dfrac{3 - 4i}{50}\right)$

$\qquad = 2(9 + 16)\left(\dfrac{1}{50}\right)$

$\qquad = \dfrac{2 \cdot 25}{50}$

$\qquad = 1$

PAGES 300-301   EXERCISES

17. $(8 - 2i)(8 + 2i)$
$\quad = 64 + 4$
$\quad = 68$

18. $(3 + 7i)(3 - 7i)$
$\quad = 9 + 49$
$\quad = 58$

19. $(5 - 2i)(5 + 2i)$
$\quad = 25 + 4$
$\quad = 29$

20. $(5)(5) = 25$

21. $(1 + i)(1 - i)$
$\quad = 1 + 1$
$\quad = 2$

22. $(12 + 5i)(12 - 5i)$
$\quad = 144 + 25$
$\quad = 169$

23. $(9i)(-9i) = -81i^2$
$\qquad\qquad = 81$

24. $(6 + 5i)(6 - 5i)$
$\quad = 36 + 25$
$\quad = 61$

25. $(-10i)(10i)$

$\quad = -100i^2$

$\quad = 100$

26. $\dfrac{4 + 5i}{1 + i} \cdot \dfrac{1 - i}{1 - i}$

$\quad = \dfrac{4 - 4i + 5i + 5}{1 + 1}$

$\quad = \dfrac{9 + i}{2}$

27. $\dfrac{3 - 2i}{1 - i} \cdot \dfrac{1 + i}{1 + i}$

$\quad = \dfrac{3 + 3i - 2i + 2}{1 + 1}$

$\quad = \dfrac{5 + i}{2}$

28. $\dfrac{1 + i}{3 + 2i} \cdot \dfrac{3 - 2i}{3 - 2i}$

$\quad = \dfrac{3 - 2i + 3i + 2}{9 + 4}$

$\quad = \dfrac{5 + i}{13}$

29. $\dfrac{11 + i}{2 - i} \cdot \dfrac{2 + i}{2 + i}$

$\quad = \dfrac{22 + 11i + 2i - 1}{4 + 1}$

$\quad = \dfrac{21 + 13i}{5}$

30. $\dfrac{3 + 5i}{2i} \cdot \dfrac{-2i}{-2i}$

$\quad = \dfrac{-6i + 10}{4}$

$\quad = \dfrac{2(5 - 3i)}{4}$

$\quad = \dfrac{5 - 3i}{2}$

31. $\dfrac{1 - i}{4 - 5i} \cdot \dfrac{4 + 5i}{4 + 5i}$

$\quad = \dfrac{4 + 5i - 4i + 5}{16 + 25}$

$\quad = \dfrac{9 + i}{41}$

32. $\dfrac{5 - 6i}{-3i} \cdot \dfrac{3i}{3i}$

$\quad = \dfrac{15i + 18}{9}$

$\quad = \dfrac{3(6 + 5i)}{9}$

$\quad = \dfrac{6 + 5i}{3}$

33. $\dfrac{2 + i}{5i} \cdot \dfrac{-5i}{-5i}$

$\quad = \dfrac{-10i + 5}{25}$

$\quad = \dfrac{5(1 - 2i)}{25}$

$\quad = \dfrac{1 - 2i}{5}$

34. $\dfrac{4 - 7i}{-3i} \cdot \dfrac{3i}{3i}$

$\quad = \dfrac{12i + 21}{9}$

$\quad = \dfrac{3(7 + 4i)}{9}$

$\quad = \dfrac{7 + 4i}{3}$

35. $\dfrac{5}{2 + i} \cdot \dfrac{2 - i}{2 - i}$

$\quad = \dfrac{10 - 5i}{4 + 1}$

$\quad = \dfrac{5(2 - i)}{5}$

$\quad = 2 - i$

36. $\dfrac{3}{4 - i} \cdot \dfrac{4 + i}{4 + i}$

$\quad = \dfrac{12 + 3i}{16 + 1}$

$\quad = \dfrac{12 + 3i}{17}$

37. $\dfrac{2}{6 + 5i} \cdot \dfrac{6 - 5i}{6 - 5i}$

$\quad = \dfrac{12 - 10i}{36 + 25}$

$\quad = \dfrac{12 - 10i}{61}$

38. $\dfrac{7}{\sqrt{2} - 3i} \cdot \dfrac{\sqrt{2} + 3i}{\sqrt{2} + 3i}$

$\quad = \dfrac{7\sqrt{2} + 21i}{2 + 9}$

$\quad = \dfrac{7\sqrt{2} + 21i}{11}$

39. $\dfrac{4}{\sqrt{3} + 2i} \cdot \dfrac{\sqrt{3} - 2i}{\sqrt{3} - 2i}$

$\quad = \dfrac{4\sqrt{3} - 8i}{3 + 4}$

$\quad = \dfrac{4\sqrt{3} - 8i}{7}$

40. $\dfrac{1 + i\sqrt{2}}{1 - i\sqrt{2}} \cdot \dfrac{1 + i\sqrt{2}}{1 + i\sqrt{2}}$

$\quad = \dfrac{1 + i\sqrt{2} + i\sqrt{2} - 2}{1 + 2}$

$\quad = \dfrac{-1 + 2i\sqrt{2}}{3}$

41. $\dfrac{\sqrt{3}}{\sqrt{3} - i} \cdot \dfrac{\sqrt{3} + i}{\sqrt{3} + i}$

$\quad = \dfrac{3 + i\sqrt{3}}{3 + 1}$

$\quad = \dfrac{3 + i\sqrt{3}}{4}$

42. $\dfrac{2 + i\sqrt{3}}{2 - i\sqrt{3}} \cdot \dfrac{2 + i\sqrt{3}}{2 + i\sqrt{3}}$

$\quad = \dfrac{4 + 2i\sqrt{3} + 2i\sqrt{3} - 3}{4 + 3}$

$\quad = \dfrac{1 + 4i\sqrt{3}}{7}$

43. $\dfrac{3 - i\sqrt{5}}{3 + i\sqrt{5}} \cdot \dfrac{3 - i\sqrt{5}}{3 - i\sqrt{5}}$

$\quad = \dfrac{9 - 3i\sqrt{5} - 3i\sqrt{5} - 5}{9 + 5}$

$\quad = \dfrac{4 - 6i\sqrt{5}}{14}$

$\quad = \dfrac{2 - 3i\sqrt{5}}{7}$

44. $\dfrac{1}{2 + i} \cdot \dfrac{2 - i}{2 - i}$

$\quad = \dfrac{2 - i}{4 + 1}$

$\quad = \dfrac{2 - i}{5}$

45. $\dfrac{1}{3-4i} \cdot \dfrac{3+4i}{3+4i}$

$= \dfrac{3+4i}{9+16}$

$= \dfrac{3+4i}{25}$

46. $\dfrac{1}{7-3i} \cdot \dfrac{7+3i}{7+3i}$

$= \dfrac{7+3i}{49+9}$

$= \dfrac{7+3i}{58}$

47. $\dfrac{1}{3+7i} \cdot \dfrac{3-7i}{3-7i}$

$= \dfrac{3-7i}{9+49}$

$= \dfrac{3-7i}{58}$

48. $\dfrac{1}{2-5i} \cdot \dfrac{2+5i}{2+5i}$

$= \dfrac{2+5i}{4+25}$

$= \dfrac{2+5i}{29}$

49. $\dfrac{1}{10-12i} \cdot \dfrac{10+12i}{10+12i}$

$= \dfrac{10+12i}{100+144}$

$= \dfrac{2(5+6i)}{244}$

$= \dfrac{5+6i}{122}$

50. $\dfrac{5-i}{2i} \cdot \dfrac{-2i}{-2i}$

$= \dfrac{-10i-2}{4}$

$= \dfrac{-1-5i}{2}$

51. $\dfrac{3+i}{4i} \cdot \dfrac{-4i}{-4i}$

$= \dfrac{-12i+4}{16}$

$= \dfrac{1-3i}{4}$

52. $\dfrac{2-3i}{-i} \cdot \dfrac{i}{i}$

$= \dfrac{2i+3}{1}$

$= 3+2i$

53. $\dfrac{8-2i}{i} \cdot \dfrac{-i}{-i}$

$= \dfrac{-8i-2}{1}$

$= -2-8i$

54. $\dfrac{3+4i}{-3i} \cdot \dfrac{3i}{3i}$

$= \dfrac{9i-12}{9}$

$= \dfrac{-4+3i}{3}$

55. $\dfrac{1}{a+bi} \cdot \dfrac{a-bi}{a-bi}$

$= \dfrac{a-bi}{a^2+b^2}$

56. $\dfrac{1-i\sqrt{3}}{2-i\sqrt{3}} \cdot \dfrac{2+i\sqrt{3}}{2+i\sqrt{3}}$

$= \dfrac{2+i\sqrt{3}-2i\sqrt{3}+3}{4+3}$

$= \dfrac{5-i\sqrt{3}}{7}$

57. $\dfrac{2-i\sqrt{7}}{2+i\sqrt{7}} \cdot \dfrac{2-i\sqrt{7}}{2-i\sqrt{7}} = \dfrac{4-2i\sqrt{7}-2i\sqrt{7}-7}{4+7}$

$= \dfrac{-3-4i\sqrt{7}}{11}$

58. $\dfrac{(2+3i)(2+3i)}{(3+i)(3+i)}$

$= \dfrac{4+6i+6i-9}{9+3i+3i-1}$

$= \dfrac{-5+12i}{8+6i} \cdot \dfrac{8-6i}{8-6i}$

$= \dfrac{-40+30i+96i+72}{64+36}$

$= \dfrac{32+126i}{100}$

$= \dfrac{16+63i}{50}$

59. $\dfrac{(3+3i)(3+3i)}{(1+i)(1+i)}$

$= \dfrac{9+9i+9i-9}{1+i+i-1}$

$= \dfrac{18i}{2i}$

$= 9$

60. $\dfrac{(4+3i)(4+3i)}{(3-i)(3-i)}$

$= \dfrac{16+12i+12i-9}{9-3i-3i-1}$

$= \dfrac{7+24i}{8-6i} \cdot \dfrac{8+6i}{8+6i}$

$= \dfrac{56+42i+192i-144}{64+36}$

$= \dfrac{-88+234i}{100}$

$= \dfrac{-44+117i}{50}$

61. $\dfrac{1-i}{(1+i)(1+i)}$

$= \dfrac{1-i}{1+i+i-1}$

$= \dfrac{1-i}{2i} \cdot \dfrac{-2i}{-2i}$

$= \dfrac{-2i-2}{4}$

$= \dfrac{-1-i}{2}$

62. $\left(-\dfrac{1}{2}+\dfrac{1}{2}i\sqrt{3}\right)^3 = \left(\dfrac{1}{4}-\dfrac{1}{2}i\sqrt{3}+\dfrac{3}{4}i^2\right)\left(-\dfrac{1}{2}+\dfrac{1}{2}i\sqrt{3}\right)$

$\qquad = \left(\dfrac{1}{4}-\dfrac{1}{2}i\sqrt{3}-\dfrac{3}{4}\right)\left(-\dfrac{1}{2}+\dfrac{1}{2}i\sqrt{3}\right)$

$\qquad = \left(-\dfrac{1}{2}-\dfrac{1}{2}i\sqrt{3}\right)\left(-\dfrac{1}{2}+\dfrac{1}{2}i\sqrt{3}\right)$

$\qquad = \left(\dfrac{1}{4}-\dfrac{3}{4}i^2\right)$

$\qquad = \dfrac{1}{4}+\dfrac{3}{4}$

$\qquad = 1$

63. $(1+i\sqrt{3})^3 = (1+i\sqrt{3})(1+i\sqrt{3})(1+i\sqrt{3})$

$\qquad = (1+2i\sqrt{3}+3i^2)(1+i\sqrt{3})$

$\qquad = (1+2i\sqrt{3}-3)(1+i\sqrt{3})$

$\qquad = (-2+2i\sqrt{3})(1+i\sqrt{3})$

$\qquad = -2-2i\sqrt{3}+2i\sqrt{3}+6i^2$

$\qquad = -2+6i^2$

$\qquad = -2-6$

$\qquad = -8$

64. a. $\qquad (70+j226) = I \cdot (6+j8)$

$\dfrac{6-8j}{6-8j} \cdot \dfrac{70+226j}{6+8j} = I$

$\dfrac{2228-796j}{100} = I$

$\dfrac{557-199j}{25} = I$

$\dfrac{557-199j}{25}$ amps

b. $\dfrac{85+110j}{3-4j} \cdot \dfrac{3+4j}{3+4j} = I$

$\dfrac{255+340j+330j-440}{9+16} = I$

$\dfrac{-185+670j}{25} = I$

$\dfrac{-37+134j}{5} = I$

$\dfrac{-37+134j}{5}$ amps

c. $\dfrac{60+112j}{10-6j} \cdot \dfrac{10+6j}{10+6j} = I$

$\dfrac{600+360j+1120j-672}{100+36} = I$

$\dfrac{-72+1480j}{136} = I$

$\dfrac{-9+185j}{17} = I$

$\dfrac{-9+185j}{17}$ amps

d.
$$\frac{-50 + 100j}{-6 - 2j} \cdot \frac{-6 + 2j}{-6 + 2j} = Z$$

$$\frac{300 - 100j - 600j - 200}{36 + 4} = Z$$

$$\frac{100 - 700j}{40} = Z$$

$$\frac{5 - 35j}{2} = Z$$

$$\frac{5 - 35j}{2} \text{ ohms}$$

e.
$$\frac{100 + 10j}{-8 + 3j} \cdot \frac{-8 - 3j}{-8 - 3j} = Z$$

$$\frac{-800 - 300j - 80j + 30}{64 + 9} = Z$$

$$\frac{-770 - 380j}{73} = Z$$

$$\frac{-770 - 380j}{73} \text{ ohms}$$

f.
$$\frac{-70 + j240}{-5 + j4} \cdot \frac{-5 - j4}{-5 - j4} = Z$$

$$\frac{350 + 280j - 1200j + 960}{25 + 16} = Z$$

$$\frac{1310 - 920j}{41} = Z$$

$$\frac{1310 - 920j}{41} \text{ ohms}$$

65. $(3 + 2i) + (4 + 5i)$ **66.** $(4 + 3i)(16 - 28i)$

$= (3 + 4) + (2i + 5i)$ $= 64 - 112i + 48i + 84$

$= 7 + 7i$ $= 148 - 64i$

67. $\sqrt[3]{\sqrt{64n^6}} = \left[(64n^6)^{\frac{1}{2}}\right]^{\frac{1}{3}} = [8n^3]^{\frac{1}{3}} = 2n$

68. $\dfrac{1000}{5085.8 \times 10^{-8}} = 0.1966 \times 10^{8}$

$= 1.966 \times 10^{6}$ wavelengths

69. $\begin{vmatrix} 5 & 1 & 3 \\ 5 & 1 & -1 \\ 1 & -1 & 5 \end{vmatrix} = 5 \cdot 1 \cdot 5 + 1 \cdot (-1) \cdot 1 + 3$

$\cdot 5 \cdot (-1) - 1 \cdot 1 \cdot 3$

$- (-1) \cdot (-1) \cdot 5 - 5 \cdot 5 \cdot 1$

$= -24$

The system has a unique solution.

$a = \dfrac{\begin{vmatrix} 3 & 1 & 3 \\ -9 & 1 & -1 \\ 9 & -1 & 5 \end{vmatrix}}{-24}$

$= \dfrac{3 \cdot 1 \cdot 5 + 1(-1)9 + 3(-9)(-1) - (9)1 \cdot 3 - (-1)(-1)3 - (5)(-9)1}{-24}$

$= \dfrac{48}{-24}$

$= -2$

$b = \dfrac{\begin{vmatrix} 5 & 3 & 3 \\ 5 & -9 & -1 \\ 1 & 9 & 5 \end{vmatrix}}{-24}$

$= \dfrac{5(-9)5 + 3(-1)1 + 3 \cdot 5 \cdot 9 - 1(-9)3 - 9(-1)5 - 5 \cdot 5 \cdot 3}{-24}$

$= \dfrac{-96}{-24}$

$= 4$

$c = \dfrac{\begin{vmatrix} 5 & 1 & 3 \\ 5 & 1 & -9 \\ 1 & -1 & 9 \end{vmatrix}}{-24}$

$= \dfrac{5 \cdot 1 \cdot 9 + 1(-9)1 + 3 \cdot 5(-1) - 1 \cdot 1 \cdot 3 - (-1)(-9)5 - 9 \cdot 5 \cdot 1}{-24}$

$= \dfrac{-72}{-24}$

$= 3$

$\{-2, 4, 3\}$

70. $(1 + 2 + 3 + \ldots + 30)$

$s = \dfrac{1}{2}(30)(31)$

$= 15(31)$

$= 465$

71. $3x + 8y < 11$

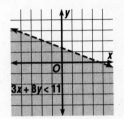

72. $|x + 9| = 22$

$x + 9 = 22$ or $x + 9 = -22$

$x = 13$ or $x = -31$

Chapter 6 Summary and Review

PAGES 302-304   SKILLS AND CONCEPTS

1. $\sqrt{49x^2} = \sqrt{49}\sqrt{x^2}$

$= 7|x|$

2. $\sqrt[3]{-64a^6 b^9}$

$= \sqrt[3]{-4^3(a^2)^3(b^3)^3}$

$= -4a^2 b^3$

3. $\sqrt{(3p - 5q)^2}$

$= |3p - 5q|$

4. $\sqrt{4n^2 + 12n + 9}$

$= \sqrt{(2n + 3)^2}$

$= |2n + 3|$

5. $\sqrt{96} = \sqrt{16 \cdot 6}$

$= 4\sqrt{6}$

6. $\sqrt{50x^3 y^2}$

$= \sqrt{25 \cdot 2x^2 xy^2}$

$= 5x|y|\sqrt{2x}$

7. $\sqrt{6ab} \cdot \sqrt{3a}$

$= \sqrt{18a^2 b}$

$= \sqrt{9 \cdot 2a^2 b}$

$= 3|a|\sqrt{2b}$

8. $\sqrt[3]{\dfrac{s}{27}} = \dfrac{\sqrt[3]{s}}{\sqrt[3]{27}}$

$= \dfrac{\sqrt[3]{s}}{3}$

9. $\dfrac{15}{2\sqrt{5}} \cdot \dfrac{\sqrt{5}}{\sqrt{5}} = \dfrac{15\sqrt{5}}{2 \cdot 5}$

$= \dfrac{3\sqrt{5}}{2}$

10. $\dfrac{4}{\sqrt{2}} \cdot \dfrac{\sqrt{8}}{\sqrt{8}} = \dfrac{4\sqrt{8}}{\sqrt{16}}$

$= \dfrac{4\sqrt{8}}{2}$

$= 2\sqrt{8}$

11. $\sqrt{5}(2\sqrt{10} + 3\sqrt{2})$

$= 2\sqrt{50} + 3\sqrt{10}$

$= 10\sqrt{2} + 3\sqrt{10}$

12. $\sqrt[3]{4}\left(2\sqrt[3]{4} - 5\sqrt[3]{2}\right)$

$= 2\sqrt[3]{16} - 5\sqrt[3]{8}$

$= 4\sqrt[3]{2} - 10$

13. $5 + 2\sqrt{6} - 3\sqrt{6} + 9$

$= 14 - \sqrt{6}$

14. $3\sqrt{27} - 5\sqrt{3} + 2\sqrt{48}$

$= 9\sqrt{3} - 5\sqrt{3} + 8\sqrt{3}$

$= 12\sqrt{3}$

15. $7\sqrt[3]{24x^2} + \sqrt[3]{81x^2}$

$= 14\sqrt[3]{3x^2} + 3\sqrt[3]{3x^2}$

$= 17\sqrt[3]{3x^2}$

16. $(6 + \sqrt{3})(2\sqrt{5} - \sqrt{3})$

$= 12\sqrt{5} - 6\sqrt{3} + 2\sqrt{15} - 3$

17. $(5\sqrt{2} - \sqrt{3})(5\sqrt{2} + \sqrt{3})$

$= 50 + 0 - 3$

$= 47$

18. $\dfrac{4 - \sqrt{3}}{1 + 2\sqrt{3}} \cdot \dfrac{1 - 2\sqrt{3}}{1 - 2\sqrt{3}}$

$= \dfrac{4 - 9\sqrt{3} + 6}{1 - 12}$

$= \dfrac{10 - 9\sqrt{3}}{-11}$

$= \dfrac{9\sqrt{3} - 10}{11}$

19. $\sqrt[4]{r^3} = r^{\frac{3}{4}}$

20. $\sqrt[3]{8m^2n^7} = 2\sqrt[3]{m^2n^7}$

$= 2m^{\frac{2}{3}}n^{\frac{7}{3}}$

21. $5^{\frac{1}{3}} = \sqrt[3]{5}$

22. $2^{\frac{2}{3}}x^{\frac{5}{6}}y^{\frac{1}{2}} = 2^{\frac{4}{6}}x^{\frac{5}{6}}y^{\frac{3}{6}}$

$= \sqrt[6]{2^4x^5y^3}$

23. $125^{\frac{1}{3}} = \sqrt[3]{125}$

$= 5$

24. $4^{-\frac{1}{2}} = \dfrac{1}{4^{\frac{1}{2}}}$

$= \dfrac{1}{\sqrt{4}}$

$= \dfrac{1}{2}$

25. $16^{1.25} = 16^{\frac{5}{4}}$

$= \sqrt[4]{16^5}$

$= \sqrt[4]{16^4} \cdot \sqrt[4]{16}$

$= 16 \cdot 2$

$= 32$

26. $8^{\frac{2}{3}} \cdot 8^{\frac{2}{3}} = 8^{\frac{4}{3}}$

$= \sqrt[3]{8^4}$

$= 16$

27. $\dfrac{\frac{1}{5^{\frac{1}{3}}}}{} \cdot \dfrac{5^{\frac{2}{3}}}{5^{\frac{2}{3}}} = \dfrac{5^{\frac{2}{3}}}{5}$

28. $\dfrac{2^{\frac{1}{2}}}{2^{\frac{1}{3}}} \cdot \dfrac{2^{\frac{2}{3}}}{2^{\frac{2}{3}}} = \dfrac{2^{\frac{7}{6}}}{2}$

$= 2^{\frac{1}{6}}$

29. $a^{-\frac{3}{4}} = \dfrac{1}{a^{\frac{3}{4}}} \cdot \dfrac{a^{\frac{1}{4}}}{a^{\frac{1}{4}}}$

$= \dfrac{a^{\frac{1}{4}}}{a}$

30. $\dfrac{p^{\frac{1}{2}} - 2q^{\frac{1}{2}}}{p^{\frac{1}{2}} + q^{\frac{1}{2}}} \cdot \dfrac{p^{\frac{1}{2}} - q^{\frac{1}{2}}}{p^{\frac{1}{2}} - q^{\frac{1}{2}}}$

$= \dfrac{p - 3p^{\frac{1}{2}}q^{\frac{1}{2}} + 2q}{p - q}$

31. $a + 3 = a\sqrt{2}$

$3 = a(\sqrt{2} - 1)$

$\dfrac{\sqrt{2} + 1}{\sqrt{2} + 1} \cdot \dfrac{3}{\sqrt{2} - 1} = a$

$3\sqrt{2} + 3 = a$

32. $4x - \sqrt{2} = x\sqrt{3} + 2\sqrt{2}$

$4x - x\sqrt{3} = 2\sqrt{2} + \sqrt{2}$

$x(4 - \sqrt{3}) = 3\sqrt{2}$

$x = \dfrac{3\sqrt{2}}{4 - \sqrt{3}} \cdot \dfrac{4 + \sqrt{3}}{4 + \sqrt{3}}$

$x = \dfrac{12\sqrt{2} + 3\sqrt{6}}{13}$

33. $5 - \sqrt{3x + 4} = 0$

$5 = \sqrt{3x + 4}$

$25 = 3x + 4$

$21 = 3x$

$7 = x$

34. $\sqrt{x + 11} - \sqrt{15 + 2x} = 1$

$\sqrt{x + 11} = 1 + \sqrt{15 + 2x}$

$x + 11 = 1 + 2\sqrt{15 + 2x} + 15 + 2x$

$x + 11 = 2x + 16 + 2\sqrt{15 + 2x}$

$-x - 5 = 2\sqrt{15 + 2x}$

$(-x - 5)(-x - 5) = 4(15 + 2x)$

$x^2 + 10x + 25 = 60 + 8x$

$x^2 + 2x - 35 = 0$

$(x + 7)(x - 5) = 0$

$x = -7 \text{ or } x = 5$

does not check

Solution: $x = -7$

35. $\sqrt{x - 2} + \sqrt{7x - 6} = 8$

$\sqrt{7x - 6} = 8 - \sqrt{x - 2}$

$7x - 6 = x + 62 - 16\sqrt{x - 2}$

$6x - 68 = -16\sqrt{x - 2}$

$3x - 34 = -8\sqrt{x - 2}$

$9x^2 - 204x + 1156 = 64x - 128$

$9x^2 - 268x + 1284 = 0$

$(9x - 214)(x - 6) = 0$

$9x = 214 \text{ or } x = 6$

$x = 23.78$ does not check

Solution: $x = 6$

36. $\sqrt[3]{5n + 4} - 4 = 0$

$\sqrt[3]{5n + 4} = 4$

$5n + 4 = 64$

$5n = 60$

$n = 12$

37. $\sqrt{-121} = \sqrt{-1} \cdot \sqrt{121}$

$= 11i$

38. $\sqrt{-32} = \sqrt{16} \cdot \sqrt{2} \cdot \sqrt{-1}$

$= 4i\sqrt{2}$

39. $5i(3i) = 15i^2$

$= -15$

40. $(8i)^3 = 8^3 i^3$

$= 512(i^2)(i)$

$= -512i$

41. $(8 + 7i) + (13 - 2i)$

$= 21 + 5i$

42. $(29 - 37i) - (19 + 21i) = 10 - 58i$

43. $(7 + 6i)(4 - 3i) = 28 - 21i + 24i + 18$

$= 46 + 3i$

44. $(5 - 7i)(5 - 7i) = 25 - 35i - 35i - 49$

$= -24 - 70i$

45. $8 + 13i$

46. $-3 - 11i$

47. $\dfrac{11 + 8i}{2i} \cdot \dfrac{-2i}{-2i}$

$= \dfrac{-22i - 16i^2}{4}$

$= \dfrac{16 - 22i}{4}$

$= \dfrac{8 - 11i}{2}$

48. $\dfrac{2 + 3i}{2 - 3i} \cdot \dfrac{2 + 3i}{2 + 3i}$

$= \dfrac{4 + 12i - 9}{4 + 9}$

$= \dfrac{-5 + 12i}{13}$

49. $\dfrac{1}{8 - i} \cdot \dfrac{8 + i}{8 + i}$

$= \dfrac{8 + i}{64 + 1}$

$= \dfrac{8 + i}{65}$

50. $\dfrac{1}{12i} \cdot \dfrac{-12i}{-12i}$

$= \dfrac{-12i}{144}$

$= \dfrac{-i}{12}$

PAGE 304   APPLICATIONS AND CONNECTIONS

51. $t = \dfrac{1}{4}\sqrt{200}$

$t = \dfrac{10\sqrt{2}}{4}$

$= \dfrac{5\sqrt{2}}{2}$

$= 3.54$

$\dfrac{5\sqrt{2}}{2}$ or about 3.54 seconds

52. Multiples of 2: $2 + 4 + 6 + \ldots + 500$

$= 2(1 + 2 + 3 + \ldots + 250)$

$= 2\left(\dfrac{250(251)}{2}\right)$

$= 250 \cdot 251$

$= 62,750$

Multiples of 3: $3 + 6 + 9 + \ldots + 498$

$= 3(1 + 2 + \ldots + 166)$

$= 3\left(\dfrac{166(167)}{2}\right)$

$= \dfrac{3}{2}(27,722)$

$= 41,583$

Sum 1 to 500 $= \dfrac{500(501)}{2}$

$= 125,250$

Multiples of 6: $6(1 + 2 + \ldots + 83)$

$= 6\dfrac{(83)(84)}{2}$

$= 3(6972)$

$= 20,916$

Sum $= 125,250 - 62,750 - 41,583 + 20,916$

$= 41,833$

53. $\pi r^2 = \dfrac{18}{0.01}$

$\pi r^2 = 1800$

$r^2 = \dfrac{1800}{\pi}$

$r^2 = 572.96$

$r = 23.94$

about 23.94 cm

54. $E = (20 + 12j)(15 + 3j)$

$= 300 + 60j + 180j + 36j^2$

$= 300 - 36 + 240j$

$= 264 + 240j$

$264 + 240j$ volts

Chapter 6 Test

PAGE 305

1. $\sqrt{324} = 18$

2. $\sqrt{512} = 16\sqrt{2}$

3. $\sqrt{169a^3 b^2}$

$= 13a|b|\sqrt{a}$

4. $\sqrt[3]{-16y^3} = -2y\sqrt[3]{2}$

5. $\sqrt{9x^2 - 30xy + 25y^2}$

$= \sqrt{(3x - 5y)^2}$

$= |3x - 5y|$

6. $\sqrt{x^2(x - 3)^2}$

$= |x(x - 3)|$

7. $\sqrt{5a^3} \cdot \sqrt{10ab^3}$

$= \sqrt{50a^4 b^3}$

$= 5a^2 b\sqrt{2b}$

8. $\sqrt{6}(3\sqrt{2} - 2\sqrt{12})$

$= 3\sqrt{12} - 2\sqrt{72}$

$= 6\sqrt{3} - 12\sqrt{2}$

9. $\sqrt[3]{2}\left(\sqrt[3]{54} - 3\sqrt[3]{16}\right)$

$= \sqrt[3]{108} - 3\sqrt[3]{32}$

$= \sqrt[3]{27 \cdot 4} - 3\sqrt[3]{8 \cdot 4}$

$= -3\sqrt[3]{4}$

10. $5\sqrt{8} - 6\sqrt{50} + 4\sqrt{18} = 10\sqrt{2} - 30\sqrt{2} + 12\sqrt{2}$

$= -8\sqrt{2}$

11. $(5 + \sqrt{3})(7 - 2\sqrt{3}) = 35 - 10\sqrt{3} + 7\sqrt{3} - 2 \cdot 3$

$= 29 - 3\sqrt{3}$

12. $(2\sqrt{5} - \sqrt{3})(2\sqrt{5} + \sqrt{3}) = 20 + 6\sqrt{5} - 6\sqrt{5} - 3$

$= 17$

13. $(\sqrt{2} - 3\sqrt{6})(\sqrt{3} + 6)$

$= \sqrt{6} + 6\sqrt{2} - 3\sqrt{18} - 18\sqrt{6}$

$= -17\sqrt{6} - 3\sqrt{2}$

14. $\dfrac{6}{\sqrt{3}} \cdot \dfrac{\sqrt{3}}{\sqrt{3}} = \dfrac{6\sqrt{3}}{3}$

$= 2\sqrt{3}$

15. $\dfrac{3}{\sqrt{54}} \cdot \dfrac{\sqrt[4]{24}}{\sqrt[4]{24}} = \dfrac{3\sqrt[4]{24}}{\sqrt[4]{1296}}$ 16. $\dfrac{3 - \sqrt{2}}{4 + \sqrt{2}} \cdot \dfrac{4 - \sqrt{2}}{4 - \sqrt{2}}$

$\quad = \dfrac{3\sqrt[4]{24}}{6} \qquad\qquad = \dfrac{14 - 7\sqrt{2}}{14}$

$\quad = \dfrac{\sqrt[4]{24}}{2} \qquad\qquad = \dfrac{2 - \sqrt{2}}{2}$

17. Odd perfect squares < 100: {1, 9, 25, 49, 81} ⇒ 5

Odd whole numbers < 100: {1, 3, 5,...99} ⇒ 50

$\dfrac{5}{50} = \dfrac{1}{10}$

18. $\dfrac{1}{4^{\frac{1}{3}}} \cdot \dfrac{4^{\frac{2}{3}}}{4^{\frac{2}{3}}} = \dfrac{4^{\frac{2}{3}}}{4}$ 19. $p^{-\frac{3}{4}} = \dfrac{1}{p^{\frac{3}{4}}} \cdot \dfrac{p^{\frac{1}{4}}}{p^{\frac{1}{4}}}$

$\qquad\qquad\qquad\qquad = \dfrac{p^{\frac{1}{4}}}{p}$

20. $\dfrac{3}{a^{-1} + b^{-2}} \cdot \dfrac{a}{a}$ 21. $\dfrac{m^{\frac{1}{2}}}{m^{\frac{1}{2}} - n^{\frac{1}{2}}} \cdot \dfrac{m^{\frac{1}{2}} + n^{\frac{1}{2}}}{m^{\frac{1}{2}} + n^{\frac{1}{2}}}$

$\quad = \dfrac{3a}{1 + ab^{-2}} \cdot \dfrac{b^2}{b^2} \qquad = \dfrac{m + m^{\frac{1}{2}}n^{\frac{1}{2}}}{m - n}$

$\quad = \dfrac{3ab^2}{b^2 + a(1)} \qquad\qquad = \dfrac{m + \sqrt{mn}}{m - n}$

$\quad = \dfrac{3ab^2}{a + b^2}$

22. $\sqrt{3t - 2} = 5$

$\quad 3t - 2 = 25$

$\quad\quad 3t = 27$

$\quad\quad\ t = 9$

23. $\sqrt{x + 5} + \sqrt{x + 13} = 4$

$\qquad\qquad \sqrt{x + 13} = 4 - \sqrt{x + 5}$

$\qquad\quad x + 13 = x + 21 - 8\sqrt{x + 5}$

$\qquad\qquad\quad -8 = -8\sqrt{x + 5}$

$\qquad\qquad\qquad 1 = \sqrt{x + 5}$

$\qquad\qquad\qquad 1 = x + 5$

$\qquad\qquad\quad -4 = x$

24. $\sqrt[3]{4n + 9} = 5$

$\quad 4n + 9 = 125$

$\quad\quad 4n = 116$

$\quad\quad\ n = 29$

25. $\qquad \sqrt{n^2 - 7} = \sqrt{4n + 25}$

$\qquad\quad n^2 - 7 = 4n + 25$

$\quad n^2 - 4n - 32 = 0$

$\quad (n - 8)(n + 4) = 0$

$\quad\quad n = 8 \text{ or } n = -4$

26. $x^2 + 100 = 0$ 27. $6x^2 + 42 = 0$

$\quad\quad x^2 = -100 \qquad\qquad 6x^2 = -42$

$\quad\quad x = \pm\sqrt{-100} \qquad\quad x^2 = -7$

$\quad\quad x = \pm 10i \qquad\qquad\quad x = \pm\sqrt{-7}$

$\qquad\qquad\qquad\qquad\qquad\quad x = \pm i\sqrt{7}$

28. $-8 - 5i$ 29. $-4i$

30. $\dfrac{1}{3 - 9i} \cdot \dfrac{3 + 9i}{3 + 9i}$ 31. $\dfrac{1}{11i} \cdot \dfrac{-11i}{-11i}$

$\quad = \dfrac{3 + 9i}{9 + 81} \qquad\qquad = \dfrac{-11i}{121}$

$\quad = \dfrac{3 + 9i}{90} \qquad\qquad\ = \dfrac{-i}{11}$

$\quad = \dfrac{1 + 3i}{30}$

32. $5^{\frac{2}{3}}a^{\frac{1}{2}}b^{\frac{3}{8}}$ 33. $\sqrt[6]{36x^5 y^9 z^4}$

$\quad = 5^{\frac{16}{24}}a^{\frac{12}{24}}b^{\frac{9}{24}} \qquad = 36^{\frac{1}{6}}x^{\frac{5}{6}}y^{\frac{9}{6}}z^{\frac{4}{6}}$

$\quad = \sqrt[24]{5^{16}a^{12}b^9} \qquad = 6^{\frac{2}{6}}x^{\frac{5}{6}}y^{\frac{3}{2}}z^{\frac{2}{3}}$

$\qquad\qquad\qquad\qquad\quad = 6^{\frac{1}{3}}x^{\frac{5}{6}}y^{\frac{3}{2}}z^{\frac{2}{3}}$

PAGE 305   BONUS

$12^3 = 1728$

Chapter 6
College Entrance Exam Preview
PAGES 306-307

1. $\dfrac{8a + 12}{2} = \dfrac{2(4a + 6)}{2} = 4a + 6$

   The two columns are equal.

   The correct choice is C.

2. $(-9)^{72}$ is a positive number.

   $(-9)^{83}$ is a negative number.

   $(-9)^{72} > (-9)^{83}$

   The correct choice is A.

3. $-3 < n < 0 \longrightarrow -6(-3) > -6n > -6(0)$

   Therefore, $-3(n + n) = -6n > 0$.

   $n < 0$ so $(n)(n)(n) = n^3$ is a negative number.

   Therefore, $-3(n + n) > (n)(n)(n)$.

   The correct choice is A.

146

4. From given, $n + 11 > 12$

   Therefore, $n > 1$

   $$3n > 3$$

   $$3n + 8 > 11.$$

   Also, $-2n < -2$

   $16 - 2n < 14.$

   Since there is no other information given, the expressions cannot be further ordered.

   The correct choice is D.

5. Given $a < 0$,　　Given $b > 0$,

   $$\frac{a}{2} < 0.\qquad\qquad b^2 > 0.$$

   Therefore, $\frac{a}{2} < 0 < b^2$.

   The correct choice is B.

6. Consider two possible choices for x and y.

   $$(-3)^2 > 2^2 \text{ and } 3^2 > 2^2$$

   $$(-3 + 1)^2 = 4 \qquad (3 + 1)^2 = 16$$

   $$(2 + 1)^2 = 9 \qquad (2 + 1)^2 = 9$$

   $$4 < 9 \qquad\qquad 16 > 9$$

   The correct choice is D.

7. $\frac{1}{2}$% of $400 = 0.005(400) = 2$

   $0.5(400) = 20$

   The correct choice is B.

8. $\frac{0.05}{x} = \frac{0.2}{0.06}$

   $x = 0.015$

   $0.015 < 0.02$

   The correct choice is B.

9. Consider two possible values for b.

   If $b = 1$, $\frac{1}{5} < 5$.

   If $b = -1$, $-\frac{1}{5} > -5$.

   The correct choice is D.

10. If 30% of r is 6, then $0.3r = 6$ and $r = 20$.
    If $x = $ the percent in Column A, $60 = x(20)$ and $x = 300\%$. If $y = $ the percent in Column B, $20 = 6y$ and $y = 333\frac{1}{3}\%$.

    The correct choice is B.

11. $0.8 \times 6d = 4.8d$

    $\frac{3}{5}$ of $8d = 0.6 \times 8d = 4.8d$

    The correct choice is C.

12. $23 - 4(2)0 = 23 - 0 = 23$

    $6 + 10(3 - 2) = 6 + 10(1) = 16$

    The correct choice is A.

13. Since z is a real number, $z^2 > 0$. Therefore, $\frac{x}{2} > 0$ and $x > 0$. But z can be positive or negative.

    The correct choice is D.

14. Since the hypotenuse of the right triangle has the same measure as the diameter of the circle, the triangle can be inscribed in the circle. Therefore, the area of the circle is greater than the area of the triangle.

    The correct choice is A.

15. a and b are both positive reals less than one. For all x, $0 < x < 1$, $0 < x^2 < x$.

    Thus, $a^2 < a$, and $b^2 < b$, and $a^2 + b^2 < a + b$.

    The correct choice is A.

16. Since $3a < 23$ and $23 < 3b$, $3a < 23 < 3b$ and $a < \frac{23}{3} < b$.

    The correct choice is B.

17. The perimeter of a square is $4s$ while the perimeter of a rectangle $= 2w + 2\ell$. Since $4s = 2w + 2\ell$, $s = \frac{w + \ell}{2}$. Area of a square is s^2 so $s^2 = \frac{(w + \ell)^2}{2} = \frac{1}{2}(w^2 + 2w\ell + \ell^2)$ which is greater than $w \times \ell$ (area of a rectangle).

    The correct choice is A.

18. Consider two possible choices for x and y.

    $x = 1$, $y = 1$ and $x = 2$, $y = 3$, then

    $(1, 1): \frac{x}{y} = \frac{1}{1} = \frac{y}{x}$ and $(2, 3): \frac{x}{y} = \frac{2}{3} \neq \frac{3}{2} = \frac{y}{x}$.

    We need to know more about x and y.

    The correct choice is D.

19. $4a - 3a = a(4 - 3) = a < 4 \times 3a$ when a is positive.

    The correct choice is B.

20. The slope of $2x + 3y = 7$ is $-\frac{2}{3}$ while the slope of $3x - 2y = 7$ is $\frac{3}{2}$.

    The correct choice is B.

21. Consider two choices for x.

    $$x = 2 \text{ or } x = \left(-\frac{1}{2}\right)$$

    2: $-x = -2$, $\frac{1}{x} = \frac{1}{2} \Rightarrow \frac{1}{x} > -x$

    -2: $-x = 2$, $\frac{1}{x} = \frac{1}{-2} \Rightarrow -x > \frac{1}{x}$

    The correct choice is D.

22. e_{mn} means the nth element in the mth row.

$$\begin{bmatrix} 3 & -4 & 5 \\ -2 & 1 & -3 \\ 6 & -5 & -7 \end{bmatrix} \qquad e_{23} = -3 \qquad e_{32} = -5$$

Since $2 + 3 = 5$, which is odd, the signed minor will be -1 times the minor of each element.

$$\begin{bmatrix} 3 & -4 & 5 \\ -2 & 1 & -3 \\ 6 & -5 & -7 \end{bmatrix} \rightarrow \begin{bmatrix} 3 & -4 & 5 \\ -2 & 1 & -3 \\ 6 & -5 & -7 \end{bmatrix} \rightarrow -1 \begin{vmatrix} 3 & -4 \\ 6 & -5 \end{vmatrix}$$

$= -[-15 - (-24)] = -9$

$$\begin{bmatrix} 3 & -4 & 5 \\ -2 & 1 & -3 \\ 6 & -5 & -7 \end{bmatrix} \rightarrow \begin{bmatrix} 3 & -4 & 5 \\ -2 & 1 & -3 \\ 6 & -5 & -7 \end{bmatrix} \rightarrow -1 \begin{vmatrix} 3 & 5 \\ 6 & -7 \end{vmatrix}$$

$= -(-21 - 30) = 51$

The signed minor of e_{32} is greater than the signed minor of e_{23}.

The correct choice is B.

23. $5x - 2y = 4$ can be reduced to $\frac{5}{2}x - 2 = y$.

Since the two lines contain the same point, the parallel line will have a positive slope $\left(\frac{5}{2}\right)$ and the perpendicular line a negative slope $\left(-\frac{2}{5}\right)$.

Thus, the parallel line will be greater.

The correct choice is A.

24. $\sqrt{r^2}$ will be r if $r < 0$ but $\sqrt[3]{r^3}$ will be $-r$ if $r < 0$.

The correct choice is A.

25. Since $x = -3y + 5$ and

$y = 3x + 5$, y will always be greater than the value of x.

The correct choice is B.

26. Since $i^x = -i$, x must be an odd integer greater than or equal to 3. We need to know more about x to determine if it is greater than or less than 6.

The correct answer is D.

Chapter 7   Quadratic Equations

<table>
<tr><td>

7-1   Problem-Solving Strategy: Guess-and-Check

PAGE 311   CHECKING FOR UNDERSTANDING

1. a square, yes

2. If the sum of the digits of a number is divisible by 3, the number is divisible by 3.   If a number ends in 0 or 5, it is divisible by 5.

3. Both prime factors cannot be greater than the square root of the number.

4. Let x = the number of dogs
   Let y = the number of puffins

$$x + y = 120 \quad -2x - 2y = -240 \quad x + y = 120$$
$$4x + 2y = 400 \Rightarrow \underline{4x + 2y = 400} \quad 80 + y = 120$$
$$2x = 160 \quad y = 40$$
$$x = 80$$

80 dogs, 40 puffins

PAGE 311   EXERCISES

5. Using guess-and-check, A = 2, B = 1, C = 9, D = 7, E = 8.

6.

no. of people	no. of handshakes
1	0
2	1
3	3
4	6
5	10
6	15
.	.
.	.
.	.
18	153

+1, +2, +3, +4, +5

7.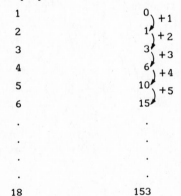

8. B, because 64 is the square of 8 and 64 is also the cube of 4.

PAGE 311   COOPERATIVE LEARNING ACTIVITY
Answers will vary.   Three other perfect numbers are 28, 496, and 8128.

</td><td>

Graphing Calculator Exploration: Quadratic Equations

PAGE 315   EXERCISES

1.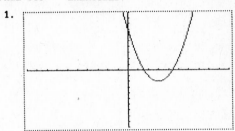

2.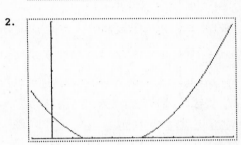

3.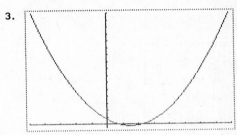

4.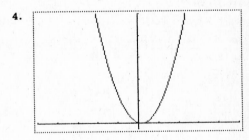

5.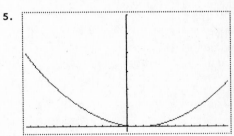

6. 1, 3, 4, 5

7. two

</td></tr>
</table>

8.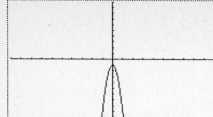

9.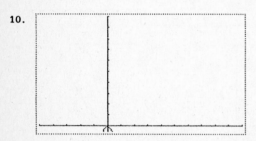

10.

11.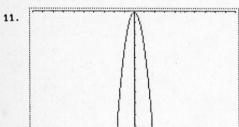

12.

13. 8, 11, 12

14. no solutions

15-20. Answers may vary. Sample answers given.

15. [-10, 10] by [-15, 30]

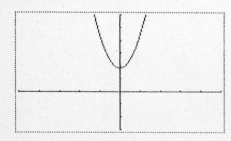

16. [-2, 6] by [-2, 12]

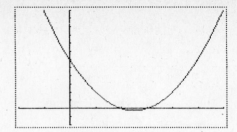

17. [-15, 1] by [-10, 30]

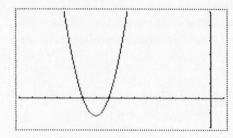

18. [-10, 5] by [-30, 10]

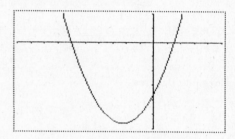

19. [-10, 10] by [-15, 10]

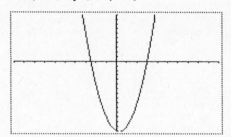

20. [-10, 10] by [-5, 15]

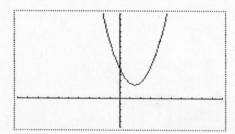

21. 3.0000, -2.5000   **22.** 1.5000, 0.2460

23. no real solutions   **24.** 0.3333, -1.3600

25. -20.2000, -11.3400   **26.** -2.6000, 0.7142

7-2 **Solving Quadratic Equations**

1. $16 \text{ m} \times 12 \text{ m}$

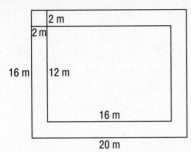

2. a. the value that satisfies an equation
   b. the value that satisfies a quadratic equation
   c. the x-value of a function when $y = 0$
   d. where the graph intersects the x-axis
   All can name solutions of a quadratic equation.

3. parabola

4. no; The maximum number of zeros a quadratic equation can have is two.

5. 100 ft

6. yes   7. no   8. yes   9. no

10. $12m^2 + 25m + 12 = (4m + 3)(3m + 4)$

11. $(1, 0), (-2, 0)$ 12. $(-4, 0)$

13. $(0, 0), (16, 0)$

14. $(y - 3)(y + 7) = 0$
    $y - 3 = 0$ or $y + 7 = 0$
    $y = 3$ $y = -7$

15. $(a + 6)(a + 2) = 0$
    $a + 6 = 0$ or $a + 2 = 0$
    $a = -6$ $a = -2$

16. $z(z - 1)^2 = 0$
    $z(z - 1)(z - 1) = 0$
    $z = 0$ or $z - 1 = 0$
                $z = 1$

17. $(3y + 7)(y + 5) = 0$
    $3y + 7 = 0$ or $y + 5 = 0$
    $3y = -7$ $y = -5$
    $y = -\dfrac{7}{3}$

18. $(2x + 3)(3x - 1) = 0$
    $2x + 3 = 0$ or $3x - 1 = 0$
    $2x = -3$ $3x = 1$
    $x = -\dfrac{3}{2}$ $x = \dfrac{1}{3}$

19. $d^2 + 6d + 8 = 0$
    Solutions: $-4, -2$

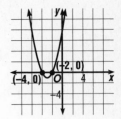

20. $z^2 + 4z + 3 = 0$
    Solutions: $-3, -1$

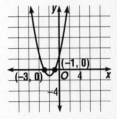

21. $c^2 + 4c + 4 = 0$
    Solution: -2

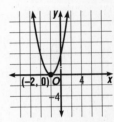

22. $n^2 - 3n = 0$
    Solutions: $0, 3$

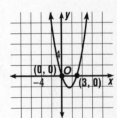

23. $2w^2 - 3w = 9$
    $2w^2 - 3w - 9 = 0$
    Solutions: $-1.5, 3$

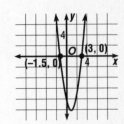

24. $4s^2 - 11s = 3$
    $4s^2 - 11s - 3 = 0$
    Solutions: $-\dfrac{1}{4}, 3$

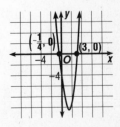

25. $y^2 - y = 12$

$y^2 - y - 12 = 0$

$(y - 4)(y + 3) = 0$

$y - 4 = 0$ or $y + 3 = 0$

$y = 4 \qquad y = -3$

26. $z^2 - 5z = 0$

$z(z - 5) = 0$

$z = 0$ or $z - 5 = 0$

$z = 5$

27. $p^2 - 12p + 36 = 0$

$(p - 6)(p - 6) = 0$

$(p - 6)^2 = 0$

$p - 6 = 0$

$p = 6$

28. $r^2 + r = 30$

$r^2 + r - 30 = 0$

$(r - 5)(r + 6) = 0$

$r - 5 = 0$ or $r + 6 = 0$

$r = 5 \qquad r = -6$

29. $d^2 - 3d = 4$

$d^2 - 3d - 4 = 0$

$(d - 4)(d + 1) = 0$

$d - 4 = 0$ or $d + 1 = 0$

$d = 4 \qquad d = -1$

30. $3c^2 = 5c$

$3c^2 - 5c = 0$

$c(3c - 5) = 0$

$c = 0$ or $3c - 5 = 0$

$3c = 5$

$c = \dfrac{5}{3}$

31. $2q^2 + 11q = 21$

$2q^2 + 11q - 21 = 0$

$(2q - 3)(q + 7) = 0$

$2q - 3 = 0$ or $q + 7 = 0$

$2q = 3 \qquad q = -7$

$q = \dfrac{3}{2}$

32. $18u^2 - 3u = 1$

$18u^2 - 3u - 1 = 0$

$(6u + 1)(3u - 1) = 0$

$6u + 1 = 0$ or $3u - 1 = 0$

$6u = -1 \qquad 3u = 1$

$u = -\dfrac{1}{6} \qquad u = \dfrac{1}{3}$

33. $3t^2 + 4t = 15$

$3t^2 + 4t - 15 = 0$

$(3t - 5)(t + 3) = 0$

$3t - 5 = 0$ or $t + 3 = 0$

$t = \dfrac{5}{3} \qquad t = -3$

34. $4y^2 = 25$

$4y^2 - 25 = 0$

$(2y - 5)(2y + 5) = 0$

$2y - 5 = 0$ or $2y + 5 = 0$

$2y = 5 \qquad 2y = -5$

$y = \dfrac{5}{2} \qquad y = -\dfrac{5}{2}$

35. $6r^2 + 7r = 3$

$6r^2 + 7r - 3 = 0$

$(2r + 3)(3r - 1) = 0$

$2r + 3 = 0$ or $3r - 1 = 0$

$2r = -3 \qquad 3r = 1$

$r = -\dfrac{3}{2} \qquad r = \dfrac{1}{3}$

36. $9y^2 + 16 = -24y$

$9y^2 + 24y + 16 = 0$

$(3y + 4)(3y + 4) = 0$

$3y + 4 = 0$

$y = -\dfrac{4}{3}$

37. $s = v_i t - \dfrac{1}{2}gt^2$

$0 = 64t - \dfrac{1}{2}(32)t^2$

$0 = 64t - 16t^2$

$16t^2 - 64t = 0$

$16t(t - 4) = 0$

$16t = 0$ or $t - 4 = 0$

$t = 0 \qquad t = 4$

The ball will return to the ground in 4 seconds.

$s = 64t - \dfrac{1}{2}(32)t^2 \qquad s = 64t - \dfrac{1}{2}(32)t^2$

$\quad = 64(1) - \dfrac{1}{2}(32)(1)^2 \quad = 64(3) - \dfrac{1}{2}(32)(3)^2$

$\quad = 64 - 16 \qquad\qquad = 192 - 144$

$\quad = 48 \qquad\qquad\qquad = 48$

after 1 second: \qquad after 3 seconds:

48 feet \qquad\qquad 48 feet

38. $4a^2 - 17a + 4 = 0$

$(4a - 1)(a - 4) = 0$

$4a - 1 = 0$ or $a - 4 = 0$

$a = \dfrac{1}{4} \qquad a = 4$

39.
$$b^2 + 3b = 40$$
$$b^2 + 3b - 40 = 0$$
$$(b + 8)(b - 5) = 0$$
$$b + 8 = 0 \text{ or } b - 5 = 0$$
$$b = -8 \qquad b = 5$$

40.
$$12m^2 + 25m + 12 = 0$$
$$(4m + 3)(3m + 4) = 0$$
$$4m + 3 = 0 \text{ or } 3m + 4 = 0$$
$$4m = -3 \qquad 3m = -4$$
$$m = -\frac{3}{4} \qquad m = -\frac{4}{3}$$

41.
$$18n^2 - 3n = 15$$
$$18n^2 - 3n - 15 = 0$$
$$3(6n + 5)(n - 1) = 0$$
$$6n + 5 = 0 \text{ or } n - 1 = 0$$
$$n = -\frac{5}{6} \qquad n = 1$$

42.
$$n^3 = 9n$$
$$n^3 - 9n = 0$$
$$n(n^2 - 9) = 0$$
$$n(n - 3)(n + 3) = 0$$
$$n = 0 \text{ or } n - 3 = 0 \text{ or } n + 3 = 0$$
$$n = 3 \qquad n = -3$$

43.
$$a^3 = 81a$$
$$a^3 - 81a = 0$$
$$a(a - 9)(a + 9) = 0$$
$$a = 0 \text{ or } a - 9 = 0 \text{ or } a + 9 = 0$$
$$a = 9 \qquad a = -9$$

44.
$$35z^3 + 16z^2 = 12z$$
$$35z^3 + 16z^2 - 12z = 0$$
$$z(35z^2 + 16z - 12) = 0$$
$$z(5z - 2)(7z + 6) = 0$$
$$z = 0 \text{ or } 5z - 2 = 0 \text{ or } 7z + 6 = 0$$
$$z = \frac{2}{5} \qquad z = -\frac{6}{7}$$

45.
$$18r^3 + 16r = 34r^2$$
$$18r^3 - 34r^2 + 16r = 0$$
$$2r(9r^2 - 17r + 8) = 0$$
$$2r(9r - 8)(r - 1) = 0$$
$$2r = 0 \text{ or } 9r - 8 = 0 \text{ or } r - 1 = 0$$
$$r = 0 \qquad r = \frac{8}{9} \qquad r = 1$$

46. a. $s = 16t - \frac{1}{2}(32)t^2 + 96$
$$s = 16t - 16t^2 + 96$$

b.
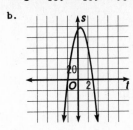

c. $s = 16t - 16t^2 + 96$
$$0 = 16t - 16t^2 + 96$$
$$0 = t - t^2 + 6$$
$$0 = (t - 3)(t + 2)$$
$$t - 3 = 0 \text{ or } t + 2 = 0$$
$$t = 3 \qquad t = -2$$
3 seconds   not reasonable

47.
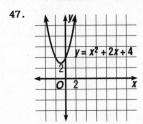

There are no real roots since the graph does not intersect the x-axis.

48. Let x = width of strips.
$$A = \ell w$$
For new playground: $2A = (\ell + x)(w + x)$
$$2(20)(30) = (30 + x)(20 + x)$$
$$1200 = 600 + 50x + x^2$$
$$0 = x^2 + 50x - 600$$
$$(x + 60)(x - 10) = 0$$
$$x + 60 = 0 \text{ or } x - 10 = 0$$
$$x = -60 \qquad x = 10$$
not reasonable

width of strips: 10 m

length of new playground: 30 + 10 = 40; 40 m

width of new playground: 20 + 10 = 30; 30 m

49. Let x = width of strips.

new ice-skating rink: $\quad A = (\ell - x)(w - x)$
$$1000 = (60 - x)(30 - x)$$
$$1000 = 1800 - 90x + x^2$$
$$0 = x^2 - 90x + 800$$
$$0 = (x - 80)(x - 10)$$
$$x = 80 \text{ or } x = 10$$
not reasonable

width of strips: 10 m

length of new rink: 60 - 10 = 50; 50 m

width of new rink: 30 - 10 = 20; 20 m

50. Use guess-and-check.

first number	second number	sum	product
30	51	81	1530
20	61	81	1220
21	60	81	1260
25	56	81	1400 √

The numbers are 25 and 56.

51. $(3a)(5a^2b) + (6ab)(10a^2) = 15a^3b + 60a^3b$

$$= 75a^3b$$

52. $\sqrt{3mn^4} \cdot \sqrt{25m^6} = n^2\sqrt{3m} \cdot 5m^3$

$$= 5m^3n^2\sqrt{3m}$$

53. $\begin{cases} 6x - 2y - 3z = -10 \\ -6x + y + 9z = 3 \\ 8x - 3y = -16 \end{cases}$ $\begin{array}{l} 18x - 6y - 9z = -30 \\ \underline{-6x + y + 9z = 3} \\ 12x - 5y = -27 \end{array}$

$\begin{array}{l} 12x - 5y = -27 \\ 8x - 3y = -16 \end{array}$ ⟹ $\begin{array}{l} 24x - 10y = -54 \\ \underline{-24x + 9y = 48} \\ -y = -6 \\ y = 6 \end{array}$ $\begin{array}{l} 8x - 3y = -16 \\ 8x - 3(6) = -16 \\ 8x = 2 \\ x = \frac{1}{4} \end{array}$

$6x - 2y - 3z = -10$

$6\left(\frac{1}{4}\right) - 2(6) - 3z = -10$

$\frac{3}{2} - 12 - 3z = -10$

$-3z = \frac{1}{2}$

$z = -\frac{1}{6}$ $\left(\frac{1}{4}, 6, -\frac{1}{6}\right)$

54. Let d = cost of deluxe doughnuts.

Let g = cost of glazed doughnuts.

Let c = cost of cake doughnuts.

$\begin{array}{l} 6d + 5g + 2c = 4.00 \\ 4d + 2g + 7c = 3.40 \\ d = 2c - 0.05 \end{array}$ $\begin{array}{l} 12d + 10g + 4c = 8.00 \\ \underline{-20d - 10g - 35c = -17.00} \\ -8d \quad\quad - 31c = -9.00 \end{array}$

$\begin{array}{l} -8d - 31c = -9.00 \\ d - 2c = -0.05 \end{array}$ ⟹ $\begin{array}{l} -8d - 31c = -9.00 \\ \underline{8d - 16c = -0.40} \\ -47c = -9.40 \\ c = 0.20 \end{array}$

$d = 2c - 0.05$

$= 2(0.20) - 0.05$

$= 0.35$

$4d + 2g + 7c = 3.40$

$4(0.35) + 2g + 7(0.20) = 3.40$

$1.40 + 2g + 1.40 = 3.40$

$2g = 0.60$

$g = 0.30$

deluxe, $0.35; glazed, $0.30; cake, $0.20

---

55. $I = \dfrac{E}{R + r}$

$= \dfrac{1.5}{2.35 + 0.15}$

$= \dfrac{1.5}{2.5}$

$= 0.6$

0.6 amperes

7-3 **Completing the Square**

1. $13,000 = (110 + s)^2$

$\sqrt{13,000} = \sqrt{(110 + s)^2}$

$\pm\sqrt{13,000} = 110 + s$

$\pm\sqrt{13,000} - 110 = s$

$s \approx -224.02$ or $s \approx 4.02$

width of parking strip: 4.02 ft

2. One of the solutions may be unreasonable, such as a negative measurement for a geometric figure.

3. yes $z^2 + 4z - 96 = 0$

$(z - 8)(z + 12) = 0$

$z = 8, z = -12$

4. yes

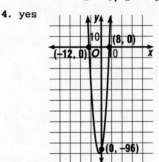

5. no **6.** yes **7.** no

8. $x^2 + 2x + c$

$c = (2 + 2)^2$

$= 1^2$ or 1

9. $t^2 + 40t + c$

$c = (40 + 2)^2$

$= 20^2$ or 400

10. $x^2 + 18x + c$

$c = (18 + 2)^2$

$= 9^2$ or 81

11. $r^2 - 9r + c$

$c = (-9 + 2)^2$

$= \left(-\frac{9}{2}\right)^2$ or $\frac{81}{4}$

12. $a^2 - 100a + c$

$c = (-100 + 2)^2$

$= (-50)^2$ or 2500

13. $x^2 + 15x + c$

$c = (15 + 2)^2$

$= \left(\frac{15}{2}\right)^2$ or $\frac{225}{4}$

14.
$$y^2 - 2y = 24$$
$$y^2 - 2y + 1 = 24 + 1$$
$$(y - 1)^2 = 25$$
$$y - 1 = \pm 5$$
$$y = 6 \text{ or } y = -4$$

15.
$$z^2 + 3z = 88$$
$$z^2 + 3z + \frac{9}{4} = 88 + \frac{9}{4}$$
$$\left(z + \frac{3}{2}\right)^2 = \frac{361}{4}$$
$$z + \frac{3}{2} = \pm \frac{19}{2}$$
$$z = 8 \text{ or } z = -11$$

16. $x^2 + 8x - 84 = 0$
$$x^2 + 8x = 84$$
$$x^2 + 8x + 16 = 84 + 16$$
$$(x + 4)^2 = 100$$
$$x + 4 = \pm 10$$
$$x = 6 \text{ or } x = -14$$

17. $m^2 + 3m - 180 = 0$
$$m^2 + 3m = 180$$
$$m^2 + 3m + \frac{9}{4} = 180 + \frac{9}{4}$$
$$\left(m + \frac{3}{2}\right)^2 = \frac{729}{4}$$
$$m + \frac{3}{2} = \pm \frac{27}{2}$$
$$m = 12 \text{ or } m = -15$$

18. $n^2 - 8n + 14 = 0$
$$n^2 - 8n = -14$$
$$n^2 - 8n + 16 = -14 + 16$$
$$(n - 4)^2 = 2$$
$$n - 4 = \pm\sqrt{2}$$
$$n = 4 \pm \sqrt{2}$$

19. $x^2 - 7x + 5 = 0$
$$x^2 - 7x = -5$$
$$x^2 - 7x + \frac{49}{4} = -5 + \frac{49}{4}$$
$$\left(x - \frac{7}{2}\right)^2 = \frac{29}{4}$$
$$x - \frac{7}{2} = \pm \frac{\sqrt{29}}{2}$$
$$x = \frac{7 \pm \sqrt{29}}{2}$$

20. $a^2 - 5a - 10 = 0$
$$a^2 - 5a + \frac{25}{4} = 10 + \frac{25}{4}$$
$$\left(a - \frac{5}{2}\right)^2 = \frac{65}{4}$$
$$a - \frac{5}{2} = \pm \frac{\sqrt{65}}{2}$$
$$a = \frac{5 \pm \sqrt{65}}{2}$$

21. $t^2 + 3t - 8 = 0$
$$t^2 + 3t = 8$$
$$t^2 + 3t + \frac{9}{4} = 8 + \frac{9}{4}$$
$$\left(t + \frac{3}{2}\right)^2 = \frac{41}{4}$$
$$t + \frac{3}{2} = \pm \frac{\sqrt{41}}{2}$$
$$t = \frac{-3 \pm \sqrt{41}}{2}$$

22. $12r^2 - 17r - 5 = 0$
$$r^2 - \frac{17}{12}r = \frac{5}{12}$$
$$r^2 - \frac{17}{12}r + \frac{289}{576} = \frac{5}{12} + \frac{289}{576}$$
$$\left(r - \frac{17}{24}\right)^2 = \frac{529}{576}$$
$$r - \frac{17}{24} = \pm \frac{23}{24}$$
$$r = \frac{5}{3} \text{ or } r = -\frac{1}{4}$$

23. $b^2 - \frac{3}{4}b + \frac{1}{8} = 0$
$$b^2 - \frac{3}{4}b + \frac{9}{64} = -\frac{1}{8} + \frac{9}{64}$$
$$\left(b - \frac{3}{8}\right)^2 = \frac{1}{64}$$
$$b - \frac{3}{8} = \pm\frac{1}{8}$$
$$b = \frac{1}{2} \text{ or } b = \frac{1}{4}$$

24. $3t^2 + 4t - 15 = 0$
$$t^2 + \frac{4}{3}t = 5$$
$$t^2 + \frac{4}{3}t + \frac{4}{9} = 5 + \frac{4}{9}$$
$$\left(t + \frac{2}{3}\right)^2 = \frac{49}{9}$$
$$t + \frac{2}{3} = \pm\frac{7}{3}$$
$$t = \frac{5}{3} \text{ or } t = -3$$

25. $3z^2 - 12z + 4 = 0$

$$z^2 - 4z = -\frac{4}{3}$$

$$z^2 - 4z + 4 = -\frac{4}{3} + 4$$

$$(z - 2)^2 = \frac{8}{3}$$

$$z - 2 = \pm \frac{2\sqrt{6}}{3}$$

$$z = 2 \pm \frac{2\sqrt{6}}{3}$$

26. $6s^2 + 2s + 3 = 0$

$$s^2 + \frac{1}{3}s = -\frac{1}{2}$$

$$s^2 + \frac{1}{3}s + \frac{1}{36} = -\frac{1}{2} + \frac{1}{36}$$

$$\left(s + \frac{1}{6}\right)^2 = -\frac{17}{36}$$

$$s + \frac{1}{6} = \pm \frac{i\sqrt{17}}{6}$$

$$s = \frac{-1 \pm i\sqrt{17}}{6}$$

no real solutions

27. $ax^2 + c = 0$

$ax^2 + bx + c = 0$ where $b = 0$

$$ax^2 + bx = -c$$

$$x^2 + \frac{b}{a}x = -\frac{c}{a}$$

$$x^2 + \frac{b}{a}x + \frac{b^2}{4a^2} = -\frac{c}{a} + \frac{b^2}{4a^2}$$

$$\left(x + \frac{b}{2a}\right)^2 = \frac{-4ac + b^2}{4a^2}$$

$$x + \frac{b}{2a} = \frac{\pm\sqrt{-4ac + b^2}}{2a}$$

$$x = \frac{-b \pm \sqrt{-4ac + b^2}}{2a}$$

But $b = 0$: $x = \frac{\pm\sqrt{-4ac}}{2a}$

$$x = \frac{\pm i\sqrt{ac}}{a}$$

28. $x^2 + bx + c = 0$

$$x^2 + bx = -c$$

$$x^2 + bx + \frac{b^2}{4} = -c + \frac{b^2}{4}$$

$$\left(x + \frac{b}{2}\right)^2 = \frac{b^2 - 4c}{4}$$

$$x + \frac{b}{2} = \frac{\pm\sqrt{b^2 - 4c}}{2}$$

$$x = \frac{-b \pm \sqrt{b^2 - 4c}}{2}$$

29. $ax^2 + bx + c = 0$

$$x^2 + \frac{b}{a}x = -\frac{c}{a}$$

$$x^2 + \frac{b}{a}x + \frac{b^2}{4a^2} = -\frac{c}{a} + \frac{b^2}{4a^2}$$

$$\left(x + \frac{b}{2a}\right)^2 = \frac{b^2 - 4ac}{4a^2}$$

$$x + \frac{b}{2a} = \frac{\pm\sqrt{b^2 - 4ac}}{2a}$$

$$x = \frac{-b \pm \sqrt{b^2 - 4ac}}{2a}$$

30. If the equation is easily factored, use factoring. If you have a graphing calculator, graphing might be easier. Completing the square is often longer, but it will always work.

31.
$$A = lw \qquad\qquad \pm\sqrt{324} = \sqrt{(w + 3)^2}$$
$$315 = (w + 6)w \qquad \pm 18 = w + 3$$
$$315 = w^2 + 6w \qquad\qquad w = \pm 18 - 3$$
$$315 + 9 = w^2 + 6w + 9 \qquad w = 15 \text{ or } w = -21$$
$$324 = (w + 3)^2 \qquad\qquad \text{not reasonable}$$

width: 15 in.

length: 15 + 6 = 21; 21 in.

32. a. $s = v_i t + \frac{1}{2}at^2$

$$100 = 24t + \frac{1}{2}(8)t^2$$

$$100 = 24t + 4t^2$$

$$25 = t^2 + 6t$$

$$25 + 9 = t^2 + 6t + 9$$

$$34 = (t + 3)^2$$

$$\pm\sqrt{34} = \sqrt{(t + 3)^2}$$

$$\pm\sqrt{34} = t + 3$$

$$t = \pm\sqrt{34} - 3$$

$$t \approx 2.8 \text{ or } t \approx -8.8$$

not reasonable

It will take 2.8 seconds to travel 100 ft.

b. $s = v_i t + \frac{1}{2}at^2$

$$200 = 24t + \frac{1}{2}(8)t^2$$

$$200 = 24t + 4t^2$$

$$50 = t^2 + 6t$$

$$50 + 9 = t^2 + 6t + 9$$

$$59 = (t + 3)^2$$

$$\pm\sqrt{59} = t + 3$$

$$t = \pm\sqrt{59} - 3$$

$$t \approx 4.7 \text{ or } t \approx -10.7$$

not reasonable

It will take 4.7 seconds to travel 200 ft.

c. $300 = 24t + 4t^2$

$75 = t^2 + 6t$

$75 + 9 = t^2 + 6t + 9$

$84 = (t + 3)^2$

$\pm\sqrt{84} = t + 3$

$t = \pm\sqrt{84} - 3$

$t \approx 6.2$ or $t \approx -12.2$

not reasonable

It will take 6.2 seconds to travel 300 ft.

d. No, the formula is not a direct variation.

33. $s = v_i t + \frac{1}{2}at^2$

$600 = 60t + \frac{1}{2}(-3)t^2$

$600 = 60t - \frac{3}{2}t^2$

$400 = 40t - t^2$

$0 = t^2 - 40t + 400$

$0 = (t - 20)^2$

$t = 20$

It will take 20 seconds to stop.

34. a. 49   35. $x^2 - 20x = -75$

b. 16 $x^2 - 20x + 75 = 0$

c. 4 $(x - 15)(x - 5) = 0$

d. 25 $x = 15$ or $x = 5$

e. 25

f. 9

36. $\sqrt{3w - 2} = 8$ 37. $a^2 - 6$

$3w - 2 = 64$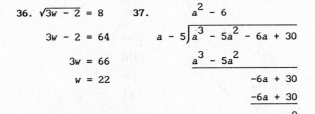

$3w = 66$

$w = 22$

38.

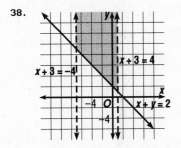

39. 2, 8, 18, 32, 50, ___

    +6 +10 +14 +18 +22

The next number is 72.

1. Try factoring 841, 842,.... The answer is 853.

2.
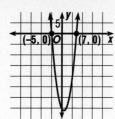
          3.
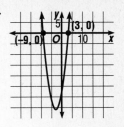

4. $4x^2 - 13x = 12$

$4x^2 - 13x - 12 = 0$

$(4x + 3)(x - 4) = 0$

$4x + 3 = 0$ or $x - 4 = 0$

$x = -\frac{3}{4}$ $x = 4$

5. $4t^2 = 25$

$4t^2 - 25 = 0$

$(2t - 5)(2t + 5) = 0$

$2t - 5 = 0$ or $2t + 5 = 0$

$t = \frac{5}{2}$ $t = -\frac{5}{2}$

6. $a^3 = 81a$

$a^3 - 81a = 0$

$a(a^2 - 81) = 0$

$a(a - 9)(a + 9) = 0$

$a = 0$ or $a - 9 = 0$ or $a + 9 = 0$

$a = 9$ $a = -9$

7. $4x^2 + 19x - 5 = 0$

$x^2 + \frac{19}{4}x = \frac{5}{4}$

$x^2 + \frac{19}{4}x + \frac{361}{64} = \frac{5}{4} + \frac{361}{64}$

$\left(x + \frac{19}{8}\right)^2 = \frac{441}{64}$

$x + \frac{19}{8} = \pm\frac{21}{8}$

$x = \frac{1}{4}$ or $x = -5$

8. $y^2 + 12y + 4 = 0$

$y^2 + 12y = -4$

$y^2 + 12y + 36 = -4 + 36$

$(y + 6)^2 = 32$

$y + 6 = \pm\sqrt{32}$

$y = -6 \pm 4\sqrt{2}$

9. Let x = width of frame

$$A = \ell w$$

$$164 = (16 - 2x)(12 - 2x)$$

$$164 = 192 - 56x + 4x^2$$

$$-28 = 4x^2 - 56x$$

$$-7 = x^2 - 14x$$

$$-7 + 49 = x^2 - 14x + 49$$

$$42 = (x - 7)^2$$

$$\pm\sqrt{42} = x - 7$$

$$x = \pm\sqrt{42} + 7$$

$$x \approx 13.48 \text{ or } x \approx 0.52$$

not reasonable

The width is about 0.52 in.

7-4 The Quadratic Formula and the Discriminant

PAGE 330   CHECKING FOR UNDERSTANDING

1. 8.99 cm is larger than the width.

2. The decimal value of $\sqrt{907.24}$ is not an exact number.

3. 2 real   4. 0   5. 2 imaginary

6. $a = 1$, $b = 6$, $c = 9$

$$b^2 - 4ac$$
$$= 6^2 - 4(1)(9)$$
$$= 36 - 36 = 0$$
$$x = \frac{-b \pm \sqrt{b^2 - 4ac}}{2a}$$
$$= \frac{-6 \pm 0}{2(1)}$$
$$= -3$$

7. $a = 1$, $b = 0$, $c = -16$

$$b^2 - 4ac$$
$$= 0^2 - 4(1)(-16)$$
$$= 64$$
$$x = \frac{-0 \pm \sqrt{64}}{2(1)}$$
$$= \frac{\pm 8}{2}$$
$$= \pm 4$$

8. $a = 5$, $b = 16$, $c = 3$

$$b^2 - 4ac$$
$$= (16)^2 - 4(5)(3)$$
$$= 256 - 60 = 196$$
$$x = \frac{-16 \pm \sqrt{196}}{2(5)}$$
$$= \frac{-16 \pm 14}{0}$$
$$x = -3 \text{ or } x = -\frac{1}{5}$$

9. $a = 6$, $b = 2$, $c = 1$

$$b^2 - 4ac$$
$$= 2^2 - 4(6)(1)$$
$$= 4 - 24 = -20$$
$$x = \frac{-2 \pm \sqrt{-20}}{2(6)}$$
$$= \frac{-2 \pm 2i\sqrt{5}}{12}$$
$$= \frac{-1 \pm i\sqrt{5}}{6}$$

10. $a = -3$, $b = 1$, $c = -2$

$$b^2 - 4ac =$$
$$1^2 - 4(-3)(-2)$$
$$= 1 - 24 = -23$$
$$x = \frac{-1 \pm \sqrt{-23}}{2(-3)}$$
$$= \frac{-1 \pm i\sqrt{23}}{-6}$$

11. $a = 3$, $b = -1$, $c = 3$

$$b^2 - 4ac$$
$$= (-1)^2 - 4(3)(3)$$
$$= 1 - 36 = -35$$
$$x = \frac{-(-1) \pm \sqrt{-35}}{2(3)}$$
$$= \frac{1 \pm i\sqrt{35}}{6}$$

PAGE 331   EXERCISES

12. $b^2 - 4ac = (12)^2 - 4(1)(32)$
$$= 144 - 128$$
$$= 16$$

two real, rational roots

$$a = \frac{-12 \pm \sqrt{16}}{2(1)}$$
$$= \frac{-12 \pm 4}{2}$$
$$a = -8 \text{ or } a = -4$$

13. $b^2 - 4ac = (-4)^2 - 4(1)(4)$
$$= 16 - 16$$
$$= 0$$

one real, rational root

$$y = \frac{-(-4) \pm \sqrt{0}}{2(1)}$$
$$= \frac{4}{2}$$
$$= 2$$

14. $b^2 - 4ac = (-4)^2 - 4(1)(1)$
$$= 16 - 4$$
$$= 12$$

two real, irrational roots

$$x = \frac{-(-4) \pm \sqrt{12}}{2(1)}$$
$$= \frac{4 \pm 2\sqrt{3}}{2}$$
$$= 2 \pm \sqrt{3}$$
$$x \approx 3.73 \text{ or } x \approx 0.27$$

15. $b^2 - 4ac = (-2)^2 - 4(1)(-35)$
$$= 4 + 140$$
$$= 144$$

two real, rational roots

$$x = \frac{-(-2) \pm \sqrt{144}}{2(1)}$$
$$= \frac{2 \pm 12}{2}$$
$$x = 7 \text{ or } x = -5$$

16. $b^2 - 4ac = (-10)^2 - 4(1)(25)$
$$= 100 - 100$$
$$= 0$$

one real, rational root

$$x = \frac{-(-10) \pm \sqrt{0}}{2(1)}$$
$$= \frac{10}{2}$$
$$= 5$$

17. $b^2 - 4ac = 8^2 - 4(4)(3)$

   $= 64 - 48$

   $= 16$

   two real, rational roots

   $x = \dfrac{-8 \pm \sqrt{16}}{2(4)}$

   $= \dfrac{-8 \pm 4}{8}$

   $x = -\dfrac{3}{2}$ or $x = -\dfrac{1}{2}$

18. $b^2 - 4ac = 11^2 - 4(3)(4)$

   $= 121 - 48$

   $= 73$

   two real, irrational roots

   $x = \dfrac{-11 \pm \sqrt{73}}{2(3)}$

   $= \dfrac{-11 \pm \sqrt{73}}{6}$

   $x \approx -0.41$ or $x \approx -3.26$

19. $b^2 - 4ac = 16^2 - 4(4)(15)$

   $= 256 - 240$

   $= 16$

   two real, rational roots

   $y = \dfrac{-16 \pm \sqrt{16}}{2(4)}$

   $= \dfrac{-16 \pm 4}{8}$

   $= -2 \pm \dfrac{1}{2}$

   $y = -\dfrac{5}{2}$ or $y = -\dfrac{3}{2}$

20. $b^2 - 4ac = (-2)^2 - 4(1)(5)$

   $= 4 - 20$

   $= -16$

   two imaginary roots

   $m = \dfrac{-(-2) \pm \sqrt{-16}}{2(1)}$

   $= \dfrac{2 \pm 4i}{2}$

   $= 1 \pm 2i$

21. $b^2 - 4ac = (-6)^2 - 4(1)(13)$

   $= 36 - 52$

   $= -16$

   two imaginary roots

   $y = \dfrac{-(-6) \pm \sqrt{-16}}{2(1)}$

   $= \dfrac{6 \pm 4i}{2}$

   $= 3 \pm 2i$

22. $b^2 - 4ac = (-12)^2 - 4(1)(42)$

   $= 144 - 168$

   $= -24$

   two imaginary roots

   $c = \dfrac{-(-12) \pm \sqrt{-24}}{2(1)}$

   $= \dfrac{12 \pm 2i\sqrt{6}}{2}$

   $= 6 \pm i\sqrt{6}$

23. $b^2 - 4ac = (-6)^2 - 4(1)(0)$

   $= 36$

   two real, rational roots

   $a = \dfrac{-(-6) \pm \sqrt{36}}{2(1)}$

   $= \dfrac{6 \pm 6}{2}$

   $a = 0$ or $a = 6$

24. $3m^2 = 108m$

   $3m^2 - 108m = 0$

   $b^2 - 4ac = (-108)^2 - 4(3)(0)$

   $= 11{,}664$

   two real, rational roots

   $m = \dfrac{-(-108) \pm \sqrt{11{,}664}}{2(3)}$

   $= \dfrac{108 \pm 108}{6}$

   $m = 0$ or $m = 36$

25. $b^2 - 4ac = (-8)^2 - 4(4)(13)$

   $= 64 - 208$

   $= -144$

   two imaginary roots

   $x = \dfrac{-(-8) \pm \sqrt{-144}}{2(4)}$

   $= \dfrac{8 \pm 12i}{8}$

   $= \dfrac{2 \pm 3i}{2}$

26. $b^2 - 4ac = (-1)^2 - 4(1)(1)$

   $= -3$

   two imaginary roots

   $x = \dfrac{-(-1) \pm \sqrt{-3}}{2(1)}$

   $= \dfrac{1 \pm i\sqrt{3}}{2}$

27. $b^2 - 4ac = 4^2 - 4(1)(29)$

   $= 16 - 116$

   $= -100$

   two imaginary roots

   $n = \dfrac{-4 \pm \sqrt{-100}}{2(1)}$

   $= \dfrac{-4 \pm 10i}{2}$

   $= -2 \pm 5i$

28. $b^2 - 4ac = (-13)^2 - 4(2)(-7)$

$= 169 + 56$

$= 225$

two real, rational roots

$a = \dfrac{-(-13) \pm \sqrt{225}}{2(2)}$

$= \dfrac{13 \pm 15}{4}$

$a = 7$ or $a = -\dfrac{1}{2}$

29. $b^2 - 4ac = 1^2 - 4(1)(-5)$

$= 1 + 20$

$= 21$

two real, irrational roots

$a = \dfrac{-1 \pm \sqrt{21}}{2(1)}$

$= \dfrac{-1 \pm \sqrt{21}}{2}$

$a \approx -2.79$ or $a \approx 1.79$

30. $b^2 - 4ac = (-12)^2 - 4(11)(-10)$

$= 144 + 440$

$= 584$

two real, irrational roots

$m = \dfrac{-(-12) \pm \sqrt{584}}{2(11)}$

$= \dfrac{12 \pm 2\sqrt{146}}{22}$

$= \dfrac{6 \pm \sqrt{146}}{11}$

$x \approx 1.64$ or $x \approx -0.55$

31. $b^2 - 4ac = 3^2 - 4(4)(-2)$

$= 9 + 32$

$= 41$

two real, irrational roots

$a = \dfrac{-3 \pm \sqrt{41}}{2(4)}$

$= \dfrac{-3 \pm \sqrt{41}}{8}$

$a \approx 0.43$ or $a \approx -1.18$

32. $b^2 - 4ac = (-16)^2 - 4(1)(4)$

$= 256 - 16$

$= 240$

two real, irrational roots

$t = \dfrac{-(-16) \pm \sqrt{240}}{2(1)}$

$= \dfrac{16 \pm 4\sqrt{15}}{2}$

$= 8 \pm 2\sqrt{15}$

$t \approx 15.75$ or $t \approx 0.25$

33. $b^2 - 4ac = 5^2 - 4(2)(-9)$

$= 25 + 72$

$= 97$

two real, irrational roots

$x = \dfrac{-5 \pm \sqrt{97}}{2(2)}$

$= \dfrac{-5 \pm \sqrt{97}}{4}$

$x \approx 1.21$ or $x \approx -3.71$

34. one real root: two real roots:

$b^2 - 4ac = 0$ $b^2 - 4ac > 0$

$3^2 - 4(1)(k) = 0$ $9 - 4k > 0$

$9 - 4k = 0$ $k > \dfrac{9}{4}$

$k = \dfrac{9}{4}$ k can be any real number

greater than $\dfrac{9}{4}$.

two imaginary roots:

$b^2 - 4ac < 0$

$9 - 4k < 0$

$k < \dfrac{9}{4}$

k can be any real number less than $\dfrac{9}{4}$.

35. one real root: two real roots:

$b^2 - 4ac = 0$ $b^2 - 4ac > 0$

$3^2 - 4k(-2) = 0$ $9 + 8k > 0$

$9 + 8k = 0$ $k > -\dfrac{9}{8}$

$k = -\dfrac{9}{8}$ k can be any real number

greater than $-\dfrac{9}{8}$.

two imaginary roots:

$b^2 - 4ac < 0$

$9 + 8k < 0$

$k < -\dfrac{9}{8}$

k can be any real number less than $-\dfrac{9}{8}$.

36. one real root:

$b^2 - 4ac = 0$

$(-5)^2 - 4(2)(k) = 0$

$25 - 8k = 0$

$k = \dfrac{25}{8}$

two real roots:

$b^2 - 4ac > 0$

$25 - 8k > 0$

$k > \dfrac{25}{8}$

k can be any real number greater than $\dfrac{25}{8}$.

two imaginary roots:

$b^2 - 4ac < 0$

$25 - 8k < 0$

$k < \dfrac{25}{8}$

k can be any real number less than $\dfrac{25}{8}$.

37. Let x = width of strips

$$2A = (\ell + x)(w + x)$$

$$2(17.5)(12.2) = (17.5 + x)(12.2 + x)$$

$$427 = 213.5 + 29.7x + x^2$$

$$x^2 + 29.7x - 213.5 = 0$$

$$x = \frac{-29.7 \pm \sqrt{(29.7)^2 - 4(1)(-213.5)}}{2(1)}$$

$$= \frac{-29.7 \pm \sqrt{1736.09}}{2}$$

$$x \approx -35.7 \text{ or } x \approx 6.0$$

not reasonable

new width: $12.2 + 6.0 = 18.2$; 18.2 m

new length: $17.5 + 6.0 = 23.5$; 23.5 m

38. Earth:

$$s = v_i t + \frac{1}{2}at^2$$

$$0 = 25t + \frac{1}{2}(-9.8)t^2$$

$$0 = 25t - 4.9t^2$$

$$0 = -4.9t^2 + 25t$$

$$t = \frac{-25 \pm \sqrt{25^2 - 4(-4.9)(0)}}{2(-4.9)}$$

$$= \frac{-25 \pm 25}{-9.8}$$

$$t = 0 \text{ or } t \approx 5.1$$

5.1 seconds

Mars:

$$0 = 25t + \frac{1}{2}(-3.7)t^2$$

$$= -1.85t^2 + 25t$$

$$t = \frac{-25 \pm \sqrt{25^2 - 0}}{2(-1.85)}$$

$$t = \frac{-25 \pm 25}{-3.7}$$

$$t = 0 \text{ or } t \approx 13.5$$

13.5 seconds

Venus:

$$0 = 25t + \frac{1}{2}(-8.9)t^2$$

$$0 = -4.45t^2 + 25t$$

$$t = \frac{-25 \pm \sqrt{25^2 - 0}}{2(-4.45)}$$

$$= \frac{-25 \pm 25}{-8.9}$$

$$t = 0 \text{ or } t \approx 5.6$$

5.6 seconds

39. $x^2 + 14x - 12 = 0$

$$x^2 + 14x + 49 = 12 + 49$$

$$(x + 7)^2 = 61$$

$$x + 7 = \pm\sqrt{61}$$

$$x = -7 \pm \sqrt{61}$$

40. $d = 8, -3$

41. $(4a + 7)(3a - 9)$

$$= 12a^2 - 36a + 21a - 63$$

$$= 12a^2 - 15a - 63$$

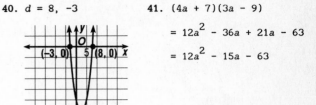

42. $\begin{bmatrix} 1 & 1 & 1 & 10 \\ 1 & 0 & -1 & 1 \\ 1 & -1 & -1 & 0 \end{bmatrix}$

43. $f(5, -2) = 3(5) + 2(-2)$

$$= 15 - 4$$

$$= 11$$

Technology: Discriminants and Roots

PAGE 332   EXERCISES

1. $-0.1396, -1.1937$; real, irrational

2. $-0.5 \pm 0.645i$; imaginary

3. $3 \pm 2i$; imaginary

4. 1st: Discriminant, -8;

   Two complex roots, $2 + 1.41i$, $2 - 1.41i$

   2nd: Discriminant, -8;

   Two complex roots, $-2 + 1.41i$, $-2 - 1.41i$

   The roots are additive inverses of one another.

   The discriminants are the same.

5. 1st: Discriminant, 100;

   Two real rational roots, $5, -5$

   2nd: Discriminant, 80;

   Two real irrational roots, $2.236, -2.236$

   3rd: Discriminant, 768;

   Two real irrational roots, $0.866, -0.866$

   The roots are additive inverses of one another.

6. 1st: Discriminant, 121;

   Two real rational roots, $7, -4$

   2nd: Discriminant, 484;

   Two real rational roots, $7, -4$

   3rd: Discriminant, 3025;

   Two real rational roots, $7, -4$

   When coefficients are multiplied by the same value, the roots remain the same but the discriminant changes.

161

7. 1st: Discriminant, 0;
   One real rational root, -2
   2nd: Discriminant, 0;
   One real rational root, 5
   3rd: Discriminant, 0;
   One real rational root, -4
   A zero discriminant implies there is one real
   root.

7-5 Sum and Product of Roots

PAGE 336   CHECKING FOR UNDERSTANDING

1. zero product property   2. $\frac{c}{a}$

3. $-\frac{b}{a}$ 4. $-\frac{b}{a} = -\frac{-14}{5} = \frac{14}{5}$ 5. $\frac{c}{a} = \frac{-20}{5} = -4$

6. $-\frac{b}{a} = -\frac{8}{2} = -4$ 7. $-\frac{b}{a} = -\frac{3}{4}$

   $\frac{c}{a} = -\frac{3}{2}$ $\frac{c}{a} = \frac{-12}{4} = -3$

8. $-\frac{b}{a} = -\frac{0}{2} = 0$ 9. $-\frac{b}{a} = -\frac{0}{5} = 0$

   $\frac{c}{a} = \frac{7}{2}$ $\frac{c}{a} = -\frac{3}{5}$

10. $-\frac{b}{a} = -\frac{4}{1} = -4$ 11. $-\frac{b}{a} = -\frac{-\frac{1}{5}}{3} = \frac{1}{15}$

    $\frac{c}{a} = \frac{-\frac{5}{3}}{1} = -\frac{5}{3}$ $\frac{c}{a} = \frac{-\frac{4}{5}}{3} = -\frac{4}{15}$

12. $x^2 + x - 6 = 0$ $-\frac{b}{a} = -1$

    $(x - 2)(x + 3) = 0$ $s_1 + s_2 = 2 + (-3) = -1$ ✓

        $x = 2$ or $x = -3$ $\frac{c}{a} = -6$

                                $s_1 s_2 = (2)(-3) = -6$ ✓

13. $m^2 + 5m + 6 = 0$ $-\frac{b}{a} = -5$

    $(m + 2)(m + 3) = 0$ $s_1 + s_2 = -2 + (-3) = -5$ ✓

        $m = -2$ or $m = -3$ $\frac{c}{a} = 6$

                                $s_1 s_2 = (-2)(-3) = 6$ ✓

14. $s^2 + 5s - 24 = 0$ $-\frac{b}{a} = -5$

    $(s + 8)(s - 3) = 0$ $s_1 + s_2 = (-8) + 3 = -5$ ✓

        $s = -8$ or $s = 3$ $\frac{c}{a} = -24$

                                $s_1 s_2 = (-8)(3) = -24$ ✓

15. $a^2 - 9a + 20 = 0$ $-\frac{b}{a} = 9$

    $(a - 5)(a - 4) = 0$ $s_1 + s_2 = 5 + 4 = 9$ ✓

        $a = 5$ or $a = 4$ $\frac{c}{a} = 20$

                                $s_1 s_2 = (5)(4) = 20$ ✓

16. $x^2 + 6x - 7 = 0$ $-\frac{b}{a} = -6$

    $(x + 7)(x - 1) = 0$ $s_1 + s_2 = -7 + 1 = -6$ ✓

        $x = -7$ or $x = 1$ $\frac{c}{a} = -7$

                                $s_1 s_2 = (-7)(1) = -7$ ✓

17. $2z^2 - 5z - 3 = 0$ $-\frac{b}{a} = \frac{5}{2}$

    $(2z + 1)(z - 3) = 0$ $s_1 + s_2 = -\frac{1}{2} + 3 = \frac{5}{2}$ ✓

        $z = -\frac{1}{2}$ or $z = 3$ $\frac{c}{a} = -\frac{3}{2}$

                                $s_1 s_2 = \left(-\frac{1}{2}\right)(3) = -\frac{3}{2}$ ✓

18. $y^2 + 5y + 6 = 0$ $-\frac{b}{a} = -5$

    $(y + 2)(y + 3) = 0$ $s_1 + s_2 = -2 + (-3) = -5$ ✓

        $y = -2$ or $y = -3$ $\frac{c}{a} = 6$

                                $s_1 s_2 = (-2)(-3) = 6$ ✓

19. $2c^2 - 5c + 1 = 0$

    $c = \frac{-(-5) \pm \sqrt{(-5)^2 - 4(2)(1)}}{2(2)}$

    $= \frac{5 \pm \sqrt{17}}{4}$

    $-\frac{b}{a} = \frac{5}{2}$

    $s_1 + s_2 = \frac{5 + \sqrt{17}}{4} + \frac{5 - \sqrt{17}}{4}$

    $= \frac{10}{4}$ or $\frac{5}{2}$ ✓

    $\frac{c}{a} = \frac{1}{2}$

    $s_1 s_2 = \left(\frac{5 + \sqrt{17}}{4}\right)\left(\frac{5 - \sqrt{17}}{4}\right)$

    $= \frac{25 - 17}{16}$

    $= \frac{8}{16}$ or $\frac{1}{2}$ ✓

20. $6t^2 + 28t - 10 = 0$

    $(2t + 10)(3t - 1) = 0$

        $t = -5$ or $t = \frac{1}{3}$

    $-\frac{b}{a} = -\frac{28}{6} = -\frac{14}{3}$

    $s_1 + s_2 = (-5) + \frac{1}{3} = -\frac{14}{3}$ ✓

    $\frac{c}{a} = -\frac{10}{6} = -\frac{5}{3}$

    $s_1 s_2 = (-5)\left(\frac{1}{3}\right) = -\frac{5}{3}$ ✓

21. $$4a^2 + 21a = 18$$
$$4a^2 + 21a - 18 = 0$$
$$(4a - 3)(a + 6) = 0$$
$$a = \frac{3}{4} \text{ or } a = -6$$
$$-\frac{b}{a} = -\frac{21}{4}$$
$$s_1 + s_2 = \frac{3}{4} + (-6)$$
$$= \frac{3}{4} + \left(-\frac{24}{4}\right)$$
$$= -\frac{21}{4} \checkmark$$
$$\frac{c}{a} = -\frac{18}{4} = -\frac{9}{2}$$
$$s_1 s_2 = \left(\frac{3}{4}\right)(-6) = -\frac{18}{4} \text{ or } -\frac{9}{2} \checkmark$$

22. $$-\frac{b}{a} = s_1 + s_2 \qquad \frac{c}{a} = s_1 s_2$$
$$-\frac{b}{a} = 6 + 4 \qquad \frac{c}{a} = (6)(4)$$
$$-\frac{b}{a} = 10 \qquad \frac{c}{a} = 24$$
So, $a = 1$, $b = -10$, and $c = 24$.
The equation is $x^2 - 10x + 24 = 0$.

23. $$-\frac{b}{a} = s_1 + s_2 \qquad \frac{c}{a} = s_1 s_2$$
$$= 8 + (-2) \qquad = 8(-2)$$
$$= 6 \qquad = -16$$
So, $a = 1$, $b = -6$, and $c = -16$.
The equation is $x^2 - 6x - 16 = 0$.

24. $$-\frac{b}{a} = 6 + (-6) \qquad \frac{c}{a} = (6)(-6)$$
$$= 0 \qquad = -36$$
So $a = 1$, $b = 0$, and $c = -36$.
The equation is $x^2 - 36 = 0$.

25. $$-\frac{b}{a} = 3 + \frac{1}{2} \qquad \frac{c}{a} = (3)\left(\frac{1}{2}\right)$$
$$= \frac{7}{2} \qquad = \frac{3}{2}$$
So, $a = 2$, $b = -7$, and $c = 3$.
The equation is $2x^2 - 7x + 3 = 0$.

26. $$-\frac{b}{a} = 5 + \frac{2}{3} \qquad \frac{c}{a} = (5)\left(\frac{2}{3}\right)$$
$$= \frac{17}{3} \qquad = \frac{10}{3}$$
So, $a = 3$, $b = -17$, and $c = 10$.
The equation is $3x^2 - 17x + 10 = 0$.

27. $$-\frac{b}{a} = -\frac{2}{5} + \frac{2}{5} \qquad \frac{c}{a} = \left(-\frac{2}{5}\right)\left(\frac{2}{5}\right)$$
$$= 0 \qquad = -\frac{4}{25}$$
So, $a = 25$, $b = 0$, and $c = -4$.
The equation is $25x^2 - 4 = 0$.

28. $$-\frac{b}{a} = \frac{5}{8} + \frac{1}{4} \qquad \frac{c}{a} = \left(\frac{5}{8}\right)\left(\frac{1}{4}\right)$$
$$= \frac{7}{8} \qquad = \frac{5}{32}$$
So that denominators will be equal, change $\frac{7}{8}$ to $\frac{28}{32}$.
So, $a = 32$, $b = -28$, and $c = 5$.
The equation is $32x^2 - 28x + 5 = 0$.

29. $$-\frac{b}{a} = \sqrt{3} + 2\sqrt{3} \qquad \frac{c}{a} = (\sqrt{3})(2\sqrt{3})$$
$$= 3\sqrt{3} \qquad = 6$$
So, $a = 1$, $b = -3\sqrt{3}$, and $c = 6$.
The equation is $x^2 - (3\sqrt{3})x + 6 = 0$.

30. $$9n^2 - 1 = 0 \qquad -\frac{b}{a} = 0$$
$$(3n - 1)(3n + 1) = 0 \qquad s_1 + s_2 = \frac{1}{3} + \left(-\frac{1}{3}\right) = 0 \checkmark$$
$$n = \pm\frac{1}{3} \qquad \frac{c}{a} = -\frac{1}{9}$$
$$s_1 s_2 = \left(\frac{1}{3}\right)\left(-\frac{1}{3}\right) = -\frac{1}{9} \checkmark$$

31. $$s^2 - 16 = 0 \qquad -\frac{b}{a} = 0$$
$$(s - 4)(s + 4) = 0 \qquad s_1 + s_2 = 4 + (-4) = 0 \checkmark$$
$$s = \pm 4 \qquad \frac{c}{a} = -16$$
$$s_1 s_2 = (4)(-4) = -16 \checkmark$$

32. $$2x^2 - 7x = 15 \qquad -\frac{b}{a} = \frac{7}{2}$$
$$2x^2 - 7x - 15 = 0 \qquad s_1 + s_2 = -\frac{3}{2} + 5 = \frac{7}{2} \checkmark$$
$$(2x + 3)(x - 5) = 0 \qquad \frac{c}{a} = -\frac{15}{2}$$
$$x = -\frac{3}{2} \text{ or } x = 5 \qquad s_1 s_2 = \left(-\frac{3}{2}\right)(5) = -\frac{15}{2} \checkmark$$

33. $$15c^2 - 2c - 8 = 0 \qquad -\frac{b}{a} = \frac{2}{15}$$
$$(5c - 4)(3c + 2) = 0 \qquad s_1 + s_2 = \frac{4}{5} + \left(-\frac{2}{3}\right)$$
$$c = \frac{4}{5} \text{ or } c = -\frac{2}{3} \qquad = \frac{12 - 10}{15}$$
$$= \frac{2}{5} \checkmark$$
$$\frac{c}{a} = -\frac{8}{15}$$
$$s_1 s_2 = \left(\frac{4}{5}\right)\left(-\frac{2}{3}\right) = -\frac{8}{15} \checkmark$$

34. $7s^2 + 5s - 1 = 0$

$$s = \frac{-5 \pm \sqrt{5^2 - 4(7)(-1)}}{2(7)}$$

$$= \frac{-5 \pm \sqrt{53}}{14}$$

$$-\frac{b}{a} = -\frac{5}{7}$$

$$s_1 + s_2 = \frac{-5 + \sqrt{53}}{14} + \frac{-5 - \sqrt{53}}{14}$$

$$= -\frac{10}{14} \text{ or } -\frac{5}{7} \checkmark$$

$$\frac{c}{a} = -\frac{1}{7}$$

$$s_1 s_2 = \left(\frac{-5 + \sqrt{53}}{14}\right)\left(\frac{-5 - \sqrt{53}}{14}\right)$$

$$= \frac{25 - 53}{196}$$

$$= -\frac{28}{196} \text{ or } -\frac{1}{7} \checkmark$$

35. $12x^2 + 19x + 4 = 0$ $-\frac{b}{a} = -\frac{19}{12}$

$(4x + 1)(3x + 4) = 0$ $s_1 + s_2 = -\frac{1}{4} + \left(-\frac{4}{3}\right)$

$x = -\frac{1}{4}$ or $x = -\frac{4}{3}$ $= \frac{-3 - 16}{12}$

$$= -\frac{19}{12} \checkmark$$

$$\frac{c}{a} = \frac{4}{12} = \frac{1}{3}$$

$$s_1 s_2 = \left(-\frac{1}{4}\right)\left(-\frac{4}{3}\right)$$

$$= \frac{1}{3} \checkmark$$

36. $-\frac{b}{a} = s_1 + s_2$ $\frac{c}{a} = (2 + \sqrt{3})(2 - \sqrt{3})$

$= (2 + \sqrt{3}) + (2 - \sqrt{3})$ $= 4 - 3$

$= 4$ $= 1$

So, $a = 1$, $b = -4$, and $c = 1$.

The equation is $x^2 - 4x + 1 = 0$.

37. $-\frac{b}{a} = s_1 + s_2$ $\frac{c}{a} = s_1 s_2$

$= -6i + 6i$ $= (-6i)(6i)$

$= 0$ $= 36$

So $a = 1$, $b = 0$, and $c = 36$.

The equation is $x^2 + 36 = 0$.

38. $-\frac{b}{a} = s_1 + s_2$ $\frac{c}{a} = s_1 s_2$

$= \frac{5 - 3i}{4} + \frac{5 + 3i}{4}$ $= \left(\frac{5 - 3i}{4}\right)\left(\frac{5 + 3i}{4}\right)$

$= \frac{10}{4}$ or $\frac{5}{2}$ $= \frac{25 + 9}{16}$

$$= \frac{34}{16} \text{ or } \frac{17}{8}$$

So that the denominators are equal,

change $\frac{5}{2}$ to $\frac{20}{8}$.

So, $a = 8$, $b = -20$, and $c = 17$.

The equation is $8x^2 - 20x + 17 = 0$.

39. $-\frac{b}{a} = s_1 + s_2$ $\frac{c}{a} = s_1 s_2$

$= \frac{1 + \sqrt{7}}{2} + \frac{1 - \sqrt{7}}{2}$ $= \left(\frac{1 + \sqrt{7}}{2}\right)\left(\frac{1 - \sqrt{7}}{2}\right)$

$= \frac{2}{2}$ $= \frac{1 - 7}{4}$ or $-\frac{3}{2}$

So, $a = 2$, $b = -2$, and $c = -3$.

The equation is $2x^2 - 2x - 3 = 0$.

40. $\frac{c}{a} = s_1 s_2$ $-\frac{b}{a} = s_1 + s_2$

$\frac{-5}{1} = 1 \cdot s_2$ $-\frac{k}{1} = 1 + (-5)$

$-5 = s_2$ $-k = -4$

$k = 4$

41. $\frac{c}{a} = s_1 s_2$ $-\frac{b}{a} = s_1 + s_2$

$-\frac{21}{1} = 3s_2$ $-\frac{k}{1} = 3 + (-7)$

$-7 = s_2$ $-k = -4$

$k = 4$

42. $-\frac{b}{a} = s_1 + s_2$ $\frac{c}{a} = s_1 s_2$

$-\frac{6}{1} = 3 + s_2$ $-\frac{k}{1} = (3)(-9)$

$-6 = 3 + s_2$ $-k = -27$

$-9 = s_2$ $k = 27$

43. $\frac{c}{a} = s_1 s_2$ $-\frac{b}{a} = s_1 + s_2$

$-\frac{12}{2} = \left(-\frac{3}{2}\right)s_2$ $-\frac{k}{2} = -\frac{3}{2} + 4$

$-6 = -\frac{3}{2}s_2$ $-\frac{k}{2} = \frac{5}{2}$

$4 = s_2$ $k = -5$

44. $\frac{c}{a} = s_1 s_2$

$\frac{12}{1} = s_1 s_2$

$12 = s_1 s_2$

If s_1 and s_2 are integers, the possible

solutions are 12, 1; -12, -1; 2, 6; -2, -6;

3, 4; -3, -4.

45. $s = v_i t - \frac{1}{2}gt^2$

$0 = \left(-\frac{1}{2}g\right)t^2 + v_i t - s$

$= -16t^2 + v_i t - s$

$s_1 + s_2 = -\frac{b}{a}$

$0 + 15 = -\frac{v_i}{-16}$

$(15)(16) = v_i$

$240 = v_i$

240 ft/s

46. Let x = width of strip

$A = \ell w$

$(50)(25) + 400 = (50 + 2x)(25 + 2x)$

$1650 = 1250 + 150x + 4x^2$

$4x^2 + 150x - 400 = 0$

$2x^2 + 75x - 200 = 0$

$x = \dfrac{-75 \pm \sqrt{75^2 - 4(2)(-200)}}{2(2)}$

$= \dfrac{-75 \pm 85}{4}$

$x = -40$ or $x = 2.5$

not reasonable

Each dimension will be increased by 2.5 feet.

47. $s = v_i t - \left(\dfrac{1}{2}g\right)t^2$

$0 = \left(-\dfrac{1}{2}g\right)t^2 + v_i t - s$

$= -16t^2 + v_i t - s$

$s_1 + s_2 = -\dfrac{b}{a} \qquad\qquad s_1 s_2 = \dfrac{c}{a}$

$1 + 3 = -\dfrac{v_i}{-16} \qquad\qquad (1)(3) = \dfrac{-s}{-16}$

$4 = \dfrac{v_i}{16} \qquad\qquad\qquad -48 = -s$

$64 = v_i \qquad\qquad\qquad\quad 48 = s$

64 ft/s, 48 ft

48. $2x^2 - 5x + 4 = 0$

$x = \dfrac{-(-5) \pm \sqrt{(-5)^2 - 4(2)(4)}}{2(2)}$

$= \dfrac{5 \pm \sqrt{-7}}{4}$

$= \dfrac{5 \pm i\sqrt{7}}{4}$

49. $\sqrt[3]{2x + 1} = 3$

$2x + 1 = 27$

$2x = 26$

$x = 13$

50. $\dfrac{(3 + \sqrt{5})}{(1 + \sqrt{2})} = \dfrac{(3 + \sqrt{5})}{(1 + \sqrt{2})} \cdot \dfrac{(1 - \sqrt{2})}{(1 - \sqrt{2})}$

$= \dfrac{3 - 3\sqrt{2} + \sqrt{5} - \sqrt{10}}{1 - 2}$

$= \dfrac{3 - 3\sqrt{2} + \sqrt{5} - \sqrt{10}}{-1}$

$= -3 + 3\sqrt{2} - \sqrt{5} + \sqrt{10}$

51. $ab + 7a + 4b + 28$

$a(b + 7) + 4(b + 7)$

$(a + 4)(b + 7)$

52. $\begin{bmatrix} 1 & 0 & 0 \\ 0 & 1 & 0 \\ 0 & 0 & 1 \end{bmatrix}$

53. $c = 12 + 20t$

$52 = 12 + 20t$

$40 = 20t$

$2 = t$

2 hours

54. Let x = length of a side of the square or triangle.

perimeter of square + perimeter of triangle < 50

$\quad 4x \qquad\qquad + \qquad\qquad 3x \qquad\quad < 50$

$\qquad\qquad\qquad\qquad\qquad\qquad\qquad 7x < 50$

$\qquad\qquad\qquad\qquad\qquad\qquad\qquad x < \dfrac{50}{7}$

$\left\{ x \,\middle|\, x < \dfrac{50}{7} \right\}$

Whole number possibilities are 1 cm, 2 cm, 3 cm, 4 cm, 5 cm, 6 cm, 7 cm.

7-6 Quadratic Techniques to Solve Polynomial Equations

PAGE 342   CHECKING FOR UNDERSTANDING

1. Dimensions cannot be 0 or negative.

2. $V = \ell wh$

$= (3)(1)(6)$

$= 18$

18 mm^3

3. Two of the solutions are imaginary; they cannot be graphed.

4. 2   **5.** Zero product property

6. Answers will vary. Sample answers:

$x + 5\sqrt{x} + 6 = 0;\quad x^4 - 20x^2 + 64 = 0$

7. $x^4 + 5x^3 + 6x^2 = 0$ **8.** $x^3 + 10x^2 + 16x = 0$

$\quad x^2(x^2 + 5x + 6) = 0 \qquad\quad x(x^2 + 10x + 16) = 0$

$\qquad\qquad\text{yes} \qquad\qquad\qquad\qquad\qquad \text{yes}$

9. $3m^3 = 2m^2 - 7m$ **10.** $a^3 = 81a + a^5$

$\quad 3m^3 - 2m^2 + 7m = 0 \qquad\quad 0 = a^5 - a^3 + 81a$

$\quad m(3m^2 - 2m + 7) = 0 \qquad\quad 0 = a(a^4 - a^2 + 81)$

$\qquad\qquad\text{yes} \qquad\qquad\qquad\qquad\qquad \text{no}$

11. $25d^3 + 9d = 30d^2$ **12.** $16t^4 = 40t^2 - 25t$

$\quad 25d^3 - 30d^2 + 9d = 0 \qquad 16t^4 - 40t^2 + 25t = 0$

$\quad d(25d^2 - 30d + 9) = 0 \qquad t(16t^3 - 40t + 25) = 0$

$\qquad\qquad\text{yes} \qquad\qquad\qquad\qquad\qquad \text{no}$

13. $\qquad x^4 + 5x^2 + 3 = 0$ **14.** $\qquad 6x^4 + 7x = 8$

$\quad (x^2)^2 + 5(x^2) + 3 = 0 \qquad\qquad 6x^4 + 7x - 8 = 0$

$\qquad\qquad\text{yes} \qquad\qquad\qquad\qquad\qquad \text{no}$

15. $6n^4 + 8n^2 = 0$ **16.** $2p + 5\sqrt{p} = 9$

$6(n^2)^2 + 8(n^2) = 0$ $2(\sqrt{p})^2 + 5(\sqrt{p}) - 9 = 0$

yes   yes

17. $r^{\frac{1}{3}} = 2$ **18.** $x^{\frac{1}{4}} = 3$

$\left(r^{\frac{1}{3}}\right)^3 = 2^3$ $\left(x^{\frac{1}{4}}\right)^4 = 3^4$

$r = 8$ $x = 81$

19. $p^{\frac{3}{2}} - 8 = 0$ **20.** $k^{\frac{3}{4}} = 27$

$p^{\frac{3}{2}} = 8$ $\left(k^{\frac{3}{4}}\right)^{\frac{4}{3}} = 27^{\frac{4}{3}}$

$\left(p^{\frac{3}{2}}\right)^{\frac{2}{3}} = 8^{\frac{2}{3}}$ $k = 81$

$p = 4$

PAGES 342-343   EXERCISES

21. $1(x^{\frac{1}{2}})^2 - 10(x^{\frac{1}{2}}) + 25 = 0$

22. $1(x^{\frac{2}{3}})^2 - 7(x^{\frac{2}{3}}) + 12 = 0$

23. $z^2(z^2 + 6z + 8) = 0$

24. $1(y^{\frac{1}{4}})^2 - 10(y^{\frac{1}{4}}) + 16 = 0$

25. $1(r^{\frac{1}{3}})^2 - 5(r^{\frac{1}{3}}) + 6 = 0$

26. $1(s^{\frac{1}{3}})^2 - 9(s^{\frac{1}{3}}) + 20 = 0$

27. $1(x^{\frac{1}{4}})^2 + 7(x^{\frac{1}{4}}) + 12 = 0$

28. $9y^3 + 16y = -24y^2$

$9y^3 + 24y^2 + 16y = 0$

$y(9y^2 + 24y + 16) = 0$

29. $x^4 + 5x^3 + 6x^2 = 0$

$x^2(x^2 + 5x + 6) = 0$

$x^2(x + 3)(x + 2) = 0$

$x^2 = 0$ or $x + 3 = 0$ or $x + 2 = 0$

$x = 0$ $x = -3$ $x = -2$

30. $x^3 + 10x^2 + 16x = 0$

$x(x^2 + 10x + 16) = 0$

$x(x + 8)(x + 2) = 0$

$x = 0$ or $x + 8 = 0$ or $x + 2 = 0$

$x = -8$ $x = -2$

31. $16x^4 - x^2 = 0$

$x^2(16x^2 - 1) = 0$

$x^2(4x - 1)(4x + 1) = 0$

$x^2 = 0$ or $4x - 1 = 0$ or $4x + 1 = 0$

$x = 0$ $x = \frac{1}{4}$ $x = -\frac{1}{4}$

32. $a^3 = 81a$

$a^3 - 81a = 0$

$a(a^2 - 81) = 0$

$a(a - 9)(a + 9) = 0$

$a = 0$ or $a - 9 = 0$ or $a + 9 = 0$

$a = 9$ $a = -9$

33. $s^3 = 8$

$s^3 - 8 = 0$

$(s - 2)(s^2 + 2s + 4) = 0$

$s - 2 = 0$ or $s^2 + 2s + 4 = 0$

$s = 2$ $s = \dfrac{-2 \pm \sqrt{2^2 - 4(1)(4)}}{2(1)}$

$= \dfrac{-2 \pm \sqrt{-12}}{2}$

$= -1 \pm i\sqrt{3}$

34. $s^4 = 25$

$s^4 - 25 = 0$

$(s^2 - 5)(s^2 + 5) = 0$

$(s - \sqrt{5})(s + \sqrt{5})(s^2 + 5) = 0$

$s - \sqrt{5} = 0$ or $s + \sqrt{5} = 0$ or $s^2 + 5 = 0$

$s = \sqrt{5}$ $s = -\sqrt{5}$

$s = \dfrac{0 \pm \sqrt{0 - 4(1)(5)}}{2(1)}$

$= \pm \dfrac{\sqrt{-20}}{2}$

$= \pm i\sqrt{5}$

35. $b^4 - 5b^2 + 4 = 0$

$(b^2)^2 - 5(b^2) + 4 = 0$

$(b^2 - 4)(b^2 - 1) = 0$

$(b - 2)(b + 2)(b - 1)(b + 1) = 0$

$b - 2 = 0$ or $b + 2 = 0$ or $b - 1 = 0$ or $b + 1 = 0$

$b = 2$ $b = -2$ $b = 1$ $b = -1$

36. $y^4 - 3y^2 + 2 = 0$

$(y^2)^2 - 3y^2 + 2 = 0$

$(y^2 - 2)(y^2 - 1) = 0$

$(y - \sqrt{2})(y + \sqrt{2})(y - 1)(y + 1) = 0$

$y - \sqrt{2} = 0$ or $y + \sqrt{2} = 0$

$y = \sqrt{2}$ $y = -\sqrt{2}$

$y - 1 = 0$ or $y + 1 = 0$

$y = 1$ $y = -1$

37.
$$a^3 = 125$$
$$a^3 - 125 = 0$$
$$(a - 5)(a^2 + 5a + 25) = 0$$
$$a - 5 = 0 \text{ or } a^2 + 5a + 25 = 0$$
$$a = 5 \qquad a = \frac{-5 \pm \sqrt{5^2 - 4(1)(25)}}{2(1)}$$
$$= \frac{-5 \pm \sqrt{-75}}{2}$$
$$= \frac{-5 \pm 5i\sqrt{3}}{2}$$

38.
$$m - 9\sqrt{m} + 8 = 0$$
$$(\sqrt{m})^2 - 9\sqrt{m} + 8 = 0$$
$$(\sqrt{m} - 1)(\sqrt{m} - 8) = 0$$
$$\sqrt{m} - 1 = 0 \text{ or } \sqrt{m} - 8 = 0$$
$$\sqrt{m} = 1 \qquad \sqrt{m} = 8$$
$$m = 1 \qquad m = 64$$

39.
$$V = \ell wh$$
$$32(w + 3) = (w + 3)(w)(w + 4)$$
$$32w + 96 = w^3 + 7w^2 + 12w$$
$$0 = w^3 + 7w^2 - 20w - 96$$
$$0 = (w - 4)(w + 8)(w + 3)$$
$$w - 4 = 0 \text{ or } w + 8 = 0 \text{ or } w + 3 = 0$$
$$w = 4 \qquad w = -8 \qquad w = -3$$
$$\text{not reasonable} \quad \text{not reasonable}$$

$\ell = w + 3$	$h = w + 4$	$V = 32(w + 3)$
$= 4 + 3$	$= 4 + 4$	$= 32(4 + 3)$
$= 7$	$= 8$	$= 224$

$$w = 4 \text{ in., } \ell = 7 \text{ in., } h = 8 \text{ in., } V = 224 \text{ in.}^3$$

40.
$$r^{\frac{2}{3}} - 12r^{\frac{1}{3}} + 20 = 0$$
$$(r^{\frac{1}{3}})^2 - 12r^{\frac{1}{3}} + 20 = 0$$
$$(r^{\frac{1}{3}} - 2)(r^{\frac{1}{3}} - 10) = 0$$
$$(r^{\frac{1}{3}})^3 = 2^3 \text{ or } (r^{\frac{1}{3}})^3 = 10^3$$
$$r = 8 \qquad r = 1000$$

41.
$$x^{\frac{2}{3}} - 8x^{\frac{1}{3}} + 15 = 0$$
$$(x^{\frac{1}{3}})^2 - 8x^{\frac{1}{3}} + 15 = 0$$
$$(x^{\frac{1}{3}} - 3)(x^{\frac{1}{3}} - 5) = 0$$
$$(x^{\frac{1}{3}})^3 = 3^3 \text{ or } (x^{\frac{1}{3}})^3 = 5^3$$
$$x = 27 \qquad x = 125$$

42.
$$m - 11m^{\frac{1}{2}} + 30 = 0$$
$$(m^{\frac{1}{2}})^2 - 11m^{\frac{1}{2}} + 30 = 0$$
$$(m^{\frac{1}{2}} - 5)(m^{\frac{1}{2}} - 6) = 0$$
$$(m^{\frac{1}{2}})^2 = 5^2 \text{ or } (m^{\frac{1}{2}})^2 = 6^2$$
$$m = 25 \qquad m = 36$$

43.
$$y^3 - 16y^{\frac{3}{2}} + 64 = 0$$
$$(y^{\frac{3}{2}})^2 - 16y^{\frac{3}{2}} + 64 = 0$$
$$(y^{\frac{3}{2}} - 8)(y^{\frac{3}{2}} - 8) = 0$$
$$(y^{\frac{3}{2}})^{\frac{2}{3}} = 8^{\frac{2}{3}}$$
$$y = \sqrt[3]{8^2}$$
$$y = 4$$

44.
$$3g^{\frac{2}{3}} - 10g^{\frac{1}{3}} + 8 = 0$$
$$(3g^{\frac{1}{3}} - 4)(g^{\frac{1}{3}} - 2) = 0$$
$$(g^{\frac{1}{3}})^3 = \left(\frac{4}{3}\right)^3 \text{ or } (g^{\frac{1}{3}})^3 = 2^3$$
$$g = \frac{64}{27} \qquad g = 8$$

45.
$$3m + m^{\frac{1}{2}} - 2 = 0$$
$$3(m^{\frac{1}{2}})^2 + m^{\frac{1}{2}} - 2 = 0$$
$$(3m^{\frac{1}{2}} - 2)(m^{\frac{1}{2}} + 1) = 0$$
$$(m^{\frac{1}{2}})^2 = \left(\frac{2}{3}\right)^2 \text{ or } (m^{\frac{1}{2}})^2 = -1^2$$
$$m = \frac{4}{9} \qquad m = 1$$

The answer 1 does not check.

Thus, the only solution is $\frac{4}{9}$.

46.
$$|a - 4|^2 - 7|a - 4| = -6$$
$$|a - 4|^2 - 7|a - 4| + 6 = 0$$
$$(|a - 4| - 6)(|a - 4| - 1) = 0$$
$$|a - 4| - 6 = 0 \text{ or } |a - 4| - 1 = 0$$
$$|a - 4| = 6 \qquad |a - 4| = 1$$
$$a - 4 = 6 \text{ or } a - 4 = -6 \quad a - 4 = 1 \text{ or } a - 4 = -1$$
$$a = 10 \qquad a = -2 \qquad a = 5 \qquad a = 3$$

47. $A = \ell w$

$425 = (32 - 2x)(24 - 2x)$

$425 = 768 - 112x + 4x^2$

$0 = 4x^2 - 112x + 343$

$x = \dfrac{-(-112) \pm \sqrt{(-112)^2 - 4(4)(343)}}{2(4)}$

$= \dfrac{112 \pm 84}{8}$

$x = 24.5$ or $x = 3.5$

24.5 m is not reasonable.

The walkway is 3.5 m.

48. $(R + r)^2 = \dfrac{R^2 \cdot w_E}{w_s}$

$(3960 + r)^2 = \dfrac{(3960)^2 \cdot (135)}{125}$

$15{,}681{,}600 + 7920r + r^2 = 16{,}936{,}128$

$r^2 + 7920r - 1{,}254{,}528 = 0$

$r = \dfrac{-7920 \pm \sqrt{(7920)^2 - 4(1)(-1{,}254{,}528)}}{2(1)}$

$= \dfrac{-7920 \pm \sqrt{67{,}744{,}512}}{2}$

$\approx \dfrac{-7920 \pm 8230.71}{2}$

$r \approx 155.35$ or $r \approx -8075.36$

not reasonable

The astronaut is 155.35 miles above Earth's surface.

49. $x^2 - 3x + 1 = 0$

$x = \dfrac{-(-3) \pm \sqrt{(-3)^2 - 4(1)(1)}}{2(1)}$

$= \dfrac{3 \pm \sqrt{5}}{2}$

$-\dfrac{b}{a} = 3$

$s_1 + s_2 = \dfrac{3 + \sqrt{5}}{2} + \dfrac{3 - \sqrt{5}}{2}$

$= \dfrac{6}{2}$ or 3 ✓

$\dfrac{c}{a} = 1$

$s_1 s_2 = \left(\dfrac{3 + \sqrt{5}}{2}\right)\left(\dfrac{3 - \sqrt{5}}{2}\right)$

$= \dfrac{9 - 5}{4}$ or 1 ✓

50. $\sqrt{600} = \sqrt{2 \cdot 2 \cdot 2 \cdot 3 \cdot 5 \cdot 5}$

$= \sqrt{2^2 \cdot 2 \cdot 3 \cdot 5^2}$

$= 2 \cdot 5\sqrt{2 \cdot 3}$

$= 10\sqrt{6}$

51.

$\begin{array}{r|rrrr} -3 & 2 & 15 & 22 & -15 \\ & & -6 & -27 & 15 \\ \hline & 2 & 9 & -5 & 0 \end{array}$

52. $6a^2 + a - 35 = 6a^2 + (15a - 14a) - 35$

$= (6a^2 + 15a) + (-14a - 35)$

$= 3a(2a + 5) - 7(2a + 5)$

$= (3a - 7)(2a + 5)$

53. A matrix I such that $A \cdot I = A$.

$I_{3 \times 3} = \begin{bmatrix} 1 & 0 & 0 \\ 0 & 1 & 0 \\ 0 & 0 & 1 \end{bmatrix}$

54.

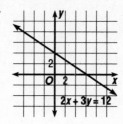

Chapter 7 Summary and Review

PAGES 344–346   SKILLS AND CONCEPTS

1. Using guess-and-check: 41312432

2.

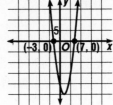

3.

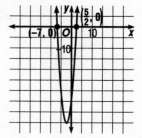

4. $2x^2 + 5x + 3 = 0$

$(2x + 3)(x + 1) = 0$

$2x + 3 = 0$ or $x + 1 = 0$

$x = -\dfrac{3}{2}$ $x = -1$

5. $4p^2 + 9 = 12p$

$4p^2 - 12p + 9 = 0$

$(2p - 3)(2p - 3) = 0$

$2p - 3 = 0$

$p = \dfrac{3}{2}$

6. $2x^2 - 8x = 0$

$x^2 - 4x = 0$

$x(x - 4) = 0$

$x = 0$ or $x - 4 = 0$

$x = 4$

7. $8b^2 + 10b = 3$

$8b^2 + 10b - 3 = 0$

$(2b + 3)(4b - 1) = 0$

$2b + 3 = 0$ or $4b - 1 = 0$

$b = -\dfrac{3}{2}$ $b = \dfrac{1}{4}$

8. $x^2 + 20x + 75 = 0$

$x^2 + 20x = -75$

$x^2 + 20x + 100 = -75 + 100$

$(x + 10)^2 = 25$

$x + 10 = \pm 5$

$x = -15$ or $x = -5$

9. $x^2 - 5x - 24 = 0$

$x^2 - 5x = 24$

$x^2 - 5x + \dfrac{25}{4} = 24 + \dfrac{25}{4}$

$\left(x - \dfrac{5}{2}\right)^2 = \dfrac{121}{4}$

$x - \dfrac{5}{2} = \pm\dfrac{11}{2}$

$x = 8$ or $x = -3$

10. $2t^2 + t - 21 = 0$

$t^2 + \dfrac{1}{2}t = \dfrac{21}{2}$

$t^2 + \dfrac{1}{2}t + \dfrac{1}{16} = \dfrac{21}{2} + \dfrac{1}{16}$

$\left(t + \dfrac{1}{4}\right)^2 = \dfrac{169}{16}$

$t + \dfrac{1}{4} = \pm\dfrac{13}{4}$

$t = 3$ or $t = -\dfrac{7}{2}$

11. $r^2 + 4r = 96$

$r^2 + 4r + 4 = 96 + 4$

$(r + 2)^2 = 100$

$r + 2 = \pm 10$

$r = 8$ or $r = -12$

12. $3x^2 - 11x + 10 = 0$

$x = \dfrac{11 \pm \sqrt{121 - 4(3)(10)}}{2(3)}$

$= \dfrac{11 \pm \sqrt{1}}{6}$

$x = 2$ or $x = \dfrac{5}{3}$

13. $2p^2 - 5p + 4 = 0$

$p = \dfrac{5 \pm \sqrt{25 - 4(2)(4)}}{2(2)}$

$= \dfrac{5 \pm \sqrt{-7}}{4}$

$= \dfrac{5 \pm i\sqrt{7}}{4}$

14. $4x^2 - 40x + 25 = 0$

$x = \dfrac{40 \pm \sqrt{40^2 - 4(4)(25)}}{2(4)}$

$= \dfrac{40 \pm \sqrt{1200}}{8}$

$= \dfrac{10 \pm 5\sqrt{3}}{2}$

15. $y^2 + 3y = 0$

$y = \dfrac{-3 \pm \sqrt{9 - 4(1)(0)}}{2(1)}$

$= \dfrac{-3 \pm \sqrt{9}}{2}$

$y = 0$ or $y = -3$

16. $n^2 = 8n - 16$

$n^2 - 8n + 16 = 0$

$64 - 4(1)(16) = 0$

one real rational

$n = \dfrac{8 \pm \sqrt{0}}{2}$

$= \dfrac{8 \pm 0}{2}$

$= 4$

17. $7b^2 = 4b$

$7b^2 - 4b = 0$

$16 - 4(7)(0) = 16$

two real rational

$b = \dfrac{4 \pm \sqrt{16}}{2(7)}$

$= \dfrac{4 \pm 4}{14}$

$b = \dfrac{4}{7}$ or $b = 0$

18. $2y^2 + 6y + 5 = 0$

$36 - 4(2)(5) = -4$

two imaginary solutions

$y = \dfrac{-6 \pm \sqrt{-4}}{2(2)}$

$= \dfrac{-6 \pm 2i}{4}$

$= \dfrac{-3 \pm i}{2}$

19. $x^2 - 12x - 45 = 0$

$x = \dfrac{12 \pm \sqrt{144 - 4(1)(-45)}}{2(1)}$

$= \dfrac{12 \pm \sqrt{324}}{2}$

$x = 15$ or $x = -3$

$s_1 + s_2 = 12$

$s_1 s_2 = -45$

20. $2m^2 - 10m + 9 = 0$

$$m = \frac{10 \pm \sqrt{100 - 4(2)(9)}}{2(2)}$$

$$= \frac{10 \pm \sqrt{28}}{4}$$

$$m = \frac{5 \pm \sqrt{7}}{2}$$

$$s_1 + s_2 = 5$$

$$s_1 s_2 = \frac{9}{2}$$

21. $3s^2 - 11 = 0$

$$s = \frac{0 \pm \sqrt{0 - 4(3)(-11)}}{2(3)}$$

$$= \frac{\sqrt{132}}{6}$$

$$s = \frac{\pm\sqrt{33}}{3}$$

$$s_1 + s_2 = 0$$

$$s_1 s_2 = -\frac{11}{3}$$

22. $2x^2 = 3 - 3x$

$$2x^2 + 3x - 3 = 0$$

$$x = \frac{-3 \pm \sqrt{3^2 - 4(2)(-3)}}{2(2)}$$

$$= \frac{-3 \pm \sqrt{33}}{4}$$

$$s_1 + s_2 = -\frac{3}{2}$$

$$s_1 s_2 = -\frac{3}{2}$$

23. $s_1 + s_2 = -2$

$$s_1 s_2 = -24$$

$$a = 1, \ b = 2, \ c = -24$$

$$x^2 + 2x - 24 = 0$$

24. $s_1 + s_2 = \frac{13}{12}$

$$s_1 s_2 = \frac{3}{12}$$

$$a = 12, \ b = -13, \ c = 3$$

$$12x^2 - 13x + 3 = 0$$

25. $s_1 + s_2 = 10$

$$s_1 s_2 = 34$$

$$a = 1, \ b = -10, \ c = 34$$

$$x^2 - 10x + 34 = 0$$

26. $s_1 + s_2 = 4$

$$s_1 s_2 = 1$$

$$a = 1, \ b = -4, \ c = 1$$

$$x^2 - 4x + 1 = 0$$

27. $3x^3 + 4x^2 - 15x = 0$

$$x(3x^2 + 4x - 15) = 0$$

$$x(3x - 5)(x + 3) = 0$$

$$x = 0 \text{ or } 3x - 5 = 0 \text{ or } x + 3 = 0$$

$$x = \frac{5}{3} \qquad x = -3$$

28. $m^4 + 3m^3 = 40m^2$

$$m^4 + 3m^3 - 40m^2 = 0$$

$$m^2(m^2 + 3m - 40) = 0$$

$$m^2(m - 5)(m + 8) = 0$$

$$m^2 = 0 \text{ or } m - 5 = 0 \text{ or } m + 8 = 0$$

$$m = 0 \qquad m = 5 \qquad m = -8$$

29. $a^3 - 64 = 0$

$$(a - 4)(a^2 + 4a + 16) = 0$$

$$a - 4 = 0 \text{ or } a^2 + 4a + 16 = 0$$

$$a = 4 \qquad a = \frac{-4 \pm \sqrt{4^2 - 4(1)(16)}}{2(1)}$$

$$= \frac{-4 \pm \sqrt{-48}}{2}$$

$$= -2 \pm 2i\sqrt{3}$$

30. $r + 9\sqrt{r} = -8$

$$(\sqrt{r})^2 + 9\sqrt{r} + 8 = 0$$

$$(\sqrt{r} + 8)(\sqrt{r} + 1) = 0$$

$$\sqrt{r} + 8 = 0 \text{ or } \sqrt{r} + 1 = 0$$

$$\sqrt{r} = -8 \qquad \sqrt{r} = -1$$

The square root of a number can never be negative. Thus, there are no solutions.

31. $x^4 - 8x^2 + 16 = 0$

$$(x^2)^2 - 8x^2 + 16 = 0$$

$$(x^2 - 4)(x^2 - 4) = 0$$

$$(x - 2)(x + 2)(x - 2)(x + 2) = 0$$

$$x = \pm 2$$

32. $x^{\frac{2}{3}} - 9x^{\frac{1}{3}} + 20 = 0$

$$\left(x^{\frac{1}{3}}\right)^2 - 9x^{\frac{1}{3}} + 20 = 0$$

$$\left(x^{\frac{1}{3}} - 5\right)\left(x^{\frac{1}{3}} - 4\right) = 0$$

$$x^{\frac{1}{3}} - 5 = 0 \text{ or } x^{\frac{1}{3}} - 4 = 0$$

$$x^{\frac{1}{3}} = 5 \qquad x^{\frac{1}{3}} = 4$$

$$x = 125 \qquad x = 64$$

33. Let x = width of strip

$A = \ell w$

$270 = (12 + 2x)(9 + 2x)$

$270 = 108 + 42x + 4x^2$

$0 = 4x^2 + 42x - 162$

$0 = 2x^2 + 21x - 81$

$0 = (2x + 27)(x - 3)$

$2x + 27 = 0$ or $x - 3 = 0$

$x = -\dfrac{27}{2}$ $x = 3$

not reasonable

The strip is 3 feet wide.

34. $s = v_i t + \dfrac{1}{2}at^2$

$7040 = 2760t + \dfrac{1}{2}(200)t^2$

$0 = 100t^2 + 2760t - 7040$

$t = \dfrac{-2760 \pm \sqrt{(2760)^2 - 4(100)(-7040)}}{2(100)}$

$\approx \dfrac{-2760 \pm 3230.11}{200}$

$t \approx 2.35$ or $t \approx -29.95$

not reasonable

It took about 2.35 seconds to travel 7040 m.

35. $s = v_i t - \dfrac{1}{2}gt^2$

$0 = 960t - \dfrac{1}{2}(32)t^2 + 288$

$0 = -16t^2 + 960t + 288$

$0 = t^2 - 60t - 18$

$t = \dfrac{60 \pm \sqrt{60^2 - 4(1)(-18)}}{2(1)}$

$\approx \dfrac{60 \pm 60.60}{2}$

$t \approx -0.30$ or $t \approx 60.3$

not reasonable

It will take 60.3 seconds for the rocket to reach ground level.

36. Let x = width of the strip

$A = \ell w$

$(100)(120) - \dfrac{1}{3}(100)(120) = (120 - 2x)(100 - 2x)$

$12{,}000 - 4000 = 12{,}000 - 440x + 4x^2$

$0 = 4x^2 - 440x + 4000$

$0 = x^2 - 110x + 1000$

$0 = (x - 10)(x - 100)$

$x - 10 = 0$ or $x - 100 = 0$

$x = 10$ $x = 100$

not reasonable

The width of the strip is 10 ft.

Chapter 7 Test

PAGE 347

1.

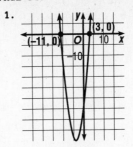

2.

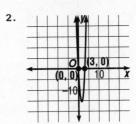

3.

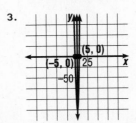

4. $6y^2 - y = 15$

$6y^2 - y - 15 = 0$

$(3x - 5)(2x + 3) = 0$

$3x - 5 = 0$ or $2x + 3 = 0$

$x = \dfrac{5}{3}$ $x = -\dfrac{3}{2}$

5. $3b^2 + b = 14$

$3b^2 + b - 14 = 0$

$(3b + 7)(b - 2) = 0$

$3b + 7 = 0$ or $b - 2 = 0$

$b = -\dfrac{7}{3}$ $b = 2$

6. $12p^2 - 5p = 3$

$12p^2 - 5p - 3 = 0$

$(3p + 1)(4p - 3) = 0$

$3p + 1 = 0$ or $4p - 3 = 0$

$p = -\dfrac{1}{3}$ $p = \dfrac{3}{4}$

7. $(-30)^2 - 4(9)(25) = 0$

one real rational

$a = \dfrac{30 \pm \sqrt{0}}{2(9)}$

$= \dfrac{30}{18}$ or $\dfrac{5}{3}$

8. $(-4)^2 - 4(3)(2) = -8$

two imaginary

$x = \dfrac{4 \pm \sqrt{-8}}{2(3)}$

$= \dfrac{4 \pm 2i\sqrt{2}}{6}$

$= \dfrac{2 \pm i\sqrt{2}}{3}$

9. $3^2 - 4(2)(3) = -15$

two imaginary

$x = \dfrac{-3 \pm \sqrt{-15}}{2(2)}$

$= \dfrac{-3 \pm i\sqrt{15}}{4}$

10. $35^2 - 4(14)(-5) = 1505$

two real, irrational

$r = \dfrac{-35 \pm \sqrt{1505}}{2(14)}$

$= \dfrac{-35 \pm \sqrt{1505}}{28}$

11. $6t^2 - 2t + 1 = 0$

$(-2)^2 - 4(6)(1) = -20$

two imaginary

$t = \dfrac{2 \pm \sqrt{-20}}{2(6)}$

$= \dfrac{2 \pm 2i\sqrt{5}}{12}$

$= \dfrac{1 \pm i\sqrt{5}}{6}$

12. $3x^2 - 7x - 20 = 0$

$(-7)^2 - 4(3)(-20) = 289$

two real, rational

$x = \dfrac{7 \pm \sqrt{289}}{2(3)}$

$= \dfrac{7 \pm 17}{6}$

$x = 4$ or $x = -\dfrac{5}{3}$

13. $(-4)^2 - 4(1)(4) = 0$

one real, rational

$n = \dfrac{4 \pm \sqrt{0}}{2(1)}$

$= 2$

14. $7k^2 - 4k - 1 = 0$

$(-4)^2 - 4(7)(-1) = 44$

two real, irrational

$k = \dfrac{4 \pm \sqrt{44}}{2(7)}$

$= \dfrac{2 \pm \sqrt{11}}{7}$

15. $4x^2 - 324 = 0$

$0^2 - 4(4)(-324) = 5184$

two real, rational

$x = \dfrac{0 \pm \sqrt{5184}}{2(4)}$

$= \pm\dfrac{72}{8}$

$= \pm 9$

16. $s_1 + s_2 = -\dfrac{(-3)}{2} = \dfrac{3}{2}$

$s_1 s_2 = \dfrac{-12}{2} = -6$

17. $2x^2 + 3x - 3 = 0$

$s_1 + s_2 = -\dfrac{3}{2}$

$s_1 s_2 = -\dfrac{3}{2}$

18. $4n^2 - n - 7 = 0$

$s_1 + s_2 = -\dfrac{(-1)}{4} = \dfrac{1}{4}$

$s_1 s_2 = -\dfrac{7}{4}$

19. $s_1 + s_2 = -3$

$s_1 s_2 = 0$

$a = 1,\ b = 3,\ c = 0$

$x^2 + 3x = 0$

20. $s_1 + s_2 = \dfrac{6}{3}$ or $\dfrac{18}{9}$

$s_1 s_2 = \dfrac{8}{9}$

$a = 9,\ b = -18,\ c = 8$

$9x^2 - 18x + 8 = 0$

21. $s_1 + s_2 = 10$

$s_1 s_2 = 29$

$a = 1,\ b = -10,\ c = 29$

$x^2 - 10x + 29 = 0$

22. $s_1 + s_2 = 16$

$s_1 s_2 = 64$

$a = 1,\ b = -16,\ c = 64$

$x^2 - 16x + 64 = 0$

23.

$p^3 + 8p^2 = 18p$

$p^3 + 8p^2 - 18p = 0$

$p(p^2 + 8p - 18) = 0$

$p = 0$ or $p^2 + 8p - 18 = 0$

$p = \dfrac{-8 \pm \sqrt{8^2 - 4(1)(-18)}}{2(1)}$

$= \dfrac{-8 \pm \sqrt{136}}{2}$

$= -4 \pm \sqrt{34}$

24.

$r^4 - 9r^2 + 18 = 0$

$(r^2)^2 - 9(r^2) + 18 = 0$

$(r^2 - 3)(r^2 - 6) = 0$

$r^2 - 3 = 0$ or $r^2 - 6 = 0$

$r = \pm\sqrt{3}$ $\qquad$ $r = \pm\sqrt{6}$

25.

$2d + 3\sqrt{d} - 9 = 0$

$2(\sqrt{d})^2 + 3\sqrt{d} - 9 = 0$

$(2\sqrt{d} - 3)(\sqrt{d} + 3) = 0$

$2\sqrt{d} - 3 = 0$ or $\sqrt{d} + 3 = 0$

$\sqrt{d} = \dfrac{3}{2}$ $\qquad$ $\sqrt{d} = -3$

$d = \dfrac{9}{4}$

The square root of a number can never be negative. Thus, $\dfrac{9}{4}$ is the only solution.

26. $2m^{\frac{2}{3}} - 5m^{\frac{1}{3}} - 12 = 0$

$2\left(m^{\frac{1}{3}}\right)^2 - 5m^{\frac{1}{3}} - 12 = 0$

$\left(2m^{\frac{1}{3}} + 3\right)\left(m^{\frac{1}{3}} - 4\right) = 0$

$2m^{\frac{1}{3}} + 3 = 0$ or $m^{\frac{1}{3}} - 4 = 0$

$2m^{\frac{1}{3}} = -3$ $\qquad$ $m^{\frac{1}{3}} = 4$

$m^{\frac{1}{3}} = -\dfrac{3}{2}$ $\qquad$ $m = 64$

$m = -\dfrac{27}{8}$

27. $x^{\frac{1}{2}} - 15x^{\frac{1}{4}} + 50 = 0$

$\left(x^{\frac{1}{4}}\right)^2 - 15x^{\frac{1}{4}} + 50 = 0$

$\left(x^{\frac{1}{4}} - 5\right)\left(x^{\frac{1}{4}} - 10\right) = 0$

$x^{\frac{1}{4}} - 5 = 0$ or $x^{\frac{1}{4}} - 10 = 0$

$x^{\frac{1}{4}} = 5$ $\qquad$ $x^{\frac{1}{4}} = 10$

$x = 625$ $\qquad$ $x = 10{,}000$

28. $x^3 + 27 = 0$

$(x + 3)(x^2 - 3x + 9) = 0$

$x + 3 = 0$ or $x^2 - 3x + 9 = 0$

$x = -3$ $\quad$ $x = \dfrac{3 \pm \sqrt{3^2 - 4(1)(9)}}{2(1)}$

$= \dfrac{3 \pm \sqrt{-27}}{2}$

$= \dfrac{3 \pm 3i\sqrt{3}}{2}$

---

29. Let x = the width of the decking

$(40 - 2x)(30 - 2x) = 600$

$1200 - 140x + 4x^2 = 600$

$x^2 - 35x + 150 = 0$

$(x - 5)(x - 30) = 0$

$x - 5 = 0$ or $x - 30 = 0$

$x = 5$ $\qquad$ $x = 30$

30 is not a reasonable answer. Thus, the width of the decking is 5 feet.

30. $s = v_i t - \dfrac{1}{2}gt^2$

$0 = 192t - \dfrac{1}{2}(32)t^2 + 32$

$0 = -16t^2 + 192t + 32$

$0 = t^2 - 12t - 2$

$t = \dfrac{12 \pm \sqrt{12^2 - 4(1)(-2)}}{2(1)}$

$\approx \dfrac{12 \pm 12.33}{2}$

$t \approx -0.16$ or $t \approx 12.16$

-0.16 is not a reasonable answer.

Thus, the cannonball returns to the ground in about 12.16 seconds.

PAGE 347 $\qquad$ **BONUS**

$\dfrac{x}{1} = \dfrac{1 - x}{x}$

$x^2 = 1 - x$

$x^2 + x - 1 = 0$

$x = \dfrac{-1 \pm \sqrt{1^2 - 4(1)(-1)}}{2(1)}$

$= \dfrac{-1 \pm \sqrt{5}}{2}$

$x \approx -1.618$ or $x \approx 0.618$

not reasonable

$\ell : w = 1 : 0.618$

Chapter 8
Quadratic Relations and Functions

Graphing Calculator Exploration: Families of Parabolas

PAGE 352

1. translates the graph vertically
2. translates the graph horizontally
3. They have the same shape and vertex, but one opens upward and one opens downward.
4. 8 units to the left
5. 5 units to the right
6. 6 units below
7. 8 units above
8. 2 units to the right
9. 7 units below
10. 10 units to the right, 9 units above
11. 6 units to the left, 5 units below
12. 11 units to the right, 7 units below
13. 9 units to the left, 4 units above
14. narrower
15. wider
16. opens upward not downward
17. narrower
18. narrower, opens downward not upward
19. wider, opens downward not upward
20. wider
21. 8 units to the right, narrower
22. narrower, opens downward not upward
23. 5 units to the left, wider
24. narrower
25. wider, opens downward not upward
26. 3 units to the right, 9 units below, narrower
27. 12 units to the left, 12 units below, wider, opens downward not upward
28. $|h|$ units to the left or right
29. $|k|$ units above or below
30. $|k|$ units above or below
31. $|h|$ units to the left or right
32. $|h|$ units to the left or right and $|k|$ units above or below
33. narrower if $|a| > 1$, wider if $|a| < 1$, opens downward not upward if $a < 0$
34. narrower if $|a| > 1$, wider if $|a| < 1$, opens downward not upward if $a < 0$
35. narrower if $|a| > 1$, wider if $|a| < 1$, opens downward not upward if $a < 0$
36. $|h|$ units to the left or right, $|k|$ units above or below, narrower if $|a| > 1$, wider if $|a| < 1$, opens downward not upward if $a < 0$

8-1 Quadratic Functions

PAGE 354   CHECKING FOR UNDERSTANDING

1. quadratic term: $-10n^2$
   linear term: $150n$
   constant term: 2500

2. $f(x) = 4(x - 1)^2 - 1$
   $= 4(x^2 - 2x + 1) - 1$
   $= 4x^2 - 8x + 4 - 1$
   $= 4x^2 - 8x + 3$

3. no; $f(x) = 3(x - 2)^2 + 5$
   $= 3(x^2 - 4x + 4) + 5$
   $= 3x^2 - 12x + 12 + 5$
   $= 3x^2 - 12x + 17$

4. yes   5. yes   6. no   7. yes
8. yes   9. no   10. no   11. no

equation	quadratic term	linear term	constant term
12. $f(x) = x^2 + x - 4$	x^2	x	-4
13. $g(x) = 5x^2 - 7x + 2$	$5x^2$	$-7x$	2
14. $g(n) = 3n^2 - 1$	$3n^2$	0	-1
15. $f(n) = \frac{1}{3}n^2 + 4$	$\frac{1}{3}n^2$	0	4
16. $n(x) = -4x^2 - 8x - 9$	$-4x^2$	$-8x$	-9
17. $f(z) = z^2 + 3z$	z^2	$3z$	0
18. $f(x) = (x + 3)^2$			
$= x^2 + 6x + 9$	x^2	$6x$	9
19. $f(t) = (3t + 1)^2 - 8$			
$= 9t^2 + 6t - 7$	$9t^2$	$6t$	-7

PAGES 354-355   EXERCISES

20. $g(x) = (x - 1)^2$
    $= x^2 - 2x + 1$

21. $f(x) = (x - 3)^2$
    $= x^2 - 6x + 9$

22. $f(m) = (2m - 5)^2$
    $= 4m^2 - 20m + 25$

23. $h(x) = (3x + 2)^2$
    $= 9x^2 + 12x + 4$

24. $f(r) = 3(r - 2)^2$

$\quad = 3(r^2 - 4r + 4)$

$\quad = 3r^2 - 12r + 12$

25. $f(x) = -4(2x - 4)^2$

$\quad = -4(4x^2 - 16x + 16)$

$\quad = -16x^2 + 64x - 64$

26. $g(x) = 2(4x + 1)^2$

$\quad = 2(16x^2 + 8x + 1)$

$\quad = 32x^2 + 16x + 2$

27. $f(x) = 4(x + 1)^2 + 10$

$\quad = 4(x^2 + 2x + 1) + 10$

$\quad = 4x^2 + 8x + 4 + 10$

$\quad = 4x^2 + 8x + 14$

28. $f(x) = -3(2x + 2)^2 + 6$

$\quad = -3(4x^2 + 8x + 4) + 6$

$\quad = -12x^2 - 24x - 12 + 6$

$\quad = -12x^2 - 24x - 6$

29. $g(x) = \frac{1}{6}(6x + 12)^2 + 5$

$\quad = \frac{1}{6}(36x^2 + 144x + 144) + 5$

$\quad = 6x^2 + 24x + 24 + 5$

$\quad = 6x^2 + 24x + 29$

30. Let n = one of the numbers.
Then, $45 - n$ = the other number.

product = $n(45 - n) = 45n - n^2$

31. Let r = the radius; area = πr^2.

32. Let n = one of the numbers.
Then, $n + 15$ = the other number.

product = $n(n + 15) = n^2 + 15n$

33. Let s = the measure of the length of a leg.

area = $\frac{1}{2}bh = \frac{1}{2}s^2$

34. Let ℓ = the length. Then $w = \frac{1}{2}(30 - 2\ell)$

area = ℓw

$\quad = \ell \cdot \frac{1}{2}(30 - 2\ell)$

$\quad = \ell(15 - \ell)$

$\quad = 15\ell - \ell^2$

35. Let x = one of the numbers.
Then, $10 - x$ = the other number.

sum = $x^2 + (10 - x)^2$

$\quad = x^2 + (100 - 20x + x^2)$

$\quad = 2x^2 - 20x + 100$

36. Let x = the lesser number.
Then, $x + 18$ = the greater number.

sum = $x^2 + (x + 18)^2$

$\quad = x^2 + (x^2 + 36x + 324)$

$\quad = 2x^2 + 36x + 324$

37. Let w = the width of the kennel.

Then, $\frac{1}{2}(100 - 2w)$ = the length.

area = $\frac{1}{2}(100 - 2w) \cdot w$

$\quad = (50 - w)w$

$\quad = 50w - w^2$

38. $a(x) = (4x + 10)x$

$\quad = 4x^2 + 10x$

39. $\quad x = 2n + 1$

$x^2 - 1 = (2n + 1)^2 - 1$

$\quad = 4n^2 + 4n + 1 - 1$

$\quad = 4n^2 + 4n$

$\quad = 4n(n + 1)$

This number is divisible by 4 since $4n$ is. We can rewrite the number as $4(n)(n + 1)$. Since either n or $(n + 1)$ must be even, this product must contain another factor of 2. Therefore, it must be divisible by 4×2 or 8.

40. Let p = the number of price increases.

$I(p) = (8 + 1p)(300 - 20p)$

$\quad = 2400 + 140p - 20p^2$

41. Let p = the number of price increases.
The number of people that attended last year: $800 + 4 = 200$.

$I(p) = (4.00 + 0.25p)(200 - 10p)$

$\quad = 800 + 10p - 2.5p^2$

42. $\quad x^6 + 3x^3 - 10 = 0$

$1(x^3)^2 + 3(x^3) - 10 = 0$

43. $\quad a - 4a^{\frac{1}{2}} + 3 = 0$

$\left(a^{\frac{1}{2}}\right)^2 - 4\left(a^{\frac{1}{2}}\right) + 3 = 0$

$\left(a^{\frac{1}{2}} - 3\right)\left(a^{\frac{1}{2}} - 1\right) = 0$

$a^{\frac{1}{2}} - 3 = 0$ or $a^{\frac{1}{2}} - 1 = 0$

$a^{\frac{1}{2}} = 3 \qquad a^{\frac{1}{2}} = 1$

$a = 9 \qquad a = 1$

44. $(2 + 9i)(2 - 9i) = 4 - 18i + 18i - 81i^2$

$\quad = 4 + 81$

$\quad = 85$

45. $(0.0016)^{\frac{1}{4}} = \left((0.0016)^{\frac{1}{2}}\right)^{\frac{1}{2}}$

$\qquad\qquad = (0.04)^{\frac{1}{2}}$

$\qquad\qquad = 0.2$

46.

$$\underline{-0.4}\,\big|\quad 1\qquad 0\qquad\quad 0\qquad\quad -2.8$$

$$\qquad\qquad\quad -0.4\quad 0.16\quad -0.064$$

$$\overline{\qquad\quad 1\quad -0.4\quad 0.16\quad -2.864}$$

$$x^2 - 0.4x + 0.16 - \frac{2.864}{x + 0.4}$$

47. $\dfrac{300{,}000 \text{ km}}{1 \text{ second}} \cdot \dfrac{86{,}400 \text{ seconds}}{1 \text{ day}} = 2.592 \times 10^{10} \text{ km/day}$

48. $\begin{bmatrix} 4 & 1 \\ 1 & 4 \end{bmatrix} \cdot \begin{bmatrix} x \\ y \end{bmatrix} = \begin{bmatrix} -5 \\ 10 \end{bmatrix}$

$\dfrac{1}{15}\begin{bmatrix} 4 & -1 \\ -1 & 4 \end{bmatrix}\begin{bmatrix} 4 & 1 \\ 1 & 4 \end{bmatrix}\begin{bmatrix} x \\ y \end{bmatrix} = \dfrac{1}{15}\begin{bmatrix} 4 & -1 \\ -1 & 4 \end{bmatrix}\begin{bmatrix} -5 \\ 10 \end{bmatrix}$

$\qquad\qquad\qquad \begin{bmatrix} x \\ y \end{bmatrix} = \dfrac{1}{15}\begin{bmatrix} -30 \\ 45 \end{bmatrix}$

$\qquad\qquad\qquad \begin{bmatrix} x \\ y \end{bmatrix} = \begin{bmatrix} -2 \\ 3 \end{bmatrix} \qquad (-2, 3)$

8-2 Problem-Solving Strategy: Make a Table

PAGE 357   CHECKING FOR UNDERSTANDING

1. Organize data and find what's missing, organize results; look for patterns.

2. no   **3.** 7

4. yes; It is also in a cycle of four:

0, 4, 4, 0, ...

5.

Half-Dollars	Quarters	Dimes	Nickels
1	0	1	0
1	0	0	2
0	2	1	0
0	2	0	2
0	1	3	1
0	1	2	3
0	1	1	5
0	1	0	7
0	0	6	0
0	0	5	2
0	0	4	4
0	0	3	6
0	0	2	8
0	0	1	10
0	0	0	12

15 combinations of coins

6.

Quarters	Dimes	Nickels	Pennies	Total of 7 Coins?
1	0	1	1	no
1	0	0	6	yes
0	3	0	1	no
0	2	2	1	no
0	2	1	6	no
0	2	0	11	no
0	1	4	1	no
0	1	3	6	no
0	1	2	11	no
0	1	1	16	no
0	1	0	21	no
0	0	6	1	yes
0	0	5	6	no
0	0	4	11	no
0	0	3	16	no
0	0	2	21	no
0	0	1	26	no
0	0	0	31	no

1 quarter and 6 pennies or

6 nickels and 1 penny

7.

n	11^n	tens' digit
1	11	1
2	121	2
3	1331	3
4	14,641	4
5	161,051	5
.	.	.
.	.	.
.	.	.

The tens' digit of 11^{10} is 0.

PAGES 357-358   EXERCISES

8.

10 points	20 points	30 points	50 points	Total of 90 points?
3	0	0	0	no
2	1	0	0	no
2	0	1	0	no
2	0	0	1	no
1	2	0	0	no
1	1	1	0	no
1	1	0	1	no
1	0	2	0	no
1	0	0	2	no
1	0	1	1	yes
0	3	0	0	no
0	2	1	0	no
0	2	0	1	yes
0	1	2	0	no
0	1	1	1	no
0	1	0	2	no
0	0	3	0	yes
0	0	0	3	no

(1) 1 - 50, 1 - 30, 1 - 10

(2) 1 - 50, 2 - 20s

(3) 3 - 30s

9.

n	$5^n \div 7$	Remainder
1	0 R5	5
2	3 R4	4
3	17 R6	6
4	89 R2	2
5	446 R3	3
6	2232 R1	1
7	11160 R5	5
8	55803 R4	4
.	.	.
.	.	.
.	.	.

Remainders of successive powers of 5 divided by 7 repeat in a cycle of six: 5, 4, 6, 2, 3, 1, ...

So $5^{100} \div 7$ will have a remainder of 2.

10. Move the four triangles to the center of the square to form a square 15 feet by 15 feet. The area of this grassy area is 15 · 15 or 225 ft^2.

11. Write out all the prime numbers up to 53. Use guess-and-check to see if any two add up to 53. The answer is 0.

12. $(n + 1)^2 - n^2 = 1993$

$n^2 + 2n + 1 - n^2 = 1993$

$2n + 1 = 1993$

$n = 996$

n can also be -996. The sum of the two consecutive integers is 1993 or -1993.

13.
$\left.\begin{array}{l} 10 = 2 \cdot 5 \\ 15 = 3 \cdot 5 \\ 20 = 2 \cdot 2 \cdot 5 \\ 21 = 3 \cdot 7 \end{array}\right\}$ $2 \cdot 2 \cdot 3 \cdot 5 \cdot 7 = 420$

14. Hornets vs. Warriors: 2 to 0; Warriors vs. Vikings: 2 to 2; Vikings vs. Hornets: 1 to 5.

15.
```
1 ⌠ T  T  T  T
2 ⌡ H  H  H  T
3 ⌠ H  T  T  H
4 ⌡ T  H  T  T
    H  H  H  H
```
The fewest number of moves is 4.

16. Sample answers:

```
   154      215
 + 782    + 478
   936      693
```

17. $2025 = 45^2$; $3136 = 56^2$; The answer is 2025.

18. $198 + 199 + 200 + 201 + 202 = 1000$

$55 + 56 + 57 + 58 + \ldots + 70 = 1000$

$28 + 29 + 30 + 31 + \ldots + 52 = 1000$

$\begin{bmatrix} H\,H\,H \\ H\,T\,H \\ H\,H\,H \end{bmatrix} \rightarrow \begin{bmatrix} T\,H\,H \\ H\,H\,H \\ H\,H\,T \end{bmatrix} \rightarrow \begin{bmatrix} T\,T\,H \\ H\,T\,H \\ H\,T\,T \end{bmatrix} \rightarrow \begin{bmatrix} T\,T\,T \\ H\,H\,H \\ T\,T\,T \end{bmatrix} \rightarrow \begin{bmatrix} H\,H\,H \\ H\,H\,H \\ T\,T\,T \end{bmatrix} \rightarrow \begin{matrix} H\,H\,H \\ H\,H\,H \\ H\,H\,H \end{matrix}$

5 moves

Graphing Calculator Exploration: Locating the Vertex of a Parabola

1. (10, 14)

2. (-8, -5)

3. (7, 21)

4. (43.50, -1915.25)

5. (30.20, -4881.20)

6. (-0.75, 3.25)

7. (37.00, 92.50)

8. (3.50, 11.50)

9. (0.56, 5.79)

10. (-0.28, 8.85)

Graphing Quadratic Functions

1. yes; Justification may vary.

2. parabola; axis of symmetry

3. A sample answer is $f(x) = (x - (-1))^2 - 1$.

4. The graphs have the same slope. The vertex of $f(x) = (x - 2)^2 + 2$ is (2, 2) and the vertex of $f(x) = (x + 2)^2 + 2$ is (-2, 2).

5. $y = (x - (-2))^2 + 1$

6. (0, 0), $x = 0$

7. (4, 0), $x = 4$

8. (-6, 0), $x = -6$

9. (0, 3), $x = 0$

10. (0, -9), $x = 0$

11. (6, 4), $x = 6$

12. (-10, -7), $x = -10$

13. $\left(\frac{1}{5}, 1\right)$, $x = \frac{1}{5}$

14. (-1.5, -3.2), $x = -1.5$

15. $y = [x - (-2)]^2 + 0$

16. $y = (x + 0)^2 + 2$

17. $y = (x - 2)^2 + 2$

18. $y = [x - (-2)]^2 + (-2)$

19. $f(x) = (x - 2)^2$; (2, 0); $x = 2$

20. $f(x) = [x - (-3)]^2$; (-3, 0); $x = -3$

21. $f(x) = (x - 0)^2 + 9$; (0, 9); $x = 0$

22. $f(x) = (x - 0)^2 + (-7)$; (0, -7); $x = 0$

23. $f(x) = [x - (-5)]^2 - 25$; (-5, -25); $x = -5$

24. $f(x) = (x - 6)^2 - 36$; (6, -36); $x = 6$

25. $f(x) = [x - (-4)]^2 + 4$; (-4, 4); $x = -4$

26. $f(x) = \left(x - \frac{3}{2}\right)^2 + \frac{3}{4}$; $\left(\frac{3}{2}, \frac{3}{4}\right)$; $x = \frac{3}{2}$

27.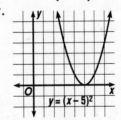

28.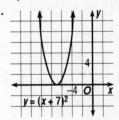

29.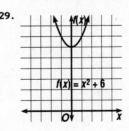

30.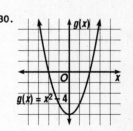

177

31.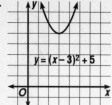

$y = (x - 3)^2 + 5$

32.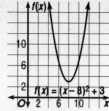

$f(x) = (x - 8)^2 + 3$

33.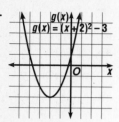

$g(x) = (x + 2)^2 - 3$

34.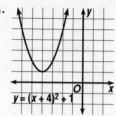

$y = (x + 4)^2 + 1$

35.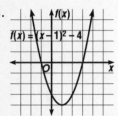

$f(x) = (x - 1)^2 - 4$

36.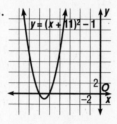

$y = (x + 11)^2 - 1$

37.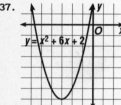

$y = x^2 + 6x + 2$

38.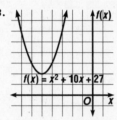

$f(x) = x^2 + 10x + 27$

39.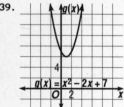

$g(x) = x^2 - 2x + 7$

40.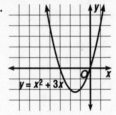

$y = x^2 + 3x$

41.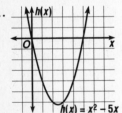

$h(x) = x^2 - 5x$

42.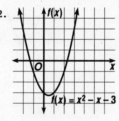

$f(x) = x^2 - x - 3$

43. $y = (x - h)^2 + k$

$-1 = (2 - 0)^2 + k$

$-5 = k$

$(0, -5); \ y = x^2 - 5$

44. $y = (x - h)^2 + k$

$9 = [-5 - (-2)]^2 + k$

$9 = 9 + k$

$0 = k$

$(-2, 0); \ y = (x + 2)^2$

45. $y = (x - h)^2 + k$

$18 = [1 - (-3)]^2 + k$

$18 = 16 + k$

$2 = k$

$(-3, 2); \ y = (x + 3)^2 + 2$

46. $y = (x - h)^2 + k$

$-2 = (-1 - 1)^2 + k$

$-2 = 4 + k$

$-6 = k$

$(1, -6); \ y = (x - 1)^2 - 6$

47. a. $h(t) = 80t - 16t^2$

$= -16(t^2 - 5t)$

$= -16\left(t^2 - 5t + \dfrac{25}{4}\right) + 100$

$= -16\left(t - \dfrac{5}{2}\right)^2 + 100$

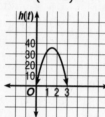

b. 2.5 seconds; 100 feet

48. a. $h(t) = 48t - 16t^2$

$= -16(t^2 - 3t)$

$= -16\left(t^2 - 3t + \dfrac{9}{4}\right) + 36$

$= -16\left(t - \dfrac{3}{2}\right)^2 + 36$

b. 3 seconds

c. at the level of the bat where the foul ball was hit

49. $f(x) = 4x^2 - 8x - 2$

quadratic term: $4x^2$

linear term: $-8x$

constant term: -2

50. $s_1 + s_2 = 8 + (-7) = 1$

$s_1 s_2 = 8(-7) = -56$

$a = 1, \ b = -1, \ c = -56$

$x^2 - x - 56 = 0$

51. $\sqrt[3]{2}(3\sqrt[3]{4} + 2\sqrt[3]{32}) = \sqrt[3]{2}(3\sqrt[3]{4}) + \sqrt[3]{2}(2\sqrt[3]{32})$

$= 3\sqrt[3]{2 \cdot 4} + 2\sqrt[3]{2 \cdot 32}$

$= 3\sqrt[3]{8} + 2\sqrt[3]{64}$

$= 3 \cdot 2 + 2 \cdot 4$

$= 14$

52. All the monomials have a degree of 6, so the degree of the polynomial is 6.

53. slope $= \dfrac{9 - 3}{-3 - 9}$

$= \dfrac{6}{-12}$

$= -\dfrac{1}{2}$

Technology: Quadratic Functions

PAGE 365

1. $(14, -10)$; $x = 14$; upward; $(11, -1)$, $(12, -6)$, $(13, -9)$, $(15, -9)$, $(16, -6)$, $(17, -1)$

2. $(-8, 100)$; $x = -8$; downward; $(-11, 91)$, $(-10, 96)$, $(-9, 99)$, $(-7, 99)$, $(-6, 96)$, $(-5, 91)$

3. $(2.2, 21.2)$; $x = 2.2$; downward; $(0, -3)$, $(1, 14)$, $(2, 21)$, $(3, 18)$, $(4, 5)$, $(5, -18)$,

4. $(1.85, -41.225)$; $x = 1.85$; upward; $(-1, 40)$, $(0, -7)$, $(1, -34)$, $(2, -41)$, $(3, -28)$, $(4, 5)$

8-4 Analyzing Graphs of Quadratic Functions

PAGE 370   CHECKING FOR UNDERSTANDING

1. If $a > 0$, it will open upward. If $a < 0$, it will open downward.

2. The graph gets wider.

3. They have the same vertex and axis of symmetry. They are the same shape, but the graph of $y = 2(x - 5)^2 + 3$ opens upward and the graph of $y = -2(x - 5)^2 + 3$ opens downward.

4. They have the same vertex and axis of symmetry. They both open upward, but the graph of $y = 2(x - 5)^2 + 3$ is much more narrow than the graph of $y = \frac{1}{2}(x - 5)^2 + 3$.

5. $(9, 0)$; $x = 9$; up

6. $(-3, 0)$; $x = -3$; down

7. $(0, -6)$; $x = 0$; up

8. $(0, 6)$; $x = 0$; down

9. $(-3, -1)$; $x = -3$; up

10. $(2, -2)$; $x = 2$; down

11. $\left(-2, -\frac{4}{3}\right)$; $x = -2$; up

12. $\left(\frac{1}{2}, \frac{1}{4}\right)$; $x = \frac{1}{2}$; up

13. $f(x) = -2x^2 + 4$

14. $f(x) = 5(x - 1)^2 - 8$

PAGES 370-372   EXERCISES

15. $f(x) = x^2 - 4x + 5$

$= (x^2 - 4x + 4) + 5 - 4$

$f(x) = (x - 2)^2 + 1$; $(2, 1)$; $x = 2$; up

16. $f(x) = -x^2 - 2x + 2$

$= -(x^2 + 2x + 1) + 2 + 1$

$f(x) = -(x + 1)^2 + 3$; $(-1, 3)$; $x = -1$; down

17. $f(x) = -3x^2 + 12x$

$= -3(x^2 - 4x)$

$= -3(x^2 - 4x + 4) + 12$

$f(x) = -3(x - 2)^2 + 12$; $(2, 12)$; $x = 2$; down

18. $f(x) = 4x^2 + 24x = 4(x^2 + 6x + 9) - 36$

$f(x) = 4(x + 3)^2 - 36$; $(-3, -36)$; $x = -3$; up

19. $f(x) = 3x^2 - 18x + 11$

$= 3(x^2 - 6x + 9) + 11 - 27$

$f(x) = 3(x - 3)^2 - 16$; $(3, -16)$; $x = 3$; up

20. $f(x) = -2x^2 - 20x - 50$

$= -2(x^2 + 10x + 25) - 50 + 50$

$f(x) = -2(x + 5)^2$; $(-5, 0)$; $x = -5$; down

21. $f(x) = -\frac{1}{2}x^2 + 5x - \frac{27}{2}$

$= -\frac{1}{2}(x^2 - 10x + 25) - \frac{27}{2} + \frac{25}{2}$

$f(x) = -\frac{1}{2}(x - 5)^2 - 1$; $(5, -1)$; $x = 5$; down

22. $f(x) = \frac{1}{3}x^2 - 4x + 15$

$= \frac{1}{3}(x^2 - 12x + 36) + 15 - 12$

$f(x) = \frac{1}{3}(x - 6)^2 + 3$; $(6, 3)$; $x = 6$; up

23. $y = 3(x - 1)^2$

24. $y = -2x^2$

25. $y = -\frac{1}{2}(x + 2)^2 - 3$

26. $y = \frac{1}{3}x^2 + 5$

27. $y = -\frac{3}{4}(x - 4)^2 + 1$

28. $y = \frac{5}{2}(x + 3)^2 - 2$

29. $0 = a(0)^2 + b(0) + c \longrightarrow 0 = c$

$6 = a(2)^2 + b(2) + c \longrightarrow 6 = 4a + 2b + c$

$3 = a(-1)^2 + b(-1) + c \longrightarrow 3 = a - b + c$

Substitute 0 for c:

$6 = 4a + 2b \longrightarrow \quad 6 = 4a + 2b \qquad 3 = a - b$

$3 = a - b \longrightarrow \quad \underline{6 = 2a - 2b} \qquad 3 = 2 - b$

$\qquad\qquad\qquad\quad 12 = 6a \qquad\qquad -1 = b$

$\qquad\qquad\qquad\quad a = 2$

$y = 2x^2 - x$

30. $6 = a(1)^2 + b(1) + c \longrightarrow 6 = a + b + c$

$27 = a(-2)^2 + b(-2) + c \longrightarrow 27 = 4a - 2b + c$

$11 = a(2)^2 + b(2) + c \longrightarrow 11 = 4a + 2b + c$

$\begin{array}{l} 12 = 2a + 2b + 2c \\ \underline{27 = 4a - 2b + c} \\ 39 = 6a + 3c \end{array}$ $\qquad$ $\begin{array}{l} 27 = 4a - 2b + c \\ \underline{11 = 4a + 2b + c} \\ 38 = 8a + 2c \end{array}$

$\begin{array}{l} 78 = 12a + 6c \\ \underline{-114 = -24a - 6c} \\ -36 = -12a \\ 3 = a \end{array}$ $\qquad$ $\begin{array}{l} 38 = 8a + 2c \\ 38 = 8(3) + 2c \\ 14 = 2c \\ 7 = c \end{array}$

$6 = a + b + c$

$6 = 3 + b + 7$

$-4 = b \qquad\qquad y = 3x^2 - 4x + 7$

31. $-3 = a(2)^2 + b(2) + c \longrightarrow -3 = 4a + 2b + c$

$-1 = a(0)^2 + b(0) + c \longrightarrow -1 = c$

$\frac{3}{2} = a(-1)^2 + b(-1) + c \longrightarrow \frac{3}{2} = a - b + c$

Substitute -1 for c:

$-3 = 4a + 2b - 1 \rightarrow -2 = 4a + 2b \rightarrow -2 = 4a + 2b$

$\frac{3}{2} = a - b - 1 \rightarrow \frac{5}{2} = a - b \rightarrow \begin{array}{l}\underline{5 = 2a - 2b} \\ 3 = 6a \\ \frac{1}{2} = a\end{array}$

$-2 = 4a + 2b$

$-2 = 4\left(\frac{1}{2}\right) + 2b \qquad y = \frac{1}{2}x^2 - 2x - 1$

$-4 = 2b$

$-2 = b$

32. $0 = a(1)^2 + b(1) + c \longrightarrow 0 = a + b + c$

$38 = a(3)^2 + b(3) + c \longrightarrow 38 = 9a + 3b + c$

$48 = a(-2)^2 + b(-2) + c \longrightarrow 48 = 4a - 2b + c$

$\begin{array}{l} 0 = -a - b - c \\ \underline{38 = 9a + 3b + c} \\ 38 = 8a + 2b \end{array}$ $\qquad$ $\begin{array}{l} 0 = -a - b - c \\ \underline{48 = 4a - 2b + c} \\ 48 = 3a - 3b \end{array}$

$\begin{array}{l} 38 = 8a + 2b \longrightarrow 114 = 24a + 66 \\ 48 = 3a - 3b \longrightarrow \underline{96 = 6a - 66} \\ 210 = 30a \\ 7 = a \end{array}$ $\qquad$ $\begin{array}{l} 38 = 8(7) + 2b \\ -18 = 2b \\ -9 = b \end{array}$

$0 = a + b + c$

$0 = 7 + (-9) + c \qquad y = 7x^2 - 9x + 2$

$2 = c$

33.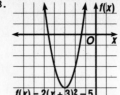

$f(x) = 2(x+3)^2 - 5$

34.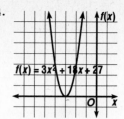

$f(x) = 3x^2 + 18x + 27$

35.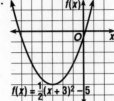

$f(x) = \frac{1}{2}(x+3)^2 - 5$

36.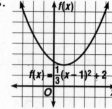

$f(x) = \frac{1}{3}(x-1)^2 + 2$

37.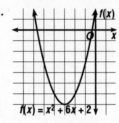

$f(x) = x^2 + 6x + 2$

38.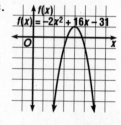

$f(x) = -2x^2 + 16x - 31$

39.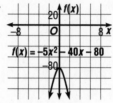

$f(x) = -5x^2 - 40x - 80$

40.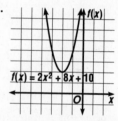

$f(x) = 2x^2 + 8x + 10$

41.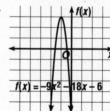

$f(x) = -9x^2 - 18x - 6$

42.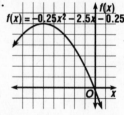

$f(x) = -0.25x^2 - 2.5x - 0.25$

43. $f(x) = ax^2 + bx + c$

$ = a\left(x^2 + \frac{b}{a}x\right) + c$

$ = a\left(x^2 + \frac{b}{a}x + \left(\frac{b}{2a}\right)^2\right) + c - a\left(\frac{b}{2a}\right)^2$

$f(x) = a\left(x + \frac{b}{2a}\right)^2 + c - \frac{b^2}{4a}$

$h = -\frac{b}{2a}; \ k = c - \frac{b^2}{4a} \text{ or } \frac{4ac - b^2}{4a}$

44. a. $f(x) = \frac{1}{315}(-2x^2 + 1260x)$

$ = \frac{1}{315}[-2(x^2 - 630x + 99{,}225)] + 630$

$f(x) = -\frac{2}{315}(x - 315)^2 + 630$

b. The arch will be tallest at $x = 315$:

$f(315) = -\frac{2}{315}(315 - 315)^2 + 630$

$ = 630 \quad$ The arch is 630 ft tall.

45. $(-2, 0)$; $x = -2$ **46.** $(3, -11)$; $x = 3$

47. $8s^2 = 200$

$s^2 = 25$

$\sqrt{s^2} = \sqrt{25}$

$s = \pm 5$

48. $(1 - \sqrt{3})^2 = 1 - \sqrt{3} - \sqrt{3} + 3$

$= 4 - 2\sqrt{3}$

49. $\dfrac{18x^3yz^2 + 27x^2yz + 45x^2y^2z^2}{9xyz}$

$= \dfrac{18x^3yz^2}{9xyz} + \dfrac{27x^2yz}{9xyz} + \dfrac{45x^2y^2z^2}{9xyz}$

$= 2x^2z + 3x + 5xyz$

50. no

51. $\begin{vmatrix} 5 & 1 & -1 \\ 2 & 1 & 0 \\ 0 & 3 & 5 \end{vmatrix}$

$= 5 \cdot 1 \cdot 5 + 1 \cdot 0 \cdot 0 + (-1) \cdot 2 \cdot 3$

$- 0 \cdot 1 \cdot (-1) - 3 \cdot 0 \cdot 5 - 5 \cdot 2 \cdot 1$

$= 25 + 0 - 6 - 0 - 0 - 10$

$= 9$

Since det $\neq 0$, the system of equations has a unique solution.

52.

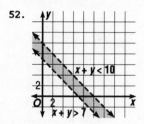

PAGE 372   MID-CHAPTER REVIEW

1. $g(x) = (x + 2)^2$

$= x^2 + 4x + 4$

2. $f(x) = 3(x - 5)^2 + 4$

$= 3(x^2 - 10x + 25) + 4$

$= 3x^2 - 30x + 75 + 4$

$= 3x^2 - 30x + 79$

3. Let n = one of the numbers.

product $= n(50 - n) = 50n - n^2$

4. Let ℓ = the length.

area $= \dfrac{1}{2}(42 - 2\ell)\ell = (21 - \ell)\ell = 21\ell - \ell^2$

5.

width	length	area
1	17	17
2	16	32
3	15	45
4	14	56
5	13	65
6	12	72
7	11	77
8	10	80
9	9	81

To get the maximum surface area, the dimensions must be 9 in. × 9 in.

6. They have the same shape, but the graph of $y = (x - 7)^2$ is shifted 7 units to the right.

7. $(2, -4)$, $x = 2$ **8.** $(-4, 0)$, $x = -4$

9. $(-2, 6)$, $x = -2$ **10.** $(0, 0)$, $x = 0$

11. $y = [(x + 2) - 2]^2 + 3$

$y = x^2 + 3$

12. $f(x) = x^2 + 6x + 3$

$= (x^2 + 6x + 9) + 3 - 9$

$f(x) = (x + 3)^2 - 6$; $(-3, -6)$; $x = -3$; up

13. $f(x) = -9x^2 - 18x - 10$

$= -9(x^2 + 2x) - 10$

$= -9(x^2 + 2x + 1) - 10 + 9$

$f(x) = -9(x + 1)^2 - 1$; $(-1, -1)$; $x = -1$; down

8–5 **Applications of Quadratic Equations**

PAGE 375   CHECKING FOR UNDERSTANDING

1. Sample answers: income and area

2. No values will be higher, or lower, than the vertex.

3. Yes, at the vertex $(3, 5)$

4. Income $= (200 - 20p)(6 + 0.5p)$

$= 1200 - 20p - 10p^2$

$= -10(p^2 + 2p + 1) + 1200 + 10$

$= -10(p + 1)^2 + 1210$

The vertex is $(-1, 1210)$. No increase should be made. The maximum income, $1210, occurs when the owner decreases the price by $0.50 one time for a fare of $5.50.

5. a. $x + 20$

b. $x(x + 20)$ or $x^2 + 20x$

c. $f(x) = x^2 + 20x$

$= (x^2 + 20x + 100) - 100$

$= (x + 10)^2 - 100$

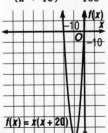

d. vertex: $(-10, 100)$; $x = -10$; $x + 20 = 10$

The numbers are 10 and -10.

6. a. $50,000 - 5000p$　　**b.** $0.40 + 0.10p$

c. $I(p) = (50,000 - 5000p)(0.40 + 0.10p)$

$$= 20,000 + 3000p - 500p^2$$

$$= -500(p^2 - 6p) + 20,000$$

$$= -500(p^2 - 6p + 9) + 20,000 + 4500$$

$$= -500(p - 3)^2 + 24,500$$

d.

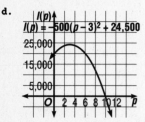

e. vertex: $(3, 24,500)$; $p = 3$

$0.40 + 0.10p = 0.40 + 0.10(3)$

$= 0.70$　　　　　　70¢ per copy

PAGES 376-378　　EXERCISES

7. Let x = one number.

Then $36 - x$ = the other number.

$g = x(36 - x)$

$$= 36x - x^2$$

$$= -(x^2 - 36x + 18^2) + 18^2$$

$$= -(x - 18)^2 + 324$$

The vertex is $(18, 324)$. The product is maximized when $x = 18$. So $36 - x$ is 18. The two numbers are 18 and 18.

8. Let x = one number.

Then $x - 40$ = the other number.

$y = x(x - 40)$

$$= (x^2 - 40x + 20^2) - 20^2$$

$$= (x - 20)^2 - 400$$

The vertex is $(20, 400)$. The product is minimized when $x = 20$. So $x - 40$ is -20. The two numbers are -20 and 20.

9. Let x = one number.

Then $37 - x$ = the other number.

$y = x(37 - x)$

$$= -x^2 + 37x$$

$$= -\left[x^2 - 37x + \left(\frac{37}{2}\right)^2\right] + \left(\frac{37}{2}\right)^2$$

$$= -\left(x - \frac{37}{2}\right)^2 + \frac{1369}{4}$$

The vertex is $\left(\frac{37}{2}, \frac{1369}{4}\right)$. The product is maximized when $x = \frac{37}{2}$. So $37 - x$ is $\frac{37}{2}$. The two numbers are $\frac{37}{2}$ and $\frac{37}{2}$.

10. Let x = one number.

Then $x + 25$ = the other number.

$y = x(x + 25)$

$$= x^2 + 25x + \left(\frac{25}{2}\right)^2 - \left(\frac{25}{2}\right)^2$$

$$= \left(x + \frac{25}{2}\right)^2 - \frac{625}{4}$$

The vertex is $\left(-\frac{25}{2}, -\frac{625}{4}\right)$. The product is minimized when $x = -\frac{25}{2}$. So $x + 25$ is $\frac{25}{2}$. The two numbers are $-\frac{25}{2}$ and $\frac{25}{2}$.

11. Let x = one number.

Then $y = -16 - x$.

$f(x) = x(-16 - x)$

$$= -x^2 - 16x$$

$$= -(x^2 + 16x + 64) + 64$$

$$= -(x + 8)^2 + 64$$

The vertex is $(-8, 64)$. The product is maximized when $x = -8$. So $-16 - x$ is -8. The two numbers are -8 and -8.

12. Let ℓ = the length.

Then $20 - \ell$ = the width.

$A = \ell(20 - \ell)$

$$= 20\ell - \ell^2$$

$$= -(\ell^2 - 20\ell + 10^2) + 10^2$$

$$= -(\ell - 10)^2 + 100$$

The vertex is $(10, 100)$. The product is maximized when $\ell = 10$. So $20 - \ell$ is 10. The dimensions are 10 m by 10 m.

13. Let ℓ = the length.

Then $12 - \ell$ = the width.

$A = \ell(12 - \ell)$

$$= 12\ell - \ell^2$$

$$= -(\ell^2 - 12\ell + 6^2) + 6^2$$

$$= -(\ell - 6)^2 + 36$$

The vertex is $(6, 36)$. The product is maximized when $\ell = 6$. So $12 - \ell$ is 6. The dimensions are 6 in. by 6 in. The maximum area is 36 sq in.

14. Let ℓ = the length.

Then $80 - \ell$ = the width.

$A = \ell(80 - \ell)$

$$= 80\ell - \ell^2$$

$$= -(\ell^2 - 80\ell + 40^2) + 40^2$$

$$= -(\ell - 40)^2 + 1600$$

The vertex is $(40, 1600)$. The product is maximized when $\ell = 40$. So $80 - \ell$ is 40. The length is 40 feet and the width is 40 feet.

15. Let ℓ = the length.

Then $60 - \frac{1}{2}\ell$ = the width.

$$A = \ell\left(60 - \frac{1}{2}\ell\right)$$

$$= 60\ell - \frac{1}{2}\ell^2$$

$$= -\frac{1}{2}(\ell^2 - 120\ell + 60^2) + \frac{1}{2}(60^2)$$

$$= -\frac{1}{2}(\ell - 60)^2 + 1800$$

The vertex is (60, 1800). The product is maximized when ℓ = 60. So $60 - \frac{1}{2}\ell$ is 30. The length is 60 feet and the width is 30 feet.

16. Let x = the number of $1 increases.

Then, $8 + x$ = most profitable charge.

And, $300 - 20x$ = number of fares sold.

$$y = (x + 8)(300 - 20x)$$

$$= -20x^2 + 140x + 2400$$

$$= -20\left(x^2 - 7x + \left(\frac{7}{2}\right)^2\right) + 2400 + 20\left(\frac{7}{2}\right)^2$$

$$= -20\left(x - \frac{7}{2}\right)^2 + 2645$$

The vertex is $\left(\frac{7}{2}, 2645\right)$. The product is maximized

when $x = \frac{7}{2}$. So $8 + x$ is $11\frac{1}{2}$. The most profitable

charge would be $11.50.

17. Let x = number of $5 increases.

Then, $300 + 5x$ = ticket price.

And, $800 - 10x$ = number of tickets sold.

$$y = (800 - 10x)(300 + 5x)$$

$$= -50x^2 + 1000x + 240,000$$

$$= -50(x^2 - 20x + 10^2) + 140,000 + 50(10^2)$$

$$= -50(x - 10)^2 + 245,000$$

The vertex is (10, 245,000). The product is maximized when x = 10. So $300 + 5x$ is 350. The price to maximize their income would be $350.

18. $h(t) = -16t^2 + 80t + 200$

$$= -16(t^2 - 5t) + 200$$

$$= -16\left(t^2 - 5t + \left(\frac{5}{2}\right)^2\right) + 200 + 16\left(\frac{5}{2}\right)^2$$

$$= -16(t - 2.5)^2 + 300$$

The vertex is (2.5, 300). The product is maximized when x = 2.5. The maximum height is 300 feet and this is reached in 2.5 seconds.

19. Let x = the number of $0.20 increases.

Then, $3 + 0.20x$ = admission price.

And, $500 - 25x$ = number of people attending.

$$y = (500 - 25x)(3 + 0.20x)$$

$$= 1500 + 25x - 5x^2$$

$$= -5(x^2 - 5x) + 1500$$

$$= -5\left(x^2 - 5x + \left(\frac{5}{2}\right)^2\right) + 1500 + 5\left(\frac{5}{2}\right)^2$$

$$= -5(x - 2.5)^2 + 1531.25$$

The vertex is (2.5, 1531.25). The profit is maximized when x = 2.5. So, $3 + 0.20x$ is 3.50. The price to maximize their income would be $3.50.

20. profit = income − cost

$$y = (300 - 2x)x - (20x + 1000)$$

$$= 300x - 2x^2 - 20x - 1000$$

$$= -2x^2 + 280x - 1000$$

$$= -2(x^2 - 140x + 70^2) - 1000 + 9800$$

$$= -2(x - 70)^2 + 8800$$

The vertex is (70, 8800). The profit is maximized when x = 70. So they should sell 70 fans each month to maximize profit.

21. Let ℓ = the length of the box.

Then $25 - \ell$ = the width of the box.

$$V = 5(\ell)(25 - \ell)$$

$$= 125\ell - 5\ell^2$$

$$= -5\left(\ell^2 - 25\ell + \left(\frac{25}{2}\right)^2\right) + 5\left(\frac{25}{2}\right)^2$$

$$= -5(\ell - 12.5)^2 + \frac{3125}{4}$$

The vertex is (12.5, 781.25). The product is maximized when ℓ = 12.5. So $25 - \ell$ is 12.5. The length is 12.5 cm, the width is 12.5 cm, and the height is 5 cm.

22. Let w = the width of the inscribed rectangle.

Then, $10 - \frac{5}{4}w$ = the length of the inscribed

rectangle.

$$A = w\left(10 - \frac{5}{4}w\right)$$

$$= 10w - \frac{5}{4}w^2$$

$$= -\frac{5}{4}(w^2 - 8w + 16) + 20$$

$$= -\frac{5}{4}(w - 4)^2 + 20$$

The vertex is (4, 20). The product is maximized

when w = 4. So, $10 - \frac{5}{4}w$ = 5. The length of the

inscribed rectangle is 5 inches.

23. Let x = width of the rectangle.

   Then, $x + 2$ = length of the rectangle.

   And, $7 - x$ = length of the side of the square.

   $g = x(x + 2) + (7 - x)^2$

   $= 2x^2 - 12x + 49$

   $= 2(x^2 - 6x + 9) + 49 - 2(9)$

   $= 2(x - 3)^2 + 31$

   The vertex is (3, 31). The product is minimized when $x = 3$.

   length of wire = $2(x) + 2(x + 2)$

   $= 2(3) + 2(3 + 2)$

   $= 16$

   The wire should be 16 in.

24. Let x = number of 25¢ increases.

   Then $2.00 + 0.25x$ = new price.

   And, $200 - 10x$ = number of tickets sold.

   $I = (2.00 + 0.25x)(200 - 10x)$

   $= 400 + 30x - 2.5x^2$

   $= -2.5(x^2 - 12x + 36) + 400 + 2.5(36)$

   $= -2.5(x - 6)^2 + 490$

   The vertex is (6, 490). The product is maximized when $x = 6$.

   $l = 2.00 + 0.25(6)$

   $= 3.50$

   The ticket price that will maximize the income is $3.50.

25. $h(t) = 64t - 16t^2$

   $h(1.5) = 64(1.5) - 16(1.5)^2$

   $= 60$

   The height after 1.5 seconds is 60 feet.

   $h(t) = 64t - 16t^2$

   $= -16(t^2 - 4t + 2^2) + 16(2^2)$

   $= -16(t - 2)^2 + 64$

   The vertex is (2, 64). The maximum height is 64 feet.

   $h(t) = 64t - 16t^2$

   $64t - 16t^2 = 0$

   $16t(4 - t) = 0$

   $t = 0$ or $4 - t = 0$

   $t = 4$

   It will return to the ground in 4 seconds.

26. profit = income - cost

   $y = (120 - 5x)(21 + 3x) - 75(21 + 3x)$

   $= 2520 + 255x - 15x^2 - 1575 - 225x$

   $= -15x^2 + 30x + 945$

   $= -15(x^2 - 2x + 1) + 945 + 15$

   $= -15(x - 1)^2 + 960$

   The vertex is (1, 960). The profit is maximized when $x = 1$. So, they should charge $120 - 5(1)$ or $115 for a camera. The maximum profit is $960.

27. Let x = one of the numbers.

   Then $a - x$ = the other number.

   $f(x) = x(a - x)$

   $= xa - x^2$

   $= -\left(x^2 - ax + \left(\frac{a}{2}\right)^2\right) + \left(\frac{a}{2}\right)^2$

   $= -\left(x - \frac{a}{2}\right)^2 + \frac{a^2}{4}$

   The vertex is $\left(\frac{a}{2}, \frac{a^2}{4}\right)$. The product is maximized when $x = \frac{a}{2}$. So, $a - x$ is $\frac{a}{2}$. The two numbers are $\frac{a}{2}$ and $\frac{a}{2}$.

28. a. 16 seconds   b. 1024 feet

   c. 4 and 12 seconds

29. a. 78 feet   b. between 5 and 6 seconds

   c. about 3 seconds   d. 126 feet

30.

n	$8^n \div 5$	remainder
1	1 R3	3
2	12 R4	4
3	102 R2	2
4	819 R1	1
5	6553 R3	3
6	52,428 R4	4
.	.	.
.	.	.
.	.	.

   The remainder of $8^{100} \div 5$ is 1.

31. $f(x) = (x - 3)^2$ 32. $x^2 - 8x + \left(\frac{8}{2}\right)^2$

   $c = \left(\frac{8}{2}\right)^2 = 16$

33. $(3 + 2i)(4 - i) = 12 - 3i + 8i - 2i^2$

   $= 12 + 5i + 2$

   $= 14 + 5i$

34. $9x^2 - 12x + 4 = (3x - 2)(3x - 2)$

   $= (3x - 2)^2$

35. Multiply first row by -4. Then add the second row to the first row.

184

1. Broken; the points on the boundary do not satisfy the inequality.

2. above; Answers may vary. A typical answer is that a test point, such as (2, 0), inside the parabola satisfies the inequality.

3. Lengths and areas cannot be negative.

4. $y \overset{?}{>} x^2$

   $2 \overset{?}{>} 3^2$

   $2 \not> 9$ no

5. $y \overset{?}{>} (x - 2)^2$

   $5 \overset{?}{>} (0 - 2)^2$

   $5 > 4$ yes

6. $y \overset{?}{\geq} x^2 - 16$

   $0 \overset{?}{\geq} (-3)^2 - 16$

   $0 \geq -7$ yes

7. $y \overset{?}{\leq} -3x^2 + 5$

   $-7 \overset{?}{\leq} -3(2)^2 + 5$

   $-7 \leq -7$ yes

8. $y \overset{?}{\leq} 2(x + 3)^2$

   $3 \overset{?}{\leq} 2(-2 + 3)^2$

   $3 \not\leq 2$ no

9. $y \overset{?}{\geq} 5x^2 - 6x$

   $1 \overset{?}{\geq} 5(1) - 6(1)$

   $1 \geq -1$ yes

10. $y \overset{?}{\geq} 4x^2 - 8x - 13$

    $-1 \overset{?}{\geq} 4(3)^2 - 8(3) - 13$

    $-1 \overset{?}{\geq} 36 - 24 - 13$

    $-1 \geq -1$ yes

11. $y \overset{?}{<} -0.5x^2 + 9x - 2$

    $15 \overset{?}{<} -0.5(16)^2 + 9(16) - 2$

    $15 \overset{?}{<} -128 + 144 - 2$

    $15 \not< 14$ no

12.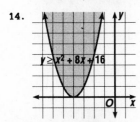

13.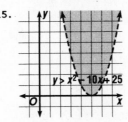

14.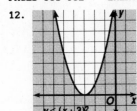

15.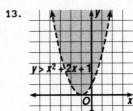

16.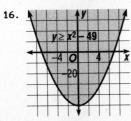

17.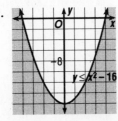

18.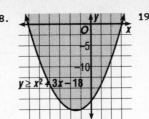

19.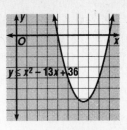

20.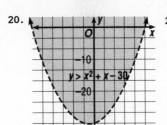

21.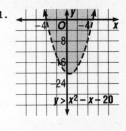

22.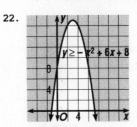

23.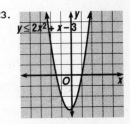

24.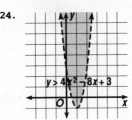

25.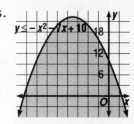

26.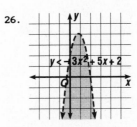

27.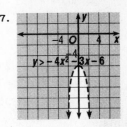

28. Let w = the width.

$$w(w + 5) > 104$$

$$w^2 + 5w - 104 > 0$$

$$\left(w^2 + 5w + \left(\frac{5}{2}\right)^2\right) - 104 - \frac{25}{4} > 0$$

$$(w + 2.5)^2 - 110.25 > 0$$

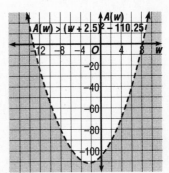

The width is greater than 8 centimeters.

29.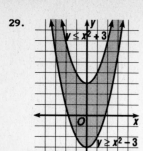

$y \le x^2 + 3$

$y \ge x^2 - 3$

30. Use the function to determine if the bullet can reach a height of 7000 ft.

31. $f(x) = -0.003x^2 + x + 4$

$30 \overset{?}{=} -0.003(410)^2 + 410 + 4$

$30 \ne -90.3$

By substituting values for x and $f(x)$, we see that the ball does not hit the scoreboard. By graphing, we see that the ball hits the ground about 337 feet from the plate.

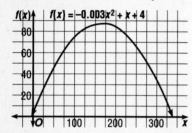

$f(x) = -0.003x^2 + x + 4$

32. Let x = the number of passengers over 100.

Then $5 - 0.02x$ = the new price.

And $100 + x$ = number of passengers.

$I = (100 + x)(5 - 0.02x)$

$\quad = 500 + 3x - 0.02x^2$

$\quad = -0.02(x^2 - 150x + 75^2) + 500 + 112.5$

$\quad = -0.02(x - 75) + 612.5$

The vertex is (75, 612.5). The profit is maximized when $x = 75$. So, $100 + x$ is 175. 175 passengers will produce a maximum profit.

33. Let x = one of the numbers.

Then $x + 40$ = the other number.

product = $x(x + 40)$

$\quad = x^2 + 40x$

$\quad = (x^2 + 40x + 20^2) - 400$

$\quad = (x + 20)^2 - 400$

The vertex is (-20, -400). So, $x = -20$ and $x + 40 = 20$. The two numbers are 20 and -20.

34. $y = \dfrac{16 \pm \sqrt{16^2 - 4(1)(10)}}{2(1)}$

$\quad = \dfrac{16 \pm \sqrt{216}}{2}$

$\quad = \dfrac{16 \pm 6\sqrt{6}}{2}$

$\quad = 8 \pm 3\sqrt{6}$

35. $\sqrt{\dfrac{8}{9}} = \dfrac{\sqrt{8}}{\sqrt{9}}$

$\quad = \dfrac{\sqrt{2 \cdot 2 \cdot 2}}{\sqrt{3 \cdot 3}}$

$\quad = \dfrac{2\sqrt{2}}{3}$

36. $(1.428 \times 10^9) - (1.08 \times 10^8) = 1.32 \times 10^9$

1.32×10^9 kilometers

8-7 Solving Quadratic Inequalities

PAGES 385–386   CHECKING FOR UNDERSTANDING

1. Sample answer: to undercut the competition

2. $\{x \mid x < -5 \text{ or } x > 3\}$

3. Sample answer: any number less than -8, any number greater than 10, and any number between -8 and 10

4. one > 0 and one < 0   **5.** both > 0 or both < 0

6. both > 0 or both < 0   **7.** one ≥ 0 and one ≤ 0

8. one > 0 and one < 0   **9.** both > 0 or both < 0

10. one ≥ 0 and one ≤ 0   **11.** one ≥ 0 and one ≤ 0

12. both > 0 or both < 0   **13.** one ≥ 0 and one ≤ 0

14. $\{x \mid -1 < x < 1\}$ **15.** $\{x \mid x \le 3 \text{ or } x \ge 6\}$

16. ø

PAGES 386–387   EXERCISES

17. $(x + 2)(x + 9) > 0$

$x + 2 > 0$ and $x + 9 > 0$ or $x + 2 < 0$ and $x + 9 < 0$

$\quad x > -2$ and $x > -9$ or $x < -2$ and $x < -9$

$\qquad\qquad x > -2$ or $x < -9$

$\qquad\qquad \{x \mid x > -2 \text{ or } x < -9\}$

18. $(a - 10)(a - 3) \le 0$

$a - 10 \le 0$ and $a - 3 \ge 0$ or $a - 10 \ge 0$ and $a - 3 \le 0$

$\quad a \le 10$ and $a \ge 3$ or $a \ge 10$ and $a \le 3$

$\qquad\quad 3 \le a \le 10$ never true

$\qquad\qquad \{a \mid 3 \le a \le 10\}$

19. $(n - 2.5)(n + 3.8) \ge 0$

$n - 2.5 \ge 0$ and $n + 3.8 \ge 0$

$\quad n \ge 2.5$ and $n \ge -3.8$

$\quad n \ge 2.5$

$\qquad$ or

$n - 2.5 \le 0$ and $n + 3.8 \le 0$

$\quad n \le 2.5$ and $n \le -3.8$

$\quad n \le -3.8$

$\{n \mid n \ge 2.5 \text{ or } n \le -3.8\}$

20. $x^2 + 4x - 21 < 0$

$(x - 3)(x + 7) < 0$

$x - 3 < 0$ and $x + 7 > 0$ or $x - 3 > 0$ and $x + 7 < 0$

$x < 3$ and $x > -7$ or $x > 3$ and $x < -7$

$-7 < x < 3$ never true

$\{x \mid -7 < x < 3\}$

21. $q^2 + 2q \geq 24$

$q^2 + 2q - 24 \geq 0$

$(q + 6)(q - 4) \geq 0$

$q + 6 \geq 0$ and $q - 4 \geq 0$ or $q + 6 \leq 0$ and $q - 4 \leq 0$

$q \geq -6$ and $q \geq 4$ or $q \leq -6$ and $q \leq 4$

$q \geq 4$ or $q \leq -6$

$\{q \mid q \geq 4$ or $q \leq -6\}$

22. $m^2 + m - 6 > 0$

$(m + 3)(m - 2) > 0$

$m + 3 > 0$ and $m - 2 > 0$ or $m + 3 < 0$ and $m - 2 < 0$

$m > -3$ and $m > 2$ or $m < -3$ and $m < 2$

$m > 2$ or $m < -3$

$\{m \mid m > 2$ or $m < -3\}$

23. $2b^2 - b < 6$

$2b^2 - b - 6 < 0$

$(2b + 3)(b - 2) < 0$

$2b + 3 < 0$ and $b - 2 > 0$ or $2b + 3 > 0$ and $b - 2 < 0$

$b < -\dfrac{3}{2}$ and $b > 2$ or $b > -\dfrac{3}{2}$ and $b < 2$

never true $-\dfrac{3}{2} < b < 2$

$\left\{ b \mid -\dfrac{3}{2} < b < 2 \right\}$

24. $6s^2 + 5s > 4$

$6s^2 + 5s - 4 > 0$

$(3s + 4)(2s - 1) > 0$

$3s + 4 > 0$ and $25 - 1 > 0$

$s > -\dfrac{4}{3}$ and $s > \dfrac{1}{2}$

$s > \dfrac{1}{2}$

or

$3s + 4 < 0$ and $2s - 1 < 0$

$s < -\dfrac{4}{3}$ and $s < \dfrac{1}{2}$

$s < -\dfrac{4}{3}$

$\left\{ s \mid s < -\dfrac{4}{3}$ or $s > \dfrac{1}{2} \right\}$

25. $p^2 - 4p \leq 5$

$p^2 - 4p - 5 \leq 0$

$(p - 5)(p + 1) \leq 0$

$p - 5 \leq 0$ and $p + 1 \geq 0$ or $p - 5 \geq 0$ and $p + 1 \leq 0$

$p \leq 5$ and $p \geq -1$ or $p \geq 5$ and $p \leq -1$

$-1 \leq p \leq 5$ never true

$\{p \mid -1 \leq p \leq 5\}$

26. $x^2 - 4x \leq 0$

$x(x - 4) \leq 0$

$x \leq 0$ and $x - 4 \geq 0$ or $x \geq 0$ and $x - 4 \leq 0$

$x \geq 4$ $x \leq 4$

never true $0 \leq x \leq 4$

$\{x \mid 0 \leq x \leq 4\}$

27. $w^2 \geq 2w$

$w^2 - 2w \geq 0$

$w(w - 2) \geq 0$

$w \geq 0$ and $w - 2 \geq 0$ or $w \leq 0$ and $w - 2 \leq 0$

$w \geq 2$ $w \leq 2$

$w \geq 2$ or $w \leq 0$

$\{w \mid w \geq 2$ or $w \leq 0\}$

28. $c^2 \leq 49$

$c^2 - 49 \leq 0$

$(c - 7)(c + 7) \leq 0$

$c - 7 \leq 0$ and $c + 7 \geq 0$ or $c - 7 \geq 0$ and $c + 7 \leq 0$

$c \leq 7$ and $c \geq -7$ or $c \geq 7$ and $c \leq -7$

$-7 \leq c \leq 7$ never true

$\{c \mid -7 \leq c \leq 7\}$

29. $d^2 \geq 3d + 28$

$d^2 - 3d - 28 \geq 0$

$(d - 7)(d + 4) \geq 0$

$d - 7 \geq 0$ and $d + 4 \geq 0$ or $d - 7 \leq 0$ and $d + 4 \leq 0$

$d \geq 7$ and $d \geq -4$ or $d \leq 7$ and $d \leq -4$

$d \geq 7$ or $d \leq -4$

$\{d \mid d \geq 7$ or $d \leq -4\}$

30. $b^2 \geq 10b - 25$

$b^2 - 10b + 25 \geq 0$

$(b - 5)(b - 5) \geq 0$

$b - 5 \geq 0$ and $b - 5 \geq 0$ or $b - 5 \leq 0$ and $b - 5 \leq 0$

$b \geq 5$ or $b \leq 5$

$\{$all reals$\}$

31. $2x^2 > 25$

$2x^2 - 25 > 0$

$\left(x - \dfrac{5\sqrt{2}}{2} \right)\left(x + \dfrac{5\sqrt{2}}{2} \right) > 0$

$x - \dfrac{5\sqrt{2}}{2} > 0$ and $x + \dfrac{5\sqrt{2}}{2} > 0$

$x > \dfrac{5\sqrt{2}}{2}$ and $x > -\dfrac{5\sqrt{2}}{2}$

$x > \dfrac{5\sqrt{2}}{2}$

or

$x - \dfrac{5\sqrt{2}}{2} < 0$ and $x + \dfrac{5\sqrt{2}}{2} < 0$

$x < \dfrac{5\sqrt{2}}{2}$ and $x < -\dfrac{5\sqrt{2}}{2}$

$x < -\dfrac{5\sqrt{2}}{2}$

$\left\{ x \mid x > \dfrac{5\sqrt{2}}{2}$ or $x < -\dfrac{5\sqrt{2}}{2} \right\}$

32.　　$t^2 + 12t \le -27$

$t^2 + 12t + 27 \le 0$

$(t + 9)(t + 3) \le 0$

$t + 9 \le 0$ and $t + 3 \ge 0$ or $t + 9 \ge 0$ and $t + 3 \le 0$

　$t \le -9$　and $t \ge -3$　or　$t \ge -9$　and $t \le -3$

　　never true　　　　　　　$-9 \le t \le -3$

$\{t \mid -9 \le t \le -3\}$

33.　$f^2 + 12f + 36 < 0$

$(f + 6)(f + 6) < 0$

$f + 6 < 0$ and $f + 6 > 0$ or $f + 6 > 0$ and $f + 6 < 0$

　$f < -6$　and $f > -6$　or $f > -6$　and $f < -6$

　　never true　　　　　　　never true

　　　　　　　　　$\varnothing$

34.　　　　$9v^2 - 6v + 1 \le 0$

$(3v - 1)(3v - 1) \le 0$

$3v - 1 \le 0$ and $3v - 1 \ge 0$

　$v \le \frac{1}{3}$　and　$v \ge \frac{1}{3}$

　　　$v = \frac{1}{3}$

　　　or

$3v - 1 \ge 0$ and $3v - 1 \le 0$

　$v \ge \frac{1}{3}$　and　$v \le \frac{1}{3}$

　　　$v = \frac{1}{3}$

　　$\left\{v \mid v = \frac{1}{3}\right\}$

35.　　　$8d + d^2 \ge -16$

$d^2 + 8d + 16 \ge 0$

$(d + 4)(d + 4) \ge 0$

$d + 4 \ge 0$ and $d + 4 \ge 0$ or $d + 4 \le 0$ and $d + 4 \le 0$

　　　$d \ge -4$　or　$d \le -4$

　　　$\{\text{all reals}\}$

36.　　　$2g^2 - 5g - 3 < 0$

$(2g + 1)(g - 3) < 0$

$2g + 1 < 0$ and $g - 3 > 0$

　$g < -\frac{1}{2}$　and　$g > 3$

　　　never true

　　　or

$2g + 1 > 0$ and $g - 3 < 0$

　$g > -\frac{1}{2}$　and　$g < 3$

　　　$-\frac{1}{2} < g < 3$

　$\left\{g \mid -\frac{1}{2} < g < 3\right\}$

37.　　　　$-5x - 3x^2 < -2$

$3x^2 + 5x - 2 > 0$

$(3x - 1)(x + 2) > 0$

$3x - 1 > 0$ and $x + 2 > 0$

　$x > \frac{1}{3}$　and　$x > -2$

　　　$x > \frac{1}{3}$

　　　or

$3x - 1 < 0$ and $x + 2 < 0$

　$x < \frac{1}{3}$　and　$x < -2$

　　　$x < -2$

　$\left\{x \mid x > \frac{1}{3} \text{ or } x < -2\right\}$

38.　　　　$n^2 \le 3$

$n^2 - 3 \le 0$

$(n - \sqrt{3})(n + \sqrt{3}) \le 0$

$n - \sqrt{3} \le 0$ and $n + \sqrt{3} \ge 0$

　$n \le \sqrt{3}$　and　$n \ge -\sqrt{3}$

　　$-\sqrt{3} \le n \le \sqrt{3}$

　　　or

$n - \sqrt{3} \ge 0$ and $n + \sqrt{3} \le 0$

　$n \ge \sqrt{3}$　and　$n \le -\sqrt{3}$

　　　never true

　　$\{n \mid -\sqrt{3} \le n \le \sqrt{3}\}$

39.　　$4t^2 - 9 < -4t$　　$t = \dfrac{-4 \pm \sqrt{4^2 - 4(4)(-9)}}{2(4)}$

$4t^2 + 4t - 9 < 0$　　　$= \dfrac{-4 \pm \sqrt{160}}{8}$

$4t^2 + 4t - 9 = 0$　　　$= \dfrac{-1 \pm \sqrt{10}}{2}$

$\left(t - \dfrac{-1 + \sqrt{10}}{2}\right)\left(t - \dfrac{-1 - \sqrt{10}}{2}\right) < 0$

$t - \dfrac{-1 + \sqrt{10}}{2} < 0$ and $t - \dfrac{-1 - \sqrt{10}}{2} > 0$

　$t < \dfrac{-1 + \sqrt{10}}{2}$ and $t > \dfrac{-1 - \sqrt{10}}{2}$

　　$\dfrac{-1 - \sqrt{10}}{2} < t < \dfrac{-1 + \sqrt{10}}{2}$

　　　or

$t - \dfrac{-1 + \sqrt{10}}{2} > 0$ and $t - \dfrac{-1 - \sqrt{10}}{2} < 0$

　$t > \dfrac{-1 + \sqrt{10}}{2}$ and $t < \dfrac{-1 - \sqrt{10}}{2}$

　　　never true

　$\left\{t \mid \dfrac{-1 - \sqrt{10}}{2} < t < \dfrac{-1 + \sqrt{10}}{2}\right\}$

40. $-2 > -6r - 9r^2$ $r = \dfrac{-6 \pm \sqrt{6^2 - 4(9)(-2)}}{2(9)}$

$9r^2 + 6r - 2 > 0$ $= \dfrac{-6 \pm \sqrt{108}}{18}$

$9r^2 + 6r - 2 = 0$ $= \dfrac{-1 \pm \sqrt{3}}{3}$

$\left(r - \dfrac{-1 + \sqrt{3}}{3}\right)\left(r - \dfrac{-1 - \sqrt{3}}{3}\right) > 0$

$r - \dfrac{-1 + \sqrt{3}}{3} > 0$ and $r - \dfrac{-1 - \sqrt{3}}{3} > 0$

$r > \dfrac{-1 + \sqrt{3}}{3}$ and $r > \dfrac{-1 - \sqrt{3}}{3}$

$r > \dfrac{-1 + \sqrt{3}}{3}$

or

$r - \dfrac{-1 + \sqrt{3}}{3} < 0$ and $r - \dfrac{-1 - \sqrt{3}}{3} < 0$

$r < \dfrac{-1 + \sqrt{3}}{3}$ and $r < \dfrac{-1 - \sqrt{3}}{3}$

$r < \dfrac{-1 - \sqrt{3}}{3}$

$\left\{r \middle| r > \dfrac{-1 + \sqrt{3}}{3} \text{ or } r < \dfrac{-1 - \sqrt{3}}{3}\right\}$

41. $(x - 1)(x - 3)(x + 4) > 0$

$x - 1 > 0$ and $x - 3 > 0$ and $x + 4 > 0$

$x > 1$ and $x > 3$ and $x > -4$

$x > 3$

$x - 1 > 0$ and $x - 3 < 0$ and $x + 4 < 0$

$x > 1$ and $x < 3$ and $x < -4$;

never true

$x - 1 < 0$ and $x - 3 > 0$ and $x + 4 < 0$

$x < 1$ and $x > 3$ and $x < -4$;

never true

$x - 1 < 0$ and $x - 3 < 0$ and $x + 4 > 0$

$x < 1$ and $x < 3$ and $x > -4$;

$-4 < x < 1$

$\{x \mid -4 < x < 1 \text{ or } x > 3\}$

42. $(x - 8)(x + 2)(x + 4) \le 0$

$x - 8 \le 0$ and $x + 2 \le 0$ and $x + 4 \le 0$

$x \le 8$ and $x \le -2$ and $x \le -4$;

$x \le -4$

$x - 8 \le 0$ and $x + 2 \ge 0$ and $x + 4 \ge 0$

$x \le 8$ and $x \ge -2$ and $x \ge -4$;

$-2 \le x \le 8$

$x - 8 \ge 0$ and $x + 2 \le 0$ and $x + 4 \ge 0$

$x \ge 8$ and $x \le -2$ and $x \ge -4$;

never true

$x - 8 \ge 0$ and $x + 2 \ge 0$ and $x + 4 \le 0$

$x \ge 8$ and $x \ge -2$ and $x \le -4$;

never true

$\{x \mid x \le -4 \text{ or } -2 \le x \le 8\}$

43. $(x - 3)(x + 6)(x + 2) < 0$

$x - 3 < 0$ and $x + 6 < 0$ and $x + 2 < 0$

$x < 3$ and $x < -6$ and $x < -2$

$x < -6$

$x - 3 < 0$ and $x + 6 > 0$ and $x + 2 > 0$

$x < 3$ and $x > -6$ and $x > -2$;

$-2 < x < 3$

$x - 3 > 0$ and $x + 6 < 0$ and $x + 2 > 0$

$x > 3$ and $x < -6$ and $x > -2$;

never true

$x - 3 > 0$ and $x + 6 > 0$ and $x + 2 < 0$

$x > 3$ and $x > -6$ and $x < -2$;

never true

$\{x \mid x < -6 \text{ or } -2 < x < 3\}$

44. $(x + 5)(x + 6)(x + 7) \ge 0$

$x + 5 \ge 0$ and $x + 6 \ge 0$ and $x + 7 \ge 0$

$x \ge -5$ and $x \ge -6$ and $x \ge -7$

$x \ge -5$

$x + 5 \le 0$ and $x + 6 \le 0$ and $x + 7 \ge 0$

$x \le -5$ and $x \le -6$ and $x \ge -7$;

$-7 \le x \le -6$

$x + 5 \le 0$ and $x + 6 \ge 0$ and $x + 7 \ge 0$

$x \le -5$ and $x \ge -6$ and $x \ge -7$;

never true

$x + 5 \ge 0$ and $x + 6 \le 0$ and $x + 7 \le 0$

$x \ge -5$ and $x \le -6$ and $x \le -7$;

never true

$\{x \mid x \ge -5 \text{ or } -7 \le x \le -6\}$

45. $(x + 5)(x + 1)(x - 4)(x - 6) > 0$

$x + 5 > 0$ and $x + 1 > 0$ and $x - 4 > 0$ and $x - 6 > 0$

$\quad x > -5$ and $\quad x > -1$ and $\quad x > 4$ and $\quad x > 6$;

$$x > 6$$

$x + 5 > 0$ and $x + 1 > 0$ and $x - 4 < 0$ and $x - 6 < 0$

$\quad x > -5$ and $\quad x > -1$ and $\quad x < 4$ and $\quad x < 6$;

$$-1 < x < 4$$

$x + 5 > 0$ and $x + 1 < 0$ and $x - 4 > 0$ and $x - 6 < 0$

$\quad x > -5$ and $\quad x < -1$ and $\quad x > 4$ and $\quad x < 6$;

never true

$x + 5 > 0$ and $x + 1 < 0$ and $x - 4 < 0$ and $x - 6 > 0$

$\quad x > -5$ and $\quad x < -1$ and $\quad x < 4$ and $\quad x > 6$;

never true

$x + 5 < 0$ and $x + 1 > 0$ and $x - 4 > 0$ and $x - 6 < 0$

$\quad x < -5$ and $\quad x > -1$ and $\quad x > 4$ and $\quad x < 6$;

never true

$x + 5 < 0$ and $x + 1 > 0$ and $x - 4 < 0$ and $x - 6 > 0$

$\quad x < -5$ and $\quad x > -1$ and $\quad x < 4$ and $\quad x > 6$;

never true

$x + 5 < 0$ and $x + 1 < 0$ and $x - 4 > 0$ and $x - 6 > 0$

$\quad x < -5$ and $\quad x < -1$ and $\quad x > 4$ and $\quad x > 6$;

never true

$x + 5 < 0$ and $x + 1 < 0$ and $x - 4 < 0$ and $x - 6 < 0$

$\quad x < -5$ and $\quad x < -1$ and $\quad x < 4$ and $\quad x < 6$;

$$x < -5$$

$\{x \mid x < -5 \text{ or } -1 < x < 4 \text{ or } x > 6\}$

46. $(x - 2)(x + 2)(x - 1)(x + 3) \geq 0$

$x - 2 \geq 0$ and $x + 2 \geq 0$ and $x - 1 \geq 0$ and $x + 3 \geq 0$

$\quad x \geq 2$ and $\quad x \geq -2$ and $\quad x \geq 1$ and $\quad x \geq -3$;

$$x \geq 2$$

$x - 2 \geq 0$ and $x + 2 \geq 0$ and $x - 1 \leq 0$ and $x + 3 \leq 0$

$\quad x \geq 2$ and $\quad x \geq -2$ and $\quad x \leq 1$ and $\quad x \leq -3$;

never true

$x - 2 \geq 0$ and $x + 2 \leq 0$ and $x - 1 \geq 0$ and $x + 3 \leq 0$

$\quad x \geq 2$ and $\quad x \leq -2$ and $\quad x \geq 1$ and $\quad x \leq -3$;

never true

$x - 2 \geq 0$ and $x + 2 \leq 0$ and $x - 1 \leq 0$ and $x + 3 \geq 0$

$\quad x \geq 2$ and $\quad x \leq -2$ and $\quad x \leq 1$ and $\quad x \geq -3$;

never true

$x - 2 \leq 0$ and $x + 2 \geq 0$ and $x - 1 \geq 0$ and $x + 3 \leq 0$

$\quad x \leq 2$ and $\quad x \geq -2$ and $\quad x \geq 1$ and $\quad x \leq -3$;

never true

$x - 2 \leq 0$ and $x + 2 \geq 0$ and $x - 1 \leq 0$ and $x + 3 \geq 0$

$\quad x \leq 2$ and $\quad x \geq -2$ and $\quad x \leq 1$ and $\quad x \geq -3$;

$$-2 \leq x \leq 1$$

$x - 2 \leq 0$ and $x + 2 \leq 0$ and $x - 1 \geq 0$ and $x + 3 \geq 0$

$\quad x \leq 2$ and $\quad x \leq -2$ and $\quad x \geq 1$ and $\quad x \geq -3$;

never true

$x - 2 \leq 0$ and $x + 2 \leq 0$ and $x - 1 \leq 0$ and $x + 3 \leq 0$

$\quad x \leq 2$ and $\quad x \leq -2$ and $\quad x \leq 1$ and $\quad x \leq -3$;

$$x \leq -3$$

$\{x \mid x \leq -3 \text{ or } -2 \leq x \leq 1 \text{ or } x \geq 2\}$

47. $h(t) = -16t^2 + 65t$

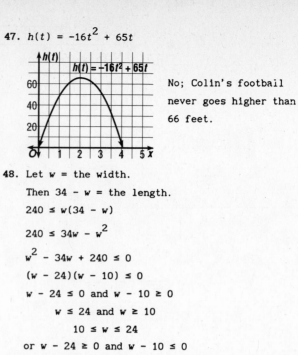

No; Colin's football never goes higher than 66 feet.

48. Let w = the width.

Then $34 - w$ = the length.

$240 \leq w(34 - w)$

$240 \leq 34w - w^2$

$w^2 - 34w + 240 \leq 0$

$(w - 24)(w - 10) \leq 0$

$w - 24 \leq 0$ and $w - 10 \geq 0$

$\quad w \leq 24$ and $w \geq 10$

$$10 \leq w \leq 24$$

or $w - 24 \geq 0$ and $w - 10 \leq 0$

$w \geq 24$ and $w \leq 10$

never true

The width of the garden can be between 10 and 24 feet.

49. Let n = number of fare decreases.

$66 \geq (100 + 5n)(1 - 0.20n)$

$66 \geq 100 - 15n - n^2$

$n^2 + 15n - 34 \geq 0$

$(n + 17)(n - 2) \geq 0$

$n + 17 \geq 0$ and $n - 2 \geq 0$ or $n + 17 \leq 0$ and $n - 2 \leq 0$

$\quad n \geq -17$ and $\quad n \geq 2 \quad$ or $\quad n \leq -17$ and $n \leq 2$

$\quad\quad n \geq -17 \quad\quad$ or $\quad\quad n \leq 2$

$\{n \mid -17 \leq n \leq 2\}$

Judy can make up to 2 decreases in fare.

50. $-4 \leq -(4^2) + 5(4)$

$-4 \leq -16 + 20$

$-4 \leq 4$

yes

51.

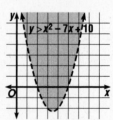

52. $f(x) = x^2 + 3x - 2$

quadratic term: x^2

linear term: $3x$

constant term: -2

53. $d^{\frac{1}{3}} = 4$

$\left(d^{\frac{1}{3}}\right)^3 = 4^3$

$d = 64$

54. $(\sqrt{3a} + \sqrt{2b})(\sqrt{15a} - \sqrt{3b})$

$= \sqrt{45a^2} - \sqrt{9ab} + \sqrt{30ab} - \sqrt{6b^2}$

$= 3a\sqrt{5} - 3\sqrt{ab} + \sqrt{30ab} - b\sqrt{6}$

55. $a^2 - b^2 + 8b - 16 = a^2 - (b^2 - 8b + 16)$

$\qquad\qquad\qquad = a^2 - (b - 4)^2$

$\qquad\qquad\qquad = [a - (b - 4)][a + (b - 4)]$

$\qquad\qquad\qquad = (a - b + 4)(a + b - 4)$

56. Let x = the ones' digit.

$\quad$ Let y = the tens' digit.

$\quad$ Let z = the hundreds' digit.

$\quad x + y + z = 13 \qquad\longrightarrow\qquad x + y + z = 13$

$\qquad y = x - 1 \qquad\longrightarrow\qquad -x + y = -1$

$\qquad z = 2(x + y) - 2 \longrightarrow 2x + 2y - z = 2$

$\quad$
$x + y + z = 13$	$x + y = 5$	$-x + y = -1$
$2x + 2y - z = 2$	$-x + y = -1$	$-x + 2 = -1$
$3x + 3y \quad = 15$	$2y = 4$	$-x = -3$
$x + y = 5$	$y = 2$	$x = 3$

$\quad x + y + z = 13$

$\quad 3 + 2 + z = 13$

$\qquad\qquad z = 8$ $\qquad$ The number is 823.

Chapter 8 Summary and Review

PAGES 388-390 $\qquad$ SKILLS AND CONCEPTS

1. $f(x) = (x + 2)^2$

$\qquad = x^2 + 4x + 4$

2. $h(x) = 2(x - 4)^2 + 6$

$\qquad = 2(x^2 - 8x + 16) + 6$

$\qquad = 2x^2 - 16x + 32 + 6$

$\qquad = 2x^2 - 16x + 38$

3. $3x^2$; $2x$; -1 $\qquad$ 4. x^2; $4x$; -2

5. $y = (x - 7)^2$ $\qquad$ 6. $y = x^2 + 6$

7. 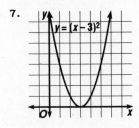 $\qquad$ 8.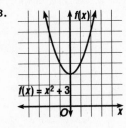

9. $f(x) = x^2 - 2x + 1$

$\qquad f(x) = (x - 1)^2$

$\qquad (1, 0)$; $x = 1$

10. $g(x) = x^2 + 6x + 3$

$\qquad = (x^2 + 6x + 9) + 3 - 9$

$\qquad g(x) = (x + 3)^2 - 6$

$\qquad (-3, -6)$; $x = -3$

11. $f(x) = x^2 - 2x + 4$

$\qquad = (x^2 - 2x + 1) + 4 - 1$

$\qquad f(x) = (x - 1)^2 + 3$

$\qquad (1, 3)$; $x = 1$; up

12. $h(x) = -3x^2 + 18x$

$\qquad = -3(x^2 - 6x + 9) + 27$

$\qquad h(x) = -3(x - 3)^2 + 27$

$\qquad (3, 27)$; $x = 3$; down

13. $f(x) = -2x^2 - 40x + 10$

$\qquad = -2(x^2 + 20x + 100) + 10 + 200$

$\qquad f(x) = -2(x + 10)^2 + 210$

$\qquad (-10, 210)$; $x = -10$; down

14. $g(x) = \frac{1}{3}x^2 + 2x + 7$

$\qquad = \frac{1}{3}(x^2 + 6x + 9) + 7 - 3$

$\qquad g(x) = \frac{1}{3}(x + 3)^2 + 4$

$\qquad (-3, 4)$; $x = -3$; up

15. Let x = one of the numbers.

$\quad$ Then $x - 5$ = the other number.

$\quad$ product = $x(x - 5)$

$\qquad = x^2 - 5x$

$\qquad = \left(x^2 - 5x + \left(\frac{5}{2}\right)^2\right) - \frac{25}{4}$

$\qquad = \left(x - \frac{5}{2}\right)^2 - \frac{25}{4}$

$\quad$ The vertex is $\left(\frac{5}{2}, -\frac{25}{4}\right)$. The product is maximized

$\quad$ when $x = \frac{5}{2}$. So, the two numbers are $\frac{5}{2}$ and $-\frac{5}{2}$.

16. Let w = the width. Then $40 - w$ = the length.

$\quad$ area = $(40 - w)w$

$\qquad = 40w - w^2$

$\qquad = -(w^2 - 40w + 400) + 400$

$\qquad = -(w - 20)^2 + 400$

$\quad$ The vertex is $(20, 400)$. The area is maximized

$\quad$ when $w = 20$. So, the dimensions are 20 cm $\times$

$\quad$ 20 cm, and the area is 400 cm^2.

17. $y > x^2 + 3x + 4$

$\quad y > \left(x^2 + 3x + \left(\frac{3}{2}\right)^2\right) + 4 - \frac{9}{4}$

$\quad y > \left(x + \frac{3}{2}\right)^2 + \frac{7}{4}$

18. $y < x^2 + 5x + 6$

$y < \left(x + 5x + \left(\frac{5}{2}\right)^2\right) + 6 - \frac{25}{4}$

$y < \left(x + \frac{5}{2}\right)^2 - \frac{1}{4}$

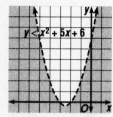

19.

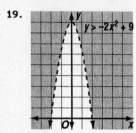

20. $y \geq 3x^2 - 15x + 22$

$y \geq 3\left(x^2 - 5x + \left(\frac{5}{2}\right)^2\right) + 22 - \frac{75}{4}$

$y \geq 3\left(x - \frac{5}{2}\right)^2 + \frac{13}{4}$

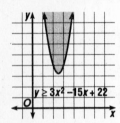

21. $(x - 10)(x + 1) < 0$

$x - 10 < 0$ and $x + 1 > 0$ or $x - 10 > 0$ and $x + 1 < 0$

$\quad x < 10 \quad$ and $\quad x > -1 \quad$ or $\quad x > 10 \quad$ and $\quad x < -1$

$\qquad -1 < x < 10 \qquad\qquad\qquad$ never true

$\qquad\qquad\qquad \{x \mid -1 < x < 10\}$

22. $x^2 + 8x - 9 > 0$

$(x + 9)(x - 1) > 0$

$x + 9 > 0$ and $x - 1 > 0$ or $x + 9 < 0$ and $x - 1 < 0$

$\quad x > -9 \quad$ and $\quad x > 1 \quad$ or $\quad x < -9 \quad$ and $\quad x < 1$

$\qquad x > 1 \qquad\qquad$ or $\qquad\qquad x < -9$

$\qquad\qquad \{x \mid x > 1 \text{ or } x < -9\}$

23. $\quad 6 - 5a - 4a^2 \leq 0$

$\quad (3 - 4a)(2 + a) \leq 0$

$3 - 4a \leq 0$ and $2 + a \geq 0$ or $3 - 4a \geq 0$ and $2 + a \leq 0$

$\quad a \geq \frac{3}{4} \quad$ and $\quad a \geq -2 \quad$ or $\quad a \leq \frac{3}{4} \quad$ and $\quad a \leq -2$

$\qquad a \geq \frac{3}{4} \qquad\qquad$ or $\qquad\qquad a \leq -2$

$\qquad\qquad \{a \mid a \geq \frac{3}{4} \text{ or } a \leq -2\}$

24. $\qquad m^2 - 20m \geq -100$

$\qquad m^2 - 20m + 100 \geq 0$

$\qquad (m - 10)(m - 10) \geq 0$

$m - 10 \geq 0$ or $m - 10 \leq 0$

$\qquad m \geq 10 \quad$ or $\quad m \leq 10$

$\qquad\qquad \{\text{all reals}\}$

PAGE 390   **APPLICATIONS AND CONNECTIONS**

25.

n	$6^n + 5$	remainder
1	1 R1	1
2	7 R1	1
3	43 R1	1
4	259 R1	1
.	.	.
.	.	.
.	.	.

The remainder of $6^{100} + 5$ is 1.

26. Let w = the width. Then $3 - w$ = the length.

area $= (3 - w)w$

$\qquad = 3w - w^2$

$\qquad = -1\left(w^2 - 3w + \left(\frac{3}{2}\right)^2\right) + \frac{9}{4}$

$\qquad = -1\left(w - \frac{3}{2}\right)^2 + \frac{9}{4}$

The vertex is $\left(\frac{3}{2}, \frac{9}{4}\right)$. The area is maximized when

$w = \frac{3}{2}$. So, the dimensions are 1.5 ft by 1.5 ft.

27. Let x = the number of \$1.50 price increases.

Then, $320 - 30x$ = number of passengers per day.

Add $11.50 + 1.50x$ = fare price.

$y = (320 - 30x)(11.50 + 1.50x)$

$\quad = 3680 + 135x - 45x^2$

$\quad = -45\left(x^2 - 3x + \frac{9}{4}\right) + 3680 + \frac{405}{4}$

$\quad = -45\left(x - \frac{3}{2}\right)^2 + 3781.25$

The vertex is $\left(\frac{3}{2}, 3781.25\right)$. The product is

maximized when $x = \frac{3}{2}$. So, $11.50 + 1.50x$ is

13.75. The maximum income is produced by a

\$13.75 fare.

28. Let w = the width. Then $80 - 2w$ = the length.

area $= (80 - 2w)w$

$\qquad = 80w - 2w^2$

$\qquad = -2(w^2 - 40w + 400) + 800$

$\qquad = -2(w - 20)^2 + 800$

The vertex is $(20, 800)$. The area is maximized

when $w = 20$. So, the dimensions are 20 ft by

$80 - 2(20)$ or 40 ft. The area is 800 square feet.

29. $0 = -16t^2 + 35t + 1250$

$$t = \frac{-35 \pm \sqrt{35^2 - 4(-16)(1250)}}{2(-16)}$$

$$= \frac{-35 \pm 285}{-32}$$

$t \approx -7.81$ or $t = 10$

It will take 10 seconds for the object to hit the ground.

Chapter 8 Test

PAGE 391

1. $y = (x + 2)^2 + 4$

$\quad = x^2 + 4x + 4 + 4$

$\quad = x^2 + 4x + 8$

2. $y = 2(x - 3)^2 + 5$

$\quad = 2(x^2 - 6x + 9) + 5$

$\quad = 2x^2 - 12x + 18 + 5$

$\quad = 2x^2 - 12x + 23$

3. $y = (x + 1)^2 - 1$

4. $y = 2(x - 2)^2 - 5$

5. $y = -\frac{2}{3}(x + 4)^2 + 3$

6. $(-3, 0)$; $x = -3$; up

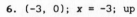
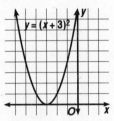

7. $(2, 0)$; $x = 2$; down

8. $(-2, 1)$; $x = -2$; up

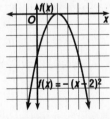
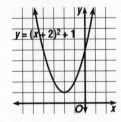

9. $(-4, 6)$; $x = -4$; down

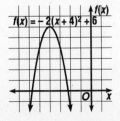

10. $g(x) = x^2 + 3x + 6$

$\quad = \left(x^2 + 3x + \frac{9}{4}\right) + 6 - \frac{9}{4}$

$\quad = \left(x + \frac{3}{2}\right)^2 + \frac{15}{4}$

$\left(-\frac{3}{2}, \frac{15}{4}\right)$; $x = -\frac{3}{2}$; up

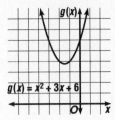
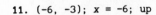

11. $(-6, -3)$; $x = -6$; up

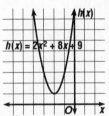

12. $h(x) = 2x^2 + 8x + 9$

$\quad = 2(x^2 + 4x + 4) + 9 - 2(4)$

$\quad = 2(x + 2)^2 + 1$

$(-2, 1)$; $x = -2$; up

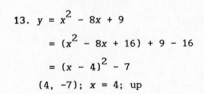

13. $y = x^2 - 8x + 9$

$\quad = (x^2 - 8x + 16) + 9 - 16$

$\quad = (x - 4)^2 - 7$

$(4, -7)$; $x = 4$; up

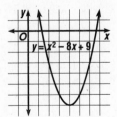
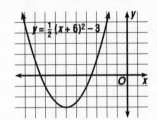

14. $f(x) = -x^2 - 10x + 10$

$= -(x^2 + 10x + 25) + 10 + 25$

$= -(x + 5)^2 + 35$

$(-5, 35)$; $x = -5$; down

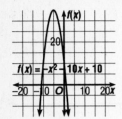

15. $f(x) = -\frac{2}{3}x^2 + 4x - 3$

$= -\frac{2}{3}(x^2 - 6x + 9) - 3 + 6$

$= -\frac{2}{3}(x - 3)^2 + 3$

$(3, 3)$; $x = 3$; down

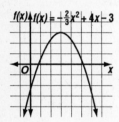

16.

n	8^n	ones' digit
1	8	8
2	64	4
3	512	2
4	4,096	6
5	32,768	8
6	262,144	4
7	2,097,152	2
.	.	.
.	.	.
.	.	.

The ones' digit of 8^{50} is 4.

17. Let x = one of the numbers. Then, $x + 22$ = the other number.

product $= x(x + 22)$

$= x^2 + 22x$

$= (x^2 + 22x + 121) - 121$

$= (x + 11)^2 - 121$

The vertex is $(-11, -121)$. The product is minimized when $x = -11$. So the two numbers are -11 and 11.

18. Let w = the width of the rectangle. Then $30 - w$ = the length of the rectangle.

Area $= w(30 - w)$

$= 30w - w^2$

$= -[w^2 - 30w + (15)^2] + 15^2$

$= -(w - 15)^2 + 225$

The vertex is $(15, 225)$. The area is maximized when $w = 15$. So $30 - w = 15$. The dimensions of the rectangle are 15 cm by 15 cm, with a maximum area of 225 sq. cm.

19. Let w = the width. Then $60 - 2w$ = the length.

area $= w(60 - 2w)$

$= 60w - 2w^2$

$= -2(w^2 - 30w + 225) + 450$

$= -2(w - 15)^2 + 450$

The vertex is $(15, 450)$. The area is maximized when $w = 15$. So $60 - 2w = 30$. The width is 15 ft, the length is 30 ft, and the area is 450 ft^2.

20. $h(t) = -16t^2 + 40t$

$= -16\left(t^2 - \frac{5}{2}t + \left(\frac{5}{4}\right)^2\right) + 25$

$= -16\left(t - \frac{5}{4}\right)^2 + 25$

The vertex is $\left(\frac{5}{4}, 25\right)$. So, the maximum height is 25 feet.

$0 = -16t^2 + 40t$

$0 = -16t(t - 2.5)$

$t = 0$ or $t = 2.5$

The rocket will land in 2.5 seconds.

21. $y < -(x - 2)^2$

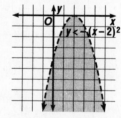

22. $y \le x^2 + 6x - 7$

$y \le (x + 3)^2 - 16$

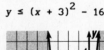

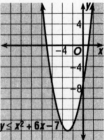

23. $(x + 6)(x - 3) < 0$

$x + 6 < 0$ and $x - 3 > 0$ or $x + 6 > 0$ and $x - 3 < 0$

$x < -6$ and $x > 3$ or $x > -6$ and $x < 3$

never true $\qquad -6 < x < 3$

$\{x | -6 < x < 3\}$

24. $3x^2 + 2x - 5 \geq 0$

$(3x + 5)(x - 1) \geq 0$

$3x + 5 \geq 0$ and $x - 1 \geq 0$ or $3x + 5 \leq 0$ and $x - 1 \leq 0$

$x \geq -\dfrac{5}{3}$ and $x \geq 1$ or $x \leq -\dfrac{5}{3}$ and $x \leq 1$

$x \geq 1$ or $x \leq -\dfrac{5}{3}$

$\left\{ x \,\middle|\, x \geq 1 \text{ or } x \leq -\dfrac{5}{3} \right\}$

25. $a^2 - 8a \geq -16$

$a^2 - 8a + 16 \geq 0$

$(a - 4)(a - 4) \geq 0$

$a - 4 \geq 0$ or $a - 4 \leq 0$

$a \geq 4$ or $a \leq 4$

{all reals}

PAGE 391   BONUS

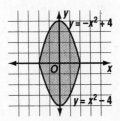

Chapter 8
College Entrance Exam Preview

PAGES 392-393

1. $10 - 4y = 18 + 2y$

$-6y = 8$

$3y = -4$

The correct choice is A.

2. Rate for 4 people is $\dfrac{1}{6}$ house per hour. Rate for one person is $\dfrac{1}{24}$ house per hour. Rate for 5 people is $\dfrac{5}{24}$ house per hour. If $x =$ time to paint house, $\dfrac{5}{24}x = 1$

$x = 4\dfrac{4}{5}$.

The correct choice is B.

3. Let $r =$ number of rows.

$\dfrac{350}{r} = r - 25$

$350 = r^2 - 25r$

$0 = r^2 - 25r - 350$

$0 = (r - 35)(r + 10)$

Since r cannot be negative, $r = 35$.

The correct choice is D.

4. Let $s =$ number of small bars.

Let $t =$ number of large bars.

$s + t = 500 \longrightarrow 2s + 2t = 1000$

$0.40s + 0.65t = 255 \longrightarrow \underline{-2s - 3.25t = -1275}$

$-1.25t = -275$

$t = 220$

$s + 220 = 500$

$s = 280$

The correct choice is D.

5. Let $B =$ cost of bottle B.

Let $C =$ cost of bottle C.

$B = 2C + 2 \qquad 2C + 2 + C = 32$

$B + C = 32 \qquad\qquad 3C = 30$

$C = 10$

$B = 2(10) + 2$

$= 22$

The correct choice is B.

6. I Since $x > 1$, $\dfrac{1}{x}$ decreases as x increases so $x - \dfrac{1}{x}$ increases as x increases.

II Since $x > 1$, $x^2 > x$, and $x^2 - x > 0$. When $0 < x^2 - x < 1$, $\dfrac{1}{x^2 - x}$ will decrease as x increases.

III $4x^3 - 2x^2 = 2x^2(2x - 1)$. x^2 and $2x - 1$ increase as x increases so $2x^2(2x - 1)$ increases as x increases.

The correct choice is C.

7. $3(-1)^3 - 2(-1)^2 + (-1) - 1 = -3 - 2 - 1 - 1 = -7$

The correct choice is A.

8. Let $x =$ cost of pencil.

Let $y =$ cost of pen.

$8x + 5y = 5.41$

$9x + 3y = 3.75$

$-24x - 15y = -16.23$

$\underline{45x + 15y = 18.75}$

$21x = 2.52$

$x = 0.12$

The correct choice is A.

9. If Sam sold x, John sold $2x - 3$. The difference is $2x - 3 - x = x - 3$

The correct choice is D.

10. $y = x + 3 \rightarrow y - x = 3 \rightarrow x - y = -3$

$(x - y)^3 = (-3)^3 = -27$

The correct choice is A.

11. $21xy + 77 = 32xy$

$77 = 11xy$

$7 = xy$

The correct choice is D.

12. $4a^6 = 4(a^3)^2$

   $= 4(7)^2$

   $= 196$

   The correct choice is C.

13. $y - 3x = 2$

   $y = 3x + 2$

   Slope is 3.

   $y = mx + b$

   $-5 = 3(2) + b$

   $b = -11$

   $y = 3x - 11$

   The correct choice is B.

14. $4 * (-2) = 4^2 + (-2)^2 + 4(-2) = 16 + 4 - 8$

   $= 12$

   The correct choice is B.

15. $3x^2 - 12x = 3(x^2 - 4x)$

   To make it a perfect square:

   $3(x^2 - 4x + 4) = 3x^2 - 12x + 12$

   So, $c = 12$.

   The correct choice is A.

16. $2x^2 - 5x - 7$

   $b^2 - 4ac = (-5)^2 - 4(2)(-7) = 81$

   Since the discriminant is positive, there are two real roots.

   The correct choice is B.

17. number of days in w weeks: $7w$

   number of days in d days: d

   number of days in h hours: $\dfrac{h}{24}$

   $7w + d + \dfrac{h}{24}$

   The correct choice is C.

18. $\dfrac{\sqrt{108}}{\sqrt{24}} = \dfrac{6\sqrt{3}}{2\sqrt{6}} = \dfrac{6\sqrt{3}}{2\sqrt{2} \cdot \sqrt{3}} = \dfrac{3}{\sqrt{2}} = \dfrac{3\sqrt{2}}{2}$

   The correct choice is D.

19. $y = x + 2$

   $z = x + 4$

   $(x - y)(x - z)(y - z)$

   $= [x - (x + 2)][x - (x + 4)][(x + 2) - (x + 4)]$

   $= (-2)(-4)(-2)$

   $= -16$

   The correct choice is C.

20. $3 @ (-2) = 3^2 - (-2)^2 = 9 - 4 = 5$

   The correct choice is A.

21. Let x = Jana's next test score.

   $\dfrac{89 + 92 + 76 + 85 + x}{5} = 86$

   $342 + x = 430$

   $x = 88$

   The correct choice is B.

22. The travel time is $5\frac{3}{4}$ hours.

   The distance traveled:

   truck: $(52)\left(5\frac{3}{4}\right) = 299$ miles

   train: $(84)\left(5\frac{3}{4}\right) = 483$ miles

   $483 - 299 = 184$ miles

   The correct choice is C.

23. Let t = cost of an audio tape.

   Let c = cost of a CD.

   $2t = \dfrac{2}{3}c \longrightarrow 6t - 2c = 0$

   $3t + 2c = 45 \longrightarrow 3t + 2c = 45$

   $9t \quad\quad = 45$

   $t = 5$

   The cost of two audio tapes: $2(5) = 10$.

   The correct choice is B.

24. $a^2 - b^2 = -7$

   $(a + b)(a - b) = -7$

   $7(a - b) = -7$

   $a - b = -1$

   $b - a = 1$

   The correct choice is B.

Chapter 9 Conics

9-1 The Distance and Midpoint Formulas

PAGE 398 CHECKING FOR UNDERSTANDING

1. Squaring the quantity will make it positive. So the absolute value is unnecessary.

2. No. The point is only the midpoint if it lies on the segment. A point could be equidistant from both points and not lie on the line segment between them.

3. Yes. Set up the equation for the midpoint and solve.

$$(0, -2) = \left(\frac{3 + x}{2}, \frac{7 + y}{2}\right)$$

So, $0 = \frac{3 + x}{2}$ and $-2 = \frac{7 + y}{2}$

$0 = 3 + x$ $-4 = 7 + y$

$-3 = x$ $y = -11$

The second endpoint is $(-3, -11)$.

4. $d = |9 - (-8)|$
   $= 17$ units

5. $d = |0 - (-3)|$
   $= 3$ units

6. $d = |-15 - (-30)|$
   $= |-15 + 30|$
   $= 15$ units

7. $d = |-3.3 - (-12.2)|$
   $= |-3.3 + 12.2|$
   $= 8.9$ units

8. $d = |-8.1 - 4.4|$
   $= |-12.5|$
   $= 12.5$ units

9. $d = \left|-6\frac{1}{8} - 10\frac{2}{3}\right|$
   $= \left|-6\frac{3}{24} - 10\frac{16}{24}\right|$
   $= \left|-16\frac{19}{24}\right|$
   $= 16\frac{19}{24}$ units

10. $d = \sqrt{(6 - 6)^2 + (-1 - 3)^2}$
    $= \sqrt{0^2 + (-4)^2}$
    $= \sqrt{16}$ or 4

11. $d = \sqrt{(4 - 9)^2 + (-7 - 5)^2}$
    $= \sqrt{(-5)^2 + (-12)^2}$
    $= \sqrt{25 + 144}$
    $= \sqrt{169}$ or 13

12. $d = \sqrt{(10 - 0)^2 + (-3 + 5)^2}$
    $= \sqrt{10^2 + 2^2}$
    $= \sqrt{100 + 4}$
    $= \sqrt{104}$ or $2\sqrt{26}$

PAGES 398-399 EXERCISES

13. $d = \sqrt{(8 - 4)^2 + (8 - 8)^2}$
    $= \sqrt{4^2 + 0^2}$
    $= \sqrt{16}$ or 4

14. $d = \sqrt{(-4 - 0)^2 + (-2 - 5)^2}$
    $= \sqrt{(-4)^2 + (-7)^2}$
    $= \sqrt{16 + 49}$
    $= \sqrt{65}$

15. $d = \sqrt{(6 - 9)^2 + (7 - 0)^2}$
    $= \sqrt{(-3)^2 + 7^2}$
    $= \sqrt{9 + 49}$
    $= \sqrt{58}$

16. $d = \sqrt{(1 + 4)^2 + (-3 - 9)^2}$
    $= \sqrt{5^2 + (-12)^2}$
    $= \sqrt{25 + 144}$
    $= \sqrt{169}$ or 13

17. $d = \sqrt{(-3 + 4)^2 + (-11 + 10)^2}$
    $= \sqrt{1^2 + (-1)^2}$
    $= \sqrt{2}$

18. $d = \sqrt{\left(\frac{1}{3} - 1\right)^2 + \left(-2 - \frac{1}{2}\right)^2}$
    $= \sqrt{\left(-\frac{2}{3}\right)^2 + \left(-\frac{5}{2}\right)^2}$
    $= \sqrt{\frac{4}{9} + \frac{25}{4}}$
    $= \sqrt{\frac{16}{36} + \frac{225}{36}}$
    $= \sqrt{\frac{241}{36}}$ or $\frac{\sqrt{241}}{6}$

19. $d = \sqrt{(-2.2 + 0.5)^2 + (-0.3 - 1)^2}$
    $= \sqrt{(-1.7)^2 + (-1.3)^2}$
    $= \sqrt{2.89 + 1.69}$
    $= \sqrt{4.58}$

20. $d = \sqrt{(\sqrt{3} - 3)^2 + (\sqrt{3} - 3)^2}$
    $= \sqrt{(3 - 6\sqrt{3} + 9) + 3 - 6\sqrt{3} + 9}$
    $= \sqrt{24 - 12\sqrt{3}}$
    $= 2\sqrt{6 - 3\sqrt{3}}$

21. $d = \sqrt{(4\sqrt{7} + 2\sqrt{7})^2 + (8 - 10)^2}$
    $= \sqrt{(6\sqrt{7})^2 + (-2)^2}$
    $= \sqrt{252 + 4}$
    $= \sqrt{256}$ or 16

22. $d = \sqrt{(2\sqrt{3} - 2\sqrt{3})^2 + (4\sqrt{3} + \sqrt{3})^2}$

$\quad = \sqrt{0^2 + (5\sqrt{3})^2}$

$\quad = \sqrt{75} \text{ or } 5\sqrt{3}$

23. $5 = \sqrt{(7 - 3)^2 + (2 - c)^2}$

$\quad 5 = \sqrt{4^2 + 4 - 4c + c^2}$

$\quad 25 = c^2 - 4c + 20$

$\quad 0 = c^2 - 4c - 5$

$\quad 0 = (c - 5)(c + 1)$

$\quad c = 5 \text{ or } -1$

24. $5 = \sqrt{(-7 - c)^2 + (7 - 11)^2}$

$\quad 5 = \sqrt{49 + 14c + c^2 + (-4)^2}$

$\quad 25 = c^2 + 14c + 65$

$\quad 0 = c^2 + 14c + 40$

$\quad 0 = (c + 4)(c + 10)$

$\quad c = -10 \text{ or } -4$

25. $5 = \sqrt{(13 - 9)^2 + (10.1 - c)^2}$

$\quad 5 = \sqrt{4^2 + 102.1 - 20.2c + c^2}$

$\quad 25 = c^2 - 20.2 + 118.01$

$\quad 0 = c^2 - 20.2 + 93.01$

$\quad 0 = (c - 13.1)(c - 7.1)$

$\quad c = 7.1 \text{ or } 13.1$

26. $5 = \sqrt{(1.2 - c)^2 + (5.9 - 1.9)^2}$

$\quad 5 = \sqrt{1.44 - 2.4c + c^2 + 4^2}$

$\quad 25 = c^2 - 2.4c + 17.44$

$\quad 0 = c^2 - 2.4c - 7.56$

$\quad 0 = (c - 4.2)(c + 1.8)$

$\quad c = 4.2 \text{ or } -1.8$

27. $(x, y) = \left(\dfrac{8 + 16}{2}, \dfrac{3 + 7}{2}\right)$

$\quad = \left(\dfrac{24}{2}, \dfrac{10}{2}\right)$

$\quad = (12, 5)$

28. $(x, y) = \left(\dfrac{5 + 12}{2}, \dfrac{9}{2} \quad \dfrac{18}{2}\right)$

$\quad = \left(\dfrac{17}{2}, \dfrac{27}{2}\right)$

29. $(x, y) = \left(\dfrac{\frac{1}{4} + \frac{7}{8}}{2}, \dfrac{3 - \frac{1}{2}}{2}\right)$

$\quad = \left(\dfrac{\frac{2}{8} + \frac{7}{8}}{2}, \dfrac{\;}{2}\right)$

$\quad = \left(\dfrac{9}{8} \cdot \dfrac{1}{2}, \dfrac{5}{2} \cdot \dfrac{1}{2}\right)$

$\quad = \left(\dfrac{9}{16}, \dfrac{5}{4}\right)$

30. $(x, y) = \left(\dfrac{-4.3 + 2.7}{2}, \dfrac{2.8 + 4.9}{2}\right)$

$\quad = \left(\dfrac{-1.6}{2}, \dfrac{7.7}{2}\right)$

$\quad = (-0.8, 3.85)$

31. $\text{midpoint} = \left(\dfrac{9 + 11}{2}, \dfrac{0 - 14}{2}\right)$

$\quad = \left(\dfrac{20}{2}, \dfrac{-14}{2}\right)$

$\quad = (10, -7)$

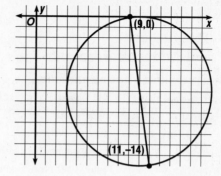

32. $(4, 5), (-4, 6)$

$\quad d = \sqrt{(4 + 4)^2 + (5 - 6)^2}$

$\qquad = \sqrt{8^2 + (-1)^2}$

$\qquad = \sqrt{65}$

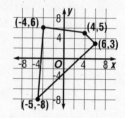

$(6, 3), (4, 5)$

$\quad d = \sqrt{(6 - 4)^2 + (3 - 5)^2}$

$\qquad = \sqrt{2^2 + (-2)^2}$

$\qquad = \sqrt{8} = 2\sqrt{2}$

$(-5, -8), (6, 3)$

$\quad d = \sqrt{(-5 - 6)^2 + (-8 - 3)^2}$

$\qquad = \sqrt{(-11)^2 + (-11)^2}$

$\qquad = \sqrt{242} = 11\sqrt{2}$

$(-5, -8), (-4, 6)$

$\quad d = \sqrt{(-5 + 4)^2 + (-8 - 6)^2}$

$\qquad = \sqrt{(-1)^2 + (-14)^2}$

$\qquad = \sqrt{197}$

$\text{perimeter} = 13\sqrt{2} + \sqrt{197} + \sqrt{65}$

33.

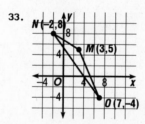

$\text{midpoint of } \overline{MN} = \left(\dfrac{3 - 2}{2}, \dfrac{5 + 8}{2}\right)$

$\qquad = \left(\dfrac{1}{2}, \dfrac{13}{2}\right)$

$\text{midpoint of } \overline{NO} = \left(\dfrac{-2 + 7}{2}, \dfrac{8 - 4}{2}\right)$

$\qquad = \left(\dfrac{5}{2}, 2\right)$

$\text{midpoint of } \overline{MO} = \left(\dfrac{3 + 7}{2}, \dfrac{5 - 4}{2}\right)$

$\qquad = \left(5, \dfrac{1}{2}\right)$

34.

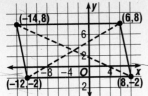

(6, 8), (-12, -2)

$d = \sqrt{(-12 - 6)^2 + (-2 - 8)^2}$

$\quad = 2\sqrt{106}$

(8, -2), (-14, 8)

$d = \sqrt{(-14 - 8)^2 + (8 - (-2))^2}$

$\quad = 2\sqrt{146}$

$2\sqrt{106}$ and $2\sqrt{146}$

35.

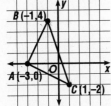

endpoints of $\overline{AB}$: (-3, 0), (-1, 4)

$d = \sqrt{(-1 - (-3))^2 + (4 - 0)^2}$

$\quad = \sqrt{20}$ or $2\sqrt{5}$

endpoints of $\overline{AC}$: (-3, 0), (1, -2)

$d = \sqrt{(1 - (-3))^2 + (-2 - 0)^2}$

$\quad = \sqrt{20}$ or $2\sqrt{5}$

$\overline{AB}$ and $\overline{AC}$ are the same lengths.

Thus, the triangle is isosceles.

36.

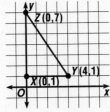

midpoint of $\overline{YZ} = \left(\dfrac{4 + 0}{2}, \dfrac{1 + 7}{2}\right)$

$\qquad\qquad\quad = (2, 4)$

Let x = distance from (2, 4) to X.

$x = \sqrt{(2 - 0)^2 + (4 - 1)^2} = \sqrt{13}$

Let y = distance from (2, 4) to Y.

$y = \sqrt{(4 - 2)^2 + (1 - 4)^2} = \sqrt{13}$

Let z = distance from (2, 4) to Z.

$z = \sqrt{(2 - 0)^2 + (4 - 7)^2} = \sqrt{13}$

37. midpoint $\overline{AB}$: $\left(\dfrac{11 + 3}{2}, \dfrac{2 - 2}{2}\right)$

$\qquad\qquad C$: (7, 0)

midpoint $\overline{AC}$: $\left(\dfrac{3 + 7}{2}, \dfrac{-2 + 0}{2}\right) = (5, -1)$

The point is (5, -1).

38. $\quad a^2 + b^2 = c^2$

$\quad 23^2 + 85^2 = c^2$

$\quad 529 + 7225 = c^2$

$\qquad\quad 7754 = c^2$

$\qquad\qquad c \approx 88$ miles

39. The distance from the edge to the center is

$\dfrac{1}{2}(12) = 6$ inches. The distance from the center

to the edge of the hole is $\dfrac{1}{2}\left(\dfrac{1}{4}\right) = \dfrac{1}{8}$ inches.

So the edge of the hole is $6 - \dfrac{1}{8} = 5\dfrac{7}{8}$ inches

from the edge.

40. $(x + 3)(x + 7) > 0$

$x + 3 > 0$ and $x + 7 > 0$ or $x + 3 < 0$ and $x + 7 < 0$

$\quad x > -3$ and $x > -7$ or $x < -3$ and $x < -7$

$\qquad\qquad\qquad x > -3$ or $x < -7$

$\qquad\qquad\qquad \{x \mid x > -3$ or $x < -7\}$

41. $(a - 1.5)(a + 2.5) \geq 0$

$a - 1.5 \geq 0$ and $a + 2.5 \geq 0$

$\qquad a \geq 1.5$ and $a \geq -2.5$

$\qquad\qquad a \geq 1.5$

$\qquad\qquad\quad$ or

$a - 1.5 \leq 0$ and $a + 2.5 \leq 0$

$\qquad a \leq 1.5$ and $a \leq -2.5$

$\qquad\qquad a \leq -2.5$

$\qquad\quad \{a \mid a \geq 1.5$ or $a \leq -2.5\}$

42. $\quad y^4 - y^2 - 30 = 0$

$\quad (y^2 - 6)(y^2 + 5) = 0$

$\quad y^2 - 6 = 0$ or $y^2 + 5 = 0$

$\qquad y^2 = 6$ or $\quad y^2 = -5$

$\qquad y^2 = \pm\sqrt{6}$ or $\quad y^2 = \pm i\sqrt{5}$

43. $2x + 5yi = 4 + 15i$

$\quad 2x = 4$ and $5yi = 15i$

$\quad\; x = 2$ and $y = 3$

44. $3m^2 + 24p^3 = 3(m^3 + 8p^3)$

$\qquad\qquad\qquad = 3(m + 2p)(m^2 - 2mp + 4p^2)$

9-2 **Parabolas**

PAGES 402-403   CHECKING FOR UNDERSTANDING

1. Some answers are: car headlights, flashlights, sound collectors, and satellite dishes.

2. The directrix and the latus rectum are parallel and are both perpendicular to the axis of symmetry. The vertex lies on the axis of symmetry and is the midpoint of the shortest segment between the latus rectum and the directrix.

3. vertex: $(-1, -2)$, axis of symmetry: $y = -2$,

focus: $\left(-\frac{7}{8}, -2\right)$, directrix: $x = -\frac{9}{8}$

4. $x^2 - bx + c$

$c = \left(\frac{1}{2}(-6)\right)^2$

$= 9$

5. $y^2 + 4y + c$

$c = \left(\frac{1}{2} \cdot 4\right)^2$

$= 4$

6. $a^2 - 8a + c$

$c = \left(\frac{1}{2}(-8)\right)^2$

$= 16$

7. $n^2 - 10n + c$

$c = \left(\frac{1}{2}(-10)\right)^2$

$= 25$

8. $q^2 + 3q + c$

$c = \left(\frac{1}{2} \cdot 3\right)^2$

$= \frac{9}{4}$

9. $s^2 - 7s + c$

$c = \left(\frac{1}{2}(-7)\right)^2$

$= \frac{49}{4}$

10. $12y = x^2$

$y = \frac{1}{12}x^2$

11. $x^2 = -4y$

$y = -\frac{1}{4}x^2$

12. $y = x^2 + 8x + 20$

$y = \left(x^2 + 8x + \left(\frac{8}{2}\right)^2\right) + 20 - \left(\frac{8}{2}\right)^2$

$y = (x + 4)^2 + 4$

13. $y = x^2 + 4x + 1$

$y = \left(x^2 + 4x + \left(\frac{4}{2}\right)^2\right) + 1 - \left(\frac{4}{2}\right)^2$

$y = (x + 2)^2 - 3$

For exercises 14-31 and 18-31, A is the vertex,
B is the axis of symmetry, C is the focus, D is the
directrix, E is the direction of opening, and F is
the length of the latus rectum.

14. $y^2 = 6x$

$x = \frac{1}{6}y^2$

A. $(0, 0)$

B. $y = 0$

C. $\left(0 + \dfrac{1}{4\left(\frac{1}{6}\right)}, \ 0\right) = \left(\frac{3}{2}, 0\right)$

D. $x = 0 - \dfrac{1}{4\left(\frac{1}{6}\right)} = -\frac{3}{2}$

E. right

F. $\left|\dfrac{1}{\left(\frac{1}{6}\right)}\right| = 6$

15. $(x + 2)^2 = y - 3$

$y = (x + 2)^2 + 3$

A. $(-2, 3)$

B. $x = -2$

C. $\left(-2, \ 3 + \dfrac{1}{4(1)}\right) = \left(-2, \ 3\frac{1}{4}\right)$

D. $y = 3 - \dfrac{1}{4(1)} = 2\frac{3}{4}$

E. up

F. $\left|\dfrac{1}{1}\right| = 1$

16. $6x = (y + 2)^2$

$x = \frac{1}{6}(y + 2)^2$

A. $(0, -2)$

B. $y = -2$

C. $\left(0 + \dfrac{1}{4\left(\frac{1}{6}\right)}, \ -2\right) = \left(\frac{3}{2}, -2\right)$

D. $x = 0 - \dfrac{1}{4\left(\frac{1}{6}\right)} = -\frac{3}{2}$

E. right

F. $\left|\dfrac{1}{\left(\frac{1}{6}\right)}\right| = 6$

17. $x^2 = (y - 1)$

$y = x^2 + 1$

A. $(0, 1)$

B. $x = 0$

C. $\left(0, \ 1 + \frac{1}{4}\right) = \left(0, \frac{5}{4}\right)$

D. $y = 1 - \frac{1}{4} = \frac{3}{4}$

E. up

F. $\left|\dfrac{1}{1}\right| = 1$

PAGES 403–404   EXERCISES

18. $-8y = x^2$

$y = -\frac{1}{8}x^2$

A. $(0, 0)$

B. $x = 0$

C. $\left(0, \ 0 + \dfrac{1}{4\left(-\frac{1}{8}\right)}\right) = (0, -2)$

D. $y = 0 - \dfrac{1}{4\left(-\frac{1}{8}\right)} = 2$

E. downward

F. $\left|\dfrac{1}{\left(-\frac{1}{8}\right)}\right| = 8$

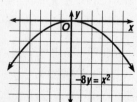

$-8y = x^2$

200

19. $4(y - 2) = (x - 4)^2$

$\qquad y = \frac{1}{4}(x - 4)^2 + 2$

A. $(4, 2)$

B. $x = 4$

C. $(4, 2 + 1) = (4, 3)$

D. $y = 2 - 1 = 1$

E. up

F. $\left|\dfrac{1}{\frac{1}{4}}\right| = 4$

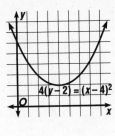

$4(y - 2) = (x - 4)^2$

20. $(x + 3)^2 = \frac{1}{4}(y - 2)$

$\qquad 4(x + 3)^2 = y - 2$

$\qquad\qquad y = 4(x + 3)^2 + 2$

A. $(-3, 2)$

B. $x = -3$

C. $\left(-3, 2 + \frac{1}{16}\right) = \left(-3, 2\frac{1}{16}\right)$

D. $y = 2 - \frac{1}{16} = 1\frac{15}{16}$

E. up

F. $\frac{1}{4}$

$(x + 3)^2 = \frac{1}{4}(y - 2)$

21. $(x - 8)^2 = \frac{1}{2}(y + 1)$

$\qquad 2(x - 8)^2 = y + 1$

$\qquad\qquad y = 2(x - 8)^2 - 1$

A. $(8, -1)$

B. $x = 8$

C. $\left(8, -1 + \frac{1}{8}\right) = \left(8, -\frac{7}{8}\right)$

D. $y = -1 - \frac{1}{8} = -\frac{9}{8}$

E. up

F. $\frac{1}{2}$

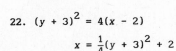

$\frac{1}{2}(y + 1) = (x - 8)^2$

22. $(y + 3)^2 = 4(x - 2)$

$\qquad x = \frac{1}{4}(y + 3)^2 + 2$

A. $(2, -3)$

B. $y = -3$

C. $(3, -3)$

D. $x = 1$

E. right

F. 4

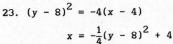

$4(x - 2) = (y + 3)^2$

23. $(y - 8)^2 = -4(x - 4)$

$\qquad x = -\frac{1}{4}(y - 8)^2 + 4$

A. $(4, 8)$

B. $y = 8$

C. $(3, 8)$

D. $x = 5$

E. left

F. 4

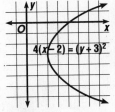

$(y - 8)^2 = -4(x - 4)$

24. $y = x^2 + 8x + 20$

$\qquad y = (x^2 + 8x + 16) + 4$

$\qquad y = (x + 4)^2 + 4$

A. $(-4, 4)$

B. $x = -4$

C. $\left(-4, 4 + \frac{1}{4}\right) = \left(-4, \frac{17}{4}\right)$

D. $y = 4 - \frac{1}{4} = \frac{15}{4}$

E. upward

F. $\left|\dfrac{1}{1}\right| = 1$

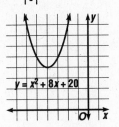

$y = x^2 + 8x + 20$

25. $x = y^2 - 14y + 25$

$\qquad x = (y - 7)^2 - 24$

A. $(-24, 7)$

B. $y = 7$

C. $\left(-23\frac{3}{4}, 7\right)$

D. $x = -24\frac{1}{4}$

E. right

F. 1

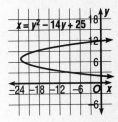

$x = y^2 - 14y + 25$

26. $y = x^2 - 6x + 33$

$\qquad y = (x^2 - 6x + 9) + 24$

$\qquad y = (x - 3)^2 + 24$

A. $(3, 24)$

B. $x = 3$

C. $\left(3, 24\frac{1}{4}\right)$

D. $y = 23\frac{3}{4}$

E. up

F. 1

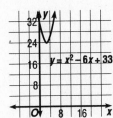

$y = x^2 - 6x + 33$

27. $y = \frac{1}{2}x^2 - 3x + \frac{19}{2}$

$\qquad y = \frac{1}{2}(x - 3)^2 + 5$

A. $(3, 5)$

B. $x = 3$

C. $\left(3, 5\frac{1}{2}\right)$

D. $y = 4\frac{1}{2}$

E. up

F. 2

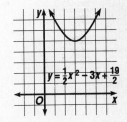

$y = \frac{1}{2}x^2 - 3x + \frac{19}{2}$

28. $y = x^2 + 4x + 1$

$\qquad y = (x + 2)^2 - 3$

A. $(-2, -3)$

B. $x = -2$

C. $= \left(-2, -\frac{11}{4}\right)$

D. $y = -\frac{13}{4}$

E. up

F. 1

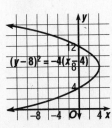

$y = x^2 + 4x + 1$

29. $x = \frac{1}{4}y^2 - \frac{1}{2}y - 3$

$x = \frac{1}{4}(y - 1)^2 - \frac{13}{4}$

A. $\left(-\frac{13}{4}, 1\right)$

B. $y = 1$

C. $\left(-\frac{9}{4}, 1\right)$

D. $x = -\frac{17}{4}$

E. right

F. 4

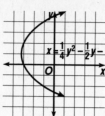

30. $x = 5y^2 - 25y + 60$

$x = 5\left(y - \frac{5}{2}\right)^2 + \frac{115}{4}$

A. $\left(\frac{115}{4}, \frac{5}{2}\right)$

B. $y = \frac{5}{2}$

C. $\left(\frac{144}{5}, \frac{5}{2}\right)$

D. $x = 28\frac{7}{10}$

E. right

F. $\frac{1}{5}$

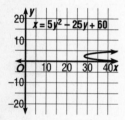

31. $y = 3x^2 - 24x + 50$

$y = 3(x - 4)^2 + 2$

A. $(4, 2)$

B. $x = 4$

C. $\left(4, 2\frac{1}{12}\right)$

D. $y = 1\frac{11}{12}$

E. up

F. $\frac{1}{3}$

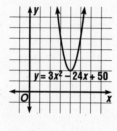

32. $\sqrt{(x - 3)^2 + (y - 8)^2} = \sqrt{(x - x)^2 + (y - 4)^2}$

$(x - 3)^2 + (y - 8)^2 = (x - x)^2 + (y - 4)^2$

$(x - 3)^2 + y^2 - 16y + 64 = y^2 - 8y + 16$

$(x - 3)^2 = 8y - 48$

$y = \frac{1}{8}(x - 3)^2 + 6$

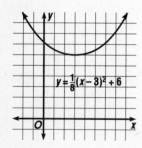

33. $\sqrt{(x - 8)^2 + (y - 0)^2} = \sqrt{(x - x)^2 + (y - 4)^2}$

$(x - 8)^2 + (y - 0)^2 = (x - x)^2 + (y - 4)^2$

$(x - 8)^2 + y^2 = y^2 - 8y + 16$

$(x - 8)^2 = -8y + 16$

$y = -\frac{1}{8}(x - 8)^2 + 2$

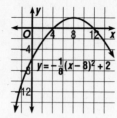

34. $\sqrt{(x - 5)^2 + (y - 5)^2} = \sqrt{(x - x)^2 + (y - (-3))^2}$

$(x - 5)^2 + y^2 - 10y + 25 = y^2 + 6y + 9$

$(x - 5)^2 = 16y - 16$

$y = \frac{1}{16}(x - 5)^2 + 1$

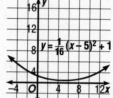

35. $\sqrt{(x - 6)^2 + (y - 2)^2} = \sqrt{(x - 4)^2 + (y - y)^2}$

$x^2 - 12x + 36 + (y - 2)^2 = x^2 - 8x + 16$

$(y - 2)^2 = 4x - 20$

$x = \frac{1}{4}(y - 2)^2 + 5$

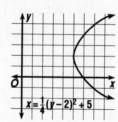

36. $\sqrt{(x - 4)^2 + (y - (-3))^2} = \sqrt{(x - x)^2 + (y - 6)^2}$

$(x - 4)^2 + y^2 + 6y + 9 = y^2 - 12y + 36$

$(x - 4)^2 = -18y + 27$

$y = -\frac{1}{18}(x - 4)^2 + \frac{3}{2}$

37. $\sqrt{(x-3)^2 + (y-(-1))^2} = \sqrt{(x-(-2))^2 + (y-y)^2}$

$x^2 - 6x + 9 + (y+1)^2 = x^2 + 4x + 4$

$(y+1)^2 = 10x - 5$

$x = \frac{1}{10}(y+1)^2 + \frac{1}{2}$

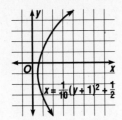

38. $\sqrt{(x-3)^2 + (y-0)^2} = \sqrt{(x+2)^2 + (y-y)^2}$

$(x-3)^2 + y^2 = (x+2)^2$

$x^2 - 6x + 9 + y^2 = x^2 + 4x + 4$

$y^2 = 10x - 5$

$\frac{1}{10}y^2 + \frac{1}{2} = x$

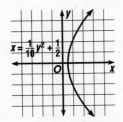

39. $\sqrt{(x-10)^2 + (y+3)^2} = \sqrt{(x-5)^2 + (y-y)^2}$

$(x-10)^2 + (y+3)^2 = (x-5)^2$

$x^2 - 20x + 100 + (y+3)^2 = x^2 - 10x + 25$

$(y+3)^2 = 10x - 75$

$\frac{1}{10}(y+3)^2 + 7.5 = x$

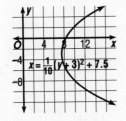

40. $h = 0$, $k = 0$

parabola opens up

$k + \frac{1}{4a} = 3$

$\frac{1}{4a} = 3$

$\frac{1}{12} = a$

$y = \frac{1}{12}x^2$

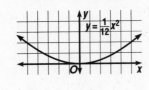

41. $h = 5$, $k = -1$

parabola opens left

$h + \frac{1}{4a} = 3$

$5 + \frac{1}{4a} = 3$

$a = -\frac{1}{8}$

$x = -\frac{1}{8}(y-(-1))^2 + 5$

$x = -\frac{1}{8}(y+1)^2 + 5$

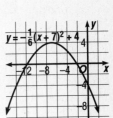

42. $h = -7$, $k = 4$

parabola opens down

$-\frac{1}{a} = 6$

$a = -\frac{1}{6}$

$y = -\frac{1}{6}(x+7)^2 + 4$

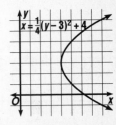

43. $h = 4$, $k = 3$

parabola opens right

$\frac{1}{a} = 4$

$a = \frac{1}{4}$

$x = \frac{1}{4}(y-3)^2 + 4$

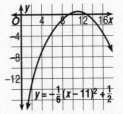

44. $\sqrt{(x-11)^2 + (y+1)^2} = \sqrt{(x-x)^2 + (y-2)^2}$

$(x-11)^2 + (y+1)^2 = (y-2)^2$

$(x-11)^2 + y^2 + 2y + 1 = y^2 - 4y + 4$

$(x-11)^2 = -6y + 3$

$-\frac{1}{6}(x-11)^2 + \frac{1}{2} = y$

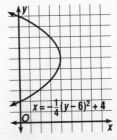

45. $\sqrt{(x-3)^2 + (y-6)^2} = \sqrt{(x-5)^2 + (y-y)^2}$

$(x-3)^2 + (y-6)^2 = (x-5)^2 + (y-y)^2$

$x^2 - 6x + 9 + (y-6)^2 = x^2 - 10x + 25$

$(y-6)^2 - 16 = -4x$

$x = -\frac{1}{4}(y-6)^2 + 4$

46.
$$\sqrt{(x-7)^2 + (y+7)^2} = \sqrt{(x+2)^2 + (y-y)^2}$$
$$(x-7)^2 + (y+7)^2 = (x+2)^2$$
$$x^2 - 14x + 49 + (y+7)^2 = x^2 + 4x + 4$$
$$(y+7)^2 = 18x - 45$$
$$\frac{1}{18}(y+7)^2 + \frac{5}{2} = x$$

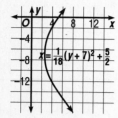

47.
$$\sqrt{(x-(-1))^2 + (y-2)^2} = \sqrt{(x-x)^2 + (y-(-1))^2}$$
$$(x+1)^2 + (y-2)^2 = (y+1)^2$$
$$(x+1)^2 + y^2 - 4y + 4 = y^2 + 2y + 1$$
$$(x+1)^2 + 3 = 6y$$
$$y = \frac{1}{6}(x+1)^2 + \frac{1}{2}$$

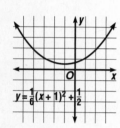

48. $h = -3,\ k = -4$

$y = a(x+3)^2 - 4$ 　　　　 $x = a(y+4)^2 - 3$

$4 = a(-1+3)^2 - 4$ 　　 $-1 = a(4+4)^2 - 3$

$8 = a(2)^2$ 　　　　　　 $2 = a \cdot 8^2$

$2 = a$ 　　　　　　　　 $\frac{1}{32} = a$

$y = 2(x+3)^2 - 4$

　　　　　　　　　　 $x = \frac{1}{32}(y+4)^2 - 3$

49. $y = \frac{1}{10}x^2$

$h = 0,\ k = 0,\ a = \frac{1}{10}$

$$\left(0,\ 0 + \frac{1}{4\left(\frac{1}{10}\right)}\right) = \left(0,\ 2\frac{1}{2}\right)$$

50.

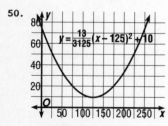

center = (125, 10)

$y = a(x-h)^2 + k$

$y = a(x-125)^2 + 10$

To find the value of a, substitute any point on the parabola into this equation, such as (0, 75).

$$y = a(x-125)^2 + 10$$
$$75 = a(0-125)^2 + 10$$
$$65 = a(-125)^2$$
$$65 = 15,625a$$
$$\frac{65}{15,625} = a$$
$$\frac{13}{3125} = a$$

The equation becomes $y = \frac{13}{3125}(x-125)^2 + 10$.

51. $d = \sqrt{(9-8)^2 + (6-0)^2}$
$$= \sqrt{1+36}$$
$$= \sqrt{37}$$

52. midpoint $= \left(\frac{9-6}{2},\ \frac{3-8}{2}\right)$
$$= \left(\frac{3}{2},\ -\frac{5}{2}\right)$$

53. Let x = the length of the side of one square. Then, $9 - x$ = the length of the side of the other square.

$A = x^2 + (9-x)^2$

$= 2x^2 - 18x + 81$

$= 2\left(x^2 - 9x + \left(\frac{9}{2}\right)^2\right) - 2\left(\frac{9}{2}\right)^2 + 81$

$= 2(x - 4.5)^2 + 40.5$

The vertex is (4.5, 40.5). The product is minimized when $x = 4.5$. The length of one side is 4.5 cm. So, the length of the wire should be 4(4.5) or 18 cm.

54. 　　 $x(x+1) = 7832$ 　　 **55.** $\dfrac{\frac{3}{4} \cdot x^{\frac{1}{5}}}{x^{\frac{1}{5}}}$

$x^2 + x - 7832 = 0$

$(x+89)(x-88) = 0$

$x = -89$ or $x = 88$ 　　　　　 $= \dfrac{\frac{3x^{\frac{1}{5}}}{x}}{}$

The numbers are

−89 and −88 or 88 and 89.

56.

$$\begin{array}{r|rrrrr} -1 & 1 & -5 & -13 & 53 & 60 \\ & & -1 & 6 & 7 & 60 \\ \hline & 1 & -6 & -7 & 60 & 0 \end{array}$$

$a^3 - 6a^2 - 7a + 60$

57. yes, coefficient: −24, degree: 5

9-3 Circles

PAGES 406-407   CHECKING FOR UNDERSTANDING

1. Yes, it would be a sphere.

2. They have the same radius, 4, but different centers, (-3, 4) and (3, 2).

3. Answers may vary. A sample answer is
$x^2 + y^2 = 9$ and $x^2 + y^2 = 16$.

4. $a < 0$, $b > 0$

5. center = (12, -3), radius = 11
$(x - 12)^2 + (y + 3)^2 = 121$

6. circle

7. parabola

8. parabola

9. circle

10. circle

11. parabola

12. (0, 0), 7

13. (0, 3), 6

14. (4, 1), 3

15. $\left(-2, \dfrac{2}{3}\right)$, $2\sqrt{2}$

16. (4, 0), $\dfrac{4}{5}$

17. (0, -5), $\dfrac{9}{8}$

18. $x^2 + y^2 = 9$
(0, 0), 3

19. $(x + 5)^2 + y^2 = 64$
(-5, 0), 8

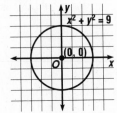

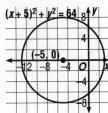

20. $(x + 6)^2 + (y - 5)^2 = 16$
(-6, 5), 4

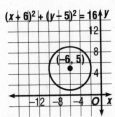

21. $(x - 3)^2 + (y + 2)^2 = 169$
(3, -2), 13

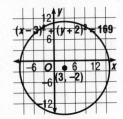

22. $x^2 + (y - 4)^2 = 49$
(0, 4), 7

23. $x^2 + (y + 2)^2 = 4$
(0, -2), 2

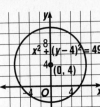

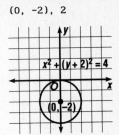

24. $(x - 3)^2 + y^2 = 16$
(3, 0), 4

25. $x^2 + y^2 = 144$
(0, 0), 12

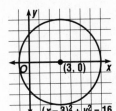

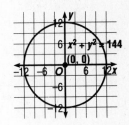

26. $(x - 3)^2 + (y - 1)^2 = 25$
(3, 1), 5

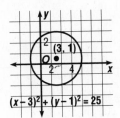

27. $(x + 2)^2 + (y - 1)^2 = 81$
(-2, 1), 9

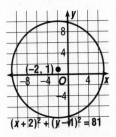

28. $(x + 3)^2 + (y + 7)^2 = 81$
(-3, -7), 9

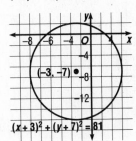

29. $(x - 4)^2 + (y - 9)^2 = 4$

(4, 9), 2

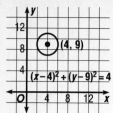

30. $x^2 + y^2 + 6x - 2y - 15 = 0$

$x^2 + 6x + 9 + y^2 - 2y + 1 = 15 + 9 + 1$

$(x + 3)^2 + (y - 1)^2 = 25$

(-3, 1), 5

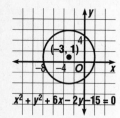

31. $x^2 + y^2 - 18x - 18y + 53 = 0$

$x^2 - 18x + 81 + y^2 - 18y + 81 = -53 + 81 + 81$

$(x - 9)^2 + (y - 9)^2 = 109$

$(9, 9), \sqrt{109}$

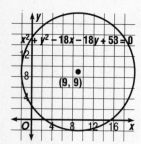

32. $x^2 + y^2 + 14x + 6y = 23$

$x^2 + 14x + 49 + y^2 + 6y + 9 = 23 + 49 + 9$

$(x + 7)^2 + (y + 3)^2 = 81$

(-7, -3); 9

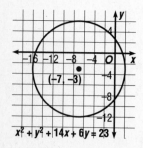

33. $x^2 + y^2 + 8x - 6y = 0$

$x^2 + 8x + 16 + y^2 - 6y + 9 = 0 + 16 + 9$

$(x + 4)^2 + (y - 3)^2 = 25$

(-4, 3); 5

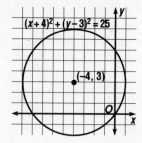

34. $x^2 - 12x + 84 = -y^2 + 16y$

$x^2 + y^2 - 12x - 16y + 84 = 0$

$x^2 - 12x + 36 + y^2 - 16y + 64 = -84 + 36 + 64$

$(x - 6)^2 + (y - 8)^2 = 16$

(6, 8); 4

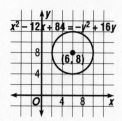

35. $x^2 + y^2 = 4x + 9$

$x^2 + y^2 - 4x = 9$

$x^2 - 4x + 4 + y^2 = 9 + 4$

$(x - 2)^2 + y^2 = 13$

$(2, 0); \sqrt{13}$

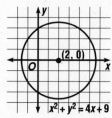

36. $x^2 + y^2 - 6y - 16 = 0$

$x^2 + y^2 - 6y = 16$

$x^2 + y^2 - 6y + 9 = 16 + 9$

$x^2 + (y - 3)^2 = 25$

(0, 3); 5

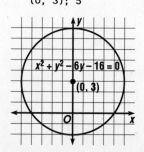

37.
$$3x^2 + 3y^2 + 6y + 9x = 2$$
$$x^2 + y^2 + 2y + 3x = \frac{2}{3}$$
$$x^2 + 3x + \frac{9}{4} + y^2 + 2y + 1 = \frac{2}{3} + \frac{9}{4} + 1$$
$$\left(x + \frac{3}{2}\right)^2 + (y + 1)^2 = \frac{47}{12}$$
$$\left(-\frac{3}{2}, -1\right); \ \sqrt{\frac{47}{12}} \text{ or } \frac{\sqrt{141}}{6}$$

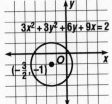

38.
$$x^2 + y^2 + 9x - 8y + 4 = 0$$
$$x^2 + y^2 + 9x - 8y = -4$$
$$x^2 + 9x + \frac{81}{4} + y^2 - 8y + 16 = -4 + \frac{81}{4} + 16$$
$$\left(x + \frac{9}{2}\right)^2 + (y - 4)^2 = \frac{129}{4}$$
$$\left(-\frac{9}{2}, 4\right); \ \frac{\sqrt{129}}{2}$$

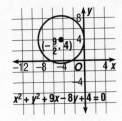

39.
$$4x^2 + 4y^2 + 36y + 5 = 0$$
$$4x^2 + 4y^2 + 36y = -5$$
$$x^2 + y^2 + 9y = -\frac{5}{4}$$
$$x^2 + y^2 + 9y + \frac{81}{4} = \frac{76}{4}$$
$$x^2 + \left(y + \frac{9}{2}\right)^2 = 19$$
$$\left(0, -\frac{9}{2}\right); \ \sqrt{19}$$

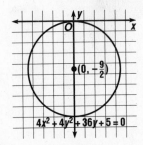

40.
$$x^2 + y^2 + 4x - 8 = 0$$
$$x^2 + y^2 + 4x = 8$$
$$x^2 + 4x + 4 + y^2 = 12$$
$$(x + 2)^2 + y^2 = 12$$
$$(-2, 0); \ 2\sqrt{3}$$

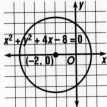

41.
$$x^2 + y^2 + 2x + 4y - 9 = 0$$
$$x^2 + 2x + y^2 + 4y = 9$$
$$x^2 + 2x + 1 + y^2 + 4y + 4 = 14$$
$$(x + 1)^2 + (y + 2)^2 = 14$$
$$(-1, -2); \ \sqrt{14}$$

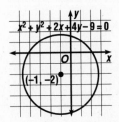

42.
$$x^2 + 14x + y^2 + 6y + 50 = 0$$
$$x^2 + y^2 + 14x + 6y = -50$$
$$x^2 + 14x + 49 + y^2 + 6y + 9 = 8$$
$$(x + 7)^2 + (y + 3)^2 = 8$$
$$(-7, -3); \ 2\sqrt{2}$$

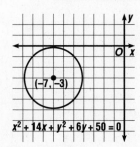

43.
$$x^2 + 2x + y^2 - 10 = 0$$
$$x^2 + 2x + y^2 = 10$$
$$x^2 + 2x + 1 + y^2 = 11$$
$$(x + 1)^2 + y^2 = 11$$
$$(-1, 0); \ \sqrt{11}$$

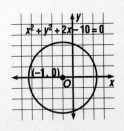

44. $(x - 4)^2 + (y - 1)^2 = 4^2$

$(x - 4)^2 + (y - 1)^2 = 16$

45. $(x - 0)^2 + (y - 3)^2 = 7^2$

$x^2 + (y - 3)^2 = 49$

46. $(x - 5)^2 + (y - 0)^2 = 8^2$

$(x - 5)^2 + y^2 = 64$

47. $(x - (-1))^2 + (y - (-5))^2 = 2^2$

$(x + 1)^2 + (y + 5)^2 = 4$

48. $(x - (-8))^2 + (y - 7)^2 = \left(\frac{1}{2}\right)^2$

$(x + 8)^2 + (y - 7)^2 = \frac{1}{4}$

49. $(x - (-3))^2 + (y - (-9))^2 = \left(\frac{5}{6}\right)^2$

$(x + 3)^2 + (y + 9)^2 = \frac{25}{36}$

50. radius $= \sqrt{(4 - 5)^2 + (-2 - 3)^2}$

$= \sqrt{26}$

$(x - 4)^2 + (y + 2)^2 = 26$

51. radius $= \sqrt{(3 - 0)^2 + (3 - 0)^2}$

$= \sqrt{18}$

$(x - 3)^2 + (y - 3)^2 = 18$

52. center $= \left(\frac{2 + 2}{2}, \frac{5 - 1}{2}\right) = (2, 2)$

radius $= \sqrt{(2 - 2)^2 + (5 - 2)^2}$

$= 3$

$(x - 2)^2 + (y - 2)^2 = 9$

53. center $= \left(\frac{-4 + 2}{2}, \frac{12 + 0}{2}\right) = (-1, 6)$

radius $= \sqrt{(-4 + 1)^2 + (12 - 6)^2}$

$= \sqrt{45}$

$(x + 1)^2 + (y - 6)^2 = 45$

54. center $= (-3, 8)$

radius $= 8$

$(x + 3)^2 + (y - 8)^2 = 64$

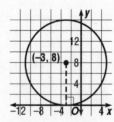

55. center $= (4, -3)$

radius $= 4$

$(x - 4)^2 + (y + 3)^2 = 16$

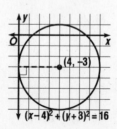

56. Answers may vary. A sample answer is

$(x - 1)^2 + (y - 1)^2 = 1$.

57. center $= (4, 16)$, radius $= 13$

$(x - 4)^2 + (y - 16)^2 = 169$

58. $r = 25$

$c = 2\pi(25) = 50\pi$

$= 157.08$

$\frac{157.08}{8} = 19.6$

about 19.6 feet per second

59.

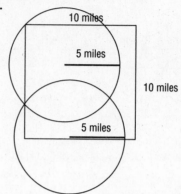

No, they cannot cover the entire city.

60. $y^2 = 6x$

$x = \frac{1}{6}y^2$

61. $6 = k - \frac{1}{4a}$ $\qquad$ $6 = 5 - \frac{1}{4a}$, $h = 2$

$\underline{4 = k + \frac{1}{4a}}$ $\qquad$ $1 = -\frac{1}{4a}$

$10 = 2k$ $\qquad\qquad$ $a = -\frac{1}{4}$

$5 = k$

$y = -\frac{1}{4}(x - 2)^2 + 5$

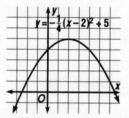

62. $y \geq x^2 - 16$

$-5 \overset{?}{\geq} (3)^2 - 16$

$-5 \geq -7$

yes

63. $y^{-6} + 4y^{-3} - 32 = 0$

$1(y^{-3})^2 + 4(y^{-3}) - 32 = 0$

64. $3x\sqrt{3} + 2 = 0$

$3x\sqrt{3} = -2$

$x = \frac{-2}{3\sqrt{3}}$

$x = \frac{-2\sqrt{3}}{3\sqrt{3} \cdot \sqrt{3}}$

$x = \frac{-2\sqrt{3}}{9}$

65. $4k^2 + 26k + 30$

$= 2(2k^2 + 13k + 15)$

$= 2(2k + 3)(k + 5)$

66. inverse $= \dfrac{1}{-32 + 0}\begin{bmatrix} -4 & 0 \\ -1 & 8 \end{bmatrix}$

$= \begin{bmatrix} \dfrac{1}{8} & 0 \\ -\dfrac{1}{32} & -\dfrac{1}{4} \end{bmatrix}$

9-4 Ellipses

PAGE 413   CHECKING FOR UNDERSTANDING

1. The result is a circle. A circle is a special ellipse.

2. The major axis is parallel or equal to the axis named in the term with the greater denominator. For example, in the equation $\dfrac{(x-3)^2}{39} + \dfrac{y^2}{22} = 1$, the x-axis is the term with the greater denominator, so the major axis is parallel or equal to the x-axis.

3. It is an ellipse with a major axis that is 4 units long and parallel to the x-axis. The minor axis is 2 units long. The center is (0, 2) and the foci are $(\sqrt{3}, 2)$, $(-\sqrt{3}, 2)$.

4. (0, 0), H   5. (0, 0), V

6. (0, 3), H   7. (11, -8), V

8. $8x^2 + 2y^2 = 32$ 9. $7x^2 + 3y^2 = 84$

   $\dfrac{x^2}{4} + \dfrac{y^2}{16} = 1$ $\dfrac{x^2}{12} + \dfrac{y^2}{28} = 1$

10. $x^2 + 4y^2 + 2x - 24y + 33 = 0$

   $x^2 + 2x + 1 + 4(y^2 - 6y + 9) = -33 + 1 + 36$

   $(x + 1)^2 + 4(y - 3)^2 = 4$

   $\dfrac{(x + 1)^2}{4} + \dfrac{(y - 3)^2}{1} = 1$

11. $4x^2 + 9y^2 + 24x - 90y = -225$

   $4(x^2 + 6x + 9) + 9(y^2 - 10y + 25) = -225 + 36 + 225$

   $4(x + 3)^2 + 9(y - 5)^2 = 36$

   $\dfrac{(x + 3)^2}{9} + \dfrac{(y - 5)^2}{4} = 1$

12. $6x^2 + 10y^2 + 54x + 20y = 122$

   $6(x^2 + 9x + 20.25) + 10(y^2 + 2y + 1)$
   $= 122 + 121.5 + 10$

   $6(x + 4.5)^2 + 10(y + 1)^2 = 253.5$

   $\dfrac{(x + 4.5)^2}{42.25} + \dfrac{(y + 1)^2}{25.35} = 1$

13. $9x^2 + 16y^2 - 54x + 64y + 1 = 0$

   $9(x^2 - 6x + 9) + 16(y^2 + 4y + 4) = -1 + 81 + 64$

   $9(x - 3)^2 + 16(y + 2)^2 = 144$

   $\dfrac{(x - 3)^2}{16} + \dfrac{(y + 2)^2}{9} = 1$

For exercises 14-17, A is the center, B is the foci, C is the length of the major axis and D is the length of the minor axis.

14. $\dfrac{x^2}{9} + \dfrac{y^2}{36} = 1$ **15.** $\dfrac{x^2}{36} + \dfrac{y^2}{16} = 1$

$a = 6,\ b = 3$ $a = 6;\ b = 4$

A. (0, 0)   A. (0, 0)

B. $b^2 = a^2 - c^2$ B. $b^2 = a^2 - c^2$

   $9 = 36 - c^2$ $16 = 36 - c^2$

   $c^2 = 27$ $c^2 = 20$

   $c = \sqrt{27}$ $c = \sqrt{20}$

   $(0, \pm 3\sqrt{3})$ $(\pm 2\sqrt{5}, 0)$

C. $2a = 12$ C. $2a = 12$

D. $2b = 6$ D. $2b = 8$

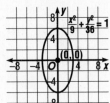   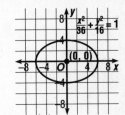

16. $3x^2 + 9y^2 = 27$ **17.** $16x^2 + 9y^2 = 144$

$\dfrac{x^2}{9} + \dfrac{y^2}{3} = 1$ $\dfrac{x^2}{9} + \dfrac{y^2}{16} = 1$

$a = 3,\ b = \sqrt{3}$ $a = 4,\ b = 3$

A. (0, 0)   A. (0, 0)

B. $b^2 = a^2 - c^2$ B. $b^2 = a^2 - c^2$

   $3 = 9 - c^2$ $9 = 16 - c^2$

   $c = \sqrt{6}$ $c^2 = 7$

   $(\pm\sqrt{6}, 0)$ $c = \sqrt{7}$

C. $2a = 6$ $(0, \pm\sqrt{7})$

D. $2b = 2\sqrt{3}$ C. $2a = 8$

   D. $2b = 6$

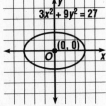   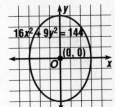

PAGES 413-415   EXERCISES

18. $b^2 = a^2 - c^2$ **19.** $b^2 = a^2 - c^2$

   $= 8^2 - 5^2$ $= 6^2 - 4^2$

   $= 39$ $= 20$

$\dfrac{x^2}{39} + \dfrac{y^2}{64} = 1$ $\dfrac{x^2}{36} + \dfrac{y^2}{20} = 1$

20. $2a = 16$

$\quad a = 8$

$\quad$ center is at $(5, 4)$

$\quad c = (5 \pm \sqrt{55}) - 5$ or $\pm\sqrt{55}$

$\quad b^2 = a^2 - c^2$

$\quad b^2 = 8^2 - (\sqrt{55})^2$

$\quad b^2 = 64 - 55$

$\quad b^2 = 9$

$\quad b = \pm 3$

$\quad \dfrac{(x - 5)^2}{64} + \dfrac{(y - 4)^2}{9} = 1$

For exercises 21-34, A is the center, B is the foci, C is the length of the major axis and D is the length of the minor axis.

21. $\dfrac{x^2}{25} + \dfrac{y^2}{9} = 1$

$\quad a = 5; \ b = 3$

A. $(0, 0)$

B. $b^2 = a^2 - c^2$

$\quad\quad 9 = 25 - c^2$

$\quad\quad c = 4$

$\quad\quad (\pm 4, 0)$

C. $2a = 10$

D. $2b = 6$

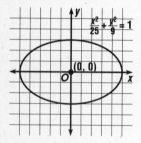

22. $\dfrac{x^2}{5} + \dfrac{y^2}{10} = 1$

$\quad a = \sqrt{10}, \ b = \sqrt{5}$

A. $(0, 0)$

B. $b^2 = a^2 - c^2$

$\quad\quad 5 = 10 - c^2$

$\quad\quad c = \sqrt{5}$

$\quad\quad (0, \pm\sqrt{5})$

C. $2a = 2\sqrt{10}$

D. $2b = 2\sqrt{5}$

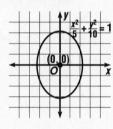

23. $x^2 + 9y^2 = 9$

$\quad \dfrac{x^2}{9} + y^2 = 1$

$\quad a = 3, \ b = 1$

A. $(0, 0)$

B. $b^2 = a^2 - c^2$

$\quad\quad 1 = 9 - c^2$

$\quad\quad c = \sqrt{8} = 2\sqrt{2}$

$\quad\quad (\pm 2\sqrt{2}, 0)$

C. $2a = 6$

D. $2b = 2$

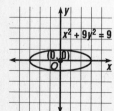

24. $36x^2 + 81y^2 = 2916$

$\quad \dfrac{x^2}{81} + \dfrac{y^2}{36} = 1$

$\quad a = 9; \ b = 6$

A. $(0, 0)$

B. $36 = 81 - c^2$

$\quad\quad c = \sqrt{45}$

$\quad\quad (\pm 3\sqrt{5}, 0)$

C. $2a = 18$

D. $2b = 12$

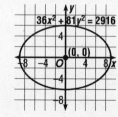

25. $27x^2 + 9y^2 = 81$

$\quad \dfrac{x^2}{3} + \dfrac{y^2}{9} = 1$

$\quad a = 3; \ b = \sqrt{3}$

A. $(0, 0)$

B. $3 = 9 - c^2$

$\quad\quad c = \sqrt{6}$

$\quad\quad (0, \pm\sqrt{6})$

C. $2a = 6$

D. $2b = 2\sqrt{3}$

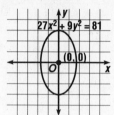

26. $\dfrac{(x + 3)^2}{36} + \dfrac{(y - 4)^2}{9} = 1$

$\quad a = 6; \ b = 3$

A. $(-3, 4)$

B. $9 = 36 - c^2$

$\quad\quad c = \sqrt{27}$

$\quad\quad (-3 \pm 3\sqrt{3}, 4)$

C. $2a = 12$

D. $2b = 6$

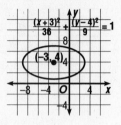

27. $\dfrac{(x - 8)^2}{4} + \dfrac{(y + 8)^2}{1} = 1$

$\quad a = 2; \ b = 1$

A. $(8, -8)$

B. $c = \sqrt{3}$

$\quad\quad (8 \pm \sqrt{3}, -8)$

C. $2a = 4$

D. $2b = 2$

28. $\dfrac{(x + 2)^2}{20} + \dfrac{(y + 3)^2}{40} = 1$

$\quad a = \sqrt{40}; \ b = \sqrt{20}$

A. $(-2, -3)$

B. $c = 2\sqrt{5}$

$\quad\quad (-2, -3 \pm 2\sqrt{5})$

C. $2a = 4\sqrt{10}$

D. $2b = 4\sqrt{5}$

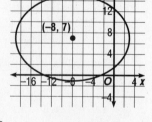

29. $\dfrac{(x + 8)^2}{121} + \dfrac{(y - 7)^2}{64} = 1$

$\quad a = 11, \ b = 8$

A. $(-8, 7)$

B. $c^2 = a^2 - b^2$

$\quad\quad = 57$

$\quad\quad c = \sqrt{57}$

$\quad\quad (-8 \pm \sqrt{57}, 7)$

C. $2a = 22$

D. $2b = 16$

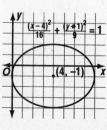

30. $\dfrac{(x - 4)^2}{16} + \dfrac{(y + 1)^2}{9} = 1$

$\quad a = 4, \ b = 3$

A. $(4, -1)$

B. $c^2 = 7$

$\quad\quad = \sqrt{7}$

$\quad\quad (4 \pm \sqrt{7}, -1)$

C. $2a = 8$

D. $2b = 6$

31. $4x^2 + 9y^2 + 16x - 18y - 11 = 0$

$4(x^2 + 4x + 4) + 9(y^2 - 2y + 1) = 36$

$$\frac{(x + 2)^2}{9} + \frac{(y - 1)^2}{4} = 1$$

$a = 3,\ b = 2$

A. $(-2, 1)$

B. $c^2 = 9 - 4$

$c = \pm\sqrt{5}$

$(-2 \pm \sqrt{5},\ 1)$

C. $2a = 6$

D. $2b = 4$

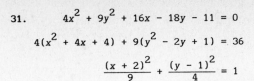

$(-2, 1)$

$4x^2 + 9y^2 + 16x - 18y - 11 = 0$

32. $9x^2 + 16y^2 - 18x + 64y = 71$

$9(x^2 - 2x + 1) + 16(y^2 + 4y + 4) = 144$

$$\frac{(x - 1)^2}{16} + \frac{(y + 2)^2}{9} = 1$$

$a = 4;\ b = 3$

A. $(1, -2)$

B. $c = \sqrt{7}$

$(1 \pm \sqrt{7},\ -2)$

C. $2a = 8$

D. $2b = 6$

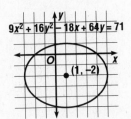

$9x^2 + 16y^2 - 18x + 64y = 71$

$(1, -2)$

33. $7x^2 + 3y^2 - 28x - 12y + 19 = 0$

$7(x^2 - 4x + 4) + 3(y^2 - 4y + 4) = 21$

$$\frac{(x - 2)^2}{3} + \frac{(y - 2)^2}{7} = 1$$

$a = \sqrt{7},\ b = \sqrt{3}$

A. $(2, 2)$

B. $c^2 = 7 - 3$

$c = 2$

$(2, 4),\ (2, 0)$

C. $2a = 2\sqrt{7}$

D. $2b = 2\sqrt{3}$

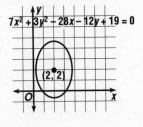

$7x^2 + 3y^2 - 28x - 12y + 19 = 0$

$(2, 2)$

34. $16x^2 + 25y^2 + 32x - 150y = 159$

$16(x^2 + 2x + 1) + 25(y^2 - 6y + 9) = 400$

$$\frac{(x + 1)^2}{25} + \frac{(y - 3)^2}{16} = 1$$

$a = 5;\ b = 4$

A. $(-1, 3)$

B. $c = 3$

$(2, 3),\ (-4, 3)$

C. $2a = 10$

D. $2b = 8$

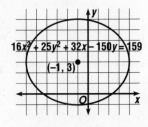

$16x^2 + 25y^2 + 32x - 150y = 159$

$(-1, 3)$

35. center: $(0, 0)$

$2a = 20 \qquad 2b = 12$

$a = 10 \qquad b = 6$

$$\frac{x^2}{36} + \frac{y^2}{100} = 1$$

36. center: $(0, 0)$

$2a = 26 \qquad 2b = 10$

$a = 13 \qquad b = 5$

$$\frac{x^2}{169} + \frac{y^2}{25} = 1$$

37. center: $(5, 4)$

$2a = 16 \qquad 2b = 9$

$a = 8 \qquad b = \frac{9}{2}$

$$\frac{(x - 5)^2}{64} + \frac{(y - 4)^2}{\frac{81}{4}} = 1$$

$$\frac{(x - 5)^2}{64} + \frac{4(y - 4)^2}{81} = 1$$

38. center: $\left(\dfrac{4 + 0}{2},\ \dfrac{-4 + 12}{2}\right)$

$= (2, 4)$

$2a = 16 \qquad 2b = 4$

$a = 8 \qquad b = 2$

$$\frac{(x - 2)^2}{4} + \frac{(y - 4)^2}{64} = 1$$

39. center: $(-2, 3)$

$2a = 12 \qquad 2b = 8$

$a = 6 \qquad b = 4$

$$\frac{(x + 2)^2}{16} + \frac{(y - 3)^2}{36} = 1$$

40. center: $\left(\dfrac{-9 + 5}{2},\ \dfrac{2 + 2}{2}\right)$

$= (-2, 2)$

$2a = 14 \qquad 2b = 6$

$a = 7 \qquad b = 3$

$$\frac{(x + 2)^2}{49} + \frac{(y - 2)^2}{9} = 1$$

41. For $k > 0$, as k increases the shape remains similar and the size increases.

42.a. $a = 23,\ b = 48$

$$\frac{x^2}{2304} + \frac{y^2}{529} = 1$$

b. The desk is on one focus point.

$c^2 = 2304 - 529$

$c \sim 42$

He had to stand about 84 feet away.

43. $(x - 6)^2 + (y - 2)^2 = 25$

44. $r = \sqrt{(1 - 0)^2 + (5 - 0)^2}$

$= \sqrt{26}$

$(x - 1)^2 + (x - 5)^2 = 26$

45. $f(x) = x^2 + 2x - 2$

$= (x^2 + 2x + 1) - 2 - 1$

$= (x + 1)^2 - 3$

$h = -1 \qquad k = -3$

vertex: $(-1, -3)$

axis of symmetry: $x = -1$

opens up

46. no

47. $(7 - 7i)(7 + 7i) = 49 - 49i^2$

$= 49 + 49$

$= 98$

48. Let n = number of cards Jim has,

$\quad 2n$ = number of cards Rose has,

$5n - 5$ = number of cards Kris has.

Total cards: $n + 2n + 5n - 5 = 8n - 5$

Since Rose is able to give 5 cards to Kris,

$2n > 5$. So $n > 3$ since one can't have a fraction

of a card. Find $8n - 5$ for $n > 3$. Since there

could not be more than 52 cards, the possible

totals are 19, 27, 35, 43, and 51.

PAGE 415   MID-CHAPTER REVIEW

1. $d = \sqrt{(-2 - 4)^2 + (7 + 1)^2}$

$\quad = \sqrt{100}$

$\quad = 10$

2. $d = \sqrt{(0 - 6)^2 + (5 - 3)^2}$

$\quad = \sqrt{40}$

$\quad = 2\sqrt{10}$

3. $m = \left(\dfrac{3 + 5}{2}, \dfrac{-1 - 7}{2}\right)$ **4.** $m = \left(\dfrac{8 - 5}{2}, \dfrac{0 + 12}{2}\right)$

$\quad = (4, -4)$ $\quad = \left(\dfrac{3}{2}, 6\right)$

5. $-12y = x^2$

$\quad y = -\dfrac{1}{12}x^2$

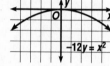

vertex: $(0, 0)$

axis of symmetry: $x = 0$

focus: $\left(0, 0 + \dfrac{1}{4\left(-\dfrac{1}{12}\right)}\right) = (0, -3)$

directrix: $y = 0 - \dfrac{1}{4\left(-\dfrac{1}{12}\right)} = 3$

opens downward

latus rectum: $\left|\dfrac{1}{\left(-\dfrac{1}{12}\right)}\right| = 12$

6. $8x = y^2 + 4y + 28$

$8x = (y^2 + 4y + 4) + 28 - 4$

$x = \dfrac{1}{8}(y + 2)^2 + 3$

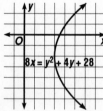

vertex: $(3, -2)$

axis of symmetry: $y = -2$

focus: $\left(3 + \dfrac{1}{4\left(\dfrac{1}{8}\right)}, -2\right) = (5, -2)$

directrix: $x = 3 - \dfrac{1}{4\left(\dfrac{1}{8}\right)} = 1$

opens right

latus rectum: $\left|\dfrac{1}{\dfrac{1}{8}}\right| = 8$

7. $h = 3$

$5 = k + \dfrac{1}{4}a$

$\dfrac{1 = k - \dfrac{1}{4}a}{6 = 2k}$

$k = 3$

$5 = 3 + \dfrac{1}{4a}$

$2 = \dfrac{1}{4a}$

$a = \dfrac{1}{8}$

$y = \dfrac{1}{8}(x - 3)^2 + 3$

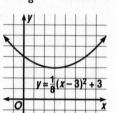

8. $0 = h + \dfrac{1}{4a}$

$\dfrac{1 = h - \dfrac{1}{4a}}{1 = 2h}$

$h = \dfrac{1}{2}, \; k = 4$

$0 = \dfrac{1}{2} + \dfrac{1}{4a}$

$-\dfrac{1}{2} = \dfrac{1}{4a}$

$a = -\dfrac{1}{2}$

$x = -\dfrac{1}{2}(y - 4)^2 + \dfrac{1}{2}$

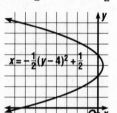

9. parabola

10. circle

11. center: $(0, 0)$

radius: $3\sqrt{3}$

12. center: $(-3, 1)$

radius: 9

13. $12x^2 + 6y^2 = 168$

$\dfrac{x^2}{14} + \dfrac{y^2}{28} = 1$

14. $8x^2 + 4y^2 - 16x - 20y = 7$

$8(x^2 - 2x + 1) + 4\left(y^2 - 5y + \dfrac{25}{4}\right) = 40$

$\dfrac{(x - 1)^2}{5} + \dfrac{(y - 2.5)^2}{10} = 1$

15. center: $\left(3, \dfrac{8 - 6}{2}\right) = (3, 1)$

$2a = 18 \qquad 2c = 14 \qquad b^2 = a^2 - c^2$

$a = 9 \qquad\quad c = 7 \qquad\quad\; = 9^2 - 7^2$

$\qquad\qquad\qquad\qquad\qquad\qquad = 32$

$\dfrac{(x - 3)^2}{32} + \dfrac{(y - 1)^2}{81} = 1$

9-5 Hyperbolas

PAGES 419-420   CHECKING FOR UNDERSTANDING

1. Answers may vary.

Similarities: two axes of symmetry, can be

defined by two foci, distance from center to

vertices is $2a$.

Differences: standard equation of hyperbola

contains subtraction and ellipse contains

addition; ellipse is a closed figure and the

hyperbola is not, relationship of a, b, and c is

different, hyperbola has asymptotes.

2. The equation of an ellipse contains addition and the equation of a hyperbola contains subtraction. That comes from the definitions of both curves.

3. A hyperbola with center at (0, 2), a vertical transverse axis, and vertices at (0, 7) and (0, -3). The slopes of the asymptotes are $\frac{5}{2}$ and $-\frac{5}{2}$ and the foci are at $(0, 2 + \sqrt{29})$ and $(0, 2 - \sqrt{29})$, or about (0, 7.4) and (0, -3.4).

4. $a = 4$, $c = 5$ $\frac{y^2}{16} - \frac{x^2}{9} = 1$

    $b^2 = c^2 - a^2$ vertices: (0, 4), (0, -4)

    $b^2 = 5^2 - 4^2$ foci: (0, 5), (0, -5)

    $b = 3$ slopes of asymptotes: $\pm\frac{4}{3}$

5. ellipse   6. hyperbola

7. hyperbola   8. ellipse

9. hyperbola   10. ellipse

11. $2x^2 - y^2 = 10$ 12. $6y^2 - 34x^2 = 204$

    $\frac{x^2}{5} - \frac{y^2}{10} = 1$ $\frac{y^2}{34} - \frac{x^2}{6} = 1$

13. $(y - 1)^2 - 4(x - 2)^2 = 168$

    $\frac{(y - 1)^2}{168} - \frac{(x - 2)^2}{42} = 1$

14. $3x^2 - 12y^2 + 45x + 60y = -60$

    $x^2 - 4y^2 + 15x + 20y = -20$

    $x^2 + 15x + 56.25 - 4(y^2 - 5y + 6.25)$

                $= -20 + 56.25 - 25$

    $(x + 7.5)^2 - 4(y - 2.5)^2 = 11.25$

    $\frac{(x + 7.5)^2}{11.25} - \frac{(y - 2.5)^2}{2.8125} = 1$

For exercises 15-18, A is vertices, B is the foci, and C is the slope of the asymptotes.

15. $\frac{x^2}{16} - \frac{y^2}{4} = 1$ 16. $\frac{x^2}{6} - \frac{y^2}{2} = 1$

    $a = 4$; $b = 2$ $a = \sqrt{6}$, $b = \sqrt{2}$

    A. $(\pm 4, 0)$ A. $(\pm\sqrt{6}, 0)$

    B. $c^2 = a^2 + b^2$ B. $c^2 = a^2 + b^2$

      $c^2 = 4 + 16$ $c^2 = 6 + 2$

      $c^2 = 20$ $c = \sqrt{8}$

      $c = 2\sqrt{5}$ $(\pm 2\sqrt{2}, 0)$

      $(\pm 2\sqrt{5}, 0)$

    C. $\pm\frac{2}{4} = \pm\frac{1}{2}$ C. $\pm\frac{\sqrt{2}}{\sqrt{6}} = \pm\frac{\sqrt{3}}{3}$

17. $\frac{x^2}{9} - \frac{y^2}{4} = 1$ 18. $x^2 - y^2 = 4$

    $a = 3$; $b = 2$ $\frac{x^2}{4} - \frac{y^2}{4} = 1$

    A. $(\pm 3, 0)$ $a = 2$; $b = 2$

    B. $c^2 = 9 + 4$ A. $(\pm 2, 0)$

      $c = \sqrt{13}$ B. $c^2 = 4 + 4$

      $(\pm\sqrt{13}, 0)$ $c = \sqrt{8}$

    C. $\pm\frac{2}{3}$ $(\pm 2\sqrt{2}, 0)$

               C. ± 1

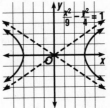

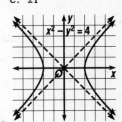

19. $c^2 = a^2 + b^2$ 20. Center: $\left(\frac{3 - 1}{2}, -2\right)$

    $4^2 = 2^2 + b^2$ $= (1, -2)$

    $b^2 = 12$ $2a = 4$ $2c = 6$

    $\frac{x^2}{4} - \frac{y^2}{12} = 1$ $a = 2$ $c = 3$

                   $c^2 = a^2 + b^2$

                   $9 = 4 + b^2$

                   $5 = b^2$

            $\frac{(x - 1)^2}{4} - \frac{(y + 2)^2}{5} = 1$

21. Center: (3, -5)

    $2a = 4$ $a = 2$

    Asymptotes have equations $y = \pm\frac{3}{2}x$. Since $a = 2$ and $y = \pm\frac{b}{a}x$, $b = 3$.

    $\frac{(x - 3)^2}{4} - \frac{(y + 5)^2}{9} = 1$

22. Center: $\left(0, \frac{-8 - 3}{2}\right)$ 23. Center: (0, 0)

        $= (0, -5.5)$ $c^2 = a^2 + b^2$

    $2a = 5$ $2c = 7$ $5^2 = 2^2 + b^2$

    $a = 2.5$ $c = 3.5$ $21 = b^2$

    $c^2 = a^2 + b^2$

    $(3.5)^2 = (2.5)^2 + b^2$ $\frac{y^2}{4} - \frac{x^2}{21} = 1$

       $6 = b^2$

    $\frac{(y + 5.5)^2}{6.25} - \frac{x^2}{6} = 1$

24. Center: $\left(3, \dfrac{1.5 - 0.5}{2}\right)$

$= (3, 0.5)$

$2a = 2 \qquad 2c = 7$

$a = 1 \qquad c = 3.5$

$c^2 = a^2 + b^2$

$(3.5)^2 = 1^2 + b^2$

$11.25 = b^2$

$$\frac{(y - 0.5)^2}{1} - \frac{(x - 3)^2}{11.25} = 1$$

For exercises 25-43, A is vertices, B is the foci, and C is the slope of the asymptotes.

25. $\dfrac{x^2}{36} - \dfrac{y^2}{1} = 1$

$a = 6;\ b = 1$

A. $(\pm 6, 0)$

B. $c^2 = a^2 + b^2$

$c^2 = 36 + 1$

$c^2 = 37$

$c = \sqrt{37}$

$(\pm\sqrt{37}, 0)$

C. $\pm\frac{1}{6}$

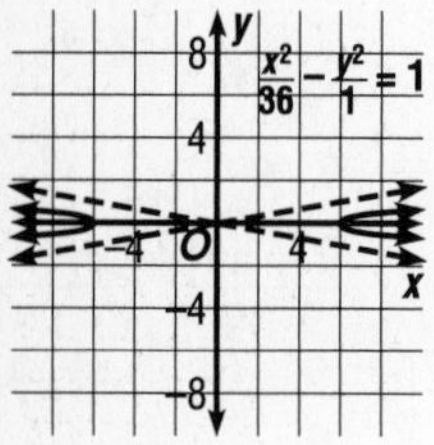

26. $\dfrac{y^2}{16} - \dfrac{x^2}{25} = 1$

$a = 4;\ b = 5$

A. $(0, \pm 4)$

B. $c^2 = 16 + 25$

$c = \sqrt{41}$

$(0, \pm\sqrt{41})$

C. $\pm\frac{4}{5}$

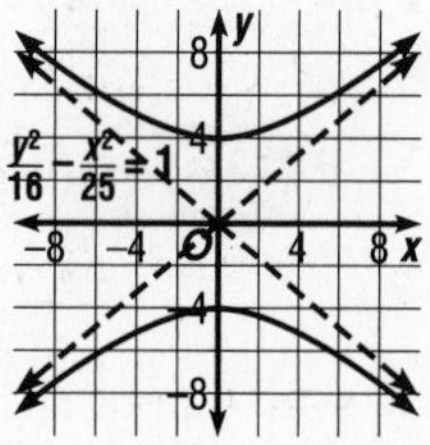

27. $\dfrac{x^2}{9} - \dfrac{y^2}{25} = 1$

$a = 3;\ b = 5$

A. $(\pm 3, 0)$

B. $c^2 = a^2 + b^2$

$c^2 = 9 + 25$

$c^2 = 34$

$c = \sqrt{34}$

$(\pm\sqrt{34}, 0)$

C. $\pm\frac{5}{3}$

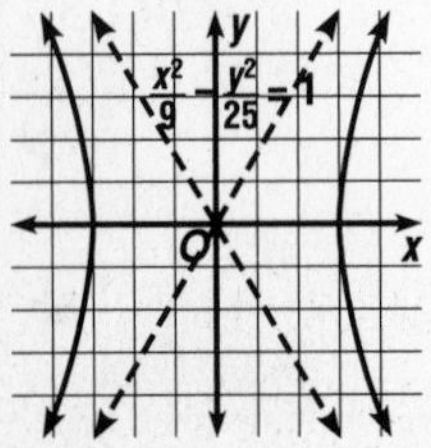

28. $\dfrac{y^2}{81} - \dfrac{x^2}{25} = 1$

$a = 9;\ b = 5$

A. $(0, \pm 9)$

B. $c^2 = a^2 + b^2$

$c^2 = 81 + 25$

$c = \sqrt{106}$

$(0, \pm\sqrt{106})$

C. $\pm\frac{9}{5}$

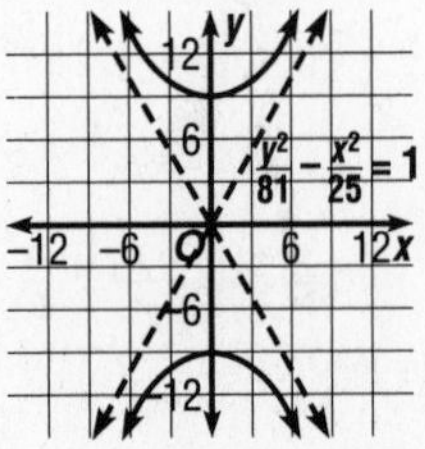

29. $\dfrac{x^2}{4} - \dfrac{y^2}{9} = 1$

$a = 2;\ b = 3$

A. $(\pm 2, 0)$

B. $c^2 = 4 + 9$

$c = \sqrt{13}$

$(\pm\sqrt{13}, 0)$

C. $\pm\frac{3}{2}$

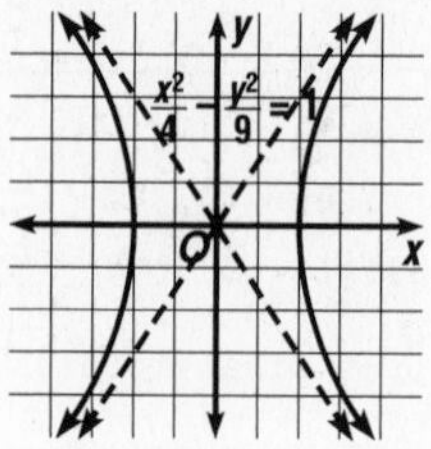

30. $\dfrac{x^2}{81} - \dfrac{y^2}{36} = 1$

$a = 9;\ b = 6$

A. $(\pm 9, 0)$

B. $c^2 = 81 + 36$

$c = \sqrt{117}$

$(\pm\sqrt{117}, 0)$

C. $\pm\frac{6}{9} = \pm\frac{2}{3}$

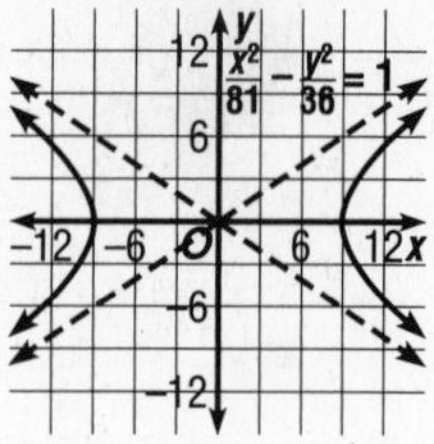

31. $\dfrac{y^2}{18} - \dfrac{x^2}{20} = 1$

$a = 3\sqrt{2};\ b = 2\sqrt{5}$

A. $(0, \pm 3\sqrt{2})$

B. $c^2 = a^2 + b^2$

$c^2 = 18 + 20$

$c = \sqrt{38}$

$(0, \pm\sqrt{38})$

C. $\pm\dfrac{3\sqrt{2}}{2\sqrt{5}} = \pm\dfrac{3\sqrt{10}}{10}$

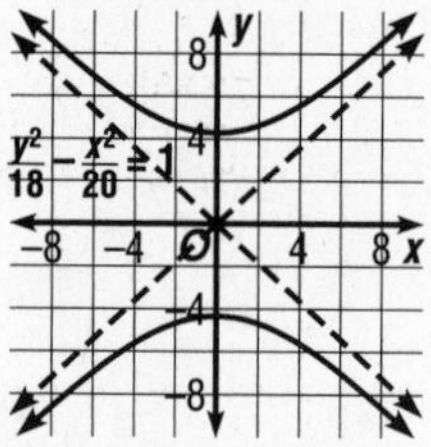

32. $\dfrac{x^2}{9} - \dfrac{y^2}{16} = 1$

$a = 3;\ b = 4$

A. $(\pm 3, 0)$

B. $c^2 = 9 + 16$

$c = 5$

$(\pm 5, 0)$

C. $\pm\frac{4}{3}$

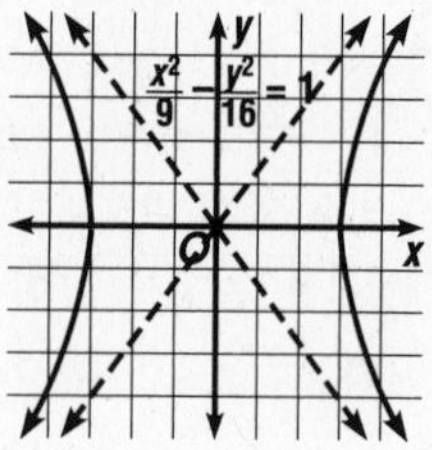

33. $\dfrac{y^2}{100} - \dfrac{x^2}{144} = 1$

$a = 10;\ b = 12$

A. $(0, \pm 10)$

B. $c^2 = 100 + 144$

$c = \sqrt{244}$

$(0, \pm 2\sqrt{61})$

C. $\pm\frac{10}{12} = \pm\frac{5}{6}$

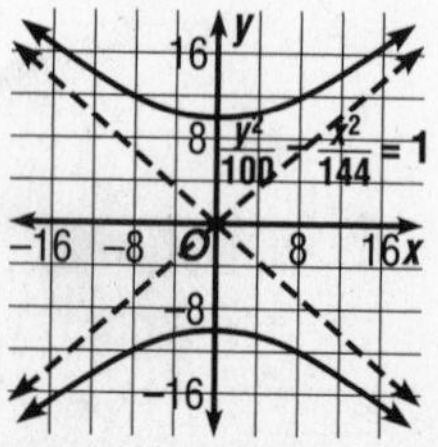

34. $x^2 - 2y^2 = 2$

$\dfrac{x^2}{2} - \dfrac{y^2}{1} = 1$

$a = \sqrt{2};\ b = 1$

A. $(\pm\sqrt{2}, 0)$

B. $c^2 = 2 + 1$

$c = \sqrt{3}$

$(\pm\sqrt{3}, 0)$

C. $\pm\dfrac{1}{\sqrt{2}} = \pm\dfrac{\sqrt{2}}{2}$

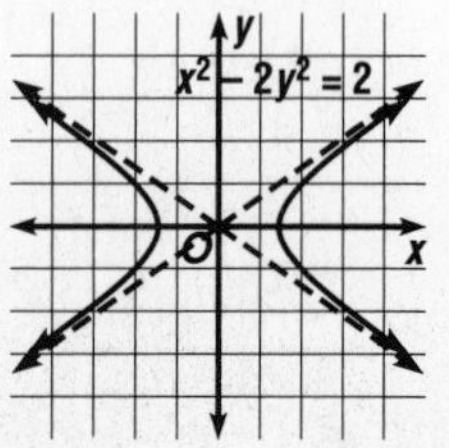

35. $y^2 = 36 + 4x^2$

$\dfrac{x^2}{36} - \dfrac{x^2}{9} = 1$

$a = 6; \ b = 3$

A. $(0, \pm 6)$

B. $c = \sqrt{36 + 9}$

$(0, \pm 3\sqrt{5})$

C. ± 2

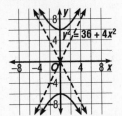

36. $\dfrac{(x + 6)^2}{36} - \dfrac{(y + 3)^2}{9} = 1$

center: $(-6, -3)$

$a = 6; \ b = 3$

A. $(-12, -3), \ (0, -3)$

B. $c = \sqrt{36 + 9}$

$(-6 \pm 3\sqrt{5}, \ -3)$

C. $\pm \dfrac{1}{2}$

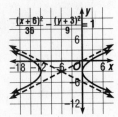

37. $\dfrac{(y - 3)^2}{25} - \dfrac{(x - 2)^2}{16} = 1$

center: $(2, 3)$

$a = 5, \ b = 4$

A. $(2, 8), \ (2, -2)$

B. $c = \sqrt{25 + 16}$

$(2, 3 \pm \sqrt{41})$

C. $\pm \dfrac{5}{4}$

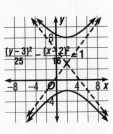

38. $\dfrac{(y - 4)^2}{16} - \dfrac{(x + 2)^2}{9} = 1$

center: $(-2, 4)$

$a = 4; \ b = 3$

A. $(-2, 8), \ (-2, 0)$

B. $c = \sqrt{16 + 9}$

$(-2, 9), \ (-2, -1)$

C. $\pm \dfrac{4}{3}$

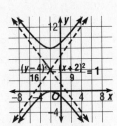

39. $\dfrac{(x + 1)^2}{4} - \dfrac{(y + 3)^2}{9} = 1$

center: $(-1, -3)$

$a = 2; \ b = 3$

A. $(-3, -3), \ (1, -3)$

B. $c = \sqrt{9 + 4} = \sqrt{13}$

$(-1 \pm \sqrt{13}, \ -3)$

C. $\pm \dfrac{3}{2}$

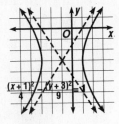

40. $(x + 3)^2 - 4(y - 2)^2 = 4$

$\dfrac{(x + 3)^2}{4} - \dfrac{(y - 2)^2}{1} = 1$

center: $(-3, 2)$

$a = 2; \ b = 1$

A. $(-1, 2), \ (-5, 2)$

B. $c = \sqrt{4 + 1}$

$(-3 \pm \sqrt{5}, \ 2)$

C. $\pm \dfrac{1}{2}$

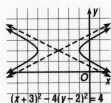

41. $5(x - 4)^2 - 4(y + 2)^2 = 100$

$\dfrac{(x - 4)^2}{20} - \dfrac{(y + 2)^2}{25} = 1$

center: $(4, -2)$

$a = 2\sqrt{5}; \ b = 5$

A. $(4 \pm 2\sqrt{5}, \ -2)$

B. $c = \sqrt{20 + 25}$

$(4 \pm 3\sqrt{5}, \ -2)$

C. $\pm \dfrac{\sqrt{5}}{2}$

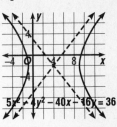

42. $y^2 - 4x^2 - 2y - 16x = -1$

$(y^2 - 2y + 1) - 4(x^2 + 4x + 4) = -16$

$\dfrac{(x + 2)^2}{4} - \dfrac{(y - 1)^2}{16} = 1$

center: $(-2, 1)$

$a = 2; \ b = 4$

A. $(0, 1), \ (-4, 1)$

B. $c = \sqrt{4 + 16}$

$(-2 \pm 2\sqrt{5}, \ 1)$

C. ± 2

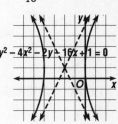

43. $y^2 - 3x^2 + 6y + 6x = 18$

$(y^2 + 6y + 9) - 3(x^2 - 2x + 1) = 24$

$(y + 3)^2 - 3(x - 1)^2 = 24$

$\dfrac{(y + 3)^2}{24} - \dfrac{(x - 1)^2}{8} = 1$

center: $(1, -3)$

$a = 2\sqrt{6}; \ b = 2\sqrt{2}$

A. $(1, -3 \pm 2\sqrt{6})$

B. $c = \sqrt{24 + 8}$

$(1, -3 \pm 4\sqrt{2})$

C. $\pm \sqrt{3}$

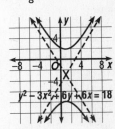

44. center: $(0, 0); \ a^2 = 1; \ b^2 = 16$

$\dfrac{x^2}{1} - \dfrac{y^2}{16} = 1$

45. center: $(5, 4); \ a^2 = 4; \ b^2 = 36$

$\dfrac{(y - 4)^2}{4} - \dfrac{(x - 5)^2}{36} = 1$

46. $3x - 2y = 0 \qquad 3x + 2y = 0$

$y = \dfrac{3}{2}x \qquad\quad y = -\dfrac{3}{2}x$

center: $(0, 0); \ a = 2; \ b = 3$

$\dfrac{x^2}{4} - \dfrac{y^2}{9} = 1$

47.

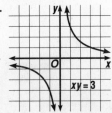

48.

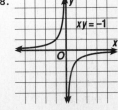

49.
$$5x + 3y = -1 \qquad\qquad 5x - 3y = 11$$
$$y = -\frac{5}{3}x - \frac{1}{3} \qquad\qquad y = \frac{5}{3}x - \frac{11}{3}$$
$$a = 5 \qquad b = 3$$
$$5x + 3y = -1$$
$$\underline{5x - 3y = 11}$$
$$10x = 10$$
$$x = 1$$
$$y = -2$$
$$\frac{(x-1)^2}{9} - \frac{(y+2)^2}{25} = 1$$

50. Sample graph:

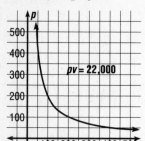

$pv = 22,000$

51. Sample graph:

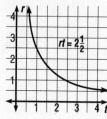

$rt = 2\frac{1}{2}$

52. $\dfrac{x^2}{4} + \dfrac{y^2}{25} = 1$

$a = 5;\ b = 2$

A. $(0, 0)$

B. $b^2 = a^2 - c^2$

$4 = 25 - c^2$

$c^2 = 21$

$c = \sqrt{21}$

$(0, \pm\sqrt{21})$

C. $2a = 10$

D. $2b = 4$

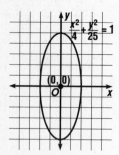

53.
$$2a = 10 \qquad 2c = 8$$
$$a = 5 \qquad c = 4$$
$$c^2 = a^2 - b^2$$
$$16 = 25 - b^2$$
$$b^2 = 9$$
$$\text{Center: } \left(\frac{5-3}{2}, 4\right)$$
$$= (1, 4)$$
$$\frac{(x-1)^2}{25} + \frac{(y-4)^2}{9} = 1$$

54. $x^2 \le 6$

$x \ge -\sqrt{6},\ x \le \sqrt{6}$

$\{x \mid -\sqrt{6} \le x \le \sqrt{6}\}$

55.
$$2x^2 + 4x = 6$$
$$x^2 + 2x - 3 = 0$$
$$(x + 3)(x - 1) = 0$$
$$x = -3 \text{ or } x = 1$$
$$\text{sum} = -3 + 1 = -2$$
$$\text{product} = (-3)(1) = -3$$

56. $\dfrac{5^{\frac{1}{3}}}{5^{\frac{1}{3}}}$

9–6 **Problem-Solving Strategy: Use a Model**

1. When it is difficult or impossible to solve a problem directly.

2. 5, you could get all five tickets right away.

3. See students' work.

4. Answers will vary depending on simulation.

5. 20

6. $4 + 8 + 12 + 16 = 40 \times 24 = 960$

$12 + 1 + 2 + 3 + 4 + 5 + 6 + 7 + 8 + 9 + 10 + 11$

$= 78 \times 2 = 156$

$960 + 156 = 1116$ per day

$1116 \times 7 = 7812$ per week

7. $120(2) = 240$

239

8. Answers may vary.

Sample answer:

$44 + 4 \times 4 - 4$

9. Answers may vary.

$67\% = 2$ out of 3 1 out of $2 = 50\%$

2 out of $2 = 100\%$

Probably won't win but a good chance of a tie.

Answers may vary.

Graphing Calculator Exploration: Conic Sections

1. $x = y^2 + 4y + 28$

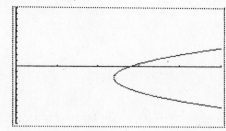

2. $(x - 2)^2 + y^2 = 9$

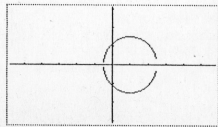

3. $5x^2 + 15y^2 = 225$

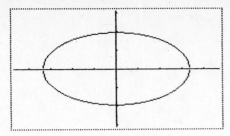

4. $9x^2 - 4y^2 - 54x - 40y - 55 = 0$

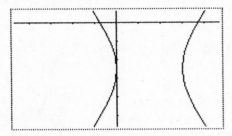

5. $x^2 + y^2 + 7x - 5 = 0$

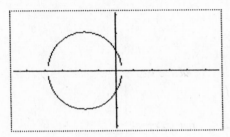

6. $y^2 - 20x^2 - 4x - 6y = 36$

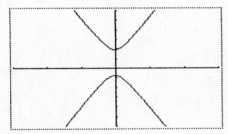

9-7 Conic Sections

1. parabola, circle, ellipse, and hyperbola; They are formed by slicing a cone.

2. parabola

3. A circle is an ellipse whose major axis and minor axis are equal.

4. circle
5. parabola
6. parabola
7. hyperbola
8. ellipse
9. hyperbola
10. circle
11. ellipse

12. $4x^2 + 2y^2 = 8$

$$\frac{x^2}{2} + \frac{y^2}{4} = 1$$

ellipse

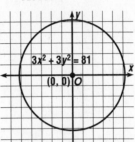

13. $x^2 = 8y$

$$y = \frac{1}{8}x^2$$

parabola

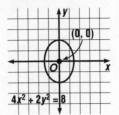
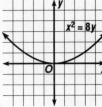

14. $6x^2 + 6y^2 = 162$

$$3x^2 + 3y^2 = 81$$

$$x^2 + y^2 = 27$$

circle

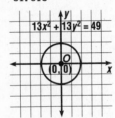

15. $4y^2 - x^2 + 4 = 0$

$$\frac{x^2}{4} - \frac{y^2}{1} = 1$$

hyperbola

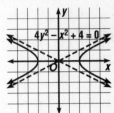

16. $13x^2 + 13y^2 = 49$

$$x^2 + y^2 = \frac{49}{13}$$

circle

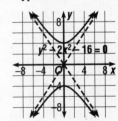

17. $y^2 - 2x^2 - 16 = 0$

$$y^2 - 2x^2 = 16$$

$$\frac{y^2}{16} - \frac{x^2}{8} = 1$$

hyperbola

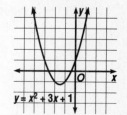

18. $3x^2 + 4y^2 + 8y = 8$

$$3x^2 + 4(y + 1)^2 = 12$$

$$\frac{x^2}{4} + \frac{(y + 1)^2}{3} = 1$$

ellipse

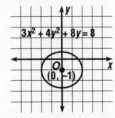

19. $y = x^2 + 3x + 1$

$$y = \left(x + \frac{3}{2}\right)^2 - \frac{5}{4}$$

parabola

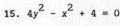

20. $x + 2 = x^2 + y$

$y = -x^2 + x + 2$

$y = -1\left(x - \frac{1}{2}\right)^2 + \frac{9}{4}$

parabola

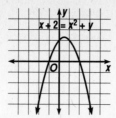

21. $\dfrac{(y - 5)^2}{4} - (x + 1)^2 = 4$

$\dfrac{(y - 5)^2}{16} - \dfrac{(x + 1)^2}{4} = 1$

hyperbola

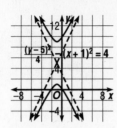

22. $x^2 - 8y + y^2 + 11 = 0$

$x^2 - 8y + y^2 = -11$

$x^2 + (y - 4)^2 = 5$

circle

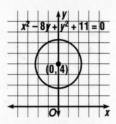

23. $(y - 4)^2 = 9(x - 4)$

$9x - 36 = (y - 4)^2$

$x = \frac{1}{9}(y - 4)^2 + 4$

parabola

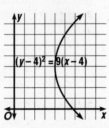

24. $3y^2 + 24y - x^2 - 2x = -41$

$3(y + 4)^2 - (x + 1)^2 = 6$

$\dfrac{(y + 4)^2}{2} - \dfrac{(x + 1)^2}{6} = 1$

hyperbola

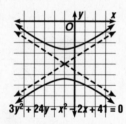

25. $25y^2 + 9x^2 - 50y - 54x = 119$

$9(x - 3)^2 + 25(y - 1)^2 = 225$

$\dfrac{(x - 3)^2}{25} + \dfrac{(y - 1)^2}{9} = 1$

ellipse

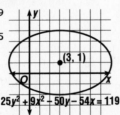

26. $x^2 + y^2 = x + 2$

$\left(x^2 - x + \frac{1}{4}\right) + y^2 = 2 + \frac{1}{4}$

$\left(x - \frac{1}{2}\right)^2 + y^2 = \frac{9}{4}$

circle

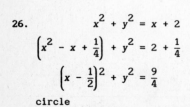

27. $6x^2 - 24x - 5y^2 - 10y - 11 = 0$

$6(x^2 - 4x + 4) - 5(y^2 + 2y + 1) = 30$

$\dfrac{(x - 2)^2}{5} - \dfrac{(y + 1)^2}{6} = 1$

hyperbola

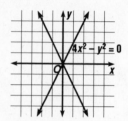

28. $4x^2 - y^2 = 0$

$y^2 = 4x^2$

$y = \pm 2x$

two intersecting lines

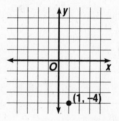

29. $3x^2 - 6x + 4y^2 + 32y + 67 = 0$

$3(x^2 - 2x + 1) + 4(y^2 + 8y + 16) = -67 + 3 + 64$

$3(x - 1)^2 + 4(y + 4)^2 = 0$

The only solution is (1, -4).

isolated point

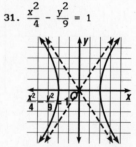

30. $x^2 - x = 0$

$x(x - 1) = 0$

$x = 0 \text{ or } x = 1$

two parallel lines

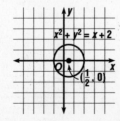

31. $\dfrac{x^2}{4} - \dfrac{y^2}{9} = 1$

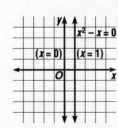

See students' graphs.
When $c = 0$, the graph
is two intersecting
lines.

32. a. circle   **b.** parabola
     c. ellipse   **d.** hyperbola

33. a. ellipse   **b.** hyperbola   **c.** circle
   d. ellipse   **e.** parabola   **f.** degenerate case

34. Answers may vary. Possible to roll a dice where
1 and 2 mean Kesia wins and 3 is Jeff wins.
Ignore other numbers. What is the chance of Jeff
winning three in a row?

35. $c^2 = a^2 - b^2$

$100 = 36 - b^2$

$b^2 = 64$

$$\frac{(y-2)^2}{36} - \frac{(x+2)^2}{64} = 1$$

36. $f(x) = 2x^2 + 3$

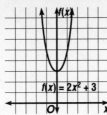

37. $6x^2 - 16x - 6 = 0$

$3x^2 - 8x - 3 = 0$

$a = 3, \ b = -8, \ c = -3$

$x = \dfrac{8 \pm \sqrt{-8^2 - 4(3)(-3)}}{2 \cdot 3}$

$= \dfrac{8 \pm \sqrt{64 + 36}}{6}$

$= \dfrac{8 \pm 10}{6}$

$x = 3, \ -\dfrac{1}{3}$

38. $\sqrt[3]{-27r^3s^3}$

$= -3rs$

Technology: Conic Sections

PAGE 431 EXERCISES

1.

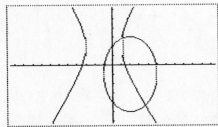

2 solutions

2.

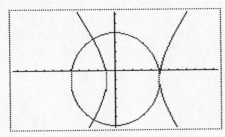

3 solutions

3.

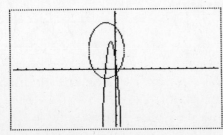

2 solutions

4.

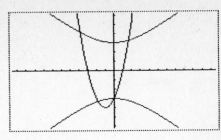

4 solutions

9-8 ## Graphing Quadratic Systems

PAGE 434 **CHECKING FOR UNDERSTANDING**

1. 0, 1, 2, 3, 4; See students' work.

2. They do not intersect. See students' work.

3. Yes; see students' work.

4. $PV = K$; $V = 15$; $K = 504$

$P(15) = 504$

$P = 33.6$

33.6 kilopascals

5. See students' work. 6. Not possible

Sample answer:

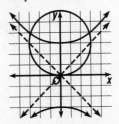

7. See students' work. 8. See students' work.

Sample answer: Sample answer:

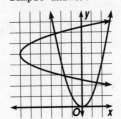

9.

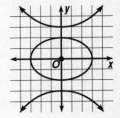

$(\pm 2\sqrt{3}, \ 2)$

10.

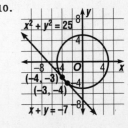

$(-4, \ -3), \ (-3, \ -4)$

219

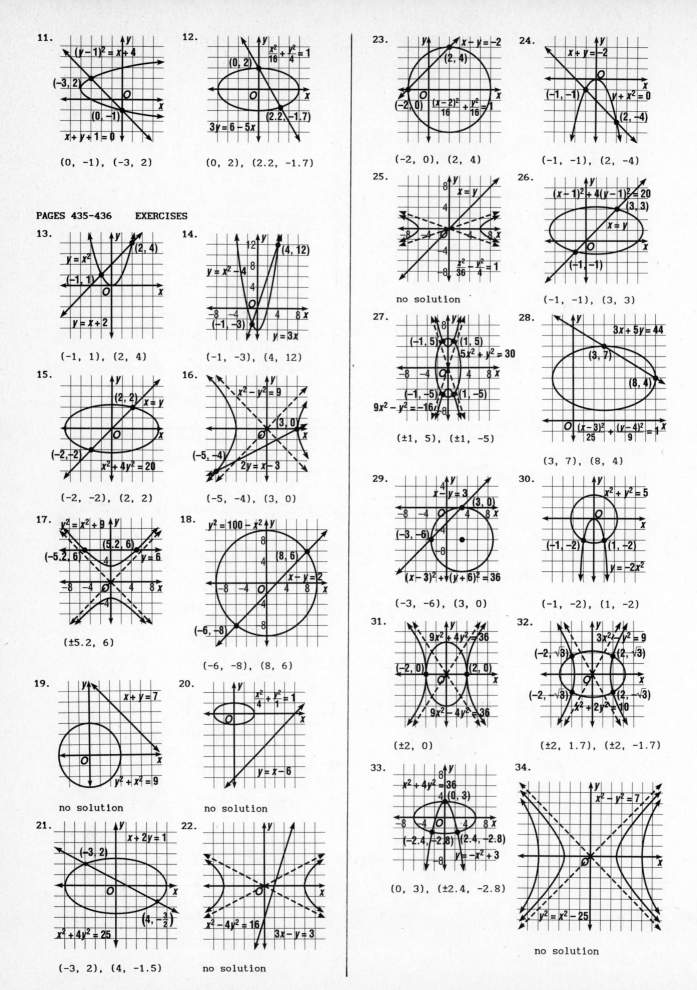

11.

$(y-1)^2 = x+4$

$(-3, 2)$

$(0, -1)$

$x + y + 1 = 0$

$(0, -1), (-3, 2)$

12.

$(0, 2)$

$\dfrac{x^2}{16} + \dfrac{y^2}{4} = 1$

$(2.2, -1.7)$

$3y = 6 - 5x$

$(0, 2), (2.2, -1.7)$

PAGES 435-436   EXERCISES

13.

$y = x^2$

$(2, 4)$

$(-1, 1)$

$y = x + 2$

$(-1, 1), (2, 4)$

14.

$(4, 12)$

$y = x^2 - 4$

$(-1, -3)$

$y = 3x$

$(-1, -3), (4, 12)$

15.

$(2, 2)$

$x = y$

$(-2, -2)$

$x^2 + 4y^2 = 20$

$(-2, -2), (2, 2)$

16.

$x^2 - y^2 = 9$

$(3, 0)$

$(-5, -4)$

$2y = x - 3$

$(-5, -4), (3, 0)$

17.

$y^2 = x^2 + 9$

$(-5.2, 6)$ $(5.2, 6)$

$y = 6$

$(\pm 5.2, 6)$

18.

$y^2 = 100 - x^2$

$(8, 6)$

$x - y = 2$

$(-6, -8)$

$(-6, -8), (8, 6)$

19.

$x + y = 7$

$y^2 + x^2 = 9$

no solution

20.

$\dfrac{x^2}{4} + \dfrac{y^2}{1} = 1$

$y = x - 6$

no solution

21.

$x + 2y = 1$

$(-3, 2)$

$(4, -\tfrac{3}{2})$

$x^2 + 4y^2 = 25$

$(-3, 2), (4, -1.5)$

22.

$x^2 - 4y^2 = 16$ $3x - y = 3$

no solution

23.

$x - y = -2$

$(2, 4)$

$(-2, 0)$ $\dfrac{(x-2)^2}{16} + \dfrac{y^2}{16} = 1$

$(-2, 0), (2, 4)$

24.

$x + y = -2$

$(-1, -1)$ $y + x^2 = 0$

$(2, -4)$

$(-1, -1), (2, -4)$

25.

$x = y$

$\dfrac{x^2}{36} - \dfrac{y^2}{4} = 1$

no solution

26.

$(x-1)^2 + 4(y-1)^2 = 20$

$(3, 3)$

$x = y$

$(-1, -1)$

$(-1, -1), (3, 3)$

27.

$(-1, 5)$ $(1, 5)$

$5x^2 + y^2 = 30$

$9x^2 - y^2 = -16$

$(-1, -5)$ $(1, -5)$

$(\pm 1, 5), (\pm 1, -5)$

28.

$3x + 5y = 44$

$(3, 7)$

$(8, 4)$

$\dfrac{(x-3)^2}{25} + \dfrac{(y-4)^2}{9} = 1$

$(3, 7), (8, 4)$

29.

$x - y = 3$

$(3, 0)$

$(-3, -6)$

$(x-3)^2 + (y+6)^2 = 36$

$(-3, -6), (3, 0)$

30.

$x^2 + y^2 = 5$

$(-1, -2)$ $(1, -2)$

$y = -2x^2$

$(-1, -2), (1, -2)$

31.

$9x^2 + 4y^2 = 36$

$(-2, 0)$ $(2, 0)$

$9x^2 - 4y^2 = 36$

$(\pm 2, 0)$

32.

$3x^2 + y^2 = 9$

$(-2, \sqrt{3})$ $(2, \sqrt{3})$

$(-2, -\sqrt{3})$ $(2, -\sqrt{3})$

$x^2 + 2y^2 = 10$

$(\pm 2, 1.7), (\pm 2, -1.7)$

33.

$x^2 + 4y^2 = 36$

$(0, 3)$

$(-2.4, -2.8)$ $(2.4, -2.8)$

$y = -x^2 + 3$

$(0, 3), (\pm 2.4, -2.8)$

34.

$x^2 - y^2 = 7$

$y^2 = x^2 - 25$

no solution

35.

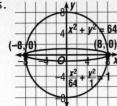

$(\pm 8, 0)$

36. $y^2 = 16 - x^2$

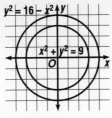

no solution

37.

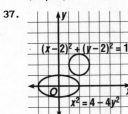

no solution

38.

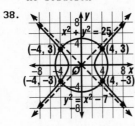

$(\pm 4, 3), (\pm 4, -3)$

39.

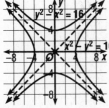

no solution

40.

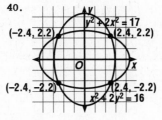

$(\pm 2.4, 2.2), (\pm 2.4, -2.2)$

41.

$(-10, 0), (6, 16)$

42. a. a parabola not as high, one as high, or one higher than the tree

b. not as high = 0, as high = 1, higher than = 2

43.
$$25 = \sqrt{(x - 0)^2 + (y - 0)^2}$$
$$25 = \sqrt{x^2 + y^2}$$
$$625 = x^2 + y^2$$
$$x^2 = 625 - y^2$$

$$42 = \sqrt{(x - 0)^2 + (y - 50)^2}$$
$$1764 = x^2 + (y - 50)^2$$
$$1764 = (625 - y^2) + (y^2 - 100y + 2500)$$
$$-1361 = -100y$$
$$13.61 = y$$
$$x^2 = 625 - (13.61)^2$$
$$x^2 = 439.77$$
$$x = 21$$

approximately $(13.6, 21)$ or $(13.6, -21)$; that is, 13.6 miles east and 21 miles north or south

44. hyperbola

45. $x^2 + 4y^2 = 4$

$$\frac{x^2}{4} + \frac{y^2}{1} = 1$$

ellipse

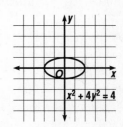

46. yes

47. $x^2 + 5x - 14 = 0$
$(x + 7)(x - 2) = 0$
$x = -7, 2$

48.

$$\begin{array}{r}
p^2 + 5p + 7 \\
2p - 3 \overline{)\, 2p^3 + 7p^2 - 29p + 29} \\
\underline{2p^3 - 3p^2} \\
10p^2 - 29p \\
\underline{10p^2 - 15p} \\
-14p + 29 \\
\underline{-14p + 21} \\
8
\end{array}$$

$$p^2 + 5p - 7 + \frac{8}{2p - 3}$$

Graphing Calculator Exploration: Solving Quadratic Systems

Answers depend on viewing window.

1. $(1.90, 4.62)$, $(-1.90, 4.62)$

2. $(2.00, 1.73)$, $(2.00, -1.73)$
   $(-2.00, 1.73)$, $(-2.00, -1.73)$

3. no solutions

4. $(3.08, 3.52)$, $(-3.08, 3.52)$
   $(2.17, -1.27)$, $(-2.17, 1.27)$

5. $(3.86, 0.87)$, $(3.86, -0.87)$
   $(-1.83, 0.97)$, $(-1.83, -0.97)$

6. $(-1.54, 1.84)$, $(-1.54, -1.84)$

9-9 Solving Quadratic Systems

1. Answers may vary. A typical answer is when the solutions are not integers.

2. They do not intersect.

3. The solution of the system of inequalities or the points that are solutions to both inequalities.

For 4-9, answers may vary. Typical answers are given.

4. substitution

$$x^2 + y^2 = 25$$
$$y - x = 1$$
$$y = 1 + x$$
$$x^2 + (1 + x)^2 = 25$$
$$2x^2 + 2x + 1 = 25$$
$$x^2 + x - 12 = 0$$
$$(x + 4)(x - 3) = 0$$
$$x = -4 \quad \text{or} \quad x = 3$$
$$y = -3 \qquad\qquad y = 4$$
$$(-4, -3) \qquad (3, 4)$$

5. elimination

$$x^2 + 2y^2 = 10 \qquad x^2 + 2y^2 = 10$$
$$3x^2 - y^2 = 9 \qquad \underline{6x^2 - 2y^2 = 18}$$
$$7x^2 = 28$$
$$x^2 = 4$$
$$x = \pm 2$$
$$2^2 + 2y^2 = 10 \qquad (-2)^2 + 2y^2 = 10$$
$$y^2 = 3 \qquad\qquad y^2 = 3$$
$$y = \pm\sqrt{3} \qquad\qquad y = \pm\sqrt{3}$$
$$(2, \pm\sqrt{3}), \ (-2, \pm\sqrt{3})$$

6. elimination

$$x^2 - y^2 = 25 \qquad\qquad 4x^2 - 4y^2 = 100$$
$$4y^2 + x^2 = 25 \qquad\qquad \underline{x^2 + 4y^2 = 25}$$
$$5x^2 = 125$$
$$x^2 = 25$$
$$x = \pm 5$$
$$5^2 - y^2 = 25 \qquad (-5)^2 - y^2 = 25$$
$$y^2 = 0 \qquad\qquad y^2 = 0$$
$$(5, 0), \ (-5, 0)$$

7. substitution

$$3x = 4y^2$$
$$4y^2 - 2x^2 = 16$$
$$3x - 2x^2 = 16$$
$$2x^2 - 3x + 16 = 0$$
$$x = \frac{3 \pm \sqrt{-119}}{4} \ \text{(complex)}$$

no solution

8. substitution

$$y = 3x^2 + 2$$
$$x^2 - 3y^2 = 27$$
$$x^2 - 3(3x^2 + 2)^2 = 27$$
$$x^2 - 27x^4 - 36x^2 - 12 = 27$$
$$27x^4 + 35x^2 + 39 = 0$$
$$x = \frac{-35 \pm \sqrt{-2987}}{54} \ \text{(complex)}$$

no solution

9. substitution

$$x^2 + y^2 = 81$$
$$x = 2y^2 - 162$$
$$x = 2(81 - x^2) - 162$$
$$2x^2 + x = 0$$
$$x(2x + 1) = 0$$
$$x = 0 \quad \text{or} \quad x = -\frac{1}{2}$$
$$0 + y^2 = 81 \qquad \frac{1}{4} + y^2 = 81$$
$$y = \pm 9 \qquad\qquad y^2 = \frac{323}{4}$$
$$y = \pm\frac{\sqrt{323}}{2}$$
$$(0, 9), \ (0, -9), \ \left(-\frac{1}{2}, \pm\frac{\sqrt{323}}{2}\right)$$

10. $x^2 + y^2 \geq 16$
    $x + y = 2$

11. $x^2 + y^2 \geq 25$
    $x^2 + y^2 \leq 100$

12. $x^2 + y^2 \leq 9$
    $y \geq \frac{1}{2}x + 1$

13. $y = x + 2$

$y = x^2$

$x^2 = x + 2$

$x^2 - x - 2 = 0$

$(x + 1)(x - 2) = 0$

$x + 1 = 0$ or $x - 2 = 0$

$x = -1$ $\qquad x = 2$

$y = (-1)^2 \qquad y = 2^2$

$y = 1 \qquad\qquad y = 4$

$(-1, 1), (2, 4)$

14. $\dfrac{x^2}{20} + \dfrac{y^2}{5} = 1$

$y = x \longrightarrow x^2 = y^2$

$\dfrac{x^2}{20} + \dfrac{y^2}{5} = 1$

$\dfrac{y^2}{20} + \dfrac{4y^2}{20} = 1$

$5y^2 = 20$

$y^2 = 4$

$y = 2 \qquad y = -2$

$x = 2 \qquad x = -2$

$(2, 2), (-2, -2)$

15. $y^2 = x^2 - 9$

$2y = x - 3$

$2y + 3 = x$

$(2y + 3)^2 - 9 = y^2$

$4y^2 + 12y + 9 - 9 = y^2$

$3y^2 + 12y = 0$

$3y(y + 4) = 0$

$3y = 0 \qquad$ or $\quad y + 4 = 0$

$y = 0 \qquad\qquad y = -4$

$2(0) + 3 = x \quad 2(-4) + 3 = x$

$3 = x \qquad\qquad -5 = x$

$(3, 0), (-5, -4)$

16. $y = x^2 - 4$

$y = 3x$

$x^2 - 3x - 4 = 0$

$(x - 4)(x + 1) = 0$

$x - 4 = 0$ or $x + 1 = 0$

$x = 4 \qquad\qquad x = -1$

$y = 3(4) \qquad y = 3(-1)$

$y = 12 \qquad\qquad y = -3$

$(4, 12), (-1, -3)$

17. $x + y + 7 = 0$

$x^2 + y^2 = 25$

$y = -7 - x$

$x^2 + (-7 - x)^2 = 25$

$x^2 + 49 + 14x + x^2 = 25$

$2x^2 + 14x + 24 = 0$

$2(x + 4)(x + 3) = 0$

$x + 4 = 0$ or $x + 3 = 0$

$x = -4 \qquad\qquad x = -3$

$y = -7 - (-4) \quad y = -7 - (-3)$

$y = -3 \qquad\qquad y = -4$

$(-4, -3), (-3, -4)$

18. $x^2 + 4y^2 = 16$

$5x + 2y = 4$

$2y = 4 - 5x$

$y = 2 - \dfrac{5}{2}x$

$x^2 + 4\left(2 - \dfrac{5}{2}x\right)^2 = 16$

$x^2 + 16 - 40x + 25x^2 = 16$

$26x^2 - 40x = 0$

$2x(13x - 20) = 0$

$2x = 0 \qquad$ or $\qquad 13x - 20 = 0$

$x = 0 \qquad\qquad\qquad x = \dfrac{20}{13}$

$2y + 5(0) = 4 \qquad 2y + 5\left(\dfrac{13}{20}\right) = 4$

$y = 2 \qquad\qquad\qquad y = -\dfrac{24}{13}$

$(0, 2), \left(\dfrac{20}{13}, -\dfrac{24}{13}\right)$

19. $y = 6$

$x^2 - y^2 + 9 = 0$

$x^2 - 36 + 9 = 0$

$x^2 = 27$

$x = \pm 3\sqrt{3}$

$(\pm 3\sqrt{3}, 6)$

20. $x + 4 = (y - 1)^2$

$x + y + 1 = 0$

$y = -x - 1$

$x + 4 = ((-x - 1) - 1)^2$

$x + 4 = (-x - 2)^2$

$x + 4 = x^2 + 4x + 4$

$x^2 + 3x = 0$

$x(x + 3) = 0$

$x = 0 \qquad$ or $\qquad x = -3$

$y = 0 - 1 \qquad\qquad y = 3 - 1$

$y = -1 \qquad\qquad\quad y = 2$

$(0, -1), (-3, 2)$

21. $x + y = 7 \longrightarrow x = 7 - y$

$x^2 + y^2 = 9$

$(7 - y)^2 + y^2 = 9$

$49 - 14y + y^2 + y^2 = 9$

$2y^2 - 14y + 40 = 0$

$2(y^2 - 7y + 20) = 0$

$y = \dfrac{7 \pm \sqrt{-31}}{3}$ (complex)

no solutions

223

22. $x - 2 = y$

$x^2 + y^2 = 100$

$x^2 + (x - 2)^2 = 100$

$x^2 + x^2 - 4x + 4 = 100$

$2x^2 - 4x + 4 = 100$

$x^2 - 2x - 48 = 0$

$(x - 8)(x + 6) = 0$

$x - 8 = 0$ or $x + 6 = 0$

$x = 8$ $x = -6$

$8 - 2 = y$ $-6 - 2 = y$

$6 = y$ $-8 = y$

  $(8, 6), (-6, -8)$

23. $x^2 + 4y^2 = 4$

$y = x - 6$

$x^2 + 4(x - 6)^2 = 4$

$x^2 + 4x^2 - 48x + 144 = 4$

$5x^2 - 48x + 140 = 0$

$x = \dfrac{48 \pm \sqrt{-496}}{10}$ (complex)

no solutions

24. $(x - 2)^2 + y^2 = 16$

$y - x = 2 \longrightarrow y = x + 2$

$(x - 2)^2 + (x + 2)^2 = 16$

$x^2 - 4x + 4 + x^2 + 4x + 4 = 16$

$2x^2 - 8 = 0$

$2(x - 2)(x + 2) = 0$

$x - 2 = 0$ or $x + 2 = 0$

$x = 2$ $x = -2$

$y = 2 + 2$ $y = -2 + 2$

$y = 4$ $y = 0$

  $(2, 4), (-2, 0)$

25. $y = -\dfrac{1}{2}x + \dfrac{1}{2} \longrightarrow y = \dfrac{1 - x}{2}$

$x^2 + 4y^2 = 25$

$x^2 + 4\left(\dfrac{1 - x}{2}\right)^2 = 25$

$x^2 + 1 - 2x + x^2 = 25$

$2x^2 - 2x - 24 = 0$

$2(x - 4)(x + 3) = 0$

$x - 4 = 0$ or $x + 3 = 0$

$x = 4$ $x = -3$

$y = \dfrac{1 - 4}{2}$ $y = \dfrac{1 + 3}{2}$

$y = -\dfrac{3}{2}$ $y = 2$

  $\left(4, -\dfrac{3}{2}\right), (-3, 2)$

26. $3x - y = 3 \longrightarrow y = 3x - 3$

$x^2 - 4y^2 = 16$

$x^2 - 4(3x - 3)^2 = 16$

$x^2 - 36x^2 + 72x - 36 = 16$

$35x^2 - 72x + 52 = 0$

$x = \dfrac{72 \pm \sqrt{-2096}}{70}$ (complex)

no solutions

27. $x^2 + y = 0 \longrightarrow y = x^2$

$x + y = -2$

$x + (-x^2) = -2$

$x^2 - x - 2 = 0$

$(x + 1)(x - 2) = 0$

$x = -1$ or $x = 2$

$y = -(-1)^2$ $y = -2^2$

$= -1$ $= -4$

  $(-1, -1), (2, -4)$

28. $x^2 - 9y^2 = 36$

$x = y$

$x^2 - 9(x)^2 = 36$

$8x^2 + 36 = 0$

$4(2x^2 + 9) = 0$

$x = \dfrac{\pm\sqrt{-72}}{4}$ (imaginary)

no solutions

29. $5x^2 + y^2 = 30$ $5x^2 + y^2 = 30$

$y^2 - 16 = 9x^2 \longrightarrow \underline{\quad 9x^2 - y^2 = -16 \quad}$

         $14x^2 = 14$

          $x^2 = 1$

          $x = \pm 1$

$y^2 - 16 = 9(1)^2$

$y^2 = 25$

$y = \pm 5$

  $(1, \pm 5), (-1, \pm 5)$

30. $(x - 3)^2 + (y + 6)^2 = 36$

$x - y = 3 \longrightarrow x = 3 + y$

$(y + 3 - 3)^2 + (y + 6)^2 = 36$

$y^2 + y^2 + 12y + 36 = 36$

$2y^2 + 12y = 0$

$2y(y + 6) = 0$

$2y = 0$ or $y + 6 = 0$

$y = 0$ $y = -6$

$0 + 3 = x$ $-6 + 3 = x$

$3 = x$ $x = -3$

  $(3, 0), (-3, -6)$

31. $3x + 5y = 44$

$\dfrac{(x - 3)^2}{25} + \dfrac{(y - 4)^2}{9} = 1$

$3x = -5y + 44$

$9x^2 = (-5y + 44)^2$

$\qquad\qquad 9(x - 3)^2 + 25(y - 4)^2 = 225$

$\qquad\qquad 9x^2 - 54x + 25y^2 - 200y + 481 = 225$

$(-5y + 44)^2 - 18(-5y + 44) + 25y^2 - 200y = -256$

$\qquad\qquad\qquad 50y^2 - 550y + 1400 = 0$

$\qquad\qquad\qquad 50(y - 7)(y - 4) = 0$

$y = 7 \qquad$ or $\qquad y = 4$

$5(7) + 3x = 44 \qquad 5(4) + 3x = 44$

$\qquad x = 3 \qquad\qquad\qquad x = 8$

$(3, 7), (8, 4)$

32. $x^2 + y^2 = 64$

$\dfrac{x^2 + 64y^2 = 64}{-63y^2 = 0}$

$y = 0$

$x^2 + 0^2 = 64$

$x = \pm 8$

$(\pm 8, 0)$

33.
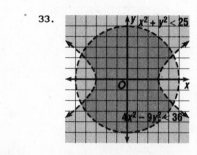

34.
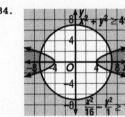

35.
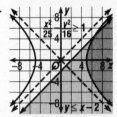

36.
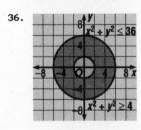

37.
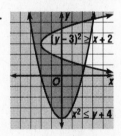

38.
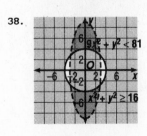

39.
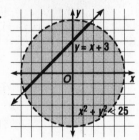

40.
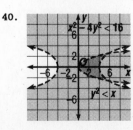

41.
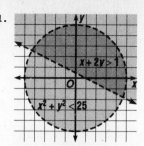

42.
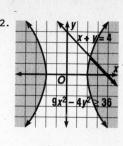

43.
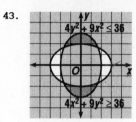

44.
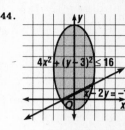

45.
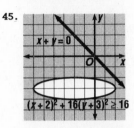

46.
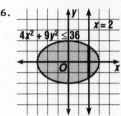

47.
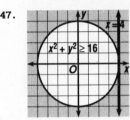

48.
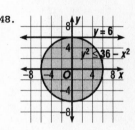

49. $x + y^2 = 2 \longrightarrow x = 2 - y^2$

$2y - 2\sqrt{2} = x(\sqrt{2} + 2)$

$\qquad y = \dfrac{x(\sqrt{2} + 2)}{2} + \sqrt{2}$

$x = -\left(\dfrac{x(\sqrt{2} + 2)}{2} + \sqrt{2}\right)^2 + 2$

$x = -\dfrac{x^2(3 + 2\sqrt{2})}{2} + x(2 + 2\sqrt{2}) + 2 + 2$

$x = -\dfrac{x^2(3 + 2\sqrt{2})}{2} - x(2 + 2\sqrt{2})$

$0 = -\dfrac{x^2(3 + 2\sqrt{2})}{2} - x(3 + 2\sqrt{2})$

$0 = -x(3 + 2\sqrt{2})\left(\dfrac{x}{2} + 1\right)$

$-x = 0 \qquad\qquad$ or $\qquad\qquad \dfrac{x}{2} + 1 = 0$

$x = 0 \qquad\qquad\qquad\qquad\qquad x = -2$

$y = \dfrac{0 \cdot (\sqrt{2} + 2)}{2} + \sqrt{2} \qquad y = \dfrac{-2(\sqrt{2} + 2)}{2} + \sqrt{2}$

$y = \sqrt{2} \qquad\qquad\qquad\qquad y = -2$

$(0, \sqrt{2}), (-2, -2)$

50. $x^2 + y^2 = 1$

$y = 3x + 1$

$x^2 + (y + 1)^2 = 4$

$x^2 + (3x + 1)^2 = 1$

$x^2 + 9x^2 + 6x + 1 = 1$

$10x^2 + 6x = 0$

$2x(5x + 3) = 0$

$x = 0$ or $x = -\dfrac{3}{5}$

$y = 3 \cdot 0 + 1$

$y = 1$ $y = 3\left(-\dfrac{3}{5}\right) + 1$

$y = -\dfrac{4}{5}$

$x^2 + (y + 1)^2 = 4$

$0 + (1 + 1)^2 = 4$ or $\left(-\dfrac{3}{5}\right)^2 + \left(-\dfrac{4}{5} + 1\right)^2 \overset{?}{=} 4$

$4 = 4$

$\dfrac{9}{25} + \dfrac{1}{25} \overset{?}{=} 4$

$\dfrac{10}{25} \neq 4$

(0, 1)

51. $xy = 480$

$2x + 2y = 88 \longrightarrow x = 44 - y$

$y(44 - y) = 480$

$y^2 - 44y + 480 = 0$

$(y - 20)(y - 24) = 0$

$y = 20$ or $y = 24$

$x + 20 = 44$ $x + 24 = 44$

$x = 24$ $x = 20$

20 ft by 24 ft

52. $50 = \sqrt{(x - 0)^2 + (y - 0)^2}$

$50 = \sqrt{x^2 + y^2}$

$2500 = x^2 + y^2$

$x^2 = 2500 - y^2$

$x^2 = 2500 - 30^2$

$x^2 = 2500 - 900$

$x^2 = 1600$

$x = \pm40$

$40 = \sqrt{(x - 0)^2 + (y - 30)^2}$

$40 = \sqrt{x^2 + (y - 30)^2}$

$1600 = x^2 + (y - 30)^2$

$1600 = 2500 - y^2 + y^2 - 60y + 900$

$0 = 1800 - 60y$

$0 = 60(30 - y)$

$y = 30$

$13 = \sqrt{(x - 35)^2 + (y - 18)^2}$

$169 = (x - 35)^2 + (y - 18)^2$

$169 \overset{?}{=} (40 - 35)^2 + (30 - 18)^2$

$169 \overset{?}{=} 25 + 144$

$169 = 169$

or

$169 \overset{?}{=} (-40 - 35)^2 + (30 - 18)^2$

$169 \overset{?}{=} (5625) + 144$

$169 \neq 5769$

(40, 30)

53.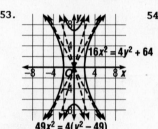

$16x^2 = 4y^2 + 64$

$49x^2 = 4(y^2 - 49)$

no solution

54. $f(x) = 4(x - 8)^2$

$h = 8,\ k = 0$

vertex: (8, 0)

axis of symmetry: $x = 8$

opens up

55. horizontal: $|12 - 9| = 3$

vertical: $|5 - 3| = 2$

Each side of grid is 10 units.

$d^2 = 30^2 + 20^2$

$= 900 + 400$

$= 1300$

$d \approx 36.06$

~ 36 miles

56. $2x^2 + 15x + 7 = 0$

$(2x + 1)(x + 7) = 0$

$x = -\dfrac{1}{2},\ x = -7$

57. $\dfrac{2 + \sqrt{6}}{2 - \sqrt{6}} \cdot \dfrac{2 + \sqrt{6}}{2 + \sqrt{6}}$

$= \dfrac{4 + 4\sqrt{6} + 6}{4 - 6}$

$= \dfrac{10 + 4\sqrt{6}}{-2}$

$= -5 - 2\sqrt{6}$

58. $(2xy^2)^3 + (2xy^2)^2(6xy^2)$

$= 8x^3y^6 + (4x^2y^4)(6xy^2)$

$= 8x^3y^6 + 24x^3y^6$

$= 32x^3y^6$

Chapter 9 Summary and Review

PAGES 444–446   SKILLS AND CONCEPTS

1. $d = \sqrt{(-8 + 2)^2 + (-7 + 1)^2}$

$= \sqrt{36 + 36}$

$= \sqrt{72}$

$= 6\sqrt{2}$

2. $d = \sqrt{(3 - 7)^2 + (6 + 8)^2}$

$= \sqrt{16 + 196}$

$= \sqrt{212}$

$= 2\sqrt{53}$

3. $d = \sqrt{(-2.4 - 1.7)^2 + (0.6 - 0.8)^2}$

    $= \sqrt{16.81 + 0.04}$

    $= \sqrt{16.85}$

4. $d = \sqrt{(2\sqrt{3} - 2\sqrt{3})^2 + (4\sqrt{3} + \sqrt{3})^2}$

    $= \sqrt{0 + (5\sqrt{3})^2}$

    $= 5\sqrt{3}$

5. $\left(\dfrac{17 - 13}{2}, \dfrac{-8 + 1}{2}\right) = \left(2, -\dfrac{7}{2}\right)$

6. $\left(\dfrac{0.2 + 0.3}{2}, \dfrac{0.6 + 0.4}{2}\right) = (0.25, 0.5)$

7. $\left(\dfrac{5 - 3}{2}, \dfrac{2 + 1}{2}\right) = \left(1, \dfrac{3}{2}\right)$

8. $\left(\dfrac{2 + \sqrt{2}}{2}, \dfrac{2 + \sqrt{2}}{2}\right) = \left(1 + \dfrac{\sqrt{2}}{2}, 1 + \dfrac{\sqrt{2}}{2}\right)$

9. $y^2 = -8x$

    $x = -\dfrac{1}{8}y^2$

    vertex: (0, 0)

    axis of symmetry:

        $y = 0$

    focus: (-2, 0)

    directrix: $x = 2$

    opens left

    latus rectum: 8

10. $(y - 8)^2 = -4(x - 4)$

    $x = -\dfrac{1}{4}(y - 8)^2 + 4$

    vertex: (4, 8)

    axis of symmetry:

        $y = 8$

    focus: (3, 8)

    directrix: $x = 5$

    opens left

    latus rectum: 4

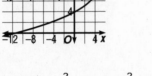

11. $x^2 + y^2 = 121$

    center: (0, 0)

    radius: 11

12. $(x - 3)^2 + (y + 7)^2 = 81$

    center: (3, -7)

    radius: 9

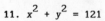

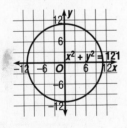

13. $9x^2 + 16y^2 = 144$

    $\dfrac{x^2}{16} + \dfrac{y^2}{9} = 1$

    $a = 4$; $b = 3$

    center: (0, 0)

    foci: $(\pm\sqrt{7}, 0)$

    major axis: 8

    minor axis: 6

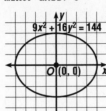

14. $\dfrac{(x - 3)^2}{25} + \dfrac{(y + 1)^2}{4} = 1$

    $a = 5$; $b = 2$

    center: (3, -1)

    foci: $(3 \pm \sqrt{21}, -1)$

    major axis: 10

    minor axis: 4

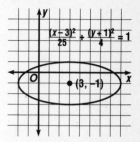

15. $49x^2 - 16y^2 = 784$

    $\dfrac{x^2}{16} - \dfrac{y^2}{49} = 1$

    $a = 4$; $b = 7$; $c = \sqrt{65}$

    vertices: $(\pm 4, 0)$

    foci: $(\pm\sqrt{65}, 0)$

    slopes of asymptotes: $\pm\dfrac{7}{4}$

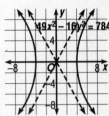

16. $25(y + 6)^2 - 20(x - 1)^2 = 500$

    $\dfrac{(y + 6)^2}{20} - \dfrac{(x - 1)^2}{25} = 1$

    $a = 2\sqrt{5}$; $b = 5$; $c = 3\sqrt{5}$

    vertices: $(1, -6 \pm 2\sqrt{5})$

    foci: $(1, -6 \pm 3\sqrt{5})$

    slopes of asymptotes: $\pm\dfrac{2\sqrt{5}}{5}$

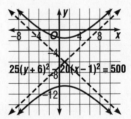

17. parabola

18. ellipse

19. circle

20. hyperbola

21.

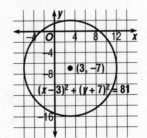

    (2, 4), (-2, 0)

22.

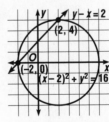

    no solutions

23. $x + y = 4 \longrightarrow x = 4 - y$

$y = x^2$

$y = (4 - y)^2$

$y = 16 - 8y + y^2$

$0 = 16 - 9y + y^2$

$y = \dfrac{9 \pm \sqrt{81 - 64}}{2}$

$= \dfrac{9 + 4.12}{2}$ and $\dfrac{9 - 4.12}{2}$

$= 6.6$ or 2.4

$x + 6.6 = 4 \qquad x + 2.4 = 4$

$\qquad x = -2.6 \qquad \qquad x = 1.6$

$(-2.6, 6.6) \qquad (1.6, 2.4)$

24. $x + y = 1 \longrightarrow x = 1 - y$

$x^2 + y^2 = 9$

$(1 - y)^2 + y^2 = 9$

$1 - 2y + y^2 + y^2 = 9$

$2y^2 - 2y - 8 = 0$

$2(y^2 - y - 4) = 0$

$y = \dfrac{1 \pm \sqrt{1 + 16}}{2}$

$y = 2.6$ or -1.6

$x + 2.6 = 1 \qquad x = 1 + 1.6$

$\qquad x = -1.6 \qquad x = 2.6$

$(-1.6, 2.6) \qquad (2.6, -1.6)$

25.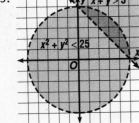

26.

PAGE 446   APPLICATIONS AND CONNECTIONS

27. $48 = \sqrt{(x - 12)^2 + (y - 25)^2}$

$2304 = (x - 12)^2 + (y - 25)^2$

28. Make it pass over the focus.

29. a hyperbola
with foci $(\pm\sqrt{13}, 0)$,
vertices $(\pm3, 0)$,
and asymptotes
$y = \pm\dfrac{3}{2}$

30. For two children,
possibilities are:

1 Boy, 1 Boy

1 Girl, 1 Girl

1 Boy, 1 Girl $\longleftarrow$ 25%

1 Girl, 1 Boy

Chapter 9 Test

1. $d = \sqrt{(6 + 6)^2 + (3 - 0)^2}$

$= \sqrt{153}$

2. $d = \sqrt{(9 + 7)^2 + (-11 - 18)^2}$

$= \sqrt{256 + 841}$

$= \sqrt{1097}$

3. $\left(\dfrac{6 - 12}{2}, \dfrac{12 + 22}{2}\right)$

$= (-3, 17)$

4. $\left(\dfrac{-3.2 + 9.8}{2}, \dfrac{2.1 - 0.6}{2}\right)$

$= (3.3, 0.75)$

5. parabola

$y = 3x^2$

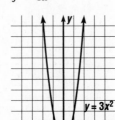

6. circle

$x^2 + 4x = -(y^2 - 6)$

$x^2 + y^2 + 4x = 6$

$(x + 2)^2 + y^2 = 10$

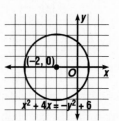

7. ellipse

$9x^2 + 49y^2 = 441$

$\dfrac{x^2}{49} + \dfrac{y^2}{9} = 1$

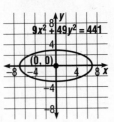

8. hyperbola

$4x^2 - y^2 = 4$

$\dfrac{x^2}{1} - \dfrac{y^2}{4} = 1$

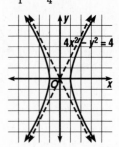

9. circle

$x^2 + 4x + y^2 - 8y = 2$

$(x + 2)^2 + (y - 4)^2 = 22$

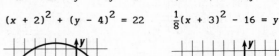

10. parabola

$(x + 3)^2 = 8(y + 2)$

$\dfrac{1}{8}(x + 3)^2 - 16 = y$

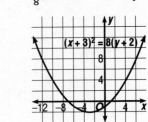

11. circle

$9x^2 + 9y^2 = 9$

$x^2 + y^2 = 1$

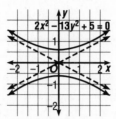

$9x^2 + 9y^2 = 9$

$(0, 0)$

12. parabola

$y - x^2 = x + 3$

$y = x^2 + x + 3$

$y = \left(x + \dfrac{1}{2}\right)^2 + 2\dfrac{3}{4}$

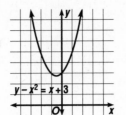

$y - x^2 = x + 3$

13. hyperbola

$2x^2 - 13y^2 + 5 = 0$

$13y^2 - 2x^2 = 5$

$\dfrac{y^2}{\frac{5}{13}} - \dfrac{x^2}{\frac{5}{2}} = 1$

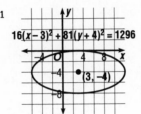

$2x^2 - 13y^2 + 5 = 0$

14. $16(x - 3)^2 + 81(y + 4)^2 = 1296$

$\dfrac{(x - 3)^2}{81} + \dfrac{(y + 4)^2}{16} = 1$

ellipse

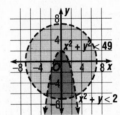

$16(x - 3)^2 + 81(y + 4)^2 = 1296$

$(3, -4)$

15. $4x^2 - y^2 = 16$

$\dfrac{x^2}{4} - \dfrac{y^2}{16} = 1$

hyperbola

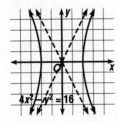

$4x^2 - y^2 = 16$

16. $x^2 + 5y^2 = 16$

$\dfrac{x^2}{16} + \dfrac{y^2}{\frac{16}{5}} = 1$

ellipse

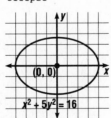

$(0, 0)$

$x^2 + 5y^2 = 16$

17. probably; 67% chance each time

18. $y = -(x + 1)$

$x^2 + y^2 = 25$

$x^2 + (x + 1)^2 = 25$

$x^2 + x^2 + 2x + 1 = 25$

$2x^2 + 2x - 24 = 0$

$2(x^2 + x - 12) = 0$

$2(x + 4)(x - 3) = 0$

$x = -4 \qquad$ or $x = 3$

$y = -(-4 + 1) \qquad y = -(3 + 1)$

$y = 3 \qquad\qquad y = -4$

$(-4, 3), (3, -4)$

19. $9x^2 - 16y^2 = 144 \qquad\qquad 9x^2 - 16y^2 = 144$

$x^2 + y^2 = 16 \quad\longrightarrow\quad \underline{9x^2 + 9y^2 = 144}$

$\qquad\qquad\qquad\qquad\qquad\qquad -25y^2 = 0$

$\qquad\qquad\qquad\qquad\qquad\qquad y^2 = 0$

$\qquad\qquad\qquad\qquad\qquad\qquad y = 0$

$x^2 + 0 = 16$

$x = \pm 4$

$(4, 0), (-4, 0)$

20. $x^2 + y < 2$

$x^2 + y^2 < 49$

21. $y = 5 - x$

$x^2 + y^2 \geq 49$

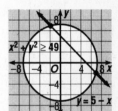

$x^2 + y^2 < 49$

$x^2 + y < 2$

$x^2 + y^2 \geq 49$

$y = 5 - x$

22. $h = 6, \ k = 1$

axis of symmetry: $y = -1$

focus $= \left(h + \dfrac{1}{4a}, \ k\right)$

$3 = 6 + \dfrac{1}{4a}$

$-3 = \dfrac{1}{4a}$

$a = -\dfrac{1}{12}$

$x = -\dfrac{1}{12}(y + 1)^2 + 6$

23. The center is the midpoint of the segment.

$M = \left(\dfrac{-2 + 4}{2}, \ \dfrac{3 + 5}{2}\right) = (1, 4)$

The radius is the distance from the center to either endpoint.

$r = \sqrt{(1 - 4)^2 + (4 - 5)^2}$

$ = \sqrt{(-3)^2 + (-1)^2}$

$ = \sqrt{9 + 1}$

$ = \sqrt{10}$

equation: $(x - 1)^2 + (y - 4)^2 = 10$

24. $2a = 12$ $\quad 2b = 8\sqrt{2}$

$\quad\ a = 6$ $\quad\ b = 4\sqrt{2}$

$\quad a^2 = 36$ $\quad b^2 = 32$

$$\frac{(y - 1)^2}{36} + \frac{(x - 3)^2}{32} = 1$$

25. $2a = 6$ $\quad 2b = 10$

$\quad\ a = 3$ $\quad\ b = 5$

$\quad a^2 = 9$ $\quad b^2 = 25$

$$\frac{(x - 2)^2}{9} - \frac{(y + 4)^2}{25} = 1$$

PAGE 447   BONUS

$x^2 + 4y^2 = 4 \longrightarrow y^2 = -\dfrac{x^2}{4} + 1$

$(x - 1)^2 + y^2 = 1$

$(x - 1)^2 + \left(-\dfrac{x^2}{4} + 1\right) = 1$

$x^2 - 2x + 1 - \dfrac{1}{4}x^2 + 1 = 1$

$\qquad \dfrac{3}{4}x^2 - 2x + 1 = 0$

$\qquad 3x^2 - 8x + 4 = 0$

$\quad (3x - 2)(x - 2) = 0$

$\qquad x = \dfrac{2}{3} \text{ or } x = 2$

$y^2 = -\dfrac{1}{4}\left(\dfrac{2}{3}\right)^2 + 1 \qquad\qquad y^2 = -\dfrac{(2)^2}{4} + 1$

$y^2 = -\dfrac{1}{9} + 1 \qquad\qquad\qquad\quad y^2 = -1 + 1$

$\qquad\qquad\qquad\qquad\qquad\qquad\qquad = 0$

$y^2 = \dfrac{8}{9} \qquad\qquad\qquad\qquad\quad (2,\ 0)$

$y = \pm\dfrac{2\sqrt{2}}{3}$

$\left(\dfrac{2}{3},\ \pm\dfrac{2\sqrt{2}}{3}\right)$

Chapter 10   Polynomial Functions

| 10-1 | **Polynomial Functions** |

PAGE 454   CHECKING FOR UNDERSTANDING

1. Answers may vary. A sample answer is $x^2 + 2x + 3$ and $a^2b^2 + 2ab + 3$. The first polynomial has real coefficients and nonnegative integer powers of one variable, x. The second polynomial has real coefficients and nonnegative integer powers of two variables, a and b.

2. polynomial function

3. $I(t) = 10 + 0.3t + 0.4t^2 - 0.01t^3$
$I(15) = 10 + 0.3(15) + 0.4(15)^2 - 0.01(15)^3$
$\quad = 10 + 4.5 + 90 - 33.75$
$\quad = 70.75$ lumens

4. For an odd function, the leftmost values of y on the graph are negative and the rightmost are positive. If the coefficient of the highest degree variable is negative, the leftmost values are positive, the rightmost negative. Even degree functions have both leftmost and rightmost values of y which are positive, or if the highest degree variable's coefficient is negative, both leftmost and rightmost will be negative.

5. yes, 5   6. no
7. yes, 0   8. yes, 2
9. no   10. yes, 3
11. no   12. yes, 2
13. yes, 3   14. no

15. $p(2) = 4(2) + 2$
$\quad = 8 + 2$
$\quad = 10$

16. $p(2) = 2(2)^2 + 6(2) - 8$
$\quad = 2(4) + 12 - 8$
$\quad = 8 + 12 - 8$
$\quad = 12$

17. $p(2) = 4(2)^3 - 2(2)^2 + 2 - 1$
$\quad = 4(8) - 2(4) + 2 - 1$
$\quad = 32 - 8 + 2 - 1$
$\quad = 25$

18. $p(2) = \frac{(2)^2}{4} - 4(2) + 11$
$\quad = \frac{4}{4} - 8 + 11$
$\quad = 1 - 8 + 11$
$\quad = 4$

19. even, 4   20. even, 3
21. odd, 2

PAGES 454-456   EXERCISES

22. $p(2) = 2(2)^4 - 3(2)^3 + 8$
$\quad = 2(16) - 3(8) + 8$
$\quad = 32 - 24 + 8$
$\quad = 16$

23. $p(2) = -3(2)^4 + 1$
$\quad = -3(16) + 1$
$\quad = -48 + 1$
$\quad = -47$

24. $p(2) = (2)^5 - (2)^2$
$\quad = 32 - 4$
$\quad = 28$

25. $p(2) = -(2)^6 + 12$
$\quad = -64 + 12$
$\quad = -52$

26. $f(-5) = 3 - 2(-5)$
$\quad = 3 + 10$
$\quad = 13$

27. $f(-5) = 6(-5) + 9$
$\quad = -30 + 9$
$\quad = -21$

28. $f(-5) = 3(-5)^2$
$\quad = 3(25)$
$\quad = 75$

29. $f(-5) = (-5)^2 - 2(-5) + 1$
$\quad = 25 + 10 + 1$
$\quad = 36$

30. $f(-5) = (-5)^3 + 4(-5)^2 + (-5) + 15$
$\quad = -125 + 4(25) - 5 + 15$
$\quad = -125 + 100 - 5 + 15$
$\quad = -15$

31. $f(-5) = (-5)^4 + 10(-5)$
$\quad = 625 - 50$
$\quad = 575$

32. $f(-5) = \frac{(-5)^4}{25} - 2$
$\quad = \frac{625}{25} - 2$
$\quad = 25 - 2$
$\quad = 23$

33. $f(-5) = 30 - \frac{(-5)^3}{6}$
$\quad = 30 - \frac{-125}{6}$
$\quad = 30 + \frac{125}{6}$
$\quad = \frac{180}{6} + \frac{125}{6}$
$\quad = \frac{305}{6}$

34. $f(x + h) = (x + h) + 1$
$\quad = x + h + 1$

35. $f(x + h) = 2(x + h) - 3$
$\quad = 2x + 2h - 3$

36. $f(x + h) = 4(x + h)^2$
$\quad = 4(x^2 + 2xh + h^2)$
$\quad = 4x^2 + 8xh + 4h^2$

37. $f(x + h) = (x + h)^2 - 2(x + h) + 5$
$\quad = x^2 + 2xh + h^2 - 2x - 2h + 5$

38. $f(x + h) = (x + h)^2 - \frac{1}{2}(x + h)$
$\quad = x^2 + 2xh + h^2 - \frac{1}{2}x - \frac{1}{2}h$

39. $f(x + h) = (x + h)^3 + 4(x + h)$
$\quad = x^3 + 3hx^2 + 3h^2x + h^3 + 4x + 4h$

40. $f(x + h) = \frac{4}{3}(x + h)^3 - 1$

$\qquad = \frac{4}{3}(x^3 + 3hx^2 + 3h^2x + h^3) - 1$

$\qquad = \frac{4}{3}x^3 + 4hx^2 + 4h^2x + \frac{4}{3}h^3 - 1$

41. $f(x + h) = 2(x + h)^3 - (x + h)^2 + 4$

$\qquad = 2(x^3 + 3hx^2 + 3h^2x + h^3)$

$\qquad\quad - (x^2 + 2xh + h^2) + 4$

$\qquad = 2x^3 + 6hx^2 + 6h^2x + 2h^3 - x^2 - 2hx$

$\qquad\quad - h^2 + 4$

42. $4[p(x)] = 4(2x - 4)$

$\qquad = 8x - 16$

43. $4[p(x)] = 4(x^2 + 5)$

$\qquad = 4x^2 + 20$

44. $4[p(x)] = 4(6x^3 - 4x^2 + 2)$

$\qquad = 24x^3 - 16x^2 + 8$

45. $4[p(x)] = 4\left(\frac{x^3}{4} + \frac{x^2}{16} - 2\right)$

$\qquad = x^3 + \frac{x^2}{4} - 8$

46. odd, 1   **47.** even, 0   **48.** odd, 3

49. $2[f(x + 3)] = 2[3(x + 3) + 8]$

$\qquad = 2[(3x + 9) + 8]$

$\qquad = 2(3x + 17)$

$\qquad = 6x + 34$

50. $2[f(x + 3)] = 2[(x + 3)^2 - 8]$

$\qquad = 2[(x^2 + 6x + 9) - 8]$

$\qquad = 2(x^2 + 6x + 1)$

$\qquad = 2x^2 + 12x + 2$

51. $2[f(x + 3)] = 2[(x + 3)^2 + 6(x + 3) - 18]$

$\qquad = 2[(x^2 + 6x + 9) + (6x + 18) - 18]$

$\qquad = 2(x^2 + 12x + 9)$

$\qquad = 2x^2 + 24x + 18$

52. $2[f(x + 3)] = 2\left[\frac{1}{2}(x + 3)^2 - \frac{3}{4}\right]$

$\qquad = 2\left[\frac{1}{2}(x^2 + 6x + 9) - \frac{3}{4}\right]$

$\qquad = 2\left(\frac{1}{2}x^2 + 3x + \frac{9}{2} - \frac{3}{4}\right)$

$\qquad = x^2 + 6x + 9 - \frac{3}{2}$

$\qquad = x^2 + 6x + \frac{15}{2}$

53. $2[p(x)] - 3[p(x + 1)]$

$\qquad = 2(5x - 7) - 3[5(x + 1) - 7]$

$\qquad = 10x - 14 - 3[(5x + 5) - 7]$

$\qquad = 10x - 14 - 3(5x - 2)$

$\qquad = 10x - 14 - 15x + 6$

$\qquad = -5x - 8$

54. $2[p(x)] - 3[p(x + 1)]$

$\qquad = 2(x^2 - 7x + 16) - 3[(x + 1)^2 - 7(x + 1) + 16]$

$\qquad = 2x^2 - 14x + 32 - 3[(x^2 + 2x + 1)$

$\qquad\quad + (-7x - 7) + 16]$

$\qquad = 2x^2 - 14x + 32 - 3(x^2 - 5x + 10)$

$\qquad = 2x^2 - 14x + 32 - 3x^2 + 15x - 30$

$\qquad = -x^2 + x + 2$

55. $2[p(x)] - 3[p(x + 1)]$

$\qquad = 2(x^3 + 1) - 3[(x + 1)^3 + 1]$

$\qquad = 2x^3 + 2 - 3[(x^3 + 3x^2 + 3x + 1) + 1]$

$\qquad = 2x^3 + 2 - 3x^3 - 9x^2 - 9x - 3 - 3$

$\qquad = -x^3 - 9x^2 - 9x - 4$

56. $2[p(x)] - 3[p(x + 1)]$

$\qquad = 2[(x - 2)^3] - 3\{[(x + 1) - 2]^3\}$

$\qquad = 2[x^3 + 3(-2)x^2 + 3(-2)^2x + (-2)^3]$

$\qquad\quad - 3[(x - 1)^3]$

$\qquad = 2[x^3 - 6x^2 + 12x - 8] - 3[x^3 + 3(-1)x^2$

$\qquad\quad + 3(-1)^2x + (-1)^3]$

$\qquad = 2x^3 - 12x^2 + 24x - 16 - 3(x^3 - 3x^2 + 3x - 1)$

$\qquad = 2x^3 - 12x^2 + 24x - 16 - 3x^3 + 9x^2 - 9x + 3$

$\qquad = -x^3 - 3x^2 + 15x - 13$

57.

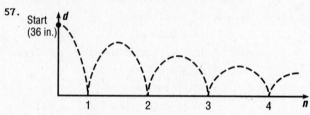

Let n = number of bounces.

Let d = distance in n bounces.

$\qquad d = f(n)$

At $n = 1$, ball has dropped 36 in.

$f(1) = 36$

At $n = 2$, ball dropped 36 in., rebounds up to

$\frac{3}{4}(36)$ in., and drops $\frac{3}{4}(36)$ in.

$f(2) = 36 + 36(0.75) + 36(0.75)$

$\qquad = 36 + 2[36(0.75)]$

At $n = 3$, ball bounces up another $\frac{3}{4}\left[\frac{3}{4}(36)\right]$ in.

and drops another $\frac{3}{4}\left[\frac{3}{4}(36)\right]$ in.

$f(3) = f(2) + 36(0.75)^2 + 36(0.75)^2$

$\qquad = 36 + 2[36(0.75)] + 2[36(0.75)^2]$

$\qquad = 36 + 2[36(0.75) + 36(0.75)^2]$

$f(4) = f(3) + 36(0.75)^3 + 36(0.75)^3$

$\qquad = 36 + 2[36(0.75) + 36(0.75)^2]$

$\qquad\quad + 2[36(0.75)^3]$

$\qquad = 36 + 2[36(0.75) + 36(0.75)^2 + 36(0.75)^3]$

In general, $f(n) = 36 + 2[36(0.75) + 36(0.75)^2$

$\qquad\qquad\qquad + \ldots + 36(0.75)^{n-1}$ for

$n > 1$. Thus, $d = 36$ for $n = 1$ and

$d = 36 + 2[36(0.75) + 36(0.75)^2 + \ldots + 36(0.75)^{n-1}]$

for $n > 1$.

58. $P(s) = \frac{s^3}{1000}$

$\qquad P(25) = \frac{(25)^3}{1000}$

$\qquad\quad = \frac{15,625}{1000}$

$\qquad\quad = 15.625$ units

59. Let t = years of appreciation.

Let p = purchase price.

Let w = current worth.

$$w = f(p_1, t_1) + f(p_2, t_2)$$

$$= p_1(1.14)^{t_1} + p_2(1.14)^{t_2}$$

$$= 20{,}000(1.14)^2 + 35{,}000(1.14)^1$$

$$= 25{,}992 + 39{,}900$$

$$= 65{,}892$$

$65,892

60. $x^2 + y^2 = 5 \longrightarrow x^2 = 5 - y^2$

$2x^2 + y = 0$

$2(5 - y^2) + y = 0$

$10 - 2y^2 + y = 0$

$-2y^2 + y + 10 = 0$

$$y = \frac{-1 \pm \sqrt{(1)^2 - 4(-2)(10)}}{2(-2)}$$

$$= \frac{-1 \pm \sqrt{1 + 80}}{-4}$$

$$= \frac{-1 \pm \sqrt{81}}{-4}$$

$$= \frac{-1 \pm 9}{-4}$$

$$= \frac{5}{2} \text{ or } -2$$

$y = \dfrac{5}{2}$ or	$y = -2$
$-2x^2 = \dfrac{5}{2}$	$-2x^2 = -2$
$x^2 = -\dfrac{5}{4}$	$x^2 = 1$
no solution	$x = \pm 1$

$(-1, -2), (1, -2)$

61.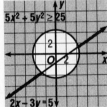

62.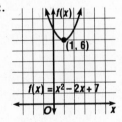

63. no

64. $x + 2yi = 3$

$x = 3, 2y = 0$ or $2yi = 3, x = 0$

$x = 3, y = 0$ $\qquad y = \dfrac{3}{2i}$

$\qquad\qquad\qquad y = -\dfrac{3}{2}i, x = 0$

65. Let k = Karl's fish,

a = Adam's fish, and

s = Sally's fish.

$k = 3a \qquad \longrightarrow \qquad a = \frac{1}{3}k$

$k = 10 + s \qquad \longrightarrow \qquad s = k - 10$

$k + a + s < 100$

$k + \frac{1}{3}k + (k - 10) < 100$

$3k + k + 3k - 30 < 300$

$7k - 30 < 300$

$k < \dfrac{330}{7}$

$k < 47.1$

Since k must be a multiple of 3, the greatest k could be is 45.

Graphing Calculator Exploration: Graphing Polynomial Equations

PAGE 458   **EXERCISES**

Sample graphs provided.

1.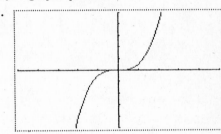

Xscl: 1, Yscl: 2

real zeros: 1

2.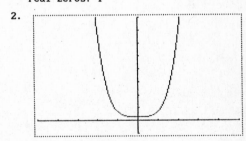

Xscl: 1, Yscl: 10

real zeros: 0

3.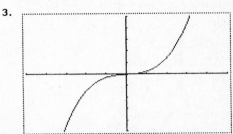

Xscl: 1, Yscl: 20

real zeros: 1

4.

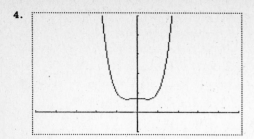

Xscl: 1, Yscl: 10

real zeros: 0

5.

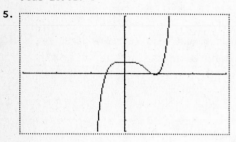

Xscl: 1, Yscl: 1

real zeros: 3

6.

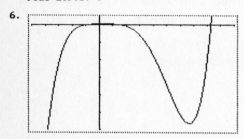

Xscl: 1, Yscl: 500

real zeros: 3

7.

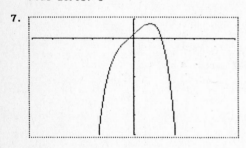

Xscl: 1, Yscl: 10

real zeros: 2

8.

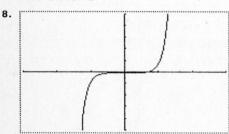

Xscl: 1, Yscl: 10

real zeros: 1

9.

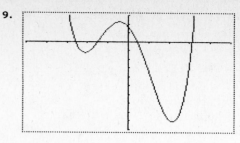

Xscl: 2, Yscl: 50

real zeros: 4

10.

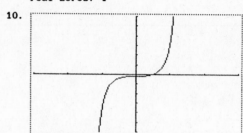

Xscl: 1, Yscl: 5

real zeros: 1

11.

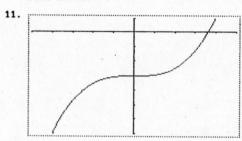

Xscl: 0.4, Yscl: 1

1.44

12.

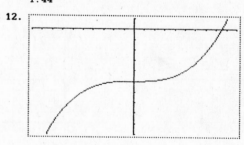

Xscl: 0.2, Yscl: 1

1.71

13.

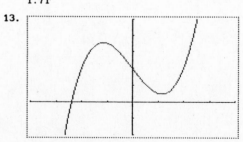

Xscl: 1, Yscl: 2

−2.38

14.

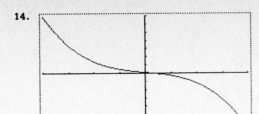

Xscl: 0.5, Yscl: 10

0.16

15.

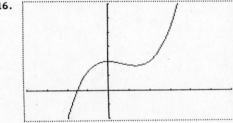

Xscl: 1, Yscl: 2

-1.34

16.

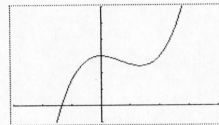

Xscl: 0.5 , Yscl: 0.5

-0.75

17.

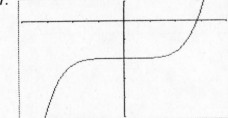

Xscl: 0.5, Yscl: 3

1.43

18.

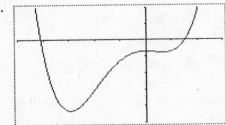

Xscl: 1, Yscl: 10

-4.08, 1.54

19.

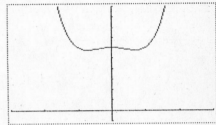

Xscl: 1, Yscl: 1

0.2

20.

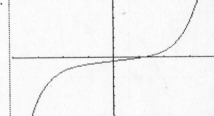

Xscl: 1, Yscl: 10

-2.38, 0.27

21.

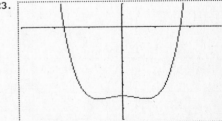

Xscl: 1, Yscl: 1

no zeros

22.

Xscl: 0.5, Yscl: 5

0.61

23.

Xscl: 1, Yscl: 1

1.73, -1.73

24.

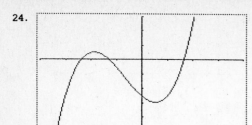

Xscl: 1, Yscl: 2

-2.38, -1.27, 1.65

25.

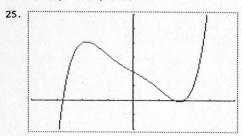

Xscl: 0.5, Yscl: 0.5

-1.38, 0.82, 1

26.

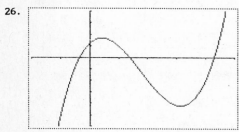

Xscl: 1, Yscl: 5

-0.34, 1.38, 4.39

27.

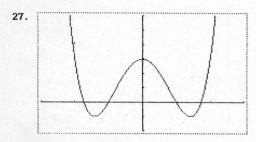

Xscl: 0.5, Yscl: 1

-1.73, -1, 1, 1.73

28.

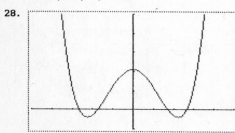

Xscl: 1, Yscl: 10

-2.65, -1.73, 1.73, 2.65

29.

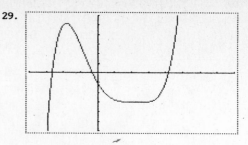

Xscl: 0.5, Yscl: 1

-1.33, -0.15, 2.09

30.

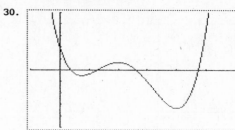

Xscl: 1, Yscl: 3

0.38, 1.27, 2.62, 4.73

31.

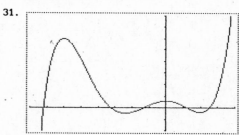

Xscl: 0.5, Yscl: 5

-3.60, -1.62, -0.66, 0.62, 1.31

32.

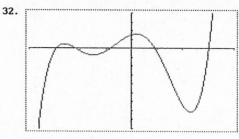

Xscl: 1, Yscl: 10

-2.93, -2.19, -0.83, 0.93, 3.10

10-2 The Remainder and Factor Theorems

PAGE 462   CHECKING FOR UNDERSTANDING

1. 12

2. A depressed polynomial is the resulting polynomial after a polynomial undergoes division by a binomial factor in the form of $(x - r)$.

3. 0   4. about 5 seconds

5. Answers may vary: quadratic formula, synthetic substitution, guess-and-check factoring, completing the square.

6. 3, 2

7. 5, 4

8. 2, 1

9. 6, 5

10.
```
2| 1  0  -5
      2   4
   1  2 |-1
```
$g(2) = -1$

11.
```
2| 1  -3   4   8
      2  -2   4
   1  -1   2 |12
```
$g(2) = 12$

12.
```
2| 1  0   0  -5   2
      2   4   8   6
   1  2   4   3 | 8
```
$g(2) = 8$

13.
```
2| 1  -4   4
      2  -4
   1  -2 | 0
```
$g(2) = 0$

PAGES 463-464   EXERCISES

14.
```
4| 1  -4   2  -6
      4   0   8
   1  0   2 | 2
```
$x^3 - 4x^2 + 2x - 6 = (x^2 + 2)(x - 4) + 2$; no

15.
```
-1| 1  -8   2  -1
      -1   9  -11
   1  -9  11 |-12
```
$x^3 - 8x^2 + 2x - 1 = (x^2 - 9x + 11)(x + 1) - 12$; no

16.
```
2| 2  8  -3  -1
      4  24  42
   2  12  21 | 41
```
$2x^3 + 8x^2 - 3x - 1 = (2x^2 + 12x + 21)(x - 2) + 41$; no

17.
```
2| 1  0  0  0  -16
      2  4  8  16
   1  2  4  8 | 0
```
$x^4 - 16 = (x^3 + 2x^2 + 4x + 8)(x - 2) + 0$; yes

18.
```
-3| 1  0   0   27
      -3   9  -27
   1  -3   9 | 0
```
$x^3 + 27 = (x^2 - 3x + 9)(x + 3) + 0$; yes

19.
```
-2| 6   9  -6  2
      -12   6  0
   6  -3   0 | 2
```
$6x^3 + 9x^2 - 6x + 2 = (6x^2 - 3x)(x + 2) + 2$; no

20.
```
4| 1  0   0  -64
      4  16   64
   1  4  16 | 0
```
$x^3 - 64 = (x^2 + 4x + 16)(x - 4) + 0$; yes

21.
```
1| 4  0  -2  1  1
      4  4   2  3
   4  4  2  3 | 4
```
$4x^4 - 2x^2 + x + 1$
$= (4x^3 + 4x^2 + 2x + 3)(x - 1) + 4$; no

22.
```
2| 1  -2  -1   1       -1| 1  -2  -1   1
      2   0  -2              -1   3  -2
   1  0  -1 |-1          1  -3   2 |-1
```
$f(2) = -1$ $f(-1) = -1$

23.
```
2| 1  2  -3   1        -1| 1   2  -3   1
      2   8  10              -1  -1   4
   1  4   5 | 11         1   1  -4 | 5
```
$f(2) = 11$ $f(-1) = 5$

24.
```
2| 2  -8   6          -1| 2  -8    6
      4  -8                 -2   10
   2  -4 |-2            2  -10 | 16
```
$f(2) = -2$ $f(-1) = 16$

25.
```
2| 1  -8  -2   5       -1| 1  -8  -2    5
      2  -12  -28           -1   9   -7
   1  -6  -14 |-23       1  -9   7 |-2
```
$f(2) = -23$ $f(-1) = -2$

26.
```
2| 3  0   8   0  -1     -1| 3   0   8    0   -1
      6  12  40  80            -3   3  -11   11
   3  6  20  40 | 79       3  -3  11  -11 | 10
```
$f(2) = 79$ $f(-1) = 10$

27.
```
2| 1  1   1   1   1     -1| 1  1  1   1   1
      2  6  14  30             -1  0  -1   0
   1  3  7  15 | 31         1  0  1   0 | 1
```
$f(2) = 31$ $f(-1) = 1$

28.
```
1| 1  2  -1  -2
      1   3   2
   1  3   2 | 0
```
$x^2 + 3x + 2$
$= (x + 1)(x + 2)$

29.
```
2| 1  -6  11  -6
      2  -8   6
   1  -4   3 | 0
```
$x^2 - 4x + 3$
$= (x - 1)(x - 3)$

30. Since $2x + 7 = 2(x + 3.5)$, factor out $x + 3.5$ and then the 2.
```
-3.5| 2  17   23  -42
        -7  -35   42
     2  10  -12 | 0
```
$2x^2 + 10x - 12$
$= 2(x^2 + 5x - 6)$
$= 2(x + 6)(x - 1)$
$(x + 6)(x - 1)$

31.
```
1| 1  0  -3   2
      1   1  -2
   1  1  -2 | 0
```
$x^2 + x - 2$
$= (x + 2)(x - 1)$

32.
```
-1| 1  -1  -5  -3
      -1   2   3
   1  -2  -3 | 0
```
$x^2 - 2x - 3$
$= (x - 3)(x + 1)$

33.
```
-2| 1  2   0  -8  -16
      -2   0   0   16
   1  0   0  -8 | 0
```
$(x^3 - 8)$
$= (x - 2)(x^2 + 2x + 4)$

34. Since $2x + 1 = 2(x + 0.5)$, factor out $x + 0.5$, then the 2.

$$
\begin{array}{r|rrrrr}
-0.5 & 8 & 32 & 0 & 1 & 4 \\
 & & -4 & -14 & 7 & -4 \\
\hline
 & 8 & 28 & -14 & 8 & 0 \\
\end{array}
$$

$8x^3 + 28x^2 - 14x + 8$
$= 2(4x^3 + 14x^2 - 7x + 4)$

$$
\begin{array}{r|rrrr}
-4 & 4 & 14 & -7 & 4 \\
 & & -16 & 8 & -4 \\
\hline
 & 4 & -2 & 1 & 0 \\
\end{array}
$$

$4x^2 - 2x + 1$
$(x + 4)(4x^2 - 2x + 1)$

35.
$$
\begin{array}{r|rrrrrr}
2 & 16 & -32 & 0 & 0 & -81 & 162 \\
 & & 32 & 0 & 0 & 0 & -162 \\
\hline
 & 16 & 0 & 0 & 0 & -81 & 0 \\
\end{array}
$$

$16x^4 - 81$
$= (4x^2 + 9)(4x^2 - 9)$
$= (4x^2 + 9)(2x + 3)(2x - 3)$

36. roots at -2, -1, 2

$$
\begin{array}{r|rrrrrr}
-2 & 1 & 1 & -3 & -3 & -4 & -4 \\
 & & -2 & 2 & 2 & 2 & 4 \\
\hline
2 & 1 & -1 & -1 & -1 & -2 & 0 \\
 & & 2 & 2 & 2 & 2 & \\
\hline
-1 & 1 & 1 & 1 & 1 & 0 & \\
 & & -1 & 0 & -1 & & \\
\hline
 & 1 & 0 & 1 & 0 & & \\
\end{array}
$$

$(x + 2)(x - 2)(x + 1)(x^2 + 1)$

37. roots at -1, 1

$$
\begin{array}{r|rrrrrr}
-1 & 1 & 1 & 0 & 0 & -1 & -1 \\
 & & -1 & 0 & 0 & 0 & 1 \\
\hline
1 & 1 & 0 & 0 & 0 & -1 & 0 \\
 & & 1 & 1 & 1 & 1 & \\
\hline
-1 & 1 & 1 & 1 & 1 & 0 & \\
 & & -1 & 0 & -1 & & \\
\hline
 & 1 & 0 & 1 & 0 & & \\
\end{array}
$$

$(x + 1)^2 (x - 1)(x^2 + 1)$

38.
$$
\begin{array}{r|rrr}
2 & 1 & k & -17 \\
 & & 2 & 4 + 2k \\
\hline
 & 1 & 2 + k & -13 + 2k = 3 \\
\end{array}
$$

$2k = 16$
$k = 8$

39.
$$
\begin{array}{r|rrr}
1 & 1 & -1 & k \\
 & & 1 & 0 \\
\hline
 & 1 & 0 & k = 3 \\
\end{array}
$$

40.
$$
\begin{array}{r|rrrr}
-1 & 1 & 4 & 1 & k \\
 & & -1 & -3 & 2 \\
\hline
 & 1 & 3 & -2 & 2 + k = 3 \\
\end{array}
$$

$k = 1$

41.
$$
\begin{array}{r|rrr}
k & 1 & 5 & 7 \\
 & & -k & -5k + k^2 \\
\hline
 & 1 & 5 - k & k^2 - 5k + 7 = 3 \\
\end{array}
$$

$k^2 - 5k + 4 = 0$
$(k - 1)(k - 4) = 0$
$k = 1$ or $k = 4$

42. a.
$$
\begin{array}{r|rrrr}
-4 & 1 & 2 & -5 & -6 \\
 & & -4 & 8 & -12 \\
\hline
 & 1 & -2 & 3 & -18 \\
\end{array}
$$
$f(-4) = -18$

$$
\begin{array}{r|rrrr}
-2 & 1 & 2 & -5 & -6 \\
 & & -2 & 0 & 10 \\
\hline
 & 1 & 0 & -5 & 4 \\
\end{array}
$$
$f(-2) = 4$

$$
\begin{array}{r|rrrr}
0 & 1 & 2 & -5 & -6 \\
 & & 0 & 0 & 0 \\
\hline
 & 1 & 2 & -5 & -6 \\
\end{array}
$$
$f(0) = -6$

$$
\begin{array}{r|rrrr}
2 & 1 & 2 & -5 & -6 \\
 & & 2 & 8 & 6 \\
\hline
 & 1 & 4 & 3 & 0 \\
\end{array}
$$
$f(2) = 0$

$$
\begin{array}{r|rrrr}
4 & 1 & 2 & -5 & -6 \\
 & & 4 & 24 & 76 \\
\hline
 & 1 & 6 & 19 & 70 \\
\end{array}
$$
$f(4) = 70$

b.

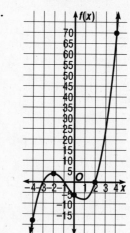

c. 3 times, yes

43. a. $A = 1000(1 + r)^6 + 1000(1 + r)^5 + 1000(1 + r)^4$
$+ 1200(1 + r)^3 + 1200(1 + r)^2$
$+ 2000(1 + r)^1$

b. Let $1 + r = x$ and define A as a function of x. Thus, $A(x) = 1000x^6 + 1000x^5 + 1000x^4 + 1200x^3 + 1200x + 2000$. When $r = 6\% = 0.06$, $1 + r = 1 + 0.06 = 1.06 = x$. Find $A(1.06)$.

$$
\begin{array}{r|rrrrrrr}
1.06 & 1000 & 1000 & 1000 & 1200 & 1200 & 2000 & 0 \\
 & & 1060 & 2183.6 & 3374.62 & 4849.09 & 6412.04 & 8916.76 \\
\hline
 & 1000 & 2060 & 3183.6 & 4574.62 & 6049.09 & 8412.04 & 8916.76 \\
\end{array}
$$

Thus, at $r = 6\%$, $A = \$8916.76$.

44. a. when the rocket is on the ground

b. $h(t) = 64t - 4.9t^2$
$= t(64 - 4.9t)$
$t = 0$ or $64 - 4.9t = 0$
$64 = 4.9t$
$13.06 = t$

about 13 seconds

45. $f(2) = -3(2)^3 + 2$
$\qquad = -3(8) + 2$
$\qquad = -24 + 2$
$\qquad = -22$

46. $\qquad p(x) = x^2 - 4$
$\qquad p(x - 1) = (x - 1)^2 - 4$
$\qquad 3[p(x - 1)] = 3[(x - 1)^2 - 4]$
$\qquad\qquad = 3(x^2 - 2x + 1 - 4)$
$\qquad\qquad = 3(x^2 - 2x - 3)$
$\qquad\qquad = 3x^2 - 6x - 9$

47. $\qquad (x + 4)^2 + y^2 = 49$
$\qquad [x - (-4)]^2 + (y - 0)^2 = 7^2$
$\qquad c = (-4, 0); \ r = 7$

48. $(y - 12)(y - 5) \leq 0$
$\qquad y - 12 \geq 0 \quad \text{and} \quad y - 5 \leq 0$
$\qquad\quad y \geq 12 \ \text{and} \qquad\quad y \leq 5$
$\qquad\qquad \text{no solution}$
$\qquad\qquad\quad \text{or}$
$\qquad y - 12 \leq 0 \quad \text{and} \quad y - 5 \geq 0$
$\qquad\quad y \leq 12 \ \text{and} \qquad\quad y \geq 5$
$\qquad\qquad 5 \leq y \leq 12$
$\qquad\qquad \{y \mid 5 \leq y \leq 12\}$

49. $169 = 9x^2$
$\qquad 0 = 9x^2 - 169$
$\qquad 0 = (3x + 13)(3x - 13)$
$\qquad 3x + 13 = 0 \quad \text{or} \quad 3x - 13 = 0$
$\qquad\quad 3x = -13 \qquad\qquad 3x = 13$
$\qquad\quad x = \dfrac{-13}{3} \qquad\qquad x = \dfrac{13}{3}$

50. $\dfrac{3^0 y + 4y^{-1}}{y^{\frac{-2}{3}}} = \dfrac{3^0(8) + 4(8)^{-1}}{(8)^{\frac{-2}{3}}}$
$\qquad = \dfrac{(1)(8) + (4)\left(\frac{1}{8}\right)}{\left[\left(\frac{1}{8}\right)^{\frac{1}{3}}\right]^2}$
$\qquad = \dfrac{8 + \frac{1}{2}}{\left(\frac{1}{2}\right)^2}$
$\qquad = \dfrac{8\frac{1}{2}}{\frac{1}{4}} = 4\left(8\frac{1}{2}\right) = 34$

51. $7\begin{bmatrix} 4 & 0 \\ 3 & -1 \end{bmatrix} = \begin{bmatrix} 28 & 0 \\ 21 & -7 \end{bmatrix}$

Problem-Solving Strategy: Combining Strategies

PAGE 466   CHECKING FOR UNDERSTANDING

1. - 3. See students' work; Answers may vary.

4. Let w = wrong answers, and
$\qquad r$ = right answers.

$w + r = 120 \qquad\qquad\qquad r - \frac{1}{4}w = 100$

$\qquad r = 120 - w \qquad\quad 120 - w - \frac{1}{4}w = 100$

$\qquad\qquad\qquad\qquad\qquad 120 - \frac{5}{4}w = 100$

$\qquad\qquad\qquad\qquad \left(-\frac{4}{5}\right)\left(-\frac{5}{4}w\right) = (-20)\left(-\frac{4}{5}\right)$

$\qquad\qquad\qquad\qquad\qquad\qquad w = 16$

$\qquad\qquad\qquad\qquad\qquad\quad r = 120 - 16$

$\qquad\qquad\qquad\qquad\qquad\quad r = 104$

PAGES 466-467   EXERCISES

5. Exactly 20% $\left(\frac{1}{5}\right)$ and $\frac{1}{7}$ means the number of books is divisible by 5 and 7. LCM(5, 7) = 35; 35 is not between 50 and 80, but $2 \times 35 = 70$ is.

6. 4-digit squares: 2000 min.
even digits: 8888 max.
$\sqrt{8888} \approx 94.28$ $\qquad$ start at $94^2 = 8836$
$\qquad\qquad\qquad\qquad\qquad\quad 93^2 = 8649$
$\qquad\qquad\qquad\qquad\qquad\boxed{92^2 = 8464}$

7.

	Math	English	Sociology
Darcy	X	✓	X
Janna	X	X	✓
Ray	✓	X	X

Eliminate each person's major.
Ray is not studying English because of the "so what" response. Thus, Ray is studying math.
Janna is studying sociology (not math). Darcy is studying English (not sociology).

8. Answers may vary. Sample answers are:
$\qquad 9 + 8 + 7 + 65 + 4 + 3 + 2 + 1 = 99$
and $\qquad 9 + 8 + 7 + 6 + 5 + 43 + 21 = 99$

9. a. By the definition of a square, $\angle ABA' \cong \angle BCB' \cong \angle CDC' \cong DAD'$, and $\overline{AB} \cong \overline{BC} \cong \overline{CD} \cong \overline{DA}$. Since A', B', C', and D' are midpoints of congruent segments, $\overline{BA'} \cong \overline{CB'} \cong \overline{DC'} \cong \overline{AD'}$. So, $\triangle ABA' \cong \triangle BCB' \cong \triangle CDC' \cong \triangle DAD'$, by SAS. $\angle BAF \cong \angle CBG \cong \angle DCH \cong \angle ADE$ since corresponding parts of congruent triangles are congruent. So $\angle FBA \cong \angle GCB \cong \angle HCD \cong \angle EAD$ by the subtraction property of equality. Therefore, $\triangle BAF \cong \triangle CBG \cong \triangle DCH \cong \triangle ADE$ by ASA. Then $\overline{BF} \cong \overline{CG} \cong \overline{DH} \cong \overline{AE}$ since they are corresponding parts of congruent triangles. $\triangle BA'F \cong \triangle CB'G \cong \triangle DC'H \cong \triangle AD'E$ by SAS. So $\angle BFA' \cong \angle CGB' \cong \angle DHC' \cong \angle AED'$ by CPCTC, and $\angle EFG \cong \angle FGH \cong \angle GHE \cong \angle HEF$ by vertical angles and substitution. $\overline{AA'} \cong \overline{BB'} \cong \overline{CC'} \cong \overline{DD'}$ by CPCTC, and $\overline{EF} \cong \overline{FG} \cong \overline{GH} \cong \overline{HE}$ by the subtraction property of equality. Therefore, $EFGH$ is a square, since all four angles and all four sides are congruent.

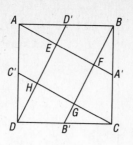

b. If you duplicate the figure next to itself as shown below, you can see that each small triangle unites with a trapezoid to make a square of the same size as $EFGH$. $ABCD$ contains 5 of these squares, so area $EFGH = \frac{1}{5}(x)$ or $\frac{x}{5}$.

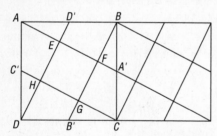

10. Let n = number attending the meeting

$\frac{1}{2}n$ = members left

$\frac{1}{3}\left(\frac{1}{2}n\right)$ = members planning

$\frac{2}{3}\left(\frac{1}{2}n\right)$ = 18 cleaning up

$n = 54$

11. Each column of rectangles has one rectangle out of four shaded. If the shaded rectangles were lined up on the bottom, they would fill the entire bottom row up. Since the horizontal lines are equidistant, $\frac{1}{4}$ of the figure is shaded.

12. Statement: The right path leads to the nearest town.

TRUE STATEMENT

You Ask:	"right=nearest?"	"other says yes?"
Nallini says:	"No"	"No"
Yassini says:	"Yes"	"No"

FALSE STATEMENT

You Ask:	"right=nearest?"	"other says yes?"
Nallini says:	"Yes"	"Yes"
Yassini says:	"No"	"Yes"

Thus, the right path does not lead to the nearest town; the left path does.

13. Cube 1 shows 0, 1, <u>2</u>, <u>6/9</u>, <u>7</u>, <u>8</u>

Cube 2 shows 3, 4, 5, <u>1</u>, <u>2</u>, <u>0</u>

To show	01	10	20	30	Both have 1 and 2.
	02	11	21	31	Both have 0 since
	03	12	22		cube 2 doesn't have
	04	13	23		enough room for 1-9.
	05	14	24		
	06	15	25		
	07	16	26		
	08	17	27		
	09	18	28		
		19	29		

14.

A six-pointed star with numbers 1, 2, 6, 3, 5, 4 arranged around the inner hexagon.

PAGE 467 COOPERATIVE LEARNING ACTIVITY

By guess-and-check, $f(0) = 120$.

```
 1| 1   2  -26  -28  145   26  -120
        1    3  -23  -51   94   120
-1| 1   3  -23  -51   94  120|    0
       -1   -2   25   26  -120
 2| 1   2  -25  -26  120|    0
        2    8  -34 -120
-3| 1   4  -17  -60|    0
       -3   -3   60
    1   1  -20|    0
```

$x^2 + x - 20$

$= (x + 5)(x - 4)(x + 3)(x - 2)(x + 1)(x - 1)$

roots: $-5, 4, -3, 2, -1, 1$

1. 4

2. $2 - i$; conjugates

3. The other possible zeros are: one negative real zero and two imaginary zeros or three negative real zeros. Justification: There must be four zeros and the imaginary zeros occur in pairs.

4. You know what kind of numbers you are looking for, so your search is easier.

5. $f(-x) = 3(-x)^5 + 7(-x)^2 - 8(-x) + 1$
   $\quad = -3x^5 + 7x^2 + 8x + 1$

6. $f(-x) = (-x)^4 - 2(-x)^3 + (-x)^2 - 1$
   $\quad = x^4 + 2x^3 + x^2 - 1$

7. $f(-x) = 4(-x)^4 - 3(-x)^3 + (-x)^2 - (-x) + 1$
   $\quad = 4x^4 + 3x^3 + 2x^2 + x + 1$

8. $f(-x) = (-x)^7 - (-x)^3 + 2(-x) - 1$
   $\quad = -x^7 + x^3 - 2x - 1$

9. $f(x) = x^3 + x^2 + x + 1$

   0 positive real zeros

   $f(-x) = (-x)^3 + (-x)^2 + (-x) + 1$
   $\quad = -x^3 + x^2 - x + 1$

   3 or 1 negative real zeros

   0 or 2 imaginary zeros

10. $f(x) = -x^4 - x^2 - x - 1$

    0 positive real zeros

    $f(-x) = -(-x)^4 - (-x)^2 - (-x) - 1$
    $\quad = -x^4 - x^2 + x - 1$

    2 or 0 negative real zeros

    2 or 4 imaginary zeros

11. $f(x) = x^4 + x^3 - 7x - 1$

    1 positive real zero

    $f(-x) = (-x)^4 + (-x)^3 - 7(-x) - 1$
    $\quad = x^4 - x^3 + 7x - 1$

    3 or 1 negative real zeros

    0 or 2 imaginary zeros

12. $f(x) = x^{10} - 1$

    1 positive real zero

    $f(-x) = (-x)^{10} - 1$
    $\quad = x^{10} - 1$

    1 negative real zero

    8 imaginary zeros

13. $f(x) - 3x^4 + 2x^3 - 3x^2 - 4x + 1$

    2 or 0 positive real zeros

    $f(-x) = 3(-x)^4 + 2(-x)^3 - 3(-x)^2 - 4(-x) + 1$
    $\quad = 3x^4 - 2x^3 - 3x^2 + 4x + 1$

    2 or 0 negative real zeros

    0, 2, or 4 imaginary zeros

14. $f(x) = x^4 + x^3 + 2x^2 - 3x - 1$

    1 positive real zero

    $f(-x) = (-x)^4 + (-x)^3 + 2(-x)^2 - 3(-x) - 1$
    $\quad = x^4 - x^3 + 2x^2 + 3x - 1$

    3 or 1 negative real zeros

    0 or 2 imaginary zeros

15. $f(x) = x^3 + 1$

    0 positive real zeros

    $f(x) = (-x)^3 + 1$
    $\quad = -x^3 + 1$

    1 negative real zero

    2 imaginary zeros

16. $f(x) = x^5 - x^3 - x + 1$

    2 or 0 positive real zeros

    $f(-x) = (-x)^5 - (-x)^3 - (-x) + 1$
    $\quad = -x^5 + x^3 + x + 1$

    1 negative real zero

    2 or 4 imaginary zeros

17. $f(x) = x^{10} - x^8 + x^6 - x^4 + x^2 - 1$

    5, 3, or 1 positive real zeros

    $f(-x) = (-x)^{10} - (-x)^8 + (-x)^6 - (-x)^4$
    $\qquad + (-x)^2 - 1$
    $\quad = x^{10} - x^8 + x^6 - x^4 + x^2 - 1$

    5, 3, or 1 negative real zeros

    0, 2, 4, 6, or 8 imaginary zeros

18. $f(x) = x^{14} + x^{10} - x^9 + x - 1$

    3 or 1 positive real zeros

    $f(-x) = (-x)^{14} + (-x)^{10} - (-x)^9 + (-x) - 1$
    $\quad = x^{14} + x^{10} + x^9 - x - 1$

    1 negative real zero

    10 or 12 imaginary zeros

19. $\begin{array}{r|rrrr} 4 & 1 & -6 & 10 & -8 \\ & & 4 & -8 & 8 \\ \hline & 1 & -2 & 2 & 0 \end{array}$

    $x^2 - 2x + 2 = 0$

    $x = \dfrac{-(-2) \pm \sqrt{(-2)^2 - 4(1)(2)}}{2(1)}$

    $\quad = \dfrac{2 \pm \sqrt{4 - 8}}{2}$

    $\quad = \dfrac{2 \pm \sqrt{-4}}{2}$

    $\quad = 1 \pm i$

    $4, 1 + i, 1 - i$

20.

$$-4\,\underline{|\,1\quad 2\quad -3\quad 20}$$
$$\underline{\ -4\quad 8\quad -20}$$
$$1\quad -2\quad 5\,|\quad 0$$

$$x^2 - 2x + 5 = 0$$

$$x = \frac{-(-2) \pm \sqrt{(-2)^2 - 4(1)(5)}}{2(1)}$$

$$= \frac{2 \pm \sqrt{4 - 20}}{2}$$

$$= \frac{2 \pm \sqrt{-16}}{2}$$

$$= 1 \pm 2i$$

$$-4,\ 1 + 2i,\ 1 - 2i$$

21.

$$-1.5\,\underline{|\,2\quad -1\quad 28\quad 51}$$
$$\underline{\ -3\quad 6\quad -51}$$
$$2\quad -4\quad 34\,|\quad 0$$

$$2x^2 - 4x + 34 = 0$$
$$x^2 - 2x + 17 = 0$$

$$x = \frac{-(-2) \pm \sqrt{(-2)^2 - 4(1)(17)}}{2(1)}$$

$$= \frac{2 \pm \sqrt{4 - 68}}{2}$$

$$= \frac{2 \pm \sqrt{-64}}{2}$$

$$= 1 \pm 4i$$

$$-\frac{3}{2},\ 1 + 4i,\ 1 - 4i$$

22.

$$0.5\,\underline{|\,2\quad -17\quad 90\quad -41}$$
$$\underline{\ 1\quad -8\quad 41}$$
$$2\quad -16\quad 82\,|\quad 0$$

$$2x^2 - 16x + 82 = 0$$
$$x^2 - 8x + 41 = 0$$

$$x = \frac{-(-8) \pm \sqrt{(-8)^2 - 4(1)(41)}}{2(1)}$$

$$= \frac{8 \pm \sqrt{64 - 164}}{2}$$

$$= \frac{8 \pm \sqrt{-100}}{2}$$

$$= 4 \pm 5i$$

$$\frac{1}{2},\ 4 + 5i,\ 4 - 5i$$

23.

$$2i\,\underline{|\,4\quad 0\quad 17\quad 0\quad 4}$$
$$\underline{\ 8i\quad -16\quad 2i\quad -4}$$
$$-2i\,\underline{|\,4\quad 8i\quad 1\quad 2i\,|\quad 0}$$
$$\underline{\ -8i\quad 0\quad -2i}$$
$$4\quad 0\quad 1\,|\quad 0$$

$$4x^2 + 1 = 0$$
$$4x^2 = -1$$
$$x^2 = -\frac{1}{4}$$
$$x = \pm\sqrt{-\frac{1}{4}}$$
$$= \pm\frac{1}{2}i$$

$$2i,\ -2i,\ \frac{1}{2}i,\ -\frac{1}{2}i$$

24.

$$-2\,\underline{|\,1\quad 6\quad 21\quad 26}$$
$$\underline{\ -2\quad -8\quad -26}$$
$$1\quad 4\quad 13\,|\quad 0$$

$$x^2 + 4x + 13 = 0$$

$$x = \frac{-4 \pm \sqrt{(4)^2 - 4(1)(13)}}{2(1)}$$

$$= \frac{-4 \pm \sqrt{16 - 52}}{2}$$

$$= \frac{-4 \pm \sqrt{-36}}{2}$$

$$= -2 \pm 3i$$

$$-2,\ -2 + 3i,\ -2 - 3i$$

25.

$$2 + 3i\,\underline{|\,1\qquad -3\qquad\quad 9\quad 13}$$
$$\underline{\ 2 + 3i\quad -11 + 3i\,|\ -13}$$
$$2 - 3i\,\underline{|\,1\quad -1 + 3i\quad -2 + 3i\,|\quad 0}$$
$$\underline{\ 2 - 3i\qquad 2 - 3i}$$
$$1\qquad\quad 1\,|\qquad 0$$

$$x + 1 = 0$$
$$x = -1$$

$$2 + 3i,\ 2 - 3i,\ -1$$

26.

$$3 - i\,\underline{|\,1\qquad -10\qquad 34\quad -40}$$
$$\underline{\ 3 - i\quad -22 + 4i\,|\ 40}$$
$$3 + i\,\underline{|\,1\quad -7 - i\quad 12 + 4i\,|\quad 0}$$
$$\underline{\ 3 + i\quad -12 - 4i}$$
$$1\qquad -4\,|\qquad 0$$

$$x - 4 = 0$$
$$x = 4$$

$$3 - i,\ 3 + i,\ 4$$

27.

$$3 + 2i\,\underline{|\,1\qquad -6\qquad 12\qquad 6\quad -13}$$
$$\underline{\ 3 + 2i\quad -13\quad -3 - 2i\,|\ 13}$$
$$3 - 2i\,\underline{|\,1\quad -3 + 2i\quad -1\quad 3 - 2i\,|\quad 0}$$
$$\underline{\ 3 - 2i\qquad 0\quad -3 + 2i}$$
$$1\qquad\quad 0\quad -1\,|\qquad 0$$

$$x^2 - 1 = 0$$
$$x = \pm 1$$

$$3 + 2i,\ 3 - 2i,\ 1,\ -1$$

28. $(x - 2)[x - (1 - i)][x - (1 + i)]$

$$= (x - 2)\,[x^2 - (1 - i)x - (1 + i)x$$
$$+ (1 - i)(1 + i)]$$
$$= (x - 2)(x^2 - x + ix - x - ix + 1 + 1)$$
$$= (x - 2)(x^2 - 2x + 2)$$
$$f(x) = x^3 - 4x^2 + 6x - 4$$

29. $(x - 3)(x - 2i)(x + 2i)$

$$= (x - 3)(x^2 + 4)$$
$$f(x) = x^3 - 3x^2 + 4x - 12$$

30. $[x - (-1)]\,(x - 1)\,[x - (2 - i)][x - (2 + i)]$

$$= (x + 1)(x - 1)[x^2 - (2 + i)x - (2 - i)x$$
$$+ (2 - i)(2 + i)]$$
$$= (x^2 - 1)(x^2 - 4x + 5)$$
$$f(x) = x^4 - 4x^3 + 4x^2 + 4x - 5$$

31. $[x - (-2 - i)][x - (-2 + i)][x - (1 + 3i)]$
$[x - (1 - 3i)]$
$= [x^2 - (-2 + i)x - (-2 - i)x + (-2 - i)(-2 + i)]$
$[x^2 - (1 - 3i)x - (1 + 3i)x + (1 + 3i)(1 - 3i)]$
$= (x^2 + 4x + 5)(x^2 - 2x + 10)$
$f(x) = x^4 + 2x^3 + 7x^2 + 30x + 50$

32. $(x - 4)(x - i)(x + i)[x - (-1 + i)][x - (-1 - i)]$
$= (x - 4)(x^2 + 1)(x^2 + 2x + 2)$
$= (x^3 - 4x^2 + x - 4)(x^2 + 2x + 2)$
$f(x) = x^5 - 2x^4 - 5x^3 - 10x^2 - 6x - 8$

33. $(x - 3i)(x + 3i)[x - (-2i)](x - 2i)[x - (1 - i)]$
$[x - (1 + i)]$
$= (x^2 + 9)(x^2 + 4)(x^2 - 2x + 2)$
$= (x^4 + 13x^2 + 36)(x^2 - 2x + 2)$
$f(x) = x^6 - 2x^5 + 15x^4 - 26x^3 + 62x^2 - 72x + 72$

34.

$-2-i$	1	k	-7	-15
		$-2-i$	$3-2i+4i-ki$	$12+36-4i+4ki$
	1	$-2+k-i$	$-4-2k+4i-ki$	$-3+3k-4i+4ki = 0$

$-3 + 3k - 4i + 4ki = 0$
$-3 + 3k = 0$ and $-4i + 4k = 0$
$\quad\quad 3k = 3 \quad\quad\quad\quad 4ki = 4i$
$\quad\quad\quad k = 1 \quad\quad\quad\quad\quad k = 1$

or

$-3 + 4ki = 0$ and $3k - 4i = 0$
$\quad\quad 4ki = 3 \quad\quad\quad\quad 3k = 4i$
$\quad\quad k = \dfrac{3}{4i} \quad\quad\quad\quad k = \dfrac{4i}{3}$

no solution

35. $V = \ell wh = 120$

$\ell = w + 7 \longrightarrow w = \ell - 7$

$6h = \ell \longrightarrow h = \frac{1}{6}\ell$

$120 = \ell(\ell - 7)\left(\frac{1}{6}\ell\right)$

$720 = \ell(\ell - 7)(\ell)$

$720 = \ell^3 - 7\ell^2$

$0 = \ell^3 - 7\ell^2 - 720 \quad\quad$ 1 positive

12	1	-7	0	-720
		12	60	720
	1	5	60	0

$\ell = 12$ cm, $w = 5$ cm, $h = 2$ cm

36. $V = \pi r^2 h = 17.89$

$h = 4r$

$V = \pi r^2(4r) = 17.89$

$4\pi r^3 = 17.89$

$4\pi r^3 - 17.89 = 0$

$4\pi(r^3 - 1.4236) = 0$

$r^3 - 1.4236 = 0$

$(1.4236)^{\frac{1}{3}}$	1	0	0	-1.4236
		$(1.4236)^{\frac{1}{3}}$	$(1.4236)^{\frac{2}{3}}$	1.4236
	1	$(1.4236)^{\frac{1}{3}}$	$(1.4236)^{\frac{2}{3}}$	

$r = (1.4236)^{\frac{1}{3}} = 1.125$ in., $h = 4.5$ in.

37.

3	2	-8	6
		6	-6
	2	-2	0

$f(3) = 0$

-2	2	-8	6
		-4	24
	2	-12	30

$f(-2) = 30$

38.

$y = a(x - h)^2 + k$
$y = ax^2$
$y = -\frac{1}{16}x^2$
$\left(h,\ k + \frac{1}{4a}\right) = (0, -4)$
$\frac{1}{4a} = -4$
$1 = -16a$
$-\frac{1}{16} = a$

39. $f(x) = x^2 + 6$
$= 1(x - 0)^2 + 6$
$= x^2 + 6 \quad\quad$ vertex: $(0, 6)$
$\quad\quad\quad\quad\quad\quad$ axis: $x = 0$

40.

$\dfrac{6 \text{ beats}}{5 \text{ sec}} \times \dfrac{60 \text{ sec}}{1 \text{ min}} \times \dfrac{60 \text{ min}}{1 \text{ hr}} \times \dfrac{24 \text{ hr}}{1 \text{ day}} \times \dfrac{\begin{pmatrix} 365 \text{ days} \\ \text{or} \\ 365\frac{1}{4} \text{ days} \end{pmatrix}}{1 \text{ yr}}$

$\times\ 18 \text{ yr}$

$= 681{,}644{,}160$ (counting leap days)

$= 681{,}177{,}600$ (not counting leap days)

PAGE 474   MID-CHAPTER REVIEW

1. $p(-3) = 6(-3)^3 - 3(-3)^2 + 4(-3) - 9$
$= 6(-27) - 3(9) + 4(-3) - 9$
$= -162 - 27 - 12 - 9$
$= -210$

2. $p(a^2) = 6(a^2)^3 - 3(a^2)^2 + 4(a^2) - 9$
$= 6a^6 - 3a^4 + 4a^2 - 9$

3. $p(x + 1) = 6(x + 1)^3 - 3(x + 1)^2 + 4(x + 1) - 9$
$= 6(x^3 + 3x^2 + 3x + 1) - 3(x^2 + 2x + 1)$
$\quad\quad + 4(x + 1) - 9$
$= 6x^3 + 18x^2 + 18x + 6 - 3x^2 - 6x - 3$
$\quad\quad + 4x + 4 - 9$
$= 6x^3 + 15x^2 + 16x - 2$

4.

$$
\begin{array}{r|rrrr}
-6 & 1 & 1 & -24 & 36 \\
  &   & -6 & 30 & -36 \\
\hline
  & 1 & -5 & 6 & 0
\end{array}
$$

$x^2 - 5x + 6$

$= (x - 2)(x - 3)$

5.

$$
\begin{array}{r|rrrr}
2 & 2 & 13 & 1 & -70 \\
  &   & 4 & 34 & 70 \\
\hline
  & 2 & 17 & 35 & 0
\end{array}
$$

$2x^2 + 17x + 35$

$= (2x + 7)(x + 5)$

6. $(x0)^5 = (10x + 0)^5 = (10x)^5 + 5(10x)^4(0)^1 +$
$\qquad \ldots + 5(10x)^1(0)^4 + (0)^5$

$(x2)^5 = (10x + 2)^5 = (10x)^5 + 5(10x)^4(2)^1 +$
$\qquad \ldots + 5(10x)^1(2)^4 + (2)^5$

$(x4)^5 = (10x + 4)^5 = (10x)^5 + 5(10x)^4(4)^1 +$
$\qquad \ldots + 5(10x)^1(4)^4 + (4)^5$

$(x6)^5 = (10x + 6)^5 = (10x)^5 + 5(10x)^4(6)^1 +$
$\qquad \ldots + 5(10x)^1(6)^4 + (6)^5$

$(x8)^5 = (10x + 8)^5 = (10x)^5 + 5(10x)^4(8)^1 +$
$\qquad \ldots + 5(10x)^1(8)^4 + (8)^5$

Parts $(10x)^5$ through $(10x)^2$ end in 00, so we
need to look at $(10x)^1$ and $(10x)^0$.
The $5(10x)^1(even)^4$ will also end in 00
because $(5)(10)(even) = $ a multiple of 100.
Thus, to find the answer, square the end
digits (0, 2, 4, 6, 8) and discover the
two-digit numbers. $0^5 = 0$ (no), $2^5 = \underline{32}$,
$4^5 = 10\underline{24}$, $6^5 = 77\underline{76}$, $8^5 = 32,7\underline{68}$

7. $f(x) = x^3 - 7x^2 - 6x + 3$

2 or 0 positive real zeros

$f(-x) = (-x)^3 - 7(-x)^2 - 6(-x) + 3$
$\qquad = -x^3 - 7x^2 + 6x + 3$

1 negative real zero

0 or 2 imaginary zeros

8. $g(x) = 2x^4 - x^3 - 9x - 12$

1 positive real zero

$g(-x) = 2(-x)^4 - (-x)^3 - 9(-x) - 12$
$\qquad = 2x^4 + x^3 + 9x - 12$

1 negative real zero

2 imaginary zeros

9. $(x - 1)[x - (1 - i)][x - (1 + i)]$
$\qquad = (x - 1)(x^2 - 2x + 2)$

$f(x) = x^3 - 3x^2 + 4x - 2$

10. $(x + 3)(x - 2)[x - (-3 + 2i)][x - (-3 - 2i)]$
$\qquad = (x^2 + x - 6)(x^2 + 6x + 13)$

$f(x) = x^4 + 7x^3 + 13x^2 - 23x - 78$

10-5 The Rational Zero Theorem

1. when coefficients are integers

2. You limit the number of possible solutions.

3. all the factors of a_n

4. Answers may vary. A sample answer is
$\qquad f(x) = x^4 + x^3 + x^2 + x + 3$.

5. $\pm 1, \pm 2$　　**6.** $\pm 1, \pm 5$　　**7.** $\pm 1, \pm 2, \pm 3, \pm 6$

8. $\pm 1, \pm 3$　　**9.** $\pm 1, \pm 2, \pm 5, \pm 10$　　**10.** ± 1

11. $\pm 1, \pm 2, \pm 4, \pm \frac{1}{3}, \pm \frac{2}{3}, \pm \frac{4}{3}$

12. $\pm 1, \pm 3, \pm \frac{1}{2}, \pm \frac{3}{2}$

13. $\pm 1, \pm 5$　　**14.** $\pm 1, \pm 2, \pm 3, \pm 4, \pm 6, \pm 12$

15. $\pm 1, \pm 2, \pm 3, \pm 6, \pm 9, \pm 18$　　**16.** $\pm 1, \pm 3, \pm \frac{1}{3}$

17. $\pm 1, \pm 2, \pm \frac{1}{6}, \pm \frac{1}{3}, \pm \frac{1}{2}, \pm \frac{2}{3}$

18. $\pm 1, \pm 3, \pm 5, \pm 15, \pm \frac{1}{3}, \pm \frac{5}{3}$

19. $\pm 1, \pm 2, \pm 3, \pm 6, \pm \frac{1}{2}, \pm \frac{3}{2}, \pm \frac{1}{4}, \pm \frac{3}{4}$

20. $\pm 1, \pm 3, \pm 9, \pm 27, \pm \frac{1}{3}, \pm \frac{1}{9}$

21.

$$
\begin{array}{r|rrrr}
10 & 1 & 1 & -80 & -300 \\
   &   & 10 & 110 & 300 \\
\hline
   & 1 & 11 & 30 & 0
\end{array}
$$

$x^2 + 11x + 30 = (x + 5)(x + 6)$

$10, -5, -6$

22.

$$
\begin{array}{r|rrrr}
-2 & 1 & -1 & -34 & -56 \\
   &   & -2 & 6 & 56 \\
\hline
   & 1 & -3 & -28 & 0
\end{array}
$$

$x^2 - 3x - 28 = (x - 7)(x + 4)$

$-2, 7, -4$

23.

$$
\begin{array}{r|rrrr}
-1 & 1 & 0 & -3 & -2 \\
   &   & -1 & 1 & 2 \\
\hline
   & 1 & -1 & -2 & 0
\end{array}
$$

$x^2 - x - 2 = (x - 2)(x + 1)$

$-1, 2, -1$

24.

$$
\begin{array}{r|rrrrr}
0 & 1 & -3 & 1 & -3 & 0 \\
  &   & 0 & 0 & 0 & 0 \\
\hline
3 & 1 & -3 & 1 & -3 & 0 \\
  &   & 3 & 0 & 3 & \\
\hline
  & 1 & 0 & 1 & 0 &
\end{array}
$$

$x^2 + 1$

$0, 3$

25.

$$
\begin{array}{r|rrrrr}
0 & 1 & -3 & -53 & -9 & 0 \\
  &   & 0 & 0 & 0 & 0 \\
\hline
9 & 1 & -3 & -53 & -9 & 0 \\
  &   & 9 & 54 & 9 & \\
\hline
  & 1 & 6 & 1 & 0 &
\end{array}
$$

$x^2 + 6x + 1$

$0, 9$

26.
```
3│ 2  -11   12    9
        6  -15   -9
   2   -5   -3 │ 0
```
$2x - 5x - 3 = (2x + 1)(x - 3)$

$3, -\frac{1}{2}, 3$

27.
```
-2│ 6   11   -3   -2
       -12    2    2
    6   -1   -1 │ 0
```
$6x^2 - x - 1 = (3x + 1)(2x - 1)$

$-2, -\frac{1}{3}, \frac{1}{2}$

28.
```
-2│ 1   10   33   38    8
        -2  -16  -34   -8
    1    8   17    4 │  0
            -4  -16   -4
    1    4    1 │  0
```
$x^2 + 4x + 1$

$-2, -4$

29.
```
 1│ 1   0   1    0   -2
        1   1    2    2
-1│ 1   1   2    2 │  0
           -1    0   -2
    1    0   2 │  0
```
$x^2 + 2$

$1, -1$

30.
```
-1│ 1   1   -9  -17   -8
       -1    0    9    8
-1│ 1   0   -9   -8 │  0
           -1    1    8
    1   -1   -8 │  0
```
$x^2 - x - 8$

$-1, -1$

31.
```
 2│ 1   4   -3  -18
        2   12   18
    1   6    9 │  0
```
$x^2 + 6x + 9 = (x + 3)(x + 3)$

$2, -3, -3$

32.
```
 2│ 1   0  -13   0   36
        2    4  -18  -36
-2│ 1   2   -9  -18 │  0
           -2    0   18
    1    0   -9 │  0
```
$x^2 - 9 = (x + 3)(x - 3)$

$2, -2, -3, 3$

33.
```
-6│ 1  -1  -40   12
       -6   42  -12
    1  -7    2 │  0
```
$x^2 - 7x + 2$

-6

34.
```
 1/2│ 48  -52    0   13   -3
          24  -14   -7    3
-1/2│ 48  -28  -14    6 │  0
         -24   26   -6
     48  -52   12 │  0
```
$48x^2 - 52x + 12 = 4(12x^2 - 13x + 3)$
$= 4(3x - 1)(4x - 3)$

$\frac{1}{2}, -\frac{1}{2}, \frac{1}{3}, \frac{3}{4}$

35.
```
 0│ 1   0   -6    0    8    0
        0    0    0    0    0
 2│ 1   0   -6    0    8 │  0
        2    4   -4   -8
-2│ 1   2   -2   -4 │  0
       -2    0    4
    1    0   -2 │  0
```
$x^2 - 2$

$0, 2, -2$

36.
```
 1│ 2  -1   0    0   -2    1
        2   1    1    1   -1
-1│ 2   1   1    1   -1 │  0
       -2   1   -2    1
 1/2│ 2  -1   2   -1 │  0
        1   0    1
    2    0   2 │  0
```
$2x^2 + 2 = 2(x^2 + 1)$

$1, -1, \frac{1}{2}$

37. $V = \ell wh = 144$

$w = 2h \longrightarrow h = \frac{1}{2}w$

$\ell = w + 2$

$V = (w + 2)(w)\left(\frac{1}{2}\,w\right) = 144$

$(w + 2)(w)(w) = 288$

$w^3 + 2w^2 = 288$

$w^3 + 2w^2 - 288 = 0$

```
6│ 1   2    0  -288
       6   48   288
   1   8   48 │  0
```

$w = 6$ units, $h = 3$ units, $\ell = 8$ units

38.
```
-1/2│ 8  -36   22   21
         -4   20  -21
     8  -40   42 │  0
```
$8x^2 - 40x + 42 = 2(4x^2 - 20x + 21)$
$= 2(2x - 3)(2x - 7)$

$-\frac{1}{2}, \frac{3}{2}, \frac{7}{2}$

39.

```
2/3 | 6   5   -9    2
            4    6   -2
        6   9   -3 |  0
```

$6x^2 + 9x - 3 = 3(2x^2 + 3x - 1)$

$$x = \frac{-3 \pm \sqrt{9 - 4(2)(-1)}}{2(2)}$$

$$= \frac{-3 \pm \sqrt{9 + 8}}{4}$$

$$= \frac{-3 \pm \sqrt{17}}{4}$$

$\dfrac{2}{3},\ \dfrac{-3 + \sqrt{17}}{4},\ \dfrac{-3 - \sqrt{17}}{4}$

40.

```
  0 | 12   4   -3   -1   0
            0    0    0   0
1/2 | 12   4   -3   -1 | 0
            6    5    1
       12  10    2 |  0
```

$12x^2 + 10x + 2 = 2(6x^2 + 5x + 1)$
$$= 2(3x + 1)(2x + 1)$$

$0,\ \dfrac{1}{2},\ -\dfrac{1}{3},\ -\dfrac{1}{2}$

41.

```
 -2 | 6   22   11   -38   -40
          -12  -20   18    40
4/3 | 6   10   -9   -20 |   0
            8   24    20
        6  18   15 |   0
```

$6x^2 + 18x + 15 = 3(2x^2 + 6x + 5)$

$$x = \frac{-6 \pm \sqrt{(6)^2 - 4(2)(5)}}{2(2)}$$

$$= \frac{-6 \pm \sqrt{-4}}{4}$$

$$= -\frac{3}{2} \pm \frac{1}{2}i$$

$-2,\ \dfrac{4}{3},\ \dfrac{-3 + i}{2},\ \dfrac{-3 - i}{2}$

42.

```
  0 | 5  -29   55   -28   0
           0    0     0   0
4/5 | 5  -29   55   -28 | 0
           4   -20    28
        5 -25   35 |  0
```

$5x^2 - 25x + 35 = 5(x^2 - 5x + 7)$

$$x = \frac{-(-5) \pm \sqrt{(-5)^2 - 4(1)(7)}}{2(1)}$$

$$= \frac{5 \pm \sqrt{25 - 28}}{2}$$

$$= \frac{5 \pm \sqrt{-3}}{2}$$

$$= \frac{5 \pm i\sqrt{3}}{2}$$

$0,\ \dfrac{4}{5},\ \dfrac{5 + i\sqrt{3}}{2},\ \dfrac{5 - i\sqrt{3}}{2}$

43.

```
   3 | 9    0   -94   27    40   -12
           27   81   -39   -36    12
 2/3 | 9   27   -13   -12    4 |   0
            6   22     6    -4
-2/3 | 9   33    9    -6 |   0
           -6  -18     6
        9  27    -9 |   0
```

$9x^2 + 27x - 9 = 9(x^2 + 3x - 1)$

$$x = \frac{-3 \pm \sqrt{3^2 - 4(1)(-1)}}{2(1)}$$

$$= \frac{-3 \pm \sqrt{9 + 4}}{2}$$

$$= \frac{-3 \pm \sqrt{13}}{2}$$

$3,\ \dfrac{2}{3},\ -\dfrac{2}{3},\ \dfrac{-3 + \sqrt{13}}{2},\ \dfrac{-3 - \sqrt{13}}{2}$

44.

```
 -1 | 1   -2   -12   -12   -13   -10
          -1    3     9     3    10
 -2 | 1   -3   -9    -3   -10 |  0
          -2   10    -2    10
  5 | 1   -5    1    -5 |   0
           5    0     5
       1   0    1 |   0
```

$x^2 + 1 = (x + i)(x - i)$

$-1,\ -2,\ 5,\ -i,\ i$

45.

```
  k | 1    4        9k          -90
          k    4k + k²    13k² + k³
 2k | 1  4 + k   13k + k²  | k³ + 13k² - 90 = 0
          2k      8k + 6k²
       1  4 + 3k  | 21k + 7k² = 0
                    7k(3 + k) = 0
                    k = 0   or   k = -3
```

Test:
```
   0 | 1   13    0   -90
           0     0    0
       1   13    0 | -90       no
  -3 | 1   13    0   -90
          -3   -30    90
       1   10  -30 |   0       yes
```

$k = -3$; roots: -3, -6 and $\underline{?}$

```
  -3 | 1    4   -27   -90
          -3    -3    90
  -6 | 1    1   -30 |   0
          -6    30
       1   -5 |   0
```

$x - 5$

roots: -3, -6, 5

246

46. s = length of one side of base

h = height

$V = Bh = s^2h = 200$

$h = s + 3$

$V = s^2(s + 3) = 200$

$s^2 + 3s^2 = 200$

$s^3 + 3s^2 - 200 = 0$

5	1	3	0	-200
		5	40	200
	1	8	40	0

$s = 5$ in.; $h = 8$ in. 5 in. × 5 in. × 8 in.

47. $V = \frac{1}{3}\pi r^2h = 5.24$

$h = r + 4$

$V = \frac{1}{3}\pi r^2(r + 4) = 5.24$

$r^2(r + 4) = 5$

$r^3 + 4r^2 = 5$

$r^3 + 4r^2 - 5 = 0$

1	1	4	0	-5
		1	5	5
	1	5	5	0

$r = 1$ in.; $h = 5$ in.

48. $f(x) = 3x^5 - 8x^2 + 1$

2 or 0 positive real zeros

$f(-x) = 3(-x)^5 - 8(-x)^2 + 1$

$= -3x^5 - 8x^2 + 1$

1 negative real zero

2 or 4 imaginary zeros

49. $(x + 2)[x - (2 + 3i)][x - (2 - 3i)]$

$= (x + 2)(x^2 - 4x + 13)$

$f(x) = x^3 - 2x^2 + 5x + 26$

50. {(3, 0), (-3, 0)}

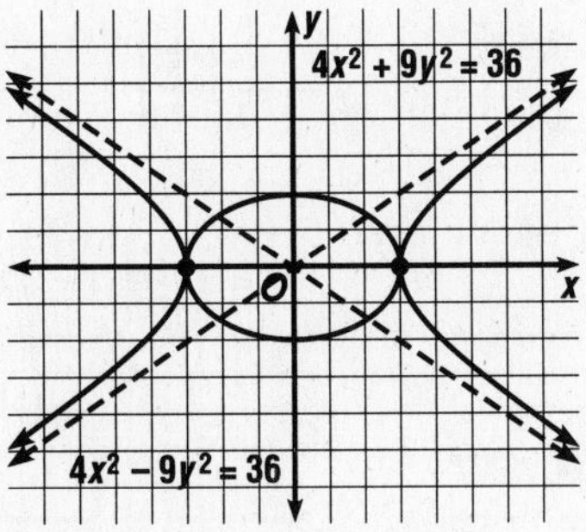

51. $2(1) - 4(-1) - (0) = 6$

$2 + 4 - 0 = 6$

$6 = 6$ ✓

$3(1) + 4(-1) + 3(0) = -1$

$3 - 4 + 0 = -1$

$-1 = -1$ ✓

$(1) + (-1) + (0) = 0$

$1 - 1 + 0 = 0$

$0 = 0$ ✓

Thus, (1, -1, 0) is a solution.

PAGE 480 LANGUAGE CONNECTION

1. factor
2. zero
3. solution
4. root
5. factor
6. function
7. equation
8. zero
9. solution
10. solution
11. function
12. expression

10-6 Graphing Polynomials and Approximating Zeros

PAGE 484 CHECKING FOR UNDERSTANDING

1. A negative height makes no sense.
2. List values for x and then find $f(x)$. Wherever a sign change occurs in $f(x)$ values, a zero lies between those two x values.
3. See students' work. Answers will vary.
4. degree 4; 1 positive, 1 negative, 2 imaginary roots
5. a.

x	$f(x)$
-4	138
-3	19
-2	-6
-1	3
0	10
1	3
2	-6
3	19
4	138

b. zeros between:

-3 and -2: -2.6

-2 and -1: -1.2

1 and 2: 1.2

2 and 3: 2.6

c. Negative: between -2.5 and -1.2
between 1.2 and 2.5

Positive: between -1.2 and 1.2
less than -2.5
greater than 2.5

d. apparent minimums at -2 and 2, maximum at 0

e.

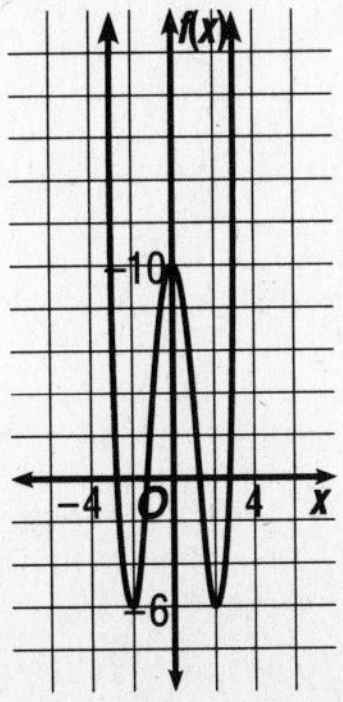

6. $f(x) = x^3 - 2x^2 + 6$

    2 or 0 positive real zeros

    $f(-x) = (-x)^3 - 2(-x)^2 + 6$

    $\qquad = -x^3 - 2x^2 + 6$

    1 negative real zero

x	$f(x)$
-1	3
-2	-10

$f(-1.4) = -0.66$

$f(-1.3) = 0.42$ ✓

The zero is approximately -1.3.

7. $g(x) = 2x^5 + 3x - 2$

    1 positive real zero

    $g(-x) = 2(-x)^5 + 3(-x) - 2$

    $\qquad = -2x^5 - 3x - 2$

    0 negative real zeros

x	$g(x)$
0	-2
1	3

$g(0.6) = -0.04$ ✓

$g(0.7) = 0.44$

The zero is approximately 0.6.

8. $g(x) = x^5 - 6$

    1 positive real zero

    $g(-x) = (-x)^5 - 6$

    $\qquad = -x^5 - 6$

    0 negative real zeros

$\sqrt[5]{6} =$

x	$g(x)$
1.43	0

$g(1.4) = -0.62$ ✓

$g(1.5) = 1.59$

The zero is approximately 1.4.

9. $h(x) = x^3 + 2x^2 - 3x - 5$

    1 positive real zero

    $h(-x) = (-x)^3 + 2(-x)^2 - 3(-x) - 5$

    $\qquad = -x^3 + 2x^2 + 3x - 5$

    2 or 0 negative real zeros

x	$h(x)$
1	-5
2	5
-1	-1
-2	1
-3	-5

$h(1.7) = 0.59$

$h(1.6) = -0.58$ ✓

$h(-1.3) = 0.083$ ✓

$h(-1.4) = 0.376$

$h(-2.3) = 0.313$

$h(-2.4) = 0.104$ ✓

The zeros are approximately 1.6, -1.3, and -2.4.

10. $n(x) = x^3 - x^2 + 1$

    2 or 0 positive real zeros

    $n(-x) = (-x)^3 - (-x)^2 + 1$

    $\qquad = -x^3 - x^2 + 1$

    1 negative real zero

x	$n(x)$
0	1
-1	-1

$n(-0.8) = -0.152$ ✓

$n(-0.7) = 0.167$

The zero is approximately -0.8.

11. $f(x) = x^3 + 1$

    0 positive real zeros

    $f(-x) = (-x)^3 + 1$

    $\qquad = -x^3 + 1$

    1 negative real zero

x	$f(x)$
-1	0

The zero is -1.

12. $h(x) = 3x^3 - 16x^2 + 12x + 6$

    2 or 0 positive real zeros

    $h(-x) = 3(-x)^3 - 16(-x)^2 + 12(-x) + 6$

    $\qquad = -3x^3 - 16x^2 - 12x + 6$

    1 negative real zero

x	$h(x)$
0	6
-1	-25
1	5
2	-10
4	-10
5	41

$h(-0.3) = 0.879$ ✓

$h(-0.4) = -1.552$

$h(1.4) = -0.328$ ✓

$h(1.3) = 1.151$

$h(4.3) = 0.281$ ✓

$h(4.2) = 3.576$

The zeros are approximately -0.3, 1.4, and 4.3.

13. $f(x) = x^4 - 4x^2 + 6$

    2 or 0 positive real zeros

    $f(-x) = x^4 - 4x^2 + 6$

    2 or 0 negative real zeros

    There are no real zeros.

14.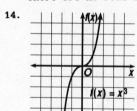

    $f(x) = x^3$

15.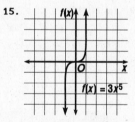

    $f(x) = 3x^5$

16.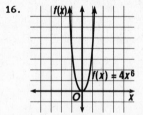

    $f(x) = 4x^6$

17.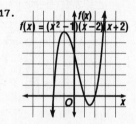

    $f(x) = (x^2 - 1)(x - 2)(x + 2)$

18.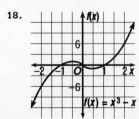

    $f(x) = x^3 - x$

19.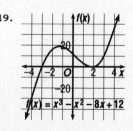

    $f(x) = x^3 - x^2 - 8x + 12$

248

20.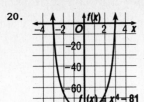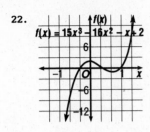

f(x) = x⁴ - 81 (in graph: $f(x) = x^4 - 81$)

21.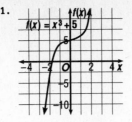

$f(x) = x^3 + 5$

22.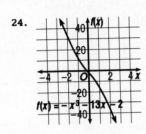

$f(x) = 15x^3 - 16x^2 - x + 2$

23.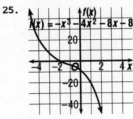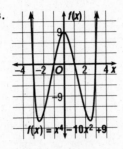

$f(x) = x^4 - 10x^2 + 9$

24.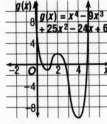

$f(x) = -x^3 - 13x - 2$

25.

$f(x) = -x^3 - 4x^2 - 8x - 8$

26. $g(x) = x^4 - 9x^3 + 25x^2 - 24x + 6$

4, 2, or 0 positive real zeros

$g(-x) = x^4 + 9x^3 + 25x^2 + 24x + 6$

0 negative real zeros

x	g(x)
0	6
1	-1
2	2
3	-3
4	-10
5	11

$g(0.4) = -0.15$ ✓

$g(0.3) = 0.815$ **A-10-54**

$g(1.3) = 0.133$ ✓

$g(1.2) = -0.278$

$g(2.6) = 0.114$ ✓

$g(2.7) = -0.553$

$g(4.7) = -0.989$ ✓

$g(4.8) = 2.314$

$g(x) = x^4 - 9x^3 + 25x^2 - 24x + 6$ (in graph)

The zeros are approximately 0.4, 1.3, 2.6, and 4.7.

27. $h(x) = x^5 + 4x^4 - x^3 - 9x^2 + 3$

2 or 0 positive real zeros

$h(-x) = -x^5 + 4x^4 + x^3 - 9x^2 + 3$

3 or 1 negative real zeros

x	h(x)
-4	-77
-3	30
-2	7
-1	-2
0	3
1	-2
2	55

$h(-3.6) = 0.20$ ✓

$h(-3.7) = -13.33$

$h(-1.6) = -0.22$ ✓

$h(-1.7) = 1.11$

$h(-0.7) = -0.27$ ✓

$h(-0.6) = 0.42$

$h(0.6) = 0.14$ ✓

$h(0.7) = -0.62$

$h(1.3) = 0.73$ ✓

$h(1.2) = -0.91$

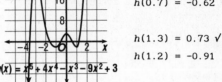

$h(x) = x^5 + 4x^4 - x^3 - 9x^2 + 3$ (in graph)

The zeros are approximately -3.6, -1.6, -0.7, 0.6, and 1.3.

28. $f(x) = x^3 - 3x^2 - 2$

1 positive real zero

$f(-x) = -x^3 - 3x^2 - 2$

0 negative real zeros

x	f(x)
3	-2
4	14

$f(3.2) = 0.048$ ✓

$f(3.1) = -1.04$

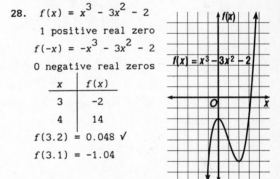

$f(x) = x^3 - 3x^2 - 2$ (in graph)

The zero is approximately 3.2.

29. $r(x) = x^3 - 3x - 4$

1 positive real zero

$r(-x) = -x^3 + 3x - 4$

2 or 0 negative real zeros

x	r(x)
2	-2
3	17

$r(2.2) = 0.048$ ✓

$r(2.1) = -1.039$

$r(x) = x^3 - 3x - 4$ (in graph)

The zero is approximately 2.2.

30. $f(x) = x^4 + 7x + 1$

0 positive real zeros

$f(-x) = x^4 - 7x + 1$

2 or 0 negative real zeros

x	$f(x)$
-2	3
-1	-5
0	1

$f(-1.9) = 0.7321$ ✓

$f(-1.8) = -1.1024$

$f(-0.1) = 0.3$ ✓

$f(-0.2) = -0.4$

The zeros are approximately -1.9 and -0.1.

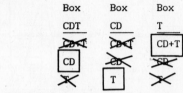

31. $g(x) = x^5 + x^4 - 2x^3 + 1$

2 or 0 positive real zeros

$g(-x) = -x^5 + x^4 + 2x^3 + 1$

1 negative real zero

x	$g(x)$
-1	3
-2	1
-3	-107

$f(-2.0) = 1$ ✓

$f(-2.1) = -20.4$

The zero is approximately -2.0.

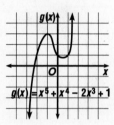

32. Answers may vary. A typical answer is that the ends of an even degree graph both point up or down, and the ends of an odd degree function point in opposite directions.

33. a.

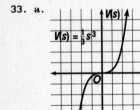

b. $V(0) = 0$

c. There is no maximum or minimum.

d. All three zeros occur at 0. However, since $V \neq 0$, we are not interested in zeros. There is no maximum or minimum volume for any value of s.

34. $r = 4.2$ $V = \frac{4}{3}\pi r^3$

$= \frac{4}{3}\pi(4.2)^3$

$= 310 \text{m}^3$

total tank volume $= 310 + 1170$

$= 1480$

1480 m^3

35. $V = \pi r^2 h,$

$2 = \pi r^2(2)$

$1 = \pi r^2$

$\frac{1}{\pi} = r^2$

$\pm\sqrt{\frac{1}{\pi}} = r$

$0.56 = r$

0.56 cm

36.

Box CDT has compact discs; thus box T has compact discs and tapes, and box CD has tapes.

37. Let x = the first number, and

y = the second number.

$x + y = 60$ maximize $xy = x(60 - x)$

$y = 60 - x$

$f(x) = x(60 - x)$

$= 60x - x^2$

$= -x^2 + 60x$

$= -1(x^2 - 60x)$

$= -1(x - 30)^2 + 900$

The vertex (maximum) is at (30, 900). Thus, when $x = 30$ and $y = 60 - x = 30$, a maximum value of 900 occurs.

38. $x^2y^2 - 25x^2 = x^2(y^2 - 25)$

$= x^2(y + 5)(y - 5)$

39. no

Technology: Zeros of Polynomial Functions

PAGE 486   EXERCISE

1. Change cells B3 through B11 to evaluate the values in cells A3 through A11 appropriately.

10-7 Composition of Functions

PAGE 489   CHECKING FOR UNDERSTANDING

1. $f(x) = x - 0.5x$ x = original price

$g(x) = x - 0.2x$

$[g \circ f](x) = g[f(x)] = g(x - 0.5x) = g(0.5x)$

$= g[(0.5)(35.99)] = g(18)$

$g(18) = 18 - 0.2(18)$

$= 18 - 3.6$

$= \$14.40$

2. $[f \circ g](x) = f[g(x)] = f(x - 0.2x) = f(0.8x)$
   $= f[(0.8)(35.99)] = f(28.8)$

   $f(28.8) = 28.8 - 0.5(28.8)$
   $= 28.8 - 14.4$
   $= \$14.40$

   No, it would be the same price.

3. f composition g or the function f performed on the function g

4. $f(x) = x^2 \qquad g(x) = x + 2$
   $[f \circ g](x) = f[g(x)] = f(x + 2)$
   $f(x + 2) = (x + 2)^2$
   $\qquad\qquad = x^2 + 4x + 4$

   $[g \circ f](x) = g[f(x)] = g(x^2)$
   $g(x^2) = x^2 + 2$

   $x^2 + 2 \neq x^2 + 4x + 4$
   So, $[g \circ f](x) \neq [f \circ g](x)$.

5. $f(3) = 9$
   $f(0) = 6$
   $f(-1) = 12$

6. $f(3) = 3 - 5 = -2$
   $f(0) = 0 - 5 = -5$
   $f(-1) = -1 - 5 = -6$

7. $f(3) = 3^2 + 3(3) + 2$
   $= 9 + 9 + 2$
   $= 20$

   $f(0) = 0) + 3(0) + 2$
   $= 0 + 0 + 2$
   $= 2$

   $f(-1) = (-1)^2 + 3(-1) + 2$
   $= 1 - 3 + 2$
   $= 0$

8. $f(3) = |3 - 3|$
   $= |0|$
   $= 0$

   $f(0) = |0 - 3|$
   $= |-3|$
   $= 3$

   $f(-1) = |(-1) - 3|$
   $= |-4|$
   $= 4$

9. $f(3) = 3^2 - 3^5$
   $= 9 - 243$
   $= -234$

   $f(0) = 0^2 - 0^5$
   $= 0$

   $f(-1) = (-1)^2 - (-1)^5$
   $= 1 - (-1)$
   $= 2$

10. $f(x) = x + 4 \qquad g(x) = x - 7$
    $[f \circ g](2) \qquad [g \circ f](2)$
    $= f[g(2)] \qquad = g[f(2)]$
    $= f(2 - 7) \qquad = g(2 + 4)$
    $= f(-5) \qquad = g(6)$
    $= -5 + 4 \qquad = 6 - 7$
    $= -1 \qquad\quad = -1$

11. $f(x) = x^2 + 1 \qquad g(x) = x + 1$
    $[f \circ g](2) \qquad [g \circ f](2)$
    $= f[g(2)] \qquad = g[f(2)]$
    $= f(2 + 1) \qquad = g(2^2 + 1)$
    $= f(3) \qquad\quad = g(5)$
    $= 3^2 + 1 \qquad = 5 + 1$
    $= 10 \qquad\quad = 6$

12. $f(x) = x^3 + 4 \qquad g(x) = x + 3$
    $[f \circ g](2) \qquad [g \circ f](2)$
    $= f[g(2)] \qquad = g[f(2)]$
    $= f(2 + 3) \qquad = g(2^3 + 4)$
    $= f(5) \qquad\quad = g(8 + 4)$
    $= 5^3 + 4 \qquad = g(12)$
    $= 125 + 4 \qquad = 12 + 3$
    $= 129 \qquad\quad = 15$

13. $f(x) = x^3 \qquad\qquad g(x) = x^2$
    $[f \circ g](2) \qquad\qquad [g \circ f](2)$
    $= f[g(2)] \qquad\qquad = g[f(2)]$
    $= f(2^2) \qquad\qquad = g(2^3)$
    $= f(4) \qquad\qquad\quad = g(8)$
    $= 4^3 = 64 \qquad\quad = 8^2 = 64$

14. $f(x) = x \qquad g(x) = -x$
    $[f \circ g](2) \qquad [g \circ f](2)$
    $= f[g(2)] \qquad = g[f(2)]$
    $= f(-2) \qquad = g(2)$
    $= -2 \qquad\quad = -2$

15. $f = \{(3, 2), (1, -7), (2, 0)\}$
    $g = \{(2, 1), (0, 11)\}$
    $[f \circ g](2) \qquad [g \circ f](2)$
    $= f[g(2)] \qquad = g[f(2)]$
    $= f(1) \qquad\quad = g(0)$
    $= -7 \qquad\quad = 11$

16. $g(x) = x + 4 \qquad h(x) = x + 9$
    $g[h(x)] \qquad\qquad h[g(x)] = h(x + 4)$
    $= g(x + 9) \qquad\qquad = (x + 4) + 9$
    $= (x + 9) + 4 \qquad\quad = x + 13$
    $= x + 13$

17. $g(x) = 2x \qquad\qquad h(x) = 5x$
    $g[h(x)] = g(5x) \qquad h[g(x)] = h(2x)$
    $\qquad\quad = 2(5x) \qquad\qquad\quad = 5(2x)$
    $\qquad\quad = 10x \qquad\qquad\qquad = 10x$

18. $g(x) = x - 1$ $\qquad$ $h(x) = x^2$

$g[h(x)] = g(x^2)$ $\qquad$ $h[g(x)] = h(x - 1)$

$\qquad = x^2 - 1$ $\qquad\qquad = (x - 1)^2$

$\qquad\qquad\qquad\qquad\qquad = x^2 - 2x + 1$

19. $g(x) = -x$ $\qquad$ $h(x) = -x$

$g[h(x)] = g(-x)$ $\qquad$ $h[g(x)] = h(-x)$

$\qquad = -(-x)$ $\qquad\qquad = -(-x)$

$\qquad = x$ $\qquad\qquad\qquad = x$

20. $g(x) = x + 1$ $\qquad$ $h(x) = x^3$

$g[h(x)] = (g(x^3)$ $\qquad$ $h[g(x)] = h(x + 1)$

$\qquad = x^3 + 1$ $\qquad\qquad = (x + 1)^3$

$\qquad\qquad\qquad\qquad\qquad = x^3 + 3x^2 + 3x + 1$

21. $g(x) = |x|$ $\qquad$ $h(x) = x - 3$

$g[h(x)] = g(x - 3)$ $\qquad$ $h[g(x)] = h(|x|)$

$\qquad = |x - 3|$ $\qquad\qquad = |x| - 3$

22. $g[f(1)] = g(1^2)$ $\qquad$ **23.** $[f \circ g](3) = f[h(3)]$

$\qquad = g(1)$ $\qquad\qquad\qquad = f(3 - 1)$

$\qquad = 3(1)$ $\qquad\qquad\qquad = f(2)$

$\qquad = 3$ $\qquad\qquad\qquad\quad = 2^2$

$\qquad\qquad\qquad\qquad\qquad\qquad = 4$

24. $[h \circ f](3) = h[f(3)]$ $\quad$ **25.** $[g \circ f](-2) = g[f(-2)]$

$\qquad\qquad = h(3^2)$ $\qquad\qquad\qquad\qquad = g[(-2)^2]$

$\qquad\qquad = h(9)$ $\qquad\qquad\qquad\qquad = g(4)$

$\qquad\qquad = 9 - 1$ $\qquad\qquad\qquad\quad = 3(4)$

$\qquad\qquad = 8$ $\qquad\qquad\qquad\qquad = 12$

26. $g[h(-2)] = g(-2 - 1)$ $\quad$ **27.** $f[h(-3)] = f(-3 - 1)$

$\qquad\qquad = g(-3)$ $\qquad\qquad\qquad = f(-4)$

$\qquad\qquad = 3(-3)$ $\qquad\qquad\qquad = (-4)^2$

$\qquad\qquad = -9$ $\qquad\qquad\qquad\quad = 16$

28. $g[f(x)] = g(x^2)$ $\qquad$ **29.** $[f \circ g](x) = f[g(x)]$

$\qquad = 3x^2$ $\qquad\qquad\qquad\qquad = f(3x)$

$\qquad\qquad\qquad\qquad\qquad\qquad = (3x)^2$

$\qquad\qquad\qquad\qquad\qquad\qquad = 9x^2$

30. $[f \circ (g \circ h)](x) = f\{g[h(x)]\}$

$\qquad\qquad\qquad = f[g(x - 1)]$

$\qquad\qquad\qquad = f[3(x - 1)]$

$\qquad\qquad\qquad = [3(x - 1)]^2$

$\qquad\qquad\qquad = 9(x - 1)^2$

$\qquad\qquad\qquad = 9(x^2 - 2x + 1)$

$\qquad\qquad\qquad = 9x^2 - 18x + 9$

31. $f = \{(1, 1), (0, -3)\}$

$g = \{(1, 0), (-3, 1), (2, 1)\}$

$f \circ g = \{(1, -3), (-3, 1), (2, 1)\}$

$g \circ f = \{(1, 0), (0, 1)\}$

32. $f = \{(3, 8), (4, 0), (6, 3), (7, -1)\}$

$g = \{(0, 4), (8, 6), (3, 6), (-1, -8)\}$

$f \circ g$ does not exist since the range of

g, $(4, 6, -8)$, is not a subset of the domain of

f, $(3, 4, 6, 7)$.

$g \circ f = \{(3, 6), (4, 4), (6, 6), (7, -8)\}$

33. Answers may vary. Sample answers are

$f(x) = 2x$, $g(x) = 4x$ $\quad$ or $\quad$ $f(x) = -x$, $g(x) = -x$.

34. K = Kelvin temperature

C = Celsius temperature

F = Fahrenheit temperature

$K = C + 273$

$C = \dfrac{5}{9}(F - 32)$

$K = \dfrac{5}{9}(F - 32) + 273$

$\quad = \dfrac{5}{9}(59 - 32) + 273$

$\quad = \dfrac{5}{9}(27) + 273$

$\quad = 15 + 273$

$\quad = 288$

35. w = wholesale

r = regular

s = sale

$r = w + 0.75w = 1.75w$

$s = r - 0.2r = 0.8r$

$s = 0.8(1.75w)$

$\quad = 0.8[(1.75)(100)]$

$\quad = 0.8(175)$

$\quad = \$140.00$

36.

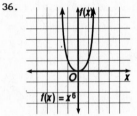

$f(x) = x^6$

37. $g(x) = x^4 - 4x^2 + 3$

2 or 0 positive real zeros

$g(-x) = x^4 - 4x^2 + 3$

2 or 0 negative real zeros

```
1| 1   0   -4   0    3
       1   1   -3   -3
1| 1   1   -3   -3 | 0
      -1   0    3
   1   0   -3 | 0
```

$x^2 - 3$

$= (x + \sqrt{3})(x - \sqrt{3})$

x	$g(x)$
2	3
$\sqrt{3} = 1.7$	0 ✓
1	0 ✓
-1	0 ✓
$-\sqrt{3} = -1.7$	0 ✓
-2	3

The zeros are 1.7, 1, -1, and -1.7.

38.
$$d = \sqrt{(4 - 8)^2 + (-3 - 5)^2}$$
$$= \sqrt{(-4)^2 + (-8)^2}$$
$$= \sqrt{16 + 64}$$
$$= \sqrt{80} \qquad \text{center } c = \left(\frac{4 + 8}{2}, \frac{-3 + 5}{2}\right)$$
$$= 4\sqrt{5}$$
$$d = 2r = 4\sqrt{5} \qquad\qquad = \left(\frac{12}{2}, \frac{2}{2}\right)$$
$$\frac{1}{2}d = r = 2\sqrt{5} \qquad\qquad = (6, 1)$$
$$(x - 6)^2 + (y - 1)^2 = (2\sqrt{5})^2$$
$$(x - 6)^2 + (y - 1)^2 = 20$$

39. $5[5^2 + 2(5) + 3]$
$$= 5(25 + 10 + 3)$$
$$= 5(38)$$
$$= 190$$

10-8 Inverse Functions and Relations

PAGES 493-494   **CHECKING FOR UNDERSTANDING**

1. Switch x and y in the equation and solve for y.

2. Answers may vary. A sample answer is $f(x) = x^2$.

3. $[f \circ g](x) = f[g(x)] = f\left(\frac{x^2 - 6}{5}\right)$
$$f\left(\frac{x^2 - 6}{5}\right) = 5\left(\frac{x^2 - 6}{5}\right)^2 + 6$$
$$= 5\frac{(x^2 - 6)^2}{25} + 6$$
$$= \frac{1}{5}(x^2 - 6)^2 + 6 \neq x$$

No, they are not inverse functions, since
$[f \circ g](x) \neq x$.

4. $\{(2, 3), (2, 4)\}$; no

5. $\{(-2, -1), (-2, -3), (-4, -1), (6, 0)\}$; no

6. $\{(8, 3), (-2, 4), (-3, 5)\}$; yes

7. $\{(4, 2), (1, -3), (8, 2)\}$; yes

8. $\{(3, 1), (-1, 1), (-3, 1), (1, 1)\}$; yes

9. $\{(11, 6), (7, -2), (3, 0), (3, -5)\}$, no

10. $y = 3x$
$$x = 3y$$
$$\frac{1}{3}x = y$$

11. $f(x) = x - 5$
$$f(x) = x - 5$$
$$x = f^{-1}(x) - 5$$
$$x + 5 = f^{-1}(x)$$

12. $y = -3x + 1$
$$x = -3y + 1$$
$$3y = -x + 1$$
$$y = -\frac{1}{3}x + \frac{1}{3}$$

---

13. $y = 8$
$$x = 8$$

14. $g(x) = 4x + 4$
$$x = 4g^{-1}(x) + 4$$
$$x - 4 = 4g^{-1}(x)$$
$$\frac{1}{4}x - 1 = g^{-1}(x)$$

15. $f(x) = \frac{1}{2}x + 2$
$$x = \frac{1}{2}f^{-1}(x) + 2$$
$$x - 2 = \frac{1}{2}f^{-1}(x)$$
$$2x - 4 = f^{-1}(x)$$

16. $h(x) = x^3$
$$x = [h^{-1}(x)]^3$$
$$\sqrt[3]{x} = h^{-1}(x)$$

17. $y = x^2 - 9$
$$x = y^2 - 9$$
$$x + 9 = y^2$$
$$\pm\sqrt{x + 9} = y$$

18. $f(x) = (x - 9)^2$
$$x = [f^{-1}(x) - 9]^2$$
$$\pm\sqrt{x} = f^{-1}(x) - 9$$
$$9 \pm \sqrt{x} = f^{-1}(x)$$

19.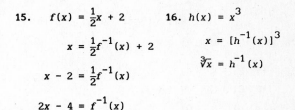

20.

21.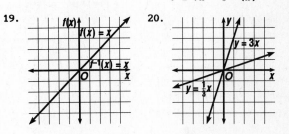

22.

23.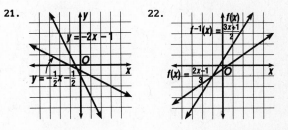

24.

25.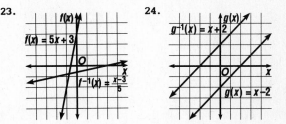

26.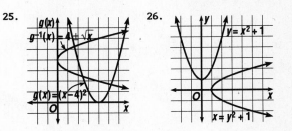

27.

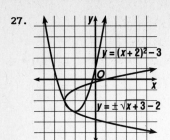

$y = (x+2)^2 - 3$

$y = \pm\sqrt{x+3} - 2$

28. {(4, 2), (4, 8), (-2, 2), (-2, 8)}

(4, 2) + (0, 6) = (4, 8)

(-2, 2) + (0, 6) = (-2, 8)

(-2, 2) + (6, 0) = (4, 2)

(-2, 8) + (6, 0) = (4, 8)

Yes, it is still a square.

29. $f(x) = x + 6$ $\qquad g(x) = x - 6$

$f[g(x)] = f(x - 6) \qquad g[f(x)] = g(x + 6)$

$\qquad\qquad = (x - 6) + 6 \qquad\qquad = (x + 6) - 6$

$\qquad\qquad = x \qquad\qquad\qquad\quad = x$

yes

30. $f(x) = -2x + 3 \qquad g(x) = 2x - 3$

$f[g(x)] = f(2x - 3)$

$\qquad\qquad = -2(2x - 3) + 3$

$\qquad\qquad = -4x + 6 + 3$

$\qquad\qquad = -4x + 9$

no

31. $f(x) = 4x - 5 \qquad\qquad g(x) = \dfrac{x + 5}{4}$

$f[g(x)] = f\left(\dfrac{x + 5}{4}\right) \qquad g[f(x)] = g(4x - 5)$

$\qquad\qquad = 4\left(\dfrac{x + 5}{4}\right) - 5 \qquad\qquad = \dfrac{(4x - 5) + 5}{4}$

$\qquad\qquad = x + 5 - 5 \qquad\qquad\qquad = \dfrac{4x}{4}$

$\qquad\qquad = x \qquad\qquad\qquad\qquad\quad = x$

yes

32. $f(x) = x \qquad\qquad g(x) = -x$

$f[g(x)] = f(-x)$

$\qquad\qquad = -x$

no

33. $f(x) = \dfrac{x - 2}{3} \qquad g(x) = 3x - 2$

$f[g(x)] = f(3x - 2)$

$\qquad\qquad = \dfrac{(3x - 2) - 2}{3}$

$\qquad\qquad = \dfrac{3x - 4}{3}$

no

34. $f(x) = \dfrac{x - 1}{2} \qquad\qquad g(x) = 2x + 1$

$f[g(x)] = f(2x + 1) \qquad g[f(x)] = g\left(\dfrac{x - 1}{2}\right)$

$\qquad\qquad = \dfrac{(2x + 1) - 1}{2} \qquad\qquad = 2\left(\dfrac{x - 1}{2}\right) + 1$

$\qquad\qquad = \dfrac{2x}{2} \qquad\qquad\qquad\quad = x - 1 + 1$

$\qquad\qquad = x \qquad\qquad\qquad\qquad = x$

yes

35.

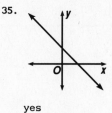

yes

36.

no

37.

no

38. Answers may vary. A sample answer is,

$f(x) = x$ and $f^{-1}(x) = x$, or

$f(x) = -x$ and $f^{-1}(x) = -x$.

39. Let I = income, and

$\qquad m$ = merchandise sold.

$I(m) = 40(7.00) + 0.03m$

$I(m) = 280 + 0.03m$

$\quad 400 = 280 + 0.03m$

$\quad 120 = 0.03m$

$4000 = m$

$4000

40. Let r = regular price,

$\qquad s$ = sale price, and

$\qquad f$ = final price.

$f = 453.20 \qquad\qquad 453.20 = 0.8r - 50$

$f = s - 50 \qquad\qquad\quad 503.20 = 0.8r$

$s = r - 0.2r = 0.8r \qquad\quad 629 = r$

$\qquad\qquad\qquad\qquad\qquad\quad \$629$

41. a. 10 DEFFNF(X) = X + 1

$\qquad$ 20 DEFFNG(X) = X - 1

$\qquad\qquad$ yes

$\quad$ b. 10 DEFFNF(X) = X + 4

$\qquad$ 20 DEFFNG(X) = X - 4

$\qquad\qquad$ yes

$\quad$ c. 10 DEFFNF(X) = (X + 7) / 5

$\qquad$ 20 DEFFNG(X) = -5 * X + 7

$\qquad\qquad$ no

42. $f(x) = 3x \qquad\qquad g(x) = x - 1$

$f[g(x)] = f(x - 1)$

$\qquad\qquad = 3(x - 1)$

$\qquad\qquad = 3x - 3$

43. $f = \{(2, 1), (3, 4), (6, -2)\}$

$g = \{(1, 5), (4, -7), (-2, -3)\}$

$g \circ f = \{(2, 5), (3, -7), (6, -3)\}$

$f \circ g$ does not exist

44. no, because of variable in denominator

45. $\dfrac{\dfrac{x^{\frac{1}{3}}}{\left(x^{\frac{2}{3}} - x^{-\frac{1}{3}}\right)} \cdot \dfrac{x^{\frac{1}{3}}}{x^{\frac{1}{3}}} = \dfrac{x^{\frac{2}{3}}}{x - 1}}$

46.

$$
\begin{array}{r}
a^3 - a^2 + 2a - 2 \\
3a + 1 \overline{\smash{\big)}\, 3a^4 - 2a^3 + 5a^2 - 4a - 2} \\
\underline{-3a^4 + -a^3} \\
-3a^3 + 5a^2 \\
\underline{+3a^3 + a^2} \\
6a^2 - 4a \\
\underline{-6a^2 + -2a} \\
-6a - 2 \\
\underline{+6a + 2} \\
0
\end{array}
$$

Chapter 10 Summary and Review

PAGES 496–498   SKILLS AND CONCEPTS

1. $p(x) = 6x + 3$

$p(x - 2) = 6(x - 2) + 3$

$\qquad = 6x - 12 + 3$

$\qquad = 6x - 9$

2. $p(x) = x^2 + 5$

$p(x - 2) = (x - 2)^2 + 5$

$\qquad = x^2 - 4x + 4 + 5$

$\qquad = x^2 - 4x + 9$

3. $f(x) = x^2 - x$

$f(x + h) = (x + h)^2 - (x + h)$

$\qquad = x^2 + 2xh + h^2 - x - h$

4. $f(x) = 2x^3 - 1$

$f(x + h) = 2(x + h)^3 - 1$

$\qquad = 2(x^3 + 3x^2h + 3xh^2 + h^3) - 1$

$\qquad = 2x^3 + 6x^2h + 6xh^2 + 2h^3 - 1$

5.
$$
\begin{array}{r|rrrr}
-1 & 1 & 5 & 8 & 4 \\
& & -1 & -4 & -4 \\
\hline
& 1 & 4 & 4 & \,|\,0
\end{array}
$$

$x^2 + 4x + 4$

$= (x + 2)(x + 2)$

6.
$$
\begin{array}{r|rrrrr}
-1 & 1 & -6 & 0 & 22 & 15 \\
& & -1 & 7 & -7 & -15 \\
\hline
-1 & 1 & -7 & 7 & 15 & \,|\,0 \\
& & -1 & 8 & -15 & \\
\hline
& 1 & -8 & 15 & \,|\,0
\end{array}
$$

$x^2 - 8x + 15$

$= (x + 1)(x - 3)(x - 5)$

7. $f(x) = 2x^4 - x^3 + 5x^2 + 3x - 9$

3 or 1 positive real zeros

$f(-x) = 2x^4 + x^3 + 5x^2 - 3x - 9$

1 negative real zero

0 or 2 imaginary zeros

8. $f(x) = 7x^3 + 5x - 1$

1 positive real zero

$f(-x) = -7x^3 - 5x - 1$

0 negative real zeros

2 imaginary zeros

9. $f(x) = -4x^4 - x^2 - x - 1$

0 positive real zeros

$f(-x) = -4x^4 - x^2 + x - 1$

2 or 0 negative real zeros

2 or 4 imaginary zeros

10. $f(x) = x^4 + x^3 - 7x + 1$

2 or 0 positive real zeros

$f(-x) = x^4 - x^3 + 7x + 1$

2 or 0 negative real zeros

0, 2, or 4 imaginary zeros

11.
$$
\begin{array}{r|rrrr}
3 & 2 & -13 & 17 & 12 \\
& & 6 & -21 & -12 \\
\hline
& 2 & -7 & -4 & \,|\,0
\end{array}
$$

$2x^2 - 7x - 4 = (2x + 1)(x - 4)$

$3, -\dfrac{1}{2}, 4$

12.
$$
\begin{array}{r|rrrrr}
-1 & 1 & 5 & 15 & 19 & 8 \\
& & -1 & -4 & -11 & -8 \\
\hline
& 1 & 4 & 11 & 8 & \,|\,0 \\
-1
\end{array}
$$

13.
$$
\begin{array}{r|rrrr}
2 & 1 & -3 & -10 & 24 \\
& & 2 & -2 & -24 \\
\hline
& 1 & -1 & -12 & \,|\,0
\end{array}
$$

$x^2 - x - 12 = (x - 4)(x + 3)$

$2, 4, -3$

14.
$$
\begin{array}{r|rrrr}
5 & 2 & -5 & -28 & 15 \\
& & 10 & 25 & -15 \\
\hline
& 2 & 5 & -3 & \,|\,0
\end{array}
$$

$2x^2 + 5x - 3 = (2x - 1)(x + 3)$

$5, \dfrac{1}{2}, -3$

15. $f(x) = x^3 - x^2 + 1$

x	$f(x)$
0	1
-1	-1

$f(-0.8) = -0.152$ ✓

$f(-0.7) = 0.167$

The zero is approximately -0.8.

16. $g(x) = 4x^3 + x^2 - 11x + 3$

x	$g(x)$
-2	-3
-1	11
0	3
1	-3
2	17

$g(-1.9) = 0.074$ ✓
$g(-2.0) = -3$

$g(0.3) = -0.102$ ✓
$g(0.2) = 0.872$

$g(1.4) = 0.536$ ✓
$g(1.3) = -0.822$

The zeros are approximately -1.9, 0.3, and 1.4.

17. $f(x) = 2x - 1 \qquad g(x) = 3x + 4$

$[f \circ g](x) \qquad\qquad [g \circ f](x)$
$= f[g(x)] \qquad\qquad = g[f(x)]$
$= f(3x + 4) \qquad\quad = g(2x - 1)$
$= 2(3x + 4) - 1 \quad = 3(2x - 1) + 4$
$= 6x + 8 - 1 \qquad = 6x - 3 + 4$
$= 6x + 7 \qquad\qquad = 6x + 1$

18. $f(x) = x^2 + 2 \qquad\qquad g(x) = x - 3$

$[f \circ g](x) \qquad\qquad\quad [g \circ f](x)$
$= f[g(x)] \qquad\qquad\quad = g[f(x)]$
$= f(x - 3) \qquad\qquad = g(x^2 + 2)$
$= (x - 3)^2 + 2 \qquad = (x^2 + 2) - 3$
$= x^2 - 6x + 9 + 2 \quad = x^2 - 1$
$= x^2 - 6x + 11$

19. $f = \{(2, 1), (-1, 6), (3, 2)\}$
$g = \{(2, 2), (6, -1), (1, 5)\}$
$f \circ g$ does not exist
$g \circ f = \{(2, 5), (-1, -1), (3, 2)\}$

20. $f(x) = 3x - 4 \qquad\qquad g(x) = \dfrac{x - 4}{3}$

$f[g(x)] = f\left(\dfrac{x - 4}{3}\right)$

$\qquad\quad = 3\left(\dfrac{x - 4}{3}\right) - 4$

$\qquad\quad = x - 4 - 4$

$\qquad\quad = x - 8$

no

21. $f(x) = -2x - 3 \qquad\qquad g(x) = \dfrac{-x - 3}{2}$

$f[g(x)] = f\left(\dfrac{-x - 3}{2}\right) \qquad g[f(x)] = g(-2x - 3)$

$\qquad\quad = -2\left(\dfrac{-x - 3}{2}\right) - 3 \qquad\qquad = \dfrac{-(-2x - 3) - 3}{2}$

$\qquad\quad = -(-x - 3) - 3 \qquad\qquad\qquad = \dfrac{2x}{2}$

$\qquad\quad = x \qquad\qquad\qquad\qquad\qquad = x$

yes

22. a. $E(x) = 200,000(1 + 0.01x)^4$
$\qquad\qquad + 500,000(1 + 0.01x)^2$
$\qquad\qquad + 100,000(1 + 0.01x)^1$

b. $E(12) = 200,000(1.12)^4 + 500,000(1.12)^2$
$\qquad\qquad + 100,000(1.12)^1$
$\qquad\quad = 314,703.87 + 627,200 + 112,000$
$\qquad\quad = 1,053,903.87$ or about $1,053,904$

23.

	DeVry	Judson	Juilliard	Case
Craig	X	X	✓	X
Vanessa	✓	X	X	X
Devin	X	X	X	✓
Anita	X	✓	X	X
Electronics	✓	X	X	X
Cello	X	X	✓	X
No Major	X	✓	X	X
Chem. Eng.	X	X	X	✓

Craig - Juilliard
Vanessa - DeVry
Devin - Case Western
Anita - Judson

24. $V = \dfrac{1}{3}\pi r^2 h = 7.07$

$\qquad \dfrac{1}{3}\pi r^2 (2r) = 7.07$

$\qquad\qquad r^3 = 3.376$

$\qquad\qquad r = \sqrt[3]{3.376}$

$\qquad\qquad r = 1.5$ in.

$h = d = 2r$, so $h = 3.0$ in.

25. $V = \ell w h = 2475$
$\ell = 2w + 3$
$h = w - 2$
$\quad (2w + 3)(w)(w - 2) = 2475$
$\quad (2w^2 + 3w)(w - 2) = 2475$
$\qquad\quad 2w^3 - w^2 - 6w = 2475$
$2w^3 - w^2 - 6w - 2475 = 0$

$\underline{11|} \quad 2 \quad -1 \quad -6 \quad -2475$
$\qquad\qquad\quad 22 \quad 231 \quad 2475$
$\qquad\quad \overline{2 \quad 21 \quad 225 \;|\quad 0}$

$w = 11,\; \ell = 25,\; h = 9$ units

26. Let w = wholesale price,
$\qquad r$ = real price, and
$\qquad s$ = sale price.

$r = 2w \qquad\qquad\qquad 15 = 2w$
$s = 0.8r = 12 \qquad\qquad 7.5 = w$
$\qquad r = 15 \qquad\qquad\qquad \$7.50$

256

Chapter 10 Test

1. $f(3) = (3)^3 - 27$
$\qquad = 27 - 27$
$\qquad = 0$

2. $f(3) = 2(3)^4 - 3(3)^3 + 8$
$\qquad = 2(81) - 81 + 8$
$\qquad = 162 - 81 + 8$
$\qquad = 89$

3. $f(a - 1) = (a - 1)^3 - (a - 1) + 7$
$\qquad = a^3 - 3a^2 + 3a - 1 - a + 1 + 7$
$\qquad = a^3 - 3a^2 + 2a + 7$

4. $f(a - 1) = (a - 1)^2 - (a - 1)^3$
$\qquad = a^2 - 2a + 1 - (a^3 - 3a^2 + 3a - 1)$
$\qquad = a^2 - 2a + 1 - a^3 + 3a^2 - 3a + 1$
$\qquad = -a^3 + 4a^2 - 5a + 2$

5.
$$\begin{array}{r|rrr} -1 & 1 & 6 & -3 \\ & & -1 & -5 \\ \hline & 1 & 5 & -8 \end{array}$$
$x^2 + 6x - 3 = (x + 5)(x + 1) - 8$; no

6.
$$\begin{array}{r|rrrr} -2 & 1 & 0 & 8 & 1 \\ & & -2 & 4 & -24 \\ \hline & 1 & -2 & 12 & -23 \end{array}$$
$x^3 + 8x + 1 = (x^2 - 2x + 12)(x + 2) - 23$; no

7.
$$\begin{array}{r|rrrr} -1 & 1 & -1 & -5 & -3 \\ & & -1 & 2 & 3 \\ \hline & 1 & -2 & -3 & 0 \end{array}$$
$x^3 - x^2 - 5x - 3 = (x^2 - 2x - 3)(x + 1) + 0$; yes

8.
$$\begin{array}{r|rrrrr} -1 & 1 & 1 & 1 & 1 & 1 \\ & & -1 & 0 & -1 & 0 \\ \hline & 1 & 0 & 1 & 0 & 1 \end{array}$$
$x^4 + x^3 + x^2 + x + 1 = (x^3 + x)(x + 1) + 1$; no

9. $g(x) = x^3 - x^2 - 14x + 24$
2 or 0 positive real zeros
$g(-x) = -x^3 - x^2 + 14x + 24$
1 negative real zero
0 or 2 imaginary zeros

10. $f(x) = x^4 + x^3 - 9x^2 - 17x - 8$
1 positive real zero
$f(-x) = x^4 + x^3 - 9x^2 + 17x - 8$
3 or 1 negative real zeros
0 or 2 imaginary zeros

11. $f(x) = x^3 - 3x^2 - 53x - 9$
1 positive real zero
$f(-x) = -x^3 - 3x^2 + 53x - 9$
2 or 0 negative real zeros
$$\begin{array}{r|rrrr} 9 & 1 & -3 & -53 & -9 \\ & & 9 & 54 & 9 \\ \hline & 1 & 6 & 1 & 0 \end{array}$$
$x^2 + 6x + 1$
9

12. $h(x) = 6x^3 + 4x^2 - 14x + 4$
2 or 0 positive real zeros
$h(-x) = -6x^3 + 4x^2 + 14x + 4$
1 negative real zero
$$\begin{array}{r|rrrr} 1 & 6 & 4 & -14 & 4 \\ & & 6 & 10 & -4 \\ \hline -2 & 6 & 10 & -4 & 0 \\ & & -12 & 4 & \\ \hline & 6 & -2 & 0 & \end{array}$$
$6x - 2 = 2(3x - 1)$
$1, -2, \dfrac{1}{3}$

13. $g(x) = x^3 - 3x - 52$
1 positive real zero
$g(-x) = -x^3 + 3x - 52$
2 or 0 negative real zeros
$$\begin{array}{r|rrrr} 4 & 1 & 0 & -3 & -52 \\ & & 4 & 16 & 52 \\ \hline & 1 & 4 & 13 & 0 \end{array}$$
$x^2 + 4x + 13$

$x = \dfrac{-4 \pm \sqrt{4^2 - 4(1)(13)}}{2(1)}$

$= \dfrac{-4 \pm \sqrt{16 - 52}}{2}$

$= \dfrac{-4 \pm \sqrt{-36}}{2}$

$= -2 \pm 3i$

$4, -2 + 3i, -2 - 3i$

14. $h(x) = 4x^4 + 11x^3 + 10x^2 - 69x - 54$
1 positive real zero
$h(-x) = 4x^4 - 11x^3 + 10x^2 + 69x - 54$
3 or 1 negative real zeros
$$\begin{array}{r|rrrrr} 2 & 4 & 11 & 10 & -69 & -54 \\ & & 8 & 38 & 96 & 54 \\ \hline -\frac{3}{4} & 4 & 19 & 48 & 27 & 0 \\ & & -3 & -12 & -27 & \\ \hline & 4 & 16 & 36 & 0 & \end{array}$$
$4x^2 + 16x + 36 = 4(x^2 + 4x + 9)$

$x = \dfrac{-4 \pm \sqrt{4^2 - 4(1)(9)}}{2(1)}$

$= \dfrac{-4 \pm \sqrt{16 - 36}}{2}$

$= \dfrac{-4 \pm \sqrt{-20}}{2}$

$= -2 \pm i\sqrt{5}$

$2, -\dfrac{3}{4}, -2 + i\sqrt{5}, -2 - i\sqrt{5}$

15.

	Tara	Alan	Lee
Cashier	✓	X	X
Pizza	X	✓	X
Typist	X	X	✓

Tara - cashier

Alan - pizza delivery person

Lee - typist

16. $f(x) = x^3 + 6x^2 + 6x - 4$

1 positive real zero

$f(-x) = -x^3 + 6x^2 - 6x - 4$

2 or 0 negative real zeros

x	$f(x)$
-5	-9
-4	4
-2	0
0	-4
1	9

$f(-4.4) = 0.576$ ✓

$f(-4.5) = -0.625$

$f(-2) = 0$ ✓

$f(0.4) = -0.576$ ✓

$f(0.5) = 0.625$

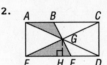

The zeros are -2 and approximately -4.4 and 0.4.

17. $g(x) = x^3 + 3x^2 - 2x + 1$

2 or 0 positive real zeros

$g(-x) = -x^3 + 3x^2 + 2x + 1$

1 negative real zero

x	$g(x)$
-3	7
-4	-7

$g(-3.6) = 0.424$

$g(-3.7) = -1.183$

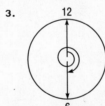

The zero is approximately -3.6.

18. $[f \circ g](4) = f[g(4)] = f(4^2 - 1)$

$\qquad\qquad\qquad = f(16-1)$

$\qquad\qquad\qquad = f(15)$

$\qquad\qquad\qquad = 2(15)$

$\qquad\qquad\qquad = 30$

19. $[g \circ f](x) = g[f(x)] = g(2x)$

$\qquad\qquad\qquad = (2x)^2 - 1$

$\qquad\qquad\qquad = 4x^2 - 1$

20. $f(x) = x^2 + 2$

$\qquad x = \left[f^{-1}(x)\right]^2 + 2$

$\qquad x - 2 = \left[f^{-1}(x)\right]^2$

$\qquad \pm\sqrt{x - 2} = f^{-1}(x)$

$f = \{(0, -3), (2, 5), (-1, 1) (3, 2)\}$

$g = \{(-1, 2), (2, 2), (1, 4), (4, 3)(0, -1)\}$

$h = \{(4, 2), (1, 0), (-3, 4), (3, -1)\}$

$f \circ g \circ h = \{(4, 5), (1, 1), (-3, 2), (3, 5)\}$

Chapter 10
College Entrance Exam Preview

PAGES 500-501

1. $A = s^2 = 25x^2$

$\qquad s = \sqrt{25x^2}$

$\qquad s = |5x|$

$\qquad s\sqrt{2} = |5x|\sqrt{2}$

The correct choice is B.

2.

$\triangle ABG \cong \triangle DEG$

$\triangle FEG + \triangle DEG = \triangle FDG$

Area $ACDF = \ell w$

$\qquad\qquad = (AC)(AF)$

Area $\triangle FDG = \frac{1}{2}bh$

$\qquad\qquad = \frac{1}{2}(FD)(GH)$

Since $AC = FD$, and $2GH = AF$: $\quad = \frac{1}{2}\left(AC\right)\left(\frac{1}{2}AF\right)$

Thus, area $\triangle FDG = 25\%$. $\qquad = \frac{1}{4}(AC)(AF)$

The correct choice is A.

3.

$1\frac{1}{2}$ hours $= 1\frac{1}{2}$ revolutions

$\qquad\qquad = 1\frac{1}{2}(360°)$

$\qquad\qquad = 540°$

The correct choice is C.

4. $m\angle a = m\angle d$

$m\angle b = m\angle f$

Thus, $a + b = f + d$

The correct choice is C.

5.

$40 = m\angle a' = m\angle a$

$180 - 40 = 140° = m\angle c' = m\angle c$

$c - a = 140° - 40°$

$\qquad = 100°$

The correct choice is B.

6.

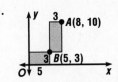

$P'Q = \frac{1}{2}PQ;\qquad QQ' = \frac{1}{2}QR\qquad P'Q + QQ' = P'Q'$

$\qquad = \frac{1}{2}(8)\qquad\qquad = \frac{1}{2}(6)\qquad\qquad 4 + 3 = 7$

$\qquad = 4\qquad\qquad\qquad = 3$

The correct choice is C.

7. $5x + 4x + x = 180°$

$\qquad\qquad 10x = 180°$

$\qquad\qquad\quad x = 18°$

$\qquad\qquad 4x = 72°$

The correct choice is D.

$\qquad\qquad$ run rise

8. $(4, 6) + (3, -2) = (7, 4)$

The correct choice is D.

9.

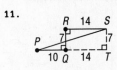

area of lower rectangle:

$5 \times 3 = 15$ sq units

area of upper rectangle:

$(8 - 5) \times (10 - 3) = 3 \times 7 = 21$ sq units

total area $= 15 + 21 = 36$ sq units

The correct choice is A.

10. All we know is that $a + b = 2a = 2b$. We don't know what a or b is.

The correct choice is D.

11.

Construct $\overline{QT}$ and $\overline{ST}$ such that $\overline{RQ} \parallel \overline{ST}$ and $\overline{RS} \parallel \overline{QT}$. We now have a right triangle, $\triangle PTS$,

where $PT = PQ + QT = 10 + 14 = 24$ and $TS = 7$.

$(PT)^2 + (TS)^2 = (PS)^2$

$\qquad 24^2 + 7^2 = (PS)^2$

$\qquad 576 + 49 = (PS)^2$

$\qquad\quad \sqrt{625} = PS$

$\qquad\qquad 25 = PS$

The correct choice is B.

12.

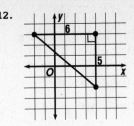

Since two of the sides parallel the x- and y-axes, a right triangle is formed with legs of length $|-2 - 4| = |-6| = 6$ and $|3 - (-2)| = |5| = 5$.

$A = \frac{1}{2}(6)(5)$

$\quad = \frac{1}{2}(30)$

$\quad = 15$

The correct choice is C.

13.

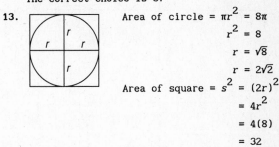

Area of circle $= \pi r^2 = 8\pi$

$\qquad\qquad\qquad r^2 = 8$

$\qquad\qquad\qquad\; r = \sqrt{8}$

$\qquad\qquad\qquad\; r = 2\sqrt{2}$

Area of square $= s^2 = (2r)^2$

$\qquad\qquad\qquad\quad = 4r^2$

$\qquad\qquad\qquad\quad = 4(8)$

$\qquad\qquad\qquad\quad = 32$

The correct choice is B.

14.

$w = 2\ell - 9$

$\quad = 2(3x + 4) - 9$

$\quad = 6x + 8 - 9$

$\quad = 6x - 1$

$A = \ell w = (3x + 4)(6x - 1)$

$\qquad\quad = 18x^2 + 24x - 3x - 4$

$\qquad\quad = 18x^2 + 21x - 4$

The correct choice is D.

15. $\dfrac{\text{circumference}}{\text{radius}} = \dfrac{2\pi r}{r} = 2\pi$

The correct choice is C.

Chapter 11
Rational Polynomial Expressions

Graphing Calculator Exploration:
Graphing Rational Functions

1.
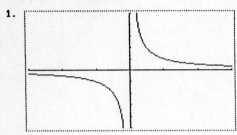
Xscl: 1, Yscl: 1

2.
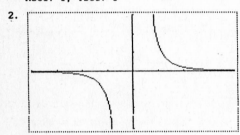
Xscl: 0.5, Yscl: 5

3.
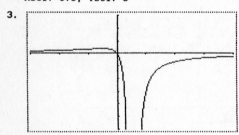
Xscl: 2, Yscl: 2

4.
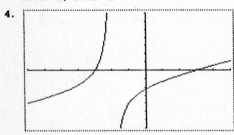
Xscl: 1, Yscl: 2

5.
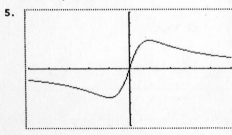
Xscl: 2, Yscl: 0.2

6.
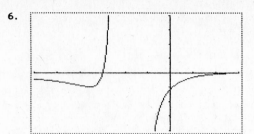
Xscl: 1, Yscl: 1

7.
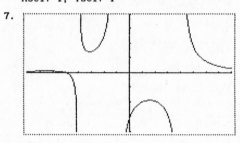
Xscl: 1, Yscl: 0.1

8.
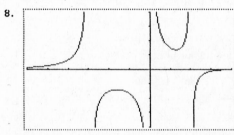
Xscl: 1, Yscl: 0.5

9.
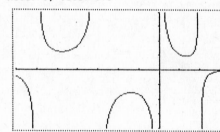
Xscl: 1, Yscl: 0.1

10. $y = 0$ 11. $y = \frac{1}{4}$ 12. $y = 0$

13. $y = 0$ 14. $y = \frac{1}{3}$ 15. $y = \frac{5}{4}$

11-1 Graphing Rational Functions

1. $x = 3$

2. $y = 0$; For table, see students' work.

3. With these values, the expressions in the denominator become powers of 10. The value of the fraction can be mentally calculated. For example,

$$\frac{2}{(102 - 2)^2} = \frac{2}{(100)^2} = \frac{2}{10,000} \text{ or } 0.0002$$

4. The value of $x - 2$ when squared will always be positive.

5. $x = 3$; $y = 0$ **6.** $x = 6$; $y = 0$

7. $x = 1$, $x = -5$, $y = 0$ **8.** $x = 0$, $y = 0$

PAGE 509   EXERCISES

9.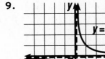
$y = \frac{1}{x}$

10.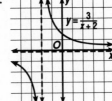
$y = \frac{3}{x+2}$

11.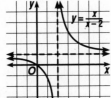
$y = \frac{x}{x-2}$

12.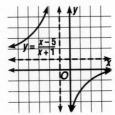
$y = \frac{x-5}{x+1}$

13.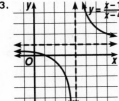
$y = \frac{x-1}{x-4}$

14.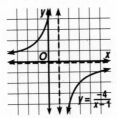
$y = \frac{-4}{x+1}$

15.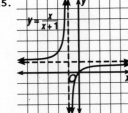
$y = \frac{x}{x+1}$

16.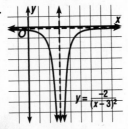
$y = \frac{-2}{(x-3)^2}$

17.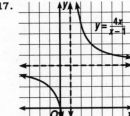
$y = \frac{4x}{x-1}$

18.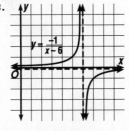
$y = \frac{-1}{x-6}$

19.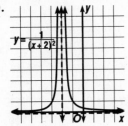
$y = \frac{1}{(x+2)^2}$

20.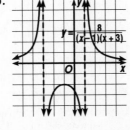
$y = \frac{8}{(x-1)(x+3)}$

21.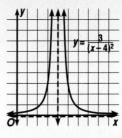
$y = \frac{3}{(x-4)^2}$

22.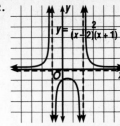
$y = \frac{2}{(x-2)(x+1)}$

23.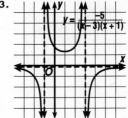
$y = \frac{-5}{(x-3)(x+1)}$

24.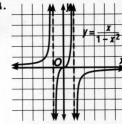
$y = \frac{x}{1-x^2}$

25.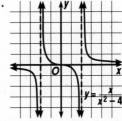
$y = \frac{x}{x^2-4}$

26.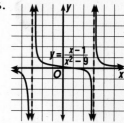
$y = \frac{x-1}{x^2-9}$

27. There will always be one horizontal asymptote. The degree of the denominator determines the number of vertical asymptotes.

degree	asymptotes
1	1
2	(diff. factors) 2
2	(squared factor) 1
3	3
.	.
.	.
.	.

28. **a.** $V = \dfrac{V_1 t_1 + V_2 t_2}{t_1 + t_2}$

$= \dfrac{60t_1 + (40)(8)}{t_1 + 8}$

$= \dfrac{60t_1 + 320}{t_1 + 8}$

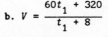

b. $V = \dfrac{60t_1 + 320}{t_1 + 8}$

$= \dfrac{60(9) + 320}{9 + 8}$

≈ 50.59

about 50.59 mph

29. a. $V_f = \dfrac{m_1 - m_2}{m_1 + m_2} \cdot v_i$

$\qquad = \dfrac{m_1 - 7}{m_1 + 7} \cdot 5$

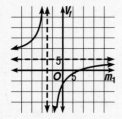

b. $V_f = \dfrac{5 - 7}{5 + 7} \cdot 5$

$\qquad \approx -0.83$

$\qquad$ about -0.83 m/s

30. $x = \dfrac{5y + 2}{2}$

$\quad 2x = 5y + 2$

$\quad \dfrac{2x - 2}{5} = y$

$\quad f^{-1}(x) = \dfrac{2x - 2}{5}$

31. $(0, 0)$; $\sqrt{25} = 5$

32. $f(-2) = 2(-2)^2 + 3(-2) - 5$

$\qquad = 8 - 6 - 5$

$\qquad = -3$

33. $4y^2 - 8y - 7 = 0$

$\quad 4(y^2 - 2y + 1) = 7 + 4$

$\qquad 4(y - 1)^2 = 11$

$\qquad (y - 1)^2 = \dfrac{11}{4}$

$\qquad y - 1 = \pm\dfrac{\sqrt{11}}{2}$

$\qquad\qquad y = 1 \pm \dfrac{\sqrt{11}}{2}$

34. $x^2 - x + 3xy - 3y$

$\quad = x(x - 1) + 3y(x - 1)$

$\quad = (x + 3y)(x - 1)$

11-2 Direct, Inverse, and Joint Variation

PAGE 513   CHECKING FOR UNDERSTANDING

1. constant of variation

2. inverse variation

3. It is the direct variation with a product of two variables instead of a single variable.

4. inverse, -3

5. direct, $-\dfrac{1}{6}$

6. direct, -4

7. direct, $\dfrac{1}{2}$

8. joint, 3

9. direct, 4

10. inverse, 3

11. joint, k

12. direct, $-\dfrac{25}{12}$

13. $\dfrac{34}{17} = \dfrac{y}{56}$

$\quad y = 112$

14. $\dfrac{25}{x} = \dfrac{30}{5}$

$\quad x = \dfrac{25}{6}$

15. $\dfrac{60}{(5)(4)} = \dfrac{y}{(4)(10)}$

$\quad 20y = 2400$

$\quad\quad y = 120$

16. $\dfrac{(40)(2)}{20} = \dfrac{y(4)}{60}$

$\quad 80y = 4800$

$\quad\quad y = 60$

PAGES 513-515   EXERCISES

17. $\dfrac{8}{2} = \dfrac{y}{9}$

$\quad 72 = 2y$

$\quad 36 = y$

18. $\dfrac{10}{-3} = \dfrac{4}{w}$

$\quad -12 = 10w$

$\quad -\dfrac{6}{5} = w$

19. $\dfrac{-6}{r} = \dfrac{-11}{14}$

$\quad -11r = -84$

$\quad\quad r = \dfrac{84}{11}$

20. $\dfrac{\frac{1}{5}}{-3} = \dfrac{y}{9}$

$\quad \dfrac{9}{5} = -3y$

$\quad -\dfrac{3}{5} = y$

21. $\dfrac{1}{15} = \dfrac{7.9}{x}$

$\quad x = (7.9)(15)$

$\quad x = 118.5$

$\quad 118.5$ km

22. $\dfrac{6}{0.7} = \dfrac{100}{x}$

$\quad 6x = 70$

$\quad x \approx 11.67$

$\quad$ about 11.67 kg

23. $\dfrac{0.5}{4} = \dfrac{y}{9}$

$\quad 4.5 = 4y$

$\quad 1.125 = y$

24. $\dfrac{1}{x} = \dfrac{40}{44}$

$\quad 40x = 44$

$\quad\quad x = 1.1$

25. $\dfrac{y}{(6)(8)} = \dfrac{12}{(4)(3)}$

$\quad 12y = 576$

$\quad\quad y = 48$

26. $\dfrac{-5}{0.25} = \dfrac{-7}{x}$

$\quad -1.75 = -5x$

$\quad 0.35 = x$

27. $\dfrac{10}{x} = \dfrac{14}{20}$

$\quad 14x = 200$

$\quad\quad x = \dfrac{100}{7}$

28. $\dfrac{180}{(15)(12)} = \dfrac{1615}{(42.5)h}$

$\quad 7650h = 290,700$

$\quad\quad h = 38$

$\quad 38$ meters

29. Heavenly Hog; $\dfrac{10}{68} \approx 0.147$ kg/person

$\quad$ Gourmet Diner: $\dfrac{6}{44} \approx 0.136$ kg/person

$\quad$ Heavenly Hog serves larger portions.

30. $\dfrac{\frac{4}{9}}{\frac{2}{3}} = \dfrac{y}{\frac{3}{8}}$

$\quad \dfrac{12}{72} = \dfrac{2}{3}y$

$\quad\quad \dfrac{1}{4} = y$

31. $\dfrac{\frac{3}{4}}{\frac{2}{5}} = \dfrac{g}{8}$

$\quad 6 = \dfrac{2}{5}g$

$\quad 15 = g$

32. $\dfrac{25}{(1)(5)} = \dfrac{y}{(8)(12)}$

$\quad 2400 = 5y$

$\quad\quad 480 = y$

33. $\dfrac{34}{(17)(2)} = \dfrac{y}{(4)(8)}$

$\quad 1088 = 34y$

$\quad\quad 32 = y$

34. $20 = k(3 + 5)(5)$

$20 = 40k$

$\frac{1}{2} = k$

general equation:

$A = \frac{1}{2}(b_1 + b_2)h$

35. $\frac{7}{9^2} = \frac{y}{7^2}$

$343 = 81y$

$\frac{343}{81} = y$

36. $\frac{4^2}{11} = \frac{y^2}{2}$

$32 = 11y^2$

$\frac{32}{11} = y^2$

$y = \pm\sqrt{\frac{32}{11}}$

$= \pm\frac{4\sqrt{22}}{11}$

37. a. $IR = (1.0)(6.0)$

$IR = 6$

$I = \frac{6}{R}$

b. 6

38. $\frac{30}{100} = \frac{p}{140}$

$4200 = 100p$

$42 = p$

42 lb/in^2

39. miles traveled in first

6 hours:

$(6)(55) = 330$ mi

miles left to travel:

$396 - 330 = 66$ mi

time left to reach

destination:

$8 - 6 - 0.5 = 1.5$ hours

$\frac{330}{(6)(55)} = \frac{66}{(1.5)x}$

$495x = 21,780$

$x = 44$

She must travel at a

minimum of 44 mph.

40.

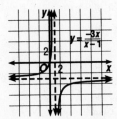

41. $f(a) = a^3 + 2a^2 - 11a - 12$

a	1	2	-11	-12	f(a)
-4	1	-2	-3	0	0
-3	1	-1	-8	12	12
-2	1	0	-11	10	10
-1	1	1	-12	0	0
1	1	3	-8	-20	-20
2	1	4	-3	-18	-18
3	1	5	4	0	0

The rational zeros are -4, -1, and 3.

42. $3x^2 - y^2 = 26$ → $3x^2 - (x + 2)^2 = 26$

$2 = y - x$ → $3x^2 - (x^2 + 4x + 4) = 26$

$2x^2 - 4x - 4 = 26$

$x^2 - 2x - 2 = 13$

$x^2 - 2x - 15 = 0$

$(x - 5)(x + 3) = 0$

$x - 5 = 0$ or $x + 3 = 0$

$x = 5$ or $x = -3$

$2 = y - 5$ or $2 = y - (-3)$

$7 = y$ $-1 = y$

The solutions are (5, 7) and (-3, -1).

43. Let x = one of the numbers.

Then $55 - x$ = the other number.

$f(x) = x(x - 55)$

44. $3\sqrt{18} + 8\sqrt{8} = 9\sqrt{2} + 16\sqrt{2}$

$= 25\sqrt{2}$

45. $3\begin{bmatrix} -4 & 0 & 1 \\ 7 & -2 & 5 \\ 1 & 1 & 4 \end{bmatrix} + \begin{bmatrix} 8 & 0 & 6 \\ -5 & 2 & -1 \\ 4 & -4 & 7 \end{bmatrix}$

$= \begin{bmatrix} -12 & 0 & 3 \\ 21 & -6 & 15 \\ 3 & 3 & 12 \end{bmatrix} + \begin{bmatrix} 8 & 0 & 6 \\ -5 & 2 & -1 \\ 4 & -4 & 7 \end{bmatrix} = \begin{bmatrix} -4 & 0 & 9 \\ 16 & -4 & 14 \\ 7 & -1 & 19 \end{bmatrix}$

46. Let g = Gladys' age.

Let m = Maria's age.

$g = 3m$ → $g - 3m = 0$

$g + 10 = 2(m + 10)$ → $\underline{-g + 2m = -10}$

$-m = -10$

$m = 10$

$g = 3(10)$

$= 30$

Gladys is 30 and Maria is 10.

11-3 **Multiplying and Dividing Rational Expressions**

PAGES 519-520   CHECKING FOR UNDERSTANDING

1. the greatest term that is a factor of each of

a group of terms

2. No. For example,

$\frac{x^2 - 4}{2x^2 + 12x + 18} = \frac{(x - 2)(x + 2)}{2(x + 3)(x + 3)}$.

There are no common factors, so the expression

is in simplest form.

3. $\frac{1}{7a}$ **4.** $\frac{4c}{11b}$ **5.** 1

6. GCF: $6y$

$$\frac{42y}{18xy} = \frac{7 \cdot 6y}{3x \cdot 6y}$$

$$= \frac{7}{3x}$$

7. GCF: $3x^2y^2$

$$\frac{-3x^2y^5}{18x^3y^2} = \frac{3x^2y^2 \cdot -y^3}{3x^2y^2 \cdot 6x}$$

$$= -\frac{y^3}{6x}$$

8. GCF: $6y^2$

$$\frac{42y^2x}{18y^7} = \frac{6y^2 \cdot 7x}{6y^2 \cdot 3y^5}$$

$$= \frac{7x}{3y^5}$$

9. $\dfrac{(-2x^2y)^3}{4x^5y} = \dfrac{-8x^6y^3}{4x^5y}$

GCF: $4x^5y$

$$= \frac{4x^5y \cdot -2xy^2}{4x^5y}$$

$$= -2xy^2$$

10. $\dfrac{a^3b^2}{(-ab)^3} = \dfrac{a^3b^2}{-a^3b^3}$

GCF: a^3b^2

$$= \frac{a^3b^2}{a^3b^2 \cdot -b}$$

$$= -\frac{1}{b}$$

11. $\dfrac{m+5}{2m+10} = \dfrac{m+5}{2(m+5)}$

GCF: $m + 5$

$$= \frac{1}{2}$$

12. $\dfrac{(-3t^2u)^3}{(6tu^2)^2} = \dfrac{-27t^6u^3}{36t^2u^4}$

GCF: $9t^2u^3$

$$= \frac{9t^2u^3 \cdot -3t^4}{9t^2u^3 \cdot 4u}$$

$$= -\frac{3t^4}{4u}$$

13. $\dfrac{4x}{x^2-x} = \dfrac{4x}{x(x-1)}$

GCF: x

$$= \frac{4}{x-1}$$

14. $\dfrac{p^3}{2q} \cdot \dfrac{4q}{-p^2} = \dfrac{4p^3q}{-2p^2q}$

$$= -2p$$

15. $\dfrac{y^2}{x+2} \cdot \dfrac{x+2}{y} = y$

16. $\dfrac{3h}{h+1} \div (h-2) = \dfrac{3h}{h+1} \cdot \dfrac{1}{h-2}$

$$= \frac{3h}{(h+1)(h-2)}$$

PAGES 520-521   EXERCISES

17. $\dfrac{3ab}{4ac} \cdot \dfrac{6a^2}{3b^2} = \dfrac{18a^3b}{12ab^2c}$

$$= \frac{6ab \cdot 3a^2}{6ab \cdot 2bc}$$

$$= \frac{3a^2}{2bc}$$

18. $-\dfrac{3}{5a} \div \left(-\dfrac{9}{15ab}\right) = \dfrac{-3}{5a} \cdot \dfrac{15ab}{-9}$

$$= \frac{-45ab}{-45a}$$

$$= b$$

19. $\dfrac{3d^3c}{a^4} \div \left(-\dfrac{6dc}{a^5}\right) = \dfrac{3d^3c}{a^4} \cdot \dfrac{-a^5}{6dc}$

$$= \frac{-3a^5d^3c}{6a^4dc}$$

$$= \frac{3a^4dc \cdot (-ad^2)}{3a^4dc \cdot 2}$$

$$= -\frac{ad^2}{2}$$

20. $\dfrac{(cd)^3}{a} \cdot \dfrac{ax^2}{xc^2d} = \dfrac{ax^2c^3d^3}{axc^2d}$

$$= \frac{axc^2d \cdot xcd^2}{axc^2d}$$

$$= xcd^2$$

21. $\left(\dfrac{x^2}{y}\right)^2 \cdot \dfrac{5}{3x} = \dfrac{5x^4}{3xy^2}$

$$= \frac{x \cdot 5x^3}{x \cdot 3y^2}$$

$$= \frac{5x^3}{3y^2}$$

22. $\dfrac{5}{m-3} \div \dfrac{10}{m-3} = \dfrac{5}{m-3} \cdot \dfrac{m-3}{10}$

$$= \frac{5(m-3)}{10(m-3)}$$

$$= \frac{1}{2}$$

23. $\dfrac{(ab)^3}{d^3} \div \dfrac{a^2b^4}{(cd)^4} = \dfrac{a^3b^3}{d^3} \cdot \dfrac{c^4d^4}{a^2b^4}$

$$= \frac{a^2b^3d^3 \cdot ac^4d}{a^2b^3d^3 \cdot b}$$

$$= \frac{ac^4d}{b}$$

24. $\left(\dfrac{3a^3}{b^2}\right)^3 \cdot \dfrac{4b^2}{3a^7} = \dfrac{27a^9}{b^6} \cdot \dfrac{4b^2}{3a^7}$

$$= \frac{3a^7b^2 \cdot 36a^2}{3a^7b^2 \cdot b^4}$$

$$= \frac{36a^2}{b^4}$$

25. $\dfrac{x+y}{a} \div \dfrac{x+y}{a^2} = \dfrac{x+y}{a} \cdot \dfrac{a^2}{x+y}$

$$= \frac{a \cdot a(x+y)}{a(x+y)}$$

$$= a$$

26. $A = \frac{1}{2}bh$

$b = \dfrac{2A}{h}$

$b = \dfrac{2(4x^2 - 2x - 6)}{x + 1}$

$\quad = \dfrac{2 \cdot 2(2x^2 - x - 3)}{x + 1}$

$\quad = \dfrac{4(2x - 3)(x + 1)}{x + 1}$

$\quad = 4(2x - 3)$

$\quad = 8x - 12 \text{ meters}$

27. $\dfrac{3x - 21}{x^2 - 49} \div \dfrac{3x}{x^2 + 7x} = \dfrac{3x - 21}{x^2 - 49} \cdot \dfrac{x^2 + 7x}{3x}$

$\quad = \dfrac{3(x - 7) \cdot x(x + 7)}{(x - 7)(x + 7) \cdot 3x}$

$\quad = \dfrac{3x(x - 7)(x + 7)}{3x(x - 7)(x + 7)}$

$\quad = 1$

28. $\dfrac{2x + 2}{x^2 + 5x + 6} \div \dfrac{3x + 3}{x^2 + 2x - 3}$

$= \dfrac{2x + 2}{x^2 + 5x + 6} \cdot \dfrac{x^2 + 2x - 3}{3x + 3}$

$= \dfrac{2(x + 1)(x + 3)(x - 1)}{(x + 2)(x + 3) \cdot 3(x + 1)}$

$= \dfrac{2(x - 1)}{3(x + 2)}$

29. $-\dfrac{x - y}{x + y} \cdot \dfrac{1}{x - y} = \dfrac{-(x + y)(x - y) \cdot 1}{(x + y)(x - y)}$

$\quad = -1$

30. $\dfrac{a^2 + 2a - 15}{a - 3} \div \dfrac{a^2 - 4}{2} = \dfrac{a^2 + 2a - 15}{a - 3} \cdot \dfrac{2}{a^2 - 4}$

$\quad = \dfrac{(a + 5)(a - 3) \cdot 2}{(a - 3)(a - 2)(a + 2)}$

$\quad = \dfrac{2(a + 5)}{(a - 2)(a + 2)}$

31. $\dfrac{y^2 - y}{w^2 - y^2} \div \dfrac{y^2 - 2y + 1}{1 - y}$

$= \dfrac{y^2 - y}{w^2 - y^2} \cdot \dfrac{1 - y}{y^2 - 2y + 1}$

$= \dfrac{y(y - 1) \cdot -1(y - 1)}{(w - y)(w + y)(y - 1)(y - 1)}$

$= \dfrac{-y(y - 1)(y - 1)}{(w - y)(w + y)(y - 1)(y - 1)}$

$= -\dfrac{y}{w^2 - y^2}$

32. $\dfrac{a^2 - b^2}{2a} \div \dfrac{a - b}{6a} = \dfrac{a^2 - b^2}{2a} \cdot \dfrac{6a}{a - b}$

$\quad = \dfrac{6a(a - b)(a + b)}{2a(a - b)}$

$\quad = 3(a + b)$

33. $\dfrac{(y - 2)^2}{(x - 4)^2} \cdot \dfrac{x - 4}{y - 2} = \dfrac{(y - 2)^2(x - 4)}{(x - 4)^2(y - 2)}$

$\quad = \dfrac{y - 2}{x - 4}$

34. $\dfrac{x^2 - y^2}{y^2} \cdot \dfrac{y^3}{y - x} = \dfrac{(x - y)(x + y) \cdot y^3}{-y^2(x - y)}$

$\quad = -y(x + y)$

35. $\dfrac{x^2 + 3x - 10}{x^2 + 8x + 15} \cdot \dfrac{x^2 + 5x + 6}{x^2 + 4x + 4}$

$= \dfrac{(x + 5)(x - 2)(x + 3)(x + 2)}{(x + 5)(x + 3)(x + 2)(x + 2)}$

$= \dfrac{x - 2}{x + 2}$

36. $\dfrac{a^3 - b^3}{a + b} \cdot \dfrac{a^2 - b^2}{a^2 + ab + b^2}$

$= \dfrac{(a - b)(a^2 + ab + b^2)(a + b)(a - b)}{(a + b)(a^2 + ab + b^2)}$

$= (a - b)^2$

37. $\dfrac{w^2 - 11w + 24}{w^2 - 18w + 80} \cdot \dfrac{w^2 - 15w + 50}{w^2 - 9w + 20}$

$= \dfrac{(w - 8)(w - 3)(w - 10)(w - 5)}{(w - 10)(w - 8)(w - 5)(w - 4)}$

$= \dfrac{w - 3}{w - 4}$

38. $\dfrac{\frac{x^2 - y^2}{2}}{\frac{x - y}{4}} = \dfrac{x^2 - y^2}{2} \div \dfrac{x - y}{4}$

$= \dfrac{x^2 - y^2}{2} \cdot \dfrac{4}{x - y}$

$= \dfrac{4(x - y)(x + y)}{2(x - y)}$

$= 2(x + y)$

39. $\qquad (x + 2)^2 + (x + 9)^2 = (x + 10)^2$

$(x^2 + 4x + 4) + (x^2 + 18x + 81) = x^2 + 20x + 100$

$\qquad\qquad x^2 + 2x - 15 = 0$

$\qquad\qquad (x + 5)(x - 3) = 0$

$\qquad\qquad x + 5 = 0 \text{ or } x - 3 = 0$

$\qquad\qquad\quad x = -5 \qquad\quad x = 3$

$x + 2 = 3 + 2 = 5$

$x + 9 = 3 + 9 = 12$

$x + 10 = 3 + 10 = 13$

5, 12, 13 inches

40. $\dfrac{\frac{w^2 + 2w + 1}{w + 1}}{\frac{w + 1}{3}} = \dfrac{w^2 + 2w + 1}{1} \div \dfrac{w + 1}{3}$

$= \dfrac{w^2 + 2w + 1}{1} \cdot \dfrac{3}{w + 1}$

$= \dfrac{3(w + 1)(w + 1)}{w + 1}$

$= 3(w + 1)$

41. $\dfrac{\dfrac{5a^2 - 20}{2a + 2}}{\dfrac{10a - 20}{4a}} = \dfrac{5a^2 - 20}{2a + 2} \div \dfrac{10a - 20}{4a}$

$= \dfrac{5(a - 2)(a + 2)}{2(a + 1)} \cdot \dfrac{4a}{10(a - 2)}$

$= \dfrac{20a(a - 2)(a + 2)}{20(a + 1)(a - 2)}$

$= \dfrac{a(a + 2)}{a + 1}$

42. $\dfrac{\dfrac{2y}{y^2 - 4}}{\dfrac{3}{y^2 - 4y + 4}} = \dfrac{2y}{y^2 - 4} \cdot \dfrac{y^2 - 4y + 4}{3}$

$= \dfrac{2y(y - 2)(y - 2)}{3(y - 2)(y + 2)}$

$= \dfrac{2y(y - 2)}{3(y + 2)}$

43. $\dfrac{\dfrac{p^2 + 7p}{3p}}{\dfrac{49 - p^2}{3p - 21}} = \dfrac{p^2 + 7p}{3p} \cdot \dfrac{3p - 21}{-(p^2 - 49)}$

$= \dfrac{p(p + 7) \cdot 3(p - 7)}{-3p(p - 7)(p + 7)}$

$= -1$

44. $\dfrac{(a^2 - 5a + 6)^{-1}}{(a - 2)^{-2}} \div \dfrac{(a - 3)^{-1}}{(a - 2)^{-2}}$

$= \dfrac{(a - 2)^2}{a^2 - 5a + 6} \div \dfrac{(a - 2)^2}{a - 3}$

$= \dfrac{(a - 2)^2}{a^2 - 5a + 6} \cdot \dfrac{a - 3}{(a - 2)^2}$

$= \dfrac{(a - 2)^2(a - 3)}{(a - 3)(a - 2)(a - 2)^2}$

$= \dfrac{1}{a - 2}$

45. $\dfrac{\dfrac{3 + 10t^2 - 17t}{5t^2 + 4t - 1}}{\dfrac{4t^2 - 9}{3 + 5t + 2t^2}}$

$= \dfrac{3 + 10t^2 - 17t}{5t^2 + 4t - 1} \cdot \dfrac{3 + 5t + 2t^2}{4t^2 - 9}$

$= \dfrac{(5t - 1)(2t - 3)(2t + 3)(t + 1)}{(5t - 1)(t + 1)(2t + 3)(2t - 3)}$

$= 1$

An equal number of men and women favor the tax.

46. a. $\dfrac{\dfrac{m^2 + 15m + 54}{m + 6}}{\dfrac{m + 9}{3}} = \dfrac{m^2 + 15m + 54}{m + 6} \cdot \dfrac{3}{m + 9}$

$= \dfrac{(m + 9)(m + 6) \cdot 3}{(m + 6)(m + 9)}$

$= 3$

There are 3 men for every woman.

b. Answers will vary. Many areas of Alaska have unfavorable weather conditions and offer little employment for a single woman. Most women in these areas are wives of men employed in mining, fishing, or trapping.

47. $\dfrac{-8}{x} = \dfrac{-3}{1.5}$

$-3x = -12$

$x = 4$

48. $\dfrac{4800}{90,000} = \dfrac{x}{219,000}$

$90,000x = 1,051,200,000$

$x = 11,680$

49. $4y^2 - x^2 - 24y + 6x = 11$

$4(y^2 - 6y) - (x^2 - 6x) = 11$

$4(y^2 - 6y + 9) - (x^2 - 6x + 9) = 11 + 36 - 9$

$4(y - 3)^2 - (x - 3)^2 = 38$

$\dfrac{(y - 3)^2}{1} - \dfrac{(x - 3)^2}{2^2} = \dfrac{17}{2}$ hyperbola

50. $(6 + i) + (5 - 2i) = 11 - i$

$(6 + i) - (5 - 2i) = 6 - 5 + i + 2i$

$= 1 + 3i$

$(6 + i)(5 - 2i) = 30 - 12i + 5i - 2i^2$

$= 30 - 7i + 2$

$= 32 - 7i$

51. complex, real, rational, integer, whole, natural

PAGE 521   MID-CHAPTER REVIEW

1.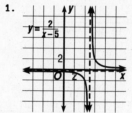

2.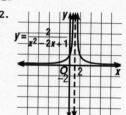

3.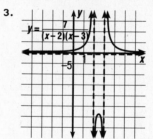

4. $\dfrac{-2}{x} = \dfrac{\dfrac{2}{3}}{-8}$

$\dfrac{2}{3}x = 16$

$x = 24$

5. $\dfrac{11}{\dfrac{1}{5}} = \dfrac{m}{\dfrac{2}{5}}$

$\dfrac{22}{5} = \dfrac{1}{5}m$

$22 = m$

6. $\dfrac{4ab}{2bc} \cdot \dfrac{11a^2b}{5b^2} = \dfrac{44a^3b^2}{10b^3c}$

$$= \dfrac{2b^2 \cdot 22a^3}{2b^2 \cdot 5bc}$$

$$= \dfrac{22a^3}{5bc}$$

7. $\dfrac{7a + 49}{16} \cdot \dfrac{48}{6a + 42} = \dfrac{7(a + 7) \cdot 48}{16 \cdot 6(a + 7)}$

$$= \dfrac{48(a + 7) \cdot 7}{48(a + 7) \cdot 2}$$

$$= \dfrac{7}{2}$$

8. $\dfrac{m^2 + 5m + 4}{6} \div \dfrac{m + 1}{18m + 24}$

$$= \dfrac{m^2 + 5m + 4}{6} \cdot \dfrac{18m + 24}{m + 1}$$

$$= \dfrac{(m + 4)(m + 1) \cdot 6(3m + 4)}{6(m + 1)}$$

$$= (m + 4)(3m + 4)$$

11-4 Adding and Subtracting Rational Expressions

PAGE 525   CHECKING FOR UNDERSTANDING

1. greatest common factor

2. least common denominator

3. fractions that have the same value

4. Use each factor the greatest number of times it occurs; $25(a + c)(a + b)$.

5. $78 = 2 \cdot 39$
   $39 = 39$
   $\text{LCD} = 2 \cdot 39$
   $\phantom{\text{LCD}} = 78$

6. $12 = 2 \cdot 2 \cdot 3$
   $27 = 3 \cdot 3 \cdot 3$
   $\text{LCD} = 2 \cdot 2 \cdot 3 \cdot 3 \cdot 3$
   $\phantom{\text{LCD}} = 108$

7. $80 = 2 \cdot 2 \cdot 2 \cdot 2 \cdot 5$
   $125 = 5 \cdot 5 \cdot 5$
   $\text{LCD} = 2 \cdot 2 \cdot 2 \cdot 2 \cdot 5 \cdot 5 \cdot 5$
   $\phantom{\text{LCD}} = 2000$

8. $36x^2y = 2 \cdot 2 \cdot 3 \cdot 3 \cdot x \cdot x \cdot y$
   $20xyz = 2 \cdot 2 \cdot 5 \cdot x \cdot y \cdot z$
   $\text{LCD} = 2 \cdot 2 \cdot 3 \cdot 3 \cdot 5 \cdot x \cdot x \cdot y \cdot z$
   $\phantom{\text{LCD}} = 180x^2yz$

9. $x(x - 2) = x(x - 2)$
   $x^2 - 4 = (x - 2)(x + 2)$
   $\text{LCD} = x(x - 2)(x + 2)$

10. $(x + 2)(x + 1) = (x + 2)(x + 1)$
    $x^2 - 1 = (x - 1)(x + 1)$
    $\text{LCD} = (x + 2)(x + 1)(x - 1)$

11. $3x + 15 = 3(x + 5)$
    $x^2 + 2x - 15 = (x + 5)(x - 3)$
    $\text{LCD} = 3(x + 5)(x - 3)$

12. $x^2 - 8x = x(x - 8)$
    $y^2 - 8y = y(y - 8)$
    $\text{LCD} = xy(x - 8)(y - 8)$

13. $\dfrac{7}{ab} + \dfrac{9}{b} = \dfrac{7}{ab} + \dfrac{9 \cdot a}{b \cdot a}$

$$= \dfrac{7}{ab} + \dfrac{9a}{ab}$$

$$= \dfrac{7 + 9a}{ab}$$

14. $\dfrac{11}{10} - \dfrac{7}{2a} - \dfrac{6}{5a} = \dfrac{11a}{10a} - \dfrac{35}{10a} - \dfrac{12}{10a}$

$$= \dfrac{11a - 47}{10a}$$

15. $3t - 7 + \dfrac{3t + 1}{t - 5} = \dfrac{(3t - 7)(t - 5)}{t - 5} + \dfrac{3t + 1}{t - 5}$

$$= \dfrac{3t^2 - 22t + 35}{t - 5} + \dfrac{3t + 1}{t - 5}$$

$$= \dfrac{3t^2 - 19t + 36}{t - 5}$$

PAGES 525-526   EXERCISES

16. $\dfrac{3a + 2}{a + b} + \dfrac{4}{2a + 2b} = \dfrac{2(3a + 2)}{2(a + b)} + \dfrac{4}{2(a + b)}$

$$= \dfrac{6a + 4}{2(a + b)} + \dfrac{4}{2(a + b)}$$

$$= \dfrac{6a + 8}{2(a + b)}$$

$$= \dfrac{3a + 4}{a + b}$$

17. $-\dfrac{18}{9xy} + \dfrac{7}{2x} - \dfrac{2}{3x^2}$

$$= -\dfrac{18 \cdot 2x}{9xy \cdot 2x} + \dfrac{7 \cdot 9xy}{2x \cdot 9xy} - \dfrac{2 \cdot 6y}{3x^2 \cdot 6y}$$

$$= -\dfrac{36x}{18x^2y} + \dfrac{63xy}{18x^2y} - \dfrac{12y}{18x^2y}$$

$$= \dfrac{-36x + 63xy - 12y}{18x^2y}$$

$$= \dfrac{-12x + 21xy - 4y}{6x^2y}$$

18. $\dfrac{3}{4a} - \dfrac{2}{5a} - \dfrac{1}{2a} = \dfrac{3 \cdot 5}{4a \cdot 5} - \dfrac{2 \cdot 4}{5a \cdot 4} - \dfrac{1 \cdot 10}{2a \cdot 10}$

$$= \dfrac{15}{20a} - \dfrac{8}{20a} - \dfrac{10}{20a}$$

$$= -\dfrac{3}{20a}$$

19. $\dfrac{7}{y - 8} - \dfrac{6}{8 - y} = \dfrac{7}{y - 8} + \dfrac{6}{y - 8}$

$$= \dfrac{13}{y - 8}$$

20. $\dfrac{x}{x^2 - 9} + \dfrac{1}{2x + 6} = \dfrac{x}{(x + 3)(x - 3)} + \dfrac{1}{2(x + 3)}$

$$= \dfrac{2x}{2(x + 3)(x - 3)} + \dfrac{x - 3}{2(x + 3)(x - 3)}$$

$$= \dfrac{2x + (x - 3)}{2(x + 3)(x - 3)}$$

$$= \dfrac{3x - 3}{2(x + 3)(x - 3)} \text{ or } \dfrac{3(x - 1)}{2(x + 3)(x - 3)}$$

21. $y - 1 + \dfrac{1}{y - 1} = \dfrac{(y - 1)(y - 1)}{y - 1} + \dfrac{1}{y - 1}$

$= \dfrac{y^2 - 2y + 1 + 1}{y - 1}$

$= \dfrac{y^2 - 2y + 2}{y - 1}$

22. $3m + 1 - \dfrac{2m}{3m + 1} = \dfrac{(3m + 1)^2}{3m + 1} - \dfrac{2m}{3m + 1}$

$= \dfrac{9m^2 + 6m + 1 - 2m}{3m + 1}$

$= \dfrac{9m^2 + 4m + 1}{3m + 1}$

23. $\dfrac{x}{x + 3} - \dfrac{6x}{x^2 - 9}$

$= \dfrac{x(x - 3)}{(x + 3)(x - 3)} - \dfrac{6x}{(x + 3)(x - 3)}$

$= \dfrac{x^2 - 3x - 6x}{(x + 3)(x - 3)}$

$= \dfrac{x^2 - 9x}{(x + 3)(x - 3)}$ or $\dfrac{x(x - 9)}{(x + 3)(x - 3)}$

24. $\dfrac{3}{a - 2} + \dfrac{2}{a - 3} = \dfrac{3(a - 3)}{(a - 2)(a - 3)} + \dfrac{2(a - 2)}{(a - 3)(a - 2)}$

$= \dfrac{3a - 9 + 2a - 4}{(a - 2)(a - 3)}$

$= \dfrac{5a - 13}{(a - 2)(a - 3)}$

25. $\dfrac{6}{x^2 + 4x + 4} + \dfrac{5}{x + 2} = \dfrac{6}{(x + 2)^2} + \dfrac{5(x + 2)}{(x + 2)^2}$

$= \dfrac{6 + 5x + 10}{(x + 2)^2}$

$= \dfrac{5x + 16}{(x + 2)^2}$

26. $\dfrac{8}{2y - 16} - \dfrac{y}{8 - y} = \dfrac{4}{y - 8} + \dfrac{y}{y - 8}$

$= \dfrac{y + 4}{y - 8}$

27. $\dfrac{2a}{3a - 15} + \dfrac{-16a + 20}{3a^2 - 12a - 15}$

$= \dfrac{2a}{3(a - 5)} + \dfrac{-16a + 20}{3(a - 5)(a + 1)}$

$= \dfrac{2a(a + 1)}{3(a - 5)(a + 1)} + \dfrac{-16a + 20}{3(a - 5)(a + 1)}$

$= \dfrac{2a^2 - 14a + 20}{3(a - 5)(a + 1)}$

$= \dfrac{2(a - 5)(a - 2)}{3(a - 5)(a + 1)}$

$= \dfrac{2(a - 2)}{3(a + 1)}$

28. $\dfrac{5}{x^2 - 3x - 28} + \dfrac{7}{2x - 14}$

$= \dfrac{5 \cdot 2}{2(x + 4)(x - 7)} + \dfrac{7(x + 4)}{2(x + 4)(x - 7)}$

$= \dfrac{10 + 7x + 28}{2(x + 4)(x - 7)}$

$= \dfrac{7x + 38}{2(x + 4)(x - 7)}$

29. $\dfrac{x}{x^2 + 2x + 1} - \dfrac{x + 2}{x + 1} - \dfrac{3x}{x + 1}$

$= \dfrac{x}{(x + 1)(x + 1)} - \dfrac{(x + 2)(x + 1)}{(x + 1)(x + 1)} - \dfrac{3x(x + 1)}{(x + 1)(x + 1)}$

$= \dfrac{x - x^2 - 3x - 2 - 3x^2 - 3x}{(x + 1)(x + 1)}$

$= \dfrac{-4x^2 - 5x - 2}{(x + 1)^2}$

30. $\dfrac{m + 3}{m^2 - 6m + 9} - \dfrac{8m - 24}{9 - m^2}$

$= \dfrac{m + 3}{(m - 3)(m - 3)} - \dfrac{-(8m - 24)}{(m + 3)(m - 3)}$

$= \dfrac{(m + 3)(m + 3)}{(m - 3)^2(m + 3)} - \dfrac{-8(m - 3)(m - 3)}{(m - 3)^2(m + 3)}$

$= \dfrac{m^2 + 6m + 9 + 8m^2 - 48m + 72}{(m - 3)^2(m + 3)}$

$= \dfrac{9m^2 - 42m + 81}{(m - 3)^2(m + 3)}$

31. $\dfrac{m^2 + n^2}{m^2 - n^2} + \dfrac{m}{n - m} + \dfrac{n}{m + n}$

$= \dfrac{m^2 + n^2}{(m - n)(m + n)} - \dfrac{m(m + n)}{(m - n)(m + n)} - \dfrac{n(m - n)}{(m - n)(m + n)}$

$= \dfrac{m^2 + n^2 - m^2 - mn + mn - n^2}{(m - n)(m + n)}$

$= \dfrac{0}{(m - n)(m + n)}$

$= 0$

32. $\dfrac{x}{x - y} + \dfrac{y}{y^2 - x^2} + \dfrac{2x}{x + y}$

$= \dfrac{x(x + y)}{(x + y)(x - y)} - \dfrac{y}{(x + y)(x - y)} + \dfrac{2x(x - y)}{(x + y)(x - y)}$

$= \dfrac{x^2 + xy - y + 2x^2 - 2xy}{(x + y)(x - y)}$

$= \dfrac{3x^2 - xy - y}{(x + y)(x - y)}$

33. $\dfrac{x^2 - 3x + 1}{x^2 - 4} - \dfrac{x^2 + 2x + 4}{2 - x} - \dfrac{x - 4}{x - 2}$

$= \dfrac{x^2 - 3x + 1}{(x + 2)(x - 2)} - \dfrac{-(x^2 + 2x + 4)}{x - 2} - \dfrac{x - 4}{x - 2}$

$= \dfrac{x^2 - 3x + 1}{(x + 2)(x - 2)} + \dfrac{x^2 + x + 8}{x - 2}$

$= \dfrac{x^2 - 3x + 1}{(x + 2)(x - 2)} + \dfrac{(x^2 + x + 8)(x + 2)}{(x + 2)(x - 2)}$

$= \dfrac{x^2 - 3x + 1 + x^3 + 3x^2 + 10x + 16}{(x + 2)(x - 2)}$

$= \dfrac{x^3 + 4x^2 + 7x + 17}{x^2 - 4}$

34. $\dfrac{3b-1}{b^2-49} - \dfrac{3b+2}{14+5b-b^2}$

$= \dfrac{3b-1}{(b+7)(b-7)} - \dfrac{-(3b+2)}{(b-7)(b+2)}$

$= \dfrac{(3b-1)(b+2)}{(b+7)(b-7)(b+2)} - \dfrac{-(3b+2)(b+7)}{(b+7)(b-7)(b-2)}$

$= \dfrac{3b^2+5b-2+3b^2+23b+14}{(b+7)(b-7)(b+2)}$

$= \dfrac{6b^2+28b+12}{(b+7)(b-7)(b+2)}$

35. $\dfrac{x+1}{x-1} + \dfrac{x+2}{x-2} + \dfrac{x}{x^2-3x+2}$

$= \dfrac{(x+1)(x-2)}{(x-1)(x-2)} + \dfrac{(x+2)(x-1)}{(x-2)(x-1)} + \dfrac{x}{(x-1)(x-2)}$

$= \dfrac{x^2-x-2+x^2+x-2+x}{(x-1)(x-2)}$

$= \dfrac{2x^2+x-4}{(x-1)(x-2)}$

36. $\dfrac{(x+y)\left(\dfrac{1}{x}-\dfrac{1}{y}\right)}{(x-y)\left(\dfrac{1}{x}+\dfrac{1}{y}\right)} = \dfrac{(x+y)\left(\dfrac{y}{xy}-\dfrac{x}{xy}\right)}{(x-y)\left(\dfrac{y}{xy}+\dfrac{x}{xy}\right)}$

$= \dfrac{(x+y)(y-x)}{xy} + \dfrac{(x-y)(x+y)}{xy}$

$= \dfrac{(x+y)(-1)(x-y)}{xy} \cdot \dfrac{xy}{(x-y)(x+y)}$

$= -1$

37. $\dfrac{\dfrac{1}{x+5} + \dfrac{1}{x-3}}{\dfrac{2x^2-3x-5}{x^2+2x-15}}$

$= \dfrac{\dfrac{x-3}{(x+5)(x-3)} + \dfrac{x+5}{(x+5)(x-3)}}{\dfrac{2x^2-3x-5}{x^2+2x-15}}$

$= \dfrac{2x+2}{(x+5)(x-3)} \div \dfrac{2x^2-3x-5}{x^2+2x-15}$

$= \dfrac{2(x+1)}{(x+5)(x-3)} \cdot \dfrac{(x+5)(x-3)}{(2x-5)(x+1)}$

$= \dfrac{2}{2x-5}$

38. $\dfrac{2x}{x^2+7x+10} + \dfrac{x-1}{x^2-25}$

$= \dfrac{2x}{(x+5)(x+2)} + \dfrac{x-1}{(x-5)(x+5)}$

$= \dfrac{2x(x-5)}{(x-5)(x+5)(x+2)} + \dfrac{(x-1)(x+2)}{(x-5)(x+5)(x+2)}$

$= \dfrac{3x^2-9x-2}{(x-5)(x+5)(x+2)}$

39. $\dfrac{3x}{4x^2-1} + \dfrac{5}{2x^2-x} + \dfrac{2x+1}{2x^2+5x+2}$

$= \dfrac{3x}{(2x+1)(2x-1)} + \dfrac{5}{x(2x-1)} + \dfrac{2x+1}{(2x+1)(x+2)}$

$= \dfrac{3x^2(x+2) + 5(2x+1)(x+2) + x(2x+1)(2x-1)}{x(2x+1)(2x-1)(x+2)}$

$= \dfrac{7x^3+16x^2+24x+10}{x(2x+1)(2x-1)\cdot(x+2)}$

40. $\dfrac{1}{p} + \dfrac{1}{q} = \dfrac{1}{f}$

$\dfrac{1}{p} + \dfrac{1}{12} = \dfrac{1}{10}$

$\dfrac{12}{12p} + \dfrac{p}{12p} = \dfrac{1}{10}$

$\dfrac{12+p}{12p} = \dfrac{1}{10}$

$120 + 10p = 12p$

$120 = 2p$

$60 = p$

The dog is 60 cm from the lens.

41. $\dfrac{4}{x+2} - \dfrac{7}{x-3} = \dfrac{4(x-3)}{(x+2)(x-3)} - \dfrac{7(x+2)}{(x+2)(x-3)}$

$= \dfrac{4x-12-7x-14}{(x+2)(x-3)}$

$= \dfrac{-3x-26}{(x+2)(x-3)}$ mph

42. $\dfrac{x}{x-3} - 189 = \dfrac{x}{x-3} - \dfrac{189(x-3)}{x-3}$

$= \dfrac{x-189x+567}{x-3}$

$= \dfrac{-188x+567}{x-3}$ mph

43. $\dfrac{1}{x} + \dfrac{2}{x-2} + \dfrac{3}{x} + \dfrac{4}{x-2} + \dfrac{x}{x-2}$

$= \dfrac{(x-2) + 2x + 3(x-2) + 4x + x(x)}{x(x-2)}$

$= \dfrac{x-2+2x+3x-6+4x+x^2}{x(x-2)}$

$= \dfrac{x^2+10x-8}{x(x-2)}$

44. $\dfrac{\dfrac{3x+5}{3x+1} - 2}{3 + \dfrac{3x}{1-2x}} = \dfrac{\dfrac{3x+5}{3x+1} - \dfrac{2(3x+1)}{3x+1}}{\dfrac{3(1-2x)}{1-2x} + \dfrac{3x}{1-2x}}$

$= \dfrac{\dfrac{-3x+3}{3x+1}}{\dfrac{-3x+3}{1-2x}}$

$= \dfrac{-3x+3}{3x+1} \cdot \dfrac{1-2x}{-3x+3}$

$= \dfrac{1-2x}{3x+1}$

45. $[f \circ g](x) = 3(x^2-1)^2$

$= 3(x^4 - 2x^2 + 1)$

$[f \circ g](2) = 3(2^4 - 2(2)^2 + 1)$

$= 3(16 - 8 + 1)$

$= 27$

46. $x^2 - 8x + 7 \geq 0$

$(x-7)(x-1) \geq 0$

$x - 7 \geq 0$ and $x - 1 \geq 0$ or $x - 7 \leq 0$ and $x - 1 \leq 0$

$x \geq 7$ and $x \geq 1$ or $x \leq 7$ and $x \leq 1$

$x \geq 7$ or $x \leq 1$

$\{x \mid x \leq 1 \text{ or } x \geq 7\}$

47. $\sqrt{z + 12} - \sqrt{z} = 2$

$\sqrt{z + 12} = 2 + \sqrt{z}$

$z + 12 = 4 + 4\sqrt{z} + z$

$8 = 4\sqrt{z}$

$2 = \sqrt{z}$

$4 = z$

48.

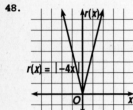

$r(x) = |-4x|$

49. $c = \pi d \Rightarrow 88 = \pi d$

$28 \approx d$

about 28 in.

11-5 Solving Rational Equations

1. By multiplying by the LCD, it removes the denominators making the equation easier to solve.

2. If you subtract $\dfrac{1}{x - 1}$ from each side, you get $x = 1$. But $x \neq 1$ because it gives 0 in the denominator.

3. Find an expression that contains each kind of factor present in each denominator with the factor raised to the highest power it has in any of the denominators.

4. $10y$; $y \neq 0$

5. $2x$; $x \neq 0$

6. $(x + 5)(x - 3)$; $x \neq 3, -5$

7. $7(2 + m)$; $m \neq -2$

8. $(1 + b)(2b + 3)$; $b \neq -1, -\dfrac{3}{2}$

9. x^2; $x \neq 0$

10. $x + 3 = \dfrac{4}{x}$

$x(x + 3) = x\left(\dfrac{4}{x}\right)$

$x^2 + 3x = 4$

$x^2 + 3x - 4 = 0$

$(x + 4)(x - 1) = 0$

$x + 4 = 0$ or $x - 1 = 0$

$x = -4$ or $x = 1$

---

11. $r^2 + \dfrac{17r}{6} = \dfrac{1}{2}$

$6\left(r^2 + \dfrac{17r}{6}\right) = 6\left(\dfrac{1}{2}\right)$

$6r^2 + 17r = 3$

$6r^2 + 17r - 3 = 0$

$(6r - 1)(r + 3) = 0$

$6r - 1 = 0$ or $r + 3 = 0$

$r = \dfrac{1}{6}$ or $r = -3$

12. $\dfrac{2y}{3} - \dfrac{y + 3}{6} = 2$

$6\left(\dfrac{2y}{3} - \dfrac{y + 3}{6}\right) = 6(2)$

$4y - (y + 3) = 12$

$3y - 3 = 12$

$3y = 15$

$y = 5$

13. $\dfrac{y + 1}{3} + \dfrac{y - 1}{3} = \dfrac{4}{3}$

$3\left(\dfrac{y + 1}{3} + \dfrac{y - 1}{3}\right) = 3\left(\dfrac{4}{3}\right)$

$y + 1 + y - 1 = 4$

$2y = 4$

$y = 2$

14. $\dfrac{2y - 5}{6} - \dfrac{y - 5}{4} = \dfrac{3}{4}$

$12\left(\dfrac{2y - 5}{6} - \dfrac{y - 5}{4}\right) = 12\left(\dfrac{3}{4}\right)$

$4y - 10 - 3y + 15 = 9$

$y + 5 = 9$

$y = 4$

15. $\dfrac{5 + 7p}{8} - \dfrac{3(5 + p)}{10} = 2$

$40\left(\dfrac{5 + 7p}{8} - \dfrac{3(5 + p)}{10}\right) = 40 \cdot 2$

$25 + 35p - 60 - 12p = 80$

$23p - 35 = 80$

$23p = 115$

$p = 5$

16. $8 - \dfrac{2 - 5x}{4} = \dfrac{4x + 9}{3}$

$12\left(8 - \dfrac{2 - 5x}{4}\right) = 12\left(\dfrac{4x + 9}{3}\right)$

$96 - 6 + 15x = 16x + 36$

$90 + 15x = 16x + 36$

$54 = x$

17.
$$x + 5 = \frac{6}{x}$$
$$x(x + 5) = x\left(\frac{6}{x}\right)$$
$$x^2 + 5x = 6$$
$$x^2 + 5x - 6 = 0$$
$$(x + 6)(x - 1) = 0$$
$$x + 6 = 0 \text{ or } x - 1 = 0$$
$$x = -6 \quad \text{or} \quad x = 1$$

18.
$$\frac{1}{y^2 - 1} = \frac{2}{y^2 + y - 2}$$
$$(y - 1)(y + 1)(y + 2)\left(\frac{1}{(y - 1)(y + 1)}\right)$$
$$= (y - 1)(y + 1)(y + 2)\left(\frac{2}{(y + 2)(y - 1)}\right)$$
$$y + 2 = 2(y + 1)$$
$$y + 2 = 2y + 2$$
$$y = 0$$

19.
$$x + \frac{12}{x} - 8 = 0$$
$$x\left(x + \frac{12}{x} - 8\right) = x(0)$$
$$x^2 - 8x + 12 = 0$$
$$(x - 2)(x - 6) = 0$$
$$x - 2 = 0 \text{ or } x - 6 = 0$$
$$x = 2 \quad \text{or} \quad x = 6$$

20.
$$\frac{5}{6} - \frac{2m}{2m + 3} = \frac{19}{6}$$
$$6(2m + 3)\left(\frac{5}{6} - \frac{2m}{2m + 3}\right) = 6(2m + 3)\left(\frac{19}{6}\right)$$
$$5(2m + 3) - 6(2m) = 38m + 57$$
$$10m + 15 - 12m = 38m + 57$$
$$-42 = 40m$$
$$-\frac{21}{20} = m$$

21.
$$\frac{1}{9} + \frac{1}{2a} = \frac{1}{a^2}$$
$$18a^2\left(\frac{1}{9} + \frac{1}{2a}\right) = 18a^2\left(\frac{1}{a^2}\right)$$
$$2a^2 + 9a = 18$$
$$2a^2 + 9a - 18 = 0$$
$$(2a - 3)(a + 6) = 0$$
$$2a - 3 = 0 \text{ or } a + 6 = 0$$
$$a = \frac{3}{2} \quad \text{or} \quad a = -6$$

22.
$$\frac{1}{1 - x} = 1 - \frac{x}{x - 1}$$
$$\frac{-1}{x - 1} = 1 - \frac{x}{x - 1}$$
$$(x - 1)\left(\frac{-1}{x - 1}\right) = (x - 1)\left(1 - \frac{x}{x - 1}\right)$$
$$-1 = x - 1 - x$$
$$-1 = -1$$

all reals except 1 $x \neq 1$

23.
$$\frac{2p}{2p + 3} - \frac{2p}{2p - 3} = 1$$
$$(2p + 3)(2p - 3)\left(\frac{2p}{2p + 3} - \frac{2p}{2p - 3}\right)$$
$$= (2p + 3)(2p - 3)(1)$$
$$2p(2p - 3) - 2p(2p + 3) = 4p^2 - 9$$
$$4p^2 - 6p - 4p^2 - 6p = 4p^2 - 9$$
$$-12p = 4p^2 - 9$$
$$4p^2 + 12p - 9 = 0$$
$$p = \frac{-12 \pm \sqrt{12^2 - 4(4)(-9)}}{2(4)}$$
$$p = \frac{-12 \pm 12\sqrt{2}}{8} \text{ or } \frac{-3 \pm 3\sqrt{2}}{2}$$

24.
$$\frac{4}{x - 2} - \frac{x + 6}{x + 1} = 1$$
$$(x - 2)(x + 1)\left(\frac{4}{x - 2} - \frac{x + 6}{x + 1}\right) = (x - 2)(x + 1)(1)$$
$$4x + 4 - (x^2 + 4x - 12) = x^2 - x - 2$$
$$-x^2 + 16 = x^2 - x - 2$$
$$0 = 2x^2 - x - 18$$
$$x = \frac{-(-1) \pm \sqrt{(-1)^2 - 4(2)(-18)}}{2(2)}$$
$$x = \frac{1 \pm \sqrt{145}}{4}$$

25.
$$\frac{x - 4}{x - 2} = \frac{x - 2}{x + 2} + \frac{1}{x - 2}$$
$$(x - 2)(x + 2)\left(\frac{x - 4}{x - 2}\right) = (x - 2)(x + 2)\left(\frac{x - 2}{x + 2} + \frac{1}{x - 2}\right)$$
$$x^2 - 2x - 8 = (x - 2)^2 + x + 2$$
$$x^2 - 2x - 8 = x^2 - 4x + 4 + x + 2$$
$$x = 14$$

26.
$$\frac{x - 3}{2x} = \frac{x - 2}{2x + 1} - \frac{1}{2}$$
$$2x(2x + 1)\left(\frac{x - 3}{2x}\right) = 2x(2x + 1)\left(\frac{x - 2}{2x + 1} - \frac{1}{2}\right)$$
$$2x^2 - 5x - 3 = 2x(x - 2) - x(2x + 1)$$
$$2x^2 - 5x - 3 = 2x^2 - 4x - 2x^2 - x$$
$$2x^2 - 3 = 0$$
$$x^2 = \frac{3}{2}$$
$$x = \pm\sqrt{\frac{3}{2}} \text{ or } \frac{\pm\sqrt{6}}{2}$$

27.
$$\frac{12}{x^2 - 16} - \frac{24}{x - 4} = 3$$
$$\frac{12}{(x - 4)(x + 4)} - \frac{24}{x - 4} = 3$$
$$(x - 4)(x + 4)\left(\frac{12}{(x - 4)(x + 4)} - \frac{24}{x - 4}\right)$$
$$= (x - 4)(x + 4)(3)$$
$$12 - 24(x + 4) = 3x^2 - 48$$
$$3x^2 + 24x + 36 = 0$$
$$3(x + 2)(x + 6) = 0$$
$$x + 2 = 0 \text{ or } x + 6 = 0$$
$$x = -2 \quad \text{or} \quad x = -6$$

28.
$$\frac{6}{a-7} = \frac{a-49}{a^2-7a} + \frac{1}{a}$$

$$a(a-7)\left[\frac{6}{a-7}\right] = a(a-7)\left[\frac{a-49}{a(a-7)} + \frac{1}{a}\right]$$

$$6a = a - 49 + a - 7$$
$$6a = 2a - 56$$
$$4a = -56$$
$$a = -14$$

29.
$$\frac{2}{y+2} - \frac{y}{2-y} = \frac{y^2+4}{y^2-4}$$

$$\frac{2}{y+2} + \frac{y}{y-2} = \frac{y^2+4}{(y+2)(y-2)}$$

$$(y+2)(y-2)\left[\frac{2}{y+2} + \frac{y}{y-2}\right]$$
$$= (y+2)(y-2)\left[\frac{y^2+4}{(y+2)(y-2)}\right]$$

$$2(y-2) + y(y+2) = y^2 + 4$$
$$2y - 4 + y^2 + 2y = y^2 + 4$$
$$4y - 4 = 4$$
$$y = 2 \qquad y \neq \pm 2$$

If $y = 2$, the denominators of the last two terms equal zero. Division by zero is not defined. Thus, there are no solutions.

30.
$$\frac{t+4}{t} + \frac{3}{t-4} = \frac{-16}{t^2-4t}$$

$$t(t-4)\left[\frac{t+4}{t} + \frac{3}{t-4}\right] = t(t-4)\left[\frac{-16}{t(t-4)}\right]$$

$$(t-4)(t+4) + 3t = -16$$
$$t^2 - 16 + 3t = -16$$
$$t^2 + 3t = 0$$
$$t(t+3) = 0$$
$$t = 0 \text{ or } t = -3 \qquad t \neq 0, 4$$

If $t = 0$, the denominator of the first term equals zero. Division by zero is not defined. Thus, 0 is not a solution.

31.
$$\frac{x+3}{x+2} = 2 - \frac{3}{x^2+5x+6}$$

$$(x+2)(x+3)\left[\frac{x+3}{x+2}\right]$$
$$= (x+2)(x+3)\left[2 - \frac{3}{(x+2)(x+3)}\right]$$

$$(x+3)^2 = 2(x^2+5x+6) - 3$$
$$x^2 + 6x + 9 = 2x^2 + 10x + 12 - 3$$
$$x^2 + 4x = 0$$
$$x(x+4) = 0$$
$$x = 0 \text{ or } x = -4$$

32.
$$\frac{x}{x^2-1} + \frac{2}{x+1} = \frac{1}{2x-2}$$

$$2(x-1)(x+1)\left[\frac{x}{(x-1)(x+1)} + \frac{2}{x+1}\right]$$
$$= 2(x-1)(x+1)\left[\frac{1}{2(x-1)}\right]$$

$$2x + 4(x-1) = x + 1$$
$$2x + 4x - 4 = x + 1$$
$$5x = 5$$
$$x = 1 \qquad x \neq \pm 1$$

If $x = 1$, the denominator of the first term equals zero. Division by zero is not defined. Thus, 1 is not a solution.

33.
$$\frac{A}{x+2} + \frac{B}{2x-3} = \frac{5x-11}{2x^2+x-6}$$

$$(2x-3)(x+2)\left[\frac{A}{x+2} + \frac{B}{2x-3}\right]$$
$$= (2x-3)(x+2)\left[\frac{5x-11}{(2x-3)(x+2)}\right]$$

$$A(2x-3) + B(x+2) = 5x - 11$$
$$2Ax - 3A + Bx + 2B = 5x - 11$$
$$2Ax + Bx - 3A + 2B = 5x - 11$$
$$(2A+B)x - (3A-2B) = 5x - 11$$

$$\begin{array}{lll} 2A + B = 5 & \rightarrow & 4A + 2B = 10 \\ 3A - 2B = 11 & & \underline{3A - 2B = 11} \\ & & 7A = 21 \\ & & A = 3 \end{array}$$

$$\begin{array}{l} 2A + B = 5 \\ 2(3) + B = 5 \\ 6 + B = 5 \\ B = -1 \end{array}$$

34.
$$r = \frac{1}{4}(40) + \frac{3}{4}(65)$$

$$4r = 4\left[\frac{40}{4} + \frac{195}{4}\right]$$
$$4r = 40 + 195$$
$$4r = 235$$
$$r = 58.75$$

35. a.
$$\frac{1}{2}\left(\frac{1}{y} + \frac{1}{z}\right) = \frac{1}{x}$$

$$\frac{1}{2y} + \frac{1}{2z} = \frac{1}{x}$$

$$\frac{1}{2y} + \frac{1}{2(20)} = \frac{1}{8}$$

$$40y\left(\frac{1}{2y} + \frac{1}{40}\right) = 40y\left(\frac{1}{8}\right)$$

$$20 + y = 5y$$
$$20 = 4y$$
$$5 = y$$

b.
$$\frac{1}{2(5)} + \frac{1}{2(8)} = \frac{1}{x}$$

$$\frac{1}{10} + \frac{1}{16} = \frac{1}{x}$$

$$80x\left(\frac{1}{10} + \frac{1}{16}\right) = 80x\left(\frac{1}{x}\right)$$

$$8x + 5x = 80$$
$$13x = 80$$
$$x \approx 6.15$$

36. $\dfrac{7x}{13y^2} + \dfrac{4x}{13y^2} = \dfrac{7x + 4x}{13y^2}$

$\qquad\qquad\qquad = \dfrac{11x}{13y^2}$

37. $\dfrac{3}{x} + 4 = \dfrac{3}{x} + \dfrac{4x}{x}$

$\qquad\qquad = \dfrac{3 + 4x}{x}$

38. $\dfrac{9}{4a} + \dfrac{-7}{5b} = \dfrac{9 \cdot 5b}{4a \cdot 5b} + \dfrac{-7 \cdot 4a}{4a \cdot 5b}$

$\qquad\qquad\qquad = \dfrac{45b - 28a}{20ab}$

39. $x = 1,\ x = 4,\ y = 0$

40. $x^2 + y^2 = 25 \qquad\quad (2)^2 + y^2 = 25$

$\qquad\quad x = 2 \quad\rightarrow\quad\qquad y^2 = 21$

$\qquad (2,\ \pm\sqrt{21}) \qquad\qquad\qquad y = \pm\sqrt{21}$

41. $x - 2 = -2y$

$\quad y - 1 = 2x + x^2 \longrightarrow y = x^2 + 2x + 1$

$\quad x - 2 = -2(x^2 + 2x + 1) \qquad\qquad$ If $x = 0$:

$\quad x - 2 = -2x^2 - 4x - 2 \qquad\qquad 0 - 2 = -2y$

$\qquad 0 = -2x^2 - 5x \qquad\qquad\qquad 1 = y$

$\qquad 0 = -x(2x + 5) \qquad\qquad$ If $x = -\dfrac{5}{2}$:

$\quad -x = 0$ or $2x + 5 = 0 \qquad -\dfrac{5}{2} - 2 = -2y$

$\quad x = 0 \quad$ or $\quad x = -\dfrac{5}{2} \qquad\qquad -\dfrac{9}{2} = -2y$

$\qquad\qquad\qquad\qquad\qquad\qquad\qquad\quad \dfrac{9}{4} = y$

$\quad (0,\ 1),\ \left(-\dfrac{5}{2},\ \dfrac{9}{4}\right)$

42. $(x,\ y) = \left(\dfrac{5 + \sqrt{5}}{2},\ \dfrac{5 + \sqrt{5}}{2}\right)$

43.

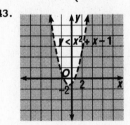

44. $(6 + \sqrt{3})(7 - \sqrt{2}) = 42 - 6\sqrt{2} + 7\sqrt{3} - \sqrt{6}$

45. a.

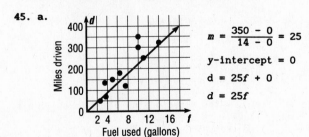

$\quad m = \dfrac{350 - 0}{14 - 0} = 25$

$\quad y\text{-intercept} = 0$

$\quad d = 25f + 0$

$\quad d = 25f$

b. $280 = 25f$

$\quad 11.2 = f$

$\quad$ about 11 gallons

Technology: Rational Expressions

1. $\dfrac{a^2 + 2a + 4}{a + 2}$ $\qquad\qquad$ **2.** $\dfrac{x + 3}{x - 3}$

3. $\dfrac{x - 2}{(x + 1)(x - 1)}$ $\qquad$ **4.** $\dfrac{1}{y}$ $\qquad$ **5.** $\dfrac{2}{x}$

11-6 Problem-Solving Strategy: Organizing Data

PAGES 533-534   CHECKING FOR UNDERSTANDING

1. graphs, diagrams, tables

2. A picture often gives a hint for the solution.

3. line, histogram, circle, bar, pictograph

4. bar graph or line graph

5.

PAGE 534   EXERCISES

6.

	4	6	
7	1	8	2
	3	5	

7.
3111	2211
1311	2121
1131	2112
1113	1221
	1212
	1122

number of possibilities: 10

So, $\dfrac{1}{n} = \dfrac{1}{10}$.

8.

14

6 9

7 13 3

2 15 11 1

10 4 5 8 12

9. Let c = number of cows.

Let p = number of pigs.

Let g = number of geese.

$\quad c + p + g = 100 \qquad\qquad c + p + g = 100$

$\quad 10c + 3p + \dfrac{1}{2}g = 100 \quad\rightarrow\quad \dfrac{-20c - 6p - g = -200}{-19c - 5p \qquad = -100}$

$\qquad\qquad\qquad\qquad\qquad\qquad\quad 19c + 5p = 100$

Since c and p must be whole numbers:

$c = 5$ and $p = 1$.

$c + p + g = 100$

$5 + 1 + g = 100$

$\qquad g = 94$

5 cows, 1 pig, 94 geese

10. $\ell w = 48$

$wh = 24 \rightarrow w = \dfrac{24}{h}$

$\ell h = 32$

$\ell w = 48$

$\ell\left(\dfrac{24}{h}\right) = 48$

$24\ell = 48h$

$\ell = 2h$

$\ell h = 32$	$\ell h = 32$	$\ell w = 48$
$(2h)h = 32$	$\ell(4) = 32$	$8w = 48$
$h^2 = 16$	$\ell = 8$	$w = 6$
$h = \pm 4$		

$V = \ell wh$

$= (8)(6)(4)$

$= 192 \qquad 192 \text{ in}^3$

PAGE 534   COOPERATIVE LEARNING ACTIVITY

$0.6x + 0.2(280 - x) = 0.3(280)$

$0.6x + 56 - 0.2x = 84$

$0.4x = 28$

$x = 70$

$280 - x = 210$

70 mL of 60% solution, 210 mL of 20% solution

11-7 Applications of Rational Equations

PAGE 537   CHECKING FOR UNDERSTANDING

1. Explore: look at all information given in problem.

Plan: select a strategy and create a way to use the given information.

Solve: find a solution.

Examine: determine if the solution is valid.

2. $\dfrac{1}{3} = \dfrac{x}{1}$

$1 = 3x$

$\dfrac{1}{3} = x$

3. The two bricklayers will complete parts of the wall. Together they will build a whole wall, represented by 1.

4. $\dfrac{1}{12} = \dfrac{x}{5}$; $\dfrac{5}{12}$ of the pool   5. $\dfrac{x}{6} - \dfrac{x}{18} = 1$; 9 hours

6. $\dfrac{12}{1} = \dfrac{d}{5}$ or $d = (12)(5)$; 60 miles

7. $r = \dfrac{524}{9}$; 58.2 mph

8. Let x = the time it takes the second panda to eat the leaves by itself.

$\dfrac{9}{14} + \dfrac{9}{x} = 1$

$14x\left(\dfrac{9}{14} + \dfrac{9}{x}\right) = 14x(1)$

$9x + 126 = 14x$

$-5x = -126$

$x = 25\dfrac{1}{5}$ hours

9. Let x = the time for the tank to fill.

$\dfrac{x}{10} - \dfrac{x}{20} = 1$

$20\left(\dfrac{x}{10} - \dfrac{x}{20}\right) = 20(1)$

$2x - x = 20$

$x = 20$ hours

10. Let x = the time it would take the painter to do the job alone.

$\dfrac{16}{x} + \dfrac{6}{30} = 1$

$5x\left(\dfrac{16}{x} + \dfrac{1}{5}\right) = 5x(1)$

$80 + x = 5x$

$-4x = -80$

$x = 20$ days

11. Let x = the number.

$\dfrac{x - 4}{x + 26} = \dfrac{1}{3}$

$3(x + 26)\dfrac{x - 4}{x + 26} = 3(x + 26)\dfrac{1}{3}$

$3x - 12 = x + 26$

$2x = 38$

$x = 19$

12. Let x = the number.

Then, $\dfrac{1}{x}$ = the multiplicative inverse.

$x + 5\dfrac{1}{x} = 10\dfrac{1}{2}$

$2x\left(x + \dfrac{5}{x}\right) = 2x\dfrac{21}{2}$

$2x^2 + 10 = 21x$

$2x^2 - 21x + 10 = 0$

$(2x - 1)(x - 10) = 0$

$2x - 1 = 0$ or $x - 10 = 0$

$x = \dfrac{1}{2}$ or $\quad x = 10$

13. Let s = the speed of the plane in still air.

$3\dfrac{1}{3}(s + 50) = 4(s - 50)$

$3\left(\dfrac{10}{3}\right)(s + 50) = 3(4)(s - 50)$

$10s + 500 = 12s - 600$

$-2s = -1100$

$s = 550$ mph

14. Let r = the rate in still water.

Let t = the time downstream.

$(r + 5)t = 26$

$$t = \frac{26}{r + 5}$$

$$(r - 5)\left(10\frac{2}{3} - t\right) = 26$$

$$3(r - 5)\left(\frac{32}{3} - t\right) = 3(26)$$

$$32r - 3rt - 160 + 15t = 78$$

$$32r - 3r\left(\frac{26}{r + 5}\right) - 160 + 15\left(\frac{26}{r + 5}\right) = 78$$

$$(r + 5)\left(32r - \frac{78r}{r + 5} - 160 + \frac{390}{r + 5}\right) = 78(r + 5)$$

$$32r^2 + 160r - 78r - 160r - 800 + 390 = 78r + 390$$

$$32r^2 - 156r - 800 = 0$$

$$4(8r^2 - 39r - 200) = 0$$

$$r = \frac{39 \pm \sqrt{39^2 - 4(8)(-200)}}{2(8)}$$

$$= \frac{39 \pm \sqrt{7921}}{16}$$

$$= 8, -3.125$$

-3.125 is not a reasonable solution.

Thus, the speed in still water is 8 mph.

15. Let x = load capacity of larger truck.

Then, $x - 3$ = load capacity of smaller truck.

$$\frac{x}{x - 3} = \frac{5}{2}$$

$$2(x - 3)\left(\frac{x}{x - 3}\right) = 2(x - 3)\left(\frac{5}{2}\right)$$

$$2x = 5(x - 3)$$

$$2x = 5x - 15$$

$$-3x = -15$$

$$x = 5 \text{ tons}$$

16. Let r = the original rate.

Let p = the original sum of money.

$rp = 108$

$$r = \frac{108}{p}$$

$$(r + 0.02)(p - 450) = 108$$

$$\left(\frac{108}{p} + 0.02\right)(p - 450) = 108$$

$$p\left(\frac{108}{p} + 0.02\right)(p - 450) = p(108)$$

$$(108 + 0.02p)(p - 450) = 108p$$

$$108p + 0.2p^2 - 48{,}600 - 9p = 108p$$

$$0.02p^2 - 9p - 48{,}600 = 0$$

$$p^2 - 450p - 2{,}430{,}000 = 0$$

$$(p - 1800)(p + 1350) = 0$$

$$p - 1800 = 0 \text{ or } p + 1350 = 0$$

$$p = 1800 \qquad p = -1350$$

The original sum of money was $1800.

$$r = \frac{108}{1800} = 0.06 \qquad \text{The original rate was 6\%.}$$

17. Let x = the numerator of the fraction.

Then $2x - 1$ = the denominator.

$$\frac{x + 7}{2x - 1 + 7} = \frac{7}{10}$$

$$\frac{x + 7}{2x + 6} = \frac{7}{10}$$

$$10(2x + 6)\frac{x + 7}{2x + 6} = 10(2x + 6)\frac{7}{10}$$

$$10x + 70 = 14x + 42$$

$$-4x = -28$$

$$x = 7$$

$$2x - 1 = 13$$

The original fraction was $\frac{7}{13}$.

18. Let x = amount of 55% solution.

$$0.55x + 0.25(1000 - x) = 0.30(1000)$$

$$250 + 0.30x = 300$$

$$0.30x = 50$$

$$x = 166.\overline{6}$$

$$1000 - 166.\overline{6} = 833.\overline{3}$$

$166\frac{2}{3}$ mL of 55% solution and $833\frac{1}{3}$ mL of 25% solution

19. a. Let x = the original sum of money.

Let y = the original interest.

$$x(0.08) = y$$

$$(x + 200)(0.06) = y + 1$$

$$(x + 200)(0.06) = x(0.08) + 1$$

$$0.06x + 12 = 0.08x + 1$$

$$11 = 0.02x$$

$$550 = x$$

$550 was originally invested.

b. $y = x(0.08)$

$$= 550(0.08)$$

$$= 44$$

$44 was the original amount of interest.

20. Let t = time pipe B will run.

$$\frac{t + 1}{4} + \frac{t}{3} = 1$$

$$12\left(\frac{t + 1}{4} + \frac{t}{3}\right) = 12(1)$$

$$3(t + 1) + 4t = 12$$

$$7t + 3 = 12$$

$$7t = 9$$

$$t = 1\frac{2}{7} \text{ hours}$$

21. It will never fill because it empties faster than it fills.

22. a. 17   b. 26   c. 23   d. 7

e. 1   f. 1   g. 2   h. 1

23. $\dfrac{x^2 - y^2}{x + y} \cdot \dfrac{1}{x - y} = \dfrac{(x + y)(x - y)}{x + y} \cdot \dfrac{1}{x - y}$

$$= 1$$

24. $\dfrac{4}{3a} - \dfrac{7}{5a} + \dfrac{1}{2a} = \dfrac{4 \cdot 10}{3a \cdot 10} - \dfrac{7 \cdot 6}{5a \cdot 6} + \dfrac{1 \cdot 15}{2a \cdot 15}$

$\qquad\qquad = \dfrac{40 - 42 + 15}{30a}$

$\qquad\qquad = \dfrac{13}{30a}$

25. $\dfrac{13x^2}{40y} \div \dfrac{26x^2}{70y^3} = \dfrac{13x^2}{40y} \cdot \dfrac{70y^3}{26x^2}$

$\qquad\qquad = \dfrac{910x^2y^3}{1040x^2y}$

$\qquad\qquad = \dfrac{130x^2y \cdot 7y^2}{130x^2y \cdot 8}$

$\qquad\qquad = \dfrac{7y^2}{8}$

26. $f(x) = (x + 2)[x - (4 + 3i)][x - (4 - 3i)]$

$\qquad = (x + 2)(x^2 - 8x + 25)$

$\qquad = x^3 - 6x^2 + 9x + 50$

27. $d = \sqrt{(7 - 3)^2 + (-8 - 6)^2}$

$\qquad = \sqrt{16 + 196}$

$\qquad = \sqrt{212}$

$\qquad = 2\sqrt{53}$

28.
$$
\begin{array}{r}
5s^2 - 9s - 2 \\
2s + 3 \,\overline{\big)\, 10s^3 - 3s^2 - 31s - 6} \\
\underline{10s^3 + 15s^2} \\
-18s^2 - 31s - 6 \\
\underline{-18s^2 - 27s} \\
-4s - 6 \\
\underline{-4s - 6} \\
0
\end{array}
$$

Chapter 11 Summary and Review

PAGES 540-542   SKILLS AND CONCEPTS

1.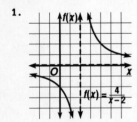

$f(x) = \dfrac{4}{x - 2}$

2.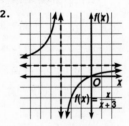

$f(x) = \dfrac{x}{x + 3}$

3.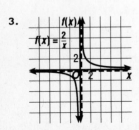

$f(x) = \dfrac{2}{x}$

4.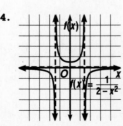

$f(x) = \dfrac{1}{2 - x^2}$

5.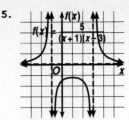

$f(x) = \dfrac{5}{(x + 1)(x - 3)}$

6. $\dfrac{7}{x} = \dfrac{21}{-5}$

$\qquad 21x = -5(7)$

$\qquad 21x = -35$

$\qquad\quad x = -\dfrac{5}{3}$

7. $\dfrac{\frac{5}{2}}{-\frac{3}{5}} = \dfrac{y}{9}$

$\quad -\dfrac{3}{5}y = \dfrac{45}{2}$

$\qquad\quad y = -\dfrac{75}{2}$

8. $\dfrac{28}{x} = \dfrac{18}{63}$

$\quad 18x = 1764$

$\qquad x = 98$

9. $\dfrac{28}{x} = \dfrac{63}{18}$

$\quad 63x = 504$

$\qquad x = 8$

10. $\dfrac{16}{(2)(4)} = \dfrac{y}{(5)(8)}$

$\qquad 8y = 640$

$\qquad\ y = 80$

11. $\dfrac{25}{(4)(2)} = \dfrac{12}{x(20)}$

$\qquad 500x = 96$

$\qquad\quad x = 0.192$

12. $\dfrac{-4ab}{21c} \cdot \dfrac{14c^2}{22a^2} = \dfrac{-56abc^2}{462a^2c}$

$\qquad\qquad = -\dfrac{14ac \cdot 4bc}{14ac \cdot 33a}$

$\qquad\qquad = -\dfrac{4bc}{33a}$

13. $\dfrac{y - 2}{a - x}(a - 3) = \dfrac{(y - 2)(a - 3)}{a - x}$

$\qquad\qquad = \dfrac{ay - 2a - 3y + 6}{a - x}$

14. $\dfrac{x + y}{a} \div \dfrac{x + y}{a^2} = \dfrac{x + y}{a} \cdot \dfrac{a^2}{x + y}$

$\qquad\qquad = \dfrac{a^2(x + y)}{a(x + y)}$

$\qquad\qquad = a$

15. $\dfrac{a^2 - b^2}{6b} \div \dfrac{a + b}{36b^2} = \dfrac{a^2 - b^2}{6b} \cdot \dfrac{36b^2}{a + b}$

$\qquad\qquad = \dfrac{36b^2(a + b)(a - b)}{6b(a + b)}$

$\qquad\qquad = 6b(a - b)$

16. $\dfrac{\frac{y^2 - y - 12}{y + 2}}{\dfrac{y - 4}{y^2 - 4y - 12}}$

$\qquad = \dfrac{y^2 - y - 12}{y + 2} \cdot \dfrac{y^2 - 4y - 12}{y - 4}$

$\qquad = \dfrac{(y - 4)(y + 3)(y - 6)(y + 2)}{(y + 2)(y - 4)}$

$\qquad = (y + 3)(y - 6)$

17. $\dfrac{\frac{1}{n^2 - 6n + 9}}{\dfrac{n + 3}{2n^2 - 18}} = \dfrac{1}{n^2 - 6n + 9} \div \dfrac{n + 3}{2n^2 - 18}$

$\qquad = \dfrac{1}{n^2 - 6n + 9} \cdot \dfrac{2n^2 - 18}{n + 3}$

$\qquad = \dfrac{2(n - 3)(n + 3)}{(n - 3)(n - 3)(n + 3)}$

$\qquad = \dfrac{2}{n - 3}$

18. $\dfrac{\dfrac{x^2 + 7x + 10}{x + 2}}{\dfrac{x^2 + 2x - 15}{x + 2}} = \dfrac{x^2 + 7x + 10}{x + 2} \div \dfrac{x^2 + 2x - 15}{x + 2}$

$\qquad = \dfrac{x^2 + 7x + 10}{x + 2} \cdot \dfrac{x + 2}{x^2 + 2x - 15}$

$\qquad = \dfrac{(x + 5)(x + 2)(x + 2)}{(x + 2)(x + 5)(x - 3)}$

$\qquad = \dfrac{x + 2}{x - 3}$

19. $-\dfrac{9}{4a} + \dfrac{7}{3b} = -\dfrac{27b}{12ab} + \dfrac{28a}{12ab}$

$\qquad = \dfrac{28a - 27b}{12ab}$

20. $\dfrac{x + 2}{x - 5} + 6 = \dfrac{x + 2}{x - 5} + \dfrac{6(x - 5)}{x - 5}$

$\qquad = \dfrac{x + 2 + 6x - 30}{x - 5}$

$\qquad = \dfrac{7x - 28}{x - 5}$ or $\dfrac{7(x - 4)}{x - 5}$

21. $\dfrac{x - 1}{x^2 - 1} + \dfrac{2}{5x + 5} = \dfrac{x - 1}{(x - 1)(x + 1)} + \dfrac{2}{5(x + 1)}$

$\qquad = \dfrac{1}{x + 1} + \dfrac{2}{5(x + 1)}$

$\qquad = \dfrac{5}{5(x + 1)} + \dfrac{2}{5(x + 1)}$

$\qquad = \dfrac{7}{5(x + 1)}$

22. $\dfrac{7}{y} - \dfrac{2}{3y} = \dfrac{21}{3y} - \dfrac{2}{3y} = \dfrac{19}{3y}$

23. $\dfrac{7}{y - 2} - \dfrac{11}{2 - y} = \dfrac{7}{y - 2} + \dfrac{11}{y - 2} = \dfrac{18}{y - 2}$

24. $\dfrac{14}{x + y} - \dfrac{9}{y^2 - x^2}$

$\qquad = \dfrac{14(y - x)}{(y + x)(y - x)} - \dfrac{9}{(y + x)(y - x)}$

$\qquad = \dfrac{14y - 14x - 9}{y^2 - x^2}$

25. $\dfrac{\dfrac{5x}{4}}{\dfrac{6x}{5}} + \dfrac{\dfrac{2x}{ab}}{\dfrac{3x}{a}} = \dfrac{5x}{4} \div \dfrac{6x}{5} + \dfrac{2x}{ab} \div \dfrac{3x}{a}$

$\qquad = \dfrac{5x}{4} \cdot \dfrac{5}{6x} + \dfrac{2x}{ab} \cdot \dfrac{a}{3x}$

$\qquad = \dfrac{25}{24} + \dfrac{2}{3b}$

$\qquad = \dfrac{25b}{24b} + \dfrac{16}{24b}$

$\qquad = \dfrac{25b + 16}{24b}$

26. $\dfrac{\dfrac{2a + 4}{a}}{6 + \dfrac{2}{a^2}} = \dfrac{\dfrac{2a + 4}{a}}{\dfrac{6a^2 + 2}{a^2}}$

$\qquad = \dfrac{2a + 4}{a} \div \dfrac{6a^2 + 2}{a^2}$

$\qquad = \dfrac{2(a + 2)}{a} \cdot \dfrac{a^2}{2(3a^2 + 1)}$

$\qquad = \dfrac{a(a + 2)}{3a^2 + 1}$

27. $\dfrac{3}{y} + \dfrac{7}{y} = 9$

$y\left(\dfrac{3}{y} + \dfrac{7}{y}\right) = y(9)$

$3 + 7 = 9y$

$\dfrac{10}{9} = y$

28. $1 + \dfrac{5}{y - 1} = \dfrac{7}{6}$

$6(y - 1)\left(1 + \dfrac{5}{y - 1}\right) = 6(y - 1)\dfrac{7}{6}$

$6y - 6 + 30 = 7y - 7$

$y = 31$

29. $\dfrac{3x + 2}{4} = \dfrac{9}{4} - \dfrac{3 - 2x}{6}$

$12\left(\dfrac{3x + 2}{4}\right) = 12\left(\dfrac{9}{4} - \dfrac{3 - 2x}{6}\right)$

$9x + 6 = 27 - 6 + 4x$

$5x = 15$

$x = 3$

30. $\dfrac{1}{r - 1} = \dfrac{2}{r^2 + r - 2}$

$\dfrac{1}{r - 1} = \dfrac{2}{(r + 2)(r - 1)}$

$(r + 2)(r - 1)\left(\dfrac{1}{r - 1}\right)$

$\qquad = (r + 2)(r - 1)\left(\dfrac{2}{(r + 2)(r - 1)}\right)$

$r + 2 = 2$

$r = 0$

31. $\dfrac{x}{x^2 - 1} + \dfrac{2}{x + 1} = 1 + \dfrac{1}{2x - 2}$

$2(x - 1)(x + 1)\left(\dfrac{x}{(x - 1)(x + 1)} + \dfrac{2}{x + 1}\right)$

$\qquad = 2(x - 1)(x + 1)\left(1 + \dfrac{1}{2(x - 1)}\right)$

$2x + 4(x - 1) = 2(x^2 - 1) + x + 1$

$2x + 4x - 4 = 2x^2 - 2 + x + 1$

$2x^2 - 5x + 3 = 0$

$(2x - 3)(x - 1) = 0$

$2x - 3 = 0$ or $x - 1 = 0$

$x = \dfrac{3}{2}$ or $x = 1$

If $x = 1$, the denominators of the first and last terms equal zero. Division by zero is not defined. Thus, 1 is not a solution.

32.

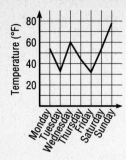

Greatest change in temperature is from Tuesday to Wednesday.

33. Let d = distance from light source.

Let x = intensity of illumination.

$$\frac{x}{d^2} = \frac{2x}{12^2}$$

$$144x = 2d^2 x$$

$$72 = d^2$$

$$\sqrt{72} = d$$

$$6\sqrt{2} = d$$

$6\sqrt{2}$ meters

34. Let x = the time it will take to do the job together.

$$\frac{x}{15} + \frac{x}{20} = 1$$

$$60\left(\frac{x}{15} + \frac{x}{20}\right) = 60(1)$$

$$4x + 3x = 60$$

$$7x = 60$$

$$x = 8\frac{4}{7} \text{ hours}$$

35. Let x = one integer.

Then, $x + 2$ = the other integer.

$$\frac{3}{x} + \frac{5}{x + 2} = \frac{7}{8}$$

$$8x(x + 2)\left(\frac{3}{x} + \frac{5}{x + 2}\right) = 8x(x + 2)\frac{7}{8}$$

$$3(8x + 16) + 8x(5) = 7x^2 + 14x$$

$$24x + 48 + 40x = 7x^2 + 14x$$

$$7x^2 - 50x - 48 = 0$$

$$(7x + 6)(x - 8) = 0$$

$$7x + 6 = 0 \text{ or } x - 8 = 0$$

$$x = -\frac{6}{7} \quad \text{or} \quad x = 8$$

$$x + 2 = 10$$

The two integers are 8 and 10.

Chapter 11 Test

PAGE 543

1. $\dfrac{7ab}{9c} \cdot \dfrac{81c^2}{91a^2 b} = \dfrac{567abc^2}{819a^2 bc}$

$$= \dfrac{63abc \cdot 9c}{63abc \cdot 13a}$$

$$= \dfrac{9c}{13a}$$

2. $\dfrac{a^2 - ab}{3a} \div \dfrac{a - b}{15b^2} = \dfrac{a(a - b)}{3a} \cdot \dfrac{15b^2}{a - b}$

$$= \dfrac{15ab^2 (a - b)}{3a(a - b)}$$

$$= 5b^2$$

3. $\dfrac{7}{5a} - \dfrac{10}{3ab} = \dfrac{21b}{15ab} - \dfrac{50}{15ab}$

$$= \dfrac{21b - 50}{15ab}$$

4. $\dfrac{6}{x - 5} + 7a = \dfrac{6}{x - 5} + \dfrac{7a(x - 5)}{x - 5}$

$$= \dfrac{6 + 7ax - 35a}{x - 5}$$

5. $\dfrac{x^2 - y^2}{a^2 - b^2} \cdot \dfrac{a + b}{x - y} = \dfrac{(x + y)(x - y)(a + b)}{(a - b)(a + b)(x - y)}$

$$= \dfrac{x + y}{a - b}$$

6. $\dfrac{x - y}{a - b} - \dfrac{x + y}{a + b}$

$$= \dfrac{(x - y)(a + b)}{(a - b)(a + b)} - \dfrac{(x + y)(a - b)}{(a + b)(a - b)}$$

$$= \dfrac{(x - y)(a + b) - (x + y)(a - b)}{(a - b)(a + b)}$$

$$= \dfrac{ax + bx - ay - by - ax + bx - ay + by}{(a - b)(a + b)}$$

$$= \dfrac{2bx - 2ay}{(a - b)(a + b)} \text{ or } \dfrac{2(bx - ay)}{a^2 - b^2}$$

7. $\dfrac{x^2 - 2x + 1}{y - 5} \div \dfrac{x - 1}{y^2 - 25}$

$$= \dfrac{(x - 1)(x - 1)}{y - 5} \cdot \dfrac{(y - 5)(y + 5)}{x - 1}$$

$$= \dfrac{(x - 1)^2 (y - 5)(y + 5)}{(y - 5)(x - 1)}$$

$$= (x - 1)(y + 5)$$

8. $\dfrac{x + 2}{x - 1} + \dfrac{6}{7x - 7} = \dfrac{x + 2}{x - 1} + \dfrac{6}{7(x - 1)}$

$$= \dfrac{7(x + 2)}{7(x - 1)} + \dfrac{6}{7(x - 1)}$$

$$= \dfrac{7x + 20}{7(x - 1)}$$

9. $\dfrac{y}{y - 9} - \dfrac{-9}{9 - y} = \dfrac{y}{y - 9} + \dfrac{-9}{y - 9}$

$$= \dfrac{y - 9}{y - 9}$$

$$= 1$$

10. $\dfrac{\dfrac{x^2 - 1}{x^2 - 3x - 10}}{\dfrac{x^2 - 12x + 35}{x^2 + 3x + 2}} = \dfrac{x^2 - 1}{x^2 - 3x - 10} \cdot \dfrac{x^2 + 3x + 2}{x^2 - 12x + 35}$

$$= \dfrac{(x - 1)(x + 1)}{(x - 5)(x + 2)} \cdot \dfrac{(x + 2)(x + 1)}{(x - 7)(x - 5)}$$

$$= \dfrac{(x + 2)(x + 1)^2(x - 1)}{(x + 2)(x - 5)^2(x - 7)}$$

$$= \dfrac{(x + 1)^2(x - 1)}{(x - 5)^2(x - 7)}$$

11. $\dfrac{\dfrac{1}{x} - \dfrac{1}{2x}}{\dfrac{2}{x} + \dfrac{4}{3x}} = \dfrac{\dfrac{2}{2x} - \dfrac{1}{2x}}{\dfrac{3 \cdot 2}{3x} + \dfrac{4}{3x}}$

$$= \dfrac{\dfrac{1}{2x}}{\dfrac{10}{3x}}$$

$$= \dfrac{1}{2x} \cdot \dfrac{3x}{10}$$

$$= \dfrac{3}{20}$$

12. $\dfrac{\dfrac{2}{x - 4} + \dfrac{5}{x + 1}}{\dfrac{3x}{x^2 - 3x - 4}} = \dfrac{\dfrac{2(x + 1) + 5(x - 4)}{(x - 4)(x + 1)}}{\dfrac{3x}{x^2 - 3x - 4}}$

$$= \dfrac{2x + 2 + 5x - 20}{(x - 4)(x + 1)} \cdot \dfrac{x^2 - 3x - 4}{3x}$$

$$= \dfrac{(7x - 18)(x - 4)(x + 1)}{3x(x - 4)(x + 1)}$$

$$= \dfrac{7x - 18}{3x}$$

13.
$$a - \dfrac{5}{a} = 4$$
$$a\left(a - \dfrac{5}{a}\right) = a(4)$$
$$a^2 - 5 = 4a$$
$$a^2 - 4a - 5 = 0$$
$$(a - 5)(a + 1) = 0$$
$$a - 5 = 0 \text{ or } a + 1 = 0$$
$$a = 5 \quad \text{or} \quad a = -1$$

14.
$$\dfrac{3}{x} + \dfrac{x}{x + 2} = \dfrac{-2}{x + 2}$$
$$x(x + 2)\left(\dfrac{3}{x} + \dfrac{x}{x + 2}\right) = x(x + 2)\dfrac{-2}{x + 2}$$
$$3x + 6 + x^2 = -2x$$
$$x^2 + 5x + 6 = 0$$
$$(x + 3)(x + 2) = 0$$
$$x + 3 = 0 \text{ or } x + 2 = 0$$
$$x = -3 \quad \text{or} \quad x = -2$$

If $x = -2$, the denominators of the last two terms equal zero. Division by zero is not defined. Thus, -2 is not a solution.

15.
$$\dfrac{y}{y - 3} + \dfrac{6}{y + 3} = 1$$
$$(y - 3)(y + 3)\left(\dfrac{y}{y - 3} + \dfrac{6}{y + 3}\right)$$
$$= (y - 3)(y + 3)(1)$$
$$y(y + 3) + 6(y - 3) = y^2 - 9$$
$$y^2 + 3y + 6y - 18 = y^2 - 9$$
$$9y = 9$$
$$y = 1$$

16.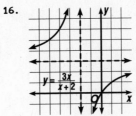

17.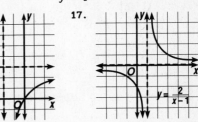

18.

19. Let x = the time it takes them to do the job together.
$$\dfrac{x}{8} + \dfrac{x}{13} = 1$$
$$104\left(\dfrac{x}{8} + \dfrac{x}{13}\right) = 104$$
$$13x + 8x = 104$$
$$21x = 104$$
$$x = 4\dfrac{20}{21} \text{ hours}$$

20. Let x = the capacity of the smaller barrel. Then, $2x - 12$ = the capacity of the larger barrel.
$$\dfrac{7}{4} = \dfrac{2x - 12}{x}$$
$$7x = 4(2x - 12)$$
$$7x = 8x - 48$$
$$x = 48, \qquad 2x - 12 = 84$$

The capacity of the smaller barrel is 48 gallons and the capacity of the larger barrel is 84 gallons.

21.
$$\dfrac{-3}{20} = \dfrac{10}{y}$$
$$-3y = 200$$
$$y = -\dfrac{200}{3}$$

22.
$$\dfrac{-\dfrac{2}{3}}{x} = \dfrac{-7}{9}$$
$$-7x = -6$$
$$x = \dfrac{6}{7}$$

23.
$$\dfrac{45}{(3)(5)} = \dfrac{y}{(2)(4)}$$
$$360 = 15y$$
$$24 = y$$

24.
$$\dfrac{250}{(10)(5)} = \dfrac{2.5}{x(4.5)}$$
$$1125x = 125$$
$$x = \dfrac{125}{1125} \text{ or } \dfrac{1}{9}$$

25.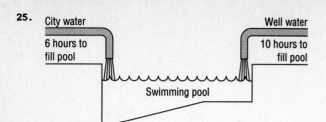

City water
6 hours to
fill pool

Well water
10 hours to
fill pool

Swimming pool

$$\frac{x}{6} + \frac{x}{10} = 1$$

$$60\left(\frac{x}{6} + \frac{x}{10}\right) = 60(1)$$

$$10x + 6x = 60$$

$$16x = 60$$

$$x = \frac{60}{16} \text{ or } 3\frac{3}{4}$$

It will take $3\frac{3}{4}$ hours to fill pool.

PAGE 543   BONUS

$$\frac{\dfrac{9x^2 - 12x + 4}{6x^2 - 13x + 6}}{\dfrac{6x^2 + 13x + 6}{4x^2 - 9}} + \frac{\dfrac{9x^2 - 4}{6x^2 - 5x - 6}}{\dfrac{6x^2 + 5x - 6}{4x^2 - 12x + 9}}$$

$$= \frac{9x^2 - 12x + 4}{6x^2 - 13x + 6} \cdot \frac{4x^2 - 9}{6x^2 + 13x + 6} \cdot \frac{6x^2 + 5x - 6}{4x^2 - 12x + 9} \cdot$$

$$\frac{6x^2 - 5x - 6}{9x^2 - 4}$$

$$= \frac{(3x - 2)(3x - 2)}{(3x - 2)(2x - 3)} \cdot \frac{(2x - 3)(2x + 3)}{(2x + 3)(3x + 2)} \cdot$$

$$\frac{(2x + 3)(3x - 2)}{(2x - 3)(2x - 3)} \cdot \frac{(2x - 3)(3x + 2)}{(3x - 2)(3x + 2)}$$

$$= \frac{(3x - 2)^3(3x + 2)(2x - 3)^2(2x + 3)^2}{(3x - 2)^2(3x + 2)^2(2x - 3)^3(2x + 3)}$$

$$= \frac{(3x - 2)(2x + 3)}{(3x + 2)(2x - 3)}$$

$$= \frac{6x^2 + 5x - 6}{6x^2 - 5x - 6}$$

Chapter 12   Exponential and Logarithmic Functions

PAGE 549   CHECKING FOR UNDERSTANDING

1. rational approximations, graph, calculator
2. 4.7111131; a calculator
3. $1^{x_1} = 1^{x_2}$ for any x_1 and x_2
4. 4.7   5. 1.6   6. 0.8
7. 2.1   8. 0.5   9. 18.9

10. $7^{\sqrt{3}} \cdot 7^{2\sqrt{3}} = 7^{\sqrt{3}+2\sqrt{3}}$
$$= 7^{3\sqrt{3}}$$

11. $(2^{\sqrt{3}})^{\sqrt{3}} = 2^{\sqrt{3}\cdot\sqrt{3}}$
$$= 2^3$$

12. $3(2^{\sqrt{2}})(2^{-\sqrt{2}}) = 3(2^{\sqrt{2}+(-\sqrt{2})})$
$$= 3(2^0)$$
$$= 3$$

13. $5^x = 5^{-3}$
$x = -3$

14. $6^x = 216$
$6^x = 6^3$
$x = 3$

15. $7^y = \frac{1}{49}$
$7^y = 7^{-2}$
$y = -2$

16. $10^x = 0.001$
$10^x = 10^{-3}$
$x = -3$

17. $2^{2x} = \frac{1}{8}$
$2^{2x} = 2^{-3}$
$2x = -3$
$x = -\frac{3}{2}$

18. $\left(\frac{1}{5}\right)^{b-3} = 125$
$\left(\frac{1}{5}\right)^{b-3} = \left(\frac{1}{5}\right)^{-3}$
$b - 3 = -3$
$b = 0$

PAGES 549-550   EXERCISES

19. 0.5   20. 0.7
21. 3.0   22. 0.5
23. 2.4   24. 3.8

25. $(3^{\sqrt{8}})^{\sqrt{2}} = 3^{\sqrt{8}\cdot\sqrt{2}}$
$$= 3^{\sqrt{16}}$$
$$= 3^4 = 81$$

26. $5^{\sqrt{3}} \cdot 5^{\sqrt{27}} = 5^{\sqrt{3}+\sqrt{27}}$
$$= 5^{\sqrt{3}+3\sqrt{3}}$$
$$= 5^{4\sqrt{3}}$$

27. $64^{\sqrt{7}} + 2^{\sqrt{7}} = (2^6)^{\sqrt{7}} + 2^{\sqrt{7}}$
$$= 2^{6\sqrt{7}} - \sqrt{7}$$
$$= 2^{5\sqrt{7}}$$

28. $(y^{\sqrt{3}})^{\sqrt{27}} = y^{\sqrt{81}}$
$$= y^9$$

29. $(x^{\sqrt{2}})^{\sqrt{8}} = x^{\sqrt{16}}$
$$= x^4$$

30. $(m^{\sqrt{2}} + n^{\sqrt{2}})^2 = (m^{\sqrt{2}})^2 + 2m^{\sqrt{2}}n^{\sqrt{2}} + (n^{\sqrt{2}})^2$
$$= m^{2\sqrt{2}} + 2(mn)^{\sqrt{2}} + n^{2\sqrt{2}}$$

31. $3^y = 3^{3y+1}$
$y = 3y + 1$
$-2y = 1$
$y = -\frac{1}{2}$

32. $5^{3y+4} = 5^y$
$3y + 4 = y$
$2y = -4$
$y = -2$

33. $3^x = 9^{x+1}$
$3^x = (3^2)^{x+1}$
$3^x = 3^{2x+2}$
$x = 2x + 2$
$x = -2$

34. $2^5 = 2^{2x-1}$
$5 = 2x - 1$
$6 = 2x$
$3 = x$

35. $8^{r-1} = 16^{3r}$
$(2^3)^{r-1} = (2^4)^{3r}$
$2^{3r-3} = 12^{12r}$
$3r - 3 = 12r$
$-3 = 9r$
$-\frac{1}{3} = r$

36. $2^{x+3} = \frac{1}{16}$
$2^{x+3} = 2^{-4}$
$x + 3 = -4$
$x = -7$

37. $9^{3y} = 27^{y+2}$
$(3^2)^{3y} = (3^3)^{y+2}$
$3^{6y} = 3^{3y+6}$
$6y = 3y+6$
$y = 2$

38. $\frac{1}{27} = 3^{x-5}$
$3^{-3} = 3^{x-5}$
$-3 = x - 5$
$2 = x$

39. $\left(\frac{1}{3}\right)^q = 3^{q-6}$
$(3^{-1})^q = 3^{q-6}$
$-q = q - 6$
$q = 3$

40. $25^{2m} = 125^{m-3}$
$(5^2)^{2m} = (5^3)^{m-3}$
$5^{4m} = 5^{3m-9}$
$4m = 3m - 9$
$m = -9$

41. $2^{2n-1} = 8^{n+7}$
$2^{2n-1} = (2^3)^{n+7}$
$2^{2n-1} = 2^{3n+21}$
$2n - 1 = 3n + 21$
$-22 = n$

42. $2^{x^2+1} = 32$
$2^{x^2+1} = 2^5$
$x^2 + 1 = 5$
$x^2 - 4 = 0$
$(x + 2)(x - 2) = 0$
$x = 2, -2$

43. $4^{x-1} = 8^x$
$(2^2)^{x-1} = (2^3)^x$
$2^{2x-2} = 2^{3x}$
$2x - 2 = 3x$
$x = -2$

44. $36^x = 6^{x^2-3}$
$(6^2)^x = 6^{x^2-3}$
$6^{2x} = 6^{x^2-3}$
$2x = x^2 - 3$
$x^2 - 2x - 3 = 0$
$(x - 3)(x + 1) = 0$
$x = 3, -1$

45.
$$9^{x^2-2x} = 27^{x^2+1}$$
$$(3^2)^{x^2-2x} = (3^3)^{x^2+1}$$
$$3^{2x^2-4x} = 3^{3x^2+3}$$
$$2x^2 - 4x = 3x^2 + 3$$
$$x^2 + 4x + 3 = 0$$
$$(x + 3)(x + 1) = 0$$
$$x = -3, -1$$

46. 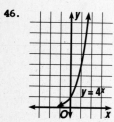   **47.**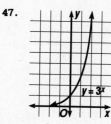

48.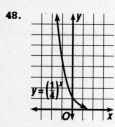

49. The graphs are reflections over the y-axis.

50. $y = 3^x$

$y = 3^3$

$y = 27$

51. a. $y = 100(1.08)^x$

b. $y = 100(1.08)^{16}$

$= 342.59$

52. Let x = amount of 60% solution.

Then $600 - x$ = amount of 35% solution.

$$0.60x + 0.35(600 - x) = 0.50(600)$$
$$0.60x + 210 - 0.35x = 300$$
$$0.25x = 90$$
$$x = 360 \text{ mL}$$

53.

```
3|   1   0   8   1      -2|  1   0   8   1
        3   9  51               -2   4 -24
   _____         _____
     1   3  17| 52           1  -2  12 |-23
```

$f(3): 52, \; f(-2): -23$

54. yes, $0 \le 4^2 - 7$

55. Let ℓ = the length.

Then $\ell - 2$ = the width.

$$\ell(\ell - 2) = 1763$$
$$\ell^2 - 2\ell - 1763 = 0$$
$$(\ell - 43)(\ell + 41) = 0$$
$$\ell - 43 = 0 \text{ or } \ell + 41 = 0$$
$$\ell = 43 \qquad \ell = -41$$
$$\ell - 2 = 41$$

The dimensions are 41 by 43 units.

56.
$$\frac{9x^{-\frac{4}{3}} - 4y^{-2}}{3x^{-\frac{2}{3}} + 2y^{-1}} = \frac{9x^{-\frac{4}{3}} - 4y^{-2}}{3x^{-\frac{2}{3}} + 2y^{-1}} \cdot \frac{3x^{-\frac{2}{3}} - 2y^{-1}}{3x^{-\frac{2}{3}} - 2y^{-1}}$$

$$= \frac{\left(9x^{-\frac{4}{3}} - 4y^{-2}\right)\left(3x^{-\frac{2}{3}} - 2y^{-1}\right)}{9x^{-\frac{4}{3}} - 4y^{-2}}$$

$$= 3x^{-\frac{2}{3}} - 2y^{-1}$$

$$= \left(3x^{-\frac{2}{3}} - 2y^{-1}\right)\frac{xy}{xy}$$

$$= \frac{3x^{\frac{1}{3}}y - 2x}{xy}$$

57. $b(3b - 2y) - (3b - 2y) = (b - 1)(3b - 2y)$

Graphing Calculator Exploration: Graphing Exponential and Logarithmic Functions

PAGE 552   EXERCISES

1. Xmin: -3
Xmax: 3
Xscl: 1.0
Ymin: -1
Ymax: 10
Yscl: 1.0

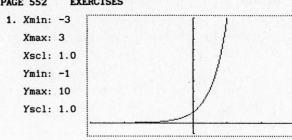

2. Xmin: -2
Xmax: 2
Xscl: 1.0
Ymin: -1
Ymax: 10
Yscl: 1.0

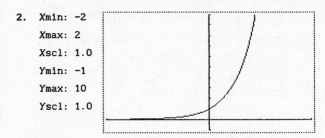

3. Xmin: -2
Xmax: 2
Xscl: 1.0
Ymin: -1
Ymax: 10
Yscl: 1.0

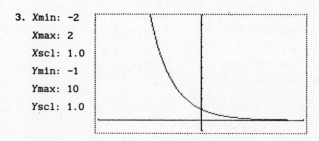

4. Xmin: -5
Xmax: 5
Xscl: 1.0
Ymin: -5
Ymax: 5
Yscl: 1.0

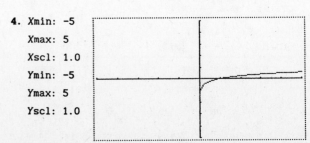

5. Xmin: -5
Xmax: 5
Xscl: 1.0
Ymin: -5
Ymax: 5
Yscl: 1.0

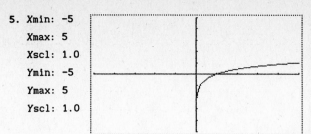

6. Xmin: -5
Xmax: 5
Xscl: 1.0
Ymin: -5
Ymax: 5
Yscl: 1.0

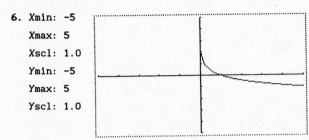

7. -6.23   **8.** 1.47
9. 0.38   **10.** -0.28
11. 4.30   **12.** 0.47
13. -3.51   **14.** 2, 4, -0.77
15. 2.48, 3   **16.** 9.17
17. 0.17   **18.** 7.30

12-2 Logarithms and Logarithmic Functions

PAGE 556   CHECKING FOR UNDERSTANDING

1. the logarithm, base 2, of x

2. Sample answer: $y = \log_2 x$

3. $30 \div 10 = 3 \to 3$ rounds of calls

$\log_4 x = 3$

$4^3 = x$

$64 = x$

4. Answers may vary.

5. $7 - 4 = 3 \to 10^3$ or 1000 times stronger

6. $\log_2 8 = 3$ **7.** $\log_{10} 1000 = 3$

8. $\log_6 \frac{1}{216} = -3$ **9.** $2^6 = 64$

10. $10^{-2} = 0.01$ **11.** $9^{\frac{3}{2}} = 27$

12. $\log_8 y = -2$ **13.** $\log_b 81 = 4$

$8^{-2} = y$ $b^4 = 81$

$\frac{1}{64} = y$ $b = 3$

14. $\log_{12} \frac{1}{12} = x$ **15.** $\log_b 64 = 6$

$12^x = \frac{1}{12}$ $b^6 = 64$

$x = -1$ $b = 2$

16. $\log_{10} \frac{1}{1000} = x$ **17.** $\log_4 y = 4$

$10^x = \frac{1}{1000}$ $4^4 = y$

$x = -3$ $256 = y$

PAGES 556-557   EXERCISES

18. $\log_{10} 10,000 = x$ **19.** $\log_4 16 = x$

$10^x = 10,000$ $4^x = 16$

$x = 4$ $x = 2$

20. $\log_{13} 169 = x$ **21.** $\log_8 \frac{1}{64} = x$

$13^x = 169$ $8^x = \frac{1}{64}$

$x = 2$ $x = -2$

22. $\log_3 \frac{1}{243} = x$ **23.** $\log_{25} 5 = x$

$3^x = \frac{1}{243}$ $25^x = 5$

$x = -5$ $x = \frac{1}{2}$

24. $\log_{\frac{1}{2}} 8 = x$ **25.** $\log_3 729 = x$

$\left(\frac{1}{2}\right)^x = 8$ $3^x = 729$

$x = -3$ $x = 6$

26. $\log_b 81 = 2$ **27.** $\log_3 y = 2$

$b^2 = 81$ $3^2 = y$

$b = 9$ $9 = y$

28. $\log_5 x = -1$ **29.** $\log_b 18 = 1$

$5^{-1} = x$ $b^1 = 18$

$\frac{1}{5} = x$ $b = 18$

30. $\log_b 81 = 4$ **31.** $\log_5 x = -2$

$b^4 = 81$ $5^{-2} = x$

$b = 3$ $x = \frac{1}{25}$

32. $\log_3 (4 + y) = \log_3 (2y)$

$4 + y = 2y$

$4 = y$

33. $\log_5 (2x - 3) = \log_5 (x + 2)$

$2x - 3 = x + 2$

$x = 5$

34. $\log_8 (3y - 1) = \log_8 (y + 4)$

$3y - 1 = y + 4$

$2y = 5$

$y = 2.5$

35. $\log_9 (5x - 1) = \log_9 (3x + 7)$

$5x - 1 = 3x + 7$

$2x = 8$

$x = 4$

36. $\log_{10} (x - 1)^2 = \log_{10} 0.01$

$(x - 1)^2 = 0.01$

$x - 1 = \pm 0.1$

$x = 1.1$ or 0.9

37. $\log_2 (x^2 + 6x) = \log_2 (x - 4)$

$x^2 + 6x = x - 4$

$x^2 + 5x + 4 = 0$

$(x + 4)(x + 1) = 0$

$x = -4, -1$

undefined, no solution

38. $\log_{12} (7x - 3) = \log_{12} (5 - x^2)$

$$7x - 3 = 5 - x^2$$
$$x^2 + 7x - 8 = 0$$
$$(x + 8)(x - 1) = 0$$
$$x = 1, -8$$
$$x = 1$$

39. $\log_{10} (x^2 + 36) = \log_{10} 100$

$$x^2 + 36 = 100$$
$$x^2 = 64$$
$$x = \pm 8$$

40. $\log_9 (x^2 + 9x) = \log_9 10$

$$x^2 + 9x = 10$$
$$x^2 + 9x - 10 = 0$$
$$(x + 10)(x - 1) = 0$$
$$x + 10 = 0 \text{ or } x - 1 = 0$$
$$x = -10 \text{ or } x = 1$$

41.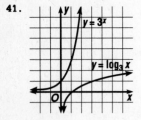

42.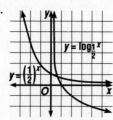

43.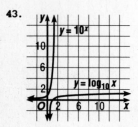

44.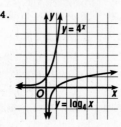

45. $\log_4 4 + \log_4 16 \stackrel{?}{=} \log_4 64$

$$1 + 2 \stackrel{?}{=} 3$$
$$3 = 3$$

46. $\log_4 16 \stackrel{?}{=} 2 \log_4 4$ **47.** $\log_2 8 \cdot \log_8 2 \stackrel{?}{=} 1$

$\quad 2 \stackrel{?}{=} 2(1)$ $\qquad\qquad\qquad 3 \cdot \frac{1}{3} \stackrel{?}{=} 1$

$\quad 2 = 2$ $\qquad\qquad\qquad\quad 1 = 1$

48. $\log_{10} [\log_3 (\log_4 64)] \stackrel{?}{=} 0$

$$\log_{10} [\log_3 3] \stackrel{?}{=} 0$$
$$\log_{10} 1 \stackrel{?}{=} 0$$
$$0 = 0$$

49. $f(g(x)) = \log_b (b^x)$

$\qquad\qquad = x$

$\quad g(f(x)) = b^{(\log_b x)}$

$\qquad\qquad = x$

50. $\text{pH} = \log_{10} \frac{1}{H+}$

$\quad 4 = \log_{10} \frac{1}{H+}$

$10^4 = \frac{1}{H+}$

$H+ = 10^{-4}$ or 0.0001 gram atoms per liter

51. $\qquad y = 2x$ **52.** $11^{\sqrt{5}} \cdot 11^{\sqrt{45}} = 11^{\sqrt{5}+\sqrt{45}}$

$\qquad 4096 = 2x \qquad\qquad\qquad\qquad = 11^{\sqrt{5}+3\sqrt{5}}$

$\log_2 4096 = x \qquad\qquad\qquad\qquad = 11^{4\sqrt{5}}$

$\qquad\quad 12 = x$

12 hours

53. $\frac{3x + 15}{9x + 45} = \frac{3(x + 5)}{9(x + 5)}$

$\qquad\qquad = \frac{1}{3}$

GCF: $x + 5$

54. $f(x) = -x^3 + x^2 - x + 1$

3 or 1 positive real zeros

$f(-x) = -(-x^3) + (-x)^2 - (-x) + 1$

$\qquad = x^3 + x^2 + x + 1$

0 negative real zeros

0 or 2 complex zeros

55. $36y^2 - 81x^2 = 2916$

$\qquad \frac{1}{2916}(36y^2 - 81x^2) = \frac{1}{2916}(2916)$

$\qquad\qquad \frac{y^2}{81} - \frac{x^2}{36} = 1$

vertices: $(0, \pm a) = (0, \pm 9)$

foci: $c^2 = a^2 + b^2$ $\quad$ asymptotes: $y = \pm\frac{a}{b}x$

$\qquad c^2 = 81 + 36 \qquad\qquad\qquad y = \pm\frac{3}{2}x$

$\qquad c^2 = 117$

$\qquad c = \pm 3\sqrt{13}$ $\qquad\qquad$ slopes: $\pm\frac{3}{2}$

$\qquad (0, \pm 3\sqrt{13})$

56. $x^2 - 18x - 120 = 0$

$a = 1, b = -18, c = -120$

sum of roots $= -\frac{b}{a}$ $\qquad$ product of roots $= \frac{c}{a}$

$\qquad\qquad = -\frac{(-18)}{1}$ $\qquad\qquad\qquad = \frac{-120}{1}$

$\qquad\qquad = 18$ $\qquad\qquad\qquad\qquad = -120$

57. $(3 - 7i)(3 + 7i) = 9 + 21i - 21i - 49i^2$

$\qquad\qquad\qquad\qquad = 9 + 49$

$\qquad\qquad\qquad\qquad = 58$

58. Let x = the ones' digit.

Let y = the tens' digit.

Let z = the hundreds' digit.

$x + y + z = 22 \qquad\qquad x + y + z = 22$

$\qquad y = z + 1 \qquad \Rightarrow \qquad y - z = 1$

$100x + 10y + z \qquad\qquad 99x - 99z = 297$

$= x + 10y + 100z + 297$

$x + y + z = 22 \qquad\qquad -99x - 198z = -2079$

$\underline{\quad -y + z = -1 \quad} \qquad\qquad \underline{\quad 99x - 99z = 297 \quad}$

$\quad x + 2z = 21 \qquad\qquad\qquad -297z = -1782$

$\qquad\qquad\qquad\qquad\qquad\qquad z = 6$

$y - z = 1 \qquad\qquad x + y + z = 22$

$y - 6 = 1 \qquad\qquad x + 7 + 6 = 22$

$\quad y = 7 \qquad\qquad\qquad x = 9$

The number is 679.

Properties of Logarithms

1. lower

2. The pH of neutral water is 7, so since $\log_{10}\left(\dfrac{1}{10^{-7}}\right) = 7$, there are 10^{-7} gram atoms of hydrogen ions in a liter of neutral water. Similarly, since $\log_{10}\left(\dfrac{1}{10^{-4.2}}\right) = 4.2$, there are $10^{-4.2}$ gram atoms of hydrogen ions in a liter of the acid rain. The ratio of acid rain to water is $\dfrac{10^{-4.2}}{10^{-7}}$ or about 630.

3. To prove this property, let $b^x = m$.

Then $\log_b m = x$.

$(b^x)^p = m^p$

$b^{xp} = m^p$ Power property of exponents

$\log_b b^{xp} = \log_b m^p$ Prop. of equal. for logs.

$xp = \log_b m^p$ Definition of inverse functions

$p \log_b m = \log_b m^p$ Substitution property

4. $\log_8 x^3 y = \log_8 x^3 + \log_8 y$
   $= 3 \log_8 x + \log_8 y$

5. $\log_5 (xy)^2 = 2 \log_5 xy$
   $= 2(\log_5 x + \log_5 y)$
   $= 2 \log_5 x + 2 \log_5 y$

6. $\log_4 \dfrac{ab}{c} = \log_4 ab - \log_4 c$
   $= \log_4 a + \log_4 b - \log_4 c$

7. $\log_2 rt^{\frac{1}{2}} = \log_2 r + \log_2 t^{\frac{1}{2}}$
   $= \log_2 r + \frac{1}{2} \log_2 t$

8. $8^{\log_8 3 + \log_8 2} = 8^{\log_8 (2 \times 3)}$
   $= 8^{\log_8 6}$
   $= 6$

9. $10^{4\log_{10} 2} = 10^{\log_{10} 2^4}$
   $= 10^{\log_{10} 16}$
   $= 16$

10. $9^{\log_9 12 - \log_9 4} = 9^{\log_9 \frac{12}{4}}$
    $= 9^{\log_9 3}$
    $= 3$

11. $\log_3 7 + \log_3 x = \log_3 14$
    $\log_3 7x = \log_3 14$
    $7x = 14$
    $x = 2$

12. $\log_2 10 - \log_2 t = \log_2 2$
    $\log_2 \dfrac{10}{t} = \log_2 2$
    $\dfrac{10}{t} = 2$
    $t = 5$

13. $\log_2 49 = \log_2 7^2$
    $= 2 \log_2 7$
    $= 2(2.807)$
    $= 5.614$

14. $\log_2 27 = \log_2 3^3$
    $= 3 \log_2 3$
    $= 3(1.585)$
    $= 4.755$

15. $\log_2 \dfrac{7}{3} = \log_2 7 - \log_2 3$
    $= 2.807 - 1.585$
    $= 1.222$

16. $\log_2 36 = \log_2 (2^2 \cdot 3^2)$
    $= \log_2 2^2 + \log_2 3^2$
    $= 2 \log_2 2 + 2 \log_2 3$
    $= 2(1) + 2(1.585)$
    $= 5.170$

17. $\log_2 0.75 = \log_2 \dfrac{3}{4}$
    $= \log_2 3 - \log_2 4$
    $= \log_2 3 - 2 \log_2 2$
    $= 1.585 - 2(1)$
    $= -0.415$

18. $\log_2 48 = \log_2 (2^4 \cdot 3)$
    $= \log_2 2^4 + \log_2 3$
    $= 4(1) + 1.585$
    $= 5.585$

19. $\log_2 108 = \log_2 (2^2 \cdot 3^3)$
    $= \log_2 2^2 + \log_2 3^3$
    $= 2 \log_2 2 + 3 \log_2 3$
    $= 2(1) + 3(1.585)$
    $= 6.755$

20. $\log_2 \dfrac{36}{49} = \log_2 36 - \log_2 49$
    $= \log_2 (2^2 \cdot 3^2) - \log_2 (7^2)$
    $= 2 \log_2 2 + 2 \log_2 3 - 2 \log_2 7$
    $= 2(1) + 2(1.585) - 2(2.807)$
    $= -0.444$

21. $\log_2 \dfrac{7}{16} = \log_2 7 = \log_2 16$
    $= \log_2 7 - \log_2 2^4$
    $= 2.807 - 4(1)$
    $= -1.193$

22. $\log_2 3 + \log_2 7 = \log_2 x$
    $\log_2 (3 \cdot 7) = \log_2 x$
    $3 \cdot 7 = x$
    $x = 21$

23. $\log_3 56 - \log_3 8 = \log_3 x$

$\log_3 \left(\dfrac{56}{8}\right) = \log_3 x$

$\dfrac{56}{8} = x$

$x = 7$

24. $\log_3 14 + \log_3 y = \log_3 42$

$14y = 42$

$y = 3$

25. $\log_9 x = \dfrac{1}{2} \log_9 144 - \dfrac{1}{3} \log_9 8$

$x = \dfrac{\sqrt{144}}{\sqrt[3]{8}}$

$x = \dfrac{12}{2}$

$x = 6$

26. $\log_{10} m = \dfrac{1}{2} \log_{10} 81$

$\log_{10} m = \log_{10} 81^{\frac{1}{2}}$

$m = 81^{\frac{1}{2}}$

$m = 9$

27. $\log_7 m = \dfrac{1}{3} \log_7 64 + \dfrac{1}{2} \log_7 121$

$m = (\sqrt[3]{64})(\sqrt{121})$

$m = 4 \cdot 11$

$m = 44$

28. $\log_{10} 7 + \log_{10} (n - 2) = \log_{10} 6n$

$7(n - 2) = 6n$

$7n - 14 = 6n$

$n = 14$

29. $3 \log_{10} x = \log_{10} 27$

$\log_{10} x^3 = \log_{10} 27$

$x^3 = 27$

$x = 3$

30. $\log_{10} (m + 3) - \log_{10} m = \log_{10} 4$

$\dfrac{m + 3}{m} = 4$

$4m = m + 3$

$m = 1$

31. $2 \log_3 x + \log_3 \dfrac{1}{10} = \log_3 5 + \log_3 2$

$x^2 \left(\dfrac{1}{10}\right) = 5 \cdot 2$

$\dfrac{1}{10} x^2 = 10$

$x = 10$

32. $3 \log_5 x - \log_5 4 = \log_5 16$

$\dfrac{x^3}{4} = 16$

$x = 4$

33. $\log_2 15 + \log_2 14 - \log_2 105 = \log_2 x$

$\dfrac{15 \cdot 14}{105} = x$

$2 = x$

34. $\log_{10} y + \log_{10} (y + 21) = 2$

$\log_{10} y(y + 21) = 2$

$y(y + 21) = 10^2$

$y^2 + 21y - 100 = 0$

$(y + 25)(y - 4) = 0$

$y = -25 \text{ or } y = 4$

Since log is not defined for negative numbers, -25 is not an acceptable solution.

35. $\log_4 (x + 3) + \log_4 (x - 3) = 2$

$\log_4 (x + 3)(x - 3) = 2$

$(x + 3)(x - 3) = 4^2$

$x^2 - 25 = 0$

$(x - 5)(x + 5) = 0$

$x = 5 \text{ or } x = -5$

Since log is not defined for negative numbers, -5 is not an acceptable solution.

36. $\log_2 (y + 2) - 1 = \log_2 (y - 2)$

$\log_2 (y + 2) - \log_2 (y - 2) = 1$

$\log_2 \left(\dfrac{y + 2}{y - 2}\right) = 1$

$\dfrac{y + 2}{y - 2} = 2^1$

$2y - 4 = y + 2$

$y = 6$

37. $\log_8 (m + 1) - \log_8 m = \log_8 4$

$\log_8 \dfrac{m + 1}{m} = \log_8 4$

$\dfrac{m + 1}{m} = 4$

$4m = m + 1$

$m = \dfrac{1}{3}$

38. $\log_n a = \log_n (y + 3) - \log_n 3$

$\log_n a = \log_n \dfrac{y + 3}{3}$

$a = \dfrac{y + 3}{3}$

$a = \dfrac{y}{3} + 1$

39. $\log_b 2a - \log_b x^3 = \log_b x$

$\log_b \dfrac{2a}{x^3} = \log_b x$

$\dfrac{20}{x^3} = x$

$a = \dfrac{x^4}{2}$

40. $\log_x a^2 + 5 \log_x y = \log_x a$

$\log_x a^2 y^5 = \log_x a$

$a^2 y^5 = a$

$a y^5 = 1$

$a = \dfrac{1}{y^5}$

41. $\log_b 4 + 2 \log_b a = 2 \log_b (n + 1)$

$\qquad \log_b 4a^2 = \log_b (n + 1)^2$

$\qquad \qquad 4a^2 = (n + 1)^2$

$\qquad \qquad a^2 = \frac{1}{4} (n + 1)^2$

$\qquad \qquad a = \frac{1}{2} (n + 1)$

42. Sample answer: Logarithms are undefined for base 1. If 1 were allowed, there would be multiple answers.

43. a. pH $= 6.1 + \log_{10} B - \log_{10} C$

b. a very weak base

c. pH $= 6.1 + \log_{10} 25 - \log_{10} 2$

$\qquad = 7.197$

44. $\log_{10} (3n) = \log_{10} (n + 2)$

$\qquad \quad 3n = n + 2$

$\qquad \quad n = 1$

45. Neither exist; the range of f is not a subset of the domain of g, and the range of g is not a subset of the domain of f.

46. $x = \dfrac{-(-8) \pm \sqrt{(-8)^2 - 4(1)(22)}}{2(1)}$

$\qquad = \dfrac{8 \pm \sqrt{-24}}{2}$

$\qquad = 4 \pm i\sqrt{6}$

47. $3pq + 3ps + q^2 - s^2 = 3p(q + s) + (q + s)(q - s)$

$\qquad \qquad \qquad \qquad = (3p + q - s)(q + s)$

48. $|x + 3| + |x - 3| > 8$

$x + 3 + x - 3 > 8$ or $-(x + 3) + -(x - 3) > 8$

$\qquad 2x > 8 \qquad \qquad -x - 3 - x + 3 > 8$

$\qquad x > 4 \qquad \qquad \qquad -2x > 8$

$\qquad \qquad \qquad \qquad \qquad \quad x < -4$

$\{x \mid x > 4 \text{ or } x < -4\}$

12-4 Common Logarithms

PAGE 565   CHECKING FOR UNDERSTANDING

1. raising 10 to this power: antilog $x = 10^x$

2. 10; common logarithms

3. logarithms of numbers $1 \leq x < 10$ (the mantissas)

4. 2

5. $5.73 = 573 \times 10^{-2}$

$\log 5.73 = \log (573 \times 10^{-2})$

$\qquad \quad = \log 573 + \log 10^{-2}$

$\qquad \quad = 2.7582 + (-2)$

$\qquad \quad = 0.7582$

6. $(-1.6383 + 10) - 10 = 8.3617 - 10$

mantissa: 0.3617

7. 2.3

8. 1.7300; 1   9. 2.9032; 2

10. 0.3522; 0   11. -1.2441; -2

12. 0.6357; 0   13. -0.5302; -1

14. 1.814   15. 167.8

16. 10.06   17. 0.5513

18. 0.0097   19. 0.0107

20. 0.0136   21. 0.1851

22. 84,000   23. 1.9925, 1, 0.9925

24. 1.1316, 1, 0.1316   25. 2.9156, 2, 0.9156

26. -7, -7, 0   27. 0.7345, 0, 0.7345

28. -0.5768, -1, 0.4232   29. -2.3010, -3, 0.6990

30. 3.8246, 3, 0.8246   31. 3, 3, 0

32. Since calculators use logarithms, finding $(-3)^3$ would proceed as follows.

$\qquad x = (-3)^3$

$\log x = \log [(-3)^3]$

$\log x = 3 \log (-3)$

Since the logarithm of -3 is undefined, the calculator sends an error message.

33. a. $10^{5.3}$ or about 199,526 times more intense

b. $10^{6.9-4.3} = 10^{2.6}$ or about 398 times stronger

34. $2 \log_6 3 + 3 \log_6 2 = \log_6 x$

$\qquad \log_6 3^2 + \log_6 2^3 = \log_6 x$

$\qquad \qquad \log_6 (9)(8) = \log_6 x$

$\qquad \qquad \qquad 72 = x$

35. $\dfrac{5}{x} = \dfrac{15}{-2}$

$\qquad 15x = -10$

$\qquad x = -\dfrac{2}{3}$

36. $f(x) = 2x^3 + 9x^2 - 20x - 75$

$p = \pm 1, \pm 3, \pm 5, \pm 15, \pm 25, \pm 75$

$q = \pm 1, \pm 2$

$\dfrac{p}{q}$	2	9	-20	-75
3	2	15	25	0

$2x^2 + 15x + 25 = 0$

$(2x + 5)(x + 5) = 0$

$2x + 5 = 0$ or $x + 5 = 0$

$\qquad x = -\dfrac{5}{2} \qquad \quad x = -5$

rational zeros: $3, -5, -\dfrac{5}{2}$

37. 2×2;

$\begin{vmatrix} 5 & 12 \\ 0 & -4 \end{vmatrix} = 5(-4) - (0)(12) = -20$

PAGE 566   MID-CHAPTER REVIEW

1. $12^5 = 12^{2x+1}$ 2. $3^{x+3} = \dfrac{1}{81}$

$\quad 5 = 2x + 1 \qquad \qquad \quad 3^{x+3} = (3)^{-4}$

$\quad 2 = x \qquad \qquad \qquad \quad x + 3 = -4$

$\qquad \qquad \qquad \qquad \qquad \qquad x = -7$

3. $5^{x^2-3} = 25^x$ **4.** $\log_{10} 100 = x$

$\quad 5^{x^2-3} = (5^2)^x$ $\quad 10^x = 100$

$\quad 5^{x^2-3} = 5^{2x}$ $\quad x = 2$

$\quad x^2 - 3 = 2x$ **5.** $\log_{36} 6 = x$

$x^2 - 2x - 3 = 0$ $\quad 36^x = 6$

$(x - 3)(x + 1) = 0$ $\quad x = \frac{1}{2}$

$(x - 3) = 0$ or $x + 1 = 0$

$\quad x = 3 \qquad x = -1$

6. $\log_5 \frac{1}{125} = x$

$\quad 5x = \frac{1}{125}$

$\quad x = -3$

7. $\log_6 8 + \log_6 3 = \log_6 x$

$\quad \log_6 (8)(3) = \log_6 x$

$\quad 24 = x$

8. $3 \log_2 x = \log_2 512$

$\quad \log_2 x^3 = \log_2 512$

$\quad x^3 = 512$

$\quad x = 8$

9. $\log_2 (9x + 5) - \log_2 (x^2 - 1) = 2$

$\quad \log_2 \frac{9x + 5}{x^2 - 1} = 2$

$\quad 2^2 = \frac{9x + 5}{x^2 - 1}$

$\quad 4(x^2 - 1) = 9x + 5$

$\quad 4x^2 - 9x - 9 = 0$

$\quad (4x + 3)(x - 3) = 0$

$\quad 4x + 3 = 0$ or $x - 3 = 0$

$\quad x = -\frac{3}{4} \qquad x = 3$

Since log is not defined for negative numbers, $-\frac{3}{4}$ is not an acceptable solution.

10. 2.3598   **11.** 0.8033

12. 0.0062   **13.** $10^{8.3-6.9} = 10^{1.4}$

or about 25 times more intense

12-5 Natural Logarithms

PAGE 569 CHECKING FOR UNDERSTANDING

1. the number e

2. $A = Pe^{rt}$

$\quad A = (1000)e^{(0.0725)(16)}$

$\quad A = 1000e^{1.16}$

$\ln A = \ln (1000e^{1.16})$

$\ln A = \ln 1000 + 1.16 \ln e$

$\ln A \approx 6.9078 + 1.16$

$\ln A \approx 8.0678$

$\quad A \approx 3189.93$ Sean has \$3189.93

3. Use natural logarithms when the base of an exponent to be simplified is e and common logarithms when the base is 10.

4. 0.9478   **5.** 1.454

6. 3.892   **7.** 1.530

8. 5.482   **9.** 0.4549

PAGES 569-570 EXERCISES

10. 2.246   **11.** 1.976

12. 0.3507   **13.** 1.598

14. 1   **15.** 9.290

16. 4.041   **17.** -0.6106

18. 4.174   **19.** 1

20. 35.16   **21.** 1.682

22. 1.334   **23.** 0.1866

24. 6.908

25. $\qquad 2000 = 5e^{0.045x}$

$\quad \ln 2000 = \ln 5 + \ln e^{0.045x}$

$\quad \ln 2000 = \ln 5 + 0.045x \ln e$

$\quad \frac{\ln 2000 - \ln 5}{0.045} = x$

$\quad 133.1 \approx x$

26. $2 = e^{5k}$ **27.** $\ln 3.6 = \ln (e^{0.031t})$

$\ln 2 = 5k \ln e$ $\ln 3.6 = 0.031t \ln e$

$\frac{\ln 2}{5} = k$ $\frac{\ln 3.6}{0.031} = t$

$0.1386 \approx k$ $41.32 \approx t$

28. $65 = e^{6n}$ **29.** $25 = e^{0.075y}$

$\ln 65 = 6n \ln e$ $\ln 25 = 0.075y \ln e$

$\frac{\ln 65}{6} = n$ $\frac{\ln 25}{0.075} = y$

$0.6957 \approx n$ $42.92 \approx y$

30. $\ln 40.5 = \ln (e^{0.21t})$

$\ln 40.5 = 0.21t \ln e$

$\frac{\ln 40.5}{0.21} = t$

$17.63 \approx t$

31. $1 + \frac{1}{1} + \frac{1}{1\cdot 2} + \frac{1}{1\cdot 2\cdot 3} + \frac{1}{1\cdot 2\cdot 3\cdot 4} + \frac{1}{1\cdot 2\cdot 3\cdot 4\cdot 5}$

$\quad + \frac{1}{1\cdot 2\cdot 3\cdot 4\cdot 5\cdot 6} + \frac{1}{1\cdot 2\cdot 3\cdot 4\cdot 5\cdot 6\cdot 7}$

$= 1 + 1 + 0.5 + 0.166\overline{6} + 0.0416\overline{6} + 0.0083\overline{3}$

$\quad + 0.0013\overline{8} + 0.00020$

$= 2.7183$

32. a. $A = Pe^{rt}$

$\quad A = (500)e^{(0.065)(7)}$

$\ln A = \ln 500 + 0.455 \ln e$

$\ln A \approx 6.2146 + 0.455$

$\ln A \approx 6.6696$

$\quad A \approx 788.09$

Mr. and Mrs. Gauser's investment is \$788.09.

b. $3P = Pe^{rt}$

$\quad 3(500) = 500e^{0.065t}$

$\quad \ln 1500 = \ln 500 + 0.065t \ln e$

$\quad \frac{\ln 1500 - \ln 500}{0.065} = t$

$\quad 16.9 \approx t$

It will triple in 16.9 years.

33. a.
$$y = ne^{kt}$$
$$50 = (100)e^{k(1800)}$$
$$\ln 50 = \ln 100 + 1800k \ln e$$
$$\frac{\ln 50 - \ln 100}{1800} = k$$
$$-0.000385 \approx k$$

b.
$$y = 1e^{(-0.000385)(10,000)}$$
$$y = e^{-3.85}$$
$$\ln y = -3.85 \ln e$$
$$\ln y = -3.85$$
$$y = 0.0213$$

approximately 0.0213 grams

34. $\log 349.948 = 2.5440$

2; 0.5440

35. $\dfrac{3}{x-2} + \dfrac{2}{x-3} = \dfrac{3(x-3)}{(x-2)(x-3)} + \dfrac{2(x-2)}{(x-3)(x-2)}$

$$= \frac{3x - 9 + 2x - 4}{(x-2)(x-3)}$$
$$= \frac{5x - 13}{(x-2)(x-3)}$$

36. $2y^2 = 10 - x^2 \qquad 2(3x^2 - 9) = 10 - x^2$

$3x^2 - 9 = y^2 \;\Rightarrow\; 6x^2 - 18 = 10 - x^2$

$$7x^2 - 28 = 0$$
$$7(x^2 - 4) = 0$$
$$(x - 2)(x + 2) = 0$$
$$x - 2 = 0 \text{ or } x + 2 = 0$$
$$x = 2 \qquad x = -2$$

$3(2)^2 - 9 = y^2 \qquad 3(-2)^2 - 9 = y^2$

$3 = y^2 \qquad\qquad 3 = y^2$

$\pm\sqrt{3} = y \qquad\qquad \pm\sqrt{3} = y$

$(2, \pm\sqrt{3}), (-2, \pm\sqrt{3})$

37.
$$x^2 \le 36$$
$$x^2 - 36 \le 0$$
$$(x - 6)(x + 6) \le 0$$

$x - 6 \le 0$ and $x + 6 \ge 0$ or $x - 6 \ge 0$ and $x + 6 \le 0$

$x \le 6$ and $\quad x \ge -6$ or $\quad x \ge 6$ and $\quad x \le -6$

$-6x \le x \le 6 \qquad\qquad$ never true

$\{x \mid -6 \le x \le 6\}$

38. Let s = the cost of the sofa.

Let ℓ = the cost of the love seat.

Let c = the cost of the coffee table.

$s + \ell + c = 1230$	$s + \ell + c = 1230$
$s = 2\ell$	$\underline{-s \qquad - c = 880}$
$s + c = 880$	$\ell \qquad = 350$

$s = 2\ell \qquad\qquad s + \ell + c = 1230$

$s = 2(350) \qquad 700 + 350 + c = 1230$

$s = 700 \qquad\qquad c = 180$

sofa - \$700, love seat - \$350,

coffee table - \$180

Problem-Solving Strategy: Using Estimation

PAGE 572   CHECKING FOR UNDERSTANDING

1. Answers may vary. Sample answers are adding prices of items at a store and figuring amounts of wallpaper or paint needed for a room.

2. To estimate an answer before performing the calculations so that you can check the reasonableness of a solution.

3. Sample answers: computation errors, wrong procedures, or a mis-key on the calculator

4. estimate: more than 9^2 or 81 sq. in.

   actual area: $(9.39)^2 = 88.1721$ sq. in.

5. **a.** Estimate the perimeter of the room to be 40 ft. Multiply by 8: 320 sq. ft. Four rolls of wallpaper will cover 300 sq. ft. So, 5 rolls are needed.

   b. area of walls: $2(9 + 12) \times 8 = 336$ sq. ft.

   $336 \div 75 = 4.48$ rolls

   c. Yes, since she can't buy 4.48 rolls, she must buy 5.

PAGE 573   EXERCISES

6. $F = C \qquad\qquad F = \dfrac{9}{5}F + 32$

   $F = \dfrac{9}{5}C + 32 \;\Rightarrow\; -\dfrac{4}{5}F = 32$

   $\qquad\qquad\qquad F = -40$

   At $-40°$, the readings are the same.

7. Grandfather, father, and son each receive \$7.

8.

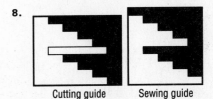

Cutting guide   Sewing guide

9. alphabetical order;

   8, 5, 4, 9, 1, 7, 6, 3, 2, 0

10. Make a table. Use a calculator.

    Rate for each quarter = 8.79% + 4 or 2.1975.

    Interest = previous balance × 0.021975

Quarter	Previous Balance	Interest	Total
1	\$1800	\$39.56	\$1839.56
2	\$1839.56	\$40.42	\$1879.98
3	\$1879.98	\$41.31	\$1921.29
4	\$1921.29	\$42.22	\$1963.51
5	\$1963.51	\$43.15	\$2006.66
6	\$2006.66	\$44.10	\$2050.76

The total interest is \$250.76 or about \$250.

11. Answers will vary.

Sample answers are shown.

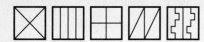

12. Let w = thousands' digit.

Let x = hundreds' digit.

Let y = tens' digit.

Let z = ones' digit.

$w + x + y + z = 23$

$x = y + 3$

$w = 1$, because the year must be between 1000 and 2000 AD.

$x = 9$, because the year must be at least 1800, and $x \neq 8$.

$x = y + 3$	$w + x + y + z = 23$
$9 = y + 3$	$1 + 9 + 6 + z = 23$
$6 = y$	$z = 7$

The year was 1967.

PAGE 573   COOPERATIVE LEARNING ACTIVITY

Some are $\frac{385}{682}$, $\frac{275}{374}$, and $\frac{572}{671}$. The sums of the ones and tens digits of the numerator and denominator of the reduced fraction are equal or less than 10. The fraction to be simplified is the original fraction multiplied by $\frac{11}{11}$. For example, for $\frac{14}{23}$:

$$1 + 4 = 5$$

$$2 + 3 = 5 \text{ and } 5 < 10$$

$$\frac{14}{23} \times \frac{11}{11} = \frac{154}{253}$$

12-7 Exponential Equations

PAGE 576   CHECKING FOR UNDERSTANDING

1. no; An exponential equation uses a variable as the exponent.

2. when finding logarithms of different bases on the calculator

3. yes

4. $6^x = 72$

$\log 6^x = \log 72$

$x \log 6 = \log 72$

$x = \dfrac{\log 72}{\log 6}$

$x \approx 2.3869$

5. $8^x = 100$

$\log 8^x = \log 100$

$x \log 8 = \log 100$

$x = \dfrac{\log 100}{\log 8}$

$x \approx 2.2146$

6. $9^{2x} = 144$

$\log 9^{2x} = \log 144$

$2x \log 9 = \log 144$

$x = \dfrac{\log 144}{2 \log 9}$

$x \approx 1.1309$

7. $x = \log_4 169$

$x = \dfrac{\log 169}{\log 4}$

$x \approx 3.7004$

8. $x = \log_6 90$

$x = \dfrac{\log 90}{\log 6}$

$x \approx 2.5114$

9. $3^x = \sqrt{34}$

$\log 3^x = \log \sqrt{34}$

$x \log 3 = \dfrac{1}{2} \log 34$

$x = \dfrac{\log 34}{2 \log 3}$

$x \approx 1.6049$

10. $2^x = 5\sqrt{2}$

$\log 2^x = \log 5\sqrt{2}$

$x \log 2 = \log 5 + \dfrac{1}{2} \log 2$

$x = \dfrac{\log 5}{\log 2} + \dfrac{1}{2}$

$x \approx 2.8219$

11. $3^{-x} = 22$

$\log 3^{-x} = \log 22$

$-x \log 3 = \log 22$

$x = \dfrac{-\log 22}{\log 3}$

$x \approx -2.8136$

12. $2^{-x} = \sqrt{7}$

$\log 2^{-x} = \log \sqrt{7}$

$-x \log 2 = \dfrac{1}{2} \log 7$

$x = -\dfrac{\log 7}{2 \log 2}$

$x \approx -1.4037$

PAGES 576-578   EXERCISES

13. $\log_5 15 = \dfrac{\log 15}{\log 5}$

≈ 1.683

14. $\log_8 72 = \dfrac{\log 72}{\log 8}$

≈ 2.057

15. $\log_{12} 169 = \dfrac{\log 169}{\log 12}$

≈ 2.064

16. $\log_4 100 = \dfrac{\log 100}{\log 4}$

≈ 3.322

17. $\log_{12} 15 = \dfrac{\log 15}{\log 12}$

≈ 1.090

18. $\log_2 36 = \dfrac{\log 36}{\log 2}$

≈ 5.170

19. $\log_{15} 5 = \dfrac{\log 5}{\log 15}$

≈ 0.594

20. $\log_9 108 = \dfrac{\log 108}{\log 9}$

≈ 2.131

21. $\log_{11} 104 = \dfrac{\log 104}{\log 11}$

≈ 1.937

22. $8^x = 45$

$\log 8^x = \log 45$

$x \log 8 = \log 45$

$x = \dfrac{\log 45}{\log 8}$

≈ 1.8306

23. $2^x = 27$

$x \log 2 = \log 27$

$x = \dfrac{\log 27}{\log 2}$

≈ 4.7549

24. $2.1^{x-5} = 9.32$

$(x - 5) \log 2.1 = \log 9.32$

$x = \dfrac{\log 9.32}{\log 2.1} + 5$

≈ 8.0086

25. $7.6^{a-2} = 41.7$

$(a - 2) \log 7.6 = \log 41.7$

$a = \dfrac{\log 41.7}{\log 7.6} + 2$

≈ 3.8394

26. $5^{x+2} = 15.3$

$(x + 2) \log 5 = \log 15.3$

$x = \dfrac{\log 15.3}{\log 5} - 2$

≈ -0.3051

27. $x = \log_4 51.6$

$= \dfrac{\log 51.6}{\log 4}$

≈ 2.8446

28. $9^{x-4} = 6.28$

$(x - 4) \log 9 = \log 6.28$

$x = \dfrac{\log 6.28}{\log 9} + 4$

≈ 4.8362

29. $x = \log_{20} 1000$

$= \dfrac{\log 1000}{\log 20}$

≈ 2.3059

30. $25^{x^2} = 50$

$x^2 \log 25 = \log 50$

$x^2 = \dfrac{\log 50}{\log 25}$

$x = \pm\sqrt{\dfrac{\log 50}{\log 25}}$

$\approx \pm 1.1024$

31. $6^{x^2} - 2 = 48$

$(x^2 - 2) \log 6 = \log 48$

$x^2 = \dfrac{\log 48}{\log 6} + 2$

$x = \pm\sqrt{\dfrac{\log 48}{\log 6} + 2}$

$\approx \pm 2.0397$

32. $4.3^{3x+1} = 78.5$

$(3x + 1) \log 4.3 = \log 78.5$

$3x = \dfrac{\log 78.5}{\log 4.3} - 1$

$x = \dfrac{1}{3}\left(\dfrac{\log 78.5}{\log 4.3} - 1\right)$

$= 0.6638$

33. $2.7^{x^2-1} = 52.3$

$(x^2 - 1) \log 2.7 = \log 52.3$

$x^2 = \dfrac{\log 52.3}{\log 2.7} + 1$

$x = \pm\sqrt{\dfrac{\log 52.3}{\log 2.7} + 1}$

$\approx \pm 2.2325$

34. $5^{x-1} = 3^x$

$\log 5^{x-1} = \log 3^x$

$(x - 1) \log 5 = x \log 3$

$x \log 5 - \log 5 = x \log 3$

$x \log 5 - x \log 3 = \log 5$

$x(\log 5 - \log 3) = \log 5$

$x = \dfrac{\log 5}{\log 5 - \log 3}$

≈ 3.1507

35. $12^{x-4} = 4^{2-x}$

$(x - 4) \log 12 = (2 - x) \log 4$

$x \log 12 - 4 \log 12 = 2 \log 4 - x \log 4$

$x(\log 12 + \log 4) = 2 \log 4 + 4 \log 12$

$x = \dfrac{2 \log 4 + 4 \log 12}{\log 12 + \log 4}$

≈ 3.2838

36. $7^{x-2} = 5^x$

$(x - 2) \log 7 = x \log 5$

$x \log 7 - 2 \log 7 = x \log 5$

$x(\log 7 - \log 5) = 2 \log 7$

$x = \dfrac{2 \log 7}{\log 7 - \log 5}$

≈ 11.5665

37. $5^{2x} = 9^{x-1}$

$2x \log 5 = (x - 1) \log 9$

$2x \log 5 = x \log 9 - \log 9$

$x(2 \log 5 - \log 9) = -\log 9$

$x = \dfrac{\log 9}{\log 9 - 2 \log 5}$

≈ -2.1507

38. $2^{2x+3} = 3^{3x}$

$(2x + 3) \log 2 = 3x \log 3$

$2x \log 2 + 3 \log 2 = 3x \log 3$

$2x \log 2 - 3x \log 3 = -3 \log 2$

$x(2 \log 2 - 3 \log 3) = -3 \log 2$

$x = \dfrac{-3 \log 2}{2 \log 2 - 3 \log 3}$

≈ 1.0890

39. $2^{3y} = 3^{y} + 1$

$3y \log 2 = (y + 1) \log 3$

$3y \log 2 = y \log 3 + \log 3$

$3y \log 2 - y \log 3 = \log 3$

$y(3 \log 2 - \log 3) = \log 3$

$y = \dfrac{\log 3}{3 \log 2 - \log 3}$

≈ 1.1201

40. $2^{5x-1} = 3^{2x+1}$

$(5x - 1) \log 2 = (2x + 1) \log 3$

$5x \log 2 - \log 2 = 2x \log 3 + \log 3$

$x(5 \log 2 - 2 \log 3) = \log 3 + \log 2$

$x = \dfrac{\log 3 + \log 2}{5 \log 2 - 2 \log 3}$

$x \approx 1.4125$

41.
$$4^{5y-6} = 3^{2y+5}$$
$$(5y - 6) \log 4 = (2y + 5) \log 3$$
$$5y \log 4 - 6 \log 4 = 2y \log 3 + 5 \log 3$$
$$y(5 \log 4 - 2 \log 3) = 5 \log 3 + 6 \log 4$$
$$y = \frac{5 \log 3 + 6 \log 4}{5 \log 4 - 2 \log 3}$$
$$y \approx 2.9172$$

42.
$$5^{4y+1} = 32^{2y}$$
$$(4y + 1) \log 5 = 2y \log 32$$
$$4y \log 5 + \log 5 = 2y \log 32$$
$$y(4 \log 5 - 2 \log 32) = -\log 5$$
$$y = \frac{-\log 5}{4 \log 5 - 2 \log 32}$$
$$\approx 3.2598$$

43.
$$24^{3x} = 6^{2x+1}$$
$$3x \log 24 = (2x + 1) \log 6$$
$$3x \log 24 = 2x \log 6 + \log 6$$
$$x(3 \log 24 - 2 \log 6) = \log 6$$
$$x = \frac{\log 6}{3 \log 24 - 2 \log 6}$$
$$\approx 0.3011$$

44.
$$2^n = \sqrt{3^{n-2}}$$
$$2^n = 3^{\frac{1}{2}(n-2)}$$
$$n \log 2 = \frac{1}{2}(n - 2) \log 3$$
$$n \log 2 = \frac{1}{2}n \log 3 - \log 3$$
$$n\left(\log 2 - \frac{1}{2} \log 3\right) = -\log 3$$
$$n = \frac{-\log 3}{\log 2 - \frac{1}{2} \log 3}$$
$$\approx -7.6377$$

45.
$$6^{x-2} = \sqrt[3]{4^{x-1}}$$
$$6^{x-2} = 4^{\frac{1}{3}(x-1)}$$
$$(x - 2) \log 6 = \frac{1}{3}(x - 1) \log 4$$
$$x \log 6 - 2 \log 6 = \frac{1}{3}x \log 4 - \frac{1}{3} \log 4$$
$$x\left(\log 6 - \frac{1}{3} \log 4\right) = 2 \log 6 - \frac{1}{3} \log 4$$
$$x = \frac{2 \log 6 - \frac{1}{3} \log 4}{\log 6 - \frac{1}{3} \log 4}$$
$$\approx \frac{1.3556}{0.5775}$$
$$\approx 2.3475$$

46.
$$x = \log_a n$$
$$a^x = a^{\log_a n}$$
$$a^x = n$$
$$\log_b a^x = \log_b n$$
$$x \log_b a = \log_b n$$
$$x = \frac{\log_b n}{\log_b a}$$

47.
$$A = P\left(1 + \frac{r}{n}\right)^{nt}$$
$$800 = 500\left(1 + \frac{0.0875}{12}\right)^{12t}$$
$$1.6 = (1.0073)^{12t}$$
$$\log 1.6 = 12t \log 1.0073$$
$$\frac{\log 1.6}{12 \log 1.0073} = t$$
$$5.38 \approx t$$
5.38 years = about 5 years, 5 months

48. a.
$$A = P\left(1 + \frac{r}{n}\right)^{nt}$$
$$2500 = 1250\left(1 + \frac{0.12}{12}\right)^{12t}$$
$$2 = (1.01)^{12t}$$
$$\log 2 = 12t \log 1.01$$
$$\frac{\log 2}{12 \log 1.01} = t$$
$$5.81 \approx t$$
5.81 years = about 5 years, 10 months

b.
$$2500 = 1500\left(1 + \frac{0.12}{12}\right)^{12t}$$
$$\frac{5}{3} = (1.01)^{12t}$$
$$\log \frac{5}{3} = 12t \log 1.01$$
$$\frac{\log 5 - \log 3}{12 \log 1.01} = t$$
$$4.28 = t$$
4.28 years = about 4 years, 3 months

49. a.
$$A = P\left(1 + \frac{r}{n}\right)^{nt}$$
$$A = 1000\left(1 + \frac{0.08}{4}\right)^{4(5)}$$
$$= 1000 (1.02)^{20}$$
$$= 1485.95$$
$$1485.95 - 1000 = 485.95$$
The company paid $485.95 into the account.

b.
$$A = 1000\left(1 + \frac{0.08}{4}\right)^{4(35)}$$
$$= 1000(1.02)^{140}$$
$$= 15,996.47$$
$$15,996.47 - 1000 = 14,996.47$$
The company paid $14,996.47 into the account.

50.
$$\ln 9.5 = \ln (e^{0.2x})$$
$$\ln 9.5 = 0.2x \ln e$$
$$\frac{\ln 9.5}{0.2} = x$$
$$11.26 = x$$

51.
$$f(x) = x^2 + 16x + 67$$
$$= (x^2 + 16x + 64) + 67 - 64$$
$$f(x) = (x + 8)^2 + 3$$
vertex: $(-8, 3)$
axis of sym: $x = -8$

52. $-5x^2 + x + 3 = 0$

$s_1 + s_2 = -\dfrac{a}{b}$

$\quad = -\dfrac{1}{-5}$

$\quad = \dfrac{1}{5}$

$s_1 s_2 = \dfrac{c}{a}$

$\quad = -\dfrac{3}{5}$

53. $T = 2\pi\sqrt{\dfrac{L}{32}}$

$\quad = 2\pi\sqrt{\dfrac{6}{32}}$

$\quad = 2.72$

A complete swing would take 2.72 seconds.

54. $\dfrac{-3w^6 t^7}{(-27w^3 t^2)(wt)^2} = \dfrac{-3w^6 t^7}{-27w^5 t^4}$

$\quad\quad = \dfrac{-3w^5 t^4 \cdot wt^3}{-3w^5 t^4 \cdot 9}$

$\quad\quad = \dfrac{wt^3}{9}$

55. domain: $\{-8, 0, 1, 9\}$

range: $\{-3, 0, 3\}$

Yes, it is a function because each element of the domain is paired with exactly one element of the range.

56. Let x = the number of games they must win.

$(0.60)(84) = 30 + x$

$50.4 = 30 + x$

$20.4 = x$

They must win at least 21 more games.

Technology: Compound Interest

PAGE 579   EXERCISES

1. Continue column B to cell B54.

2. Add a column C similar to column B.

12-8 Applications of Logarithms

PAGES 582-583   CHECKING FOR UNDERSTANDING

1. Answers may vary. Sample answers are bacteria growth and radioactive decay. If K is zero, the the population is not growing or decaying, the function is a constant function.

2. $V_n = P(1 + r)^n$, with $r = 0.15$.

3. a. Based on interest alone, you should choose the account at Lake County Savings.

b. Other factors may include service charges, minimum balances, other services available like loans and safety deposit boxes.

4.

$40 = 200\, e^{7k}$

$\ln 40 = \ln 200\, e^{7k}$

$\ln 40 = \ln 200 + 7k \ln e$

$\dfrac{\ln 40 - \ln 200}{7} = k$

$-0.2299 \approx k$

5. $50{,}000 = 25{,}000(1 + 0.1)^n$

$2 = 1.1^n$

$\log 2 = n \log 1.1$

$\dfrac{\log 2}{\log 1.1} = n$

$7.27 \approx n$

6.

$200 = 100\, e^{0.06t}$

$\ln 200 = \ln 100\, e^{0.06t}$

$\ln 200 = \ln 100 + 0.06t \ln e$

$\dfrac{\ln 200 - \ln 100}{0.06} = t$

$11.55 \approx t$

7. $2500 = 4\, e^{0.58t}$

$625 = e^{0.58t}$

$\ln 625 = 0.58t \ln e$

$\dfrac{\ln 625}{0.58} = t$

$11.1 \approx t$

PAGES 583-585   EXERCISES

8. $y = ne^{kt}$

$1000 = 2e^{0.775t}$

$500 = e^{0.775t}$

$\ln 500 = 0.775t \ln e$

$\dfrac{\ln 500}{0.775} = t$

$8.02 \approx t$

It will take 8.02 hours.

9. $A = Pe^{rt}$

$200 = 100e^{0.06t}$

$2 = e^{0.06t}$

$\ln 2 = 0.06t \ln e$

$\dfrac{\ln 2}{0.06} = t$

$11.55 \approx t$

11.55 years = about 11 years, 6 months

He opened the account about 11 years, 6 months ago.

10. $y = ne^{kt}$

$50 = 250e^{-0.08042t}$

$0.2 = e^{-0.08042t}$

$\ln 0.2 = -0.08042t \ln e$

$\dfrac{\ln 0.2}{-0.08042} = t$

$20.01 \approx t$

It will take about 20.01 years.

11.
$$y = ne^{kt}$$
$$4000 = 500e^{k(1.5)}$$
$$8 = e^{1.5k}$$
$$\ln 8 = 1.5k \ln e$$
$$\frac{\ln 8}{1.5} = k$$
$$1.3863 \approx k$$

12.
$$A = Pe^{rt}$$
$$1276 = 1000 \, e^{r(3)}$$
$$1.276 = e^{3r}$$
$$\ln 1.276 = 3r \ln e$$
$$\frac{\ln 1.276}{3} = r$$
$$0.0812 \approx r$$
The interest rate was 8.12%.

13.
$$V_n = P(1 + r)^n$$
$$5000 = 25,000 \, (1 - 0.1)^n$$
$$0.2 = 0.9^n$$
$$\log 0.2 = n \log 0.9$$
$$\frac{\log 0.2}{\log 0.9} = n$$
$$15.28 \approx n$$
In 15.28 years, it will be worth $5000.

14.
$$A = Pe^{rt}$$
$$2500 = 2000e^{0.0725t}$$
$$1.25 = e^{0.0725t}$$
$$\ln 1.25 = 0.0725t \ln e$$
$$\frac{\ln 1.25}{0.0725} = t$$
$$3.08 \approx t$$
Keith can buy the synthesizer in 3.08 years.

15. a.
$$A = Pe^{rt}$$
$$100 = 10e^{0.08t}$$
$$10 = e^{0.08t}$$
$$\ln 10 = 0.08t \ln e$$
$$\frac{\ln 10}{0.08} = t$$
$$28.78 \approx t$$
28.78 years

b.
$$1000 = 10e^{0.08t}$$
$$100 = e^{0.08t}$$
$$\ln 100 = 0.08t \ln e$$
$$\frac{\ln 100}{0.08} = t$$
$$57.56 \approx t$$
57.56 years

16.
$$V_n = P(1 + r)^n$$
$$V_n = 63,000 \, (1 + 0.08)^5$$
$$V_n \approx 92,568$$
$92,568

17.
$$V_n = P(1 + r)^n$$
$$600 = 6000(1 - r)^{10}$$
$$0.1 = (1 - r)^{10}$$
$$\log 0.1 = 10 \log (1 - r)$$
$$\frac{\log 0.1}{10} = \log (1 - r)$$
$$-0.1 = \log (1 - r)$$
$$\text{antilog} \, (-0.1) = 1 - r$$
$$0.2056 \approx r$$
Annual rate of depreciation was 20.56%.

18.
$$A = A_0 \times 10^{-0.024t}$$
$$0.5A_0 = A_0 \times 10^{-0.024t}$$
$$\frac{0.5A_0}{A_0} = 10^{-0.024t}$$
$$0.5 = 10^{-0.024t}$$
$$\log 0.5 = -0.024t \log 10$$
$$t = \frac{\log 0.5}{-0.024(1)}$$
$$t \approx 12.54$$
The half-life is 12.54 hours.

19.
$$V_n = P(1 + r)^n$$
$$1 = 500(1 - 0.10)^n$$
$$1 = 500(0.9)^n$$
$$0.002 = 0.9^n$$
$$\log 0.002 = n \log 0.9$$
$$n = \frac{\log 0.002}{\log 0.9}$$
$$n \approx 59$$
In 59 weeks, he will have less than $1.

20.
$$V_n = P(1 + r)^n$$
$$500 = 2500(1 - 0.1)^n$$
$$0.2 = 0.9^n$$
$$\log 0.2 = n \log 0.9$$
$$\frac{\log 0.2}{\log 0.9} = n$$
$$15.28 \approx n$$
The equipment will be replaced in 15.28 years.

21. Both equations find the final amount of something that is added to by the same rate over and over again.

22.
$$w = 50 \, e^{-0.004t}$$
$$20 = 50 \, e^{-0.004t}$$
$$0.4 = e^{-0.004t}$$
$$\ln 0.4 = -0.004t \ln e$$
$$\frac{\ln 0.4}{-0.004} = t$$
$$229.07 \approx t$$
The power output will be reduced in 229.07 days.

23.
$$y = ne^{kt}$$
$$50 = 100e^{k(1800)}$$
$$0.5 = e^{1800k}$$
$$\ln 0.5 = 1800k \ln e$$
$$\frac{\ln 0.5}{1800} = k$$
$$-0.000385 \approx k$$

24.
$$V_n = P(1 + r)^n$$
$$120,000 = 49,000(1 + r)^{10}$$
$$\log 120,000 = \log 49,000 + 10 \log (1 + r)$$
$$\log(1 + r) = \frac{\log 120,000 - \log 49,000}{10}$$
$$\log(1 + r) \approx \frac{5.0792 - 4.6902}{10}$$
$$\log(1 + r) \approx 0.0389$$
$$(1 + r) \approx \text{antilog } (0.0389)$$
$$1 + r \approx 1.0937$$
$$r \approx 0.0937$$
$$r \approx 9.37\%$$

25. 11

26. 16

27. 48

28. 60

29. 81

30. 157

31. 28

32. Joyce

33. $\log_7 12 = \dfrac{\log 12}{\log 7}$
$$\approx 1.277$$

34. $f(x) = 3x^4 - 5x^2 + 4$

p: ±1, ±2, ±4

q: ±1, ±3

$\dfrac{p}{q}$: ±1, ±2, ±4, ±$\dfrac{1}{3}$, ±$\dfrac{2}{3}$, ±$\dfrac{4}{3}$

35. $f(x) = (x + 9)^2$
$$= x^2 + 18x + 81$$

quadratic term: x^2

linear term: $18x$

constant term: 81

36. Let x = the amount added to length and width.
$$A = \ell w$$
$$5(4)(6) = (6 + x)(4 + x)$$
$$120 = 24 + 10x + x^2$$
$$x^2 + 10x - 96 = 0$$
$$(x + 16)(x - 6) = 0$$
$$x + 16 = 0 \quad \text{or} \quad x - 6 = 0$$
$$x = -16 \qquad x = 6$$
$$\ell = 6 + x = 6 + 6 = 12$$
$$w = 4 + x = 4 + 6 = 10$$

The new dimensions are 10 in. by 12 in.

37. $x = (11 \times 10^{-6})(70)(200)$
$$= 0.154$$

The change in the length of the bridge is 15.4 cm.

38. $3x + 1 < x + 5$
$$2x < 4$$
$$x < 2$$
$$\{x \mid x < 2\}$$

Chapter 12 Summary and Review

1. $3^{\sqrt{2}} \cdot 3^{\sqrt{2}} = 3^{\sqrt{2}+\sqrt{2}}$
$$= 3^{2\sqrt{2}}$$

2. $(9^{\sqrt{2}})^{\sqrt{2}} = 9^2$
$$= 81$$

3. $\dfrac{49^{\sqrt{2}}}{7^{\sqrt{12}}} = \dfrac{7^{2\sqrt{2}}}{7^{2\sqrt{3}}}$
$$= 7^{2\sqrt{2}-2\sqrt{3}}$$

4. $(x^{\sqrt{5}})^{\sqrt{20}} = x^{\sqrt{100}}$
$$= x^{10}$$

5. $2^{6x} = 4^{5x+2}$
$$2^{6x} = (2^2)^{5x+2}$$
$$6x = 10x + 4$$
$$x = -1$$

6. $(\sqrt{3})^{n+1} = 9^{n-1}$
$$(3)^{n+1} = (3^2)^{n-1}$$
$$\tfrac{1}{2}(n + 1) = 2(n - 1)$$
$$\tfrac{1}{2}n + \tfrac{1}{2} = 2n - 2$$
$$n = \frac{5}{3}$$

7. $49^{3p+1} = 7^{2p-5}$
$$(7^2)^{3p+1} = 7^{2p-5}$$
$$2(3p + 1) = 2p - 5$$
$$6p + 2 = 2p - 5$$
$$p = -\frac{7}{4}$$

8. $9^{x^2} = 27^{x^2-2}$
$$(3^2)^{x^2} = (3^3)^{x^2-2}$$
$$2x^2 = 3(x^2 - 2)$$
$$2x^2 = 3x^2 - 6$$
$$x^2 = 6$$
$$x = \pm\sqrt{6}$$

9. $\log_7 343 = 3$

10. $\log_5 \dfrac{1}{25} = -2$

11. $\log_4 1 = 0$

12. $\log_4 8 = \dfrac{3}{2}$

13. $4^3 = 64$

14. $8^{\frac{1}{3}} = 2$

15. $6^{-2} = \dfrac{1}{36}$

16. $6^0 = 1$

17. 7

18. 7

19. 3

20. 3

21. $\log_b 9 = 2$
$$b^2 = 9$$
$$b = 3$$

22. $\log_b 9 = \dfrac{1}{2}$
$$b^{\frac{1}{2}} = 9$$
$$b = 81$$

23. $\log_{16} 2 = x$
$$16^x = 2$$
$$2^{4x} = 2^1$$
$$4x = 1$$
$$x = \frac{1}{4}$$

24. $\log_4 x = -\dfrac{1}{2}$
$$4^{-\frac{1}{2}} = x$$
$$\frac{1}{\sqrt{4}} = x$$
$$x = \frac{1}{2}$$

25. $\log_6 12 = \log_6 (5x - 3)$
$$12 = 5x - 3$$
$$x = 3$$

26. $\log_4 (1 - 2x) = \log_4 (x + 10)$
$$1 - 2x = x + 10$$
$$x = -3$$

27. $\log_7 (x^2 + x) = \log_7 12$
$$x^2 + x = 12$$
$$x^2 + x - 12 = 0$$
$$(x + 4)(x - 3) = 0$$
$$x = -4 \text{ or } x = 3$$

28. $\log_2 (x - 1)^2 = \log_2 7$

$\qquad (x - 1)^2 = 7$

$\qquad x - 1 = \pm\sqrt{7}$

$\qquad x = 1 \pm \sqrt{7}$

29. $\log_9 28 = \log_9 7 + \log_9 4$

$\qquad = 0.8856 + 0.6309$

$\qquad = 1.5165$

30. $\log_9 49 = \log_9 7^2$

$\qquad = \log_9 7 + \log_9 7$

$\qquad = 0.8856 + 0.8856$

$\qquad = 1.7712$

31. $\log_9 144 = \log_9 (9 \cdot 16)$

$\qquad = \log_9 9 + \log_9 4^2$

$\qquad = \log_9 9 + \log_9 4 + \log_9 4$

$\qquad = 1 + 0.6309 + 0.6309$

$\qquad = 2.2618$

32. $\log_9 15.75 = \log_9 \dfrac{63}{4}$

$\qquad = \log_9 63 - \log_9 4$

$\qquad = \log_9 9 + \log_9 7 - \log_9 4$

$\qquad = 1 + 0.8856 - 0.6309$

$\qquad = 1.2547$

33. $\log_3 x - \log_3 4 = \log_3 12$

$\qquad \dfrac{x}{4} = 12$

$\qquad x = 48$

34. $\log_2 y = \dfrac{1}{3} \log_2 27$

$\qquad y = 27^{\frac{1}{3}}$

$\qquad y = 3$

35. $\log_5 7 + \dfrac{1}{2} \log_5 4 = \log_5 x$

$\qquad \log_5 (7 \cdot \sqrt{4}) = \log_5 x$

$\qquad 14 = x$

36. $2 \log_2 x - \log_2 (x + 3) = 2$

$\qquad \dfrac{x^2}{x + 3} = 2^2$

$\qquad x^2 = 4x + 12$

$\qquad x^2 - 4x - 12 = 0$

$\qquad (x - 6)(x + 2) = 0$

$\qquad x = 6 \text{ or } x = -2$

Since log is not defined for negative numbers, -2 is not an acceptable solution.

37. 1

38. 0.5587

39. -3

40. 0.9671

41. -2.5029

42. 4.6992

43. 0.0003609

44. 971.9

45. 0.8329

46. 2.2246

47. 7.21

48. 9.45

49. $2^x = 53$

$\qquad \log 2^x = \log 53$

$\qquad x \log 2 = \log 53$

$\qquad x = \dfrac{\log 53}{\log 2}$

$\qquad x \approx 5.7286$

50. $\log_4 11.2 = x$

$\qquad x = \dfrac{\log 11.2}{\log 4}$

$\qquad x \approx 1.7427$

51. $2.3^{x^2} = 66.6$

$\qquad x^2 \log 2.3 = \log 66.6$

$\qquad x^2 = \dfrac{\log 66.6}{\log 2.3}$

$\qquad x = \sqrt{\dfrac{\log 66.6}{\log 2.3}}$

$\qquad x \approx \pm2.2452$

52. $\qquad 3^{4x-7} = 4^{2x+3}$

$\qquad (4x - 7)\log 3 = (2x + 3)\log 4$

$\qquad 4x \log 3 - 7 \log 3 = 2x \log 4 + 3 \log 4$

$\qquad x(4 \log 3 - 2 \log 4) = 7 \log 3 + 3 \log 4$

$\qquad x = \dfrac{7 \log 3 + 3 \log 4}{4 \log 3 - 2 \log 4}$

$\qquad \approx \dfrac{5.1460}{0.7044}$

$\qquad \approx 7.3059$

53. $\qquad \sqrt{3^b} = 2^{b+1}$

$\qquad 3^{\frac{b}{2}} = 2^{b+1}$

$\qquad \dfrac{b}{2} \log 3 = (b + 1) \log 2$

$\qquad \dfrac{b}{2} \log 3 = b \log 2 + \log 2$

$\qquad b\left(\dfrac{1}{2} \log 3 - \log 2\right) = \log 2$

$\qquad b = \dfrac{\log 2}{\frac{1}{2} \log 3 - \log 2}$

$\qquad \approx -4.8188$

54. $\qquad 6^{3y} = 8^{y-3}$

$\qquad 3y \log 6 = (y - 3) \log 8$

$\qquad 3y \log 6 = y \log 8 - 3 \log 8$

$\qquad y(3 \log 6 - \log 8) = -3 \log 8$

$\qquad y = \dfrac{-3 \log 8}{3 \log 6 - \log 8}$

$\qquad \approx -1.8928$

55. $\qquad 300 = 20e^{5t}$

$\qquad 15 = e^{5t}$

$\qquad \ln 15 = 5t \ln e$

$\qquad \dfrac{\ln 15}{5} = t$

$\qquad 0.5416 \approx t$

56. $\qquad 500 = P(1 + 0.2)^5$

$\qquad \log 500 = \log P + 5 \log 1.2$

$\qquad \log 500 - 5 \log 1.2 = \log P$

$\qquad 2.3031 \approx \log P$

$\qquad \text{antilog } 2.3031 \approx P$

$\qquad 200.9388 \approx P$

57.
$$V = P(1 + r)^n$$
$$1000 = 14,000(1 - 0.18)^n$$
$$\frac{1}{14} = 0.82^n$$
$$\log 1 - \log 14 = n \log 0.82$$
$$\frac{\log 1 - \log 14}{\log 0.82} = n$$
$$13.30 \approx n$$

The car will depreciate to $1000 in 13.30 years.

58.
$$y = ne^{kt}$$
$$738 = 9\,e^{0.872t}$$
$$82 = e^{0.872t}$$
$$\ln 82 = 0.872t \ln e$$
$$\frac{\ln 82}{0.872} = t$$
$$5.05 \approx t$$

It will take 5.05 days.

59.
$$A = Pe^{rt}$$
$$300 = 200\,e^{0.06t}$$
$$1.5 = e^{0.06t}$$
$$\ln 1.5 = 0.06t \ln e$$
$$\frac{\ln 1.5}{0.06} = t$$
$$6.76 \approx t$$

It will be worth $300 in 6.76 years.

60.
$$y = ne^{kt}$$
$$5000 = 400\,e^{k(2)}$$
$$12.5 = e^{2k}$$
$$\ln 12.5 = 2k \ln e$$
$$\frac{\ln 12.5}{2} = k$$
$$1.2629 \approx k$$

Chapter 12 Test

PAGE 589

1. $\log_6 1296 = 4$

2. $\log_3 2187 = 7$

3. $5^4 = 625$

4. $8^{\frac{4}{3}} = 16$

5. 2

6. 3

7. 1.6

8.
$$9^x = 3^{3x-2}$$
$$3^{2x} = 3^{3x-2}$$
$$2x = 3x - 2$$
$$2 = x$$

9.
$$27^{2p+1} = 3^{4p-1}$$
$$(3^3)^{2p+1} = 3^{4p-1}$$
$$6p + 3 = 4p - 1$$
$$2p = -4$$
$$p = -2$$

10.
$$\log_m 144 = -2$$
$$m^{-2} = 144$$
$$m = \frac{1}{12}$$

11.
$$\log_2 128 = y$$
$$2^y = 128$$
$$2^y = 2^7$$
$$y = 7$$

12.
$$\log_3 x - 2 \log_3 2 = 3 \log_3 3$$
$$\frac{x}{2^2} = 3^3$$
$$x = 108$$

13.
$$\log_{\sqrt{7}} x = 4$$
$$\sqrt{7}^4 = x$$
$$49 = x$$

14.
$$\log_5 (8r - 7) = \log_5 (r^2 + 5)$$
$$8r - 7 = r^2 + 5$$
$$r^2 - 8r + 12 = 0$$
$$(r - 6)(r - 2) = 0$$
$$r = 6 \text{ or } r = 2$$

15.
$$\log_9 (x + 4) + \log_9 (x - 4) = 1$$
$$\log_9 (x + 4)(x - 4) = 1$$
$$(x + 4)(x - 4) = 9^1$$
$$x^2 - 25 = 0$$
$$(x - 5)(x + 5) = 0$$
$$x = 5 \text{ or } x = -5$$

Since log is not defined for negative numbers, -5 is not an acceptable solution.

16.
$$\log_4 21 = \log_4 (7 \cdot 3)$$
$$= \log_4 7 + \log_4 3$$
$$= 1.4037 + 0.7925$$
$$= 2.1962$$

17.
$$\log_4 9 = \log_4 3^2$$
$$= 2 \log_4 3$$
$$= 2(0.7925)$$
$$= 1.585$$

18.
$$\log_4 36 = \log_4 (9 \cdot 4)$$
$$= \log_4 3^2 + \log_4 4$$
$$= 2(0.7925) + 1$$
$$= 2.585$$

19.
$$\log_4 \frac{7}{12} = \log_4 7 - \log_4 (3 \cdot 4)$$
$$= \log_4 7 - (\log_4 3 + \log_4 4)$$
$$= 1.4037 - (0.7925 + 1)$$
$$= -0.3888$$

20. 5.8859

21. 0.7284 - 3

22. 2.2618

23. 0.006841

24. 2,156,000

25. 1.5001

26.
$$7.6^{x-1} = 431$$
$$(x - 1) \log 7.6 = \log 431$$
$$x \log 7.6 - \log 7.6 = \log 431$$
$$x \log 7.6 = \log 431 + \log 7.6$$
$$x = \frac{\log 431 + \log 7.6}{\log 7.6}$$
$$x \approx 3.9910$$

27.
$$\log_4 37 = x$$
$$x = \frac{\log 37}{\log 4}$$
$$\approx 2.6047$$

28.
$$3^x = 5^{x-1}$$
$$x \log 3 = (x - 1) \log 5$$
$$x \log 3 = x \log 5 - \log 5$$
$$x(\log 3 - \log 5) = -\log 5$$
$$x = \frac{\log 5}{\log 5 - \log 3}$$
$$\approx 3.1507$$

29.

$$\sqrt{2^{b-4}} = 6^b$$

$$2^{\frac{b-4}{2}} = 6^b$$

$$\left(\frac{1}{2}b - 2\right) \log 2 = b \log 6$$

$$\frac{1}{2}b \log 2 - 2 \log 2 = b \log 6$$

$$b\left(\frac{1}{2} \log 2 - \log 6\right) = 2 \log 2$$

$$b = \frac{2 \log 2}{\frac{1}{2}\log 2 - \log 6}$$

$$\approx -0.9592$$

30.

$$4^{2x-3} = 9^{x+2}$$

$$(2x - 3) \log 4 = (x + 2) \log 9$$

$$2x \log 4 - 3 \log 4 = x \log 9 + 2 \log 9$$

$$x(2 \log 4 - \log 9) = 3 \log 4 + 2 \log 9$$

$$x = \frac{3 \log 4 + 2 \log 9}{2 \log 4 - \log 9}$$

$$\approx 14.8659$$

31.

$$45.9 = e^{0.75t}$$

$$\ln 45.9 = 0.75t \ln e$$

$$\frac{\ln 45.9}{0.75} = t$$

$$5.102 \approx t$$

32.

$$A = Pe^{rt}$$

$$75{,}000 = 10e^{0.04t}$$

$$7500 = e^{0.04t}$$

$$\ln 7500 = 0.04t \ln e$$

$$\frac{\ln 7500}{0.04} = t$$

$$223 \approx t$$

The account was started about 223 years ago.

33.

$$y = ne^{kt}$$

$$4000 = 500e^{k(1.5)}$$

$$8 = e^{1.5k}$$

$$\ln 8 = 1.5k \ln e$$

$$\frac{\ln 8}{1.5} = k$$

$$1.3863 \approx k$$

PAGE 589   BONUS

$$\log x^2 = (\log x)^2$$

$$2 \log x = (\log x)^2$$

$$(\log x)^2 - 2 \log x = 0$$

$$\log x(\log x - 2) = 0$$

$$\log x = 0 \quad \text{or} \quad \log x - 2 = 0$$

$$x = 1 \qquad\qquad \log x = 2$$

$$x = 100$$

Chapter 12
College Entrance Exam Preview

PAGES 590–591

1. $\dfrac{x}{y} = z$ $\qquad$ $\dfrac{x}{y} = y$

$\quad y = z$ $\qquad\quad x = y^2$

$\qquad\qquad\qquad \pm\sqrt{x} = y$

The correct choice is C.

2. $\dfrac{x + y}{2} = \dfrac{x + y + z}{3}$

$\quad 3x + 3y = 2x + 2y + 2z$

$\qquad x + y = 2z$

$\qquad \dfrac{x + y}{2} = z$

The correct choice is C.

3. Let x = the number.

$$x(2b) + y = p$$

$$2xb = p - y$$

$$x = \frac{p - y}{2b}, \; b \neq 0$$

The correct choice is C.

4. $\dfrac{1}{p} = \sqrt{0.25} = \dfrac{1}{4}$

$\dfrac{1}{p} = \dfrac{1}{\sqrt{4}}$

$p = \sqrt{4}$

$p^2 = 4$

The correct choice is B.

5. Note that $\sqrt{3} > 1$ and $\sqrt{3} < 3$. If $\sqrt{3} > 1$, then

$3\sqrt{3} > 3$ and $\dfrac{1}{3\sqrt{3}} < \dfrac{1}{3}$. $\dfrac{\sqrt{3}}{3} = \dfrac{1}{\sqrt{3}}$ and since

$\sqrt{3} < 3$, $\dfrac{1}{\sqrt{3}} > \dfrac{1}{3}$. Clearly $\dfrac{1}{\sqrt{3}} < \sqrt{3}$ so we may

order the given numbers as $\dfrac{1}{3\sqrt{3}} < \dfrac{1}{3} < \dfrac{1}{\sqrt{3}} < \sqrt{3}$.

The correct choice is D.

6. $\dfrac{a + b}{a} = \dfrac{5}{4}$

$1 + \dfrac{b}{a} = \dfrac{5}{4}$

$\qquad \dfrac{b}{a} = \dfrac{1}{4}$

The correct choice is A.

7. $65.9 \approx 66$ and $0.49 \approx 0.5$

$$\frac{65.9 \times 0.49}{3.3} \approx \frac{66 \times 0.5}{3.3} = 10$$

The correct choice is A.

8. Before finding the reciprocal, simplify.

$$\frac{b}{5 - 1} + \frac{3}{b} = \frac{5b + 3(b - 1)}{b(b - 1)}$$

$$= \frac{8b - 3}{b^2 - 1}$$

The reciprocal is $\dfrac{b^2 - 1}{8b - 3}$.

The correct choice is C.

9. $1 + \dfrac{1}{b} = 1 \cdot \dfrac{b}{1} = b.$

$\dfrac{b}{\frac{1}{b}} = b \cdot b = b^2$

The correct choice is D.

10. $4b - 3a = 0$ $\qquad$ $\dfrac{16b^2}{a^2} = \dfrac{9a^2}{a^2}$

$ 4b = 3a$ $\qquad\qquad = 9$

$ 16b^2 = 9a^2$

The correct choice is B.

11. $xyz = 8$ $\qquad$ $xy^2 = 8$

$ y = z \longrightarrow x = \dfrac{8}{y^2}$

The correct choice is B.

12. $\dfrac{2b}{5a} = 12$ $\qquad$ $\dfrac{2b - 10a}{5a} = \dfrac{60a - 10a}{5a}$

$\phantom{\dfrac{2b}{5a}} 2b = 60a$ $\qquad\qquad = 10$

The correct choice is B.

13. $\dfrac{x}{6} + 4 = 1$

$ \dfrac{x}{6} = -3$

$ \dfrac{x}{3} = -6$

The correct choice is C.

14. $3 + \dfrac{d}{4} = 8\dfrac{1}{2} = \dfrac{17}{2}$

$ 12 + d = 34$

$ d = 22$

The correct choice is D.

15. Betty's Rate: $rt = d$ $\qquad$ Ted's rate: $rt = d$

$ r_1 x = 1$ $\qquad\qquad r_2 y = 1$

$ r_1 = \dfrac{1}{x}$ $\qquad\qquad r_2 = \dfrac{1}{y}$

Working together: $rt = d$

$\left(\dfrac{1}{x} + \dfrac{1}{y}\right) t = 1$

$\dfrac{y + x}{xy} t = 1$

$t = \dfrac{xy}{x + y}$

The correct choice is C.

16. The number of cents in n weeks: nc

Convert to dollars: $\dfrac{nc}{100}$

The correct choice is C.

17. $\dfrac{a}{b} = c$

$\log \dfrac{a}{b} = \log c$

$\log a - \log b = \log c$

The correct choice is B.

18. $\sqrt{(-3)^2}$: $(-3)^2$ is a positive number. The square root of a positive number is a real number.

$\sqrt[3]{(-3)^3}$: $(-3)^3$ is a negative number. The cube root of a negative number is a real number.

$\sqrt{-(3)^2}$: $-(3)^2$ is a negative number. The square root of a negative number is an imaginary number.

The correct choice is C.

19. $(5\sqrt{3})^2 = 5^2 (\sqrt{3})^2$

$\phantom{(5\sqrt{3})^2} = 25(3)$

$\phantom{(5\sqrt{3})^2} = 75$

The correct choice is A.

20. If half his share is $12,000, his whole share is worth 2(12,000) or $24,000. If this is $\dfrac{1}{4}$ of the entire business, the entire business is worth 4(24,000) or $96,000.

The correct choice is C.

21. $\dfrac{2 \text{ miles}}{25 \text{ minutes}} \cdot \dfrac{60 \text{ minutes}}{1 \text{ hour}} = 4.8 \text{ mph}$

The correct choice is B.

22. $x^2 + y^2 = 15$ $\qquad\qquad (x + y)^2 = 35$

$(x + y)^2 = 35$ $\qquad\qquad x^2 + 2xy + y^2 = 35$

$\qquad\qquad\qquad\qquad (x^2 + y^2) + 2xy = 35$

$\qquad\qquad\qquad\qquad\qquad 15 + 2xy = 35$

$\qquad\qquad\qquad\qquad\qquad\qquad 2xy = 20$

$\qquad\qquad\qquad\qquad\qquad\qquad xy = 10$

The correct choice is B.

23. $(5y + 1) + 2 = 5y + 3$

The correct choice is B.

Chapter 13
Sequences and Series

13-1 | Problem-Solving Strategy: Look for a Pattern

PAGE 595   CHECKING FOR UNDERSTANDING

1. A group of ordered numbers in which each succeeding term is related to a previous term. (Answers will vary.)

2. Any mathematical operation or group of operations.

3. Leonardo Fibonacci

4. Some daisy centers have the ratio $\frac{34}{21}$. Sunflower heads have spirals of seeds which may have ratios of $\frac{21}{13}$, $\frac{34}{21}$, or $\frac{55}{34}$.

5. 1, 1, 2, 3, 5, 8, 13, 21, 34, 55, 89, 144, 233, 377, 610, 987, 1597, 2584, 4181, 6765

6. 15,624

PAGE 595   EXERCISES

7. $9^5 = 59,049$ and $10^5 = 100,000$. Therefore the factors are somewhere near this range.
   By guess-and-check, $\underline{n = 12}$.
   $12(12 - 1)(12 - 2)(12 - 3)(12 - 4)$
   $= 12 \cdot 11 \cdot 10 \cdot 9 \cdot 8$
   $= 95,040$

8. The first 50 natural numbers are 1, 2, 3,...50. A zero can be produced by any number ending in 0 or by any number ending in 5 which can be multiplied by an even number. In this set of numbers, these numbers would be 5, 10, 15, 20, 25, 30, 35, 40, 45, and 50. There are 10 of these numbers so there are 10 zeros in the product of the first 50 natural numbers.

9. Let x = price before 3% discount.
   $x - 0.03x = 195.89$
   $\quad 0.97x = 195.89$
   $\qquad x = \$201.95$
   Let y = price before 10% discount.
   $y - 0.10y = 201.95$
   $\quad 0.90y = 201.95$
   $\qquad y = \$224.39$
   Let z = original price.
   $z - 0.25z = 224.39$
   $\quad 0.75z = 224.39$
   $\qquad z = \$299.19$

10.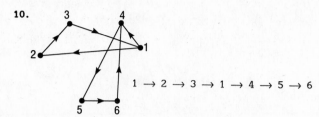
$1 \to 2 \to 3 \to 1 \to 4 \to 5 \to 6$

11. $1 \times 20 = 20 \text{ cm}^2$
$2 \times 19 = 38 \text{ cm}^2$
$3 \times 18 = 54 \text{ cm}^2$
$4 \times 17 = 68 \text{ cm}^2$
$5 \times 16 = 80 \text{ cm}^2$
$6 \times 15 = 90 \text{ cm}^2$
$7 \times 14 = 98 \text{ cm}^2$
$8 \times 13 = 104 \text{ cm}^2$
$9 \times 12 = 108 \text{ cm}^2$
$10 \times 11 = 110 \text{ cm}^2$
$11 \times 10 = 110 \text{ cm}^2$
$12 \times 9 = 108 \text{ cm}^2$

The greatest possible area is 110cm^2.

PAGE 595   COOPERATIVE LEARNING ACTIVITY

$\frac{65,000}{33} = \$1969.70$

This value should be included in the range of values of the 33 sapphires. By guess-and-check, the value of the middle sapphire is $3000.

13-2 | Arithmetic Sequences

PAGE 599   CHECKING FOR UNDERSTANDING

1. Consider three consecutive terms of the sequence. Is the same number added to each term to get the next?

2. The difference between a term and its preceeding term in an arithmetic sequence.

3. $a_n = a_1 + (n - 1)d$, where a_1 = the first term, n = the number of terms, and d = common difference.

4. arithmetic means   5. 4, 7, 10, 13, 16

6. 7, 12, 17, 22, 27   **7.** 16, 14, 12, 10, 8

8. 38, 34, 30, 26, 22   **9.** $\frac{3}{4}$, $\frac{1}{2}$, $\frac{1}{4}$, 0, $-\frac{1}{4}$

10. $\frac{3}{8}$, 1, $1\frac{5}{8}$, $2\frac{1}{4}$, $2\frac{7}{8}$ **11.** $d = 4$

17, 21, 25, 29

12. $d = 3$ **13.** $d = -5$

20, 23, 26, 29 -13, -18, -23, -28

14. $d = -6$ **15.** $d = 1$

3, -3, -9, -15 $\frac{7}{2}$, $\frac{9}{2}$, $\frac{11}{2}$, $\frac{13}{2}$

16. $d = 4$

6.6, 10.6, 14.6, 18.6

PAGES 600-601   EXERCISES

17. a_{25} = $-1 + (25 - 1)(-10)$

= $-1 - 10(24)$

= $-1 - 240$

= -241

18. a_{11} = $-3 + (11 - 1)(-9)$

= $-3 - 9(10)$

= $-3 - 90$

= -93

19. a_{14} = $7 + (14 - 1) \cdot 3$

= $7 + 13 \cdot 3$

= $7 + 39$

= 46

20. a_{17} = $-7 + (17 - 1) \cdot 3$ **21.** a_8 = $2 + (8 - 1)\frac{1}{2}$

= $-7 + 16 \cdot 3$ = $2 + 7 \cdot \frac{1}{2}$

= $-7 + 48$ = $2 + \frac{7}{2}$

= 41 = $5\frac{1}{2}$

22. a_{13} = $\frac{3}{4} + (13 - 1)\left(-\frac{5}{4}\right)$

= $\frac{3}{4} + 12 \cdot \left(-\frac{5}{4}\right)$

= $\frac{3}{4} - 15$

= $-14\frac{1}{4}$

23. a_{100} = $20 + (100 - 1)4$

= $20 + 99 \cdot 4$

= $20 + 396$

= 416

24. a_{101} = $13 + (101 - 1)3$ **25.** $d = 7$

= $13 + 100 \cdot 3$ $124 = -2 + (n - 1)7$

= $13 + 300$ $124 = -2 + 7n - 7$

= 313 $7n = 133$

$n = 19$

19th term

26. $d = 5$ **27.** $d = -5$

$142 = -3 + (n - 1)5$ $-28 = 7 + (n - 1)(-5)$

$142 = -3 + 5n - 5$ $-28 = 7 - 5n + 5$

$5n = 150$ $-5n = -40$

$n = 30$ $n = 8$

30th term   8th term

28. $d = -\frac{1}{4}$

$-\frac{17}{4} = 2\frac{1}{4} + (n - 1)\left(-\frac{1}{4}\right)$

$-\frac{17}{4} = \frac{9}{4} - \frac{1}{4}n + \frac{1}{4}$

$-\frac{1}{4}n = -\frac{27}{4}$

$n = -\frac{27}{4} \cdot -\frac{4}{1}$

$n = 27$

27th term

29. $C = 30$

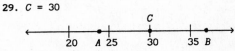

C is the midpoint of segment AB.

30. $d = 4$

a_{12} = $-17 + (12 - 1)4$

= $-17 + 11 \cdot 4$

= $-17 + 44$

= 27

31. $d = -3$

a_{21} = $10 + (21 - 1)(-3)$

= $10 + 20(-3)$

= $10 - 60$

= -50

32. $d = 3$ **33.** $d = -5$

a_{32} = $4 + (32 - 1)3$ a_{10} = $8 + (10 - 1)(-5)$

= $4 + 31 \cdot 3$ = $8 + 9(-5)$

= $4 + 93$ = $8 - 45$

= 97 = -37

34. $d = 15$ **35.** $d = \frac{11}{3}$

70, 85, 100 $-\frac{13}{3}$, $-\frac{2}{3}$

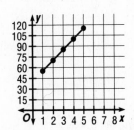   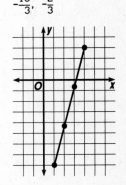

36. $d = \frac{12}{5}$ **37.** $d = 3$

$-\frac{38}{5}$, $-\frac{26}{5}$, $-\frac{14}{5}$, $-\frac{2}{5}$ 5, 8, 11, 14, 17

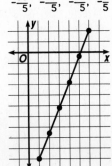   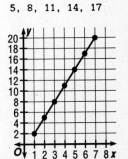

38. $d = 7$

$-13, 1, 8, 22$

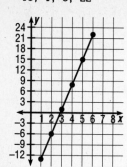

39. $d = -7$

$56, 42, 35$

40. $207 = a_1 + (14 - 1)3$

$207 = a_1 + 13 \cdot 3$

$a_1 = 207 - 39$

$a_1 = 168$

41. $d = -\frac{5}{2}$

$19, 16\frac{1}{2}, 14, 11\frac{1}{2}$

42. $d = 4$

$19 = a_1 + (5 - 1)4$

$19 = a_1 + 4 \cdot 4$

$a_1 = 19 - 16$

$a_1 = 3$

$a_{87} = 3 + (87 - 1)4$

$\quad = 3 + 86 \cdot 4$

$\quad = 3 + 344$

$\quad = 347$

43. Let x = 1st number.

$x + d$ = 2nd number, and

$x + 2d$ = 3rd number.

$\left. \begin{array}{l} x + x + d + x + 2d = 27 \\ x(x + d)(x + 2d) = 288 \end{array} \right\}$

$\left. \begin{array}{l} 3x + 3d = 27 \\ x(x^2 + 3dx + 2d^2) = 288 \end{array} \right\}$

$\left. \begin{array}{l} x + d = 9 \\ x^3 + 3dx^2 + 2d^2x = 288 \end{array} \right\}$

$d = 9 - x$

$x^3 + 3(9 - x)x^2 + 2(9 - x)^2x = 288$

$x^3 + 27x^2 - 3x^3 + 2(81 - 18x + x^2)x = 288$

$x^3 + 27x^2 - 3x^3 + 162x - 36x^2 + 2x^3 = 288$

$-9x^2 + 162x - 288 = 0$

$x^2 - 18x + 32 = 0$

$(x - 2)(x - 16) = 0$

$x = 2, 16$

$d = 7, -7$

$(2, 7), (16, -7)$

$2, 9,$ and 16

44. least multiple = 14

greatest multiple = 385

$385 = 14 + (n - 1)7$

$385 = 14 + 7n - 7$

$7n = 378$

$n = 54$

54 multiples of 7

45. a. No, there is not a common difference.

b. $F_n = F_{n-1} + F_{n-2}$

46. $d = 32$

$a_8 = 16 + (8 - 1)32$

$\quad = 16 + 7 \cdot 32$

$\quad = 16 + 224$

$\quad = 240$ ft

47. $d = 40$

$a_{20} = 20 + (20 - 1)40$

$\quad = 20 + 19 \cdot 40$

$\quad = 20 + 760$

$\quad = 780$ feet

48. $aceg, acegi, acegik$

49. $\log_8 8^5 = 5$

50. $\dfrac{3x^2 - 5x + 2}{2x^2 - 5x - 3} \div \dfrac{x^2 + x - 2}{2x^2 - x - 3}$

$= \dfrac{3x^2 - 5x + 2}{2x^2 - 5x - 3} \cdot \dfrac{2x^2 - x - 3}{x^2 + x - 2}$

$= \dfrac{(3x - 2)(x - 1)}{(2x + 1)(x - 3)} \cdot \dfrac{(2x - 3)(x + 1)}{(x + 2)(x - 1)}$

$= \dfrac{(3x - 2)(x + 1)(2x - 3)}{(x + 2)(x - 3)(2x + 1)}$

51. $f(-2) = 3(-2)^2 + 12(-2) - 5$

$\quad = 3 \cdot 4 - 24 - 5$

$\quad = 12 - 24 - 5$

$\quad = -17$

$g[f(-2)] = (-17)^3 + 5(-17)^2 - 4(-17) + 12$

$\quad = -4913 + 5 \cdot 289 + 68 + 12$

$\quad = -3388$

52.

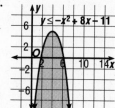

53. Let x = number of widgets made.

Let y = number of gadgets made.

$500 \le x \le 1200$

$700 \le y \le 1400$

$x + y \le 2300$

$I(x, y) = 0.40x + 0.50y$

(x, y)	$0.40x + 0.50y$
$(500, 700)$	$550
$(500, 1400)$	$900
$(900, 1400)$	$1060
$(1200, 1100)$	$1030
$(1200, 700)$	$830

a. 900 widgets and 1400 gadgets

b. $1060

Arithmetic Series

CHECKING FOR UNDERSTANDING

1. series

2. sigma, summation

3. It tells which terms to add and how many.

4. 116

5. 120

6. $S_n = \frac{100}{2}(2 + 200)$

  $= 50(202)$

  $= 10,100$

7. $S_n = \frac{200}{2}(5 + 100)$

  $= 100(105)$

  $= 10,500$

8. $S_n = \frac{15}{2}[2.4 + (15 - 1)3]$

  $= \frac{15}{2}(8 + 45 - 3)$

  $= \frac{15}{2}(50)$

  $= 375$

9. $S_n = \frac{20}{2}[2 \cdot 50 + (20 - 1)(-4)]$

  $= 10(100 - 80 + 4)$

  $= 10(24)$

  $= 240$

10. $n = 10, d = -4, a_1 = -3$

  $S_n = \frac{10}{2}[2(-3) + (10 - 1)(-4)]$

  $= 5(-6 - 40 + 4)$

  $= 5(-42)$

  $= -210$

11. $n = 12, d = 2, a_1 = 9$

  $S_n = \frac{12}{2}[2 \cdot 9 + (12 - 1)2]$

  $= 6(18 + 24 - 2)$

  $= 6(40)$

  $= 240$

12. $n = 100, d = -1, a_1 = -1$

  $S_n = \frac{100}{2}[2(-1) + (100 - 1)(-1)]$

  $= 50(-2 - 99)$

  $= 50(-101)$

  $= -5050$

13. $n = 100, d = 2, a_1 = 2$

  $S_n = \frac{100}{2}[2(2) + (100 - 1)2]$

  $= 50(4 + 99 \cdot 2)$

  $= 50(202)$

  $= 10,100$

---

14. $S_n = \frac{8}{2}(3 - 38)$

  $= 4(-35)$

  $= -140$

15. $S_n = \frac{21}{2}(85 + 25)$

  $= \frac{21}{2}(110)$

  $= 1155$

16. $S_n = \frac{9}{2}(34 + 2)$

  $= \frac{9}{2}(36)$

  $= 162$

17. $S_n = \frac{16}{2}(76 + 31)$

  $= 8(107)$

  $= 856$

18. $S_n = \frac{7}{2}[2 \cdot 4 + (7 - 1)(-1)]$

  $= \frac{7}{2}(8 - 6)$

  $= \frac{7}{2}(2)$

  $= 7$

19. $S_n = \frac{13}{2}\left[2 \cdot 5 + (13 - 1)1\frac{1}{2}\right]$

  $= \frac{13}{2}(10 + 6)$

  $= \frac{13}{2}(16)$

  $= 104$

20. $d = 6$

  $\frac{n}{2}(6 + 96) = \frac{n}{2}[2 \cdot 6 + (n - 1)6]$

  $\frac{n}{2}(102) = \frac{n}{2}(12 + 6n - 6)$

  $51n = \frac{n}{2} \cdot 6(n + 1)$

  $51n = 3n^2 + 3n$

  $3n^2 - 48n = 0$

  $3n(n - 16) = 0$

  $n = 16$

  $S_n = \frac{16}{2}(6 + 96)$

  $= 8(102)$

  $= 816$

21. $d = -4$

  $\frac{n}{2}(34 + 2) = \frac{n}{2}[2(34) + (n - 1)(-4)]$

  $\frac{n}{2}(36) = \frac{n}{2}(68 - 4n + 4)$

  $18n = \frac{n}{2}(72 - 4n)$

  $18n = \frac{n}{2} \cdot 4(18 - n)$

  $18n = 2n(18 - n)$

  $18n = 36n - 2n^2$

  $2n^2 - 18n = 0$

  $2n(n - 9) = 0$

  $n = 9$

  $S_n = \frac{9}{2}(34 + 2)$

  $= \frac{9}{2}(36)$

  $= 9 \cdot 18$

  $= 162$

22. $d = 7$

$$\frac{n}{2}(7 + 98) = \frac{n}{2}[2 \cdot 7 + (n - 1)7]$$

$$\frac{n}{2}(105) = \frac{n}{2}(14 + 7n - 7)$$

$$\frac{105n}{2} = \frac{n}{2}(7 + 7n)$$

$$\frac{105n}{2} = \frac{7n}{2} + \frac{7n^2}{2}$$

$$\frac{7n^2}{2} - \frac{98n}{2} = 0$$

$$\frac{7n^2}{2} - 49n = 0$$

$$7n\left(\frac{1}{2}n - 7\right) = 0$$

$$\frac{1}{2}n = 7$$

$$n = 14$$

$$S_n = \frac{14}{2}(7 + 98)$$

$$= 7 \cdot 105$$

$$= 735$$

23. $d = -6$

$$\frac{n}{2}(10 - 50) = \frac{n}{2}[2(10) + (n - 1)(-6)]$$

$$\frac{n}{2}(-40) = \frac{n}{2}(20 - 6n + 6)$$

$$-20n = \frac{n}{2} \cdot 2(13 - 3n)$$

$$-20n = 13n - 3n^2$$

$$3n^2 - 33n = 0$$

$$3n(n - 11) = 0$$

$$n = 11$$

$$S_n = \frac{11}{2}(10 - 50)$$

$$= \frac{11}{2}(-40)$$

$$= 11(-20)$$

$$= -220$$

24. $n = 25$, $a_1 = 2$, $a_n = a_{25} = 50$

$$S_n = \frac{25}{2}(2 + 50)$$

$$= \frac{25}{2}(52)$$

$$= 650$$

25. $n = 4$, $a_1 = 5$, $a_n = a_4 = 8$

$$S_n = \frac{4}{2}(5 + 8)$$

$$= 2(13)$$

$$= 26$$

26. $n = 30$, $a_1 = 1$, $a_n = a_{30} = 59$

$$S_n = \frac{30}{2}(1 + 59)$$

$$= 15(60)$$

$$= 900$$

27. $n = 55$, $a_1 = 47$, $a_n = a_{55} = 155$

$$S_n = \frac{55}{2}(47 + 155)$$

$$= \frac{55}{2}(202)$$

$$= 5555$$

28. $n = 41$, $a_1 = 29$, $a_n = a_{41} = 149$

$$S_n = \frac{41}{2}(29 + 149)$$

$$= \frac{41}{2}(178)$$

$$= 3649$$

29. $n = 6$, $a_1 = 15$, $a_n = a_6 = -30$

$$S_n = \frac{6}{2}(15 - 30)$$

$$= 3(-15)$$

$$= -45$$

30. $$\frac{n}{2}(91 + 15) = \frac{n}{2}[2 \cdot 91 + (n - 1)(-4)]$$

$$\frac{n}{2} \cdot 106 = \frac{n}{2}[182 - 4n + 4]$$

$$53n = \frac{n}{2} \cdot 2(93 - 2n)$$

$$53n = 93n - 2n^2$$

$$2n^2 - 40n = 0$$

$$2n(n - 20) = 0$$

$$n = 20$$

$$S_n = \frac{20}{2}(91 + 15)$$

$$= 10(106)$$

$$= 1060$$

31. $$\frac{16}{2}(a_1 + 72) = \frac{16}{2}[2a_1 + (16 - 1)5]$$

$$8a_1 + 576 = 8(2a_1 + 75)$$

$$8a_1 + 576 = 16a_1 + 600$$

$$8a_1 = -24$$

$$a_1 = -3$$

$$S_n = \frac{16}{2}(-3 + 72)$$

$$= 8(69)$$

$$= 552$$

32. $\frac{9}{2}(a_1 + 27) = \frac{9}{2}[2a_1 + (9 - 1)(-4)]$

$\frac{9}{2}a_1 + \frac{243}{2} = \frac{9}{2}(2a_1 - 32)$

$\frac{9}{2}a_1 + \frac{243}{2} = 9a_1 - 144$

$\frac{9}{2}a_1 = \frac{531}{2}$

$a_1 = \frac{531}{2}\left(\frac{2}{9}\right)$

$a_1 = 59$

$S_n = \frac{9}{2}(59 + 27)$

$= \frac{9}{2}(86)$

$= 9(43)$

$= 387$

33. $\frac{n}{2}(-2 + 5) = \frac{n}{2}\left[2(-2) + (n - 1)1\frac{1}{2}\right]$

$\frac{3}{2}n = \frac{n}{2}\left(-4 + \frac{n}{2} - \frac{1}{2}\right)$

$\frac{3}{2}n = \frac{n}{2}\left(\frac{n}{2} - \frac{9}{2}\right)$

$\frac{3}{2}n = \frac{n^2}{4} - \frac{9}{4}n$

$\frac{n^2}{4} - \frac{15}{4}n = 0$

$\frac{1}{4}n(n - 15) = 0$

$n = 15$

$S_n = \frac{15}{2}(-2 + 5)$

$= \frac{15}{2}(3)$

$= \frac{45}{2}$

34. $876 = \frac{n}{2}(7 + 139)$

$876 = \frac{n}{2}(146)$

$876 = 73n$

$n = 12$

$876 = \frac{12}{2}[2(7) + (12 - 1)d]$

$876 = 6(14 + 11d)$

$876 = 84 + 66d$

$66d = 792$

$d = 12$

1st three terms: 7, 19, 31

35. $378 = \frac{14}{2}(a_1 + 53)$

$378 = 7a_1 + 371$

$7a_1 = 7$

$a_1 = 1$

$378 = \frac{14}{2}[2(1) + (14 - 1)d]$

$378 = 7(2 + 13d)$

$378 = 14 + 91d$

$91d = 364$

$d = 4$

1st three terms: 1, 5, 9

36. $1008 = \frac{21}{2}(a_1 + 78)$

$1008 = \frac{21}{2}a_1 + 819$

$\frac{21}{2}a_1 = 189$

$a_1 = 189\left(\frac{2}{21}\right)$

$a_1 = 18$

$1008 = \frac{21}{2}[2 \cdot 18 + (21 - 1)d]$

$1008 = \frac{21}{2}(36 + 20d)$

$1008 = 378 + 210d$

$210d = 630$

$d = 3$

1st three terms: 18, 21, 24

37. $1716 = \frac{n}{2}(6 + 306)$

$1716 = \frac{n}{2}(312)$

$1716 = 156n$

$n = 11$

$1716 = \frac{11}{2}[2(6) + (11 - 1)d]$

$1716 = \frac{11}{2}(12 + 10d)$

$1716 = 66 + 55d$

$55d = 1650$

$d = 30$

1st three terms: 6, 36, 66

38. $\sum_{a=3}^{7}(a - 2)^2 = (3 - 2)^2 + (4 - 2)^2 + (5 - 2)^2$

$+ (6 - 2)^2$

$= 1^2 + 2^2 + 3^2 + 4^2$

$= 1 + 4 + 9 + 16$

$= 30$

$\sum_{a=1}^{4}a^2 = 1^2 + 2^2 + 3^2 + 4^2$

$= 1 + 4 + 9 + 16$

$= 30$

They describe the same arithmetic series.

39. $2\displaystyle\sum_{k=3}^{7} k^2 = 2(3^2 + 4^2 + 5^2 + 6^2 + 7^2)$

$\quad = 2(9 + 16 + 25 + 36 + 49)$

$\quad = 2(135)$

$\quad = 270$

$\displaystyle\sum_{k=3}^{7} 2k^2 = 2 \cdot 3^2 + 2 \cdot 4^2 + 2 \cdot 5^2 + 2 \cdot 6^2$

$\qquad\qquad + 2 \cdot 7^2$

$\quad = 2(9) + 2(16) + 2(25) + 2(36) + 2(49)$

$\quad = 18 + 32 + 50 + 72 + 98$

$\quad = 270$

Yes, they are equal.

40. $\displaystyle\sum_{n=0}^{12} 10 + n = 10 + 11 + 12 + 13 + 14 + 15 + 16$

$\qquad\qquad + 17 + 18 + 19 + 20 + 21 + 22$

$\qquad = 208 \qquad 208\text{ logs}$

41. $\displaystyle\sum_{n=0}^{29} 21 + n = 21 + 22 + 23 + 24 + 25 + 26 + 27$

$\qquad\qquad + 28 + 29 + 30 + 31 + 32 + 33 + 34$

$\qquad\qquad + 35 + 36 + 37 + 38 + 39 + 40 + 41$

$\qquad\qquad + 42 + 43 + 44 + 45 + 46 + 47 + 48$

$\qquad\qquad + 49 + 50$

$\qquad = 1065$

The auditorium seats 1065. 1200 are expected, so there will not be a seat for everyone.

42. $d = 9$

$a_{57} = 6 + (57 - 1)9$

$\quad = 6 + 56(9)$

$\quad = 6 + 504$

$\quad = 510$

43. $3x + 7 = x^2 - 4x - 1$

$\quad x^2 - 7x - 8 = 0$

$\quad (x + 1)(x - 8) = 0$

$\qquad\qquad x = -1, 8$

44. $p(-4) = 3(-4)^2 - 7(-4) + 1$

$\quad = 3(16) + 28 + 1$

$\quad = 48 + 28 + 1$

$\quad = 77$

45. $\begin{bmatrix} 1 & 2 & -3 & -13 \\ 2 & -1 & 3 & 23 \\ 3 & 1 & -3 & -8 \end{bmatrix}$ Multiply row 1 by −2 and add to row 2. Multiply row 1 by −3 and add to row 3.

$= \begin{bmatrix} 1 & 2 & -3 & -13 \\ 0 & -5 & 9 & 49 \\ 0 & -5 & 6 & 31 \end{bmatrix}$ Multiply row 2 by $-\frac{1}{5}$.

$= \begin{bmatrix} 1 & 2 & -3 & -13 \\ 0 & 1 & -\frac{9}{5} & -\frac{49}{5} \\ 0 & -5 & 6 & 31 \end{bmatrix}$ Multiply row 2 by −2 and add to row 1. Multiply row 2 by 5 and add to row 3.

$= \begin{bmatrix} 1 & 0 & \frac{3}{5} & \frac{33}{5} \\ 0 & 1 & -\frac{9}{5} & -\frac{49}{5} \\ 0 & 0 & -3 & -18 \end{bmatrix}$ Multiply row 3 by $-\frac{1}{3}$.

$= \begin{bmatrix} 1 & 0 & \frac{3}{5} & \frac{33}{5} \\ 0 & 1 & -\frac{9}{5} & -\frac{49}{5} \\ 0 & 0 & 1 & 6 \end{bmatrix}$ Multiply row 3 by $-\frac{3}{5}$ and add to row 1. Multiply row 3 by $\frac{9}{5}$ and add to row 2.

$= \begin{bmatrix} 1 & 0 & 0 & 3 \\ 0 & 1 & 0 & 1 \\ 0 & 0 & 1 & 6 \end{bmatrix}$

$x = 3, \ y = 1, \ z = 6$

46. Let b = length of base.

Length of leg = $3b - 5$.

$2(3b - 5) + b = 88$

$6b - 10 + b = 88$

$\qquad 7b = 98$

$\qquad b = 14\text{ cm}$

$3b - 5 = 3(14) - 5$

$\qquad = 37\text{ cm}$

Dimensions are 14 cm by 37 cm by 37 cm.

PAGE 607   MID-CHAPTER REVIEW

1. 3

2. 1, 3, 4, 7, 11, 18, 29, 47

3. $d = \frac{3}{4}$

$a_{12} = \frac{3}{4} + (12 - 1)\frac{3}{4}$

$\quad = \frac{3}{4} + 11\left(\frac{3}{4}\right)$

$\quad = \frac{3}{4} + \frac{33}{4}$

$\quad = 9$

4. $a_{100} = 20 + (100 - 1)4$

$\quad = 20 + 99(4)$

$\quad = 20 + 396$

$\quad = 416$

5. $\frac{16}{2}(a_1 + 72) = \frac{16}{2}[2a_1 + (16 - 1)5]$

$8(a_1 + 72) = 8(2a_1 + 75)$

$8a_1 + 576 = 16a_1 + 600$

$\qquad 8a_1 = -24$

$\qquad a_1 = -3$

$S_n = \frac{16}{2}(-3 + 72)$

$\quad = 8(69)$

$\quad = 552$

6. $S_n = \frac{14}{2}[2 \cdot 9 + (14 - 1)(-6)]$

    $= 7(18 + 13(-6))$

    $= 7(18 - 78)$

    $= 7(-60)$

    $= -420$

7. $d = 820$, $a_1 = 4500$, $n = 30$

    $S_n = \frac{30}{2}[2(4500) + (30 - 1)820]$

    $= 15[9000 + 29(820)]$

    $= 15(9000 + 23{,}780)$

    $= 15(32{,}780)$

    $= \$491{,}700$

13-4 Geometric Sequences

PAGE 612 CHECKING FOR UNDERSTANDING

1. common ratio

2. Each succeeding term contains a factor of r, so each term can be expressed as a product of a_1 and a power of r.

3. geometric means

4. A half-life is the amount of time it takes for half the mass of an element to decay.

5. $\frac{20}{4} = 5$, $\frac{100}{20} = 5$, $\frac{500}{100} = 5$

    yes; $r = 5$

6. $\frac{4}{2} = 2$, $\frac{6}{4} = \frac{3}{2}$

    no

7. $\frac{9}{4} \div \frac{3}{2} = \frac{9}{4} \cdot \frac{2}{3} = \frac{3}{2}$

    $\frac{27}{8} \div \frac{9}{4} = \frac{27}{8} \cdot \frac{4}{9} = \frac{3}{2}$

    $\frac{81}{16} \div \frac{27}{8} = \frac{81}{16} \cdot \frac{8}{27} = \frac{3}{2}$

    yes; $r = \frac{3}{2}$

8. $\frac{14}{7} = 2$, $\frac{21}{14} = \frac{3}{2}$

    no

9. $\frac{4}{1} = 4$, $\frac{9}{4} = \frac{9}{4}$

    no

10. $\frac{6}{9} = \frac{2}{3}$, $\frac{4}{6} = \frac{2}{3}$, $\frac{8}{3} \div 4 = \frac{8}{3} \cdot \frac{1}{4} = \frac{8}{12} = \frac{2}{3}$

    yes; $r = \frac{2}{3}$

11. $a_2 = a_1 r^1 = 3 \cdot -2 = -6$

    $a_3 = a_1 r^2 = 3 \cdot (-2)^2 = 3 \cdot 4 = 12$

    $a_4 = a_1 r^3 = 3 \cdot (-2)^3 = 3 \cdot -8 = -24$

    1st four terms: 3, -6, 12, -24

12. $r = \frac{10}{30} = \frac{1}{3}$

    $a_4 = a_3 \cdot \frac{1}{3}$

    $= 10 \cdot \frac{1}{3}$

    $= \frac{10}{3}$

    $a_5 = a_4 \cdot \frac{1}{3}$

    $= \frac{10}{3} \cdot \frac{1}{3}$

    $= \frac{10}{9}$

13. $r = \frac{6}{2} = 3$

    $a_4 = a_1 r^3$

    $= 2 \cdot 3^3$

    $= 2 \cdot 27$

    $= 54$

    $a_5 = a_1 r^4$

    $= 2 \cdot 3^4$

    $= 2 \cdot 81$

    $= 162$

14. $r = \frac{30}{20} = \frac{3}{2}$

    $a_4 = a_3 r$

    $= 45 \cdot \frac{3}{2}$

    $= \frac{135}{2} = 67\frac{1}{2}$

    $a_5 = a_4 r$

    $= \frac{135}{2} \cdot \frac{3}{2}$

    $= \frac{405}{4} = 101\frac{1}{4}$

15. $r = \frac{243}{729} = \frac{1}{3}$

    $a_4 = a_1 r^3$

    $= 729 \cdot \left(\frac{1}{3}\right)^3$

    $= 729 \cdot \frac{1}{27}$

    $= 27$

    $a_5 = a_1 r^4$

    $= 729 \cdot \frac{1}{81}$

    $= 9$

16. $r = \frac{1}{9} \div \frac{1}{27} = \frac{1}{9} \cdot \frac{27}{1} = 3$

    $a_4 = a_1 r^3$

    $= \frac{1}{27} \cdot 3^3$

    $= \frac{27}{27}$

    $= 1$

    $a_5 = a_1 r^4$

    $= \frac{1}{27} \cdot 3^4$

    $= \frac{81}{27}$

    $= 3$

17. $r = \frac{1}{2} \div \frac{-1}{4} = \frac{1}{2} \cdot \frac{-4}{1} = -2$

    $a_4 = a_1 r^3$

    $= -\frac{1}{4} \cdot (-2)^3$

    $= -\frac{1}{4}(-8)$

    $= 2$

    $a_5 = a_1 r^4$

    $= -\frac{1}{4} \cdot (-2)^4$

    $= -\frac{1}{4} \cdot 16$

    $= -4$

18. $a_2 = 3 \cdot -2$
$\quad = -6$
$a_3 = 3 \cdot (-2)^2$
$\quad = 3 \cdot 4$
$\quad = 12$
$a_4 = 3 \cdot (-2)^3$
$\quad = 3(-8)$
$\quad = -24$
$\quad 3, -6, 12, -24$

19. $a_2 = 27 \cdot -\frac{1}{3}$
$\quad = -9$
$a_3 = 27 \cdot \left(-\frac{1}{3}\right)^2$
$\quad = 27 \cdot \frac{1}{9}$
$\quad = 3$
$a_4 = 27 \cdot \left(-\frac{1}{3}\right)^3$
$\quad = 27\left(-\frac{1}{27}\right)$
$\quad = -1$
$\quad 27, -9, 3, -1$

20. $a_2 = 12 \cdot \frac{1}{2}$
$\quad = 6$
$a_3 = 12 \cdot \left(\frac{1}{2}\right)^2$
$\quad = 12 \cdot \frac{1}{4}$
$\quad = 3$
$a_4 = 12 \cdot \left(\frac{1}{2}\right)^3$
$\quad = 12 \cdot \frac{1}{8}$
$\quad = \frac{3}{2}$
$\quad 12, 6, 3, \frac{3}{2}$

21. $r = \frac{2}{-1} = -2$
$a_5 = a_4 r = 8(-2) = -16$
$a_6 = a_5 r = -16(-2) = 32$
$a_7 = a_6 r = 32(-6) = -64$
$a_8 = a_7 r = -64(-2) = 128$

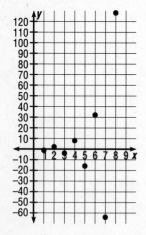

22. $a_n = a_3 = a_1 r^2$
$\quad = 4(5^2)$
$\quad = 4 \cdot 25$
$\quad = 100$

23. $a_n = a_5 = a_1 r^4$
$\quad = 2(2^4)$
$\quad = 2(16)$
$\quad = 32$

24. $a_n = a_4 = a_1 r^3$
$\quad = 7(2^3)$
$\quad = 7(8)$
$\quad = 56$

25. $a_n = a_5 = a_1 r^4$
$\quad = 243 \cdot \left(-\frac{1}{3}\right)^4$
$\quad = 243\left(\frac{1}{81}\right)$
$\quad = 3$

26. $a_3 = a_1 r^2$
$32 = a_1\left(-\frac{1}{2}\right)^2$
$32 = a_1 \cdot \frac{1}{4}$
$a_1 = 128$
$a_n = a_6 = a_1 r^5$
$\quad = 128 \cdot \left(-\frac{1}{2}\right)^5$
$\quad = 128\left(-\frac{1}{32}\right)$
$\quad = -4$

27. $a_4 = a_1 r^3$
$16 = a_1\left(\frac{1}{2}\right)^3$
$16 = a_1 \cdot \frac{1}{8}$
$a_1 = 128$
$a_n = a_8 = a_1 r^7$
$\quad = 128 \cdot \left(\frac{1}{2}\right)^7$
$\quad = 128\left(\frac{1}{128}\right)$
$\quad = 1$

28. $48 = 3 \cdot r^4$
$16 = r^4$
$r = \sqrt[4]{16}$
$r = \pm 2$
$6, 12, 24$
or $-6, 12, -24$

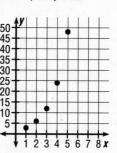
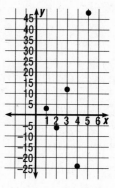

29. $8 = 1 \cdot r^3$
$8 = r^3$
$r = \sqrt[3]{8}$
$r = 2$
$2, 4$

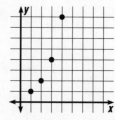

30. $\frac{1}{4} = 8 \cdot r^5$
$r^5 = \frac{1}{32}$
$r = \sqrt[5]{\frac{1}{32}}$
$r = \frac{1}{2}$
$4, 2, 1, \frac{1}{2}$

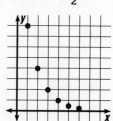

31. $75 = 3 \cdot r^2$

$r^2 = 25$

$r = \sqrt{25}$

$r = \pm 5$

15 or -15

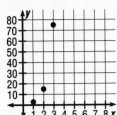

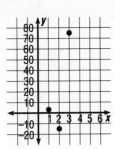

32. $80 = 5 \cdot r^4$

$16 = r^4$

$r = \sqrt[4]{16}$

$r = \pm 2$

10, 20, 40

or -10, 20, -40

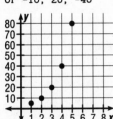

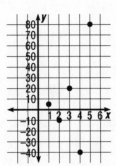

33. $112 = 7 \cdot r^4$

$r^4 = 16$

$r = \sqrt[4]{16}$

$r = \pm 2$

14, 28, 56

or -14, 28, -56

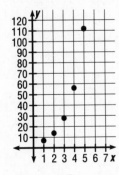

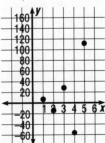

34. $96 = -12r^3$

$r^3 = -8$

$r = \sqrt[3]{-8}$

$r = -2$

$96 = a_1 r^5$

$96 = a_1(-2)^5$

$96 = -32a_1$

$a_1 = -3$

-3, 6, 24, -48

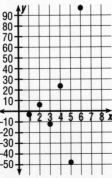

35. $384 = 24r^4$

$r^4 = 16$

$r = \sqrt[4]{16}$

$r = \pm 2$

$384 = a_1 r^7$

$384 = a_1 2^7$

$384 = a_1 128$

$a_1 = 3$

3, 6, 12, 48, 96, 192

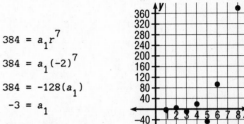

$384 = a_1 r^7$

$384 = a_1(-2)^7$

$384 = -128(a_1)$

$-3 = a_1$

-3, 6, -12, -48, 96, -192

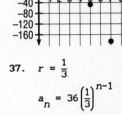

36. $r = 2$

$a_n = 2 \cdot 2^{n-1}$

$a_n = 2^n$

37. $r = \frac{1}{3}$

$a_n = 36\left(\frac{1}{3}\right)^{n-1}$

38. $r = -5$

$a_n = \frac{4}{25} \cdot (-5)^{n-1}$

39. In a geometric sequence, each subsequent term can be found by multiplying the preceding term by r. So $a_n = a_{n-1}r$, the preceding term times r, or $a_n - 1^r$. Since each term originally comes from the first term, a_1, each succeeding term has one more factor of r than its preceding term. The second term has one factor of r, the third term has 2, and so on. So a_n would have $n - 1$ factors of r times a_1, or $a_n = a_1 r^{n-1}$.

40. a. guess-and-check, make a model, work backwards (Answers will vary.)

b. $r = \frac{19}{20} = 0.95$

$a_n = (r)^{n-1}$

$0.01 = (0.95)^{n-1}$

$0.95(0.01) = 0.95(0.95)^{n-1}$

$0.0095 = 0.95^n$

$\log 0.0095 = \log 0.95^n$

$\log 0.0095 = n(\log 0.95)$

$\frac{\log 0.0095}{\log 0.95} = n$

$91 \approx n$

Since a_1 occurs at 0 strokes, a_{91} occurs at 90 strokes. 99% of the air is gone after 90 strokes.

41. $r = \frac{9}{10}$, $a_1 = \frac{9}{10}$

$a_{10} = \frac{9}{10} \cdot \left(\frac{9}{10}\right)^9$

$a_{10} = \left(\frac{9}{10}\right)^{10}$

$a_{10} \approx 0.35$

About 35% remains.

42. a. $a_1 = 20,000$, $r = 1.10$

$a_6 = 20,000 \cdot (1.10)^5$

$\approx 32,200$ people

b. $100,000 = 20,000 \cdot (1.10)^{n-1}$

$(1.10)^{n-1} = 5$

$\log (1.10)^{n-1} = \log 5$

$(n - 1) \log (1.10) = \log 5$

$n - 1 = \dfrac{\log 5}{\log (1.10)}$

$n = 1 + \dfrac{\log 5}{\log (1.10)}$

$n \approx 18$

Since a_1 occurs at 0 years, a_{18} occurs at 17 years. After 17 years, the population will be at least 100,000.

43. $a_1 = \frac{1}{2}$, $a_2 = \frac{1}{4}$, $a_n = \frac{1}{2^n}$

After a_2, 8 more reductions would be a_{10}.

$a_{10} = \dfrac{1}{2^{10}}$

$= \dfrac{1}{1024}$ or about 0.098% of the original

44. $S_n = \dfrac{23}{2}(11 + 44)$

$= \dfrac{23}{2} \cdot 55$

$= \dfrac{1265}{2} = 632.5$

45.

$$\begin{array}{r|rrrr} 2 & 1 & -4 & -11 & 30 \\ & & 2 & -4 & -30 \\ \hline & 1 & -2 & -15 & \,|\, 0 \end{array}$$

$f(x) = (x - 2)(x^2 - 2x - 15)$

$= (x - 2)(x + 3)(x - 5)$

rational zeros: 2, -3, 5

46. $f(m + 2) = 2(m + 2)^3 - 5(m + 2)^2$

$= 2(m^3 + 6m^2 + 12m + 8) - 5(m^2 + 4m + 4)$

$= 2m^3 + 12m^2 + 24m + 16 - 5m^2 - 20m - 20$

$= 2m^3 + 7m^2 + 4m - 4$

47. $(a^2 - 4b^4)(a^2 + 4b^4)$

$= (a - 2b^2)(a + 2b^2)(a^2 + 4b^4)$

48.

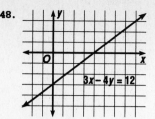

49. apothem $= 6 \cdot 1.73 = 10.38$ in.

perimeter $= 6 \cdot 6 = 36$ in.

$A = \frac{1}{2}ap$

$= \frac{1}{2}(10.38)(36)$

$= 186.84$ in^2

13-5 Geometric Series

PAGE 618   **CHECKING FOR UNDERSTANDING**

1. series

2. $S_n = \dfrac{a_1(1 - r^n)}{1 - r}$, where $r \neq 1$

and

$S_n = a_1 n$ where $r = 1$

3. If $r = 1$ the denominator would be zero and the formula would not be able to be evaluated.

4. It is possible to get two correct sets of answers depending on whether a positive or negative number is used for the common ratio.

5. 9, -2, -72, 4   **6.** 3, 0.5, 0.375, 4

7. 2, 4, 512, 5

8. -12, $-\frac{1}{2}$, $-\frac{3}{4}$, 5

9. $-\dfrac{5}{16} = 20 \cdot r^3$

$r^3 = \dfrac{-\frac{5}{16}}{20}$

$r^3 = -\dfrac{5}{16} \cdot \dfrac{1}{20}$

$r^3 = -\dfrac{1}{64}$

$r = \sqrt[3]{-\dfrac{1}{64}}$

$r = -\dfrac{1}{4}$

$a_5 = -\dfrac{5}{16} \cdot -\dfrac{1}{4}$

$a_5 = \dfrac{5}{64}$

10. $24 = 6r^2$

$r^2 = 4$

$r = \pm\sqrt{4}$

$r = \pm 2$

For $r = 2$: $a_1 = \dfrac{a_2}{r}$ $a_6 = a_4 \cdot r^2$

$= \dfrac{6}{2}$ or 3 $= 24 \cdot 2^2$

$= 96$

For $r = -2$: $a_1 = \dfrac{a_2}{r}$ $a_6 = a_4 \cdot r^2$

$= \dfrac{6}{-2}$ or -3 $= 24 \cdot (-2)^2$

$= 96$

11. $S_n = 7 \cdot 9$
$= 63$

12. $r = \dfrac{-6}{2} = -3$, $n = 6$

$S_n = \dfrac{2(1 - (-3)^6)}{1 - (-3)}$

$= \dfrac{2(1 - 729)}{4}$

$= -364$

13. $r = \dfrac{6}{3} = 2$, $n = 6$

$S_n = \dfrac{3(1 - 2^6)}{1 - 2}$

$= \dfrac{3(1 - 64)}{-1}$

$= 189$

14. $r = \dfrac{4}{8} = \dfrac{1}{2}$, $n = 6$

$S_n = \dfrac{8 - 8\left(\dfrac{1}{2}\right)^6}{1 - \dfrac{1}{2}}$

$= \dfrac{8 - 8\left(\dfrac{1}{64}\right)}{\dfrac{1}{2}}$

$= \left(8 - \dfrac{1}{8}\right)2$

$= 16 - \dfrac{1}{4} = 15\dfrac{3}{4}$

15. $r = -\dfrac{1}{3} \div \dfrac{1}{9} = -3$, $n = 5$

$S_n = \dfrac{\dfrac{1}{9}(1 - (-3)^5)}{1 - (-3)}$

$= \dfrac{\dfrac{1}{9}(244)}{4}$

$= \dfrac{61}{9}$

16. $r = \dfrac{36}{-216} = -\dfrac{1}{6}$, $n = 5$

$S_n = \dfrac{1296\left(1 - \left(-\dfrac{1}{6}\right)^5\right)}{1 - \left(-\dfrac{1}{6}\right)}$

$= \dfrac{1296\left(1 + \dfrac{1}{7776}\right)}{1 + \dfrac{1}{6}}$

$= \dfrac{1296\left(\dfrac{7777}{7776}\right)}{\dfrac{7}{6}}$

$= \dfrac{10,078,992}{7776} \cdot \dfrac{6}{7}$

$= \dfrac{1,439,856}{1296}$

$= 1111$

17. $S_n = 16 \cdot 11 = 176$

18. $n = 10$, $r = \dfrac{15}{75} = \dfrac{1}{5} = 0.2$

$S_n = \dfrac{75(1 - (0.2)^{10})}{1 - 0.2}$

$= \dfrac{75(1 - 0.000000102)}{0.8}$

$= \dfrac{74.99999232}{0.8}$

≈ 93.75

19. $S_n = \dfrac{5 - 5(3)^{12}}{1 - 3}$

$= \dfrac{5 - 5(531,441)}{-2}$

$= \dfrac{5 - 2,657,205}{-2}$

$= \dfrac{-2,657,200}{-2}$

$= 1,328,600$

20. $S_n = \dfrac{256(1 - (0.75)^9)}{1 - 0.75}$

$= \dfrac{256(1 - 0.075084686)}{0.25}$

≈ 947.11

21. $S_n = \dfrac{7(1 - 2^{14})}{1 - 2}$

$= \dfrac{7(1 - 16,384)}{-1}$

$= \dfrac{-114,681}{-1}$

$= 114,681$

22. $S_n = \dfrac{12(1 - (-3)^5)}{1 - (-3)}$

$= \dfrac{12(1 + 243)}{4}$

$= 3 \cdot 244$

$= 732$

23. $S_n = \dfrac{16\left(1 - \left(-\dfrac{1}{2}\right)^{10}\right)}{1 - \left(-\dfrac{1}{2}\right)}$

$= \dfrac{16\left(1 - \dfrac{1}{1024}\right)}{\dfrac{3}{2}}$

$= 16 \cdot \dfrac{1023}{1024} \cdot \dfrac{2}{3}$

$= \dfrac{341}{32} \approx 10.66$

24. $S_n = \dfrac{625\left(1 - \left(\frac{2}{5}\right)^8\right)}{1 - \frac{2}{5}}$

$= \dfrac{625\left(1 - \frac{256}{390,625}\right)}{\frac{3}{5}}$

$= 625 \cdot \dfrac{390,369}{390,625} \cdot \dfrac{5}{3}$

$= \dfrac{130,123}{125} \approx 1040.98$

25. $S_n = \dfrac{1\left(1 - \left(-\frac{1}{2}\right)^5\right)}{1 - \left(-\frac{1}{2}\right)}$

$= \dfrac{1 + \frac{1}{32}}{\frac{3}{2}}$

$= \dfrac{33}{32} \cdot \dfrac{2}{3}$

$= \dfrac{11}{16}$

30. $S_n = \dfrac{4\left(1 - \left(\frac{1}{2}\right)^6\right)}{1 - \frac{1}{2}}$

$= \dfrac{4\left(1 - \frac{1}{64}\right)}{\frac{1}{2}}$

$= 4 \cdot \dfrac{63}{64} \cdot 2$

$= \dfrac{63}{8}$

26. $S_n = \dfrac{243\left(1 - \left(-\frac{2}{3}\right)^5\right)}{1 - \left(-\frac{2}{3}\right)}$

$= \dfrac{243\left(1 + \frac{32}{243}\right)}{\frac{5}{3}}$

$= 243 \cdot \dfrac{275}{243} \cdot \dfrac{3}{5}$

$= 165$

27. $S_n = \dfrac{343\left(1 - \left(-\frac{1}{7}\right)^4\right)}{1 - \left(-\frac{1}{7}\right)}$

$= \dfrac{343\left(1 - \frac{1}{2401}\right)}{\frac{8}{7}}$

$= 343 \cdot \dfrac{2400}{2401} \cdot \dfrac{7}{8}$

$= 300$

28. $S_n = \dfrac{625\left(1 - \left(\frac{3}{5}\right)^5\right)}{1 - \frac{3}{5}}$

$= \dfrac{625\left(1 - \frac{243}{3125}\right)}{\frac{2}{5}}$

$= 625 \cdot \dfrac{2882}{3125} \cdot \dfrac{5}{2}$

$= 1441$

29. $S_n = \dfrac{125\left(1 - \left(\frac{1}{5}\right)^5\right)}{1 - \frac{1}{5}}$

$= \dfrac{125\left(1 - \frac{1}{3125}\right)}{\frac{4}{5}}$

$= 125 \cdot \dfrac{3124}{3125} \cdot \dfrac{5}{4}$

$= \dfrac{781}{5}$

31. $a_s = a_2 r^3$

$0.1875 = 1.5 r^3$

$r^3 - 0.125$

$r = \sqrt[3]{0.125}$

$r = 0.5$

$a_1 = \dfrac{1.5}{0.5}$

$a_1 = 3$

$S_n = \dfrac{3(1 - (0.5)^9)}{1 - 0.5}$

$= \dfrac{3(0.998046875)}{0.5}$

≈ 5.99

32. $a_6 = a_3 r^3$

$\dfrac{3}{32} = \dfrac{3}{4} r^3$

$r^3 = \dfrac{3}{32} \cdot \dfrac{4}{3}$

$r^3 = \dfrac{1}{8}$

$r = \sqrt[3]{\dfrac{1}{8}}$

$r = \dfrac{1}{2}$

$\dfrac{3}{4} = a_1\left(\dfrac{1}{2}\right)^2$

$\dfrac{3}{4} = a_1 \cdot \dfrac{1}{4}$

$a_1 = 3$

$S_n = \dfrac{3\left(1 - \left(\frac{1}{2}\right)^6\right)}{1 - \frac{1}{2}}$

$= \dfrac{3\left(1 - \frac{1}{64}\right)}{\frac{1}{2}}$

$= 3\left(\dfrac{63}{64}\right) \cdot 2$

$= \dfrac{189}{32}$

33. $a_4 = a_3 r$

$\dfrac{-5}{16} = \dfrac{5}{4} r$

$r = \dfrac{-5}{16} \cdot \dfrac{4}{5}$

$r = -\dfrac{1}{4}$

$\dfrac{5}{4} = a_1\left(-\dfrac{1}{4}\right)^2$

$\dfrac{5}{4} = a_1 \cdot \dfrac{1}{16}$

$a_1 = 16 \cdot \dfrac{5}{4}$

$a_1 = 20$

$S_n = \dfrac{20\left(1 - \left(-\frac{1}{4}\right)^6\right)}{1 - \left(-\frac{1}{4}\right)}$

$= \dfrac{20\left(1 - \frac{1}{4096}\right)}{\frac{5}{4}}$

$= 20 \cdot \dfrac{4095}{4096} \cdot \dfrac{4}{5}$

$= \dfrac{4095}{256}$

34. $a_5 = a_2 r^3$

$-324 = -12 r^3$

$r^3 = 27$

$r = \sqrt[3]{27}$

$r = 3$

$a_1 = -\dfrac{12}{3} = -4$

$S_n = \dfrac{-4(1 - 3^{10})}{1 - 3}$

$= \dfrac{-4(1 - 59,049)}{-2}$

$= 2(-59,048)$

$= -118,096$

35. $r = -\frac{6}{2} = -3$

$a_n = 2(-3)^{n-1}$

$$\sum_{n=1}^{6} 2(-3)^{n-1}$$

36. $r = \frac{-162}{243} = \frac{-6}{9} = \frac{-2}{3}$

$a_n = 243\left(-\frac{2}{3}\right)^{n-1}$

$$\sum_{n=1}^{6} 243\left(-\frac{2}{3}\right)^{n-1}$$

37. $244 = \dfrac{a_1(1 - (-3)^5)}{1 - (-3)}$

$244 = \dfrac{a_1(1 + 243)}{4}$

$a_1 = 4$

38. $32 = \dfrac{a_1(1 - 2^6)}{1 - 2}$

$32 = \dfrac{a_1(1 - 64)}{-1}$

$-32 = a_1 \cdot -63$

$a_1 = \dfrac{32}{63}$

39. $324 = a_1 3^{n-1}$

$a_1 = \dfrac{324}{3^{n-1}}$

$484 = \dfrac{a_1(1 - 3^n)}{1 - 3}$

$a_1 = \dfrac{-2 \cdot 484}{1 - 3^n}$

$a_1 = \dfrac{-968}{1 - 3^n}$

$\dfrac{324}{3^{n-1}} = \dfrac{-968}{1 - 3^n}$

$324 - 324 \cdot 3^n = -968 \cdot 3^n \cdot 3^{-1}$

$968 \cdot \dfrac{1}{3} \cdot 3^n - 324 \cdot 3^n = -324$

$3^n\left(\dfrac{1}{3} \cdot 968 - 324\right) = -324$

$3^n = \dfrac{-324}{\frac{4}{3}}$

$3^n = 243$

$\log 3^n = \log 243$

$n \log 3 = \log 243$

$n = \dfrac{\log 243}{\log 3}$

$n = 5$

$324 = a_1 3^{5-1}$

$324 = a_1 3^4$

$324 = a_1 \cdot 81$

$a_1 = 4$

40. $320 = a_1 2^{n-1}$

$a_1 = \dfrac{320}{2^{n-1}}$

$635 = \dfrac{a_1(1 - 2^n)}{1 - 2}$

$635 = \dfrac{a_1(1 - 2^n)}{-1}$

$a_1 = \dfrac{-635}{1 - 2^n}$

$\dfrac{320}{2^{n-1}} = \dfrac{-635}{1 - 2^n}$

$320(1 - 2^n) = -635 \cdot 2^{n-1}$

$635 \cdot 2^{-1} \cdot 2^n - 320 \cdot 2^n = -320$

$2^n\left(635 \cdot \dfrac{1}{2} - 320\right) = -320$

$2^n = \dfrac{-320}{\frac{-5}{2}}$

$2^n = 128$

$\log 2^n = \log 128$

$n \log 2 = \log 128$

$n = \dfrac{\log 128}{\log 2}$

$n = 7$

$320 = a_1 \cdot 2^{7-1}$

$320 = a_1 \cdot 2^6$

$320 = a_1 \cdot 64$

$a_1 = 5$

41. $0.25 = a_1 (0.5)^{n-1}$

$a_1 = \dfrac{0.25}{(0.5)^{n-1}}$

$15.75 = \dfrac{a_1(1 - 0.5)^n}{1 - 0.5}$

$15.75 = \dfrac{a_1 (1 - (0.5)^n)}{0.5}$

$a_1 = \dfrac{7.875}{1 - (0.5)^n}$

$\dfrac{0.25}{(0.5)^{n-1}} = \dfrac{7.875}{1 - (0.5)^n}$

$0.25(1 - (0.5)^n) = 7.875 \cdot (0.5)^{n-1}$

$0.25 - 0.25(0.5)^n = 7.875 \cdot (0.5)^{-1} \cdot (0.5)^n$

$7.785 \cdot 2 \cdot (0.5)^n + 0.25(0.5)^n = 0.25$

$(0.5)^n(15.75 + 0.25) = 0.25$

$(0.5)^n = \dfrac{0.25}{16}$

$(0.5)^n = 0.015625$

$\log (0.5)^n = \log 0.015625$

$n \log (0.5) = \log 0.015625$

$n = \dfrac{\log 0.015625}{\log (0.5)}$

$n = 6$

$0.25 = a_1 (0.5)^{6-1}$

$0.25 = a_1 (0.5)^5$

$0.25 = a_1 \cdot 0.03125$

$a_1 = 8$

42.
$$1022 = \frac{a_1(1 - 2^9)}{1 - 2}$$
$$1022 = \frac{a_1(1 - 512)}{-1}$$
$$-1022 = a_1 \cdot -511$$
$$a_1 = 2$$

43. $S_n = a_1 + a_1 r + a_1 r^2 + a_1 r^3 + \ldots + a_1 r^{n-1}$

Substitute 1 for r.

$$S_n = a_1 + a_1(1) + a_1(1)^2 + a_1(1)^3 + \ldots + a_1(1^{1-1})$$

$S_n = n$ addends of a_1

or

$$S_n = n \cdot a_1$$

44. a. $80 + (0.60)80 + (0.60)^2 \cdot 80 + (0.60)^3 \cdot 80$
$\quad + (0.60)^4 \cdot 80$
$\quad = 80 + 48 + 28.8 + 17.28 + 10.368$
$\quad = 184.448$ ft

b. $184.448 + (0.60)^5 \cdot 80$
$\quad = 184.448 + 6.2208$
$\quad \approx 190.67$ ft

45. $n = 7, r = 2, a_1 = 1$ **46.** $n = 5, a_1 = 1, r = 3$

$$S_n = \frac{1(1 - 2^7)}{1 - 2} \qquad S_n = \frac{1(1 - 3^5)}{1 - 3}$$

$$S_n = \frac{1 - 128}{-1} \qquad = \frac{1 - 243}{-2}$$

$\quad = 127$ people $\qquad = 121$ in.

47. $r = \frac{9}{3} = 3$ **48.** $\quad y = ne^{kt}$

$a_2 = \frac{3}{3} = 1 \qquad 164 = 80e^{3k}$

$a_1 = \frac{1}{3} \qquad e^{3k} = \frac{164}{80}$

$\frac{1}{3}, 1 \qquad\qquad e^{3k} = 2.05$

$\qquad\qquad \ln e^{3k} = \ln 2.05$

$\qquad\qquad 3k \ln e = \ln 2.05$

$\qquad\qquad k = \frac{\ln 2.05}{3}$

$\qquad\qquad k \approx 0.2393$

49.

	w	$=$	r	$\cdot$	t
Danny	1		$\frac{1}{15}$		15
Sonia	1		$\frac{1}{12}$		12

$$8 \cdot \frac{1}{15} + \frac{x}{15} + \frac{x}{12} = 1$$

$$\frac{8 + x}{15} + \frac{x}{12} = 1$$

$$\frac{4}{4} \cdot \frac{8 + x}{15} + \frac{5}{5} \cdot \frac{x}{12} = 1$$

$$\frac{32 + 4x + 5x}{60} = 1$$

$$32 + 9x = 60$$

$$9x = 28$$

$$x = \frac{28}{9} \quad \text{about 3 hours and 7 minutes}$$

50. $m = n$ **51.** $x = \dfrac{\begin{vmatrix} -1 & -7 \\ 13 & 7 \end{vmatrix}}{\begin{vmatrix} 3 & -7 \\ 3 & 7 \end{vmatrix}} \qquad y = \dfrac{\begin{vmatrix} 3 & -1 \\ 3 & 13 \end{vmatrix}}{\begin{vmatrix} 3 & -7 \\ 3 & 7 \end{vmatrix}}$

$$\qquad\qquad = \frac{-7 + 91}{21 + 21} \qquad = \frac{39 + 3}{21 + 21}$$

$$\qquad\qquad = \frac{84}{42} = 2 \qquad = \frac{42}{42} = 1$$

13-6 Infinite Geometric Series

1. because they are geometric series in which there is no "last" term, but the value of each term gets increasingly smaller

2. a. $(0.8)^n$ becomes smaller and smaller as n increases. It seems to be approaching zero.

b. a_n is decreasing and seems to be approaching zero.

c. S_n is increasing and seems to be approaching 125.

3. infinity **4.** only if $|r| < 1$

5. $a_1 = 12, r = \frac{3}{12} = \frac{1}{4}$ **6.** $a_1 = 1, r = -\frac{3}{1} = -3$

$$S = \frac{12}{1 - \frac{1}{4}} \qquad\qquad \text{There is no sum.}$$

$$= \frac{12}{\frac{3}{4}}$$

$$= 16$$

7. $a_1 = 1, r = -\frac{1}{3}$ **8.** $a_1 = \frac{1}{2}, r = \frac{1}{3} + \frac{1}{2} = \frac{2}{3}$

$$S = \frac{1}{1 - \left(-\frac{1}{3}\right)} \qquad S = \frac{\frac{1}{2}}{1 - \frac{2}{3}}$$

$$= \frac{1}{\frac{4}{3}} \qquad\qquad = \frac{\frac{1}{2}}{\frac{1}{3}}$$

$$= \frac{3}{4} \qquad\qquad = \frac{3}{2}$$

9. $a_1 = 48, r = \frac{16}{48} = \frac{1}{3}$ **10.** $a_1 = 1, r = \frac{3}{2}$

$$S = \frac{48}{1 - \frac{1}{3}} \qquad\qquad \text{There is no sum.}$$

$$= \frac{48}{\frac{2}{3}}$$

$$= 72$$

11. $a_1 = 0.7, a_2 = 0.07, r = \frac{0.07}{0.7} = 0.1$

$$S = \frac{0.7}{1 - 0.1}$$

$$= \frac{0.7}{0.9}$$

$$= \frac{7}{9}$$

12. $a_1 = 0.73$, $a_2 = 0.0073$, $r = \dfrac{0.0073}{0.73} = 0.01$

$$S = \frac{0.73}{1 - 0.01}$$

$$= \frac{0.73}{0.99}$$

$$= \frac{73}{99}$$

13. $a_1 = 0.152$, $a_2 = 0.000152$, $r = \dfrac{0.000152}{0.152} = 0.001$

$$S = \frac{0.152}{1 - 0.001}$$

$$= \frac{0.152}{0.999}$$

$$= \frac{152}{999}$$

14. $a_1 = 0.93$, $a_2 = 0.0093$, $r = \dfrac{0.0093}{0.93} = 0.01$

$$S = \frac{0.93}{1 - 0.01}$$

$$= \frac{0.93}{0.99}$$

$$= \frac{93}{99} = \frac{31}{33}$$

PAGES 623-624   EXERCISES

15. $S = \dfrac{7}{1 - \left(-\dfrac{3}{4}\right)}$

$$= \frac{7}{\dfrac{7}{4}}$$

$$= 4$$

16. $S = \dfrac{6}{1 - \dfrac{11}{12}}$

$$= \frac{6}{\dfrac{1}{12}}$$

$$= 72$$

17. $S = \dfrac{18}{1 - \left(-\dfrac{2}{7}\right)}$

$$= \frac{18}{\dfrac{9}{7}}$$

$$= 14$$

18. $a_1 = \dfrac{1}{3}$, $r = \dfrac{\dfrac{1}{9}}{\dfrac{1}{3}} = \dfrac{1}{3}$

$$S = \frac{\dfrac{1}{3}}{1 - \dfrac{1}{3}}$$

$$= \frac{\dfrac{1}{3}}{\dfrac{2}{3}}$$

$$= \frac{1}{2}$$

19. $a_1 = 9$, $r = \dfrac{6}{9} = \dfrac{2}{3}$

$$S = \frac{9}{1 - \dfrac{2}{3}}$$

$$= \frac{9}{\dfrac{1}{3}}$$

$$= 27$$

20. $a_1 = 2$, $r = \dfrac{6}{2} = 3$

S does not exist.

21. $a_1 = \dfrac{3}{4}$, $r = \dfrac{\dfrac{1}{2}}{\dfrac{3}{4}} = \dfrac{2}{3}$

$$S = \frac{\dfrac{3}{4}}{1 - \dfrac{2}{3}}$$

$$= \frac{\dfrac{3}{4}}{\dfrac{1}{3}}$$

$$= \frac{9}{4}$$

22. $a_1 = 1$, $r = -\dfrac{1}{4}$

$$= \frac{1}{1 - \left(-\dfrac{1}{4}\right)}$$

$$= \frac{1}{\dfrac{5}{4}}$$

$$= \frac{4}{5}$$

23. $a_1 = 12$, $r = -\dfrac{4}{12} = -\dfrac{1}{3}$

$$S = \frac{12}{1 - \left(-\dfrac{1}{3}\right)}$$

$$= \frac{12}{\dfrac{4}{3}}$$

$$= 9$$

24. $S = \dfrac{27}{1 - \left(-\dfrac{4}{5}\right)}$

$$= \frac{27}{\dfrac{9}{5}}$$

$$= 15$$

25. $a_1 = 10$, $r = \dfrac{-\dfrac{5}{2}}{10} = -\dfrac{1}{4}$

$$S = \frac{10}{1 - \left(-\dfrac{1}{4}\right)}$$

$$S = \frac{10}{\dfrac{5}{4}}$$

$$= 8$$

26. $a_1 = 12$, $r = \dfrac{6}{12} = \dfrac{1}{2}$

$$S = \frac{12}{1 - \dfrac{1}{2}}$$

$$= \frac{12}{\dfrac{1}{2}}$$

$$= 24$$

27. $a_1 = 3$, $r = -\dfrac{9}{3} = -3$

S does not exist.

28. $a_1 = 3$, $r = -\dfrac{2}{3}$

$$S = \frac{3}{1 - \left(-\dfrac{2}{3}\right)}$$

$$S = \frac{3}{\dfrac{5}{3}}$$

$$= \frac{9}{5}$$

29. $a_1 = 10$, $r = -\dfrac{1}{10}$

$$S = \frac{10}{1 - \left(-\dfrac{1}{10}\right)}$$

$$= \frac{10}{\dfrac{11}{10}}$$

$$= \frac{100}{11}$$

30. $a_1 = 0.9$, $a_2 = 0.09$, $r = \dfrac{0.09}{0.9} = 0.1$

$$S = \frac{0.9}{1 - 0.1}$$

$$= \frac{0.9}{0.9}$$

$$= 1$$

31. $a_1 = 0.31$, $a_2 = 0.0031$, $r = \dfrac{0.0031}{0.31} = 0.01$

$S = \dfrac{0.31}{1 - 0.01}$

$= \dfrac{0.31}{0.99}$

$= \dfrac{31}{99}$

32. $a_1 = 0.410$, $a_2 = 0.000410$, $r = \dfrac{0.000410}{0.410} = 0.001$

$S = \dfrac{0.410}{1 - 0.001}$

$= \dfrac{0.410}{0.999}$

$= \dfrac{410}{999}$

33. $a_1 = 0.05$, $a_2 = 0.005$, $r = \dfrac{0.005}{0.05} = 0.1$

$S = \dfrac{0.05}{1 - 0.1} + 0.4$

$= \dfrac{0.05}{0.9} + 0.4$

$= \dfrac{1}{18} + \dfrac{2}{5}$

$= \dfrac{41}{90}$

34. $a_1 = 50$, $r = 0.9$

a. $S_n = \dfrac{90}{1 - 0.9}$

b. $S_n = \dfrac{50}{1 - 0.9}$

$= \dfrac{50}{0.1}$

$= 500$

500 cm

35. $16 = \dfrac{a_1}{1 - \dfrac{3}{4}}$

$a_1 = 16 \cdot \dfrac{1}{4} = 4$

$a_2 = 4 \cdot \dfrac{3}{4} = 3$

$a_3 = 3 \cdot \dfrac{3}{4} = \dfrac{9}{4}$

$4 + 3 + \dfrac{9}{4}$

36. $28 = \dfrac{a_1}{1 - \left(-\dfrac{2}{7}\right)}$

$a_1 = 28 \cdot \dfrac{9}{7}$

$= 36$

$a_2 = 36 \cdot \left(-\dfrac{2}{7}\right) = -\dfrac{72}{7}$

$a_3 = -\dfrac{72}{7} \cdot \left(-\dfrac{2}{7}\right) = \dfrac{144}{49}$

$36 - \dfrac{72}{7} + \dfrac{144}{49}$

37. $\dfrac{27}{4} = \dfrac{a_1}{1 - \left(-\dfrac{1}{3}\right)}$

$a_1 = \dfrac{27}{4} \cdot \dfrac{4}{3}$

$a_1 = 9$

$a_2 = 9 \cdot \left(-\dfrac{1}{3}\right) = -3$

$a_3 = -3 \cdot \left(-\dfrac{1}{3}\right) = 1$

$9 - 3 + 1$

38. Since $-1 < r < 1$, r^n produces a smaller and smaller number with each increase in the value of n. Eventually r^n approaches 0. Thus, $a_1 - a_1 r^n$ approaches $a_1 - a_1(0)$ or a_1. That is why the numerator of S_n becomes a_1 instead of $a_1 - a_1 r^n$.'

39. $a_1 = 80$, $r = 0.9$

$S = \dfrac{80}{1 - 0.9}$

$= \dfrac{80}{0.1}$

$= 800$ 800 ft

40. $a_1 = 60$, $r = \dfrac{2}{3}$ $a_1 = 60 \cdot \dfrac{2}{3} = 40$, $r = \dfrac{2}{3}$

$S_D = \dfrac{60}{1 - \dfrac{2}{3}}$ $S_U = \dfrac{40}{1 - \dfrac{2}{3}}$

$= \dfrac{60}{\dfrac{1}{3}}$ $= \dfrac{40}{\dfrac{1}{3}}$

$= 180$ $= 120$

The ball traveled 180 in. + 120 in. = 300 in.

41. $24\left(-\dfrac{1}{2}\right)^1 + 24\left(-\dfrac{1}{2}\right)^2 + 24\left(-\dfrac{1}{2}\right)^3 + 24\left(-\dfrac{1}{2}\right)^4$

$= -\dfrac{1}{2}(24) + \dfrac{1}{4}(24) + -\dfrac{1}{8}(24) + \dfrac{1}{16}(24)$

$= -12 + 6 - 3 + \dfrac{3}{2}$

$= -7\dfrac{1}{2}$ or -7.5

42. $a_n = a_1 r^{n-1}$

$48 = 3r^{5-1}$

$48 = 3r^4$

$r^4 = 16$

$r = \pm 2$

For $r = 2$, $a_2 = 3 \cdot 2 = 6$

$a_3 = 6 \cdot 2 = 12$

$a_4 = 12 \cdot 2 = 24$

6, 12, 24

For $r = -2$, $a_2 = 3 \cdot -2 = -6$

$a_3 = -6 \cdot -2 = 12$

$a_4 = 12 \cdot -2 = -24$

-6, 12, -24

43. $f(2) = 2 \cdot 2 + 3 = 4 + 3 = 7$

$h[f(2)] = 7^2 + 4$

$= 49 + 4$

$= 53$

$g[h(f(2))] = 53 - 1$

$= 52$

44. Let x = no. of vacuums over first 10.

$25 + 1.75x = 46$

$1.75x = 21$

$x = 12$

Total vacuums sold to reach maximum

$= 10 + 12 = 22$ vacuums.

45. $2x - 4x - 8 = -2x - 8$

$-2x - 8 = -2x - 8$

$-2x = -2x$

$x = x$

all reals

316

The Binomial Theorem

1. For each coefficient, add the pair of coefficients above its location.

2. 13 terms

3. The Binomial Theorem is a system by which the coefficients are part of a series and the exponents of the two variables in succeeding terms are related in ascending and descending orders.

4. $\dfrac{1}{2}$

5. 362,880

6. 479,001,600

7. 90

8. 26,970

9. 120

10. 210

11. 5 terms

$$4a \cdot 3^3 = 27 \cdot 4a$$
$$= 108a$$

12. 8 terms

$35k^4m^3$

13. 6 terms

$10b^2(-z)^3 = -10b^2z^3$

14. $r^6 + 6r^5s + 15r^4s^2 + 20r^3s^3 + 15r^2s^4 + 6rs^5 + s^6$

15. $y^7 + 7y^6p + 21y^5p^2 + 35y^4p^3 + 35y^3p^4 + 21y^2p^5 + 7yp^6 + p^7$

16. $x^3 - 3x^2y + 3xy^2 - y^3$

17. $r^6 - 6r^5m + 15r^4m^2 - 20r^3m^3 + 15r^2m^4 - 6rm^5 + m^6$

18. $32m^5 + 80m^4y + 80m^3y^2 + 40m^2y^3 + 10my^4 + y^5$

19. $81r^4 + 108r^3y + 54r^2y^2 + 12ry^3 + y^4$

20. $64b^6 + 192b^5x + 240b^4x^2 + 160b^3x^3 + 60b^2x^4 + 12bx^5 + x^6$

21. $16x^4 + 96x^3y + 216x^2y^2 + 216xy^3 + 81y^4$

22. $243x^5 - 810x^4y + 1080x^3y^2 - 720x^2y^3 + 240xy^4 - 32y^5$

23. $64m^6 - 576m^5 + 2160m^4 - 4320m^3 + 4860m^2 - 2916m + 729$

24. $64 + 96x + 60x^2 + 20x^3 + 3.75x^4 + 0.375x^5 + 0.015625x^6$

25. $\dfrac{1}{729}y^6 + \dfrac{2}{27}y^5 + \dfrac{5}{3}y^4 + 20y^3 + 135y^2 + 486y + 729$

26. $\displaystyle\sum_{k=0}^{n} \dfrac{n!}{k!(n-k)!}a^{n-k}b^k$ if $n = 15$, $k = 6$, $a = x$, $b = -y$

$$\dfrac{15!}{6!(15-6)!}x^{15-6}(-y)^4 = 5005x^9y^6$$

27. $\displaystyle\sum_{k=0}^{n} \dfrac{n!}{k!(n-k)!}a^{n-k}b^k$ if $n = 7$, $k = 4$, $a = x$, $b = y$

$$\dfrac{7!}{4!(7-4)!}x^{7-4}y^4 = 35x^3y^4$$

28. $\displaystyle\sum_{k=0}^{n} \dfrac{n!}{k!(n-k)!}a^{n-k}b^k$ if $n = 9$, $k = 3$, $a = 2x$, $b = 3y$

$$\dfrac{9!}{3!(9-3)!}(2x)^{9-3}(3y)^3 = 84(64x^6)(27y^3)$$
$$= 145,152x^6y^3$$

29. $\displaystyle\sum_{k=0}^{n} \dfrac{n!}{k!(n-k)!}a^{n-k}b^k$ if $n = 11$, $k = 7$, $a = 3a$, $b = -5b$

$$\dfrac{11!}{(11-7)!76!}(3a)^{11-7}(-5b)^7 = 330(81a^4)(-78,125b^7)$$
$$= -2,088,281,250a^4b^7$$

30. $\dfrac{k!}{(k-1)!} = \dfrac{k(k-1)(k-2)\ldots}{(k-1)(k-2)\ldots} = k$

31. $\dfrac{(k+3)!}{(k+2)!} = \dfrac{(k+3)(k+2)(k+1)\ldots}{(k+2)(k+1)\ldots} = k+3$

32. $\dfrac{3!4(k-3)!}{(k-2)!} = \dfrac{6(4)(k-3)(k-4)\ldots}{(k-2)(k-3)(k-4)\ldots} = \dfrac{24}{k-2}$

33. $(k+1)!(k+2) = (k+2)(k+1)(k)(k-1)\ldots$ or $(k+2)!$

34. a. The tray has 4 levels at which the ball bearing can go right or left at each peg. Using the expression $(a+b)^4$ we can use the coefficients of the equation (1, 4, 6, 4, 1) whose total is 16.

b. If 64 ball bearings are used, the probability for each tray section is in the same ratio. Just multiply by 4 to get 4(1), 4(4), 4(6), 4(4), 4(1) or 4, 16, 24, 16, 4.

35. Let p = probability of completed pass, or $\dfrac{2}{3}$.

Let q = probability of incompleted pass, or $\dfrac{1}{3}$.

$$(p+q)^6 = p^6 + 6p^5q + 15p^4q^2 + 20p^3q^3 + 15p^2q^4 + 6pq^5 + q^6$$

P(exactly 5 completions) $= 6p^5q$

$$= 6\left(\dfrac{2}{3}\right)^5\left(\dfrac{1}{3}\right)$$
$$= 6\left(\dfrac{32}{243}\right)\left(\dfrac{1}{3}\right)$$
$$= \dfrac{64}{243}$$
$$\approx 0.2633 \text{ or about } 26\dfrac{1}{3}\%$$

36. Let p = probability of success, or $\frac{4}{5}$.

Let q = probability of collapse, or $\frac{1}{5}$.

$(p + q)^6 = p^6 + 6p^5q + 15p^4q^2 + 20p^3q^3 + 15p^2q^4$
$$+ 6pq^5 + q^6$$

$P(\text{exactly 4 successes}) = 15p^4q^2$
$$= 15\left(\frac{4}{5}\right)^4\left(\frac{1}{5}\right)^2$$
$$= 15\left(\frac{256}{625}\right)\left(\frac{1}{25}\right)$$
$$= \frac{768}{3125}$$
$$= 0.24576 \text{ or } 24.576\%$$

37. a. $a^4 + 4a^3b + 6a^2b^2 + 4ab^3 + b^4$

b. $a^{12} + 12a^{11}b + 66a^{10}b^2 + 220a^9b^3 + 495a^8b^4$
$$+ 792a^7b^5 + 924a^6b^6 + 792a^5b^7 + 495a^4b^8$$
$$+ 220a^3b^9 + 66a^2b^{10} + 12ab^{11} + b^{12}$$

c. $x^6 - 6x^5y + 15x^4y^2 - 20x^3y^3 + 15x^2y^4 - 6xy^5$
$$+ y^6$$

d. $x^{10} - 10x^9y + 45x^8y^2 - 120x^7y^3 + 210x^6y^4$
$$- 252x^5y^5 + 210x^4y^6 - 120x^3y^7 + 45x^2y^8$$
$$- 10xy^9 + y^{10}$$

38. $a_1 = \frac{2}{3}$, $r = \dfrac{\frac{1}{3}}{\frac{2}{3}} = \frac{1}{3} \cdot \frac{3}{2} = \frac{1}{2}$

$$S = \frac{\frac{2}{3}}{1 - \frac{1}{2}}$$
$$= \frac{\frac{2}{3}}{\frac{1}{2}}$$
$$= \frac{4}{3}$$

39. $A = Pe^{rt}$

$24{,}000{,}000 = 150e^{0.04t}$

$160{,}000 = e^{0.04t}$

$\ln 160{,}000 = \ln e^{0.04t}$

$\ln 160{,}000 = 0.04t \ln e$

$\dfrac{\ln 160{,}000}{0.04} = t$

$299.573 \approx t$ or about 300 years

40. $\dfrac{3x - 2}{3x - 2} \cdot \dfrac{1}{2x - 3} - \dfrac{2x - 3}{2x - 3} \cdot \dfrac{1}{3x - 2}$

$= \dfrac{3x - 2 - 2x + 3}{(3x - 2)(2x - 3)}$

$= \dfrac{x + 1}{(3x - 2)(2x - 3)}$

41. 2 or 0 positive real zeros; 3 or 1 negative real zeros; 0, 2, or 4 imaginary zeros

Technology: Amortization

PAGE 631   EXERCISES

1. It is figured on the balance of the account which is growing smaller.
2. Add the cells to increase the number of payments to 360.

Chapter 13 Summary and Review

PAGES 632-634   SKILLS AND CONCEPTS

1. $d = 8$

$a_5 = 6 + (5 - 1)8$
$= 6 + 4(8)$
$= 6 + 32$
$= 38$

2. $d = 7$

$a_{22} = -5 + (22 - 1)7$
$= -5 + 21(7)$
$= -5 + 147$
$= 142$

3. $a_9 = 5 + (9 - 1)(-2)$
$= 5 + 8(-2)$
$= 5 - 16$
$= -11$

4. $a_{15} = -2 + (15 - 1)(-3)$
$= -2 + 14(-3)$
$= -2 - 42$
$= -44$

5. $d = 7$

$72 = -5 + (n - 1)7$
$72 = -5 + 7n - 7$
$72 = 7n - 12$
$7n = 84$
$n = 12$
12th

6. $d = -2$

$-37 = 1 + (n - 1)(-2)$
$-37 = 1 - 2n + 2$
$-40 = -2n$
$20 = n$
20th term

7. $d = 5$

$49 = 4 + (n - 1)(5)$
$49 = 4 + 5n - 5$
$50 = 5n$
$10 = n$
10th term

8. $4 = 12 + (4 - 1)d$
$4 = 12 + 3d$
$3d = -8$
$d = -\frac{8}{3}$
$\frac{28}{3}, \frac{20}{3}$

9. $9 = -7 + (5 - 1)d$
$9 = -7 + 4d$
$4d = 16$
$d = 4$
$-3, 1, 5$

10. $-3 = 6 + (4 - 1)d$
$-3 = 6 + 3d$
$3d = -9$
$d = -3$
$9, 3, 0, -6$

11. $S_n = \frac{36}{2}[12 + 117]$
$= 18 \cdot 129$
$= 2322$

12. $d = 6$

$\frac{n}{2}(4 + 106) = \frac{n}{2}[2 \cdot 4 + (n - 1)6]$

$110 \cdot \frac{n}{2} = \frac{n}{2}(8 + 6n - 6)$

$55n = \frac{n}{2}(2 + 6n)$

$55n = n + 3n^2$

$3n^2 - 54n = 0$

$3n(n - 18) = 0$

$n = 18$

$S_n = \frac{18}{2}(4 + 106)$
$= 9(110)$
$= 990$

13. $a_1 = 7 \quad a_n = 88, \ n = 28$

$S_n = \dfrac{28}{2}(7 + 88)$

$\quad = 14 \cdot 95$

$\quad = 1330$

14. $108 = \dfrac{n}{2}(3 + 24)$

$216 = 27n$

$\quad n = 8$

$24 = 3 + (8 - 1)d$

$24 = 3 + 7d$

$21 = 7d$

$\quad d = 3$

$\quad a_1 = 3$

$\quad a_2 = 3 + 3 = 6$

$\quad a_3 = 6 + 3 = 9$

$3, \ 6, \ 9$

15. $r = \dfrac{\frac{4}{3}}{\frac{2}{3}} = \dfrac{4}{3} \cdot \dfrac{3}{2} = \dfrac{4}{2} = 2$

$a_4 = \dfrac{8}{3} \cdot 2 = \dfrac{16}{3}$

$a_5 = \dfrac{16}{3} \cdot 2 = \dfrac{32}{3}$

$a_6 = \dfrac{32}{3} \cdot 2 = \dfrac{64}{3}$

16. $a_5 = 7 \cdot 3^{5-1}$

$a_5 = 7 \cdot 3^4$

$a_5 = 7 \cdot 81$

$a_5 = 567$

17. $r = -\dfrac{12}{4} = -3$

$a_4 = 36(-3) = -108$

$a_5 = -108(-3) = 324$

18. $120 = 7.5r^{5-1}$

$120 = 7.5r^4$

$r^4 = 16$

$r = \sqrt[4]{16}$

$r = 2$

$15, \ 30, \ 60$

19. $S_n = \dfrac{12(1 - 3^5)}{1 - 3}$

$\quad = \dfrac{12(1 - 243)}{-2}$

$\quad = 1452$

20. $16 = 625\left(\dfrac{2}{5}\right)^{n-1}$

$16 = 625\left(\dfrac{2}{5}\right)^n \cdot \dfrac{5}{2}$

$\left(\dfrac{2}{5}\right)^n = 0.01024$

$\log\left(\dfrac{2}{5}\right)^n = \log 0.01024$

$n \log \dfrac{2}{5} = \log 0.01024$

$n = \dfrac{\log 0.01024}{\log \frac{2}{5}}$

$n = 5$

$S_n = \dfrac{625\left(1 - \left(\frac{2}{5}\right)^5\right)}{1 - \frac{2}{5}}$

$\quad = \dfrac{625\left(1 - \frac{32}{3125}\right)}{\frac{3}{5}}$

$\quad = 625 \cdot \dfrac{5}{3} \cdot \dfrac{3093}{3125}$

$\quad = 1031$

21. $S_n = \dfrac{4\left(1 - \left(-\frac{1}{2}\right)^6\right)}{1 - \left(-\frac{1}{2}\right)}$

$\quad = \dfrac{4\left(1 - \frac{1}{64}\right)}{\frac{3}{2}}$

$\quad = 4 \cdot \dfrac{2}{3} \cdot \dfrac{63}{64}$

$\quad = 4 \cdot \dfrac{21}{32}$

$\quad = \dfrac{21}{8}$

22. $1031 = \dfrac{a_1\left(1 - \left(\frac{2}{5}\right)^5\right)}{1 - \frac{2}{5}}$

$1031 = \dfrac{a_1\left(1 - \frac{32}{3125}\right)}{\frac{3}{5}}$

$\left(\dfrac{3}{5}\right)(1031)\left(\dfrac{3125}{3093}\right) = a_1$

$625 = a_1$

23. $30 = \dfrac{a_1(1 - (-2)^4)}{1 - (-2)}$

$30 = \dfrac{a_1(1 - 16)}{3}$

$90 = -15a_1$

$a_1 = -6$

24. $-61 = \dfrac{a_1(1 - (-1)^5)}{1 - (-1)}$

$-61 = \dfrac{a_1(1 - (-1))}{2}$

$-122 = 2a_1$

$a_1 = -61$

25. $s = \dfrac{-2}{1 - \left(-\frac{5}{8}\right)}$

$\quad = \dfrac{-2}{\frac{13}{8}}$

$\quad = -2 \cdot \dfrac{8}{13}$

$\quad = -\dfrac{16}{13}$

26. $r = \dfrac{-\frac{3}{16}}{\frac{1}{8}}$

$\quad = -\dfrac{3}{16} \cdot 8$

$\quad = -\dfrac{3}{2}$

S does not exist.

27. $a_1 = \dfrac{1}{2}\left(\dfrac{1}{3}\right)^{1-1} = \dfrac{1}{2}$

$a_2 = \dfrac{1}{2}\left(\dfrac{1}{3}\right)^{2-1} = \dfrac{1}{2} \cdot \dfrac{1}{3} = \dfrac{1}{6}$

$r = \dfrac{\frac{1}{6}}{\frac{1}{2}} = \dfrac{2}{6} = \dfrac{1}{3}$

$S = \dfrac{\frac{1}{2}}{1 - \frac{1}{3}}$

$\quad = \dfrac{\frac{1}{2}}{\frac{2}{3}}$

$\quad = \dfrac{1}{2} \cdot \dfrac{3}{2}$

$\quad = \dfrac{3}{4}$

28. $a_1 = 0.09, \ a_2 = 0.0009$

$r = \dfrac{0.0009}{0.09}$

$\quad = 0.01$

$s = \dfrac{0.09}{1 - 0.01}$

$\quad = \dfrac{0.09}{0.99}$

$\quad = \dfrac{9}{99} = \dfrac{1}{11}$

29. $a^3 + 3a^2b + 3ab^2 + b^3$

30. $x^4 - 8x^3 + 24x^2 - 32x + 16$

31. $243r^5 + 405r^4s + 270r^3s^2 + 90r^2s^3 + 15rs^4 + s^5$

32. $160x^3y^3$ 33. $-13,107,200x^9$

34. $\pi \approx 4\left(1 - \dfrac{1}{3} + \dfrac{1}{5} - \dfrac{1}{7} + \dfrac{1}{9} - \dfrac{1}{11} + \dfrac{1}{13} - \dfrac{1}{15} + \dfrac{1}{17}\right.$

$\left. - \dfrac{1}{19}\right)$

≈ 3.041839619

35. $d = 20$

$a_{10} = 40 + (10 - 1)20$

$= 40 + 9 \cdot 20$

$= 40 + 180$

$= 220 \text{ ft}$

36. $a_1 = 100, \; r = \dfrac{1}{2}, \; n = 5$

$S_n = \dfrac{100\left(1 - \left(\dfrac{1}{2}\right)^5\right)}{1 - \dfrac{1}{2}}$

$= \dfrac{100\left(1 - \dfrac{1}{32}\right)}{\dfrac{1}{2}}$

$= 100 \cdot 2 \cdot \dfrac{31}{32}$

$= \dfrac{200 \cdot 31}{32}$

$= 193\dfrac{3}{4}$ 193.75 feet

37. $a_1 = 900,000, \; r = \dfrac{3}{4}, \; n = 5$

$a_5 = 900,000 \cdot \left(\dfrac{3}{4}\right)^{5-1}$

$= 900,000 \cdot \left(\dfrac{3}{4}\right)^4$

$= 900,000 \cdot \dfrac{81}{256}$

$\approx 284,766$

$\$284,766$

38. $a_1 = 5, \; d = 2, \; n = 20$

$a_{20} = 5 + (20 - 1)2$

$= 5 + 2 \cdot 19$

$= 5 + 38$

$= 43$

43 diamonds

Chapter 13 Test

1. 360, 2160, 15,120

2. $a_1 = 27, \; a_n = 414, \; d = 9$

$414 = 27 + (n - 1)9$

$414 = 27 + 9n - 9$

$414 = 18 + 9n$

$9n = 396$

$n = 44$

44 integers

3. $d = -5$

$a_4 = 32 - 5 = 27$

$a_5 = 27 - 5 = 22$

$a_6 = 22 - 5 = 17$

$a_7 = 17 - 5 = 12$

27, 22, 17, 12

4. $r = \dfrac{\dfrac{1}{9}}{\dfrac{1}{27}} = \dfrac{1}{9} \cdot 27 = 3$

$\dfrac{1}{9} \cdot 3 = \dfrac{1}{3}$

$\dfrac{1}{3} \cdot 3 = 1$

5. $a_{27} = 2 + (27 - 1)6$ 6. $a_6 = 5(-2)^{6-1}$

$= 2 + 26 \cdot 6$ $= 5(-2)^5$

$= 2 + 156$ $= 5 \cdot -32$

$= 158$ $= -160$

7. $127 = 7 + (31 - 1)d$

$127 = 7 + 30d$

$120 = 30d$

$d = 4$

$S_n = \dfrac{31}{2}[2 \cdot 7 + (31 - 1)4]$

$= \dfrac{31}{2}(14 + 30 \cdot 4)$

$= \dfrac{31}{2}(14 + 120)$

$= \dfrac{31}{2} \cdot 134$

$= 2077$

8. $S_n = \dfrac{125\left(1 - \left(\dfrac{2}{5}\right)^4\right)}{1 - \dfrac{2}{5}}$

$= \dfrac{125\left(1 - \dfrac{16}{625}\right)}{\dfrac{3}{5}}$

$= 125 \cdot \dfrac{5}{3} \cdot \dfrac{609}{625}$

$= 125 \cdot \dfrac{203}{125}$

$= 203$

9. 1, 6, 11

10. $189 = 7r^{4-1}$

$189 = 7r^3$

$r^3 = 27$

$r = \sqrt[3]{27}$

$r = 3$

$a_2 = 7 \cdot 3 = 21$

$a_3 = 21 \cdot 3 = 63$

21, 63

11. $a_1 = 8$, $a_2 = 6$, $d = -2$

$S_n = \frac{13}{2}[2 \cdot 8 + (13 - 1)(-2)]$

$= \frac{13}{2}(16 + 12 \cdot -2)$

$= \frac{13}{2}(16 - 24)$

$= \frac{13}{2}(-8)$

$= -52$

12. $a_1 = \frac{1}{3}$, $a_2 = -\frac{2}{3}$, $r = \dfrac{-\frac{2}{3}}{\frac{1}{3}} = -2$

S does not exist.

13. $a_1 = 91$, $d = -6$

$\frac{n}{2}(91 - 29) = \frac{n}{2}[2 \cdot 91 + (n - 1)(-6)]$

$\frac{n}{2} \cdot 62 = \frac{n}{2}(182 - 6n + 6)$

$31n = \frac{n}{2}(188 - 6n)$

$31n = 94n - 3n^2$

$63n - 3n^2 = 0$

$3n(21 - n) = 0$

$n = 21$

$S_n = \frac{21}{2}[2 \cdot 91 + (21 - 1)(-6)]$

$= \frac{21}{2}(182 - 20 \cdot 6)$

$= \frac{21}{2}(182 - 120)$

$= \frac{21}{2} \cdot 62$

$= 651$

14. $a_1 = 12$, $r = \frac{-6}{12} = -\frac{1}{2}$

$S = \dfrac{12}{1 + \frac{1}{2}}$

$= \dfrac{12}{1\frac{1}{2}}$

$= 8$

15. $0.3\overline{2} = 0.3 + 0.0\overline{2}$

$0.0\overline{2} = 0.02 + 0.002 + \ldots$

$0.3\overline{2} = \frac{3}{10} + \dfrac{0.02}{1 - 0.1}$

$= \frac{3}{10} + \dfrac{0.02}{0.9}$

$= \frac{3}{10} + \frac{2}{90}$

$= \frac{27}{90} + \frac{2}{90}$ or $\frac{29}{90}$

16. $32s^5 - 240s^4t + 720s^3t^2 - 1080s^2t^3 + 810st^4$

$- 243t^5$

17. $28x^6y^2$ **18.** 8, 13

19. $a_1 = 1$, $r = \frac{6}{7}$, $n = 5$

$a_5 = 1 \cdot \left(\frac{6}{7}\right)^4$

$= \frac{1296}{2401}$

$\approx 54\%$

20. $a_1 = 20$, $d = -3$, $a_n = 0$

$0 = 20 + (n - 1)(-3)$

$-20 = -3n + 3$

$-3n = -23$

$n \approx 8$

8 rows

Total bricks = 20 + 17 + 14 + 11 + 8 + 5 + 2

$= 77$

PAGE 635   BONUS

$a_1 = 60$, $a_2 = 30$, $r = \frac{30}{60} = \frac{1}{2}$

$S = \dfrac{30}{1 - \frac{1}{2}}$

$= \dfrac{60}{\frac{1}{2}}$

$= 120$ 120 inches

Chapter 14   Statistics

14-1   Problem-Solving Strategy: Make a Graph

1. Answers may vary. Samples are: bar - number of students of each grade in a school; circle - breakdown of ages of people in American population; line - profit of a company over 10 years.

2. $(0.40)(4) = 1.60$
   $1.60 goes to the bookstore.

3. no; The people at home to answer the phone probably do not work outside the home.

4. Answers may vary.

5. a. 3,400,000 people

   b. $\frac{104}{115.5} \times 100 \approx 90\%$

   c.

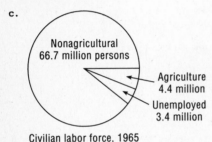

   Civilian labor force, 1965

6.

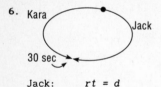

Jack: $rt = d$ $rt = d$

         $r(55) = 1$ $\frac{1}{55}(30) = d$

           $r = \frac{1}{55}$ $\frac{30}{55} = d$

Kara: $d = 1 - \frac{30}{55} = \frac{25}{55}$

           $rt = d$ $rt = d$

         $r(30) = \frac{25}{55}$ $\frac{25}{1650}t = 1$

           $r = \frac{25}{1650}$ $t = 66$

Kara can run a lap in 66 seconds.

7. $\dfrac{3^{x+3} - 3(3^x)}{3(3^{x+2})} = \dfrac{3^{x+3} - 3^{x+1}}{3^{x+3}}$

   $= \dfrac{3^{x+3}}{3^{x+3}} - \dfrac{3^{x+1}}{3^{x+3}}$

   $= 1 - 3^{(x+1)-(x+3)}$

   $= 1 - 3^{-2}$

   $= \dfrac{8}{9}$

8. Let $\ell + 0.2\ell$ = length of medium size carton.
   Let $w + 0.3w$ = width of medium size carton.
   Let h = height of medium size carton.
   $$V = (\ell + 0.2\ell)(w + 0.3w)h$$
   $$= (1.2\ell)(1.3w)h$$
   $$= 1.56\ell wh$$

   Difference in volumes: $1.56\ell wh - \ell wh = 0.56\ell wh$
   The volume of medium size carton is 56% greater.

9. $$|x - 2|^2 - 2|x - 2| = 8$$
   $$|x - 2|^2 - 2|x - 2| - 8 = 0$$
   $$(|x - 2| - 4)(|x - 2| + 2) = 0$$

   $|x - 2| - 4 = 0$ or $|x - 2| + 2 = 0$

   $|x - 2| = 4$ $|x - 2| = -2$

   $x - 2 = 4$ or $x - 2 = -4$ never true

   $x = 6$ $x = -2$

10.

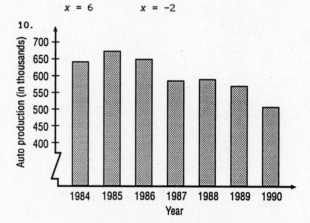

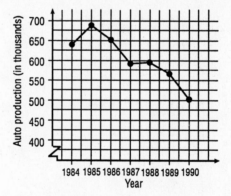

11. beginning at 12:00 midnight, the hands meet at approximately these times:
    1:05 AM, 2:10 AM, 3:15 AM, 4:20 AM, 5:25 AM,
    6:30 AM, 7:35 AM, 8:40 AM, 9:45 AM, 10:50 AM,
    11:55 AM, 12 noon, 1:05 PM, 2:10 PM, 3:15 PM,
    4:20 PM, 5:25 PM, 6:30 PM, 7:35 PM, 8:40 PM,
    9:45 PM, 10:50 PM, 11:55 PM, 12 midnight
    24 times

12. Democratic: $\frac{13}{42}(360) \approx (0.32)(360) \approx 115°$

Democratic-Rep: $\frac{4}{42}(360) \approx (0.10)(360) \approx 36°$

Federalist: $\frac{2}{42}(360) \approx (0.05)(360) \approx 18°$

Republican: $\frac{17}{42}(360) \approx (0.41)(360) \approx 148°$

Union: $\frac{1}{42}(360) \approx (0.02)(360) \approx 7°$

Whig: $\frac{4}{42}(360) \approx (0.10)(360) \approx 36°$

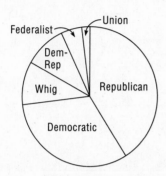

13. List possible palindromes and determine which ones are prime numbers.

11, 101, 131, 151, 181, 191, 313, 353, 373, 383, 727, 757, 787, 797, 919, and 929

14. For 17, try 2 and 3 (primes less than $\sqrt{17}$).

For 37, try 2, 3, and 5 (primes less than $\sqrt{37}$).

Etc.

The number of divisions is the number of primes less than the square root of the number.

PAGE 641   COOPERATIVE LEARNING ACTIVITY

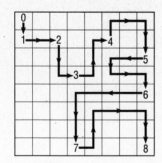

14-2 Line Plots and Stem-and-Leaf Plots

PAGE 645   CHECKING FOR UNDERSTANDING

1. Answers may vary.

2. The two plots are not very different. The distributions are similar. Neither is more accurate than the other.

3. Answers may vary. A sample answer is populations of cities in the 1980 and the 1990 national census.

4. a. 51　　**b.** 1　　**c.** 16　　**d.** 5 or 11

5. a. 299　　**b.** 277　　**c.** 11　　**d.** 280, 290

PAGES 645-647   EXERCISES

6. a.

```
                 X  XX X
              X   XXXX    X
            X XXXX XXXX   X  X
       XX  XXXXXX XXXX XXX XX   XX
      +++++++++++++++++++++++++++++
      40    45   50   55   60   65   70
```

b. 69　　**c.** 42　　**d.** 69 − 42 = 27 years

e. 42　　**f.** 51, 54, 55, 57　　**g.** 10

7. a.

Stem	Leaf
6	8
7	0 3
•	5 6 8 9
8	0 0 1 1 1 2 2 2

7 | 3 represents 73 games.

b. Ewing, Pippen, and Lewis

c. Robinson　　**d.** 82 − 68 = 14 games

e. 81 or 82　　**f.** 6 players

g.

Stem	Leaf
15	1 7 8
16	9
17	0 2 3 7
18	0 9
19	0 7
20	7
21	
22	7
23	
24	0

16 | 9 represents 1690 points.

h. Jordan　　**i.** Olajuwon

j. 2404 − 1510 = 894 points　　**k.** 12 players

l.

Stem	Leaf
2	1 1 2 2 2 2 3 3 3 3 4
•	5 6 8
3	0

2 | 3 represents 23 points.

m. Jordan　　**n.** Lewis

o. 30.1 − 20.8 = 9.3 points

p. none　　**q.** 3 players

8. a.

Men	Stem	Women
	17	3
	16	
5	15	
	14	
7	13	
	12	
3	11	
0	10	9 7
	9	
	8	2
9	7	
6		
5		2

|8| 2 represents $820,000.

b. The men earned slightly more than the women.

9. Answers may vary.

10.

```
   X     XX   X XX X    X    X   X
  ++++++++++++++++++++++++++++
  5 6 7 8 9 10 11 12 13 14 15 16 17
Monica Seles
```

11.
```
Stem | Leaf
   4 | 2 3
   • | 6 6 7 8 9 9
   5 | 0 0 1 1 1 1 2 2 4 4 4 4
   • | 5 5 5 5 6 6 6 7 7 7 7 8
   6 | 0 1 1 1 2 4 4
   • | 5 8 9
```
4 | 2 represents 42 years old.

Most of the presidents were 50-59.

12.

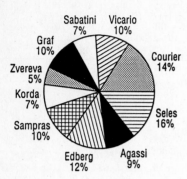

13. $a_1 = 10 + (1 - 1)(2.2)$ $a_2 = 10 + (2 - 1)(2.2)$

     $= 10$ $= 12.2$

   $a_3 = 10 + (3 - 1)(2.2)$ $a_4 = 10 + (4 - 1)(2.2)$

     $= 14.4$ $= 16.6$

   $a_5 = 10 + (5 - 1)(2.2)$

     $= 18.8$

14. $9^{\log_9 2} = 2$

15.
```
 3| 1   1    1    1    1      -2| 1   1    1   1    1
   |     3   12   39  120       |    -2   2  -6   10
   ─────────────────────        ────────────────────
     1   4   13   40 |121         1  -1   3  -5 |11
```

16. $f(x) = 5(3x - 2)^2 + 4$

     $= 5(9x^2 - 12x + 4) + 4$

     $= 45x^2 - 60x + 24$

17. Let k = Kari's age.

Let m = her mother's age.

     $k + m = 52$ $\Rightarrow$ $k + (k + 20) = 52$

        $m = k + 20$ $2k + 20 = 52$

                            $k = 16$

   $m = k + 20$ Kari is 16 and her

     $= 16 + 20$ mother is 36.

     $= 36$

14-3   Central Tendency: Median, Mode, and Mean

PAGE 651   CHECKING FOR UNDERSTANDING

1. Michael Jackson, Jane Fonda

2. 5 million to 65 million

3. See students' work.

4. whenever extreme values are present that distort the arithmetic mean

5. {0, 2, 4, 4, 5}

median: 4   mode: 4

mean: $\dfrac{0 + 2 + 4 + 4 + 5}{5} = 3$

6. {2, 4, 6, 8, 10}

median: 6   mode: none

mean: $\dfrac{2 + 4 + 6 + 8 + 10}{5} = 6$

7. {9, 9, 9, 9, 9, 9}

median: 9   mode: 9   mean: 9

8. {1, 1, 1, 2, 4}

median: 1   mode: 1

mean: $\dfrac{1 + 1 + 1 + 2 + 4}{5} = 1.8$

9. {2, 8, 43, 44, 56}

median: 43   mode: none

mean: $\dfrac{2 + 8 + 43 + 44 + 56}{5} = 30.6$

10. {239, 299, 318, 399, 399}

median: 318   mode: 399

mean: $\dfrac{239 + 299 + 318 + 399 + 399}{5} = 330.8$

PAGES 651-652   EXERCISES

11. {2.1, 2.1, 2.1, 4.8, 4.8, 5.7}

median: $\dfrac{2.1 + 4.8}{2} = 3.45$

mode: 2.1

mean: $\dfrac{3(2.1) + 2(4.8) + 5.7}{6} = 3.6$

12. {179, 180, 216, 219, 399, 399}

median: $\dfrac{216 + 219}{2} = 217.5$

mode: 399

mean: $\dfrac{179 + 180 + 216 + 219 + 2(399)}{6} \approx 265.3$

13. {10, 11, 12, 12, 13, 13, 15}

median: 12

mode: 12 and 13

mean: $\dfrac{10 + 11 + 2(12) + 2(13) + 15}{7} \approx 12.3$

14. {50, 50, 55, 65, 65, 70, 75, 80}

median: 65

mode: 50 and 65

mean: $\dfrac{2(50) + 55 + 2(65) + 70 + 75 + 80}{8} \approx 63.8$

15. {45, 97, 98, 100, 101, 105}

median: $\dfrac{98 + 100}{2} = 99$

mode: none

mean: $\dfrac{45 + 97 + 98 + 100 + 101 + 105}{6} = 91$

16. {2.0, 2.1, 2.2, 2.2, 2.2, 2.3, 2.4}

median: 2.2

mode: 2.2

mean: $\dfrac{2.0 + 2.1 + 3(2.2) + 2.3 + 2.4}{7} = 2.2$

17. {1, 1, 1, 1, 1, 2, 2, 2, 3, 3, 4, 4, 4, 4, 4, 5, 5, 5, 5, 6, 6, 6, 6, 6, 6}

median: 4   mode: 6

mean: $\dfrac{5(1) + 3(2) + 2(3) + 5(4) + 4(5) + 6(6)}{25}$

≈ 3.7

18. {25,895; 25,910; 25,925; 26,000; 26,041; 26,090; 26,291; 26,360; 26,400; 26,470; 26,504; 26,660; 26,750; 26,760; 26,810; 27,790; 27,890; 28,208; 29,064; 29,108}

median: $\dfrac{26{,}470 + 26{,}504}{2} = 26{,}487$

mode: none

mean: $\dfrac{\text{sum of above numbers}}{20} = 26{,}846.3$

19. 10 at $7.75
10 at 6.25
60 at 5.90
100 at 5.00
20 at 4.50

median: $5.00   mode: $5.00

mean:

$\dfrac{10(7.75)+10(6.25)+60(5.90)+100(5.00)+20(4.50)}{200}$

$= \$5.42$

20. median: 27   mode: 16, 27

mean: $\dfrac{\text{sum of the scores}}{25} = 29$

21. a. mean; It is higher.

b. mode; It is lower and is what most employees make. It reflects the most representative worker.

22. The mean of a set of data {x_1, x_2, x_3, ..., x_n} is the sum of the data divided by the number of pieces of data.

This can be written as $\dfrac{1}{n}\displaystyle\sum_{i=1}^{n} x_i$.

23. See students' work.

24. Male: median: $420

mode: $420

mean: $\dfrac{\text{sum of male incomes}}{13} \approx 432.31$

Female: median: $290

mode: $240

mean: $\dfrac{\text{sum of female incomes}}{13} \approx 313.08$

Male workers make more than female workers.

25. $\dfrac{1}{25} = \dfrac{8.2}{x}$

$x = (8.2)(25)$

$= 205$ miles

26. focus: $\left(h, \ k + \dfrac{1}{4a}\right) = (0, 3)$

$h = 0$

$k + \dfrac{1}{4a} = 3$

directrix: $k - \dfrac{1}{4a} = -1$ $\left.\right\}\longrightarrow$

$k + \dfrac{1}{4a} = 3$

$k - \dfrac{1}{4a} = -1$

$\overline{\qquad\qquad}$

$2k \quad = 2$

$k = 1$

$k + \dfrac{1}{4a} = 3$ $y = a(x - h)^2 + k$

$1 + \dfrac{1}{4a} = 3$ $y = \dfrac{1}{8}(x - 0)^2 + 1$

$\dfrac{1}{4a} = 2$ $y = \dfrac{1}{8}x^2 + 1$

$a = \dfrac{1}{8}$

27. $6\begin{bmatrix} 5 & 6 \\ 0 & -2 \end{bmatrix} = \begin{bmatrix} 6(5) & 6(6) \\ 6(0) & 6(-2) \end{bmatrix} = \begin{bmatrix} 30 & 36 \\ 0 & -12 \end{bmatrix}$

28. $\left| x - \dfrac{7}{3} \right| = 6$

$x - \dfrac{7}{3} = 6$ or $x - \dfrac{7}{3} = -6$

$x = \dfrac{25}{3}$ $x = -\dfrac{11}{3}$

14-4 **Variation: Range, Interquartile Range, and Outliers**

PAGE 655   CHECKING FOR UNDERSTANDING

1. 14 - (-80) = 94   **2.** record low temperatures

3. See students' work.   **4.** See students' work.

5. 325 - 175 = 150   **6.** 51 - 29 = 22

7. 82 - 3 = 79   **8.** 77 - 41 = 36

9. 46 - 30 = 16

10. {175, 200, 225, 250, 275, 300, 325}

lower quartile: 200

median: 250

upper quartile: 300

interquartile range: 300 - 200 = 100

11. {29, 36, 37, 38, 38, 40, 45, 47, 48, 51}

lower quartile: 37

median: 39

upper quartile: 47

interquartile range: 47 - 37 = 10

12. {3, 7, 8, 9, 12, 13, 15, 19, 19, 22, 31, 81}

lower quartile: $\dfrac{8 + 9}{2} = 8.5$

median: $\dfrac{13 + 15}{2} = 14$

upper quartile: $\dfrac{19 + 22}{2} = 20.5$

interquartile range: 20.5 - 8.5 = 12

13. lower quartile: $\dfrac{49 + 52}{2} = 50.5$

         median: 59

   upper quartile: $\dfrac{65 + 72}{2} = 68.5$

   interquartile range: $68.5 - 50.5 = 18$

14. lower quartile: 34

         median: 38

   upper quartile: 44

   interquartile range: $44 - 34 = 10$

PAGES 656-657   EXERCISES

15. {1, 1, 1, 2, 3, 4, 4, 5, 7, 7, 7, 7, 8, 11, 20}

         range: $20 - 1 = 19$

   lower quartile: 2

         median: 5

   upper quartile: 7

   interquartile range: $7 - 2 = 5$

16. {23, 47, 47, 49, 49, 51, 54, 57, 58, 82}

         range: $82 - 23 = 59$

   lower quartile: 47

         median: $\dfrac{49 + 51}{2} = 50$

   upper quartile: 57

   interquartile range: $57 - 47 = 10$

17. {975, 1005, 1025, 1055, 1075, 1075, 1095, 1100, 1125, 1125, 1145}

         range: $1145 - 975 = 170$

   lower quartile: 1025

         median: 1075

   upper quartile: 1125

   interquartile range: $1125 - 1025 = 100$

18. {53, 57, 59, 63, 64, 65, 65, 66, 71, 75, 76, 81, 82, 85, 88, 95, 96, 98}

         range: $98 - 53 = 45$

   lower quartile: 64

         median: $\dfrac{71 + 75}{2} = 73$

   upper quartile: 85

   interquartile range: $85 - 64 = 21$

19.   range: $490 - 10 = 480$

   lower quartile: $\dfrac{150 + 170}{2} = 160$

         median: $\dfrac{250 + 280}{2} = 265$

   upper quartile: $\dfrac{330 + 360}{2} = 345$

   interquartile range: $345 - 160 = 185$

20.   range: $8.9 - 4.0 = 4.9$

   lower quartile: $\dfrac{6.4 + 6.5}{2} = 6.45$

         median: 6.8

   upper quartile: 7.2

   interquartile range: $7.2 - 6.45 = 0.75$

21. $2 - 1.5(5) = -5.5$

   $7 + 1.5(5) = 14.5$

   outliers: 20

22. $47 - 1.5(10) = 32$

   $57 + 1.5(10) = 72$

   outliers: 23, 82

23. $1025 - 1.5(100) = 875$

   $1125 + 1.5(100) = 1275$

   outliers: none

24. $64 - 1.5(21) = 32.5$

   $85 + 1.5(21) = 116.5$

   outliers: none

25. $160 - 1.5(185) = -117.5$

   $345 + 1.5(185) = 622.5$

   outliers: none

26. $6.45 - 1.5(0.75) = 5.325$

   $7.2 + 1.5(0.75) = 8.325$

   outliers: 4.0, 8.5, 8.9

27. {130, 140, 150, 150, 175, 180, 180, 200, 230, 235, 239, 265, 275, 275, 290, 298, 350, 350, 396, 500}

         range: $500 - 130 = 370$

   lower quartile: $\dfrac{175 + 180}{2} = 177.5$

         median: $\dfrac{235 + 239}{2} = 237$

   upper quartile: $\dfrac{290 + 298}{2} = 294$

   interquartile range: $294 - 177.5 = 116.5$

   $177.5 - 1.5(116.5) = 2.75$

   $294 + 1.5(116.5) = 468.75$

   outliers: 500

28. See students' work.

29. {19, 19, 21, 21, 25, 26, 33, 34, 35, 48, 49, 60, 80, 92, 121}

         range: $121 - 19 = 102$

   lower quartile: 21

         median: 34

   upper quartile: 60

   interquartile range: $60 - 21 = 39$

   $21 - 1.5(39) = -37.5$

   $60 + 1.5(39) = 118.5$

   outliers: 121

30. {30, 35, 39, 40, 40, 40, 41, 45, 47, 47, 49, 50, 51, 52, 54, 58, 60, 60, 65, 66, 87}

         range: $87 - 30 = 57$

   lower quartile: 40

         median: 49

   upper quartile: $\dfrac{58 + 60}{2} = 59$

   interquartile range: $59 - 40 = 19$

   $40 - 1.5(19) = 11.5$

   $59 + 1.5(19) = 87.5$

   outliers: none

31. median: 49   mode: 40

mean: $\dfrac{\text{sum of bike helmet prices}}{21} = 50.3$

32. first term: 2   common ratio: $\dfrac{6}{2} = 3$

last term: 162   number of terms: 5

33. $x = 3y - 4$

$3y = x + 4$

$y = \dfrac{x + 4}{3}$

$f^{-1}(x) = \dfrac{x + 4}{3}$

34. $x\sqrt{5} + x = 3$

$x(\sqrt{5} + 1) = 3$

$x = \dfrac{3}{\sqrt{5} + 1}$

$= \dfrac{3}{\sqrt{5} + 1} \cdot \dfrac{\sqrt{5} - 1}{\sqrt{5} - 1}$

$= \dfrac{3\sqrt{5} - 3}{5 - 1}$

$= \dfrac{3\sqrt{5} - 3}{4}$

35. $3a^3b^2(-2ab^2 + 4a^2b - 7a)$

$= -6a^4b^4 + 12a^5b^3 - 21a^4b^2$

36. $c = 10\left(t - \dfrac{1}{2}\right) + 35$

PAGE 657   MID-CHAPTER REVIEW

1.

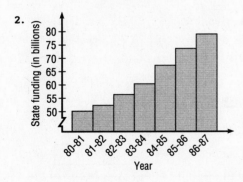

2.

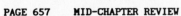

3. Federal: $\dfrac{9,956,009}{149,004,882} = 6.7\%$

State: $\dfrac{73,673,174}{149,004,882} = 49.4\%$

Local: $\dfrac{63,375,698}{149,004,882} = 43.9\%$

Sources of funding
for 1985-1986

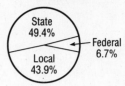

4.

rounded	stem	truncated
6	4	5 9
7 3 0	5	2 7
5 1	6	1 5 9
0	7	

Using rounded data, 1 | 6 | represents
\$60,500,000,000 to \$61,499,999,000.

Using truncated data, | 6 | 1 represents
\$61,000,000,000 to \$61,999,999,000.

5.

```
X  X   X   X       X       X        X
+++++++++++++++++++++++++++++++++++++
50        60        70        80
          Billions ($)
```

6. median: 9,105,569,000

mode: none

mean: $\dfrac{\text{sum of federal funding}}{7} = 9,154,106,000$

7. range: 158,827,473,000 - 105,949,087,000

$= 52,878,386,000$

lower quartile: 110,191,257,000

median: 126,055,419,000

upper quartile: 149,004,882,000

interquartile range:

149,004,882,000 - 110,191,257,000

$= 38,813,625,000$

110,191,257,000 - 1.5(38,813,625,000)

$= 51,970,819,500$

149,004,882,000 - 1.5(38,813,625,000)

$= 207,225,319,500$

outliers: none

14-5 **Box-and-Whisker Plots**

PAGE 660   CHECKING FOR UNDERSTANDING

1. Roy Roger's cheeseburger   **2.** 25% each

3. Sample answers: quartiles, range, outliers, dispersion

4. It is greatly dispersed.

5. a. 30 - 10 = 20   **b.** 26   **c.** 25%   **d.** 21 and 28

6. a. 50%   **b.** 75%   **c.** 50%

d. The least value and the lower quartile are the same value.

7. a. 700 - 490 = 210   **b.** 670, 700

c. 50%   **d.** 75%

8. {125, 200, 211, 220, 239, 240, 240, 250, 327}

lower quartile: $\dfrac{200 + 211}{2}$ = 205.5

median: 239

upper quartile: $\dfrac{240 + 250}{2}$ = 245

interquartile range: 245 - 205.5 = 44.5

205.5 - 1.5(44.5) = 138.75

245 + 1.5(44.5) = 311.75

outliers: 125, 327

least value: 200

greatest value: 250

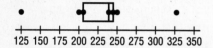

9. {57.7, 61.5, 63.6, 67, 67.4, 68.7, 69.1, 69.2, 70, 71.9, 72.8, 73.3, 75.8, 75.8, 76.7, 78.4, 82.5, 83.3, 113.3, 126.7}

lower quartile: $\dfrac{67.4 + 68.7}{2}$ = 68.05

median: $\dfrac{71.9 + 72.8}{2}$ = 72.35

upper quartile: $\dfrac{76.7 + 78.4}{2}$ = 77.55

interquartile range: 77.55 - 68.05 = 9.5

68.05 - 1.5(9.5) = 53.8

77.55 + 1.5(9.5) = 91.8

outliers: 113.3, 126.7

least value: 57.7

greatest value: 83.3

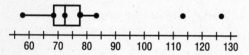

10. lower quartile: $\dfrac{19 + 20}{2}$ = 19.5

median: 28

upper quartile: $\dfrac{54 + 31}{2}$ = 42.5

interquartile range: 42.5 - 19.5 = 23

19.5 - 1.5(23) = -15

42.5 + 1.5(23) = 77

outliers: 82, 108, 112

least value: 18

greatest value: 54

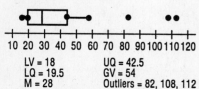

LV = 18   UQ = 42.5
LQ = 19.5   GV = 54
M = 28   Outliers = 82, 108, 112

11. median: 210   outliers: none

lower quartile: 195   greatest value: 255

upper quartile: 225   least value: 178

interquartile range: 30

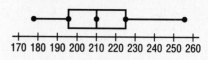

12. a. median: 166

lower quartile: 158

upper quartile: 176

interquartile range: 18

outliers: 129, 204, 221

greatest value: 201

least value: 134

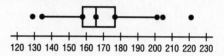

b.

Stem	Leaf
12	9
13	4 9
14	4 9
15	3 4 4 8
16	0 1 1 2 3 5 5
	6 6 6 7 7 7 8 9
17	0 0 1 2 6 8
18	7 8
19	0 7
20	0 1 4
21	
22	1

c. mode: 166, 167

median: 166

The medians should be the same. You cannot find a mode comparison.

13. a. <u>Men</u>:

median: 24.6   outliers: none

lower quartile: 23.2   greatest value: 26.2

upper quartile: 25.9   least value: 22.8

interquartile range: 2.7

<u>Women</u>:

median: 21.5   outliers: 25.1

lower quartile: 20.8   greatest value: 22.0

upper quartile: 22.0   least value: 20.3

interquartile range: 1.2

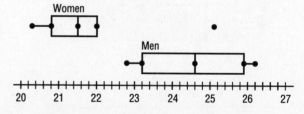

b. Men marry at a later age than women.

c. See students' work.

14. The upper quartile is the same as the greatest value, and the lower quartile is the same as the least value.

15. median: 961   outliers: none

lower quartile: 877   greatest value: 1450

upper quartile: 1399   least value: 775

interquartile range: 522

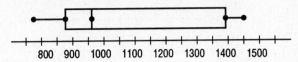

16. median: 225   outlier: 342

lower quartile: 196.5   greatest value: 290

upper quartile: 249   least value: 194

interquartile range: 52.5

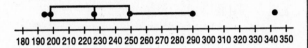

17. range: $342 - 194 = 148$

lower quartile: 196.5

median: $\dfrac{214 + 236}{2} = 225$

upper quartile: $\dfrac{254 + 244}{2} = 249$

interquartile range: $249 - 196.5 = 52.5$

$196.5 - 1.5(52.5) = 117.75$

$249 + 1.5(52.5) = 327.75$

outlier: 342

18. $\displaystyle\sum_{n=0}^{5} 4^{n-2} = 4^{0-2} + 4^{1-2} + 4^{2-2} + 4^{3-2} + 4^{4-2} + 4^{5-2}$

$= \dfrac{1}{16} + \dfrac{1}{4} + 1 + 4 + 16 + 64$

$= 85\dfrac{5}{16}$

19. $\log_{10}(y - 1) + \log_{10}(y + 2) = \log_7 7$

$\log_{10}(y - 1)(y + 2) = \log_7 7$

$\log_{10}(y^2 + y - 2) = 1$

$10^1 = y^2 + y - 2$

$y^2 + y - 12 = 0$

$(y - 3)(y + 4) = 0$

$y - 3 = 0$ or $y + 4 = 0$

$y = 3$ $y = -4$

Since log is not defined for negative numbers, -4 is not an acceptable solution.

20. $\dfrac{x^2 - y^2}{x} \div \dfrac{y - x}{x^2} = \dfrac{x^2 - y^2}{x} \cdot \dfrac{x^2}{y - x}$

$= \dfrac{x^2(x - y)(x + y)}{-x(x - y)}$

$= -x(x + y)$

$= -x^2 - xy$

21. $(x + 8)^2 + (y - 3)^2 = 25$

center: $(-8, 3)$

radius: $\sqrt{25} = 5$

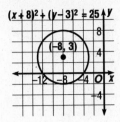

PAGE 662   **CHALLENGE**

Make a list:

$A = 2, 14, 26, 38, 50, 62, 74, 86, 98, 110, 122, 134, \ldots$

$B = 1, 8, 15, 22, 29, 36, 43, 50, 57, 64, 71, 78, 85, 92, 99, 106, 113, 120, 127, 134, \ldots$

three common terms: 50, 134, 218

Technology: Statistical Graphs

PAGE 663   **EXERCISES**

1.

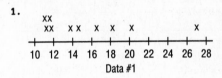

2.

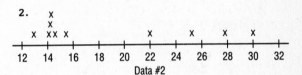

3.

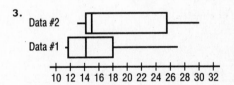

4.

Data #2	Stem	Data #1
	11	4 5 7 8
9	12	
	13	8
6 3 2 1	14	6
4	15	
	16	3
	17	
	18	1
	19	
	20	2
	21	
0	22	
	23	
	24	
4	25	
	26	
9	27	0
	28	
	29	
0	30	

$30 \mid 0 = 30.0$

14-6 Variation: Standard Deviation

1. See students' work.   2. vary greatly

3. do not vary greatly

4. $\bar{x} = \dfrac{55+40+39+32+61+53+60+40+33+44}{10} = 45.7$

standard deviation:

$$\sqrt{\dfrac{\begin{array}{l}(9.3)^2 + (5.7)^2 + (6.7)^2 + (13.7)^2 \\ + (15.3)^2 + (7.3)^2 + (14.3)^2 \\ + (5.7)^2 + (12.7)^2 + (1.7)^2\end{array}}{10}}$$

= 10.2   \$10.2 million

The revenues vary less than those of the top 16.

5. mean: $\dfrac{11 + 7 + 4 + 2 + 1}{5} = 5$

standard deviation:

$$\sqrt{\dfrac{(6)^2 + (2)^2 + (-1)^2 + (-3)^2 + (-4)^2}{5}}$$

$= \sqrt{\dfrac{66}{5}} = 3.6$

6. mean: $\dfrac{14 + 8 + 6 + 4 + 2 + 2}{6} = 6$

standard deviation:

$$\sqrt{\dfrac{(8)^2 + (2)^2 + (0)^2 + (-2)^2 + (-4)^2 + (-4)^2}{6}}$$

$= \sqrt{\dfrac{104}{6}} = 4.2$

7. mean: 250

standard deviation:

$$\sqrt{\dfrac{\begin{array}{l}(0)^2 + (25)^2 + (75)^2 + (50)^2 \\ + (-50)^2 + (-25)^2 + (-75)^2\end{array}}{7}}$$

$= \sqrt{\dfrac{17,500}{7}} = 50$

8. mean:

$\dfrac{39 + 47 + 51 + 38 + 45 + 29 + 37 + 40 + 36 + 48}{10}$

= 41

standard deviation:

$$\sqrt{\dfrac{\begin{array}{l}(2)^2 + (6)^2 + (10)^2 + (-3)^2 + (4)^2 \\ +(-12)^2 + (-4)^2 + (-1)^2 + (-5)^2 + (7)^2\end{array}}{10}}$$

$= \sqrt{\dfrac{400}{10}} = 6.3$

9. mean: 82.2

standard deviation:

$$\sqrt{\dfrac{\begin{array}{l}(-1.2)^2 + (12.8)^2 + (-3.2)^2 + (2.8)^2 \\ + (-0.2)^2 + (7.8)^2 + (-19.2)^2 + (1.8)^2 \\ + (1.8)^2 + (2.8)^2 + (-2.2)^2 + (-10.2)^2 \\ + (-0.2)^2 + (2.8)^2 + (3.8)^2\end{array}}{15}}$$

= 7.1

10. mean: 4

standard deviation:

$$\sqrt{\dfrac{3^2 + 2(1)^2 + 8(0)^2 + 3(-1)^2 + (-2)^2}{15}}$$

= 1.1

11. mean: 1075

standard deviation:

$$\sqrt{\dfrac{\begin{array}{l}(70)^2 + (25)^2 + (50)^2 + (-25)^2 \\ + (100)^2 + (-240)^2 + 0^2 + (20)^2\end{array}}{8}}$$

= 97.9

12. mean: 3.9

standard deviation:

$$\sqrt{\dfrac{\begin{array}{l}(-0.9)^2 + (-0.9)^2 + (-0.8)^2 \\ + (-0.7)^2 + (-0.5)^2 + (-0.4)^2 \\ + (-0.3)^2 + (-0.3)^2 + (-0.2)^2 \\ + (-0.1)^2 + (0)^2 + (0.2)^2 \\ + (0.2)^2 + (0.4)^2 + (0.5)^2 \\ + (0.5)^2 + (0.6)^2 + (0.6)^2 \\ + (0.7)^2 + (0.7)^2\end{array}}{20}}$$

= 0.55

13. mean: 60

standard deviation:

$$\sqrt{\dfrac{\begin{array}{l}(-19)^2 + (-17)^2 + (-11)^2 + (-8)^2 \\ + (-7)^2 + (-4)^2 + (-1)^2 + (4)^2 + (4)^2 \\ + (5)^2 + (7)^2 + (8)^2 + (12)^2 + (14)^2 \\ + (17)^2\end{array}}{15}}$$

= 10.6

14. a. mean: 200

standard deviation:

$$\sqrt{\dfrac{\begin{array}{l}(-40)^2 + (-20)^2 + (-10)^2 + (0)^2 \\ + (10)^2 + (-30)^2 + (50)^2 + (20)^2 \\ + (-20)^2 + (0)^2 + (40)^2\end{array}}{11}}$$

= 27

b. mean: 200

standard deviation:

$$\sqrt{\dfrac{\begin{bmatrix}(-40)^2 + (-10)^2 + (10)^2 + (30)^2 \\ + (40)^2 + (20)^2 + (-50)^2 + (-10)^2 \\ + (10)^2 + (-40)^2 + (40)^2\end{bmatrix}}{11}}$$

= 31

c. mean: 202

standard deviation:

$$\sqrt{\dfrac{\begin{bmatrix}(-32)^2 + (-17)^2 + (3)^2 + (8)^2 + (3)^2 \\ + (13)^2 + (-17)^2 + (18)^2 + (3)^2 \\ + (-32)^2 + (48)^2\end{bmatrix}}{11}}$$

= 22

d. Ridgemont

15. a. mean: 21.5

standard deviation:

$$\sqrt{\dfrac{\begin{bmatrix}(0.5)^2 + (-7.5)^2 + (11.5)^2 \\ + (-10.5)^2 + (3.5)^2 + (-10.5)^2 \\ + (0.5)^2 + (-7.5)^2 + (14.5)^2 \\ + (13.5)^2 + (6.5)^2 + (-1.5)^2 \\ + (14.5)^2 + (-6.5)^2 + (-0.5)^2 \\ + (-9.5)^2 + (0.5)^2 + (-11.5)^2\end{bmatrix}}{18}}$$

$$= \sqrt{\dfrac{1390.5}{18}} = 8.8$$

b. mean: 22.4

standard deviation:

$$\sqrt{\dfrac{\begin{bmatrix}(9.6)^2 + (-6.4)^2 + (-0.4)^2 \\ + (1.6)^2 + (0.6)^2 + (-9.4)^2 \\ + (0.6)^2 + (8.6)^2 + (-7.4)^2 \\ + (-1.4)^2 + (1.6)^2 + (4.6)^2 \\ + (7.6)^2 + (-1.4)^2 + (-10.4)^2 \\ + (1.6)^2\end{bmatrix}}{16}}$$

$$= \sqrt{\dfrac{549.76}{16}} = 5.9$$

c. mean: 22.1

standard deviation:

$$\sqrt{\dfrac{\begin{bmatrix}(2.9)^2 + (-9.1)^2 + (1.9)^2 \\ + (-4.1)^2 + (6.9)^2 + (-10.1)^2 \\ + (7.9)^2 + (-6.1)^2 + (2.9)^2 \\ + (-1.1)^2 + (5.9)^2 + (2.9)^2 \\ + (10.9)^2 + (-11.1)^2 + (-0.1)^2 \\ + (-10.1)^2 + (7.9)^2 + (-6.1)^2 \\ + (5.9)^2 + (0.9)^2\end{bmatrix}}{20}}$$

$$= \sqrt{\dfrac{893}{20}} = 6.7$$

d. Selby Sales

16.

Stem	Leaf
27	1 2
28	4 4
29	6
30	3 6 6 7
31	1 1 2 7
32	3 5 9
33	1 5
34	0 5 7 8
35	0 6
36	5
37	1 9
38	4
39	
40	
41	
42	
43	
44	8
45	
46	
47	
48	
49	
50	4

36 | 5 represents
36.5 points.

mode: 28.4, 30.6, 31.1

mean: 33.53

lower quartile: 30.6

median: 32.7

upper quartile: 35.0

interquartile range: 4.4

standard deviation: 4.8

outliers: 44.8, 50.4

17. when all the data are equal

18. mean: $8.74

standard deviation:

$$\sqrt{\dfrac{\begin{bmatrix}(-4.29)^2 + 2(-3.24)^2 + (-2.44)^2 \\ + (-0.94)^2 + (2.26)^2 + (3.46)^2 \\ + (8.46)^2\end{bmatrix}}{8}}$$

= $4.11

19. mean: 11.09°

standard deviation:

$$\sqrt{\dfrac{\begin{bmatrix}(0.11)^2 + (0.08)^2 + (-0.17)^2 \\ + (-0.03)^2 + (0.1)^2 + (-0.12)^2 \\ + 0^2 + (-0.04)^2 + (0.13)^2 + (-0.06)^2\end{bmatrix}}{10}}$$

= 0.097

20. $2.7^x = 52.3$

$x \log 2.7 = \log 52.3$

$$x = \dfrac{\log 52.3}{\log 2.7}$$

$$= 3.9839$$

21. $f(x) = x^4 - 6x^3 - 3x^2 - 24x - 28$

$\dfrac{p}{q}$: ±1, ±2, ±4, ±7, ±14, ±28

$\dfrac{p}{q}$	1	-6	-3	-24	-28
-1	1	-7	4	-28	0

$\dfrac{p}{q}$	1	-7	4	-28
7	1	0	4	0

$x^2 + 4 = 0 \longrightarrow$ no rational zeros

So, the rational zeros are -1 and 7.

22. $x^2 - 7x - 8 \leq 0$

$(x - 8)(x + 1) \leq 0$

$x - 8 \leq 0$ and $x + 1 \geq 0$

$\quad x \leq 8 \quad$ and $\quad x \geq 1$

$\qquad -1 \leq x \leq 8$

$\qquad\qquad$ or

$x - 8 \geq 0$ and $x + 1 \leq 0$

$\quad x \geq 8 \quad$ and $\quad x \leq -1$

$\qquad\qquad$ never true

$\qquad \{x \mid -1 \leq x \leq 8\}$

23. $2\ell + 2w = 44 \longrightarrow \ell = 22 - w$

$\quad \ell w = 117$

$\ell w = 117$	$\ell w = 117$
$(22 - w)w = 117$	$\ell(9) = 117$
$22w - w^2 = 117$	$\ell = 13$

$w^2 - 22w + 117 = 0$

$(w - 9)(w - 13) = 0 \qquad\qquad \ell w = 117$

$w - 9 = 0$ or $w - 13 = 0 \qquad \ell(13) = 117$

$\quad w = 9 \qquad\quad w = 13 \qquad\quad \ell = 9$

The dimensions are 9 by 13 units.

14-7 The Normal Distribution

PAGE 670   CHECKING FOR UNDERSTANDING

1. See students' work.   **2.** x; y

3. the center

4. 13.5% + 34% + 34% + 13.5% = 95%

5. Answers may vary. A sample answer is the number of days students attend school in a year.

6. a. 34% + 34% = 68%

$\quad (0.68)(500) = 340$

b. 13.5% + 34% + 34% + 13.5% = 95%

$\quad (0.95)(500) = 475$

c. 2% + 13.5% + 34% + 34% + 13.5% + 2% = 99%

$\quad (0.99)(500) = 495$

d. $(0.34)(500) = 170$

e. 34% + 13.5% = 47.5%

$\quad (0.475)(500) = 237.5$

---

7. a. 34% + 34% = 68%   **b.** 34%

c. 13.5% + 34% + 34% + 13.5% + 2% + 0.5% = 97.5%

d. 2% + 13.5% + 34% + 34% + 13.5% = 97%

$\quad (0.97)(100) = 97$

8. a. 34% + 34% = 68%

$\quad (10,000)(0.68) = 6800$

b. 13.5% + 34% + 34% + 13.5% = 95%

$\quad (10,000)(0.95) = 9500$

c. 34% + 13.5% + 2% + 0.5% = 50%

$\quad (10,000)(0.50) = 5000$

d. 34% + 13.5% + 2% + 0.5% = 50%

$\quad (10,000)(0.50) = 5000$

e. 2% + 0.5% = 2.5%

$\quad (10,000)(0.025) = 250$

f. 0.5%

$\quad (10,000)(0.005) = 50$

9. a. 50%   **b.** 2% + 13.5% = 15.5%

c. 13.5% + 34% + 34% + 13.5% = 95%

10. a. $(0.50)(1000) = 500$

b. 13.5% + 34% + 34% = 81.5%

$\quad (0.815)(1000) = 815$

c. $(0.005)(1000) = 5$

d. 0.5% + 2% = 2.5%

$\quad (0.025)(1000) = 25$

11. Answers may vary. A typical answer will be no, since the sample is so small.

12. a.

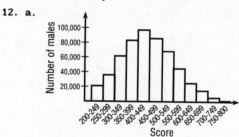

b.

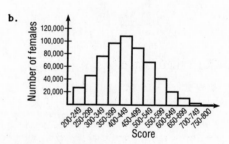

c. male student scores

d. Answers may vary.

13. a. rejected

b. X1 = 10 * 0.3 = 3

$\quad$ X2 = 10 * 0.7 = 7

$\quad$ Since X1 is less than 5, the procedure is stopped.

c. yes

14. $a_8 = 2(8) + 1 \qquad a_9 = 2(9) + 1 \qquad a_{10} = 2(10) + 1$

$\qquad = 17 \qquad\qquad = 19 \qquad\qquad = 21$

15.
$$\log_5(4x) = \log_5(x^2 - 5)$$
$$4x = x^2 - 5$$
$$x^2 - 4x - 5 = 0$$
$$(x - 5)(x + 1) = 0$$
$$x - 5 = 0 \text{ or } x + 1 = 0$$
$$x = 5 \qquad x = -1$$

Since log is not defined for negative numbers, -1 is not an acceptable solution.

16. $\dfrac{a + 1}{a^2 - 1} + \dfrac{2}{4a - 4} = \dfrac{a + 1}{(a + 1)(a - 1)} + \dfrac{2}{4(a - 1)}$

$$= \frac{1}{a - 1} + \frac{1}{2(a - 1)}$$

$$= \frac{2}{2(a - 1)} + \frac{1}{2(a - 1)}$$

$$= \frac{3}{2(a - 1)}$$

17.
$$8x^2 - 16x + 4y^2 - 20y = 7$$
$$8(x^2 - 2x + 1) + 4(y^2 - 5y + 6.25) = 7 + 8 + 25$$
$$8(x - 1)^2 + 4(y - 2.5)^2 = 40$$
$$\frac{(x - 1)^2}{5} + \frac{(y - 2.5)^2}{10} = 1$$

ellipse

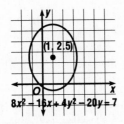

PAGE 673   APPLICATION

No, sum = 112%. The most possible is 100%.

Chapter 14 Summary and Review

PAGES 674-676   SKILLS AND CONCEPTS

1.

```
              X        X       X
              X    X X X X XXXXX X
        +--+--+--+--+--+--+--+--+--+
        2.0      2.5     3.0     3.5
```
Average number of goals per game

2.

Stem	Leaf
25	3 3
26	
27	
28	1 9 9
29	
30	0 9
31	3 5 9
32	2 2 6
33	5

33 | 5 represents 3.35.

3. {2.7, 5.0, 6.3, 7.1, 8.1, 8.5, 9.1}

median: 7.1   mode: none

mean: $\dfrac{2.7 + 5.0 + 6.3 + 7.1 + 8.1 + 8.5 + 9.1}{7}$

≈ 6.7

4. {2.1, 2.1, 2.1, 2.1, 4.8, 4.8, 5.7}

median: 2.1   mode: 2.1

mean: $\dfrac{4(2.1) + 2(4.8) + 5.7}{7} \approx 3.4$

5. {14,255; 15,781; 18,700; 19,344; 20,270; 21,201; 22,835; 25,263; 28,146; 29,002}

median: $\dfrac{20{,}270 + 21{,}201}{2} = 20{,}735.5$

mode: none

mean: $\dfrac{\text{sum of above numbers}}{10} = 21{,}479.7$

6. {3, 6, 7, 7, 7, 7, 9, 10, 10, 10, 10, 10, 13, 14, 14, 16, 17, 17, 19, 20, 21, 31}

median: 10   mode: 10

mean: $\dfrac{\text{sum of above numbers}}{22} \approx 12.6$

7. {78, 79, 84, 85, 86, 88, 89, 90, 92, 93}

range: 93 - 78 = 15

lower quartile: 84

median: $\dfrac{88 + 86}{2} = 87$

upper quartile: 90

interquartile range: 90 - 84 = 6

84 - 1.5(6) = 75

90 + 1.5(6) = 99

outliers: none

8. {0.1, 0.2, 0.2, 0.3, 0.4, 0.4, 0.4, 0.5, 0.5, 0.5, 0.6, 0.7, 0.8, 0.9, 1.9}

range: 1.9 - 0.1 = 1.8

lower quartile: 0.3

median: 0.5

upper quartile: 0.7

interquartile range: 0.7 - 0.3 = 0.4

0.3 - 1.5(0.4) = -0.3

0.7 + 1.5(0.4) = 1.3

outliers: 1.9

9. {19, 93, 94, 94, 95, 96, 98, 99, 100, 100, 101, 104, 104, 106, 108, 109, 125}

range: 125 - 19 = 106

lower quartile: 94.5

median: 100

upper quartile: 105

interquartile range: 105 - 94.5 = 10.5

94.5 - 1.5(10.5) = 78.75

105 + 1.5(10.5) = 120.75

outliers: 19, 125

10. {0, 10, 40, 40, 50, 50, 60, 90, 90}

range: $90 - 0 = 90$

lower quartile: $\dfrac{10 + 40}{2} = 25$

median: 50

upper quartile: $\dfrac{60 + 90}{2} = 75$

interquartile range: $75 - 25 = 50$

$25 - 1.5(50) = -50$

$75 + 1.5(50) = 150$

outliers: none

11. range: $58 - 11 = 47$

lower quartile: $\dfrac{22 + 25}{2} = 23.5$

median: $\dfrac{35 + 36}{2} = 35.5$

upper quartile: $\dfrac{41 + 42}{2} = 41.5$

interquartile range: $41.5 - 23.5 = 18$

$23.5 - 1.5(18) = -3.5$

$41.5 + 1.5(18) = 68.5$

outliers: none

12. LV = 32,206   UQ = 227,009.5

LQ = 104,569   UV = 364,080

M = 127,258   Outlier = None

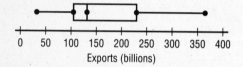

Exports (billions)

13. median: 4.98

standard deviation:

$$\sqrt{\dfrac{\begin{bmatrix}(0.22)^2 + (0.72)^2 + (1.02)^2 \\ + (0.62)^2 + (-2.58)^2\end{bmatrix}}{5}}$$

≈ 1.3

14. median: 14.75

standard deviation:

$$\sqrt{\dfrac{\begin{bmatrix}2(-1.05)^2 + 2(0.05)^2 + (0.25)^2 \\ + (2.15)^2 + (-1.15)^2 + (-0.45)^2 \\ + (0.35)^2 + (0.65)^2 + (0.15)^2\end{bmatrix}}{11}}$$

≈ 0.9

15. median: 3407

standard deviation:

$$\sqrt{\dfrac{\begin{bmatrix}(-917)^2 + (293)^2 + (893)^2 + (-1037)^2 \\ + (1323)^2 + (-302)^2 + (649)^2 \\ + (-502)^2 + (-1277)^2 + (-477)^2 \\ + (-637)^2 + (-87)^2 + (-23)^2 \\ + (1343)^2 + (93)^2 + (671)^2\end{bmatrix}}{16}}$$

≈ 784.6

16. median: 2193

standard deviation:

$$\sqrt{\dfrac{\begin{bmatrix}(1396)^2 + (4288)^2 + (-2076)^2 \\ + (1557)^2 + (-1693)^2 + (1649)^2 \\ + (-445)^2 + (1166)^2 + (-818)^2 \\ + (1469)^2 + (-317)^2 + (-1392)^2 \\ + (-1993)^2\end{bmatrix}}{13}}$$

$= 1819.8$

17. $(0.5)(3000) = 1500$

18. $13.5\% + 34\% + 34\% = 81.5\%$

$(0.815)(3000) = 2445$

19. $2\% + 0.5\% = 2.5\%$

PAGE 676   APPLICATIONS AND CONNECTIONS

20. a.

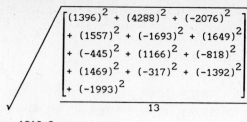

b.

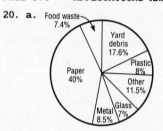

21. a. median: $\dfrac{6,066,136 + 5,976,588}{2} = 6,021,362$

mode: none

mean: $\dfrac{\text{sum of the numbers}}{12} = 6,706,047.4$

b. range: $11,781,270 - 4,908,985 = 6,872,285$

lower quartile: 5,448,988.5

median: 6,021,362

upper quartile: 7,464,143.5

interquartile range: 2,015,155

$5,448,988.5 - 1.5(2,015,155) = 2,426,256$

$7,464,143.5 + 1.5(2,015,155) = 10,486,876$

outlier: 11,781,270

22. a.

Stem	Leaf
1	0 3 5 6 7 9
2	1 3 4 5
3	9 9

2 | 1 represents 21.

b.

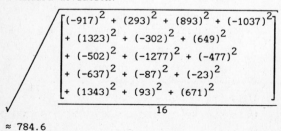

c. median: $\dfrac{19 + 21}{2} = 20$ mode: 39

   mean: $\dfrac{10+13+15+16+17+19+21+23+24+25+2(39)}{12}$

   $= 21.75$

23. a. 13.5% + 2% + 0.5% = 16%

   (0.16)(10,000) = 1600

   b. 0.5% + 2% = 2.5%

   (0.025)(10,000) = 250

   c. 2% + 13.5% + 34% + 34% + 13.5% = 97%

   d. 0.5% + 2% + 13.5% + 34% + 34% + 13.5% = 97.5%

Chapter 14 Test

PAGE 677

1.

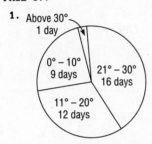

Above 30°
1 day

0° – 10°
9 days

21° – 30°
16 days

11° – 20°
12 days

2.

```
                              x
              x               x                x  x
              x x       x     x x x      x x  x x x  x x
x  x   x x x  x         x x    x x x   x  x x  x x x  x x x
+--+--+--+--+--+--+--+--+--+--+--+--+--+--+--+--+
0  2  4  6  8  10 12 14 16 18 20 22 24 26 28 30
```

3. $31 - 0 = 31°F$

4. median: $18°F$ mode: $16°F$

   mean: $\dfrac{\text{sum of above numbers}}{40} = 17.97°F$

5.

Stem	Leaf
0	0 2 4
•	5 5 5 6 6 8
1	2 2 3
•	6 6 6 6 7 7 8 8
2	0 2 2 3 3
•	5 5 6 6 7 7 7 9 9 9
3	0 0 1

   1 | 2 = 12°

   • | 6 = 16°

6. lower quartile: $12°$

   median: $18°$

   upper quartile: $26°$

   interquartile range: $14°$

7. 12 - (1.5)14 = -9

   26 + (1.5)14 = 37

   outliers: none

8.

```
        +---+---+
  •-----|   •   |-----•
        +---+---+
+--+--+--+--+--+--+--+
0  5  10 15 20 25 30 35
```

9. standard deviation ≈ 9.1

10.
   20 at $4.50
   100 at $5.00   median: $5.00
   60 at $5.25   mode: $5.00
   10 at $5.75   mean: $5.15
   10 at $6.75

11.

Stem	Leaf
4	0
5	0
6	0
7	0 5 9
8	0 0 5
9	0 0
10	0
11	
12	0 0 5
13	
14	8 9
15	0
16	0
17	
18	
19	0
.	
.	
.	
40	0

12. median: $90

   mode: $80, $90, and $120

   mean: $117.19

13. range: $360

   lower quartile: $77

   median: $90

   upper quartile: $148.50

   interquartile range: $71.50

   77 - 1.5(71.50) = -30.25

   148.50 + 1.5(71.50) = 255.75

   outliers: $400

14.

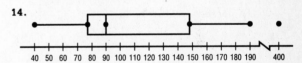

```
        +-----+--------------+
  •-----|     |              |-----•     •
        +-----+--------------+
+--+--+--+--+--+--+--+--+--+--+--+--+--/\--+
40 50 60 70 80 90 100 110 120 130 140 150 160 170 180 190   400
```

15. standard deviation:

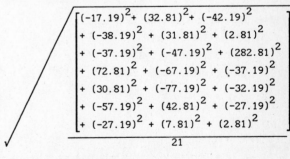

$$\sqrt{\dfrac{\begin{matrix}(-17.19)^2+ (32.81)^2+ (-42.19)^2 \\ + (-38.19)^2 + (31.81)^2 + (2.81)^2 \\ + (-37.19)^2 + (-47.19)^2 + (282.81)^2 \\ + (72.81)^2 + (-67.19)^2 + (-37.19)^2 \\ + (30.81)^2 + (-77.19)^2 + (-32.19)^2 \\ + (-57.19)^2 + (42.81)^2 + (-27.19)^2 \\ + (-27.19)^2 + (7.81)^2 + (2.81)^2\end{matrix}}{21}}$$

$= \sqrt{\dfrac{115015.2381}{21}} = 74.01$

   (calc = 74.0061896)

16. (0.5)(50,000) = 25,000

17. (0.68)(50,000) = 34,000

18. 0.5% + 2% + 13.5% + 34% + 34% + 13.5% = 97.5%

19. 0.5%

20. 6 at $85,000   median: $85,000

    3 at $100,000   mode: $85,000

    1 at $225,000   mean: $103,500

                  the mean

PAGE 677   BONUS

variance = (standard diviation)^2

$$= (74.01)^2$$

$$= \$5477.48 \quad \text{calc} = \$5476.9161 \approx \$5476.92$$

Chapter 14
College Entrance Exam Preview

PAGES 678–679

1. $0 < 0.4 < 1$, therefore $\sqrt{0.4} > 0.4$.

The correct choice is B.

2. Since the intervals overlap, and since no other information is given, then no conclusion can be drawn.

The correct choice is D.

3. Recall the rules for adding and subtracting signed numbers. Since $n < 0$ and $b < 0$, $n + b = -(|n| + |b|) < 0$. If $n = b$, $n - b = 0$ and $n + b < n - b$. If $n > b$, $n - b > 0$ and $n + b < n - b$. If $n < b$, $|n| > |b|$ and $n - b = -(|n| - |b|)$. Clearly $|n| + |b| > |n| - |b|$ so $-(|n| + |b|) < -(|n| - |b|)$ and $n + b < n - b$.

The correct choice is B.

4. $\frac{1}{10}(1 \cdot 2 \cdot 3 \cdot 4 \cdot 5 \cdot 6 \cdot 7 \cdot 8 \cdot 9 \cdot 10)$

$= 1 \cdot 2 \cdot 3 \cdot 4 \cdot 5 \cdot 6 \cdot 7 \cdot 8 \cdot 9 \cdot \frac{10}{10}$

$= 1 \cdot 2 \cdot 3 \cdot 4 \cdot 5 \cdot 6 \cdot 7 \cdot 8 \cdot 9$

The correct choice is C.

5. $(0.12)(1600) = 192$

$(0.165)(1200) = 198$

The correct choice is B.

6. If $y = 2$, $\frac{y}{3} = \frac{2}{3}$ and $\frac{3}{y} = \frac{3}{2}$,

$\frac{2}{3} < \frac{3}{2}$.

If $y = 6$, $\frac{y}{3} = 2$, and $\frac{3}{y} = \frac{1}{2}$,

$2 > \frac{1}{2}$.

The correct choice is D.

7. $\frac{2}{3} \div \frac{5}{7} = \frac{2}{3} \cdot \frac{7}{5} = \frac{14}{15}$ $\frac{14}{15} > \frac{6}{17}$

The correct choice is A.

8. $*0.4 = 1$ $*1.0 = 1$

The correct choice is C.

9. $\frac{a + b + c}{3} = \frac{a + d + c + 1}{3}$

$= \frac{a + d + c}{3} + \frac{1}{3}$

The correct choice is A.

10. Let $c = 2$. If $d = 2$, $[1 + (-c)]^d = 1$ and $(-c)^d = 4$. $1 < 4$. If $d = 3$, $[1 + (-c)]^d = -1$ and $(-c)^d = -8$. $-1 > -8$.

The correct choice is D.

11. $\frac{b^9}{b^4} = b^5$ $\frac{b^{10}}{b^5} = b^5$

The correct choice is C.

12. $5 = \frac{2}{c}$ $\frac{5}{b} = 2$

$c = \frac{2}{5}$ $b = \frac{5}{2}$

$c + \frac{1}{3} = \frac{2}{5} + \frac{1}{3}$ $b - \frac{11}{6} = \frac{5}{2} - \frac{11}{6}$

$= \frac{11}{15}$ $= \frac{2}{3} = \frac{10}{15}$

$\frac{11}{15} > \frac{2}{3}$

The correct choice is A.

13. Since $\frac{4}{k} < 0$, $\frac{1}{k} < 0$ and $-\frac{1}{k} > 0$.

Since $\frac{1}{k} < 0$, $k < 0$ and $4k < 0$.

The correct choice is A.

14. Since $\frac{1}{k} < 0$, $-\frac{1}{k} > 0$.

Since $\frac{1}{k} < 0$, $k > 0$.

The correct choice is A.

15. $\frac{3^4 + 3^5}{3^4} = \frac{3^4}{3^4} + \frac{3^5}{3^4} = 1 + 3 = 4$

$\frac{3^2 + 3^3}{3^2} = \frac{3^2}{3^2} + \frac{3^3}{3^2} = 1 + 3 = 4$

The correct choice is C.

16. $\frac{8!}{2!6!} = \frac{8 \cdot 7}{2 \cdot 1} = 28$

$4! = 4 \cdot 3 \cdot 2 \cdot 1 = 24$

The correct choice is A.

17. $2 + (-4) + 8 + (-16) + 32 + (-64) + 128$

The sum of the first six terms is a negative number. The sum of the first seven terms is a positive number.

The correct choice is B.

18. If $x \geq 0$, $3^x \geq 3^{-x}$.

If $x < 0$, $3^x < 3^{-x}$.

The correct choice is D.

19. Since a and b are supplementary, $a + b = 180$.

So, $a = 180 - b$.

The correct choice is C.

20. $0 < 0.2 < 1$, therefore $\sqrt{0.2} > 0.2$ and

$(0.2)^2 < 0.2$. So, $\sqrt{0.2} > (0.2)^2$.

The correct choice is A.

21. $\quad a > b \qquad\qquad c > d$

$a - d > b - d \qquad\qquad -c < -d$

$\qquad\qquad\qquad\qquad b - c < b - d$

$a - d > b - d > b - c$

The correct choice is A.

22. area of inner circle: πx^2

area of shaded region: $\pi(2x)^2 - \pi x^2$

$\qquad\qquad\qquad = 4\pi x^2 - \pi x^2$

$\qquad\qquad\qquad = 3\pi x^2$

The correct choice is B.

23.
$$\begin{array}{cccc} A & B & C & D \end{array}$$

—●——●——●——●—: 4 points

The correct choice is B.

24. $RA = \frac{1}{2}RB \qquad\qquad SB = \frac{1}{2}(SA)$

$\quad = \frac{1}{2}(2AB) \qquad\qquad = \frac{1}{2}(2AB)$

$\quad = AB \qquad\qquad\quad = AB$

The correct choice is C.

Chapter 15   Probability

15-1   **Problem-Solving Strategy:**
Using Models

1. lists, tree diagrams

2. The numbers may be too great to physically assemble each situation.

3. **a.** (1, 1), (1, 2), (1, 3), (1, 4),
   (1, 5), (1, 6), (2, 1), (2, 2),
   (2, 3), (2, 4), (2, 5), (2, 6),
   (3, 1), (3, 2), (3, 3), (3, 4),
   (3, 5), (3, 6), (4, 1), (4, 2),
   (4, 3), (4, 4), (4, 5), (4, 6),
   (5, 1), (5, 2), (5, 3), (5, 4),
   (5, 5), (5, 6), (6, 1), (6, 2),
   (6, 3), (6, 4), (6, 5), (6, 6)

   b. 1 + 1 = 2

   c. 6 + 6 = 12

   d. 7, because more combinations for 7 exist than for any other number between 2 and 12.

4. Find the LCM of 12, 16, and 20.
   LCM = 3 · 4 · 4 · 5 = 240

5. Matrix logic can be used.

   Clue 1: If a coin is black, then it cannot be small or worth 17 cents.

   If a coin is small, then it cannot be black or worth 17 cents.

   If a coin is worth 17 cents, then it cannot be black or small.

   Clue 2: If a coin is gold, then it cannot be large or worth 36 cents.

   If a coin is large, it cannot be gold or worth 36 cents.

   If a coin is worth 36 cents, it cannot be gold or large.

   Clue 3: The large coin is worth more than the silver, so the silver is not large.

	$0.17	$0.36	$0.55	Sm.	Med.	Lar.
Black	X			X		
Silver						X
Gold		X				X
Small	X					
Medium						
Large		X				

Conclusion 1:

From the three clues, we find the black coin must be the large coin.

Therefore the large coin must be worth 36 cents or 55 cents.

However, the chart says the gold coin can be worth 17 cents or 55 cents--but it cannot be large, so we can eliminate the 55 cents as a possibility for gold.

Conclusion 2:

Since the small one cannot be worth 17 cents and gold is worth 17 cents, the gold is not small. It must be medium, which makes the silver the small one. Since the large is worth more than the silver, the large (which is black) must be worth 55 cents, making the silver one worth 36 cents.

	$0.17	$0.36	$0.55	Sm.	Med.	Lar.
Black	X	X	yes	X	X	yes
Silver	X	yes	X	yes	X	X
Gold	yes	X	X	X	yes	X
Small	X					
Medium						
Large		X				

6. exterior cubes with no paint: 4 · 4 = 16

   interior cubes: $2^3 = 8$

   total: 16 + 8 = 24 cubes

7.
length	width	perimeter
12	1	26
6	2	16
4	3	14

   maximum: 26 units, minimum: 14 units

8. George: $rt = d$ $rt = d$

   $r(40) = 1$ $\frac{1}{40}(15) = d$

   $r = \frac{1}{40}$ $\frac{3}{8} = d$

   Amanda: $rt = d$ $rt = d$

   $r(15) = \frac{5}{8}$ $\frac{1}{24}t = 1$

   $r = \frac{1}{24}$ $t = 24$

   It takes Amanda 24 minutes to walk around trail.

$GAGAGA = 3 \cdot 3 \cdot 2 \cdot 2 \cdot 1 \cdot 1 = 36$

$AGAGAG = 3 \cdot 3 \cdot 2 \cdot 2 \cdot 1 \cdot 1 = 36$

$AGGAGA = 3 \cdot 3 \cdot 2 \cdot 2 \cdot 1 \cdot 1 = 36$

$AGAGGA = 3 \cdot 3 \cdot 2 \cdot 2 \cdot 1 \cdot 1 = \underline{36}$

144

PAGE 686   CHECKING FOR UNDERSTANDING

1. With independent events, one choice for an event does not affect any of the possibilities for another event. Dependent events have each choice affected by the previous choice.

2. Answers will vary. Sample answers are rolling dice, picking a marble out of a sack, replacing the marble, and picking again.

3. Answers will vary. Sample answers are selecting members of a team from a group and the lottery.

4. independent

5. a. independent   b. dependent

   c. dependent or independent, based upon the availability of each color for a particular model

6. 8! or 40,320 orders

7. 6! or 720 schedules

PAGES 686-688   EXERCISES

8. independent

9. dependent, if a person can only hold one office

10. dependent   11. dependent

12. independent   13. dependent

14. $5^5 = 3125$ 15. $15 \cdot 12 \cdot 10 = 1800$

16.   17.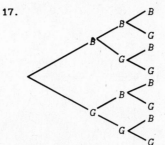

18. $24 \cdot 24 \cdot 10 \cdot 10 \cdot 9 = 518,400$

19. $5 \cdot 6 \cdot 3 = 90$

20. $6 \cdot 18 \cdot 7 = 756$

21. $6 \cdot 5 \cdot 4 \cdot 3 \cdot 2 \cdot 1 = 720$

22. $6 \cdot 6 \cdot 6 = 216$

23. $5 \cdot 4 \cdot 3 \cdot 2 \cdot 1 \cdot 1 + 1 \cdot 1 \cdot 5 \cdot 4 \cdot 3 \cdot 2 \cdot 1 = 240$

24. $1 \cdot 1 \cdot 6 \cdot 5 \cdot 4 + 6 \cdot 1 \cdot 1 \cdot 5 \cdot 4$
    $+ 6 \cdot 5 \cdot 1 \cdot 1 \cdot 4 + 6 \cdot 5 \cdot 4 \cdot 1 \cdot 1 = 480$

25. a. $7 \cdot 6 \cdot 5 \cdot 4 = 840$

    b. $4 \cdot 5 \cdot 4 \cdot 3 = 240$

26. $1 \cdot 4 \cdot 8 \cdot 7 \cdot 6 = 1344$

27. a. $26 \cdot 25 \cdot 24 \cdot 26 \cdot 25 = 10,140,000$

    b. $26 \cdot 25 \cdot 24 \cdot 6 \cdot 20 = 1,872,000$

28. $4 \cdot 3 \cdot 5 = 60$ meals

29. a. $4 \cdot 4 = 16$ ways

    b. $4 \cdot 3 = 12$ ways

30. 6×7 or 42, since 7 is the most probable total each time the dice are rolled

31. $a_n = a_1 r^{n-1}$

    $a_{27} = 3(2)^{27-1}$

    $= 3(2)^{26}$

32. $a_n = a_1 r^n$

    $45,000 = 60,000(0.9)^n$

    $0.75 = (0.9)^n$

    $\log 0.75 = \log(0.9)^n$

    $\log 0.75 = n \log 0.9$

    $n = \dfrac{\log 0.75}{\log 0.9}$

    $= 2.73$ years

33.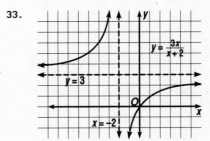

34. $[-6.2] + [4.3] + [-2.87] + [0.5]$
    $= -7 + 4 + (-3) + 0$
    $= -6$

PAGES 691-692   CHECKING FOR UNDERSTANDING

1. an arrangement in which order is important

2. $P(5, 5) = \dfrac{5!}{(5 - 5)!}$

   $= \dfrac{5!}{0!}$

   $= 5!$ or 120

3. $P(7, 3)$, or 210

4. $5! - 3! \overset{?}{=} 2!$

   $5040 - 6 \overset{?}{=} 2$

   $5034 \neq 2$

   false

5. $6 \cdot 5! \overset{?}{=} 6!$

   $6 \cdot 120 \overset{?}{=} 720$

   $720 = 720$

   true

6. $\dfrac{6!}{3!} \overset{?}{=} 2!$

   $\dfrac{720}{6} \overset{?}{=} 2$

   $120 \neq 2$

   false

7. $(6 - 3)! \overset{?}{=} 6! - 3!$

   $3! \overset{?}{=} 720 - 6$

   $6 \neq 714$

   false

8. $6! = 720$

9. $5! = 120$

10. $\dfrac{3!}{2!} = 3$

PAGES 692-693   EXERCISES

11. $\dfrac{6!}{8!} \cdot \dfrac{8!}{6!} \overset{?}{=} 1$

    $1 = 1$

    true

12. $3! + 4! \overset{?}{=} 5 \cdot 3!$

    $6 + 24 \overset{?}{=} 5 \cdot 6$

    $30 = 30$

    true

13. $\frac{6!}{30} \stackrel{?}{=} 4!$

$\frac{720}{30} \stackrel{?}{=} 24$

$24 = 24$

true

14. $\frac{P(9, 9)}{9!} \stackrel{?}{=} 1$

$\frac{9!}{9!} \stackrel{?}{=} 1$

$1 = 1$

true

15. $\frac{3!}{3} \stackrel{?}{=} \frac{2!}{2}$

$\frac{6}{3} \stackrel{?}{=} \frac{2}{2}$

$2 \neq 1$

false

16. $1!2!3!2! \stackrel{?}{=} 4!$

$1 \cdot 2 \cdot 6 \cdot 2 \stackrel{?}{=} 24$

$24 = 24$

true

17. $\frac{3!}{2!} = 3$ 18. $\frac{5!}{2!} = 60$ 19. $\frac{5!}{2!2!} = 30$

20. $\frac{11!}{4!4!2!} = 34,650$ 21. $\frac{6!}{3!} = 120$

22. $\frac{7!}{2!} = 2520$ 23. $\frac{8!}{2!3!} = 3360$

24. $\frac{9!}{2!2!} = 90,720$ 25. $\frac{13!}{2!2!2!} = 778,377,600$

26. $\frac{P(10, 3)}{P(5, 3)} = \frac{\frac{10!}{(10 - 3)!}}{\frac{5!}{(5 - 3)!}} = \frac{720}{60} = 12$

27. $\frac{P(6, 4)}{P(5, 3)} = \frac{\frac{6!}{(6 - 4)!}}{\frac{5!}{(5 - 3)!}} = \frac{\frac{720}{2}}{\frac{120}{2}} = 6$

28. $\frac{P(5, 3)}{P(8, 5) \cdot P(5, 5)} = \frac{60}{6720 \cdot 120} = \frac{1}{13,440}$

29. $\frac{P(6, 3) \cdot P(4, 2)}{P(5, 2)} = \frac{120 \cdot 12}{20} = 72$

30. $\frac{(5 + 3 + 4)!}{5!3!4!} = 27,720$ 31. $\frac{6!}{2!2!} = 180$

32. There are $P(5, 5)$ or 5! ways of arranging the books in the algebra group.

There are $P(4, 4)$ or 4! ways of arranging the books in the geometry group.

There are 5 ways that the algebra books can be together.

$5! \cdot 4! \cdot 5 = 14,400$

33. $\frac{9!}{4!5!} = 126$

34. 6! = 720 arrangements of 6 books

4! = 24 arrangements of 4 green books

There are 5 places the red and blue books can be placed together, 2 ways for each.

$6! - 5 \cdot 2 \cdot 4! = 480$

35. $P(n, 4) = 3[P(n, 3)]$

$n(n - 1)(n - 2)(n - 3) = 3[n(n - 1)(n - 2)]$

$n - 3 = 3$

$n = 6$

36. $n[P(5, 3)] = P(7, 5)$

$60n = 2520$

$n = 42$

37. $7[P(n, 5)] = P(n, 3) \cdot P(9, 3)$

$7n(n - 1)(n - 2)(n - 3)(n - 4) = n(n - 1)(n - 2) \cdot 504$

$n^2 - 7n + 12 = 72$

$n^2 - 7n - 60 = 0$

$(n - 12)(n + 5) = 0$

$n = 12$ or $n = -5$

-5 is not a reasonable solution.

38. $P(n, 4) = 40[P(n - 1, 2)]$

$n(n - 1)(n - 2)(n - 3) = 40[(n - 1)(n - 2)]$

$n(n - 3) = 40$

$n^2 - 3n - 40 = 0$

$(n - 8)(n + 5) = 0$

$n = 8$ or $n = -5$

-5 is not a reasonable solution.

39. $208P(n, 2) = P(16, 4)$

$208n(n - 1) = 43,680$

$n^2 - n = 210$

$n^2 - n - 210 = 0$

$(n - 15)(n + 14) = 0$

$n = 15$ or $n = -14$

-14 is not a reasonable solution.

40. $9P(n, 5) = P(n, 3) \cdot P(9, 3)$

$9n(n - 1)(n - 2)(n - 3)(n - 4) = n(n - 1)(n - 2) \cdot 504$

$(n - 3)(n - 4) = 56$

$n^2 - 7n + 12 = 56$

$n^2 - 7n - 44 = 0$

$(n - 11)(n + 4) = 0$

$n = 11$ or $n = -4$

-4 is not a reasonable solution.

41.

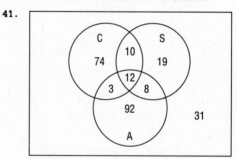

Use a Venn diagram, filling in the center and working backwards.

A = algebra, C = chemistry, S = Spanish, + means "and"

$A + C + S = 12$

$C + S = 22$, but 12 are already accounted for in $A + C + S$, leaving 10.

$A + S = 20$, but 12 are already accounted for in $A + C + S$, leaving 8.

$A + C = 15$, but 12 are already accounted for in $A + C + S$, leaving 3.

Total A = 115, but circle A already has

3 + 12 + 8, leaving 92.

Total C = 99, but circle C already has

3 + 12 + 10, leaving 74.

Total S = 49, but circle S already has

10 + 12 + 8 in it, leaving 19.

31 goes outside the three circles. Add the

parts to get the total.

31 + 92 + 3 + 12 + 13 + 19 + 74 = 249

There are 249 students.

42. $\frac{16!}{8!5!3!}$ = 720,720 designs

43. a. $\frac{9!}{2!2!2!}$ = 45,360 ways

  b. $\frac{82 + 2(91) + 2(75) + 2(83) + 64 + 77}{9} \approx 80.1$

44. $\frac{8!}{3!5!}$ = 56 signals

45.

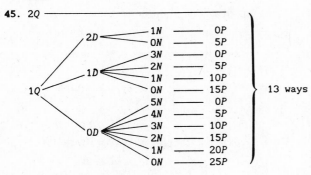

46. 2, 3, 4, 5, 6, 7, 8

47. $\log_3 (x + 6) = 2 \log_3 x$

   $\log_3 (x + 6) = \log_3 x^2$

   $x + 6 = x^2$

   $x^2 - x - 6 = 0$

   $(x - 3)(x + 2) = 0$

   $x - 3 = 0$ or $x + 2 = 0$

   $x = 3 \qquad x = -2$

Since log is undefined for negative numbers, -2

is not an acceptable solution.

48. $r_1 t_1 = r_2 t_2$

  $(x + 120)2.5 = (x - 120)(3.75)$

  $2.5x + 300 = 3.75x - 450$

  $750 = 1.25x$

  $600 = x$

  $rt = d$

  $(600 + 120)(2.5) = d$

  $1800 = d$

1800 km

49. $\begin{cases} x + 2y = 11 \\ x - 4y = 2 \end{cases} \longrightarrow \begin{array}{r} x + 2y = 11 \\ -x + 4y = -2 \\ \hline 6y = 9 \end{array}$

$y = \frac{3}{2}$

$x + 2\left(\frac{3}{2}\right) = 11$

$x + 3 = 11$

$x = 8 \qquad \left(8, \frac{3}{2}\right)$

50. $a^3 b^2 + 4ac + 2d \geq 6c^2 - 4ab$

  $(2)^3(-6)^2 + 4(2)(3) + 2d \geq 6(3)^2 - 4(2)(-6)$

  $288 + 24 + 2d \geq 54 + 48$

  $2d \geq -210$

  $d \geq -105$

15-4 Circular Permutations

PAGE 697   **CHECKING FOR UNDERSTANDING**

1. In a circular permutation, there is no reference point for the exact beginning of the arrangement.

2. It reduces the number by half as many.

3. when there is a fixed reference point

4. circular, reflection, $\frac{(8 - 1)!}{2}$ = 2520

5. circular, not reflection, (11 - 1)! = 3,628,800

6. circular, not reflection, (6 - 1)! = 120

7. linear, reflection, $\frac{10!}{2}$ = 1,814,400

PAGES 697-698   **EXERCISES**

8. linear, reflection

9. circular, not reflection

10. linear, not reflection

11. linear, not reflection

12. $\frac{P(6, 4) \cdot P(5, 2)}{5!} = \frac{360 \cdot 20}{120} = 60$

13. $\frac{P(8, 3) \cdot P(5, 4)}{P(6, 6)} = \frac{336 \cdot 120}{720} = 56$

14. $\frac{P(12, 6)}{P(12, 3) \cdot P(8, 2)} = \frac{665,280}{1320 \cdot 56} = 9$

15. $\frac{(6 - 1)!}{2} = 60$ 16. $(6 - 1)! = 120$

17. $\frac{(8 - 1)!}{2} = 2520$ 18. $(4 - 1)!(4 - 1)!2 = 72$

19. $(5 - 1)! = 24$ 20. $6! = 720$

21. $\frac{(5 - 1)!}{2!} = 12$

22. $\frac{P(20, 6)}{6! \cdot 2} = \frac{20!}{14!6!2!} = 19,380$

23.

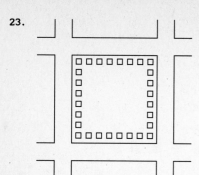

total houses: 28

number of arrangements: 5^{28}

24. $\dfrac{40!}{28!12!2!} = 2{,}793{,}426{,}740$

25. $2^8 - 1 = 255$

26. $6 + 4 + 2 = 12$

$(12 - 1)! = 39{,}916{,}800$

27. $5! = 120$

28. $\displaystyle\sum_{n=1}^{20} \dfrac{n+1}{2n+1}$

29. $0 = x^3 - x^2 + 2x - 3$

2 sign changes $\longrightarrow$ 3 or 1 positive real roots

$0 = -x^3 - x^2 - 2x - 3$

0 sign changes $\longrightarrow$ no negative real roots

3 positive real roots, or 1 positive real root

and 2 imaginary roots

30. $35 = 3b^2 - 8b$ $s_1 + s_2 = -\dfrac{b}{a}$

$0 = 3b^2 - 8b - 35$ $-\dfrac{7}{3} + 5 = \dfrac{-8}{3}$

$0 = (3b + 7)(b - 5)$ $\dfrac{8}{3} = \dfrac{8}{3}$ ✓

$3b + 7 = 0$ or $b - 5 = 0$ $s_1 s_2 = \dfrac{c}{a}$

$b = -\dfrac{7}{3}$ $b = 5$ $\left(-\dfrac{7}{3}\right)(5) = \dfrac{-35}{3}$

$-\dfrac{35}{3} = -\dfrac{35}{3}$ ✓

31.

$$\begin{array}{r|rrrr} 1 & 1 & -4 & -7 & 10 \\ & & 1 & -3 & -10 \\ \hline & 1 & -3 & -10 & 0 \end{array}$$

$x^2 - 3x - 10 = 0$

32. Parallel lines have equal slopes, whereas the slopes of perpendicular lines are negative reciprocals of each other.

15-5 Combinations

PAGE 701   CHECKING FOR UNDERSTANDING

1. A permutation is an arrangement in which the order is important. A combination is an arrangement in which order is not important.

2. The team bats in a certain order.

3. the student, because the order is important

4. permutation   **5.** combination

6. permutation   **7.** combination

8. $C(5, 3) = \dfrac{5!}{(5 - 3)!3!} = 10$

9. $C(12, 5) = \dfrac{12!}{(12 - 5)!5!} = 792$

10. $C(3, 2) \cdot C(8, 3) = \dfrac{3!}{(3 - 2)!2!} \cdot \dfrac{8!}{(8 - 3)!3!}$

$= 3 \cdot 56$

$= 168$

11. $\dfrac{C(10, 3)}{C(5, 2)} = \dfrac{\frac{10!}{(10 - 3)!3!}}{\frac{5!}{(5 - 2)!2!}} = \dfrac{10!}{7!3!} \cdot \dfrac{3!2!}{5!}$

$= \dfrac{10!2!}{7!5!}$

$= 12$

PAGES 702-704   EXERCISES

12. permutation   **13.** combination

14. combination   **15.** permutation

16. permutation   **17.** permutation

18. permutation   **19.** combination

20. $C(7, 2) = \dfrac{7!}{(7 - 2)!2!} = 21$

21. $C(8, 3) = \dfrac{8!}{(8 - 3)!3!} = 56$

22. $C(8, 5) \cdot C(7, 3) = \dfrac{8!}{(8 - 5)!5!} \cdot \dfrac{7!}{(7 - 3)!3!}$

$= 56 \cdot 35$

$= 1960$

23. $C(24, 21) = \dfrac{24!}{(24 - 21)!21!} = 2024$

24. $C(9, 3) = \dfrac{9!}{(9 - 3)!3!} = 84$

25. $C(9, 4) = \dfrac{9!}{(9 - 4)!4!} = 126$

26. $C(9, 5) = \dfrac{9!}{(9 - 5)!5!} = 126$

27. $C(9, 6) = \dfrac{9!}{(9 - 6)!6!} = 84$

28. $C(9, 8) = \dfrac{9!}{(9 - 8)!8!} = 9$

29. $C(9, 10)$ not possible

30. $C(12, 5) = \dfrac{12!}{(12 - 5)!5!} = 792$

31. $C(85, 2) = \dfrac{85!}{(85 - 2)!2!} = 3570$

32. $C(14, 9) = \dfrac{14!}{(14 - 9)!9!} = 2002$

33. $C(27, 25) = \dfrac{27!}{(27 - 25)!25!} = 351$

34. $C(8, 3) = \dfrac{8!}{(8 - 3)!3!} = 56$

35. a. $C(13, 5) \cdot 4 = \dfrac{13!}{(13 - 5)!5!} \cdot 4$

$= 5148$

b. $C(13, 1) \cdot C(13, 1) \cdot C(13, 1) \cdot C(13, 1)$

$= 13^4 = 28{,}561$

36.
$$C(n, 8) = C(n, 3)$$
$$\frac{n!}{(n - 8)!8!} = \frac{n!}{(n - 3)!3!}$$
$$n!(n - 3)!3! = n!(n - 8)!8!$$
$$(n - 3)!3! = (n - 8)!8!$$
$$(n-3)(n-4)(n-5)(n-6)(n-7) = 8 \cdot 7 \cdot 6 \cdot 5 \cdot 4$$
$$n = 11$$

37.
$$C(n, 12) = C(30, 18)$$
$$\frac{n!}{(n - 12)!12!} = \frac{30!}{(30 - 18)!18!}$$
$$n!(12)!18! = 30!(n - 12)!12!$$
$$n!18! = 30!(n - 12)!$$
$$n = 30$$

38.
$$C(n, 5) = C(n, 7)$$
$$\frac{n!}{(n - 5)!5!} = \frac{n!}{(n - 7)!7!}$$
$$n!(n - 7)!7! = n!(n - 5)!5!$$
$$(n - 7)!7! = (n - 5)!5!$$
$$7 \cdot 6 = (n - 5)(n - 6)$$
$$n = 12$$

39.
$$C(14, 3) = C(n, 11)$$
$$\frac{14!}{(14 - 3)!3!} = \frac{n!}{(n - 11)!11!}$$
$$14!(n - 11)!11! = n!(11)!3!$$
$$14!(n - 11)! = n!3!$$
$$n = 14$$

40. $C(6, 5) = \dfrac{6!}{(6 - 5)!5!} = 6$

41. $C(9, 5) = \dfrac{9!}{(9 - 5)!5!} = 126$

42. $C(4, 2) \cdot C(6, 2) \cdot C(9, 1) = 6 \cdot 15 \cdot 9 = 810$

43. $C(4, 5) = \dfrac{4!}{(4 - 5)!5!}$

not possible; 0

44. $C(9, 2) \cdot C(10, 3) = 36 \cdot 120 = 4320$

45. 2 red, 3 white $= C(4, 2) \cdot C(6, 3) = 6 \cdot 20$
$$= 120$$
2 red, 3 blue $= C(4, 2) \cdot C(9, 3) = 6 \cdot 84$
$$= 504$$
2 white, 3 red $= C(6, 2) \cdot C(4, 3) = 15 \cdot 4$
$$= 60$$
2 white, 3 blue $= C(6, 2) \cdot C(9, 3) = 15 \cdot 84$
$$= 1260$$
2 blue, 3 red $= C(9, 2) \cdot C(4, 3) = 36 \cdot 4$
$$= 144$$
2 blue, 3 white $= C(9, 2) \cdot C(6, 3) = 36 \cdot 20$
$$= 720$$
$$120 + 504 + 60 + 1260 + 144 + 720 = 2808$$

46. $C(8, 5) = \dfrac{8!}{(8 - 5)!5!} = 56$

47. $C(8, 3) \cdot C(10, 2) = 168 \cdot 15 = 2520$

48. $C(8, 1) \cdot C(10, 4) = 8 \cdot 210 = 1680$

49. $C(10, 5) = \dfrac{10!}{(10 - 5)!5!} = 252$

50. $P(n, r) = \dfrac{n!}{(n - r)!}$
$$= \frac{n!}{(n - r)!} \cdot \frac{r!}{r!}$$
$$= r! \frac{n}{(n - r)!r!}$$
$$= r!C(n, r)$$

51. $C(12, 8) \cdot C(4, 1) = \dfrac{12!}{8!4!} \cdot \dfrac{4!}{1!3!}$
$$= \frac{12 \cdot 11 \cdot 10 \cdot 9}{4 \cdot 3 \cdot 2} \cdot 4$$
$$= 1980$$
There are 1980 teams.

52. a. $C(53, 6) = \dfrac{53!}{(53 - 6)!6!} = 22{,}957{,}480$

b. $P(53, 6) = \dfrac{53!}{(53 - 6)!} = 16{,}529{,}385{,}600$

c. part a: combination

part b: permutation, because of order

53. $C(8, 4) \cdot C(2, 1) + C(8, 3) \cdot C(2, 2)$
$$= \frac{8!}{4!4!} \cdot \frac{2!}{1!1!} + \frac{8!}{5!3!} \cdot \frac{2!}{0!2!}$$
$$= 70 \cdot 2 + 56 \cdot 1$$
$$= 196$$

54. $(5 - 1)! = 4! = 24$ ways

55.
$$V_n = P(1 + r)^n$$
$$15{,}000 = 75{,}000(1 - 0.08)^n$$
$$0.2 = 0.92^n$$
$$\log 0.2 = n \log 0.92$$
$$n = \frac{\log 0.2}{\log 0.92}$$
$$n \approx 19.3 \text{ years}$$

56.
$$A = Pe^{rt}$$
$$400 = 200e^{0.08t}$$
$$2 = e^{0.08t}$$
$$\ln 2 = 0.08t \ln e$$
$$\frac{\ln 2}{0.08} = t$$
$$t \approx 8.7 \text{ years}$$

57.

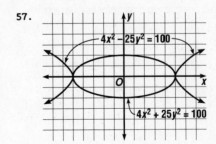

$4x^2 + 25y^2 = 100$: ellipse

$4x^2 - 25y^2 = 100$: hyperbola

58.

$$\begin{bmatrix} 2 & -1 & -5 & 3 \\ 1 & 4 & -2 & 3 \\ 5 & 3 & 2 & 1 \end{bmatrix} = \begin{bmatrix} 2 & -1 & -5 & 3 \\ 9 & 0 & -22 & 15 \\ 11 & 0 & -13 & 10 \end{bmatrix}$$

$$= \begin{bmatrix} 9 & 0 & -22 & 15 \\ 18 & -9 & -45 & 27 \\ 11 & 0 & -13 & 10 \end{bmatrix} = \begin{bmatrix} 9 & 0 & -22 & 15 \\ 0 & -9 & -1 & -3 \\ 11 & 0 & -13 & 10 \end{bmatrix}$$

$$= \begin{bmatrix} 9 & 0 & -22 & 15 \\ 0 & -9 & -1 & -3 \\ 99 & 0 & -117 & 90 \end{bmatrix} = \begin{bmatrix} 9 & 0 & -22 & 15 \\ 0 & -9 & -1 & -3 \\ 0 & 0 & 125 & -75 \end{bmatrix}$$

$$= \begin{bmatrix} 9 & 0 & 0 & \frac{9}{5} \\ 0 & -9 & 0 & -\frac{18}{5} \\ 0 & 0 & 1 & -\frac{3}{5} \end{bmatrix} = \begin{bmatrix} 1 & 0 & 0 & \frac{1}{5} \\ 0 & 1 & 0 & \frac{2}{5} \\ 0 & 0 & 1 & -\frac{3}{5} \end{bmatrix}$$

$$\left(\frac{1}{5}, \frac{2}{5}, -\frac{3}{5} \right)$$

59. $a^2b^2c^2$, $a^2b^2c^2d$, $a^2b^2c^2d^2$

60. List the possibilities.

(1, 64), (2, 32), (4, 16), (8, 8), (16, 4),
(32, 2), (64, 1), (-1, -64), (-2, -32),
(-4, -16), (-8, -8), (-16, -4), (-32, -2),
(-64, -1)

PAGE 704   MID-CHAPTER REVIEW

1. a. squares, pencils, buttons--arranged in a
straight line

  b. 24 ways

2. a. tree diagram   b. $2 \cdot 2 \cdot 2 \cdot 3 = 24$

3. $P(100, 100) = \dfrac{100!}{(100 - 100)!} = \dfrac{100!}{0!} = 100!$

4. $24 \cdot 24 \cdot 24 \cdot 10 \cdot 10 \cdot 10 = 13,824,000$

5. $3!2! = 12$ ways

6. $C(52, 13) = \dfrac{52!}{(52 - 13)!13!} = \dfrac{52!}{39!13!}$

15-6 Probability

PAGES 707-708   CHECKING FOR UNDERSTANDING

1. the probability of success

2. 1, $s + f$ = all possibilities

3. $P(s) = 1 - P(f)$

$\quad = 1 - \dfrac{4}{5}$

$\quad = \dfrac{1}{5}$

4. no, $0 \leq P(s) \leq 1$

5. yes, because s can be greater than f

6. $s = 2$

$f = 3 - 2 = 1$

odds $= \dfrac{2}{1}$

7. $s = 5$

$f = 9 - 5 = 4$

odds $= \dfrac{5}{4}$

8. $s = 1$

$f = 2 - 1 = 1$

odds $= \dfrac{1}{1}$

9. $s = 3$

$f = 7 - 3 = 4$

odds $= \dfrac{3}{4}$

10. $s = 3$, $f = 5$

$s + f = 8$

probability $= \dfrac{3}{8}$

11. $s = 4$, $f = 3$

$s + f = 7$

probability $= \dfrac{4}{7}$

12. $s = 8$, $f = 1$

$s + f = 9$

probability $= \dfrac{8}{9}$

13. $s = 1$, $f = 5$

$s + f = 6$

probability $= \dfrac{1}{6}$

PAGES 708-709   EXERCISES

14. $s = 3$

$f = 4 - 3 = 1$

odds $= \dfrac{3}{1}$

15. $s = 1$

$f = 7 - 1 = 6$

odds $= \dfrac{1}{6}$

16. $s = 5$

$f = 8 - 5 = 3$

odds $= \dfrac{5}{3}$

17. $s = 7$

$f = 15 - 7 = 8$

odds $= \dfrac{7}{8}$

18. $s = 3$, $f = 7$

$s + f = 10$

probability $= \dfrac{3}{10}$

19. $s = 5$, $f = 1$

$s + f = 6$

probability $= \dfrac{5}{6}$

20. $s = 6$, $f = 5$

$s + f = 11$

probability $= \dfrac{6}{11}$

21. $s = 1$, $f = 1$

$s + f = 2$

probability $= \dfrac{1}{2}$

22. $s = 6$, $f = 1$

$s + f = 7$

probability $= \dfrac{6}{7}$

23. $s = 3$

$f = 4 - 3 = 1$

odds of not getting A

$\quad = \dfrac{1}{3}$

24. $P(2 \text{ strawberry}) = \dfrac{C(5, 2)}{C(20, 2)}$

$\quad = \dfrac{10}{190}$

$\quad = \dfrac{1}{19} \approx 0.053$

25. $P(2 \text{ watermelon}) = \dfrac{C(9, 2)}{C(20, 2)}$

$\quad = \dfrac{36}{190}$

$\quad = \dfrac{18}{95} \approx 0.189$

26. $P(2 \text{ mint}) = \dfrac{C(6, 2)}{C(20, 2)}$

$\quad = \dfrac{15}{190}$

$\quad = \dfrac{3}{38} \approx 0.079$

27. $P(1 \text{ strawberry and 1 mint}) = \dfrac{C(5, 1) \cdot C(6, 1)}{C(20, 2)}$

$\quad = \dfrac{5 \cdot 6}{190}$

$\quad = \dfrac{3}{19} \approx 0.158$

28. $P(2 \text{ juice bars}) = \dfrac{C(5, 2)}{C(13, 2)}$

$= \dfrac{10}{78}$

$= \dfrac{5}{39} \approx 0.128$

$s = 5, \ f = 39 - 5 = 34$

odds $= \dfrac{5}{34}$

29. $P(2 \text{ yogurt bars}) = \dfrac{C(8, 2)}{C(13, 2)}$

$= \dfrac{28}{78}$

$= \dfrac{14}{39} \approx 0.359$

$s = 14, \ f = 39 - 14 = 25$

odds $= \dfrac{14}{25}$

30. $P(1 \text{ of each kind of bar}) = \dfrac{C(5, 1) \cdot C(8, 1)}{C(13, 2)}$

$= \dfrac{5 \cdot 8}{78}$

$= \dfrac{20}{39} \approx 0.513$

$s = 20, \ f = 39 - 20 = 19$

odds $= \dfrac{20}{19}$

31. $P(\text{all pennies}) = \dfrac{C(7, 3)}{C(16, 3)}$

$= \dfrac{35}{560}$

$= \dfrac{1}{16} \approx 0.063$

32. $P(\text{all nickels}) = \dfrac{C(4, 3)}{C(16, 3)}$

$= \dfrac{4}{560}$

$= \dfrac{1}{140} \approx 0.007$

33. $P(1 \text{ dime, 2 nickels}) = \dfrac{C(5, 1) \cdot C(4, 2)}{C(16, 3)}$

$= \dfrac{5 \cdot 6}{560}$

$= \dfrac{3}{56} \approx 0.054$

34. $P(2 \text{ pennies, 1 dime}) = \dfrac{C(7, 2) \cdot C(5, 1)}{C(16, 3)}$

$= \dfrac{21 \cdot 5}{560}$

$= \dfrac{3}{16} \approx 0.188$

35. $P(1 \text{ dime, 1 nickel, 1 penny})$

$= \dfrac{C(7, 1) \cdot C(5, 1) \cdot C(4, 1)}{C(16, 3)}$

$= \dfrac{7 \cdot 5 \cdot 4}{560}$

$= \dfrac{1}{4} = 0.25$

36. $P(2 \text{ dimes, 1 quarter}) = 0$

There are no quarters in Tommie's bank.

37. $P(2 \text{ consonants}) = \dfrac{C(4, 2)}{C(7, 2)} = \dfrac{6}{21} = \dfrac{2}{7} \approx 0.286$

38. $P(2 \text{ vowels}) = \dfrac{C(3, 2)}{C(7, 2)} = \dfrac{3}{21} = \dfrac{1}{7} \approx 0.143$

39. $P(1 \text{ vowel, 1 consonant}) = \dfrac{C(3, 1) \cdot C(4, 1)}{C(7, 2)}$

$= \dfrac{3 \cdot 4}{21} = \dfrac{4}{7} \approx 0.571$

40. a. $P(\text{all aces}) = \dfrac{C(4, 5)}{C(52, 5)}$

not possible; 0

b. $P(\text{all face cards}) = \dfrac{C(12, 5)}{C(52, 5)}$

$= \dfrac{33}{108,290}$ odds $= \dfrac{33}{108,257}$

c. $P(\text{all from one suit}) = \dfrac{C(4, 1) \cdot C(13, 5)}{C(52, 5)}$

$= \dfrac{4 \cdot 1287}{2,598,960}$

$= \dfrac{33}{16,660}$ odds $= \dfrac{33}{16,627}$

41. a. $P(\text{all hearts}) = \dfrac{C(13, 5)}{C(52, 5)} = \dfrac{33}{66,640}$

odds against $= \dfrac{66,607}{33}$

b. $P(\text{all face cards}) = \dfrac{C(12, 5)}{C(52, 5)} = \dfrac{33}{108,290}$

odds against $= \dfrac{108,257}{33}$

c. $P(\text{all from one suit}) = \dfrac{C(4, 1) \cdot C(13, 5)}{C(52, 5)}$

$= \dfrac{33}{16,660}$

odds against $= \dfrac{16,627}{33}$

d. $P(\text{the first 3 from one suit and the last 2 from another})$

$= \dfrac{P(4, 2) \cdot C(13, 3) \cdot C(13, 2)}{C(52, 5)}$

$= \dfrac{267,696}{2,598,960} = \dfrac{429}{4165}$

odds against $= \dfrac{3736}{429}$

42. Let (r, g) be all possible rolls of 2 dice. This is 36. The 15 ordered pairs for $g > r$ are $(1, 2), (1, 3), (1, 4), (1, 5), (1, 6), (2, 3), (2, 4), (2, 5), (2, 6), (3, 4), (3, 5), (3, 6), (4, 5), (4, 6),$ and $(5, 6)$. So $\dfrac{15}{36} = \dfrac{5}{12}$.

43. $P(\text{winning}) = \dfrac{C(6, 6)}{C(46, 6)} = \dfrac{1}{9,366,819}$

44. a. area of $A = 3^2\pi = 9\pi$

area of dart board $= 9^2\pi = 81\pi$

$P(\text{landing in the } A \text{ ring}) = \dfrac{9\pi}{81\pi} = \dfrac{1}{9}$

b. area of $B = 6^2\pi - 3^2\pi = 36\pi - 9\pi = 27\pi$

$P(\text{landing in the } B \text{ ring}) = \dfrac{27\pi}{81\pi} = \dfrac{1}{3}$

c. area of $C = 9^2\pi - 6^2\pi = 81\pi - 36\pi = 45\pi$

$P(\text{landing in the } C \text{ ring}) = \dfrac{45\pi}{81\pi} = \dfrac{5}{9}$

45. $C(6, 2) \cdot C(8, 2) = \dfrac{6!}{4!\,2!} \cdot \dfrac{8!}{6!\,2!}$

$= 15 \cdot 28$

$= 420 \text{ ways}$

46. $(4r + s)^5 = (4r)^5 s^0 + \dfrac{5}{1}(4r)^4 s^1 + \dfrac{5(5-1)}{1 \cdot 2}(4r)^3 s^2$

$\qquad + \dfrac{5(5-1)}{1 \cdot 2}(4r)^2 s^3 + \dfrac{5}{1}(4r)^1 s^4$

$\qquad + (4r)^0 s^5$

$= 1024r^5 + 1280r^4 s + 640r^3 s^2 + 160r^2 s^3$

$\qquad + 20rs^4 + s^5$

47. $\log_7 y = 4$

$7^4 = y$

$2401 = y$

48. $f[g(x)] = 2(x^2 + 1) + 3$

$= 2x^2 + 5$

49.

$2x^2 - x - 6 < y$

50. $6x^2 + 7x - 3 = 0$

$x^2 + \dfrac{7}{6}x = \dfrac{1}{2}$

$x^2 + \dfrac{7}{6}x + \left(\dfrac{7}{12}\right)^2 = \dfrac{1}{2} + \left(\dfrac{7}{12}\right)^2$

$\left(x + \dfrac{7}{12}\right)^2 = \dfrac{121}{144}$

$x + \dfrac{7}{12} = \pm\dfrac{11}{12}$

$x = -\dfrac{7}{12} \pm \dfrac{11}{12}$

$x = \dfrac{1}{3} \text{ or } x = -\dfrac{3}{2}$

51. $\left(-\dfrac{1}{2} + \dfrac{i\sqrt{3}}{2}\right)^3 = \left(-\dfrac{1}{2} + \dfrac{i\sqrt{3}}{2}\right)^2\left(-\dfrac{1}{2} + \dfrac{i\sqrt{3}}{2}\right)$

$= \left(\dfrac{1}{4} + 2\left(-\dfrac{1}{2}\right)\left(\dfrac{i\sqrt{3}}{2}\right) + \dfrac{-3}{4}\right)\left(-\dfrac{1}{2} + \dfrac{i\sqrt{3}}{2}\right)$

$= \left(-\dfrac{1}{2} - \dfrac{i\sqrt{3}}{2}\right)\left(-\dfrac{1}{2} + \dfrac{i\sqrt{3}}{2}\right)$

$= \dfrac{1}{4} - \dfrac{-3}{4}$

$= 1$

15-7 Multiplying Probabilities

PAGE 712   CHECKING FOR UNDERSTANDING

1. Dependent events are affected by previous choices; independent events are not.
2. It makes the probability greater.
3. less
4. dependent; $P(\text{red, green, blue})$

$= \dfrac{5}{16} \cdot \dfrac{3}{15} \cdot \dfrac{8}{14} = \dfrac{1}{28}$

5. dependent; $P(2 \text{ iced teas}) = \dfrac{4}{7} \cdot \dfrac{3}{6} = \dfrac{2}{7}$

PAGES 713-714   EXERCISES

6. independent; $P(2 \text{ apricots}) = \dfrac{5}{9} \cdot \dfrac{5}{9} = \dfrac{25}{81}$

7. independent; $P(\text{winning 4 games})$

$= \dfrac{3}{5} \cdot \dfrac{3}{5} \cdot \dfrac{3}{5} \cdot \dfrac{3}{5} = \dfrac{81}{625}$

8. $P(\text{both vowels}) = \dfrac{3}{7} \cdot \dfrac{2}{6} = \dfrac{1}{7} \approx 0.143$

9. $P(\text{both vowels}) = \dfrac{3}{7} \cdot \dfrac{3}{7} = \dfrac{9}{49} \approx 0.184$

10. $P(\text{both same letter}) = \dfrac{1}{7} \cdot \dfrac{0}{6} = 0$

11. $P(2 \text{ plates}) = \dfrac{6}{16} \cdot \dfrac{5}{15} = \dfrac{1}{8} \approx 0.125$

12. $P(2 \text{ bowls}) = \dfrac{5}{16} \cdot \dfrac{4}{15} = \dfrac{1}{12} \approx 0.083$

13. $P(\text{a bowl, then a glass}) = \dfrac{5}{16} \cdot \dfrac{5}{15} = \dfrac{5}{48} \approx 0.104$

14. $P(\text{a bowl and a glass}) = \dfrac{5}{16} \cdot \dfrac{5}{15} \cdot C(2, 1)$

$= \dfrac{5}{24} \approx 0.208$

15. $P(\text{two 3s}) = \dfrac{1}{6} \cdot \dfrac{1}{6} = \dfrac{1}{36} \approx 0.028$

16. $P(\text{no 3s}) = \dfrac{5}{6} \cdot \dfrac{5}{6} = \dfrac{25}{36} \approx 0.694$

17. $P(3 \text{ and } 4) = \dfrac{1}{6} \cdot \dfrac{1}{6} = \dfrac{1}{36} = 0.028$

18. $P(3 \text{ and any other number}) = \dfrac{1}{6} \cdot \dfrac{5}{6} = \dfrac{5}{36} \approx 0.139$

19. $P(2 \text{ numbers alike}) = \dfrac{6}{6} \cdot \dfrac{1}{6} = \dfrac{1}{6} \approx 0.167$

20. $P(2 \text{ different numbers}) = \dfrac{6}{6} \cdot \dfrac{5}{6} = \dfrac{5}{6} \approx 0.833$

21. **a.** $P(\text{one of each}) = \dfrac{5}{15} \cdot \dfrac{3}{14} \cdot \dfrac{7}{13} = \dfrac{1}{26} \approx 0.038$

b. $P(\text{one of each}) = \dfrac{5}{15} \cdot \dfrac{3}{15} \cdot \dfrac{7}{15} = \dfrac{7}{225} \approx 0.031$

22. **a.** $P(\text{each is a different color}) = \dfrac{8}{18} \cdot \dfrac{7}{17} \cdot \dfrac{3}{16}$

$= \dfrac{7}{204} \approx 0.034$

b. $P(\text{each is a different color}) = \dfrac{8}{18} \cdot \dfrac{7}{18} \cdot \dfrac{3}{18}$

$= \dfrac{7}{243} \approx 0.029$

23. P(selecting all odd numbers)

$$= \frac{50}{100} \cdot \frac{50}{100} \cdot \frac{50}{100} \cdot \frac{50}{100} \cdot \frac{50}{100}$$

$$= \left(\frac{1}{2}\right)^5$$

$$= \frac{1}{32} \approx 0.031$$

24. P(selecting all odd numbers)

$$= \frac{50}{100} \cdot \frac{49}{99} \cdot \frac{48}{98} \cdot \frac{47}{97} \cdot \frac{46}{96}$$

$$= \frac{1081}{38,412} \approx 0.028$$

25. P(selecting 5 consecutive numbers)

$$= \frac{1}{100} \cdot \frac{1}{99} \cdot \frac{1}{98} \cdot \frac{1}{97} \cdot \frac{1}{96} \cdot C(96, 1)$$

$$= \frac{1}{94,109,400} \approx 1.06 \times 10^{-8}$$

26. P(all diamonds) $= \frac{13}{52} \cdot \frac{12}{51} \cdot \frac{11}{50} \cdot \cdots \cdot \frac{1}{40}$

$$= \frac{1}{635,013,559,600}$$

$$\approx 1.57 \times 10^{-12}$$

27. P(all one suit) $= \frac{52}{52} \cdot \frac{12}{51} \cdot \frac{11}{50} \cdot \frac{10}{49} \cdot \cdots \cdot \frac{1}{40}$

$$= \frac{4}{635,013,559,600}$$

$$\approx 6.3 \times 10^{-12}$$

28. P(all red cards) $= \frac{26}{52} \cdot \frac{25}{52} \cdot \frac{24}{52} \cdot \cdots \cdot \frac{14}{40}$

$$= \frac{19}{1,160,054}$$

$$\approx 1.64 \times 10^{-5}$$

29. P(all face cards) $= \frac{12}{52} \cdot \frac{11}{52} \cdot \frac{10}{52} \cdot \cdots \cdot \frac{0}{52}$

$$= 0$$

Only 12 face cards exist in a deck.

30. Answers will vary. Sample: When the coins are tossed, give double credit for tossing heads.

31. **a.** area of $A = 9\pi$, area of dart board $= 81\pi$

$$P(\text{landing in center ring}) = \frac{9\pi}{81\pi} \cdot \frac{9\pi}{81\pi} \cdot \frac{9\pi}{81\pi}$$

$$= \frac{1}{9} \cdot \frac{1}{9} \cdot \frac{1}{9}$$

$$= \frac{1}{729}$$

b. area of $B = 27\pi$, area of $C = 45\pi$

$P(\text{landing in 3 different rings})$

$$= \frac{9\pi}{81\pi} \cdot \frac{27\pi}{81\pi} \cdot \frac{45\pi}{81\pi}$$

$$= \frac{1}{9} \cdot \frac{1}{3} \cdot \frac{5}{9}$$

$$= \frac{5}{243}$$

c. P(one dart in second ring, two in outer ring)

$$= \frac{27\pi}{81\pi} \cdot \frac{45\pi}{81\pi} \cdot \frac{45\pi}{81\pi}$$

$$= \frac{1}{3} \cdot \frac{5}{9} \cdot \frac{5}{9}$$

$$= \frac{25}{243}$$

32. P(yellow pencil, red pencil) $= \frac{3}{20} \cdot \frac{12}{19}$

$$= \frac{9}{95}$$

33. P(odd number, even number) $= \frac{3}{6} \cdot \frac{3}{6} = \frac{1}{4}$

34. $$\frac{2z^2}{z^2 - 2z - 35} - \frac{z + 7}{z + 5} = \frac{2z^2}{(z - 7)(z + 5)} - \frac{z + 7}{z + 5}$$

$$= \frac{2z^2}{(z - 7)(z + 5)} - \frac{(z - 7)(z + 7)}{(z - 7)(z + 5)}$$

$$= \frac{2z^2 - z^2 + 49}{(z - 7)(z + 5)}$$

$$= \frac{z^2 + 49}{(z - 7)(z + 5)}$$

35. midpoint of $\overline{RS} = \left(\frac{0 + 2}{2}, \frac{4 + 6}{2}\right) = (1, 5)$

midpoint of $\overline{ST} = \left(\frac{2 + 4}{2}, \frac{6 - 2}{2}\right) = (3, 2)$

midpoint of $\overline{RT} = \left(\frac{0 + 4}{2}, \frac{4 - 2}{2}\right) = (2, 1)$

36. $\begin{bmatrix} 1 & 0 \\ 0 & 1 \end{bmatrix}$

15-8 Adding Probabilities

PAGE 717   CHECKING FOR UNDERSTANDING

1. rolling two dice, spinning a spinner twice

2. picking a face card or a black card; buying a 1993 model car or a blue car

3. How many even numbers are there, how many multiples of 7 are there, and how many even numbers are also multiples of 7?

4.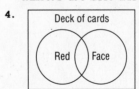

5. inclusive

$$P(\text{2 on only one}) = \frac{1}{10} + \frac{1}{6} - \frac{1}{10} \cdot \frac{1}{6}$$

$$= \frac{16}{60} - \frac{1}{60}$$

$$= \frac{1}{4} = 0.25$$

6. exclusive

$$P(\text{both kings or both queens}) = \frac{4}{52} \cdot \frac{3}{51} + \frac{4}{52} \cdot \frac{3}{51}$$

$$= \frac{2}{221} \approx 0.009$$

7. exclusive

P(3 photos of children or 3 photos of

grandchildren) $= \frac{5}{15} \cdot \frac{4}{14} \cdot \frac{3}{13} + \frac{7}{15} \cdot \frac{6}{14} \cdot \frac{5}{13}$

$\qquad = \frac{2}{91} + \frac{1}{13}$

$\qquad = \frac{9}{91} \approx 0.099$

8. exclusive

P(at least 3 heads) $= P$(3 heads) $+ P$(4 heads)

$\qquad\qquad\qquad + P$(5 heads)

$= \frac{1}{2} \cdot \frac{1}{2} \cdot \frac{1}{2} \cdot \frac{1}{2} \cdot \frac{1}{2} \cdot C(5, 3)$

$\quad + \frac{1}{2} \cdot \frac{1}{2} \cdot \frac{1}{2} \cdot \frac{1}{2} \cdot \frac{1}{2} \cdot C(5, 4)$

$\quad + \frac{1}{2} \cdot \frac{1}{2} \cdot \frac{1}{2} \cdot \frac{1}{2} \cdot \frac{1}{2} \cdot C(5, 5)$

$= \frac{1}{32} \cdot 10 + \frac{1}{32} \cdot 5 + \frac{1}{32} \cdot 1 = \frac{1}{2}$

9. inclusive

P(not red and not ace) $= \frac{24}{52} \cdot \frac{23}{51}$

So, P(black or ace) $= 1 - \frac{24}{52} \cdot \frac{23}{51}$

$\qquad\qquad\qquad = 1 - \frac{552}{2652}$

$\qquad\qquad\qquad = \frac{175}{221}$ or about 0.79

10. inclusive

P(boy or redhead) $= P$(boy) $+ P$(redhead)

$\qquad\qquad\qquad - P$(redhead boy)

$\qquad\qquad = \frac{15}{31} + \frac{5}{31} - \frac{2}{31}$

$\qquad\qquad = \frac{18}{31} \approx 0.581$

11. P(all 3 cork or all 3 plastic)

$= P$(all 3 cork) $+ P$(all 3 plastic)

$= \frac{6}{11} \cdot \frac{5}{10} \cdot \frac{4}{9} + \frac{5}{11} \cdot \frac{4}{10} \cdot \frac{3}{9}$

$= \frac{4}{33} + \frac{2}{33}$

$= \frac{2}{11} \approx 0.181$

12. P(exactly 2 plastic)

$= \frac{5}{11} \cdot \frac{4}{10} \cdot \frac{6}{9} \cdot C(3, 1)$

$= \frac{4}{11} \approx 0.363$

13. P(at least 2 plastic)

$= P$(2 plastic) $+ P$(3 plastic)

$= \frac{5}{11} \cdot \frac{4}{10} \cdot \frac{6}{9} \cdot C(3, 1) + \frac{5}{11} \cdot \frac{4}{10} \cdot \frac{3}{9}$

$= \frac{4}{11} + \frac{2}{33}$

$= \frac{14}{33} \approx 0.424$

14. P(at least 2 cork)

$= P$(2 cork) $+ P$(3 cork)

$= \frac{6}{11} \cdot \frac{5}{10} \cdot \frac{5}{9} \cdot C(3, 1) + \frac{6}{11} \cdot \frac{4}{10} \cdot \frac{4}{9}$

$= \frac{5}{11} + \frac{4}{33}$

$= \frac{19}{33} \approx 0.576$

15. P(both black or both face cards)

$= P$(both black) $+ P$(both face cards)

$\quad - P$(both black face cards)

$= \frac{26}{52} \cdot \frac{25}{51} + \frac{12}{52} \cdot \frac{11}{51} - \frac{6}{52} \cdot \frac{5}{51}$

$= \frac{188}{663} \approx 0.284$

16. P(both aces or both face cards)

$= P$(both aces) $+ P$(both face cards)

$= \frac{4}{52} \cdot \frac{3}{51} + \frac{12}{52} \cdot \frac{11}{51}$

$= \frac{12}{221} \approx 0.054$

17. P(both aces or both red)

$= P$(both aces) $+ P$(both red) $- P$(both red aces)

$= \frac{4}{52} \cdot \frac{3}{51} + \frac{26}{52} \cdot \frac{25}{51} - \frac{2}{52} \cdot \frac{1}{51}$

$= \frac{55}{221} \approx 0.249$

18. P(both either red or an ace)

$= P$(both red or both aces)

$\quad + P$(red (not an ace), 1 ace)

$= \frac{55}{221} + \frac{24}{52} \cdot \frac{4}{51} \cdot C(2, 1)$

$= \frac{55}{221} + \frac{16}{221}$

$= \frac{71}{221} \approx 0.321$

19. P(3 heads or 2 tails) $= P$(3 heads) $+ P$(2 tails)

$= \frac{1}{2} \cdot \frac{1}{2} \cdot \frac{1}{2} \cdot \frac{1}{2} \cdot \frac{1}{2} \cdot \frac{1}{2} \cdot \frac{1}{2} \cdot C(7, 3)$

$\quad + \frac{1}{2} \cdot \frac{1}{2} \cdot \frac{1}{2} \cdot \frac{1}{2} \cdot \frac{1}{2} \cdot \frac{1}{2} \cdot \frac{1}{2} \cdot C(7, 5)$

$= \frac{35}{128} + \frac{21}{128}$

$= \frac{7}{16} \approx 0.438$

20. P(at least 5 heads)

$= P$(5 heads) $+ P$(6 heads) $+ P$(7 heads)

$= \left(\frac{1}{2}\right)^7 C(7, 5) + \left(\frac{1}{2}\right)^7 C(7, 6) + \left(\frac{1}{2}\right)^7 C(7, 7)$

$= \frac{21}{128} + \frac{7}{128} + \frac{1}{128}$

$= \frac{29}{128} \approx 0.227$

21. P(3 heads or 3 tails)

= P(3 heads) + P(4 heads)

= $\left(\frac{1}{2}\right)^7 C(7, 3) + \left(\frac{1}{2}\right)^7 C(7, 4)$

= $\frac{35}{128} + \frac{35}{128}$

= $\frac{35}{64} \approx 0.547$

22. P(all tails or all heads)

= P(0 heads) + P(7 heads)

= $\left(\frac{1}{2}\right)^7 C(7, 0) + \left(\frac{1}{2}\right)^7 C(7, 7)$

= $\frac{1}{128} + \frac{1}{128}$

= $\frac{1}{64} \approx 0.016$

23. P(all men or all women)

= P(all men) + P(all women)

= $\dfrac{C(6, 6) \cdot C(8, 0)}{C(14, 6)} + \dfrac{C(6, 0) \cdot C(8, 6)}{C(14, 6)}$

= $\frac{1}{3003} + \frac{28}{3003}$

= $\frac{29}{3003} \approx 0.010$

24. P(5 men or 5 women)

= P(5 men) + P(5 women)

= $\dfrac{C(6, 5) \cdot C(8, 1)}{C(14, 6)} + \dfrac{C(6, 1) \cdot C(8, 5)}{C(14, 6)}$

= $\frac{48}{3003} + \frac{336}{3003}$

= $\frac{128}{1001} \approx 0.128$

25. P(4 men or 4 women)

= P(4 men) + P(4 women)

= $\dfrac{C(6, 4) \cdot C(8, 2)}{C(14, 6)} + \dfrac{C(6, 2) \cdot C(8, 4)}{C(14, 6)}$

= $\frac{420}{3003} + \frac{1050}{3003}$

= $\frac{70}{143} \approx 0.490$

26. P(at least 3 men)

= P(3 men) + P(4 men) + P(5 men) + P(6 men)

= $\dfrac{C(6, 3) \cdot C(8, 3)}{C(14, 6)} + \dfrac{C(6, 4) \cdot C(8, 2)}{C(14, 6)}$

$+ \dfrac{C(6, 5) \cdot C(8, 1)}{C(14, 6)} + \dfrac{C(6, 6) \cdot C(8, 0)}{C(14, 6)}$

= $\frac{1120}{3003} + \frac{420}{3003} + \frac{48}{3003} + \frac{1}{3003}$

= $\frac{1589}{3003} \approx 0.529$

27. P(each is a 20) = $\frac{1}{25} \cdot \frac{1}{21} = \frac{1}{525} \approx 0.002$

28. P(neither is a 20) = $\frac{24}{25} \cdot \frac{20}{21} = \frac{32}{35} \approx 0.914$

29. P(at least one is a 22)

= $1 - P$(neither is a 22)

= $1 - \frac{24}{25} \cdot \frac{20}{21}$

= $\frac{3}{35} \approx 0.086$

30. P(each is greater than 10) = $\frac{15}{25} \cdot \frac{21}{21}$

$= \frac{3}{5} \approx 0.6$

31. a. P(ceramic urn given blue marble) = 0

b. P(gold urn given blue marble)

= $\dfrac{P\text{(blue given gold)}}{P\text{(bl.g.gold)}+P\text{(bl.g.silver)}+P\text{(bl.g.ceramic)}}$

= $\dfrac{\frac{1}{6}}{\frac{1}{6} + \frac{7}{14} + \frac{0}{10}}$

= $\dfrac{\frac{1}{6}}{\frac{4}{6}} = \frac{1}{4}$

32. P(at least one left-hander)

= P(one left-hander) + P(2 left-handers)

= $\frac{4}{11} \cdot \frac{7}{10} \cdot C(2, 1) + \frac{4}{11} \cdot \frac{3}{10} = \frac{28}{55} + \frac{6}{55}$

= $\frac{34}{55} \approx 0.618$

33. P(all first shift or all third shift)

= P(all first shift) + P(all third shift)

= $\frac{8}{23} \cdot \frac{7}{22} \cdot \frac{6}{21} + \frac{3}{23} \cdot \frac{2}{22} \cdot \frac{1}{21}$

= $\frac{56}{1771} + \frac{1}{1771}$

= $\frac{57}{1771} \approx 0.032$

34. a. 0.317460, 0.039683, 0.007937

b. 0.220588, 0.485294

c. 0.909090, 0.090909

35. P(each outfit) = $\frac{1}{4} \cdot \frac{1}{5} = \frac{1}{20}$

36. $C(8, 3) \cdot C(7, 4) = \dfrac{8!}{5!3!} \cdot \dfrac{7!}{3!4!}$

$= 56 \cdot 35 = 1960$

37. $\quad a_n = a_1 r^{n-1} \qquad a_2 = 6(2.5)^{2-1}$

$93.75 = 6r^{4-1} \qquad\quad = 15$

$15.625 = r^3 \qquad\quad a_3 = 6(2.5)^{3-1}$

$2.5 = r \qquad\qquad\quad = 37.5$

38. $\log_6 (x + 5) + \log_6 (x - 4) = 2$

$\log_6 (x + 5)(x - 4) = 2$

$(x + 5)(x - 4) = 6^2$

$x^2 + x - 20 = 36$

$x^2 + x - 56 = 0$

$(x + 8)(x - 7) = 0$

$x + 8 = 0$ or $x - 7 = 0$

$x = -8 \qquad x = 7$

Since log is not defined for negative numbers, -8 is not an acceptable solution.

39. $p = 0.5$ *ans*
$= 0.5(10.4)(6)(12)$
$= 374.4$

15-9 Simulation and Binomial Experiments

1. no

2. A binomial experiment exists if and only if these conditions occur.
   - There are exactly 2 possible outcomes for any trial.
   - There is a fixed number of trials.
   - The trials are independent.
   - The probability of each trial is the same.

3. $P(s) + P(f) = 1$
$n + P(f) = 1$
$P(f) = 1 - n$

4. coins, dice, spinners, random draws from a bag

5. binomial
$C(3, 2)H^2T = 3\left(\frac{1}{2}\right)^2\left(\frac{1}{2}\right) = \frac{3}{8}$

6. a. binomial
$C(4, 4)A^4 = 1 \cdot \left(\frac{1}{13}\right)^4 = \frac{1}{28,561}$
   b. not binomial

7. a. binomial
$C(2, 2)A^2 = 1 \cdot \left(\frac{8}{18}\right)^2 = \frac{16}{81}$
   b. binomial
$C(2, 2)G^2 = 1 \cdot \left(\frac{4}{18}\right)^2 = \frac{4}{81}$
   c. binomial
$C(2, 2)T^2 = 1 \cdot \left(\frac{6}{18}\right)^2 = \frac{1}{9}$
   d. not binomial   **e.** not binomial
   f. not binomial

8. $C(4, 0)T^4 = 1\left(\frac{1}{2}\right)^4 = \frac{1}{16} \approx 0.063$

9. $C(4, 2)H^2T^2 = 6\left(\frac{1}{2}\right)^2\left(\frac{1}{2}\right)^2 = \frac{3}{8} = 0.375$

10. $C(4, 3)HT^3 + C(4, 4)T^4 = 4\left(\frac{1}{2}\right)\left(\frac{1}{2}\right)^3 + 1\left(\frac{1}{2}\right)^4$
$= \frac{1}{4} + \frac{1}{16}$
$= \frac{5}{16} \approx 0.313$

11. $C(5, 1)WL^4 = 5\left(\frac{1}{6}\right)\left(\frac{5}{6}\right)^4 = \frac{3125}{7776}$
≈ 0.402

12. $C(5, 3)W^3L^2 + C(5, 4)W^4L + C(5, 5)W^5$
$= 10\left(\frac{1}{6}\right)^3\left(\frac{5}{6}\right)^2 + 5\left(\frac{1}{6}\right)^4\left(\frac{5}{6}\right) + \left(\frac{1}{6}\right)^5$
$= \frac{250}{7776} + \frac{25}{7776} + \frac{1}{7776}$
$= \frac{23}{648} \approx 0.035$

13. $C(5, 0)W^0L^5 + C(5, 1)WL^4 + C(5, 2)W^2L^3$
$= 1\left(\frac{5}{6}\right)^5 + 5\left(\frac{1}{6}\right)\left(\frac{5}{6}\right)^4 + 10\left(\frac{1}{6}\right)^2\left(\frac{5}{6}\right)^3$
$= \frac{3125}{7776} + \frac{3125}{7776} + \frac{1250}{7776}$
$= \frac{625}{648} \approx 0.965$

14. $C(4, 0)N^4 = 1\left(\frac{2}{3}\right)^4$
$= \frac{16}{81} \approx 0.198$

15. $C(4, 3)L^3N + C(4, 4)L^4 = 4\left(\frac{1}{3}\right)^3\left(\frac{2}{3}\right) + 1\left(\frac{1}{3}\right)^4$
$= \frac{8}{81} + \frac{1}{81}$
$= \frac{1}{9} \approx 0.111$

16. $C(4, 0)N^4 + C(4, 1)LN^3 + C(4, 2)L^2N^2$
$\quad + C(4, 3)L^3N$
$= 1\left(\frac{2}{3}\right)^4 + 4\left(\frac{1}{3}\right)\left(\frac{2}{3}\right)^3 + 6\left(\frac{1}{3}\right)^2\left(\frac{2}{3}\right)^2 + 4\left(\frac{1}{3}\right)^3\left(\frac{2}{3}\right)$
$= \frac{16}{81} + \frac{32}{81} + \frac{24}{81} + \frac{8}{81}$
$= \frac{80}{81} \approx 0.988$

17. $C(10, 7)R^7W^3 = 120\left(\frac{1}{2}\right)^7\left(\frac{1}{2}\right)^3 = \frac{15}{128} \approx 0.117$

18. $C(10, 6)R^6W^4 + C(10, 7)R^7W^3 + C(10, 8)R^8W^2$
$\quad + C(10, 9)R^9W + C(10, 10)R^{10}$
$= 210\left(\frac{1}{2}\right)^6\left(\frac{1}{2}\right)^4 + 120\left(\frac{1}{2}\right)^7\left(\frac{1}{2}\right)^3 + 45\left(\frac{1}{2}\right)^8\left(\frac{1}{2}\right)^2$
$\quad + 10\left(\frac{1}{2}\right)^9\left(\frac{1}{2}\right) + 1\left(\frac{1}{2}\right)^{10}$
$= \frac{210}{1024} + \frac{120}{1024} + \frac{45}{1024} + \frac{10}{1024} + \frac{1}{1024} = \frac{193}{512} \approx 0.377$

19. $C(10, 10)W^{10} = 1\left(\frac{1}{2}\right)^{10} = \frac{1}{1024} \approx 0.001$

20. $C(5, 3)H^3M^2 = 10\left(\frac{1}{5}\right)^3\left(\frac{4}{5}\right)^2 = \frac{32}{625} \approx 0.051$

21. $C(5, 4)H^4M + C(5, 5)H^5 = 5\left(\frac{1}{5}\right)^4\left(\frac{4}{5}\right) + 1\left(\frac{1}{5}\right)^5$
$= \frac{20}{3125} + \frac{1}{3125}$
$= \frac{21}{3125} \approx 0.007$

22. $C(5, 2)H^2M^3 + C(5, 3)H^3M^2 + C(5, 4)H^4M$
$+ C(5, 5)H^5$

$= 10\left(\frac{1}{5}\right)^2\left(\frac{4}{5}\right)^3 + 10\left(\frac{1}{5}\right)^3\left(\frac{4}{5}\right)^2 + 5\left(\frac{1}{5}\right)^4\left(\frac{4}{5}\right) + 1\left(\frac{1}{5}\right)^5$

$= \frac{640}{3125} + \frac{160}{3125} + \frac{20}{3125} + \frac{1}{3125} = \frac{821}{3125} \approx 0.263$

23. $C(3, 0)T^3 = 1\left(\frac{1}{2}\right)^3 = \frac{1}{8}$

24. $C(3, 3)H^3 = 1\left(\frac{1}{2}\right)^3 = \frac{1}{8}$

25. $C(3, 2)H^2T + C(3, 3)H^3 = 3\left(\frac{1}{2}\right)^2\left(\frac{1}{2}\right) + 1\left(\frac{1}{2}\right)^3$

$= \frac{1}{2} = 0.5$

26. $C(3, 1)HT^2 = 3\left(\frac{1}{2}\right)\left(\frac{1}{2}\right)^2 = \frac{3}{8} = 0.375$

27. $C(10, 10)U^{10} = 1\left(\frac{2}{5}\right)^{10} = \frac{1024}{9,765,625}$

≈ 0.0001049

28. $C(10, 3)U^3D^7 = 120\left(\frac{2}{5}\right)^3\left(\frac{3}{5}\right)^7 = \frac{419,904}{1,953,125}$

≈ 0.2149908

29. $C(10, 6)U^6D^4 + C(10, 7)U^7D^3 + C(10, 8)U^8D^2$
$+ C(10, 9)U^9D + C(10, 10)U^{10}$

$= 210\left(\frac{2}{5}\right)^6\left(\frac{3}{5}\right)^4 + 120\left(\frac{2}{5}\right)^7\left(\frac{3}{5}\right)^3 + 45\left(\frac{2}{5}\right)^8\left(\frac{3}{5}\right)^2$

$+ 10\left(\frac{2}{5}\right)^9\left(\frac{3}{5}\right) + \left(\frac{2}{5}\right)^{10}$

$= \frac{1,088,640}{9,765,625} + \frac{414,720}{9,765,625} + \frac{103,680}{9,765,625} + \frac{15,360}{9,765,625}$

$+ \frac{1024}{9,765,625} = \frac{1,623,424}{9,765,625}$

≈ 0.1662386

30. 2 or more complete

$(C + I)^5 = C^5 + 5C^4I + 10C^3I^2 + 10C^2I^3$
$+ 5CI^4 + I^5$

P(2 or more complete)

$= \left(\frac{2}{3}\right)^5 + 5\left(\frac{2}{3}\right)^4\left(\frac{1}{3}\right) + 10\left(\frac{1}{3}\right)^3\left(\frac{1}{3}\right)^2 + 10\left(\frac{2}{3}\right)^2\left(\frac{1}{3}\right)^3$

$= \frac{32 + 80 + 80 + 40}{243}$

$= \frac{232}{243}$ or about 0.95

31. $C(7, 3)G^4R^3 = 35\left(\frac{3}{5}\right)^4\left(\frac{2}{5}\right)^3 = \frac{4536}{15,625} \approx 0.290$

32. $C(5, 4)S^4H^1 = 5\left(\frac{4}{7}\right)^4\left(\frac{3}{7}\right)^1 = \frac{3840}{16,807} \approx 22.8\%$

33. a. $C(12, 0)M^{12} = 1\left(\frac{1}{10}\right)^{12} = \left(\frac{1}{10}\right)^{12} = 1 \times 10^{-12}$

b. $C(12, 7)H^7M^5 = 792\left(\frac{9}{10}\right)^7\left(\frac{1}{10}\right)^5 \approx 0.0037881$

c. $C(12, 12)H^{12} = 1\left(\frac{9}{10}\right)^{12} = \left(\frac{9}{10}\right)^{12} \approx 0.2824295$

d. $C(12, 10)H^{10}M^2 + C(12, 11)H^{11}M + C(12, 12)H^{12}$

$= 66\left(\frac{9}{10}\right)^{10}\left(\frac{1}{10}\right)^2 + 12\left(\frac{9}{10}\right)^{11}\left(\frac{1}{10}\right) + 1\left(\frac{9}{10}\right)^{12}$

≈ 0.8891300

34. $P(\text{not a junior}) = \frac{16 - 3}{16} = \frac{13}{16}$

35. $S_D = \frac{a_1}{1 - r}$ $S_U = \frac{a_1}{1 - r}$

$= \frac{120}{1 - \frac{2}{3}}$ $= \frac{80}{1 - \frac{2}{3}}$

$= 360$ $= 240$

$360 + 240 = 600$ ft

36. $9^{3y} = 27^{y-1}$

$(3^2)^{3y} = (3^3)^{y-1}$

$3^{6y} = 3^{3y-3}$

$6y = 3y - 3$

$3y = -3$

$y = -1$

37. Let n = numerator.

Let d = denominator.

$\frac{n}{d} = \frac{6}{7}$

$\frac{n + 1}{d} = \frac{7}{8} \longrightarrow \frac{n}{d} + \frac{1}{d} = \frac{7}{8}$

$\frac{6}{7} + \frac{1}{d} = \frac{7}{8}$

$48d + 56 = 49d$

$56 = d$

$\frac{n}{d} = \frac{6}{7}$

$\frac{n}{56} = \frac{6}{7}$

$n = 48$

The fraction is $\frac{48}{56}$.

Technology: Coin Toss Simulation

1. See students' work.

2. $P(H, H, H) = P(H) \cdot P(H) \cdot P(H)$

$$= \left(\frac{1}{2}\right)^3 = \frac{1}{8}$$

$P(T, T, T) = P(T) \cdot P(T) \cdot P(T)$

$$= \left(\frac{1}{2}\right)^3 = \frac{1}{8}$$

$P(H, H, T) = P(H) \cdot P(H) \cdot P(T)$

$$= \left(\frac{1}{2}\right)^3 = \frac{1}{8}$$

$P(H, T, T) = P(H) \cdot P(T) \cdot P(T)$

$$= \left(\frac{1}{2}\right)^3 = \frac{1}{8}$$

3. Change line 30 to FOR I = 1 to 1000. See students' work.

4. The greater the sample, the more likely the probability is closer to the theoretical probability.

Chapter 15 Summary and Review

1. $5 \cdot 5 \cdot 5 = 125$

2. $5 \cdot 4 \cdot 3 = 60$

3. $\dfrac{P(7, 3)}{P(5, 2)} = \dfrac{\frac{7!}{(7-3)!}}{\frac{5!}{(5-2)!}} = \dfrac{7!}{4!} \cdot \dfrac{3!}{5!} = 10.5$

4. $\dfrac{P(8, 5)}{P(5, 3)} = \dfrac{\frac{8!}{(8-5)!}}{\frac{5!}{(5-3)!}} = \dfrac{8!}{3!} \cdot \dfrac{2!}{5!} = 112$

5. $8!8! = 1,625,702,400$

6. $8!7!2! = 406,425,600$

7. $(8-1)! = 7! = 5040$

8. $\dfrac{10!}{2} = \dfrac{3,628,800}{2} = 1,814,400$

9. $\dfrac{5!}{2} = 60$

10. $C(3, 1) \cdot C(12, 8) = 3 \cdot 495 = 1485$

11. $C(52, 4) = 270,725$

12. $P(\text{queen}) = \dfrac{4}{52} = \dfrac{1}{13} \approx 0.077$

odds $= \dfrac{s}{f} = \dfrac{1}{13-1} = \dfrac{1}{12}$

13. $P(\text{red, white}) = \dfrac{C(6, 1) \cdot C(2, 1)}{C(8, 2)}$

$$= \dfrac{6 \cdot 2}{28} = \dfrac{3}{7} \approx 0.429$$

14. $P(\text{2 dimes, 2 pennies}) = \dfrac{C(5, 2) \cdot C(4, 2)}{C(16, 4)}$

$$= \dfrac{10 \cdot 6}{1820} = \dfrac{3}{91} \approx 0.033$$

15. $P(\text{2 black}) = \dfrac{C(4, 2)}{C(10, 2)}$

$$= \dfrac{6}{45} = \dfrac{2}{15} \approx 0.133$$

16. $P(\text{ace or face}) = P(\text{ace}) + P(\text{face})$

$$= \dfrac{4}{52} + \dfrac{12}{52} = \dfrac{4}{13} \approx 0.308$$

17. $P(\text{multiple of 5 or multiple of 7})$

$= P(\text{multiple of 5}) + P(\text{multiple of 7})$

$$= \dfrac{4}{20} + \dfrac{2}{20}$$

$$= \dfrac{3}{10} = 0.3$$

18. $P(\text{CAT or SKATE}) = P(\text{CAT}) + P(\text{SKATE})$

$- P(\text{CAT and SKATE})$

$$= \dfrac{3}{26} + \dfrac{5}{26} - \dfrac{2}{26} = \dfrac{3}{13}$$

19. $P(\text{not red or not face})$

$= P(\text{not red}) + P(\text{not face})$

$- P(\text{not red and not face})$

$$= \dfrac{1}{2} + \dfrac{10}{13} - \dfrac{1}{2} \cdot \dfrac{10}{13}$$

$$= \dfrac{23}{26} \approx 0.885$$

20. $P(\text{3 heads, 1 tail}) = C(4, 3)H^3 T$

$$= 4 \cdot \left(\dfrac{1}{2}\right)^3 \cdot \left(\dfrac{1}{2}\right) = \dfrac{1}{4} = 0.25$$

21. $P(\text{at least two 3's})$

$= P(\text{two 3's}) + P(\text{three 3's}) + P(\text{four 3's})$

$+ P(\text{five 3's})$

$= C(5, 2)W^2 L^3 + C(5, 3)W^3 L^2 + C(5, 4)W^4 L$

$+ C(5, 5)W^5$

$$= 10\left(\dfrac{1}{6}\right)^2\left(\dfrac{5}{6}\right)^3 + 10\left(\dfrac{1}{6}\right)^3\left(\dfrac{5}{6}\right)^2 + 5\left(\dfrac{1}{6}\right)^4\left(\dfrac{5}{6}\right) + 1\left(\dfrac{1}{6}\right)^5$$

$$= \dfrac{1526}{7776} = \dfrac{763}{3888} \approx 0.196$$

22. $C(20, 2) = \dfrac{20!}{18!2!} = 190$

$190 - 20 = 170$ diagonals

23. $C(6, 4) = \dfrac{6!}{2!4!} = 15$ groups

Chapter 15 Test

1. $P(6, 4) = \dfrac{6!}{(6-4)!} = 360$

2. $P(8, 3) = \dfrac{8!}{(8-3)!} = 336$

3. $C(8, 3) = \dfrac{8!}{(8-3)!3!} = 56$

4. $C(6, 4) = \dfrac{6!}{(6-4)!4!} = 15$

5. $8 \cdot 7 \cdot 6 \cdot 5 \cdot 4 = 6720$

6. $8 \cdot 6 \cdot 4 = 192$

7. $\dfrac{10!}{2!2!} = 907,200$

8. $C(12, 5) = \dfrac{12!}{(12-5)!5!} = 792$

9. $11! = 39,916,800$ **10.** $\dfrac{(6-1)!}{2} = 60$

11. $C(9, 3) = \dfrac{9!}{(9-3)!3!} = 84$

12. $P(2\text{ men, }1\text{ woman}) = \dfrac{C(4, 2) \cdot C(5, 1)}{C(9, 3)}$

$= \dfrac{6 \cdot 5}{84} = \dfrac{5}{14}$

13. $P(\text{even red, green} > 4) = \dfrac{3}{6} \cdot \dfrac{2}{6} = \dfrac{1}{6}$

14. $P(4\text{ followed by }7) = \dfrac{4}{52} \cdot \dfrac{4}{51} = \dfrac{4}{663}$

15. $P(\text{vowel}) = \dfrac{2}{6} = \dfrac{1}{3}$

16. $P(5\text{ smallest population states}) = \dfrac{5}{50} = \dfrac{1}{10}$

17. $C(9, 2) = \dfrac{9!}{7!2!} = 36$

18. $C(6, 2) \cdot C(4, 3) = \dfrac{6!}{4!2!} \cdot \dfrac{4!}{1!3!} = 15 \cdot 4 = 60$

19. $P(\text{no more than 2 heads})$

$= P(0\text{ heads}) + P(1\text{ head}) + P(2\text{ heads})$

$= C(5, 0)T^5 + C(5, 1)HT^4 + C(5, 2)H^2T^3$

$= 1\left(\dfrac{1}{3}\right)^5 + 5\left(\dfrac{2}{3}\right)\left(\dfrac{1}{3}\right)^5 + 10\left(\dfrac{2}{3}\right)^2\left(\dfrac{1}{3}\right)^5$

$= \dfrac{51}{243} = \dfrac{17}{81} \approx 0.210$

20. $C(7, 4)H^4M^3 = 35\left(\dfrac{9}{10}\right)^4\left(\dfrac{1}{10}\right)^3 = \dfrac{45,927}{2,000,000} \approx 0.023$

$C(w + 1, 2) = 9 \cdot C(w, 1)$

$\dfrac{(w + 1)!}{[(w + 1) - 2]!2!} = 9 \cdot \dfrac{w!}{(w - 1)!1!}$

$\dfrac{w + 1!}{(w - 1)!2!} = \dfrac{9w!}{(w - 1)!}$

$\dfrac{(w + 1)!}{2} = 9w!$

$\dfrac{(w + 1)!}{w} = 18$

$w + 1 = 18$

$w = 17$

Chapter 16 Trigonometric Functions

16-1 Angles and the Unit Circle

PAGE 734   CHECKING FOR UNDERSTANDING

1. standard position
2. Coterminal angles are angles in standard position with the same terminal side. An example is $50°$, $410°$, $770°$.
3. a circle centered at the origin with a radius one unit long
4. $150°$ or $\frac{5\pi}{6}$ radians
5. II   6. IV   7. IV   8. II
9. I   10. III   11. no   12. yes
13. no   14. yes   15. no   16. no

PAGES 734-736   EXERCISES

17. no   18. yes   19. no
20. yes   21. yes   22. yes
23. $180° \cdot \frac{\pi}{180} = \pi$ 24. $-90° \cdot \frac{\pi}{180} = -\frac{\pi}{2}$
25. $45° \cdot \frac{\pi}{180} = \frac{\pi}{4}$ 26. $540° \cdot \frac{\pi}{180} = 3\pi$
27. $-225° \cdot \frac{\pi}{180} = -\frac{5\pi}{4}$ 28. $315° \cdot \frac{\pi}{180} = \frac{7\pi}{4}$
29. $135° \cdot \frac{\pi}{180} = \frac{3\pi}{4}$ 30. $-210° \cdot \frac{\pi}{180} = -\frac{7\pi}{6}$
31. $-120° \cdot \frac{\pi}{180} = -\frac{2\pi}{3}$ 32. $\frac{2\pi}{3} \cdot \frac{180}{\pi} = 120°$
33. $\pi \cdot \frac{180}{\pi} = 180°$ 34. $\frac{5\pi}{6} \cdot \frac{180}{\pi} = 150°$
35. $-\frac{7\pi}{4} \cdot \frac{180}{\pi} = -315°$ 36. $-\frac{8\pi}{3} \cdot \frac{180}{\pi} = -480°$
37. $\frac{9\pi}{4} \cdot \frac{180}{\pi} = 405°$ 38. $5 \cdot \frac{180}{\pi} = \frac{900}{\pi}$
$\approx 286.48°$
39. $-\frac{7}{3} \cdot \frac{180}{\pi} = -\frac{420}{\pi}$ 40. $-\frac{13}{2} \cdot \frac{180}{\pi} = -\frac{1170}{\pi}$
$\approx -133.69°$ $\approx -372.42°$

41. Coterminal angles have the same terminal side, so they differ only by the number of complete revolutions made. Since a complete revolution measures $360°$, the measures must differ by an integral multiple of $360°$. Radian measures of coterminal angles will differ by an integral multiple of 2π.

42. a. $18° + 180° = 198°$
    b. $234° - 180° = 54°$

43. $0°$ 44. $293.56°$ 45. $99°$
46. yes   47. no   48. yes

49. 30 IF A < 2 * 3.1415927 THEN 70
    40 LET A = A - 2 * 3.1415927
    70 LET A = A + 2 * 3.1415927

50. $\left(\frac{1}{2}\right)^{10}\left(\frac{1}{2}\right)^{0} = \frac{1}{1024}$ 51. $S_n = \frac{a_1 - a_1 r^n}{1 - r}$
≈ 0.001 $S_8 = \frac{5 - 5(4)^8}{1 - 4}$
$= 109,225$

52. $\log_3 27 + \log_3 3 \overset{?}{=} \log_3 81$
$3 + 1 = 4 \checkmark$

53. $f(x) = -x^2 - 4x - 10$

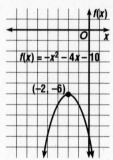

$f(x) = -x^2 - 4x - 10$

$(-2, -6)$

54. $5^{-3}b^3x^4y^{-1} = \dfrac{b^3 x^4}{5^3 y}$

PAGE 736   CHALLENGE

Unit circle: $a^2 + b^2 = 1$
a. $a^2 + (-b)^2 = a^2 + b^2 = 1$
b. $b^2 + a^2 = a^2 + b^2 = 1$
c. $b^2 + (-a)^2 = a^2 + b^2 = 1$

16-2 Sine and Cosine Functions

PAGES 739-740   CHECKING FOR UNDERSTANDING

1. a. cosine θ
   b. sine θ
2. Sine and cosine are both negative.
3. They are coterminal angles.
4. −   5. +   6. −   7. +   8. −   9. +
10. $-\frac{\sqrt{3}}{2}$ 11. $\frac{1}{2}$ 12. $-\frac{1}{2}$
13. $-\frac{\sqrt{2}}{2}$ 14. $\frac{\sqrt{3}}{2}$ 15. $-\frac{\sqrt{3}}{2}$

PAGES 740-741   EXERCISES

16. $680° - 360° = 320°$ 17. $-70° + 360° = 290°$
18. $1020° - 360° = 660° - 360° = 300°$
19. $-450° + 360° = -90° + 360° = 270°$
20. $3\pi - 2\pi = \pi$ 21. $\frac{9\pi}{2} - \frac{8\pi}{2} = \frac{\pi}{2}$

22. $-\frac{\pi}{4} + \frac{8\pi}{4} = \frac{7\pi}{4}$

23. $\frac{27\pi}{4} - \frac{8\pi}{4} = \frac{19\pi}{4} - \frac{8\pi}{4} = \frac{11\pi}{4} - \frac{8\pi}{4} = \frac{3\pi}{4}$

24. $-760° + 360° = -400° + 360° = -40° + 360° = 320°$

25. $\frac{\sqrt{2}}{2}$ 26. $-\frac{\sqrt{3}}{2}$ 27. $\frac{1}{2}$

28. $\sin\left(-\frac{5}{3}\pi\right) = \sin\left(-\frac{5}{3}\pi + \frac{6\pi}{3}\right)$

$$= \sin\frac{\pi}{3}$$

$$= \frac{\sqrt{3}}{2}$$

29. -1 30. $\frac{\sqrt{2}}{2}$

31. $\sin(-180°) = \sin(-180 + 360)° = \sin 180° = 0$

32. $\cos\left(-\frac{7}{4}\pi\right) = \cos\left(-\frac{7}{4}\pi + \frac{8\pi}{4}\right) = \cos\frac{\pi}{4} = \frac{\sqrt{2}}{2}$

33. $\cos(-60°) = \cos(-60 + 360)° = \cos 300° = \frac{1}{2}$

34. $\sin 300° = -\frac{\sqrt{3}}{2}$

35. $\sin\left(-\frac{\pi}{6}\right) = \sin\left(-\frac{\pi}{6} + \frac{12\pi}{6}\right) = \sin\frac{11\pi}{6} = -\frac{1}{2}$

36. $\sin\frac{4}{3}\pi = -\frac{\sqrt{3}}{2}$

37. $4(\sin 30°)(\cos 60°)$

$$= 4\left(\frac{1}{2}\right)\left(\frac{1}{2}\right)$$

$$= 1$$

38. $\dfrac{\sin 30° + \cos 60°}{2}$

$$= \frac{\frac{1}{2} + \frac{1}{2}}{2}$$

$$= \frac{1}{2}$$

39. $\dfrac{4\sin 300° + 2\cos 30°}{3}$

$$= \frac{4\left(-\frac{\sqrt{3}}{2}\right) + 2\left(\frac{\sqrt{3}}{2}\right)}{3}$$

$$= -\frac{2\sqrt{3}}{2} \cdot \frac{1}{3}$$

$$= -\frac{\sqrt{3}}{3}$$

40. $\sin 30° + \sin 60°$

$$= \frac{1}{2} + \frac{\sqrt{3}}{2}$$

$$= \frac{1 + \sqrt{3}}{2}$$

41. $(\sin 60°)^2 + (\cos 60°)^2$

$$= \left(\frac{\sqrt{3}}{2}\right)^2 + \left(\frac{1}{2}\right)^2$$

$$= \frac{3}{4} + \frac{1}{4}$$

$$= 1$$

42. $8(\sin 120°)(\cos 120°)$

$$= 8\left(\frac{\sqrt{3}}{2}\right)\left(-\frac{1}{2}\right)$$

$$= -2\sqrt{3}$$

43.

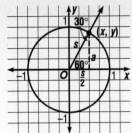

$s = 1$, so $a^2 = 1^2 - \left(\frac{1}{2}\right)^2$

$$a^2 = \frac{3}{4}$$

$$a = \frac{\sqrt{3}}{2}$$

The y-coordinate of the point (x, y) is $\frac{\sqrt{3}}{2}$

so, $\sin 60° = \frac{\sqrt{3}}{2}$.

44. a.

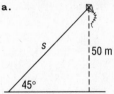

b. $\sin 45° = \cos 45°$

So, height = 50 and ground distance = 50.

So, $50^2 + 50^2 = s^2$

$$5000 = s^2$$

$$70.7 \approx s$$

Kite string is about 70.7 meters.

45. Here we have a radius of 6, so we need to divide each side by 6 so the support is $\frac{1}{2}$. Then, cosine $60° = \frac{1}{2}$.

46.

31	25	17	7
31	25	17	6
31	24	16	5
30	24	16	5
29	23	16	5
29	22	16	4
29	22	13	-7
27	20	13	
27	20	12	
27	19	12	
26	18	12	
26	18	8	

Median: 22nd score = 19

Mode: 16

Mean: $\frac{796}{43} = 18.5$

47. $1 + 4 + 9 + 16 + 25 + 36 + 49 + 64 + 81 + 100 + 121 + 144 = 650$

48. $\dfrac{\dfrac{3x}{4x-1}}{1+\dfrac{2x}{x-1}} = \dfrac{\dfrac{3x}{4x-1}}{\dfrac{4x-1}{x-1}}$

$\qquad = \dfrac{3x}{4x-1} \cdot \dfrac{x-1}{4x-1}$

$\qquad = \dfrac{3x(x-1)}{(4x-1)^2}$

49. $f(x) = x^3 - 2x^2 - 13x - 10$

The possible rational zeros are $\pm 1, \pm 2, \pm 5, \pm 10$.

$\dfrac{p}{q}$	1	-2	-13	-10
1	1	-1	-14	-24
-1	1	-3	-10	0

$x^2 - 3x - 10 = 0$

$(x-5)(x+2) = 0$

$x = 5$ or $x = -2$

The zeros are $-1, -2, 5$.

50. $(9 + 6i) - (3 + 2i)$

$= 6 + 4i$

51. $4y - x \le 6$

$\qquad 4y \le 6 + x$

$\qquad y \le \dfrac{1}{4}x + \dfrac{3}{2}$

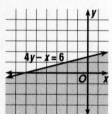

16-3 Other Trigonometric Functions

PAGE 743 CHECKING FOR UNDERSTANDING

1. $\tan \theta = \dfrac{3}{4}$; $\sec \theta = \dfrac{5}{4}$; $\cot \theta = \dfrac{4}{3}$; $\csc \theta = \dfrac{5}{3}$

2. $\csc \theta \le -1$ or $\csc \theta \ge 1$

3. $y = \sec x$; $y = \cot x$

4. none $\qquad\qquad$ **5.** $90°$, $270°$

6. none $\qquad\qquad$ **7.** $0°$, $180°$, $360°$

8. $0°$, $180°$, $360°$ $\qquad$ **9.** $90°$, $270°$

10. $\sin 60° = \dfrac{\sqrt{3}}{2}$; $\cos 60° = \dfrac{1}{2}$; $\tan 60° = \sqrt{3}$;

$\sec 60° = 2$; $\cot 60° = \dfrac{\sqrt{3}}{3}$; $\csc 60° = \dfrac{2\sqrt{3}}{3}$

11. $-225° + 360° = 135°$

$\sin -225° = \dfrac{\sqrt{2}}{2}$; $\cos -225° = -\dfrac{\sqrt{2}}{2}$; $\tan -225° = -1$

$\sec -225° = -\sqrt{2}$; $\cot -225° = -1$; $\csc -225° = \sqrt{2}$

12. $\sin \dfrac{3\pi}{2} = -1$; $\cos \dfrac{3\pi}{2} = 0$; $\tan \dfrac{3\pi}{2}$ is undefined;

$\sec \dfrac{3\pi}{2}$ is undefined; $\cot \dfrac{3\pi}{2} = 0$; $\csc \dfrac{3\pi}{2} = -1$

PAGES 744-745 EXERCISES

13. $\cot 135° = \dfrac{-\dfrac{\sqrt{2}}{2}}{\dfrac{\sqrt{2}}{2}} = -1$

14. $\csc 45° = \dfrac{1}{\dfrac{\sqrt{2}}{2}} = \sqrt{2}$

15. $\sec 300° = \dfrac{1}{\dfrac{1}{2}} = 2$

16. $\tan\left(-\dfrac{\pi}{3}\right) = \tan \dfrac{5\pi}{3} = \dfrac{-\dfrac{\sqrt{3}}{2}}{\dfrac{1}{2}} = -\sqrt{3}$

17. $\csc(-210°) = \csc 150° = \dfrac{1}{\dfrac{1}{2}} = 2$

18. $\tan \dfrac{7\pi}{6} = \dfrac{-\dfrac{1}{2}}{-\dfrac{\sqrt{3}}{2}} = \dfrac{\sqrt{3}}{3}$

19. $\cot(-60°) = \cot 300° = \dfrac{\dfrac{1}{2}}{-\dfrac{\sqrt{3}}{2}} = -\dfrac{\sqrt{3}}{3}$

20. $\sec 240° = \dfrac{1}{-\dfrac{1}{2}} = -2$

21. $\cot\left(-\dfrac{\pi}{6}\right) = \cot \dfrac{5\pi}{6} = \dfrac{-\dfrac{\sqrt{3}}{2}}{\dfrac{1}{2}} = -\sqrt{3}$

22. $\csc\left(-\dfrac{\pi}{6}\right) = \csc \dfrac{5\pi}{6} = \dfrac{1}{-\dfrac{1}{2}} = -2$

23. $\sec(-120°) = \sec 240° = \dfrac{1}{-\dfrac{1}{2}} = -2$

24. $\cot 210° = \dfrac{-\dfrac{\sqrt{3}}{2}}{-\dfrac{1}{2}} = \sqrt{3}$

25. $\csc \dfrac{\pi}{2} = \dfrac{1}{1} = 1$

26. $\tan \dfrac{9\pi}{4} = \dfrac{\dfrac{\sqrt{2}}{2}}{\dfrac{\sqrt{2}}{2}} = 1$

27. $\tan -\dfrac{5\pi}{6} = \tan \dfrac{\pi}{6} = \dfrac{\dfrac{1}{2}}{\dfrac{\sqrt{3}}{2}} = \dfrac{\sqrt{3}}{3}$

28. $\cot \dfrac{7\pi}{4} = \dfrac{\dfrac{\sqrt{2}}{2}}{-\dfrac{\sqrt{2}}{2}} = -1$

29. $\tan(-300°) = \tan 60° = \dfrac{\dfrac{\sqrt{3}}{2}}{\dfrac{1}{2}} = \sqrt{3}$

30. $\cot 540° = -\dfrac{1}{0}$ is undefined

31. $\sec(-30°) = \sec 330° = \dfrac{1}{\frac{\sqrt{3}}{2}} = \dfrac{2\sqrt{3}}{3}$

32. $\tan 405° = \tan 45° = \dfrac{\frac{\sqrt{2}}{2}}{\frac{\sqrt{2}}{2}} = 1$

33. $\csc 180° = \dfrac{1}{0}$ is undefined

34. $\sec 390° = \sec 30° = \dfrac{1}{\frac{\sqrt{3}}{2}} = \dfrac{2\sqrt{3}}{3}$

35. $\cot(-600°) = \cot 120° = \dfrac{\frac{-1}{2}}{\frac{\sqrt{3}}{2}} = \dfrac{-\sqrt{3}}{3}$

36. $\csc\left(-\dfrac{7}{6}\pi\right) = \csc\dfrac{5\pi}{6} = \dfrac{1}{\frac{1}{2}} = 2$

37. $\dfrac{\tan 300°}{\csc 540°} = \dfrac{\frac{-\frac{\sqrt{3}}{2}}{\frac{1}{2}}}{\frac{1}{0}}$

undefined

38. $\tan\dfrac{13\pi}{4} - \sec\pi = \dfrac{-\frac{\sqrt{2}}{2}}{-\frac{\sqrt{2}}{2}} - \left(-\dfrac{1}{1}\right)$

$\qquad\qquad = 1 + 1$

$\qquad\qquad = 2$

39. $\csc\left(-\dfrac{5}{2}\pi\right)\sec\left(-\dfrac{11}{6}\pi\right) = \csc\left(\dfrac{3\pi}{2}\right)\sec\dfrac{\pi}{6}$

$\qquad\qquad = \left(-\dfrac{1}{1}\right)\left|\dfrac{1}{\frac{\sqrt{3}}{2}}\right|$

$\qquad\qquad = -\dfrac{2\sqrt{3}}{3}$

40. If $x° + y° = 90°$, then:

$\sin x° = \cos y°$
$\tan x° = \cot y°$
$\sec x° = \csc y°$
$\cos x° = \sin y°$
$\cot x° = \tan y°$
$\csc x° = \sec y°$

41. $\tan 12.7° = \dfrac{9}{40}$;

$\sec 12.7° = \dfrac{41}{40}$;

$\cot 12.7° = \dfrac{40}{9}$;

$\csc 12.7° = \dfrac{41}{9}$

42.

$\sin 67.4° = \dfrac{144}{156} = \dfrac{12}{13}$

$\cos 67.4° = \dfrac{60}{156} = \dfrac{5}{13}$

$\tan 67.4° = \dfrac{12}{5}$

$\sec 67.4° = \dfrac{13}{5}$

$\csc 67.4° = \dfrac{13}{12}$

$\cot 67.4° = \dfrac{5}{12}$

$60^2 + 144^2 = h^2$

$156 = h$

43. $P(p \text{ or } n) = \left(\dfrac{7}{14}\right) + \dfrac{1}{14}$

$\qquad\qquad = \dfrac{8}{14} = \dfrac{4}{7}$

44. $a_1 = 12$

$12r^3 = \dfrac{3}{2}$

$r^3 = \dfrac{1}{8}$

$r = \dfrac{1}{2}$

$a_6 = 12\left(\dfrac{1}{2}\right)^5$

$\quad = \dfrac{12}{32} = \dfrac{3}{8}$

$n = 6$

45. $4x^2 + 9y^2 = 36$

$\underline{4x^2 - 9y^2 = 36}$

$\qquad 8x^2 = 72$

$\qquad\quad x = \pm 3$

$\qquad\quad (\pm 3, 0)$

46. $\sqrt[3]{3y - 1} - 2 = 0$

$\sqrt[3]{3y - 1} = 2$

$3y - 1 = 8$

$3y = 9$

$y = 3$

47. Let x = longest side.
Let y = shortest side.
Let z = third side.
$x + y + z = 56$
$x = 3(z - y)$
$x = 2y$
$2y = 3z - 3y$
$\dfrac{5}{3}y = z$
$2y + y + \dfrac{5}{3}y = 56$
$\dfrac{14}{3}y = 56$
$y = 12$ feet
$x = 24$ feet
$z = 20$ feet

48. $m = \dfrac{22 - 8}{10 - 6}$

$\quad = \dfrac{14}{4}$

$\quad = \dfrac{7}{2}$

16-4 Inverse Trigonometric Functions

PAGE 749   CHECKING FOR UNDERSTANDING

1. They are inverses of each other.

2. The trigonometric functions are not one-to-one functions.

3. Restricted domains are denoted with a capital letter.

4. $b = \text{Cos}^{-1} a$ 5. $y = \text{Sin}^{-1} x$

6. $\alpha = \text{Tan}^{-1} \beta$ 7. $30° = \text{Sin}^{-1}\dfrac{1}{2}$

8. $45° = \text{Cos}^{-1}\dfrac{y}{2}$ 9. $x = \text{Tan}^{-1}\left(-\dfrac{4}{3}\right)$

10. $\sin\left[\text{Cos}^{-1}\left(\frac{2}{3}\right)\right]$

$= \sin\left(\cos\theta = \frac{2}{3}\right)$

$= \sin\theta$

$= \frac{\sqrt{5}}{3}$

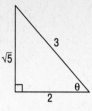

$2^2 + y^2 = 3^2$

$y^2 = 5$

$y = \sqrt{5}$

11. $\cos\left(\text{Cos}^{-1}\frac{4}{5}\right) = \frac{4}{5}$ 12. $\cos\left(\text{Cos}^{-1}\frac{1}{2}\right) = \frac{1}{2}$

PAGES 749-750   EXERCISES

13. $\theta = 120°$

14. $\frac{1}{2}$

15. $\text{Sin}^{-1}\left(\cos\frac{\pi}{2}\right) = \text{Sin}^{-1}(0)$

$= 0$

16. $\text{Tan}^{-1}(-1) = -\frac{\pi}{4}$

$= -45°$

17. $\text{Sin}\frac{\pi}{6} = \frac{1}{2}$

18. $\text{Sin}^{-1} 1 = 90°$

19. $\text{Cos}^{-1}\frac{6}{7} = x$

$\cos x = \frac{6}{7};\ \sin x = \frac{\sqrt{13}}{7}$

$\tan\left(\text{Cos}^{-1}\frac{6}{7}\right) = \tan x$

$= \frac{\frac{\sqrt{13}}{7}}{\frac{6}{7}} = \frac{\sqrt{13}}{6}$

20. $\text{Sin}^{-1}\frac{5}{6} = x$

$\sin x = \frac{5}{6};\ \cos x = \frac{\sqrt{11}}{6}$

$\cot\left(\text{Sin}^{-1}\frac{5}{6}\right) = \cot x$

$= \frac{\frac{\sqrt{11}}{6}}{\frac{5}{6}} = \frac{\sqrt{11}}{5}$

21. $\text{Sin}^{-1}\frac{7}{9} = x$

$\sin x = \frac{7}{9};\ \cos x = \frac{4\sqrt{2}}{9}$

$\cot\left(\text{Sin}^{-1}\frac{7}{9}\right) = \cot x$

$= \frac{\frac{4\sqrt{2}}{9}}{\frac{7}{9}} = \frac{4\sqrt{2}}{7}$

22. $\sin\left(\text{Arctan}\frac{\sqrt{3}}{3}\right)$

$= \sin 30°$

$= \frac{1}{2}$

23. $\text{Arcsin}\frac{3}{5} = x$

$\sin x = \frac{3}{5};\ \cos = \frac{4}{5}$

$\cos\left(\text{Arcsin}\frac{3}{5}\right) = \frac{4}{5}$

24. $\tan(\text{Arctan } 3)$

$= \tan 60°$

$= 3$

25. $\text{Sin}^{-1}\left(\tan\frac{\pi}{4}\right)$

$= \text{Sin}^{-1}(1)$

$= 90°$

26. $\text{Arctan}\sqrt{3} = 60°$

27. $\text{Arccos}\frac{\sqrt{3}}{2} = 30°$

28. $\cos(\text{Tan}^{-1}\sqrt{3})$

$= \cos 60°$

$= \frac{1}{2}$

29. $\cos\left[\text{Arcsin}\left(-\frac{1}{2}\right)\right]$

$= \cos(-30°)$

$= \frac{\sqrt{3}}{2}$

30. $\cos(\text{Tan}^{-1} 1)$

$= \cos 45°$

$= \frac{\sqrt{2}}{2}$

31. $\cos\left[\text{Cos}^{-1}\left(-\frac{\sqrt{2}}{2}\right) - \frac{\pi}{2}\right]$

$= \cos\left(\frac{3\pi}{4} - \frac{\pi}{2}\right)$

$= \cos\frac{\pi}{4}$

$= \frac{\sqrt{2}}{2}$

32. $\text{Sin}^{-1}\frac{1}{2} = x$

$\sin x = \frac{1}{2};\ \cos x = \frac{\sqrt{3}}{2}$

$\sin\left(2\,\text{Sin}^{-1}\frac{1}{2}\right) = \sin(2x)$

$= 2\sin x\cos x$

$= 2\cdot\frac{1}{2}\cdot\frac{\sqrt{3}}{2}$

$= \frac{\sqrt{3}}{2}$

33. $\text{Cos}^{-1}\frac{3}{5} = x$

$\cos x = \frac{3}{5};\ \sin x = \frac{4}{5}$

$\sin\left(2\,\text{Cos}^{-1}\frac{3}{5}\right) = \sin 2x$

$= 2\sin x\cos x$

$= 2\cdot\frac{4}{5}\cdot\frac{3}{5}$

$= \frac{24}{25}$

34. $\text{Cos}^{-1}\left(-\frac{3}{5}\right) = x$

$\cos x = -\frac{3}{5};\ \sin x = \frac{4}{5}$

$\tan\left[\text{Cos}^{-1}\left(-\frac{3}{5}\right)\right]$

$= \tan x$

$= \frac{\frac{4}{5}}{-\frac{3}{5}}$

$= -\frac{4}{3}$

35. $\text{Sin}^{-1} \dfrac{\sqrt{3}}{2} = x$

$\sin x = \dfrac{\sqrt{3}}{2}$

36. $\sin [\text{Arctan} (-\sqrt{3})]$

$= \sin (-60°)$

$= -\dfrac{\sqrt{3}}{2}$

37. $\text{Cos}^{-1} \left(\sin \dfrac{3\pi}{2} \right)$

$= \text{Cos}^{-1} (-1)$

$= \pi \text{ or } 180°$

38. $\text{Tan}^{-1} \left(\cos \dfrac{3\pi}{2} \right)$

$= \text{Tan}^{-1} 0$

$= 0$

39. $\text{Sin}^{-1} \left(\cos \dfrac{\pi}{6} \right)$

$= \text{Sin}^{-1} \left(\dfrac{\sqrt{3}}{2} \right)$

$= \dfrac{\pi}{3} \text{ or } 60°$

40. $(\text{Cos}^{-1} \circ \text{Cos})(x)$

$= \text{Cos}^{-1} (\text{Cos } x)$

$= \text{Cos}^{-1} y$

$= x$

$(\text{Cos} \circ \text{Cos}^{-1})x$

$= \text{Cos} (\text{Cos}^{-1} x)$

$= \text{Cos } y$

$= x$

41. a.

48 mi

θ

24 mi

b. $\cos \theta = \dfrac{1}{2}$

$\theta = 60°$

60° north of east

42. $\sin \theta = \dfrac{40}{41}$

$40^2 + s^2 = 41^2$

$1600 + s^2 = 1681$

$s^2 = 81$

$s = 9$

$\cos \theta = \dfrac{9}{41}$

$\tan \theta = \dfrac{\frac{40}{41}}{\frac{9}{41}} = \dfrac{40}{9}$

43. Range: $53{,}000{,}000 - 16{,}000{,}000 = 37{,}000{,}000$

Quartiles: $18{,}000{,}000, 22{,}000{,}000, 31{,}000{,}000$

Interquartile range: $31{,}000{,}000 - 18{,}000{,}000$

$= 13{,}000{,}000$

Outlier: $53{,}000{,}000$

44. $\displaystyle\sum_{k=1}^{10} (2 + k) = 3 + 4 + 5 + 6 + 7 + 8 + 9 + 10 + 11$

$+ 12 = 75$

45. $y = ne^{kt}$

$164 = 80e^{3k}$

$2.05 = e^{3k}$

$\log 2.05 = \log e^{3k}$

$\log 2.05 = 3k \log e$

$\dfrac{\log 2.05}{3 \log e} = k$

$\dfrac{0.312}{3(0.434)} = k$

$0.2392 = k$

46. $55(4) = 45x$

$220 = 45x$

$\dfrac{44}{9} = x$

$4\dfrac{8}{9}$ hours

47. $x = 120(2 \text{ hrs}) \left(60 \dfrac{\text{min}}{\text{hr}} \right) (14 \text{ days})$

$= 201{,}600$

$= 2.016 \times 10^5$

48. $AA = \begin{bmatrix} 2 & 7 \\ 0 & -1 \end{bmatrix} \begin{bmatrix} 2 & 7 \\ 0 & -1 \end{bmatrix} = \begin{bmatrix} 4 & 7 \\ 0 & 1 \end{bmatrix}$

16-5 Finding Values for Trigonometric Functions

PAGE 753   CHECKING FOR UNDERSTANDING

1. Convert the minutes to a decimal first.

2. ENTER: $48 \boxed{=} \boxed{\text{TAN}} \boxed{\frac{1}{x}}$; 0.9004

3. Multiply the decimal portion by 60.

4. 0.6691   **5.** 0.1564   **6.** 0.0875

7. 0.7392   **8.** 0.0552   **9.** 343.8

10. 47.4256   **11.** 7.6067   **12.** 30.6383

13. $\sec x = \dfrac{1}{\cos x}$

$\cos x = \dfrac{1}{2.7504}$

$x = 68.6796$

14. $\csc x = \dfrac{1}{\sin x}$

$\sin x = \dfrac{1}{1.9735}$

$x = 30.4452$

15. $\cot x = \dfrac{1}{\tan x}$

$\tan x = \dfrac{1}{3.1376}$

$x = 17.6779$

PAGES 753-755   EXERCISES

16. $\csc 75° = \dfrac{1}{\sin 75°}$

$= 1.0353$

17. $\sin 730° = 0.1736$

18. $\tan -90°$ is undefined

19. $\cos 5\pi = -1$

20. $\cot -\dfrac{3\pi}{5} = \dfrac{1}{\tan \left(-\dfrac{3\pi}{5} \right)}$

$= 0.3249$

21. $\sin \dfrac{7\pi}{3} = 0.8660$

22. $\tan -\dfrac{11\pi}{8} = -2.4142$

23. $\sec -\dfrac{8\pi}{5} = \dfrac{1}{\cos \left(-\dfrac{8\pi}{5} \right)}$

$= 3.2361$

24. $\cot 250° = \dfrac{1}{\tan 250°}$

$= 0.3640$

25. $\sec 600° = \dfrac{1}{\cos 600°}$

$= -2$

26. $\sec 540° = \dfrac{1}{\cos 540°}$

$= -1$

27. $\csc 7\pi = \dfrac{1}{\sin 7\pi}$

undefined

28. $\csc (-890°) = \dfrac{1}{\sin (-890°)}$

$= -5.7588$

29. $(\sin 95°)(\tan 37°) = 0.7507$

30. $\left(\sin \dfrac{\pi}{3}\right)\left(\cos \dfrac{\pi}{8}\right) = 0.8001$

31. $\dfrac{3(\sin 50°) + 9(\cos 10°)}{\tan 290°} = -4.0624$

32. $\operatorname{Sin}^{-1} \dfrac{15}{16} = 69.6359°$

33. $\operatorname{Cos}^{-1} 0.89 = 27.1268°$

34. $\operatorname{Tan}^{-1} \dfrac{3}{2} = 56.3099°$

35. $\dfrac{3 \tan \frac{\pi}{6}}{2 \sin \frac{\pi}{3} - \sec 3\pi} = \dfrac{3 \tan \frac{\pi}{6}}{2 \sin \frac{\pi}{3} - \frac{1}{\cos 3\pi}} = 0.6340$

36. $\tan \left(\operatorname{Cos}^{-1} \dfrac{\sqrt{3}}{3}\right) = 1.4142$

37. $\sin \left[\operatorname{Tan}^{-1}(-\sqrt{6})\right] = -0.9258$

38. a. $\sin 100$ grads $= 1$

$\cos 100$ grads $= 0$

$\tan 100$ grads is undefined

$\sec 100$ grads is undefined

$\csc 100$ grads $= 1$

$\cot 100$ grads $= 0$

b. 100 grads $= 90°$

$= \dfrac{\pi}{2}$ radians

39. $H = \dfrac{(100^2) \sin 65°}{2(32)}$

$= 128.3$ feet

40. $P = 2(120) \cos 70°$

$= 82.1$ watts

41. $2 \sin 60° = 3 \sin r$

$\dfrac{2 \sin 60°}{3} = \sin r$

$r = 35°16'$

42. Let L = Lynn wins.

Let M = Maria wins.

$P(M \geq 3) = M^8 + C(8, 7)M^7L + C(8, 6)M^6L^2$

$+ C(8, 5)M^5L^3 + C(8, 4)M^4L^4$

$+ C(8, 3)M^3L^5$

$= \left(\dfrac{1}{3}\right)^8 + 8\left(\dfrac{1}{3}\right)^7\left(\dfrac{2}{3}\right) + 28\left(\dfrac{1}{3}\right)^6\left(\dfrac{2}{3}\right)^2$

$+ 56\left(\dfrac{1}{3}\right)^5\left(\dfrac{2}{3}\right)^3 + 70\left(\dfrac{1}{3}\right)^4\left(\dfrac{2}{3}\right)^4$

$+ 56\left(\dfrac{1}{3}\right)^3\left(\dfrac{2}{3}\right)^5$

$= \dfrac{3489}{6561}$

≈ 0.532

43. 40 34 31 30 30 30 24 24 24

23 23 21 20 17

Median: 24

Mode: 24 and 30

Mean: $\dfrac{371}{14} = 26.5$

Standard Deviation:

$$\sqrt{\dfrac{\begin{bmatrix} (13.5)^2 + 7.5^2 + 4.5^2 + 3(3.5)^2 \\ + 3(-2.5)^2 + 2(-3.5)^2 + (-5.5)^2 \\ + (-6.5)^2 + (9.5)^2 \end{bmatrix}}{14}}$$

$= \sqrt{\dfrac{501.5}{14}}$

$= 5.98$

≈ 6

44. $\log_3 35 = \dfrac{\log 35}{\log 3} \approx 3.2362$

45. $\dfrac{\dfrac{x}{x^2 - 16}}{\dfrac{4x - 4}{x^2 - 2x - 8}} = \dfrac{x}{(x - 4)(x + 4)} \cdot \dfrac{(x - 4)(x + 2)}{4(x - 1)}$

$= \dfrac{x(x + 2)}{4(x - 1)(x + 4)}$

46. $\dfrac{1}{3}|6x + 5| = 7$

$6x + 5 = 21$ or $-6x - 5 = 21$

$6x = 16$ $\qquad -6x = 26$

$x = \dfrac{8}{3}$ $\qquad x = -\dfrac{13}{3}$

PAGE 755   MID-CHAPTER REVIEW

1. $90 \cdot \dfrac{\pi}{180} = \dfrac{\pi}{2}$

2. $150 \cdot \dfrac{\pi}{180} = \dfrac{5\pi}{6}$

3. $-135 \cdot \dfrac{\pi}{180} = -\dfrac{3\pi}{4}$

4. $\dfrac{3\pi}{2} \cdot \dfrac{180}{\pi} = 270°$

5. $-\dfrac{7\pi}{4} \cdot \dfrac{180}{\pi} = -315°$

6. $2 \cdot \dfrac{180}{\pi} = \dfrac{360}{\pi} \approx 114.59°$

7. $420° - 360° = 60°$

8. $1400° - 1080° = 320°$

9. $-\frac{8\pi}{9} + \frac{18\pi}{9} = \frac{10\pi}{9}$

10. $-\frac{\sqrt{3}}{2}$

11. $\tan 900° = \frac{\sin 180°}{\cos 180°}$

$= 0$

12. $\csc \frac{4}{3}\pi = \frac{1}{\sin \frac{4}{3}\pi}$

$= -\frac{2\sqrt{3}}{3}$

13. $\sec \frac{9\pi}{4} = \frac{1}{\cos \frac{9\pi}{4}}$

$= \frac{2\sqrt{2}}{2}$

$= \sqrt{2}$

14. $\frac{\tan(-135°)}{\sec 270°}$

undefined

15. $\left[\cot\left(-\frac{3\pi}{4}\right)\right]\left[\sec\left(-\frac{\pi}{4}\right)\right]$

$= \frac{1}{\tan\left(-\frac{3\pi}{4}\right)} \cdot \frac{1}{\cos -\frac{\pi}{4}}$

$= (1)(\sqrt{2})$

$= \sqrt{2}$

16. $45°$ **17.** $-90°$ **18.** $\frac{\sqrt{2}}{2}$

19. $-30°$ **20.** $30°$ **21.** (-1)

22. 1.0038 **23.** -0.1736 **24.** 3.5387

25. $512 = \frac{(128)^2 \sin 2\theta}{32}$

$1 = \sin 2\theta$

$\theta = 45°$

16-6 **Solving Right Triangles**

PAGE 759 CHECKING FOR UNDERSTANDING

1. Find the measures of all angles and sides.

2. Answers may vary. One answer is that their sum is $90°$.

3. They are equal.

4. $\sin 15° = \frac{a}{37}$

$a = 37 \sin 15°$

$a = 9.6$

5. $\tan 76° = \frac{13}{b}$

$b = \frac{13}{\tan 76°}$

$b = 3.2$

6. $\sin 49°13' = \frac{10}{c}$

$c = \frac{10}{\sin 49°13'}$

$c = 13.2$

7. $\tan 71°13' = \frac{21.2}{b}$

$b = \frac{21.2}{\tan 71°13'}$

$b = 7.2$

8. $\cos 16° = \frac{13}{c}$

$c = \frac{13}{\cos 16°}$

$c = 13.5$

9. $\cos 19°7' = \frac{11}{c}$

$c = \frac{11}{\cos 19°7'}$

$c = 11.6$

---

10. $b = \sqrt{10^2 - 8^2} = 6$

$\sin A = \frac{8}{10} = 0.8$

$A = 53°8'$

$B = 90° - A = 36°52'$

11. $b = \sqrt{13^2 - 12^2} = 5$

$\sin A = \frac{12}{13} = 0.9231$

$A = 67°23'$

$B = 90° - A = 22°37'$

12. $c = \sqrt{2^2 + 7^2} = \sqrt{53} = 7.28$

$\sin A = \frac{2}{\sqrt{53}} = 0.2747$

$A = 15°57'$

$B = 90° - A = 74°3'$

13. $a = \sqrt{21^2 - 18^2} = \sqrt{117} = 10.82$

$\sin A = \frac{\sqrt{117}}{21} = 0.5151$

$A = 31°$

$B = 90° - A = 59°$

14. $c = \sqrt{11^2 + 21^2} = \sqrt{562} = 23.71$

$\sin A = \frac{11}{\sqrt{562}} = 0.4640$

$A = 27°39'$

$B = 90° - A = 62°21'$

15. $a = \sqrt{13^2 - 6^2} = \sqrt{133} = 11.53$

$\sin A = \frac{\sqrt{133}}{13} = 0.8871$

$A = 62°31'$

$B = 90° - A = 27°29'$

16. $\sin 63° = \frac{9.7}{c}$

$0.8910 = \frac{9.7}{c}$

$c = 10.89$

$b = \sqrt{10.89^2 - 9.7^2} = 4.94$

$B = 90° - A = 27°$

17. $\sin 16° = \frac{a}{14}$

$0.2756 = \frac{a}{14}$

$a = 3.86$

$b = \sqrt{14^2 - 3.86^2} = 13.46$

$B = 90° - A = 74°$

18. $\cos 37°15' = \frac{11}{c}$

$0.7960 = \frac{11}{c}$

$c = 13.82$

$a = \sqrt{13.82^2 - 11^2} = 8.36$

$B = 90° - A = 52°45'$

19. $\cos 42°10' = \dfrac{9}{c}$

$\qquad c = 12.14$

$b = \sqrt{12.14^2 - 9^2} = 8.15$

$A = 90° - B = 47°50'$

20. $\sin 64° = \dfrac{b}{19.2}$

$\qquad b = 17.26$

$a = \sqrt{19.2^2 - 17.26^2} = 8.42$

$B = 90° - A = 26°$

21. $\sin 83° = \dfrac{\sqrt{31}}{c}$

$\qquad c = 5.61$

$a = \sqrt{5.61^2 - 31} = 0.68$

$A = 90° - B = 7°$

22. $\tan 33° = \dfrac{b}{33}$

$\qquad b = 21.43$

$c = \sqrt{33^2 + 21.43^2} = 39.35$

$A = 90° - B = 57°$

23. $\sin 13° = \dfrac{b}{6}$

$\qquad b = 1.35$

$a = \sqrt{6^2 - 1.35^2} = 5.85$

$A = 90° - B = 77°$

24. $\tan 77° = \dfrac{a}{42}$

$\qquad a = 181.92$

$c = \sqrt{181.92^2 + 42^2} = 186.71$

$B = 90° - A = 13°$

25. $\cos 49° = \dfrac{9}{c}$

$\qquad c = 13.72$

$b = \sqrt{13.72^2 - 9^2} = 10.35$

$A = 90°° - B = 41°$

26. $\tan 22°22' = \dfrac{a}{22}$

$\qquad a = 9.05$

$c = \sqrt{9.05^2 + 22^2} = 23.79$

$B = 90° - A = 67°38'$

27. $\tan 44°44' = \dfrac{b}{44}$

$\qquad b = 43.59$

$c = \sqrt{44^2 + 43.59^2} = 61.94$

$A = 90° - B = 45°16'$

28. $\tan 18° = \dfrac{b}{\sqrt{15}}$

$\qquad b = 1.26$

$c = \sqrt{15 + 1.26^2} = 4.07$

$A = 90° - B = 72°$

29. $\sin 55°55' = \dfrac{a}{16}$

$\qquad a = 13.25$

$b = \sqrt{16^2 - 13.25^2} = 8.97$

$B = 90° - A = 34°5'$

30. $\sin 45° = \dfrac{a}{7\sqrt{2}}$

$\qquad a = 7$

$b = \sqrt{98 - 49} = 7$

$B = 90° - A = 45°$

31. $\sin 15° = \dfrac{a}{25}$

$\qquad a = 6.47$

$b = \sqrt{25^2 - 6.47^2} = 24.15$

$B = 90° - A = 75°$

32. $\tan 30° = \dfrac{11}{a}$

$\qquad a = 19.05$

$c = \sqrt{19.05^2 + 11^2} = 22$

$A = 90° - 30° = 60°$

33. $\tan A = \dfrac{7}{8}$

$\qquad A = 41°11'$

$B = 90° - A = 48°49'$

$a = 7, \; b = 8$

$c = \sqrt{7^2 + 8^2} = 10.63$

34. $\sin 27° = \dfrac{7}{c}$

$\qquad c = 15.42$

$b = \sqrt{15.42^2 - 7^2} = 13.74$

$B = 90° - A = 63°$

35. $\tan B = \dfrac{8}{6}$

$\qquad B = 53°8'$

$A = 90° - B = 36°52'$

$a = 6$

$c = \sqrt{6^2 + 8^2} = 10$

36. $\sin A = \dfrac{1}{3}$

$\qquad A = 19°28'$

$B = 90° - A = 70°32'$

$a = 5, \; c = 15$

$225 = \sqrt{5^2 + b^2}$

$b = 14.14$

37. $2x - 1 = x + 2$

$\qquad x = 3$

$a = b = 5, \; c = 7.07$

a, b, and c are sides of an isosceles right triangle.

$A = B = 45°$

38. $3x - 20 = x + 16$

$2x = 36$

$x = 18$, $a = b = c = 34$

a, b, and c are sides of an equilateral triangle.

$A = B = C = 60°$

39. Yes; justifications may vary.

40. $\tan A = \dfrac{1.7}{3}$

$A = 29°32'$

41.

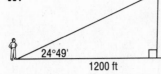

$\tan 24°49' = \dfrac{m}{1200}$

$m = 555$ feet

42. $7 \cdot 3 \cdot 4 = 84$

43. $\displaystyle\sum_{n=1}^{5} 3^{n-1} = 3^0 + 3^1 + 3^2 + 3^3 + 3^4$

$= 1 + 3 + 9 + 27 + 81$

$= 121$

44. $A = P\left(1 + \dfrac{r}{n}\right)^{nt}$

$6230 = 150\left(1 + \dfrac{0.05}{4}\right)^{4t}$

$41.53 = (1.0125)^{4t}$

$\log 41.53 = 4t \log (1.0125)$

$\dfrac{\log 41.53}{4 \log 1.01} = t$

$75 = t$

75 years ago

45. Let x = amount of 35% salt solution.

$0.35x + 0.10(250 - x) = 0.20(250)$

$0.25x + 25 = 50$

$0.25x = 25$

$x = 100$

100 mL of 35% solution

46. $y^2 - 8y + 12 = 0$

Discriminant: 16

Two real roots

$(y - 6)(y - 2) = 0$

$y = 6$ or $y = 2$

47. $r + s = 12$ $s = 3r$

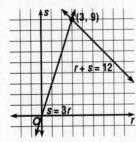

$r = 3$, $s = 9$

Technology: Solving Triangles

1. one; 1.9487   **2.** one; 0.1743

3. none; 4.8719   **4.** none; 7.6604

5. two; 9.9864   **6.** two; 0.3653

7. one; 4.8127   **8.** two; 1.0333

16-7   Applications of Right Triangles

PAGE 764   CHECKING FOR UNDERSTANDING

1. Angle of elevation is the angle formed by a line of sight and the horizontal when the observer is looking up.

2. They are alternate interior angles formed by a transversal cutting two parallel lines, so they are congruent.

3. $7^2 + b^2 = 16^2$ **4.** $a^2 + 10^2 = 20^2$

$b^2 = 207$ $a^2 = 300$

$b = 14.4$ $a = 17.3$

5. $\tan A = \dfrac{7}{12}$ **6.** $a^2 + a^2 = 12^2$

$A = 30°15'$ $2a^2 = 12^2$

$a = 8.5$

$\cos B = \dfrac{8.5}{12}$

$B = 45°$

PAGES 765-766   EXERCISES

7. $a^2 + 2^2 = 6^2$

$a = 5.6569$

$\sin A = \dfrac{5.6569}{6} = 0.9428$

$\cos A = \dfrac{2}{6} = 0.333\overline{3}$

$\tan A = \dfrac{5.6569}{2} = 2.8284$

8. $b^2 + 5^2 = 11^2$

$b = 9.7980$

$\sin A = \dfrac{5}{11} = 0.4545$

$\cos A = \dfrac{9.7980}{11} = 0.8907$

$\tan A = \dfrac{5}{9.7980} = 0.5103$

9. $9^2 + 13^2 = c^2$

$c = 15.8114$

$\sin A = \dfrac{9}{15.8114} = 0.5692$

$\cos A = \dfrac{13}{15.8114} = 0.8222$

$\tan A = \dfrac{9}{13} = 0.6923$

10. $\tan 31°20' = \dfrac{h}{40}$

$h = 24.35$ ft

11. $\tan 40° = \dfrac{h}{300}$

$h = 251.73$ m

12. $\sin 63°18' = \dfrac{1000}{d}$

$d = 1119.36$ ft

13. $\sin 70° = \dfrac{d}{65}$

$d = 61.08$ m

14. Let x = distance from ground to break.

$\tan 29° = \dfrac{x}{13}$

$x = 7.21$

Let y = distance from break to top.

$y = \sqrt{13^2 + 7.21^2}$

$y = 14.86$

$x + y = 22.07$ m

15. $\sin x = \dfrac{20}{120} = 0.1667$

$x = 9°36'$

16. $\sin x = \dfrac{10}{400} = 0.025$

$x = 1°26'$

17. $\tan x = \dfrac{555}{\frac{1}{4}(5280)} = 0.42$

$x = 22°48'$

18. $\tan x = 2$

$x = 63°26'$

$y = 90° - x = 26°34'$

$z = 90° - y = 63°26'$

19. Let h = height of building.

Let k = distance from closer point.

$\tan 45° = \dfrac{h}{x}$ $\tan 38°20' = \dfrac{h}{50 + x}$

$1 = \dfrac{h}{x}$ $h = (\tan 38°20')(50 + x)$

$x = h$

$x = (\tan 38°20')(50 + x)$

$x = 0.7907(50 + x)$

$0.2093x = 39.535$

$x = 188.89$ ft $= h$

20. Let w = width of alley.

$\tan 40° = \dfrac{w}{60}$

$w = 50.34$

Let $60 + x$ = height of second building.

$\tan 40° = \dfrac{x}{50.34}$

$x = 42.25$ ft

$60 + x = 102.25$ ft

21. $\cos 40° = \dfrac{x}{50}$

$x = 38.30$

$50 - x = 11.7$ cm

22. Let h = height of flagpole.

Let x = distance from Jason to flagpole.

$\tan 30° = \dfrac{h}{x + 200}$ $\tan 60 = \dfrac{h}{x}$

$(\tan 60°)x = h$

$(\tan 30°)(x + 200) = h$

$(\tan 30°)(x + 200) = (\tan 60°)x$

$0.5774 + 115.47 = 1.732x$

$x = 100$ ft from Jason

$x + 200 = 300$ ft from Olivia

23. $\tan 39° = \dfrac{h}{5}$

$h = 4.05$ cm

24. Let E = angle of elevation.

Let D = angle of depression.

$90° = (90° - E) + D$

$0 = D - E$

$E = D$

25. $\sin 2° = \dfrac{h}{5000}$

$h = 174.5$ meters

26. $\tan 80° = \dfrac{y}{200}$

$y = 1134.26$

$\tan 75° = \dfrac{x}{200}$

$x = 746.41$

$y - x = 387.85$ ft

27. $160^2 + 40^2 = d^2$

$d = 164.92$ km

28. $\dfrac{n!}{5!(n - 5)!} = \dfrac{n!}{15!(n - 15)!}$

$15!n!(n - 15)! = n!5!(n - 5)!$

$(n - 15)!15! = (n - 5)!5!$

$15 \cdot 14 \cdot 13 \cdot 12 \cdot 11 \cdot 10 \cdot 9 \cdot 8 \cdot 7 \cdot 6 = (n - 5)(n - 6)$

$(n - 7)(n - 8)$

$(n - 9)(n - 10)$

$(n - 11)(n - 12)$

$(n - 13)(n - 14)$

$n = 20$

29. $3^5 = 3^{2n-1}$

$5 \log 3 = (2n - 1) \log 3$

$5 = 2n - 1$

$n = 3$

30. $g(x) = 24x^4 - 94x^3 + 61x^2 + 21x - 18$

$p = \pm 1, \pm 2, \pm 3, \pm 6, \pm 9, \pm 18$

$q = \pm 1, \pm 2, \pm 3, \pm 4, \pm 6, \pm 8, \pm 12, \pm 24$

$\frac{p}{q}$	24	-94	61	21	-18
3	24	-22	-5	6	0

$24x^3 - 22x^2 - 5x + 6 = 0$

$\frac{p}{q}$	24	-22	-5	6
$\frac{2}{3}$	24	-6	-9	0

$24x^2 - 6x - 9 = 0$

$8x^2 - 2x - 3 = 0$

$x = \dfrac{2 \pm \sqrt{(-2)^2 - 4(8)(-3)}}{2(8)}$

$\quad = \dfrac{2 \pm \sqrt{100}}{16}$

$\quad = \dfrac{2 \pm 10}{16}$

$x = -\dfrac{1}{2}$ or $x = \dfrac{3}{4}$

zeros: $3, \dfrac{2}{3}, \dfrac{3}{4}, -\dfrac{1}{2}$

16-8 Law of Sines

PAGE 769   CHECKING FOR UNDERSTANDING

1. area $= \frac{1}{2}b(c \sin A)$, $A = \frac{1}{2}ac \sin B$, $A = \frac{1}{2}ab \sin C$

2. any triangle

3. $\dfrac{\sin 45^\circ 34'}{x} = \dfrac{\sin 34^\circ}{17.06}$

$\quad x = \dfrac{17.06 \sin 45^\circ 34'}{\sin 34^\circ}$

$\quad x \approx 21.8$ miles

4. area $= \frac{1}{2}(15)(20) \sin 63^\circ$

$\quad = 133.7$

5. area $= \frac{1}{2}(10)(17) \sin 46^\circ$

$\quad = 61.1$

6. area $= \frac{1}{2}(6)(4) \sin 52^\circ$

$\quad = 9.5$

7. area $= \frac{1}{2}(15)(30) \sin 90^\circ$

$\quad = 225$

8. $\dfrac{\sin 40^\circ}{20} = \dfrac{\sin 60^\circ}{b}$

$\quad b = \dfrac{20 \sin 60^\circ}{\sin 40^\circ}$

$\quad b = 26.9$

9. $\dfrac{\sin 50^\circ}{14} = \dfrac{\sin B^\circ}{10}$

$\quad \dfrac{10 \sin 50^\circ}{14} = \sin B^\circ$

$\quad B = 33^\circ 10'$

10. $\dfrac{\sin 53^\circ}{a} = \dfrac{\sin 61^\circ}{2.8}$

$\quad \dfrac{28 \sin 53^\circ}{\sin 61^\circ} = a$

$\quad a = 2.6$

11. $\dfrac{\sin 42^\circ}{16} = \dfrac{\sin C}{12}$

$\quad \dfrac{12 \sin 42^\circ}{16} = \sin C$

$\quad C = 30^\circ 7'$

PAGES 769-770   EXERCISES

12. $A = \frac{1}{2}(15)(22) \sin 90^\circ$

$\quad = 165$

13. $A = \frac{1}{2}(12)(12) \sin 50^\circ$

$\quad = 55.155$

14. $A = \frac{1}{2}(11.5)(14) \sin 20^\circ$

$\quad = 27.533$

15. $A = \frac{1}{2}(11)(5) \sin 50^\circ 6'$

$\quad = 21.097$

16. $A = \frac{1}{2}(4)(19) \sin 73^\circ 24'$

$\quad = 36.4162$

17. $A = \frac{1}{2}(9.4)(13.5) \sin 95^\circ$

$\quad = 63.2086$

18. $C = 80^\circ$

$\quad \dfrac{\sin 80^\circ}{20} = \dfrac{\sin 40^\circ}{a} = \dfrac{\sin 60^\circ}{b}$

$\quad a = 13.05$

$\quad b = 17.59$

19. $C = 180^\circ - 49^\circ - 57^\circ = 74^\circ$

$\quad \dfrac{\sin 57^\circ}{b} = \dfrac{\sin 49^\circ}{8} = \dfrac{\sin 74^\circ}{c}$

$\quad b = 8.89$

$\quad c = 10.19$

20. $\dfrac{\sin B}{70} = \dfrac{\sin 83^\circ 10'}{80}$

$\quad B = 60^\circ 19'$

$\quad C = 36^\circ 31'$

$\quad \dfrac{\sin C}{c} = \dfrac{\sin 83^\circ 10'}{80}$

$\quad C = 47.95$

21. $A = 52^\circ$

$\quad \dfrac{\sin 52^\circ}{84} = \dfrac{\sin 70^\circ}{b} = \dfrac{\sin 58^\circ}{c}$

$\quad b = 100.17$

$\quad c = 90.40$

22. $B = 80^\circ$

$\quad \dfrac{\sin 70^\circ}{8} = \dfrac{\sin 30^\circ}{a} = \dfrac{\sin 80^\circ}{b}$

$\quad a = 4.26$

$\quad b = 8.38$

23.
$$\frac{\sin B}{15} = \frac{\sin 64°40'}{17}$$
$$B = 52°53'$$
$$A = 62°27'$$
$$\frac{\sin 62°27'}{a} = \frac{\sin 64°40'}{17}$$
$$a = 16.68$$

24.
$$\frac{\sin B}{7.5} = \frac{\sin 103°}{14}$$
$$B = 31°28'$$
$$C = 45°32'$$
$$\frac{\sin 45°32'}{c} = \frac{\sin 103°}{14}$$
$$c = 10.25$$

25. $B = 180° - C - A = 82°5'$
$$\frac{\sin 24°30'}{c} = \frac{\sin 73°25'}{23} = \frac{\sin 82°5'}{b}$$
$$c = 9.95$$
$$b = 23.77$$

26. $A = 180° - B - C = 24°24'$
$$\frac{\sin 119°}{c} = \frac{\sin 36°36'}{8} = \frac{\sin 24°24'}{a}$$
$$c = 11.74$$
$$a = 5.54$$

27. $\frac{\sin B}{14} = \frac{\sin 105°}{18}$
$$B = 48°42'$$
$$C = 180° - 105° - 48°42' = 26°18'$$
$$\frac{\sin 26°18'}{c} = \frac{\sin 105°}{18}$$
$$c = 8.3$$

28. $(180 - 36)° ÷ 2 = 72°$
Base angles are $72°$ each.
$$\frac{\sin 72°}{a} = \frac{\sin 36°}{22}$$
$$a = 35.597$$
$$P = 2a + 22 = 71.194 + 22 = 93.194 \text{ cm}$$

29. $180° - (40° + 65°) = 75°$
$$\frac{\sin 75°}{34} = \frac{\sin 40°}{x} = \frac{\sin 65°}{y}$$
$$x = 22.6 \text{ yds}$$
$$y = 31.9 \text{ yds}$$

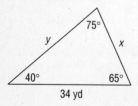

30. $(180 - 85)° ÷ 2 = 47.5°$
Base angles are $47.5°$ each.
$$\frac{\sin 85°}{a} = \frac{\sin 47°5'}{160}$$
$$a = 216.19$$
$$P = 2(160) + 216.19$$
$$= 536.19 \text{ ft}$$

31. $Y = 180° - (108 + 35)° = 37°$
$$\frac{\sin 37°}{60} = \frac{\sin 35°}{c}$$
$$c = \frac{60 \sin 35°}{\sin 37°}$$
$$= 57.2 \text{ km}$$

32. $\frac{\sin 45°}{28} = \frac{\sin A}{36}$
$$A = 180° - 65° = 115°$$
$$C = 180° - 45° - 115° = 20°$$
$$\frac{\sin 45°}{28} = \frac{\sin 20°}{c}$$
$$c = 13.5 \text{ ft}$$

33.
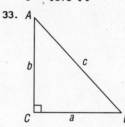

$C = 90°$ and $A + B = 90°$
$$\sin A = \frac{a}{c} \Rightarrow c = \frac{a}{\sin A}$$
$$\sin B = \frac{b}{c} \Rightarrow c = \frac{b}{\sin B}$$
$$\sin C = \frac{c}{c} \Rightarrow c = \frac{c}{\sin C}$$
$$\frac{a}{\sin A} = \frac{b}{\sin B} = \frac{c}{\sin C}$$
or $\frac{\sin A}{a} = \frac{\sin B}{b} = \frac{\sin C}{c}$

34. a.
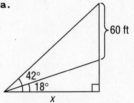

b.
$$\frac{60}{\sin (42 - 18)°} = \frac{x}{\sin (90 - 42)°}$$
$$x = \frac{60 \sin 48}{\sin 24°} = 109.63 \text{ ft}$$

35. a.
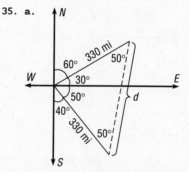

b. Let d = distance apart.
After 3 hours, each plane is (110 mph)(3 hr) or 330 miles from its starting point.
$$180° - 60° - 40° = 80°$$
$$(180 - 80)° ÷ 2 = 50°$$
$$\frac{\sin 80°}{d} = \frac{\sin 50°}{330}$$
$$d = 424.24 \text{ mi}$$

36.

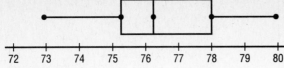

Median: 76.2

Lower quartile: 75.2

Upper quartile: 78

Interquartile range: 2.8

Outliers: none

Greatest value: 79.9

Least value: 72.9

37. $(x + 4)^6 = x^6 + 24x^5 + 240x^4 + 1280x^3 + 3840x^2$
$$+ 6144x + 4096$$

38.
$$y = ne^{kt}$$
$$500 = 10e^{0.782t}$$
$$50 = e^{0.782t}$$
$$\log 50 = 0.782t \log e$$
$$\frac{\log 50}{0.782 \log e} = t$$
$$t = 5.003 \text{ hours}$$

39. $f[g(x)] = f(x^2)$ $\qquad$ $g[f(x)] = g(x + 1)$

$\qquad = x^2 + 1$ $\qquad\qquad = (x + 1)^2$

$\qquad\qquad\qquad\qquad = x^2 + 2x + 1$

40. $A = \frac{8}{2}(12 + 20)$

$\qquad = 128 \text{ cm}^2$

16-9 Problem-Solving Strategy: Examine the Solution

PAGE 773   CHECKING FOR UNDERSTANDING

1. none, one, or two

2. none or one

3. no solution exists

4. $A > 90°$ and $a < b$; no solution exists

5. $A < 90°$, $b \sin A < a < b$

two solutions

$$\frac{\sin 36°52'}{6} = \frac{\sin B}{8}$$

$B = 53°7'$ or $126°53'$ $\qquad \dfrac{\sin 36°52'}{6} = \dfrac{\sin 90°1'}{c}$

$C = 90°1'$ or $16°15'$ $\qquad\qquad c = 10$

$$\frac{\sin 36°52'}{6} = \frac{\sin 16°15'}{c}$$
$$c = 2.8$$

6. $C > 90°$, $c > a$

one solution

$$\frac{\sin A}{64} = \frac{\sin 98°}{90}$$
$$A = 44°46'$$
$$B = 37°14'$$
$$\frac{\sin 37°14'}{b} = \frac{\sin 98°}{90}$$
$$b = 54.99$$

7. $A < 90°$, $a < b \sin A$

no solution exists

---

8. $A < 90°$, $a < b \sin A$

no solution exists

9. $A \geq 90°$, $a < b$; no solution exists

10. $A < 90°$, $b \sin A < a < b$

two solutions

$$\frac{\sin B}{150} = \frac{\sin 25°}{125}$$
$$B = 30°28' \text{ or } 149°32'$$
$$C = 124°32' \text{ or } 5°28'$$
$$\frac{\sin 124°32'}{C_1} = \frac{\sin 25°}{125}$$
$$C_1 = 243.66$$
$$\frac{\sin 5°28'}{C_2} = \frac{\sin 25°}{125}$$
$$C_2 = 28.18$$

11. $A < 90°$, $a < b \sin A$

no solution exists

12. $A \geq 90°$, $a < b$; no solution exists

13. $A < 90°$; $b \sin A < a < b$

two solutions

$$\frac{\sin B}{10} = \frac{\sin 40°}{8}$$
$$B = 53°28' \text{ or } 126°32'$$
$$C = 86°32' \text{ or } 13°28'$$

$\dfrac{\sin 86°32'}{C_1} = \dfrac{\sin 40°}{8}$ $\qquad$ $\dfrac{\sin 13°28'}{C_2} = \dfrac{\sin 40°}{8}$

$C_1 = 12.4$ $\qquad\qquad\qquad$ $C_2 = 2.9$

PAGE 774   EXERCISES

14. $A < 90°$, $b \sin A < a < b$

two solutions

$$\frac{\sin 48°19'}{32} = \frac{\sin B}{40}$$
$$B = 68°59' \text{ or } 111°01'$$
$$C = 62°42' \text{ or } 30°40'$$
$$\frac{\sin 62°42'}{C_1} = \frac{\sin 48°19'}{32}$$
$$\frac{\sin 20°40'}{C_2} = \frac{\sin 48°19'}{32}$$
$$C_1 = 38.1 \text{ mm}, C_2 = 15.1 \text{ mm}$$

15. $\left[\left(\frac{1}{2}\right)^{-1} + \left(\frac{1}{3}\right)^{-1} + \left(\frac{1}{4}\right)^{-1} + \left(\frac{1}{5}\right)^{-1} \right]^{-1}$

$= [2 + 3 + 4 + 5]^{-1}$

$= \dfrac{1}{14}$

16.

Rolls Possible With Two Special Dice		Numbers on First Die					
		1	2	5	4	5	6
Numbers on Second Die	3	4	5	8	7	8	9
	2	3	4	7	6	7	8
	3	4	5	8	7	8	9
	4	5	6	9	8	9	10
	5	6	7	10	9	10	11
	6	7	8	11	10	11	12

There are 3 possible rolls whose sum is 6 out of 36 possible rolls.

$\frac{3}{36} = \frac{1}{12}$ or about 0.0833

17.

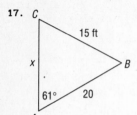

$\dfrac{\sin A}{a} = \dfrac{\sin C}{c}$

$\dfrac{\sin 61°}{15} = \dfrac{\sin C}{20}$

$\dfrac{4}{3} \sin 61° = \sin C$

$1.1662 = \sin C$

Since $\sin C$ cannot be greater than 1, there is no $\angle C$ to fit the solution.
The triangle cannot exist.

18. Paul goes first, so he has to lose the most points.

19. 6: has factors 1, 2, 3, 6.
12: has factors 1, 2, 3, 4, 6

20.

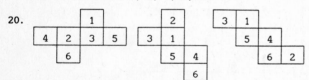

21. Answers may vary. A sample answer is
$6 + 3 - 6 - 2 + 4 = 5$.

PAGE 774   COOPERATIVE LEARNING ACTIVITY

Part 1:

Let a, b, and c represent the sides of triangle ABC. Let h_a = the altitude from $\angle A$, h_b = the altitude from $\angle B$, and h_c = the altitude from $\angle C$.

From the area formula, $A = \frac{1}{2}bh$, we get three possible equations,

$A = \frac{1}{2}a(h_a)$, $A = \frac{1}{2}b(h_b)$, and $A = \frac{1}{2}c(h_c)$.

Since the area of the triangle, if it exists, does not change for whatever base and height you use, these quantities are equal.

So $\frac{1}{2}a(h_a) = \frac{1}{2}b(h_b) = \frac{1}{2}c(h_c)$ or $a(h_a) = b(h_b) = c(h_c)$

The problem gives altitudes of 3 cm, 5 cm, and 6 cm. Substitute these values for each of the h's in the equation: $3a = 5b = 6c$.

Since the triangle inequality states that the sum of any two sides of a triangle must be greater than the third side, you can use this relationship to test each possibility.

$a + b$? c	$b + c$? a	$a + c$? b
$2c + \frac{6}{5}c$? c	$\frac{3}{5}a + \frac{1}{2}a$? a	$\frac{5}{3}b + \frac{5}{6}b$? b
$\frac{16}{5}c > c$	$\frac{11}{10}a > a$	$\frac{15}{6}b > b$

Since all inequalities work, the triangle is possible.

Part 2:

Use the same strategy as above, but with the altitudes 2, 6, and 9.
Thus, $2a = 6b = 9c$.

$a + b$? c	$b + c$? a
$9c + 1.5c > c$	$\frac{1}{3}a + \frac{2}{9}a$? a
	$\frac{5}{9}a < a$ Since the inequality does not work, this triangle is impossible.

16-10 **Law of Cosines**

PAGES 777-778   CHECKING FOR UNDERSTANDING

1. length of third side

2. any of the angles

3. Law of Cosines: given all three sides or two sides and the included angle;
Law of Sines: given two sides and a non-included angle or two angles and a side

4. $b^2 = a^2 + c^2 - 2ac \cos B$

     $300^2 = 228.38^2 + 75^2 - 2(228.38)(75) \cos B$

     $90,000 = 57,782.42 - 34,257 \cos B$

     $0.9405 = \cos B$

       $B = 19°53'$

5. sines;

     $\dfrac{\sin 40°}{10} = \dfrac{\sin C}{8}$

        $C = 30°57'$

   $B = 180 - 40 - 30°57' = 109°3'$

         $\dfrac{\sin 109°3'}{b} = \dfrac{\sin 40°}{10}$

            $b = 14.7$

6. cosines;

     $a^2 = 6^2 + 7^2 - 2 \cdot 6 \cdot 7 \cos 40°$

     $a = 4.5$

     $6^2 = 4.5^2 + 7^2 - 2 \cdot 4.5 \cdot 6 \cos B$

     $B = 58°59'$

     $7^2 = 4.5^2 + 6^2 - 2 \cdot 4.5 \cdot 6 \cos C$

     $C = 81°1'$

7. cosines;

     $b^2 = 14^2 + 21^2 - 2 \cdot 14 \cdot 21 \cos 60°$

     $b = 18.5$

     $14^2 = 18.5^2 + 21^2 - 2 \cdot 18.5 \cdot 21 \cos A$

      $A = 40°57'$

   $C = 180° - 60 - 40°57' = 79°3'$

8. cosines;

     $14^2 = 15^2 + 16^2 - 2 \cdot 15 \cdot 16 \cos A$

     $A = 53°35'$

     $15^2 = 14^2 + 16^2 - 2 \cdot 14 \cdot 16 \cos B$

     $B = 59°33'$

   $C = 180 - 53°35' - 59°33' = 65°52'$

9. sines;

     $\dfrac{\sin 40°}{a} = \dfrac{\sin 70°}{14}$

       $a = 9.6$

   $B = 180° - 40° - 70° = 70°$

        $\dfrac{\sin 70°}{b} = \dfrac{\sin 40°}{9.6}$

          $b = 14$

10. cosines;

     $c^2 = 11^2 + 10.5^2 - 2 \cdot 11 \cdot 10.5 \cos 35°$

     $c = 6.5$

     $11^2 = 10.5^2 + 6.5^2 - 2 \cdot 10.5 \cdot 6.5 \cos A$

      $A = 76°5'$

   $B = 180° - 35° - 76°5' = 68°55'$

11. sines;

     $\dfrac{\sin 42°58'}{17} = \dfrac{\sin A}{11}$

       $A = 26°10'$

  $C = 180 - 42°58' - 26°10' = 110°52'$

        $\dfrac{\sin 110°52'}{c} = \dfrac{\sin 42°58'}{17}$

          $c = 23.3$

12. sines;

     $\dfrac{\sin 22°34'}{12.2} = \dfrac{\sin 56°}{a}$

       $a = 26.4$

  $B = 180° - 56° - 22°34' = 101°26'$

       $\dfrac{\sin 101°26'}{b} = \dfrac{\sin 56°}{26.4}$

         $b = 31.2$

PAGES 778-779   EXERCISES

13. $a^2 = 16^2 + 19^2 - 2 \cdot 16 \cdot 19 \cos 35°$

     $a = 10.91$

     $\dfrac{\sin B}{16} = \dfrac{\sin 35°}{10.91}$

       $B = 57°16'$

  $C = 180° - 57°16' - 35° = 87°44'$

14. $140^2 = 185^2 + 166^2 - 2 \cdot 185 \cdot 166 \cos A$

    $\cos A = \dfrac{140^2 - 185^2 - 166^2}{-2 \cdot 185 \cdot 166}$

        $= 0.6868$

       $A = 46°37'$

   $\dfrac{\sin B}{185} = \dfrac{\sin 46°37'}{140}$

       $B = 73°50'$

   $C = 180° - 46°37' - 73°50'$

     $= 59°33'$

15. $5^2 = 12^2 + 13^2 - 2 \cdot 12 \cdot 13 \cos A$

    $\cos A = \dfrac{5^2 - 12^2 - 13^2}{-2 \cdot 12 \cdot 13}$

        $= 0.9231$

       $A = 22°37'$

   $\dfrac{\sin B}{12} = \dfrac{\sin 22°37'}{5}$

       $B = 67°23'$

   $C = 180° - 22°37' - 67°23' = 90°$

16. $b^2 = 20^2 + 24^2 - 2 \cdot 20 \cdot 24 \cos 47°$

     $b = 17.92$

     $\dfrac{\sin A}{20} = \dfrac{\sin 47°}{17.92}$

       $A = 54°42'$

       $C = 78°18'$

17. $c^2 = 13^2 + 21.5^2 - 2 \cdot 13 \cdot 21.5 \cos 38°20'$

    $c = 13.88$

    $\dfrac{\sin B}{13} = \dfrac{\sin 38°20'}{13.88}$

    $B = 35°31'$

    $A = 106°9'$

18. $C = 180° - 40° - 59° = 81°$

    $\dfrac{\sin 40°}{a} = \dfrac{\sin 59°}{b} = \dfrac{\sin 81°}{14}$

    $a = 9.11$

    $b = 12.15$

19. $b^2 = 51^2 + 61^2 - 2 \cdot 51 \cdot 61 \cos 19°$

    $b = 20.95$

    $\dfrac{\sin A}{51} = \dfrac{\sin 19°}{20.95}$

    $A = 52°25'$

    $C = 108°35'$

20. $C = 180° - 25°26' - 78° = 76°34'$

    $\dfrac{\sin 25°26'}{13.7} = \dfrac{\sin 78°}{b} = \dfrac{\sin 76°34'}{c}$

    $b = 31.20$

    $c = 31.03$

21. $11^2 = 13^2 + 15^2 - 2 \cdot 13 \cdot 15 \cos A$

    $\cos A = \dfrac{11^2 - 13^2 - 15^2}{-2 \cdot 13 \cdot 15}$

    $A = 45°34'$

    $\dfrac{\sin 45°34'}{11} = \dfrac{\sin B}{13}$

    $B = 57°34'$

    $C = 180 - 45°34' - 57°34' = 76°52'$

22. $345^2 = 648^2 + 442^2 - 2 \cdot 648 \cdot 442 \cos A$

    $\cos A = \dfrac{345^2 - 648^2 - 442^2}{-2 \cdot 648 \cdot 442}$

    $A = 29°58'$

    $\dfrac{\sin B}{648} = \dfrac{\sin 29°58'}{345}$

    $B = 110°15'$

    $C = 39°47'$

23. $21.5^2 = 16.71^2 + 10.3^2 - 2 \cdot 16.71 \cdot 10.3 \cos A$

    $\cos A = \dfrac{21.5^2 - 16.71^2 - 10.3^2}{-2 \cdot 16 \cdot 71}$

    $A = 102°55'$

    $\dfrac{\sin 102°55'}{21.5} = \dfrac{\sin B}{16.71}$

    $B = 49°15'$

    $C = 27°50'$

24. $a^2 = 5^2 + 4.9^2 - 2 \cdot 5 \cdot 4.9 \cos 28°50'$

    $a = 2.47$

    $\dfrac{\sin 28°50'}{2.47} = \dfrac{\sin B}{5}$

    $B = 77°29'$

    $C = 73°41'$

25. $a^2 = 7.6^2 + 14.1^2 - 2 \cdot 7.6 \cdot 14.1 \cos 29°$

    $a = 8.31$

    $\dfrac{\sin 29°}{8.31} = \dfrac{\sin B}{7.6}$

    $B = 26°19'$

    $C = 124°41'$

26. $8^2 = 24^2 + 18^2 - 2 \cdot 24 \cdot 18 \cos A$

    $\cos A = \dfrac{8^2 - 24^2 - 18^2}{-2 \cdot 24 \cdot 18}$

    $A = 14°38'$

    $\dfrac{\sin 14°38'}{8} = \dfrac{\sin B}{24}$

    $B = 130°45'$

    $C = 34°37'$

27. $b^2 = 400^2 + 600^2 - 2 \cdot 400 \cdot 600 \cos 46°20'$

    $b = 434.26$

    $P = 400 + 600 + 434.26 = 1434.26 \text{ ft}$

    $A = \dfrac{1}{2} \cdot 400 \cdot 600 \cdot \sin 46°20'$

    $= 86{,}804.28 \text{ ft}^2$

28. $4.9^2 = 6.8^2 + 8.4^2 - 2 \cdot 6.8 \cdot 8.4 \cos A$

    $A = 35°41'$

29. $d^2 = 55^2 + 71^2 - 2 \cdot 55 \cdot 71 \cos 106°$

    $d = 101.09 \text{ cm}$

    $c^2 = 55^2 + 71^2 - 2 \cdot 55 \cdot 71 \cos 74°$

    $c = 76.90 \text{ cm}$

30. $x^2 = 15^2 + 15^2 - 2 \cdot 15 \cdot 15 \cos 15°$

    $x = 26.4 \text{ cm}$

31. $50^2 = 70^2 + 85^2 - 2 \cdot 70 \cdot 85 \cos A$

    $A = 36°1'$

32. no; multiple solutions

    You can, however, determine the ratio of the three sides.

33.

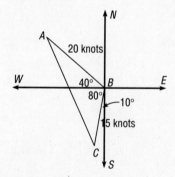

The time is 11 hours.

$a = BC = 15(11)$ or 165 knots

$c = AB = 20(11)$ or 220 knots

$\angle ABC = 40° + 80° = 120°$

Let $\angle B$ represent $\angle ABC$.

$b^2 = a^2 + c^2 - 2ac(\cos B)$

$b^2 = (165)^2 + (220)^2 - 2(165)(220)(\cos 120°)$

$b^2 = 225 + 48,400 - 72,600(-0.5)$

$b^2 = 111,925$

$b = \pm334.55$

The ships are approximately 334.6 nautical miles apart.

34. Let x = distance from point on ground to top of building.

$$\frac{\sin(90-56)°}{x} = \frac{\sin(56-42)°}{40}$$

$$x = 92.5$$

$$\sin 42° = \frac{h}{92.5}; \quad h = 61.87 \text{ ft}$$

35.

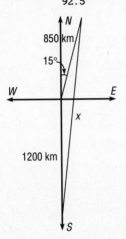

$x^2 = 1200^2 + 850^2 - 2(1200)(850)\cos 165°$

$x = 2032.98$

about 2033 km

36. $x^2 = 70^2 + 130^2 - 2 \cdot 70 \cdot 130 \cos 130°$

$x = 183.03$ miles

37.

Rounded	Stem	Truncated
9 8 8 5 3	2	2 5 7 7 9
9 7	3	6 9 9
0	4	
9 3 1	5	1 2 8
	6	
8 7	7	6 8
7 4	8	3 7
6	9	5

Using rounded data, 7|3| represents 365,000 to 374,000 people.

Using truncated data, |3|6 represents 360,000 to 369,000 people.

38. $\log_x \sqrt{5} = \frac{1}{4}$

$$x^{\frac{1}{4}} = \sqrt{5}$$

$$\left(x^{\frac{1}{4}}\right)^4 = (\sqrt{5})^4$$

$$x = 25$$

39. $\dfrac{x^2 + 49}{x^2 - 49} + \dfrac{x}{7 - x} + \dfrac{7}{x + 7}$

$$= \frac{x^2 + 49}{(x-7)(x+7)} + \frac{-x(x+7)}{(x-7)(x+7)}$$

$$+ \frac{7(x-7)}{(x+7)(x-7)}$$

$$= \frac{x^2 + 49 - x^2 - 7x + 7x - 49}{x^2 - 49}$$

$$= \frac{0}{x^2 - 49}$$

$$= 0$$

40. $g(x) = (x - 4)^2$

$$y = (x - 4)^2$$

$$x = (y - 4)^2$$

$$\pm\sqrt{x} = y - 4$$

$$y = \pm\sqrt{x} + 4$$

Chapter 16 Summary and Review

PAGES 780-782   SKILLS AND CONCEPTS

1. $255° \cdot \dfrac{\pi}{180} = \dfrac{17\pi}{12}$ **2.** $-315° \cdot \dfrac{\pi}{180} = -\dfrac{7\pi}{4}$

3. $270° \cdot \dfrac{\pi}{180} = \dfrac{3\pi}{2}$ **4.** $120° \cdot \dfrac{\pi}{180} = \dfrac{2\pi}{3}$

5. $\dfrac{\pi}{3} \cdot \dfrac{180}{\pi} = 60°$ **6.** $\dfrac{7\pi}{4} \cdot \dfrac{180}{\pi} = 315°$

7. $-\dfrac{5\pi}{12} \cdot \dfrac{180}{\pi} = -75°$ **8.** $\dfrac{4}{3} \cdot \dfrac{180}{\pi} = \dfrac{240°}{\pi}$

9. $\cos 210° = -\dfrac{\sqrt{3}}{2}$ **10.** $\cos 3\pi = -1$

11. $\sin(-150°) = -\dfrac{1}{2}$ **12.** $\sin \dfrac{5}{4}\pi = -\dfrac{\sqrt{2}}{2}$

13. $\cos(-135)° = -\dfrac{\sqrt{2}}{2}$ **14.** $\cos 300° = \dfrac{1}{2}$

15. $(\sin 30°)^2 + (\cos 30°)^2 = 1$

16. $(\sin 45°)(\sin 225°) = \left(\dfrac{\sqrt{2}}{2}\right)\left(-\dfrac{\sqrt{2}}{2}\right)$

$$= -\dfrac{1}{2}$$

17. $\csc 135° = \dfrac{1}{\sin 135°} = \dfrac{1}{\dfrac{\sqrt{2}}{2}} = \sqrt{2}$

18. $\csc \pi = \dfrac{1}{\sin \pi} = \dfrac{1}{0}$:   undefined

19. $\sec(-30°) = \dfrac{1}{\cos 330°} = \dfrac{1}{\dfrac{\sqrt{3}}{2}} = \dfrac{2\sqrt{3}}{3}$

20. $\cot \dfrac{7}{6}\pi = \dfrac{\cos 210^\circ}{\sin 210^\circ} = \dfrac{\frac{\sqrt{3}}{2}}{\frac{1}{2}} = \sqrt{3}$

21. $\tan 120^\circ = \dfrac{\sin 120^\circ}{\cos 120^\circ} = \dfrac{\frac{\sqrt{3}}{2}}{-\frac{1}{2}} = -\sqrt{3}$

22. $\sec(-60^\circ) = \dfrac{1}{\cos 300^\circ} = \dfrac{1}{\frac{1}{2}} = 2$

23. -90° 24. 30° 25. 60°

26. $\text{Sin}^{-1}\left(\tan \dfrac{\pi}{4}\right) = \text{Sin}^{-1}(1) = 90^\circ$

27. $\cos(\text{Sin}^{-1} 1) = \cos 90^\circ = 0$

28. $\sin\left(2 \text{ Sin}^{-1} \dfrac{1}{2}\right) = \sin(2 \cdot 30^\circ)$

$\qquad\qquad = \sin 60^\circ = \dfrac{\sqrt{3}}{2}$

29. 37.5896° 30. 46.7512°

31. -0.3536 32. 0.2362

33. $b^2 = \sqrt{16^2 - 7^2}$ 34. $\tan A = \dfrac{7}{12}$

$\quad b = 14.4$ $A = 30^\circ 15'$

35. $a^2 = \sqrt{400 - 100}$ 36. $a^2 + a^2 = 12^2$

$\quad a = 17.3$ $a^2 = 72$

$\qquad\qquad\qquad\qquad\qquad a = 8.5$

$\qquad\qquad\qquad\qquad\quad \sin B = \dfrac{8.5}{12}$

$\qquad\qquad\qquad\qquad\qquad B = 45^\circ$

37. $\cos 25^\circ = \dfrac{b}{6}$ 38. $\tan A = \dfrac{1}{3}$

$\quad b = 5.4$ $A = 18^\circ 26'$

39. $\dfrac{\sin 83^\circ 10'}{80} = \dfrac{\sin B}{10}$

$\qquad\qquad B = 7^\circ 8'$

$C = 180^\circ - 83^\circ 10' - 7^\circ 8'$

$\quad = 89^\circ 42'$

$\dfrac{\sin 89^\circ 42'}{c} = \dfrac{\sin 83^\circ 10'}{80}$

$\qquad\qquad c = 80.57$

40. $\dfrac{\sin B}{12} = \dfrac{\sin 50^\circ}{10}$

$\qquad B = 66^\circ 49' \text{ or } 113^\circ 11'$

$C = 180^\circ - 50^\circ - 66^\circ 49'$

$\quad = 63^\circ 11'$

$\dfrac{\sin 63^\circ 11'}{c} = \dfrac{\sin 50^\circ}{10}$

$\qquad\qquad c = 11.65$

$C = 180^\circ - 50^\circ - 113^\circ 11'$

$\quad = 16^\circ 49'$

$\dfrac{\sin 16^\circ 49'}{c} = \dfrac{\sin 50^\circ}{10}$

$\qquad\qquad c = 3.78$

41. $A = 180^\circ - 46^\circ - 83^\circ = 51^\circ$

$\dfrac{\sin 51^\circ}{a} = \dfrac{\sin 46^\circ}{65} = \dfrac{\sin 83^\circ}{c}$

$\qquad\qquad a = 70.22$

$\qquad\qquad c = 89.69$

42. $C = 180^\circ - 45^\circ - 30^\circ = 105^\circ$

$\dfrac{\sin 45^\circ}{a} = \dfrac{\sin 30^\circ}{20} = \dfrac{\sin 105^\circ}{c}$

$\qquad\qquad a = 28.28$

$\qquad\qquad c = 38.63$

43. $c^2 = 4^2 + 7^2 - 2 \cdot 4 \cdot 7 \cos 65^\circ$

$\quad c = 6.43$

$\dfrac{\sin A}{4} = \dfrac{\sin 65^\circ}{6.43}$

$\qquad A = 34^\circ 19'$

$B = 180^\circ - 65^\circ - 34^\circ 19' = 80^\circ 41'$

44. $a^2 = 2^2 + 5^2 - 2 \cdot 2 \cdot 5 \cos 60^\circ$

$\quad a = 4.36$

$\dfrac{\sin B}{2} = \dfrac{\sin 60^\circ}{4.36}$

$\qquad B = 23^\circ 24'$

$C = 180^\circ - 60^\circ - 23^\circ 24' = 96^\circ 36'$

45. $c^2 = 6^2 + 7^2 - 2 \cdot 6 \cdot 7 \cos 40^\circ$

$\quad c = 4.54$

$\dfrac{\sin 40^\circ}{4.54} = \dfrac{\sin A}{6}$

$\qquad A = 58^\circ 4'$

$B = 180^\circ - 58^\circ 4' - 40^\circ$

$B = 81^\circ 56'$

46. $b^2 = 42^2 + 6.5^2 - 2 \cdot 6.5 \cdot 42 \cos 24^\circ$

$\quad b = 36.16$

$\dfrac{\sin A}{42} = \dfrac{\sin 24^\circ}{36.16}$

$\qquad A = 151^\circ 47'$

$C = 180^\circ - 24^\circ - 151^\circ 47' = 4^\circ 13'$

PAGE 782   APPLICATIONS AND CONNECTIONS

47. Let x = distance from the plane to the ship.

$\quad \sin 42^\circ = \dfrac{3000}{x}$

$\qquad\quad x = 4483.48 \text{ ft}$

48. Let h = height of the flagpole.

$\quad \tan 48^\circ = \dfrac{h}{50}$

$\qquad\quad h = 55.53 \text{ m}$

49. $a^2 = 14^2 - 13.5^2$ 50. $a = 15, b = 20, A = 61^\circ$

$\quad a = 3.7 \text{ m}$ $15 < 20 \sin 61^\circ$

$\qquad\qquad\qquad\qquad\qquad$ no solution exists

Chapter 16 Test
PAGE 783

1. $-45^\circ \cdot \dfrac{\pi}{180} = -\dfrac{\pi}{4}$ 2. $275^\circ \cdot \dfrac{\pi}{180} = \dfrac{55\pi}{36}$

3. $330^\circ \cdot \dfrac{\pi}{180} = \dfrac{11\pi}{6}$ 4. $-600^\circ \cdot \dfrac{\pi}{180} = -\dfrac{10\pi}{3}$

5. $-\dfrac{\pi}{6} \cdot \dfrac{180}{\pi} = -30°$ 6. $\dfrac{11}{2}\pi \cdot \dfrac{180}{\pi} = 990°$

7. $-\dfrac{7\pi}{4} \cdot \dfrac{180}{\pi} = -315°$

8. $-2\dfrac{1}{3} \cdot \dfrac{180}{\pi} = -\dfrac{420°}{\pi} \approx -133.69°$

9. $\cos(-120°) = -\dfrac{1}{2}$ 10. $\sin\dfrac{7\pi}{4} = -\dfrac{\sqrt{2}}{2}$

11. $\cos\dfrac{3\pi}{4} = -\dfrac{\sqrt{2}}{2}$ 12. $\sin 390° = \dfrac{1}{2}$

13. $\tan 135° = \dfrac{\sin 135°}{\cos 135°} = \dfrac{\frac{\sqrt{2}}{2}}{-\frac{\sqrt{2}}{2}} = -1$

14. $\cot 300° = \dfrac{\cos 300°}{\sin 300°} = \dfrac{\frac{1}{2}}{-\frac{\sqrt{3}}{2}} = -\dfrac{\sqrt{3}}{3}$

15. $\sec\left(-\dfrac{7}{6}\pi\right) = \dfrac{1}{\cos 210°} = \dfrac{1}{-\frac{\sqrt{3}}{2}} = -\dfrac{2\sqrt{3}}{3}$

16. $\csc\dfrac{5\pi}{6} = \dfrac{1}{\sin 150°} = \dfrac{1}{\frac{1}{2}} = 2$

17. $\text{Sin}^{-1}\left(-\dfrac{\sqrt{3}}{2}\right) = -60°$ 18. $\text{Arctan } 1 = 45°$

19. $\text{Cos}^{-1}(\sin -60°) = 150°$

20. $\sin 2\left(\text{Arccos }\dfrac{1}{2}\right)$ 21. $42°10'$

   $= \sin 120°$

   $= \dfrac{\sqrt{3}}{2}$

22. $82°1'$ 23. $50°32'$ 24. $41°59'$

25. $\sin 49° = \dfrac{7}{b}$

   $b = 6.1$

   $7^2 + 6.1^2 = c^2$

   $c = 9.3$

   $B = 90° - 49° = 41°$

26. $b = \sqrt{16^2 - 7^2}$

   $= 14.4$

   $\sin A = \dfrac{7}{16}$

   $A = 25°57'$

   $B = 90° - 25°57' = 64°3'$

27. $A = 90° - 75° = 15°$

   $\sin 75° = \dfrac{6}{c}$

   $c = 6.21$ or 6.2

   $a = \sqrt{6.21^2 - 6^2} = 1.60$ or 1.6

28. $B = 90° - 22° = 68°$

   $\sin 22° = \dfrac{a}{8}$

   $a = 3.0$

   $b = \sqrt{8^2 - 3^2} = 7.42$ or 7.4

29. one solution;

   $\dfrac{\sin 40°}{14} = \dfrac{\sin B}{10}$

   $B = 27°20'$

   $C = 180° - 40° - 27°20' = 112°40'$

   $\dfrac{\sin 112°40'}{c} = \dfrac{\sin 40°}{14}$

   $c = 20.1$

30. $\sin A = \dfrac{26}{32}$

   $A = 54°20'$

31. Let x = distance from starting point.

   $x^2 = 1000^2 + 700^2 - 2(1000)700 \cos 160°$

   $x = 1675$ km

32. Let x = distance from deer to the cliff.

   $\tan(90° - 70°) = \dfrac{x}{50}$

   $x = 18.2$ m

33. $180° - (23° + 49°) = 108°$

   $\dfrac{\sin 108°}{23} = \dfrac{\sin 49°}{x} = \dfrac{\sin 23°}{y}$

   $x = 18.25$ yd

   $y = 9.45$ yd

PAGE 783   BONUS

$x = 145°32'$

Chapter 16
College Entrance Exam Preview

PAGES 784-785

1. $P_1 = 2(1) + 2w = 2 + 2w$

   $P_2 = 2(1) + 2(w + 3) = 8 + 2w$

   $P_2 - P_1 = (8 + 2w) - (2 + 2w)$

   $= 6$

   The correct choice is B.

2. $A_t = \dfrac{1}{2}bh = \dfrac{1}{2}r^2$

   $\dfrac{1}{2}r^2 = 40$

   $r^2 = 80$

   $A_c = \pi r^2$

   $= 80\pi$

   The correct choice is A.

3. $d = \sqrt{(-4 - 4)^2 + (0 - 0)^2} = 8$

   $d = \sqrt{(0 - 4)^2 + (4\sqrt{3} - 0)^2} = 8$

   $d = \sqrt{(0 - 4)^2 - (-4\sqrt{3} - 0)^2} = 8$

   $d = \sqrt{(8 - 4)^2 + (0 - 0)^2} = 4 \neq 8$

   The correct choice is D.

4. $x^2 + y^2 = 16$

$\underline{ 2xy = 16}$

$x^2 + 2xy + y^2 = 32$

$(x + y)^2 = 32$

The correct choice is A.

5. $x = -6$ $\qquad$ $\frac{1}{2y} = -12$

$2x = -12$ $\qquad$ $\frac{1}{2y} = 2x$

$ \qquad 1 = 4xy$

$ \qquad y = \frac{1}{4x}$

The correct choice is D.

6. $(0.05)n = 81$

$n = 1620$

The correct choice is B.

7. Area $= \frac{1}{2}bh$ $\qquad$ $\sin 45° = \frac{AB}{AC}$ $\qquad$ $\cos 45° = \frac{BC}{AC}$

$8 = \frac{1}{2}(AB)(BC)$ $\qquad$ $\frac{\sqrt{2}}{2} = \frac{AB}{AC}$ $\qquad$ $\frac{\sqrt{2}}{2} = \frac{BC}{AC}$

$16 = (AB)(BC)$ $\qquad$ $AB = \frac{\sqrt{2}}{2}(AC)$ $\qquad$ $BC = \frac{\sqrt{2}}{2}AC$

$ \qquad 16 = \left(\frac{\sqrt{2}}{2}AC\right)\left(\frac{\sqrt{2}}{2}AC\right)$

$ \qquad 16 = \frac{1}{2}(AC)^2$

$ \qquad AC = \sqrt{32} = 4\sqrt{2}$

The correct choice is B.

8.

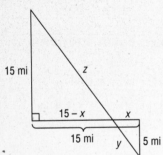

$\frac{5}{15} = \frac{x}{15 - x}$

$5^2 + \left(\frac{15}{4}\right)^2 = y^2$

$15^2 + \left(15 - \frac{15}{4}\right)^2 = z^2$

$x = \frac{15}{4} \qquad y = \frac{25}{4} \qquad z = \frac{75}{4}$

$y + z = \frac{25}{4} + \frac{75}{4} = \frac{100}{4} = 25$

The correct choice is D.

9. $n^2 - 4 = -3n$

$n^2 + 3n - 4 = 0$

$(n + 4)(n - 1) = 0$

$n = -4$ or $n = 1$

$\left(-4 + \frac{3}{2}\right)^2 = \left(\frac{-5}{2}\right)^2 = \frac{25}{4} = 6\frac{1}{4}$

The correct choice is B.

10. $x^2 = 25$

$ x = \pm 5$

$2^{5-1} = 2^4 = 16$

The correct choice is D.

11. If $\frac{x}{6} > x$ then $x > 6x$ and $-5x > 0$. Then x must be negative.

The correct choice is A.

12. Let $0 < x < y < 1$. Then $0 < x^2 < y^2 < 1$ since $f(a) = a^2$ is an increasing function.

Then for $x < y$, $x^2 < y^2$.

Then $-x^2 > -y^2$ and $1 - x^2 > 1 - y^2$.

Thus case I is decreasing.

For case II, $0 < x < y$ and $x - 1 < y - 1$.

Since the original order is preserved, case II is increasing. For case III, recall

$0 < x < y < 1$ and $x^2 < y^2 < 1$. But $\frac{1}{x^2} > \frac{1}{y^2}$ so

case III is decreasing.

The correct choice is A.

13. If $-a < 0 < -b$ then $-a < 0$ and $0 < -b$.

Multiplying by -1, $a > 0$ and $0 > b$.

Thus $b < 0 < a$.

The correct choice is C.

14. Since b is odd, b^3 is odd and $b^3 - 1$ is even, as is $1 + b^3$. $b^3 - b^2 = b^2(b - 1)$ is even.

$\frac{3b - 3}{b - 1} = \frac{3(b - 1)}{(b - 1)} = 3$ which is always odd.

The correct choice is D.

15. If $x = 6k$ then $\frac{x}{2} = 3k$.

Since k is odd, $3k$ is also odd.

The correct choice is A.

16. $a + b = 8$ $\qquad\longrightarrow\qquad$ $-3a - 3b = -24$

$3b - 4 = -13a$ $\qquad\qquad\quad$ $\underline{13a + 3b = 4}$

$ 10a = -20$

$ a = -2$

The correct choice is C.

17. Since $z < 0$ and $x > y$, $xz < yz$.

Case I is true.

Since $x > y$, $x + z > y + z$.

Case II is true.

Since $x > y$, $x - z > y - z$.

Case III is false.

The correct choice is C.

Chapter 17   Trigonometric Graphs, Identities, and Equations

Graphing Calculator Exploration: Graphing Trigonometric Functions

PAGE 789   EXERCISES

1.

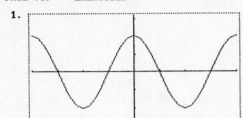

Xscl: 90, Yscl: 0.5

2.

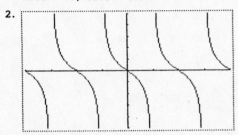

Xscl: 90, Yscl: 1

3.

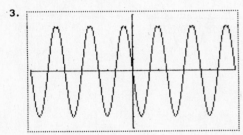

Xscl: 90, Yscl: 0.5

4.

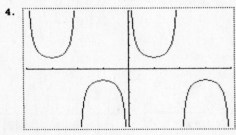

Xscl: 90, Yscl: 1

5.

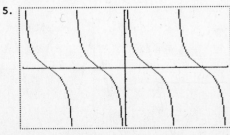

Xscl: 90, Yscl: 1

6.

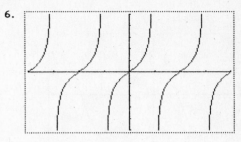

Xscl: 90, Yscl: 1

7.

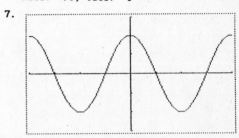

Xscl: 180, Yscl: 1

8.

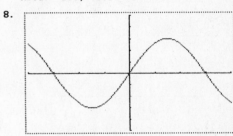

Xscl: 90, Yscl: 1

9.

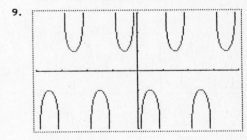

Xscl: 90, Yscl: 5

10.

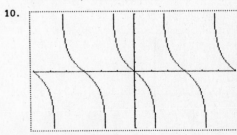

Xscl: 2, Yscl: 2

11.

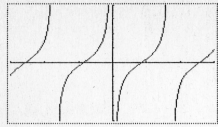

Xscl: 30, Yscl: 10

12.

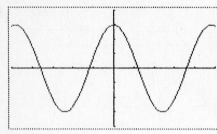

Xscl: 5, Yscl: 5

13.

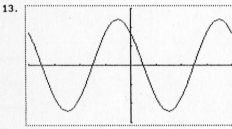

Xscl: 90, Yscl: 5

14.

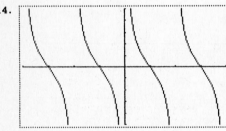

Xscl: 90, Yscl: 2

15.

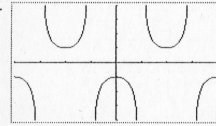

Xscl: 45, Yscl: 0.5

16.

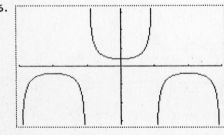

Xscl: 30, Yscl: 0.5

17-1 | **Graphs of Trigonometric Functions**

PAGE 795   CHECKING FOR UNDERSTANDING

1. The values of the function repeat in 180° intervals.

2. A typical answer is given. The amplitude of a graph of a periodic function is the absolute value of half the difference between its maximum value and its minimum value.

3. no amplitude; period = $\dfrac{360°}{|b|}$ or $\dfrac{2\pi}{|b|}$

4. 1, 2π	**5.** 3, 2π	**6.** $\frac{1}{2}$, 2π	**7.** 3, 4π
8. $\frac{2}{3}$, 2π	**9.** 6, 3π	**10.** 2, 2π	**11.** 3, 3π
12. 4, 4π	**13.** $\frac{1}{2}$, $\frac{8\pi}{3}$	**14.** $\frac{2}{3}$, 4π	**15.** 6, π
16. $\frac{2\pi}{3}$	**17.** 2π	**18.** π	**19.** $\frac{\pi}{5}$
20. 3π	**21.** $\frac{\pi}{3}$	**22.** 2π	**23.** π
24. $\frac{8\pi}{3}$	**25.** 4π	**26.** $\frac{\pi}{2}$	**27.** 3π

PAGES 795-796   EXERCISES

28.

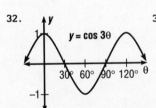

$y = \sin \theta$

29.

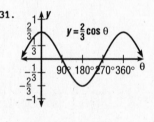

$y = 3 \sin \theta$

30.

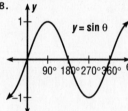

$y = \frac{1}{2} \cos \theta$

31.

$y = \frac{2}{3} \cos \theta$

32.

$y = \cos 3\theta$

33.

$y = \sin 4\theta$

34.

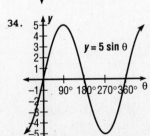

$y = 5 \sin \theta$

35.

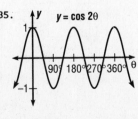

$y = \cos 2\theta$

36. 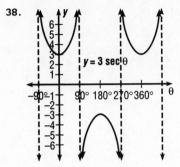 $y = -2 \sin \theta$

37. 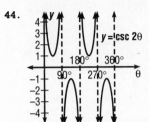 $y = \cot \theta$

38. 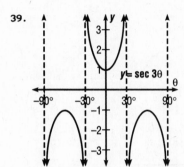 $y = 3 \sec \theta$

39. 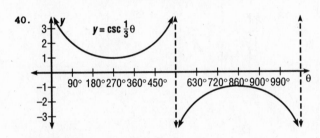 $y = \sec 3\theta$

40. 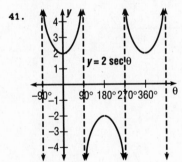 $y = \csc \frac{1}{3}\theta$

41. 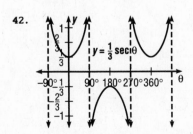 $y = 2 \sec \theta$

42. 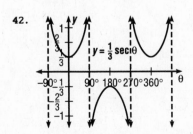 $y = \frac{1}{3} \sec \theta$

43. 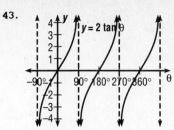 $y = 2 \tan \theta$

44. 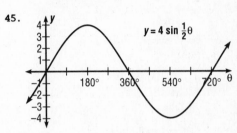 $y = \csc 2\theta$

45. 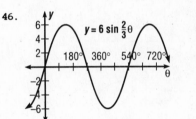 $y = 4 \sin \frac{1}{2}\theta$

46. 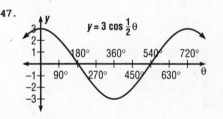 $y = 6 \sin \frac{2}{3}\theta$

47. 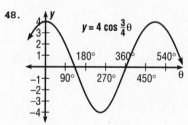 $y = 3 \cos \frac{1}{2}\theta$

48. 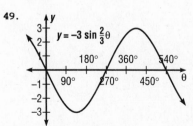 $y = 4 \cos \frac{3}{4}\theta$

49. $y = -3 \sin \frac{2}{3}\theta$

377

50.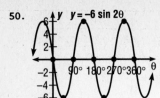

$y = -6 \sin 2\theta$

51.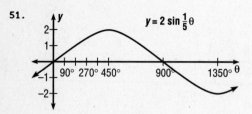

$y = 2 \sin \frac{1}{5}\theta$

52.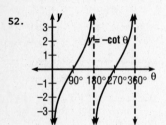

$y = -\cot\theta$

53.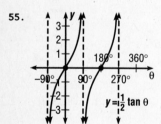

$y = 3 \csc \frac{1}{2}\theta$

54.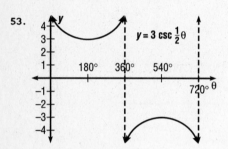

$y = -\frac{1}{2}\cot 2\theta$

55.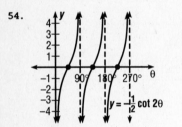

$y = \frac{1}{2}\tan\theta$

56.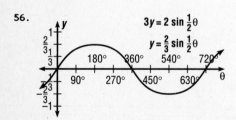

$3y = 2 \sin \frac{1}{2}\theta$

$y = \frac{2}{3} \sin \frac{1}{2}\theta$

57.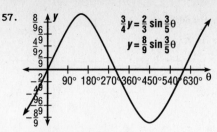

$\frac{3}{4}y = \frac{2}{3} \sin \frac{3}{5}\theta$

$y = \frac{8}{9} \sin \frac{3}{5}\theta$

58.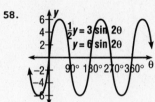

$\frac{1}{2}y = 3 \sin 2\theta$

$y = 6 \sin 2\theta$

59.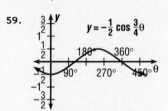

$y = -\frac{1}{2} \cos \frac{3}{4}\theta$

60.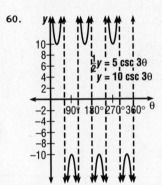

$\frac{1}{2}y = 5 \csc 3\theta$

$y = 10 \csc 3\theta$

61. $y = 3 \sin \frac{2}{3}\theta$

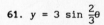

$y = 3 \sin \frac{2}{3}\theta$

62. a.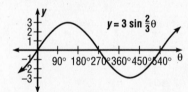

$R = 1000 + 250 \sin \frac{\pi t}{2}$

b. 1000 rabbits

c. 1250 rabbits; first reached on Jan. 1, 1961

d. 750 rabbits; first reached on Jan. 1, 1963

378

63. $434° + x = 794°$

$\qquad x = 360°$ yes

64. {81, 82, 83, 87, 89, 90, 94, 95, 97, 98, 99, 100}

median = 92

no mode

mean = 91.25

65. $\displaystyle\sum_{n=1}^{6} (3 + 3n)$

66. $\left(4^{\sqrt{3}}\right)^{\sqrt{2}} = 4^{\sqrt{3}\cdot\sqrt{2}} = 4^{\sqrt{6}}$

67.

$$
\begin{array}{r|rrrrr}
3 & 4 & -35 & 78 & 28 & -165 \\
  &   & 12 & -69 & 27 & 165 \\ \hline
  & 4 & -23 & 9 & 55 & \big| \ 0
\end{array}
$$

$$
\begin{array}{r|rrrr}
-\frac{5}{4} & 4 & -23 & 9 & 55 \\
             &   & -5 & 35 & -55 \\ \hline
             & 4 & -28 & 44 & \big| \ 0
\end{array}
$$

$4x^2 - 28x + 44 = 0$

$x = \dfrac{28 \pm \sqrt{784 - 16 \cdot 44}}{2 \cdot 4}$

$\quad = \dfrac{28 \pm \sqrt{80}}{8}$

$\quad = \dfrac{28 \pm 4\sqrt{5}}{8}$

$\quad = \dfrac{7 \pm \sqrt{5}}{2}$

zeros: $3,\ -\dfrac{5}{4},\ \dfrac{7 \pm \sqrt{5}}{2}$

68. $36 - i^2$

$= 36 - (-1) = 37$

69. Let f = number of floor lamps made

Let t = number of table lamps

$18f + 12t \le 14{,}400$

$\quad f + 2t \le 1200$

$\qquad\quad f \ge 0$

$\qquad\quad t \ge 0$

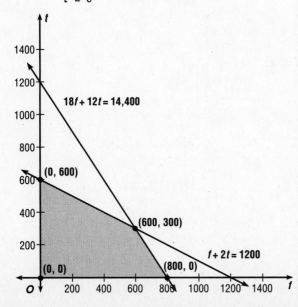

(f, t)	(0, 0)	(0, 600)	(600, 300)	(800, 0)
$85f + 75t$	\$0	\$45,000	\$73,500	\$68,000

a. 600 floor lamps and 300 table lamps

b. \$73,500

17-2   Trigonometric Identities

PAGE 799   **CHECKING FOR UNDERSTANDING**

1. Given an angle in standard position whose measurement is θ and which intersects the unit circle at point (x, y), $x = \cos\theta$ and $y = \sin\theta$.

2. Write the expression as a numerical value or in terms of a single trigonometric function.

3. III   **4.** II or IV

5. $\dfrac{\sin\theta}{\cos\theta} \cdot \cos^2\theta = \sin\theta\cos\theta$

6. $\dfrac{1}{\sin^2\theta} = \csc^2\theta$

7. $\dfrac{1}{\sin^2\theta} - \dfrac{\cos^2\theta}{\sin^2\theta} = \dfrac{1 - \cos^2\theta}{\sin^2\theta}$

$\qquad\qquad\qquad\quad = \dfrac{\sin^2\theta}{\sin^2\theta}$

$\qquad\qquad\qquad\quad = 1$

8. $\dfrac{1}{\sin^2\gamma} - \dfrac{\cos^2\gamma}{\sin^2\gamma} = \dfrac{1 - \cos^2\gamma}{\sin^2\gamma}$

$\qquad\qquad\qquad\quad = \dfrac{\sin^2\gamma}{\sin^2\gamma}$

$\qquad\qquad\qquad\quad = 1$

9. $\cos\alpha \cdot \dfrac{1}{\sin\alpha} = \dfrac{\cos\alpha}{\sin\alpha}$

$\qquad\qquad\qquad\ = \cot\alpha$

10. $\dfrac{\sin x}{\cos x} \cdot \dfrac{1}{\sin x} = \dfrac{1}{\cos x}$

$\qquad\qquad\qquad = \sec x$

11. $\dfrac{\cos x \cdot \dfrac{1}{\sin x}}{\dfrac{\sin x}{\cos x}} = \cos x \cdot \dfrac{1}{\sin x} \cdot \dfrac{\cos x}{\sin x}$

$\qquad\qquad\qquad = \dfrac{\cos^2 x}{\sin^2 x}$

$\qquad\qquad\qquad = \cot^2 x$

12. $\dfrac{\dfrac{\sin x}{\cos x}}{\sin x} = \dfrac{\sin x}{\cos x} \cdot \dfrac{1}{\sin x}$

$\qquad\quad = \dfrac{1}{\cos x}$

$\qquad\quad = \sec x$

13. $\sin\theta \cdot \dfrac{\cos\theta}{\sin\theta} = \cos\theta$ **14.** $\dfrac{\cos^2\alpha}{\sin^2\alpha} = \cot^2\alpha$

15. $\dfrac{\sec^2 x}{\csc^2 x} = \dfrac{\dfrac{1}{\cos^2 x}}{\dfrac{1}{\sin^2 x}}$

$= \dfrac{1}{\cos^2 x} \cdot \sin^2 x$

$= \dfrac{\sin^2 x}{\cos^2 x}$

$= \tan^2 x$

16. $\dfrac{\dfrac{\sin \beta}{\cos \beta}}{\dfrac{\cos \beta}{\sin \beta}} = \dfrac{\sin \beta}{\cos \beta} \cdot \dfrac{\sin \beta}{\cos \beta}$

$= \dfrac{\sin^2 \beta}{\cos^2 \beta}$

$= \tan^2 \beta$

17. $\tan \theta = \dfrac{1}{\cot \theta}$

$= \dfrac{1}{2}$

18. $\sin^2 \theta + \cos^2 \theta = 1$

$\left(\dfrac{4}{5}\right)^2 + \cos^2 \theta = 1$

$\cos^2 \theta = 1 - \dfrac{16}{25}$

$\cos^2 \theta = \dfrac{9}{25}$

$\cos \theta = \sqrt{\dfrac{9}{25}}$

$\cos \theta = \dfrac{3}{5}$

19. $\sin^2 \theta + \cos^2 \theta = 1$

$\sin^2 \theta + \left(\dfrac{2}{3}\right)^2 = 1$

$\sin^2 \theta = 1 - \left(\dfrac{2}{3}\right)^2$

$\sin^2 \theta = 1 - \dfrac{4}{9}$

$\sin^2 \theta = \dfrac{5}{9}$

$\sin \theta = \sqrt{\dfrac{5}{9}}$

$\sin \theta = \dfrac{\sqrt{5}}{3}$

20. $\sin^2 \theta + \cos^2 \theta = 1$

$\sin^2 \theta + \left(\dfrac{2}{3}\right)^2 = 1$

$\sin^2 \theta = 1 - \dfrac{4}{9}$

$\sin^2 \theta = \dfrac{5}{9}$

$\sin \theta = \dfrac{\sqrt{5}}{3}$

$\csc \theta = \dfrac{1}{\sin \theta}$

$= \dfrac{1}{\dfrac{\sqrt{5}}{3}}$

$= \dfrac{3}{\sqrt{5}} \cdot \dfrac{\sqrt{5}}{\sqrt{5}}$

$= \dfrac{3\sqrt{5}}{5}$

PAGES 799-800   EXERCISES

21. $\sin^2 \theta + \cos^2 \theta = 1$

$\sin^2 \theta + \left(\dfrac{4}{5}\right)^2 = 1$

$\sin^2 \theta = 1 - \dfrac{16}{25}$

$\sin^2 \theta = \dfrac{9}{25}$

$\sin \theta = \sqrt{\dfrac{9}{25}}$

$\sin \theta = \dfrac{3}{5}$

$\tan \theta = \dfrac{\sin \theta}{\cos \theta}$

$= \dfrac{\dfrac{3}{5}}{\dfrac{4}{5}}$

$= \dfrac{3}{5} \cdot \dfrac{5}{4}$

$= \dfrac{3}{4}$

22. $\sin^2 \theta + \cos^2 \theta = 1$

$\left(\dfrac{1}{2}\right)^2 + \cos^2 \theta = 1$

$\cos^2 \theta = 1 - \dfrac{1}{4}$

$\cos^2 \theta = \dfrac{3}{4}$

$\cos \theta = \sqrt{\dfrac{3}{4}}$

$= \dfrac{\sqrt{3}}{2}$

23. $\sin^2 \theta + \cos^2 \theta = 1$

$\left(\dfrac{3}{4}\right)^2 + \cos^2 \theta = 1$

$\cos^2 \theta = 1 - \dfrac{9}{16}$

$\cos^2 \theta = \dfrac{7}{16}$

$\cos \theta = \sqrt{\dfrac{7}{16}}$

$\cos \theta = \dfrac{\sqrt{7}}{4}$

$$\sec \theta = \frac{1}{\cos \theta}$$

$$= \frac{1}{\frac{\sqrt{7}}{4}}$$

$$= \frac{4}{\sqrt{7}} \cdot \frac{\sqrt{7}}{\sqrt{7}}$$

$$= \frac{4\sqrt{7}}{7}$$

24. $\tan^2 \theta + 1 = \sec^2 \theta$

$$4^2 + 1 = \sec^2 \theta$$

$$\sec^2 \theta = 16 + 1$$

$$\sec^2 \theta = 17$$

$$\sec \theta = \sqrt{17}$$

$$\cos \theta = \frac{1}{\sec \theta}$$

$$= \frac{1}{\sqrt{17}} \cdot \frac{\sqrt{17}}{\sqrt{17}}$$

$$= \frac{\sqrt{17}}{17}$$

$$\tan \theta = \frac{\sin \theta}{\cos \theta}$$

$$4 = \frac{\sin \theta}{\frac{\sqrt{17}}{17}}$$

$$\sin \theta = \frac{4\sqrt{17}}{17}$$

25. $\sin^2 \theta + \cos^2 \theta = 1$

$$\left(\frac{1}{2}\right)^2 + \cos^2 \theta = 1$$

$$\cos^2 \theta = 1 - \frac{1}{4}$$

$$\cos^2 \theta = \frac{3}{4}$$

$$\cos \theta = -\sqrt{\frac{3}{4}}$$

$$\cos \theta = -\frac{\sqrt{3}}{2}$$

$$\tan \theta = \frac{\sin \theta}{\cos \theta}$$

$$= \frac{\frac{1}{2}}{-\frac{\sqrt{3}}{2}}$$

$$= \frac{1}{2} \cdot -\frac{2}{\sqrt{3}}$$

$$= -\frac{1}{\sqrt{3}} \cdot \frac{\sqrt{3}}{\sqrt{3}}$$

$$= -\frac{\sqrt{3}}{3}$$

26. $\sin^2 \theta + \cos^2 \theta = 1$

$$\sin^2 \theta + \left(-\frac{3}{5}\right)^2 = 1$$

$$\sin^2 \theta = 1 - \frac{9}{25}$$

$$\sin^2 \theta = \frac{16}{25}$$

$$\sin \theta = \sqrt{\frac{16}{25}}$$

$$\sin \theta = \frac{4}{5}$$

$$\csc \theta = \frac{1}{\sin \theta}$$

$$= \frac{1}{\frac{4}{5}}$$

$$= \frac{5}{4}$$

27. $\tan^2 \theta + 1 = \sec^2 \theta$

$$(-2)^2 + 1 = \sec^2 \theta$$

$$\sec^2 \theta = 1 + 4$$

$$\sec^2 \theta = 5$$

$$\sec \theta = -\sqrt{5}$$

28. $\sin^2 \theta + \cos^2 \theta = 1$

$$\left(\frac{3}{5}\right)^2 + \cos^2 \theta = 1$$

$$\cos^2 \theta = 1 - \frac{9}{25}$$

$$\cos^2 \theta = \frac{16}{25}$$

$$\cos \theta = -\sqrt{\frac{16}{25}}$$

$$\cos \theta = -\frac{4}{5}$$

29. $\tan^2 \theta + 1 = \sec^2 \theta$

$$\tan^2 \theta + 1 = (-3)^2$$

$$\tan^2 \theta = 9 - 1$$

$$\tan^2 \theta = 8$$

$$\tan \theta = \sqrt{8}$$

$$\tan \theta = 2\sqrt{2}$$

30. $\sin^2 \theta + \cos^2 \theta = 1$

$\quad \sin^2 \theta + \left(-\frac{3}{5}\right)^2 = 1$

$\quad \sin^2 \theta = 1 - \frac{9}{25}$

$\quad \sin^2 \theta = \frac{16}{25}$

$\quad \sin \theta = -\sqrt{\frac{16}{25}}$

$\quad \sin \theta = -\frac{4}{5}$

$\quad \csc \theta = \frac{1}{\sin \theta}$

$\quad = \frac{1}{-\frac{4}{5}}$

$\quad = -\frac{5}{4}$

31. $\sin^2 \theta + \cos^2 \theta = 1$

$\quad \left(-\frac{1}{2}\right)^2 + \cos^2 \theta = 1$

$\quad \cos^2 \theta = 1 - \frac{1}{4}$

$\quad \cos^2 \theta = \frac{3}{4}$

$\quad \cos \theta = -\sqrt{\frac{3}{4}}$

$\quad \cos \theta = -\frac{\sqrt{3}}{2}$

32. $\cot^2 \theta + 1 = \csc^2 \theta$

$\quad \left(\frac{1}{4}\right)^2 + 1 = \csc^2 \theta$

$\quad \csc^2 \theta = 1 + \frac{1}{16}$

$\quad \csc^2 \theta = \frac{17}{16}$

$\quad \csc \theta = -\sqrt{\frac{17}{16}}$

$\quad \csc \theta = -\frac{\sqrt{17}}{4}$

33. $\tan^2 \theta + 1 = \sec^2 \theta$

$\quad (-1)^2 + 1 = \sec^2 \theta$

$\quad \sec^2 \theta = 2$

$\quad \sec \theta = \sqrt{2}$

34. $\sin^2 \theta + \cos^2 \theta = 1$

$\quad \sin^2 \theta + \left(\frac{5}{13}\right)^2 = 1$

$\quad \sin^2 \theta = 1 - \frac{25}{169}$

$\quad \sin^2 \theta = \frac{144}{169}$

$\quad \sin \theta = -\sqrt{\frac{144}{169}}$

$\quad \sin \theta = -\frac{12}{13}$

35. $\sin \theta = \frac{1}{\csc \theta}$

$\quad = \frac{1}{-\frac{5}{3}}$

$\quad = -\frac{3}{5}$

$\quad \sin^2 \theta + \cos^2 \theta = 1$

$\quad \left(-\frac{3}{5}\right)^2 + \cos^2 \theta = 1$

$\quad \cos^2 \theta = 1 - \frac{9}{25}$

$\quad \cos^2 \theta = \frac{16}{25}$

$\quad \cos \theta = \sqrt{\frac{16}{25}}$

$\quad \cos \theta = \frac{4}{5}$

36. $\sec \theta = \frac{1}{\cos \theta}$

$\quad \frac{5}{3} = \frac{1}{\cos \theta}$

$\quad \cos \theta = \frac{1}{\frac{5}{3}}$

$\quad \cos \theta = \frac{3}{5}$

37. $\tan^2 \theta$

38. $\frac{1}{\sin \alpha} \cdot \cos \alpha \cdot \frac{\sin \alpha}{\cos \alpha} = 1$

39. $\frac{\sin \beta}{\cos \beta} \cdot \frac{\cos \beta}{\sin \beta} = 1$

40. $\sin x + \cos x \cdot \frac{\sin x}{\cos x} = \sin x + \sin x$

$\quad = 2 \sin x$

41. $\frac{1 - \cos^2 \theta}{\sin^2 \theta} = \frac{\sin^2 \theta}{\sin^2 \theta}$

$\quad = 1$

42. $\sin \beta (\csc^2 \beta) = \sin \beta \cdot \frac{1}{\sin^2 \beta}$

$\quad = \frac{1}{\sin \beta}$

$\quad = \csc \beta$

43. $2\left(\frac{1}{\sin^2 \theta} - \frac{\cos^2 \theta}{\sin^2 \theta}\right) = 2\left(\frac{1 - \cos^2 \theta}{\sin^2 \theta}\right)$

$\quad = 2\left(\frac{\sin^2 \theta}{\sin^2 \theta}\right)$

$\quad = 2$

44.
$$\frac{\dfrac{\sin^2 \theta}{\cos^2 \theta} - \sin^2 \theta}{\dfrac{\sin^2 \theta}{\cos^2 \theta} \cdot \sin^2 \theta} = \frac{\dfrac{\sin^2 \theta}{\cos^2 \theta} - \sin^2 \theta}{\dfrac{\sin^4 \theta}{\cos^2 \theta}}$$

$$= \left(\frac{\sin^2 \theta}{\cos^2 \theta} - \sin^2 \theta\right)\frac{\cos^2 \theta}{\sin^4 \theta}$$

$$= \frac{\sin^2 \theta}{\cos^2 \theta} \cdot \frac{\cos^2 \theta}{\sin^4 \theta} - \sin^2 \theta \cdot \frac{\cos^2 \theta}{\sin^4 \theta}$$

$$= \frac{1}{\sin^2 \theta} - \frac{\cos^2 \theta}{\sin^2 \theta}$$

$$= \csc^2 \theta - \cot^2 \theta$$

$$= 1$$

45. $1 + \cot^2 \theta = 1 + \dfrac{\cos^2 \theta}{\sin^2 \theta}$

$$= \frac{\sin^2 \theta}{\sin^2 \theta} + \frac{\cos^2 \theta}{\sin^2 \theta}$$

$$= \frac{\sin^2 \theta + \cos^2 \theta}{\sin^2 \theta}$$

$$= \frac{1}{\sin^2 \theta}$$

$$= \csc^2 \theta$$

46. $\sin x \sec x = \sin x \cdot \dfrac{1}{\cos x}$

$$= \frac{\sin x}{\cos x}$$

$$= \tan x$$

47. $\dfrac{\sec \theta}{\csc \theta} = \dfrac{\dfrac{1}{\cos \theta}}{\dfrac{1}{\sin \theta}}$

$$= \frac{1}{\cos \theta} \cdot \sin \theta$$

$$= \frac{\sin \theta}{\cos \theta}$$

$$= \tan \theta$$

48. $\sec \alpha - \cos \alpha = \dfrac{1}{\cos \alpha} - \cos \alpha$

$$= \frac{1}{\cos \alpha} - \frac{\cos^2 \alpha}{\cos \alpha}$$

$$= \frac{1 - \cos^2 \alpha}{\cos \alpha}$$

$$= \frac{\sin^2 \alpha}{\cos \alpha}$$

$$= \sin \alpha \cdot \frac{\sin \alpha}{\cos \alpha}$$

$$= \sin \alpha \cdot \tan \alpha$$

49. $\dfrac{\sin \beta \sec \beta}{\cot \beta} = \dfrac{\sin \beta \cdot \dfrac{1}{\cos \beta}}{\dfrac{\cos \beta}{\sin \beta}}$

$$= \frac{\dfrac{\sin \beta}{\cos \beta}}{\dfrac{\cos \beta}{\sin \beta}}$$

$$= \frac{\sin \beta}{\cos \beta} \cdot \frac{\sin \beta}{\cos \beta}$$

$$= \frac{\sin^2 \beta}{\cos^2 \beta}$$

$$= \tan^2 \beta$$

$$= \left(\frac{3}{4}\right)^2$$

$$= \frac{9}{16}$$

50. a. $\sin^2 \theta + \cos^2 \theta = 1$

$$\left(\frac{5}{9}\right)^2 + \cos^2 \theta = 1$$

$$\cos^2 \theta = 1 - \frac{25}{81}$$

$$\cos^2 \theta = \frac{56}{81}$$

$$\cos \theta = \sqrt{\frac{56}{81}}$$

$$\cos \theta = \frac{\sqrt{56}}{9}$$

b. $\cot \theta = \dfrac{\cos \theta}{\sin \theta}$

$$= \frac{-\dfrac{\sqrt{56}}{9}}{\dfrac{5}{9}}$$

$$= -\frac{\sqrt{56}}{9} \cdot \frac{9}{5}$$

$$= -\frac{\sqrt{56}}{5}$$

c. $\sec \theta = \dfrac{1}{\cos \theta}$

$$\sec \theta = \frac{1}{\dfrac{\sqrt{56}}{9}}$$

$$= \frac{9}{\sqrt{56}} \cdot \frac{\sqrt{56}}{\sqrt{56}}$$

$$= \frac{9\sqrt{56}}{56}$$

51. $\dfrac{10!}{2!2!} = 907,200$ different ways

52. $x \neq 0, -\dfrac{3}{2}$

$$\dfrac{2x+1}{3x} - \dfrac{3}{3} \cdot \dfrac{x-1}{x} = \dfrac{1}{2x+3}$$

$$\dfrac{2x+1-3x+3}{3x} = \dfrac{1}{2x+3}$$

$$\dfrac{-x+4}{3x} = \dfrac{1}{2x+3}$$

$$(-x+4)(2x+3) = 3x$$

$$-2x^2 + 5x + 12 = 3x$$

$$-2x^2 + 2x + 12 = 0$$

$$-x^2 + x + 6 = 0$$

$$(-x+3)(x+2) = 0$$

$$x = 3, -2$$

53. $(x-6)^2 + y^2 = 36$

54. Let x = length of side adjacent to existing fence.

Then $200 - 2x$ = width of garden.

area $= x(200 - 2x)$

$\qquad = 200x - 2x^2$

55.
$$\begin{array}{r} 4b + \dfrac{1}{2b-1} \\ 2b-1\overline{)8b^2 - 4b + 1} \\ \underline{8b^2 - 4b} \\ 0 + 1 \end{array}$$

56. domain: $\{0, 8\}$

range: $\{-12, -8, 0, 3, 4\}$

not a function

Graphing Calculator Exploration: Verifying Trigonometric Identities

PAGE 802 EXERCISES

1. yes	2. no	3. yes	4. yes
5. yes	6. yes	7. yes	8. no
9. no	10. no	11. no	12. no
13. no	14. yes	15. yes	16. yes
17. no	18. yes	19. yes	20. yes

17-3   Verifying Trigonometric Identities

1. Transform the more complicated side of the equation into the form of the simpler side; transform each side separately into the same form; use substitution with basic trigonometric identities; factor or multiply to simplify; multiply numerator and denominator by the same trigonometric expression.

2.
$$\dfrac{v_o^2 \sin^2 \theta}{2g} \cdot \dfrac{\cos^2 \theta}{\cos^2 \theta} = v_o^2 \dfrac{\sin^2 \theta}{\cos^2 \theta} \cdot \dfrac{\cos^2 \theta}{2g}$$

$$\dfrac{v_o^2 \tan^2 \theta \cos^2 \theta}{2g} = \dfrac{v_o^2 \tan^2 \theta \cos^2 \theta}{2g}$$

3. $\sin \theta \sec \theta \cot \theta \overset{?}{=} 1$

$\sin \theta \cdot \dfrac{1}{\cos \theta} \cdot \dfrac{\cos \theta}{\sin \theta} \overset{?}{=} 1$

$\qquad\qquad 1 = 1$

4. $\tan^2 x \cos^2 x \overset{?}{=} 1 - \cos^2 x$

$\dfrac{\sin^2 x}{\cos^2 x} \cdot \cos^2 x \overset{?}{=} \sin^2 x$

$\qquad\qquad \sin^2 x = \sin^2 x$

5. $\csc y \sec y \overset{?}{=} \cot y + \tan y$

$\csc y \sec y \overset{?}{=} \dfrac{\cos y}{\sin y} + \dfrac{\sin y}{\cos y}$

$\csc y \sec y \overset{?}{=} \dfrac{\sin^2 y + \cos^2 y}{\sin y \cos y}$

$\csc y \sec y \overset{?}{=} \dfrac{1}{\sin y \cos y}$

$\csc y \sec y = \csc y \sec y$

6. $\tan \alpha \sin \alpha \cos \alpha \csc^2 \alpha \overset{?}{=} 1$

$\dfrac{\sin \alpha}{\cos \alpha} \cdot \sin \alpha \cdot \cos \alpha \cdot \dfrac{1}{\sin^2 \alpha} \overset{?}{=} 1$

$\qquad\qquad \dfrac{\sin^2 \alpha}{\sin^2 \alpha} \overset{?}{=} 1$

$\qquad\qquad 1 = 1$

---

7. $\dfrac{1}{\cos^2 x} - \dfrac{\sin^2 x}{\cos^2 x} \overset{?}{=} \tan x \cot x$

$\dfrac{1 - \sin^2 x}{\cos^2 x} \overset{?}{=} \dfrac{\sin x}{\cos x} \cdot \dfrac{\cos x}{\sin x}$

$\dfrac{\cos^2 x}{\cos^2 x} \overset{?}{=} 1$

$\qquad 1 = 1$

8. $\cos^2 \theta + \sin^2 \theta \overset{?}{=} 1$

$\qquad\qquad 1 = 1$

9. $\dfrac{\dfrac{1}{\cos \alpha}}{\sin \alpha} - \dfrac{\sin \alpha}{\cos \alpha} \overset{?}{=} \cot \alpha$

$\dfrac{1}{\sin \alpha \cos \alpha} - \dfrac{\sin^2 \alpha}{\sin \alpha \cos \alpha} \overset{?}{=} \cot \alpha$

$\dfrac{1 - \sin^2 \alpha}{\sin \alpha \cos \alpha} \overset{?}{=} \cot \alpha$

$\dfrac{\cos^2 \alpha}{\sin \alpha \cos \alpha} \overset{?}{=} \cot \alpha$

$\dfrac{\cos \alpha}{\sin \alpha} \overset{?}{=} \cot \alpha$

$\cot \alpha = \cot \alpha$

10.
$$\tan^2 \theta - \sin^2 \theta \overset{?}{=} \tan^2 \theta \, \sin^2 \theta$$

$$\frac{\sin^2 \theta}{\cos^2 \theta} - \sin^2 \theta \overset{?}{=} \tan^2 \theta \, \sin^2 \theta$$

$$\frac{\sin^2 \theta}{\cos^2 \theta} - \frac{\cos^2 \theta \, \sin^2 \theta}{\cos^2 \theta} \overset{?}{=} \tan^2 \theta \, \sin^2 \theta$$

$$\frac{\sin^2 \theta - \cos^2 \theta \, \sin^2 \theta}{\cos^2 \theta} \overset{?}{=} \tan^2 \theta \, \sin^2 \theta$$

$$\frac{\sin^2 \theta \,(1 - \cos^2 \theta)}{\cos^2 \theta} \overset{?}{=} \tan^2 \theta \, \sin^2 \theta$$

$$\frac{\sin^2 \theta}{\cos^2 \theta} \cdot \sin^2 \theta \overset{?}{=} \tan^2 \theta \, \sin^2 \theta$$

$$\tan^2 \theta \, \sin^2 \theta = \tan^2 \theta \, \sin^2 \theta$$

11.
$$\frac{\sin \alpha}{\sin \alpha} \cdot \frac{\sin \alpha}{1 - \cos \alpha} + \frac{1 - \cos \alpha}{1 - \cos \alpha} \cdot \frac{1 - \cos \alpha}{\sin \alpha} \overset{?}{=} 2 \csc \alpha$$

$$\frac{\sin^2 \alpha}{\sin \alpha \,(1 - \cos \alpha)} + \frac{1 - 2 \cos \alpha + \cos^2 \alpha}{\sin \alpha \,(1 - \cos \alpha)} \overset{?}{=} 2 \csc \alpha$$

$$\frac{\sin^2 \alpha + \cos^2 \alpha + 1 - 2 \cos \alpha}{\sin \alpha \,(1 - \cos \alpha)} \overset{?}{=} 2 \csc \alpha$$

$$\frac{2 - 2 \cos \alpha}{\sin \alpha \,(1 - \cos \alpha)} \overset{?}{=} 2 \csc \alpha$$

$$\frac{2(1 - \cos \alpha)}{\sin \alpha \,(1 - \cos \alpha)} \overset{?}{=} 2 \csc \alpha$$

$$\frac{2}{\sin \alpha} \overset{?}{=} 2 \csc \alpha$$

$$2 \csc \alpha = 2 \csc \alpha$$

12.
$$\frac{\dfrac{1}{\cos \beta} + \dfrac{1}{\sin \beta}}{1 + \dfrac{\sin \beta}{\cos \beta}} \overset{?}{=} \csc \beta$$

$$\frac{\dfrac{\sin \beta + \cos \beta}{\sin \beta \cos \beta}}{\dfrac{\sin \beta + \cos \beta}{\cos \beta}} \overset{?}{=} \csc \beta$$

$$\frac{\sin \beta + \cos \beta}{\sin \beta \cos \beta} \cdot \frac{\cos \beta}{\sin \beta + \cos \beta} \overset{?}{=} \csc \beta$$

$$\frac{\cos \beta}{\sin \beta \cos \beta} \overset{?}{=} \csc \beta$$

$$\frac{1}{\sin \beta} \overset{?}{=} \csc \beta$$

$$\csc \beta = \csc \beta$$

13.
$$\frac{1 - \cos x}{\sin x} \cdot \frac{1 + \cos x}{1 + \cos x} \overset{?}{=} \frac{\sin x}{1 + \cos x}$$

$$\frac{1 - \cos^2 x}{\sin x \,(1 + \cos x)} \overset{?}{=} \frac{\sin x}{1 + \cos x}$$

$$\frac{\sin^2 x}{\sin x \,(1 + \cos x)} \overset{?}{=} \frac{\sin x}{1 + \cos x}$$

$$\frac{\sin x}{1 + \cos x} = \frac{\sin x}{1 + \cos x}$$

14.
$$\frac{\sin \theta}{\sec \theta} \overset{?}{=} \frac{1}{\dfrac{\sin \theta}{\cos \theta} + \dfrac{\cos \theta}{\sin \theta}}$$

$$\frac{\sin \theta}{\sec \theta} \overset{?}{=} \frac{1}{\dfrac{\sin^2 \theta + \cos^2 \theta}{\sin \theta \cos \theta}}$$

$$\frac{\sin \theta}{\sec \theta} \overset{?}{=} \frac{\sin \theta \cos \theta}{\sin^2 \theta + \cos^2 \theta}$$

$$\frac{\sin \theta}{\sec \theta} \overset{?}{=} \frac{\sin \theta \cos \theta}{1}$$

$$\frac{\sin \theta}{\sec \theta} = \frac{\sin \theta}{\sec \theta}$$

15.
$$\frac{1 - \cos x}{1 + \cos x} \overset{?}{=} \csc^2 x - 2 \cot x \csc x + \cot^2 x$$

$$\frac{1 - \cos x}{1 + \cos x} \overset{?}{=} \frac{1}{\sin^2 x} - 2 \cdot \frac{\cos x}{\sin x} \cdot \frac{1}{\sin x} + \frac{\cos^2 x}{\sin^2 x}$$

$$\frac{1 - \cos x}{1 + \cos x} \overset{?}{=} \frac{1}{\sin^2 x} - \frac{2 \cos x}{\sin^2 x} + \frac{\cos^2 x}{\sin^2 x}$$

$$\frac{1 - \cos x}{1 + \cos x} \overset{?}{=} \frac{1 - 2 \cos x + \cos^2 x}{\sin^2 x}$$

$$\frac{1 - \cos x}{1 + \cos x} \overset{?}{=} \frac{1 - \cos x + \cos^2 x - \cos x}{\sin^2 x}$$

$$\frac{1 - \cos x}{1 + \cos x} \overset{?}{=} \frac{1 - \cos x + \cos x \,(\cos x - 1)}{1 - \cos^2 x}$$

$$\frac{1 - \cos x}{1 + \cos x} \overset{?}{=} \frac{(1 - \cos x) - \cos x \,(1 - \cos x)}{(1 - \cos x)(1 + \cos x)}$$

$$\frac{1 - \cos x}{1 + \cos x} \overset{?}{=} \frac{(1 - \cos x)(1 - \cos x)}{(1 - \cos x)(1 + \cos x)}$$

$$\frac{1 - \cos x}{1 + \cos x} = \frac{1 - \cos x}{1 + \cos x}$$

16.
$$\frac{\sec \theta + 1}{\tan \theta} \overset{?}{=} \frac{\tan \theta}{\sec \theta - 1} \cdot \frac{\sec \theta + 1}{\sec \theta + 1}$$

$$\frac{\sec \theta + 1}{\tan \theta} \overset{?}{=} \frac{\tan \theta \cdot (\sec \theta + 1)}{\sec^2 \theta - 1}$$

$$\frac{\sec \theta + 1}{\tan \theta} \overset{?}{=} \frac{\tan \theta \,(\sec \theta + 1)}{\tan^2 \theta}$$

$$\frac{\sec \theta + 1}{\tan \theta} = \frac{\sec \theta + 1}{\tan \theta}$$

17.
$$\frac{\cot \theta + \csc \theta}{\sin \theta + \tan \theta} \overset{?}{=} \cot \theta \csc \theta$$

$$\frac{\dfrac{\cos \theta}{\sin \theta} + \dfrac{1}{\sin \theta}}{\sin \theta + \dfrac{\sin \theta}{\cos \theta}} \overset{?}{=} \cot \theta \csc \theta$$

$$\frac{\dfrac{\cos \theta + 1}{\sin \theta}}{\dfrac{\sin \theta \cos \theta + \sin \theta}{\cos \theta}} \overset{?}{=} \cot \theta \csc \theta$$

$$\frac{\dfrac{\cos \theta + 1}{\sin \theta}}{\dfrac{\sin \theta \,(\cos \theta + 1)}{\cos \theta}} \overset{?}{=} \cot \theta \csc \theta$$

$$\frac{\cos \theta + 1}{\sin \theta} \cdot \frac{\cos \theta}{\sin \theta \,(\cos \theta + 1)} \overset{?}{=} \cot \theta \csc \theta$$

$$\frac{\cos \theta}{\sin \theta} \cdot \frac{1}{\sin \theta} \overset{?}{=} \cot \theta \csc \theta$$

$$\cot \theta \csc \theta = \cot \theta \csc \theta$$

18.
$$\cos^2 x + \tan^2 x \cos^2 x \stackrel{?}{=} 1$$
$$\cos^2 x + \frac{\sin^2 x}{\cos^2 x} \cdot \cos^2 x \stackrel{?}{=} 1$$
$$\cos^2 x + \sin^2 x \stackrel{?}{=} 1$$
$$1 = 1$$

19.
$$\frac{1 - 2\cos^2 \beta}{\sin \beta \cos \beta} \stackrel{?}{=} \tan \beta - \cot \beta$$
$$\frac{(1 - \cos^2 \beta) - \cos^2 \beta}{\sin \beta \cos \beta} \stackrel{?}{=} \tan \beta - \cot \beta$$
$$\frac{\sin^2 \beta - \cos^2 \beta}{\sin \beta \cos \beta} \stackrel{?}{=} \tan \beta - \cot \beta$$
$$\frac{\sin^2 \beta}{\sin \beta \cos \beta} - \frac{\cos^2 \beta}{\sin \beta \cos \beta} \stackrel{?}{=} \tan \beta - \cot \beta$$
$$\frac{\sin \beta}{\cos \beta} - \frac{\cos \beta}{\sin \beta} \stackrel{?}{=} \tan \beta - \cot \beta$$
$$\tan \beta - \cot \beta = \tan \beta - \cot \beta$$

20.
$$\frac{1 + \tan^2 \theta}{\csc^2 \theta} \stackrel{?}{=} \tan^2 \theta$$
$$\frac{\sec^2 \theta}{\csc^2 \theta} \stackrel{?}{=} \tan^2 \theta$$
$$\frac{\frac{1}{\cos^2 \theta}}{\frac{1}{\sin^2 \theta}} \stackrel{?}{=} \tan^2 \theta$$
$$\frac{1}{\cos^2 \theta} \cdot \sin^2 \theta \stackrel{?}{=} \tan^2 \theta$$
$$\tan^2 \theta = \tan^2 \theta$$

21.
$$\frac{\cos y}{1 + \sin y} \cdot \frac{1 - \sin y}{1 - \sin y} + \frac{\cos y}{1 - \sin y} \cdot \frac{1 + \sin y}{1 + \sin y}$$
$$\stackrel{?}{=} 2 \sec y$$
$$\frac{\cos y (1 - \sin y) + \cos y (1 + \sin y)}{(1 + \sin y)(1 - \sin y)} \stackrel{?}{=} 2 \sec y$$
$$\frac{\cos y - \sin y \cos y + \cos y + \sin y \cos y}{1 - \sin^2 y}$$
$$\stackrel{?}{=} 2 \sec y$$
$$\frac{2 \cos y}{\cos^2 y} \stackrel{?}{=} 2 \sec y$$
$$\frac{2}{\cos y} \stackrel{?}{=} 2 \sec y$$
$$2 \sec y = 2 \sec y$$

22.
$$\frac{1 + \sin x}{\sin x} \stackrel{?}{=} \frac{\cot^2 x}{\csc x - 1} \cdot \frac{\csc x + 1}{\csc x + 1}$$
$$\frac{1 + \sin x}{\sin x} \stackrel{?}{=} \frac{\cot^2 x (\csc x + 1)}{\csc^2 x - 1}$$
$$\frac{1 + \sin x}{\sin x} \stackrel{?}{=} \frac{\cot^2 x (\csc x + 1)}{\cot^2 x}$$
$$\frac{1 + \sin x}{\sin x} \stackrel{?}{=} \csc x + 1$$
$$\frac{1 + \sin x}{\sin x} \stackrel{?}{=} \frac{1}{\sin x} + \frac{\sin x}{\sin x}$$
$$\frac{1 + \sin x}{\sin x} = \frac{1 + \sin x}{\sin x}$$

23.
$$\cot x (\cot x + \tan x) \stackrel{?}{=} \csc^2 x$$
$$\cot^2 x + \tan x \cot x \stackrel{?}{=} \csc^2 x$$
$$\csc^2 x - 1 + \frac{\sin x}{\cos x} \cdot \frac{\cos x}{\sin x} \stackrel{?}{=} \csc^2 x$$
$$\csc^2 x - 1 + 1 \stackrel{?}{=} \csc^2 x$$
$$\csc^2 x = \csc^2 x$$

24.
$$\cos^4 \theta - \sin^4 \theta \stackrel{?}{=} \cos^2 \theta - \sin^2 \theta$$
$$(\cos^2 \theta - \sin^2 \theta)(\cos^2 \theta + \sin^2 \theta)$$
$$\stackrel{?}{=} \cos^2 \theta - \sin^2 \theta$$
$$(\cos^2 \theta - \sin^2 \theta) \cdot 1 \stackrel{?}{=} \cos^2 \theta - \sin^2 \theta$$
$$\cos^2 \theta - \sin^2 \theta = \cos^2 \theta - \sin^2 \theta$$

25.
$$\frac{1 + \tan \gamma}{1 + \cot \gamma} \stackrel{?}{=} \frac{\sin \gamma}{\cos \gamma}$$
$$\frac{1 + \frac{\sin \gamma}{\cos \gamma}}{1 + \frac{\cos \gamma}{\sin \gamma}} \stackrel{?}{=} \frac{\sin \gamma}{\cos \gamma}$$
$$\frac{\frac{\sin \gamma + \cos \gamma}{\cos \gamma}}{\frac{\sin \gamma + \cos \gamma}{\sin \gamma}} \stackrel{?}{=} \frac{\sin \gamma}{\cos \gamma}$$
$$\frac{\sin \gamma + \cos \gamma}{\cos \gamma} \cdot \frac{\sin \gamma}{\sin \gamma + \cos \gamma} \stackrel{?}{=} \frac{\sin \gamma}{\cos \gamma}$$
$$\frac{\sin \gamma}{\cos \gamma} = \frac{\sin \gamma}{\cos \gamma}$$

26.
$$\frac{\tan^2 x}{\sec x - 1} \cdot \frac{\sec x + 1}{\sec x + 1} \stackrel{?}{=} 1 + \frac{1}{\cos x}$$
$$\frac{\tan^2 x (\sec x + 1)}{\sec^2 x - 1} \stackrel{?}{=} 1 + \frac{1}{\cos x}$$
$$\frac{\tan^2 x (\sec x + 1)}{\tan^2 x} \stackrel{?}{=} 1 + \frac{1}{\cos x}$$
$$\sec x + 1 \stackrel{?}{=} 1 + \frac{1}{\cos x}$$
$$1 + \frac{1}{\cos x} = 1 + \frac{1}{\cos x}$$

27.
$$1 + \sec^2 x \sin^2 x \stackrel{?}{=} \sec^2 x$$
$$1 + \frac{1}{\cos^2 x} \cdot \sin^2 x \stackrel{?}{=} \sec^2 x$$
$$1 + \tan^2 x \stackrel{?}{=} \sec^2 x$$
$$\sec^2 x = \sec^2 x$$

28.
$$\sin \theta + \cos \theta \stackrel{?}{=} \frac{1 + \frac{\sin \theta}{\cos \theta}}{\frac{1}{\cos \theta}}$$
$$\sin \theta + \cos \theta \stackrel{?}{=} \frac{\frac{\sin \theta + \cos \theta}{\cos \theta}}{\frac{1}{\cos \theta}}$$
$$\sin \theta + \cos \theta \stackrel{?}{=} \frac{\sin \theta + \cos \theta}{\cos \theta} \cdot \cos \theta$$
$$\sin \theta + \cos \theta = \sin \theta + \cos \theta$$

29. See students' work.

30. a.
$$\frac{I \cos \theta}{R^2} \stackrel{?}{=} \frac{I \cot \theta}{R^2 \csc \theta}$$

$$\frac{I \cos \theta}{R^2} \stackrel{?}{=} \frac{I \cdot \dfrac{\cos \theta}{\sin \theta}}{R^2 \cdot \dfrac{1}{\sin \theta}}$$

$$\frac{I \cos \theta}{R^2} \stackrel{?}{=} I \cdot \frac{\cos \theta}{\sin \theta} \cdot \frac{\sin \theta}{R^2}$$

$$\frac{I \cos \theta}{R^2} = \frac{I \cos \theta}{R^2}$$

b. $E = \dfrac{12 \cos 0^\circ}{10^2}$

$\qquad = \dfrac{12}{100}$

$\qquad = 0.12$ footcandles

c. $20 = \dfrac{90 \cos 30^\circ}{R^2}$

$\qquad R^2 = \dfrac{90 \cos 30^\circ}{20}$

$\qquad R = \sqrt{\dfrac{90 \cos 30^\circ}{20}}$

$\qquad R = 1.97$ feet

31. $\left(\dfrac{3}{4}\right)^7 = \dfrac{2187}{16,384} \approx 0.133$

32.

Stem	Leaf
0	4 4 4 4
•	5 6 6 6 6 7 7 8 9 9
1	1 1 2 2
•	6 9 9 9

1 | 1 represents 11 cents.

33. $\log_5 82 = \dfrac{\log 82}{\log 5}$

$\qquad \approx 2.738$

34. $s_1 + s_2 = \dfrac{-b}{a} \qquad\qquad s_1 s_2 = \dfrac{c}{a}$

$\qquad = \dfrac{-10}{2} \qquad\qquad\qquad = \dfrac{8}{2}$

$\qquad = -5 \qquad\qquad\qquad\quad = 4$

$$x = \frac{-10 \pm \sqrt{10^2 - 4(2)(8)}}{2 \cdot 2}$$

$$= \frac{-10 \pm \sqrt{100 - 64}}{4}$$

$$= \frac{-10 \pm \sqrt{36}}{4}$$

$$= \frac{-10 \pm 6}{4}$$

$$= \frac{-4}{4}, \frac{-16}{4}$$

$$= -1, -4$$

35. $\begin{bmatrix} -10 & 0 \\ 3 & -2 \end{bmatrix}; \dfrac{1}{20} \begin{bmatrix} -2 & -3 \\ 0 & -10 \end{bmatrix}$

$$= \begin{bmatrix} \dfrac{-2}{20} & \dfrac{-3}{20} \\ 0 & \dfrac{-10}{20} \end{bmatrix}$$

$$= \begin{bmatrix} \dfrac{-1}{10} & \dfrac{-3}{20} \\ 0 & \dfrac{-1}{2} \end{bmatrix}$$

17-4 **Problem-Solving Strategy: Working Backwards**

PAGE 808   CHECKING FOR UNDERSTANDING

1. when it is faster to start from the end than from the beginning

2. $4 \cdot 9 = 36$ rungs

3. Work backward from the final statement in the proof to the given information.

4. $x + y = 4$ $\qquad \left(\dfrac{1}{x}\right)^2 + \left(\dfrac{1}{y}\right)^2 = \dfrac{1}{x^2} \cdot \dfrac{y^2}{y^2} + \dfrac{1}{y^2} \cdot \dfrac{x^2}{x^2}$
   $xy = 7$

$\qquad\qquad\qquad\qquad\qquad = \dfrac{x^2 + y^2}{x^2 y^2}$

$x^2 y^2 = 7^2 = 49$

$(x + y)^2 = x^2 + 2xy + y^2 = 16$

where $2xy = 2 \cdot 7 = 14$.

$\qquad x^2 + y^2 + 14 = 16$

$\qquad\qquad x^2 + y^2 = 2$

So, $\dfrac{x^2 + y^2}{x^2 y^2} = \dfrac{2}{49}$.

5. $4550 \cdot 2 \cdot 2 = 18,200$ coins

6. $10.25 + 7.45 + 10.25 + 7.45 + 10.25 + 7.45 + 10.25 + 7.45 + 15 = \$85.80$

PAGES 808-809   EXERCISES

7. List the multiples of 7 and then use guess-and-check to find the answer, 301.

8. Let $x = \sqrt{11 + \sqrt{72}} + \sqrt{11 - \sqrt{72}}$

then $x^2 = (\sqrt{11 + \sqrt{72}})^2 + 2(\sqrt{11 + \sqrt{72}})(\sqrt{11 + \sqrt{72}})$
$\qquad\qquad + (\sqrt{11 + \sqrt{72}})^2$

$x^2 = 11 + \sqrt{72} + 2\sqrt{121 - 72} + 11 - \sqrt{72}$

$x^2 = 22 + 2\sqrt{49}$

$x^2 = 22 + 14$

$x^2 = 36$

$x = 6$ (x must be positive since principal roots of $\sqrt{11 + \sqrt{72}}$ and $\sqrt{11 - \sqrt{72}}$ are positive.)

So, $\sqrt{11 + \sqrt{72}} + \sqrt{11 - \sqrt{72}} = 6$.

9. 6 or 12. By listing the possibilities, you see that there are four possible ways to get each of these products.

10. Factors of numbers occur in pairs, so unless the two numbers in a pair are the same number, as for a square, the number of factors for a number is even. Since squares are the only numbers that have an odd number of factors, we need to count the squares less than 500. The greatest square less than 500 is 484 or 22^2. So, there are 22 squares less than 500, namely 1^2, 2^2, 3^2, ..., 22^2. Therefore, there are 22 positive integers less than 500 with an odd number of factors.

11. $x + y = 2$
    $xy = 3$

$$\left(\frac{1}{x}\right)^2 + \left(\frac{1}{y}\right)^2$$

$$= \frac{1}{x^2} \cdot \frac{y^2}{y^2} + \frac{1}{y^2} \cdot \frac{x^2}{x^2}$$

$$= \frac{x^2 + y^2}{x^2 y^2}$$

$x^2 y^2 = 9$

$(x + y)^2 = x^2 + 2xy + y^2 = 4$

where $2xy = 2 \cdot 3 = 6$

$x^2 + y^2 + 6 = 4$

$x^2 + y^2 = -2$

So, $\dfrac{x^2 + y^2}{x^2 y^2} = -\dfrac{2}{9}$.

12. The store lost $10, consisting of the $3.50 magazine and the $6.50 in change given to the customer.

The exchange with the record store manager has no effect on the loss, because the bookstore manager gave him a good $10 bill and received $10 in change.

13. Answers may vary. A sample answer is $5[5(5 + 5) - (5 + 5)]$.

14.
$$(\log x)^2 = \log(x^2)$$
$$(\log x)^2 = 2 \log x$$
$$(\log x)^2 - 2 \log x = 0$$
$$\log x (\log x - 2) = 0$$
$$\log x = 0 \text{ or } \log x - 2 = 0$$
$$x = 1 \qquad \log x = 2$$
$$x = 100$$

15. $24^5 = 7,962,624$
    $25^5 = 9,765,625$
    $32^5 = 33,554,432$
    $43^5 = 147,008,443$
    $49^5 = 282,475,249$
    $51^5 = 345,025,251$
    $57^5 = 6,016,922,057$
    $68^5 = 1,453,933,568$
    $75^5 = 2,373,046,875$
    $76^5 = 2,535,525,376$
    $93^5 = 6,956,883,693$
    $99^5 = 9,509,900,499$

    So, $x = 24, 25, 32, 43, 49, 51, 57, 68, 75, 76, 93,$ or 99.

16. Area of entire rectangle $= 12 \cdot 6 = 72$

    Area of triangle $= \frac{1}{2} \cdot 6 \cdot 8 = 24$

    $72 - 24 = 48$

    $\dfrac{48}{72} = \dfrac{2}{3}$

17. $1 + 2 + 4 = 7$

PAGE 809   COOPERATIVE LEARNING ACTIVITY

Sample answers are:

2	3	4
6		6
2	12	1

3	4	6
2		2
12	1	6

17-5 Sum and Difference of Angles Formulas

PAGE 813   CHECKING FOR UNDERSTANDING

1. no; A counter example is:
   $$\sin(30° + 45°) = \sin 30° + \sin 45°$$
   $$= \frac{1}{2} + \frac{\sqrt{2}}{2}$$
   $$= \frac{1 + \sqrt{2}}{2}$$
   $$\approx 1.2071$$

   Since a sine value cannot be greater than 1, this statement must be false.

2. See students' work.;
   $$\cos 15° = \cos(45° - \cos 30°)$$
   $$= \cos 45° \cos 30° + \sin 45° \sin 30°$$
   $$= \frac{\sqrt{2}}{2} \cdot \frac{\sqrt{3}}{2} + \frac{\sqrt{2}}{2} \cdot \frac{1}{2}$$
   $$= \frac{\sqrt{6} + \sqrt{2}}{4}$$

3. $30° - 45°$ 4. $135° + 30°$ 5. $30° + 45°$
6. $225° + 60°$ 7. $225° + 30°$ 8. $300° + 45°$

9. $\sin (30° + 45°) = \sin 30° \cos 45°$
$+ \cos 30° \sin 45°$
$= \dfrac{1}{2} \cdot \dfrac{\sqrt{2}}{2} + \dfrac{\sqrt{3}}{2} \cdot \dfrac{\sqrt{2}}{2}$
$= \dfrac{\sqrt{2} + \sqrt{6}}{4}$

10. $\sin (225° + 60°) = \sin 225° \cos 60°$
$+ \cos 225° \sin 60°$
$= -\dfrac{\sqrt{2}}{2} \cdot \dfrac{1}{2} + -\dfrac{\sqrt{2}}{2} \cdot \dfrac{\sqrt{3}}{2}$
$= \dfrac{-\sqrt{2} - \sqrt{6}}{4}$

11. $\cos (30° + 45°) = \cos 30° \cos 45°$
$- \sin 30° \sin 45°$
$= \dfrac{\sqrt{3}}{2} \cdot \dfrac{\sqrt{2}}{2} - \dfrac{1}{2} \cdot \dfrac{\sqrt{2}}{2}$
$= \dfrac{\sqrt{6} - \sqrt{2}}{4}$

12. $\sin (135° + 30°) = \sin 135° \cos 30°$
$+ \cos 135° \sin 30°$
$= \dfrac{\sqrt{2}}{2} \cdot \dfrac{\sqrt{3}}{2} + -\dfrac{\sqrt{2}}{2} \cdot \dfrac{1}{2}$
$= \dfrac{\sqrt{6} - \sqrt{2}}{4}$

13. $\cos (135° + 60°) = \cos 135° \cos 60°$
$- \sin 135° \sin 60°$
$= -\dfrac{\sqrt{2}}{2} \cdot \dfrac{1}{2} - \dfrac{\sqrt{2}}{2} \cdot \dfrac{\sqrt{3}}{2}$
$= \dfrac{-\sqrt{2} - \sqrt{6}}{4}$

14. $\sin (60° + 45°) = \sin 60° \cos 45°$
$+ \cos 60° \sin 45°$
$= \dfrac{\sqrt{3}}{2} \cdot \dfrac{\sqrt{2}}{2} + \dfrac{1}{2} \cdot \dfrac{\sqrt{2}}{2}$
$= \dfrac{\sqrt{6} + \sqrt{2}}{4}$

15. $\cos (225° + 30°) = \cos 225° \cos 30°$
$- \sin 225° \sin 30°$
$= -\dfrac{\sqrt{2}}{2} \cdot \dfrac{\sqrt{3}}{2} - \left(-\dfrac{\sqrt{2}}{2}\right) \cdot \dfrac{1}{2}$
$= \dfrac{-\sqrt{6} + \sqrt{2}}{4}$

16. $\cos (300° + 45°) = \cos 300° \cos 45°$
$- \sin 300° \sin 45°$
$= \dfrac{1}{2} \cdot \dfrac{\sqrt{2}}{2} - \left(-\dfrac{\sqrt{3}}{2}\right) \cdot \dfrac{\sqrt{2}}{2}$
$= \dfrac{\sqrt{2} + \sqrt{6}}{4}$

17. $\cos (135° + 30°) = \cos 135° \cos 30°$
$- \sin 135° \sin 30°$
$= -\dfrac{\sqrt{2}}{2} \cdot \dfrac{\sqrt{3}}{2} - \dfrac{\sqrt{2}}{2} \cdot \dfrac{1}{2}$
$= \dfrac{-\sqrt{6} - \sqrt{2}}{4}$

18. $\sin (40° + 20°) = \sin 60° = \dfrac{\sqrt{3}}{2}$

19. $\sin (65° - 35°) = \sin 30° = \dfrac{1}{2}$

20. $\cos (25° + 5°) = \cos 30° = \dfrac{\sqrt{3}}{2}$

21. $\cos (80° - 20°) = \cos 60° = \dfrac{1}{2}$

22. $\cos (270° - \theta) \overset{?}{=} \cos 270° \cos \theta + \sin 270° \sin \theta$
$\overset{?}{=} 0 + (-1 \sin \theta)$
$= -\sin \theta$

23. $\sin (270° - \theta) \overset{?}{=} \sin 270° \cos \theta - \cos 270° \sin \theta$
$\overset{?}{=} -1 \cos \theta - 0$
$= -\cos \theta$

24. $\sin (180° + \theta) \overset{?}{=} \sin 180° \cos \theta + \cos 180° \sin \theta$
$\overset{?}{=} 0 + (-1 \sin \theta)$
$= -\sin \theta$

25. $\sin (90° + \theta) \overset{?}{=} \sin 90° \cos \theta + \cos 90° \sin \theta$
$\overset{?}{=} 1 \cdot \cos \theta + 0$
$= \cos \theta$

26. $\cos (180° + \theta) \overset{?}{=} \cos 180° \cos \theta - \sin 180° \sin \theta$
$\overset{?}{=} -1 \cos \theta - 0$
$= -\cos \theta$

27. $\cos (90° + \theta) \overset{?}{=} \cos 90° \cos \theta - \sin 90° \sin \theta$
$\overset{?}{=} 0 - 1 \cdot \sin \theta$
$= -\sin \theta$

28. $\sin \left(\theta + \dfrac{\pi}{3}\right) - \cos \left(\theta + \dfrac{\pi}{6}\right)$
$\overset{?}{=} \sin \theta \cos \dfrac{\pi}{3} + \cos \theta \sin \dfrac{\pi}{3} - \cos \theta \cos \dfrac{\pi}{6}$
$+ \sin \theta \sin \dfrac{\pi}{6}$
$\overset{?}{=} \dfrac{1}{2} \sin \theta + \dfrac{\sqrt{3}}{2} \cos \theta - \dfrac{\sqrt{3}}{2} \cos \theta + \dfrac{1}{2} \sin \theta$
$\overset{?}{=} \dfrac{1}{2} \sin \theta + \dfrac{1}{2} \sin \theta$
$= \sin \theta$

29. $\sin (x + y) \sin (x - y)$
$\overset{?}{=} [\sin x \cos y + \cos x \sin y]$
$[\sin x \cos y - \cos x \sin y]$
$\overset{?}{=} \sin^2 x \cos^2 y - \cos^2 x \sin^2 y$
$\overset{?}{=} \sin^2 x(1 - \sin^2 y) - (1 - \sin^2 x) \sin^2 y$
$\overset{?}{=} \sin^2 x - \sin^2 x \sin^2 y - \sin^2 y$
$+ \sin^2 x \sin^2 y$
$= \sin^2 x - \sin^2 y$

30. $\sin(60° + \theta) + \sin(60° - \theta)$

$\overset{?}{=} \sin 60° \cos \theta + \cos 60° \sin \theta + \sin 60° \cos \theta$
$\quad - \cos 60° \sin \theta$

$\overset{?}{=} \frac{\sqrt{3}}{2} \cos \theta + \frac{1}{2} \sin \theta + \frac{\sqrt{3}}{2} \cos \theta - \frac{1}{2} \sin \theta$

$= \sqrt{3} \cos \theta$

31. $\sin(x + 30°) + \cos(x + 60°)$

$\overset{?}{=} \sin x \cos 30° + \cos x \sin 30° + \cos x \cos 60°$
$\quad - \sin x \sin 60°$

$\overset{?}{=} \frac{\sqrt{3}}{2} \sin x + \frac{1}{2} \cos x + \frac{1}{2} \cos x - \frac{\sqrt{3}}{2} \sin x$

$\overset{?}{=} \frac{1}{2} \cos x + \frac{1}{2} \cos x = \cos x$

32. $\dfrac{\tan 315° - \tan 120°}{1 + \tan 315° \tan 120°} = \dfrac{-1 + \sqrt{3}}{1 + (-1)(-\sqrt{3})}$

$= \dfrac{\sqrt{3} - 1}{1 + \sqrt{3}} \cdot \dfrac{1 - \sqrt{3}}{1 - \sqrt{3}}$

$= \dfrac{\sqrt{3} + \sqrt{3} - 1 - 3}{1 - 3}$

$= \dfrac{2\sqrt{3} - 4}{-2}$

$= -\sqrt{3} + 2$

$= 2 - \sqrt{3}$

33. $\dfrac{\tan 225° - \tan 120°}{1 + \tan 225° \tan 120°} = \dfrac{1 + \sqrt{3}}{1 + 1 \cdot (-\sqrt{3})}$

$= \dfrac{1 + \sqrt{3}}{1 - \sqrt{3}} \cdot \dfrac{1 + \sqrt{3}}{1 + \sqrt{3}}$

$= \dfrac{1 + 2\sqrt{3} + 3}{1 - 3}$

$= \dfrac{4 + 2\sqrt{3}}{-2}$

$= -2 - \sqrt{3}$

34. $\tan(30° + 30°) = \tan 60°$

$= \tan(120° - 60°)$

$= \dfrac{\tan 120° - \tan 60°}{1 + \tan 120° \tan 60°}$

$= \dfrac{-\sqrt{3} - \sqrt{3}}{1 + \sqrt{3}(-\sqrt{3})}$

$= \dfrac{-2\sqrt{3}}{1 - 3}$

$= \dfrac{-2\sqrt{3}}{-2}$

$= \sqrt{3}$

35. $\tan 195° = \tan(225° - 30°)$

$= \dfrac{\tan 225° - \tan 30°}{1 + \tan 225° \tan 30°}$

$= \dfrac{1 - \frac{\sqrt{3}}{3}}{1 + 1 \cdot \frac{\sqrt{3}}{3}} \cdot \dfrac{1 - \frac{\sqrt{3}}{3}}{1 - \frac{\sqrt{3}}{3}}$

$= \dfrac{1 - \frac{2\sqrt{3}}{3} + \frac{1}{3}}{1 - \frac{1}{3}}$

$= \dfrac{\frac{4}{3} - \frac{2}{3}\sqrt{3}}{\frac{2}{3}}$

$= 2 - \sqrt{3}$

36. $\tan(\alpha + \beta) = \dfrac{\sin(\alpha + \beta)}{\cos(\alpha + \beta)}$

$= \dfrac{\sin \alpha \cos \beta + \cos \alpha \sin \beta}{\cos \alpha \cos \beta - \sin \alpha \sin \beta}$

$= \dfrac{\frac{\sin \alpha \cos \beta}{\cos \alpha \cos \beta} + \frac{\cos \alpha \sin \beta}{\cos \alpha \sin \beta}}{\frac{\cos \alpha \cos \beta}{\cos \alpha \cos \beta} - \frac{\sin \alpha \sin \beta}{\cos \alpha \cos \beta}}$

$= \dfrac{\tan \alpha + \tan \beta}{1 - \tan \alpha \tan \beta}$

37. a. $\sin(13° - 12°) = \sin 13° \cos 12°$
$\quad - \cos 13° \sin 12°$

b.

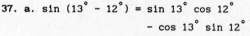
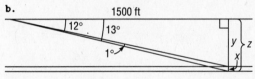

$\tan 12° = \dfrac{y}{1500}$

$y = 318.8$

$\tan 13° = \dfrac{z}{1500}$

$z = 346.3$

$x = 346.3 - 318.8$

$= 27.5 \text{ ft}$

38. $-120° + 360° = 240°$

39. $512 = 2r^{9-1}$

$512 = 2r^8$

$r^8 = 256$

$r = 2$

$S_n = \dfrac{2 - 2(2^{10})}{1 - 2}$

$= \dfrac{2 - 2048}{-1}$

$= 2046$

40. $\dfrac{2x^6 y^3}{a^3 b^7} \cdot \dfrac{ab^3}{4x^2 y} = \dfrac{2ab^3 x^2 y(x^4 y^2)}{2ab^3 x^2 y(2a^2 b^4)}$

$= \dfrac{x^4 y^2}{2a^2 b^4}$

41. $[f \circ g](3) = (x - 3)^2 + 8$

$\qquad = (3 - 3)^2 + 8$

$\qquad = 8$

$\quad [g \circ f](3) = (x^2 + 8) - 3$

$\qquad = x^2 + 5$

$\qquad = 3^2 + 5$

$\qquad = 14$

42. $f(x) = (x - 3)^2$

43. Symmetric property of equality

PAGE 814   MID-CHAPTER REVIEW

1. $1, \dfrac{\pi}{2}$ or $90°$ **2.** $5, 2\pi$ or $360°$

3. $4, \dfrac{8\pi}{3}$ or $480°$ **4.** $\dfrac{\pi}{2}$ or $90°$

5. π or $180°$ **6.** 5π or $900°$

7. $\cot^2 \theta + 1 = \csc^2 \theta$

$\left(-\dfrac{3}{5}\right)^2 + 1 = \csc^2 \theta$

$\csc^2 \theta = \dfrac{9}{25} + 1$

$\csc^2 \theta = \dfrac{34}{25}$

$\csc \theta = \sqrt{\dfrac{34}{25}}$

$\csc \theta = \dfrac{\sqrt{34}}{5}$

8. $\tan^2 \alpha + 1 = \sec^2 \alpha$

$\left(-\dfrac{3}{5}\right)^2 + 1 = \sec^2 \alpha$

$\sec^2 \alpha = \dfrac{9}{25} + 1$

$\sec^2 \alpha = \dfrac{34}{25}$

$\sec \alpha = -\sqrt{\dfrac{34}{25}}$

$\sec \alpha = -\dfrac{\sqrt{34}}{5}$

$\cos \alpha = \dfrac{1}{\sec \alpha}$

$\qquad = \dfrac{1}{-\dfrac{\sqrt{34}}{5}}$

$\qquad = -\dfrac{5}{\sqrt{34}} \cdot \dfrac{\sqrt{34}}{\sqrt{34}}$

$\qquad = -\dfrac{5\sqrt{34}}{34}$

9. $\cot \beta \overset{?}{=} \cos \beta \csc \beta$

$\cot \beta \overset{?}{=} \cos \beta \left(\dfrac{1}{\sin \beta}\right)$

$\cot \beta \overset{?}{=} \dfrac{\cos \beta}{\sin \beta}$

$\cot \beta = \cot \beta$

10. $1 \overset{?}{=} \dfrac{1}{\sec^2 \alpha - \sec^2 \alpha \sin^2 \alpha}$

$1 \overset{?}{=} \dfrac{1}{\sec^2 \alpha(1 - \sin^2 \alpha)}$

$1 \overset{?}{=} \dfrac{1}{\dfrac{1}{\cos^2 \alpha}(\cos^2 \alpha)}$

$1 \overset{?}{=} \dfrac{1}{1}$

$1 = 1$

11. $15 + 12 + 15 + 12 + 4 = 58$ tickets

12. $\sin (135° + 60°)$

$= \sin 135° \cos 60° + \cos 135° \sin 60°$

$= \dfrac{\sqrt{2}}{2} \cdot \dfrac{1}{2} + \left(-\dfrac{\sqrt{2}}{2}\right) \cdot \dfrac{\sqrt{3}}{2}$

$= \dfrac{\sqrt{2} - \sqrt{6}}{4}$

13. $\cos (225° + 60°)$

$= \cos 225° \cos 60° - \sin 225° \sin 60°$

$= \left(-\dfrac{\sqrt{2}}{2}\right) \cdot \dfrac{1}{2} - \left(-\dfrac{\sqrt{2}}{2}\right) \cdot \dfrac{\sqrt{3}}{2}$

$= \dfrac{\sqrt{6} - \sqrt{2}}{4}$

14. $\sin (60° - 135°)$

$= \sin 60° \cos 135° - \cos 60° \sin 135°$

$= \dfrac{\sqrt{3}}{2} \cdot \left(-\dfrac{\sqrt{2}}{2}\right) - \dfrac{1}{2} \cdot \dfrac{\sqrt{2}}{2}$

$= \dfrac{-\sqrt{6} - \sqrt{2}}{4}$

17-6 ### Double-Angle and Half-Angle Formulas

PAGES 817-818   CHECKING FOR UNDERSTANDING

1. $\sin^2 x + \cos^2 x = 1$

$\left(\dfrac{1}{2}\right)^2 + \cos^2 x = 1$

$\cos^2 x = 1 - \dfrac{1}{4}$

$\cos^2 x = \dfrac{3}{4}$

$\cos x = -\dfrac{\sqrt{3}}{2}$

$\sin 2x = 2\left(\dfrac{1}{2}\right)\left(-\dfrac{\sqrt{3}}{2}\right)$

$\qquad = -\dfrac{2\sqrt{3}}{4}$

$\qquad = -\dfrac{\sqrt{3}}{2}$

2. x will be in quadrant II.

Use the double-angle formula for sin knowing that $\sin x$ will be positive.

3. $\sin \frac{x}{2} = \pm\sqrt{\dfrac{1 - \dfrac{40}{41}}{2}}$

$= \pm\sqrt{\dfrac{\dfrac{1}{41}}{2}}$

$= \pm\sqrt{\dfrac{1}{82}} \cdot \dfrac{\sqrt{82}}{\sqrt{82}}$

$= \pm\dfrac{\sqrt{82}}{82}$

Since x is in quadrant IV, $\frac{x}{2}$ in in quadrant II where sin values are positive.

Therefore $\sin \frac{x}{2} = \dfrac{\sqrt{82}}{82}$.

4. I or II   **5.** III or IV   **6.** III or IV

7. I or II   **8.** I   **9.** I

10. $\sin^2 x + \cos^2 x = 1$

$\left(\dfrac{5}{13}\right)^2 + \cos^2 x = 1$

$\cos^2 x = 1 - \dfrac{25}{169}$

$\cos^2 x = \dfrac{144}{169}$

$\cos x = -\sqrt{\dfrac{144}{169}}$

$\cos x = -\dfrac{12}{13}$

$\sin 2x = 2 \cdot \dfrac{5}{13} \cdot \left(-\dfrac{12}{13}\right)$ $\cos 2x = \left(-\dfrac{12}{13}\right)^2 - \left(\dfrac{5}{13}\right)^2$

$= 2 \cdot \left(-\dfrac{60}{169}\right)$ $= \dfrac{144 - 25}{169}$

$= -\dfrac{120}{169}$ $= \dfrac{119}{169}$

$\sin \dfrac{x}{2} = \sqrt{\dfrac{1 - \left(-\dfrac{12}{13}\right)}{2}}$ $\cos \dfrac{x}{2} = \sqrt{\dfrac{1 + \left(-\dfrac{12}{13}\right)}{2}}$

$= \sqrt{\dfrac{\dfrac{25}{13}}{2}}$ $= \sqrt{\dfrac{\dfrac{1}{13}}{2}}$

$= \sqrt{\dfrac{25}{26}}$ $= \dfrac{1}{\sqrt{26}} \cdot \dfrac{\sqrt{26}}{\sqrt{26}}$

$= \dfrac{5}{\sqrt{26}} \cdot \dfrac{\sqrt{26}}{\sqrt{26}}$ $= \dfrac{\sqrt{26}}{26}$

$= \dfrac{5\sqrt{26}}{26}$

11. $\sin^2 x + \cos^2 x = 1$

$\sin^2 x + \left(\dfrac{1}{5}\right)^2 = 1$

$\sin^2 x = 1 - \dfrac{1}{25}$

$\sin^2 x = \dfrac{24}{25}$

$\sin x = -\sqrt{\dfrac{24}{25}}$

$\sin x = -\dfrac{2\sqrt{6}}{5}$

$\sin 2x = 2 \cdot \left(-\dfrac{2\sqrt{6}}{5}\right) \cdot \dfrac{1}{5}$ $\cos 2x = \left(\dfrac{1}{5}\right)^2 - \left(-\dfrac{2\sqrt{6}}{5}\right)^2$

$= -\dfrac{4\sqrt{6}}{25}$ $= \dfrac{1 - 24}{25}$

$= -\dfrac{23}{25}$

$\sin \dfrac{x}{2} = \sqrt{\dfrac{1 - \dfrac{1}{5}}{2}}$ $\cos \dfrac{x}{2} = -\sqrt{\dfrac{1 + \dfrac{1}{5}}{2}}$

$= \sqrt{\dfrac{\dfrac{4}{5}}{2}}$ $= -\sqrt{\dfrac{\dfrac{6}{5}}{2}}$

$= \dfrac{2}{\sqrt{10}} \cdot \dfrac{\sqrt{10}}{\sqrt{10}}$ $= -\sqrt{\dfrac{6}{10}} \cdot \dfrac{\sqrt{10}}{\sqrt{10}}$

$= \dfrac{2\sqrt{10}}{10}$ $= -\dfrac{\sqrt{60}}{10}$

$= \dfrac{\sqrt{10}}{5}$ $= -\dfrac{2\sqrt{15}}{10}$

$= -\dfrac{\sqrt{15}}{5}$

PAGES 818-819   EXERCISES

12. $\sin^2 x + \left(\dfrac{3}{5}\right)^2 = 1$

$\sin^2 x = 1 - \dfrac{9}{25}$

$\sin^2 x = \dfrac{16}{25}$

$\sin x = \sqrt{\dfrac{16}{25}}$

$\sin x = \dfrac{4}{5}$

$\sin 2x = 2 \cdot \dfrac{4}{5} \cdot \dfrac{3}{5}$ $\cos 2x = 1 - 2 \cdot \left(\dfrac{4}{5}\right)^2$

$= \dfrac{24}{25}$ $= 1 - 2 \cdot \dfrac{16}{25}$

$= 1 - \dfrac{32}{25}$

$= -\dfrac{7}{25}$

$\sin \dfrac{x}{2} = \sqrt{\dfrac{1 - \dfrac{3}{5}}{2}}$ $\cos \dfrac{x}{2} = \sqrt{\dfrac{1 + \dfrac{3}{5}}{2}}$

$= \sqrt{\dfrac{\dfrac{2}{5}}{2}}$ $= \sqrt{\dfrac{\dfrac{8}{5}}{2}}$

$= \dfrac{\sqrt{2}}{\sqrt{10}} \cdot \dfrac{\sqrt{10}}{\sqrt{10}}$ $= \dfrac{\sqrt{8}}{\sqrt{10}} \cdot \dfrac{\sqrt{10}}{\sqrt{10}}$

$= \dfrac{\sqrt{20}}{10}$ $= \dfrac{\sqrt{80}}{10}$

$= \dfrac{2\sqrt{5}}{10}$ $= \dfrac{4\sqrt{5}}{10}$

$= \dfrac{\sqrt{5}}{5}$ $= \dfrac{2\sqrt{5}}{5}$

13. $\left(\frac{4}{5}\right)^2 + \cos^2 x = 1$

$\qquad \cos^2 x = 1 - \frac{16}{25}$

$\qquad \cos^2 x = \frac{9}{25}$

$\qquad \cos x = -\sqrt{\frac{9}{25}}$

$\qquad \cos x = -\frac{3}{5}$

$\sin 2x = 2 \cdot \frac{4}{5} \cdot \left(-\frac{3}{5}\right) \qquad \cos 2x = 1 - 2 \cdot \left(\frac{4}{5}\right)^2$

$\qquad = -\frac{24}{25} \qquad\qquad\qquad = 1 - \frac{32}{25}$

$\qquad\qquad\qquad\qquad\qquad\qquad = -\frac{7}{25}$

$\sin \frac{x}{2} = \sqrt{\dfrac{1 - \left[-\frac{3}{5}\right]}{2}} \qquad \cos \frac{x}{2} = \sqrt{\dfrac{1 + \left[-\frac{3}{5}\right]}{2}}$

$\qquad = \sqrt{\dfrac{\frac{8}{5}}{2}} \qquad\qquad\qquad = \sqrt{\dfrac{\frac{2}{5}}{2}}$

$\qquad = \frac{\sqrt{8}}{\sqrt{10}} \cdot \frac{\sqrt{8}}{\sqrt{10}} \qquad\qquad = \frac{\sqrt{2}}{\sqrt{10}} \cdot \frac{\sqrt{10}}{\sqrt{10}}$

$\qquad = \frac{2\sqrt{5}}{5} \qquad\qquad\qquad = \frac{\sqrt{5}}{5}$

14. $\sin^2 x + \left(-\frac{2}{3}\right)^2 = 1$

$\qquad \sin^2 x = 1 - \frac{4}{9}$

$\qquad \sin^2 x = \frac{5}{9}$

$\qquad \sin x = -\frac{\sqrt{5}}{\sqrt{9}}$

$\qquad \sin x = -\frac{\sqrt{5}}{3}$

$\sin 2x = 2 \cdot \left(-\frac{\sqrt{5}}{3}\right) \cdot \left(-\frac{2}{3}\right)$

$\qquad = \frac{4\sqrt{5}}{9}$

$\cos 2x = \left(-\frac{2}{3}\right)^2 - \left(-\frac{\sqrt{5}}{3}\right)^2$

$\qquad = \frac{4}{9} - \frac{5}{9}$

$\qquad = -\frac{1}{9}$

$\sin \frac{x}{2} = \sqrt{\dfrac{1 - \left[-\frac{2}{3}\right]}{2}} \qquad \cos \frac{x}{2} = -\sqrt{\dfrac{1 + \left[-\frac{2}{3}\right]}{2}}$

$\qquad = \sqrt{\dfrac{\frac{5}{3}}{2}} \qquad\qquad\qquad = -\sqrt{\dfrac{\frac{1}{3}}{2}}$

$\qquad = \frac{\sqrt{5}}{\sqrt{6}} \cdot \frac{\sqrt{6}}{\sqrt{6}} \qquad\qquad = -\sqrt{\frac{1}{6}}$

$\qquad = \frac{\sqrt{30}}{6} \qquad\qquad\qquad = -\frac{1}{\sqrt{6}} \cdot \frac{\sqrt{6}}{\sqrt{6}}$

$\qquad\qquad\qquad\qquad\qquad\qquad = -\frac{\sqrt{6}}{6}$

15. $\sin^2 x + \left(-\frac{1}{3}\right)^2 = 1$

$\qquad \sin^2 x = 1 - \frac{1}{9}$

$\qquad \sin^2 x = \frac{8}{9}$

$\qquad \sin x = -\sqrt{\frac{8}{9}}$

$\qquad\qquad = -\frac{2\sqrt{2}}{3}$

$\sin 2x = 2 \cdot \left(-\frac{2\sqrt{2}}{3}\right) \cdot \left(-\frac{1}{3}\right)$

$\qquad = \frac{4\sqrt{2}}{9}$

$\cos 2x = \left(-\frac{1}{3}\right)^2 - \left(-\frac{2\sqrt{2}}{3}\right)^2$

$\qquad = \frac{1}{9} - \frac{8}{9}$

$\qquad = \frac{-7}{9}$

$\sin \frac{x}{2} = \sqrt{\dfrac{1 - \left[-\frac{1}{3}\right]}{2}}$

$\qquad = \sqrt{\dfrac{\frac{4}{3}}{2}}$

$\qquad = \frac{2}{\sqrt{6}} \cdot \frac{\sqrt{6}}{\sqrt{6}}$

$\qquad = \frac{2\sqrt{6}}{6}$

$\qquad = \frac{\sqrt{6}}{3}$

$\cos \frac{x}{2} = -\sqrt{\dfrac{1 + \left[-\frac{1}{3}\right]}{2}}$

$\qquad = -\sqrt{\dfrac{\frac{2}{3}}{2}}$

$\qquad = -\frac{\sqrt{2}}{\sqrt{6}} \cdot \frac{\sqrt{6}}{\sqrt{6}}$

$\qquad = -\frac{\sqrt{12}}{6}$

$\qquad = -\frac{2\sqrt{3}}{6}$

$\qquad = -\frac{\sqrt{3}}{3}$

16. $\left(\frac{-3}{4}\right)^2 + \cos^2 x = 1$

$$\cos^2 x = 1 - \frac{9}{16}$$

$$\cos^2 x = \frac{7}{16}$$

$$\cos x = \sqrt{\frac{7}{16}}$$

$$= \frac{\sqrt{7}}{4}$$

$$\sin 2x = 2 \cdot \left(-\frac{3}{4}\right) \cdot \frac{\sqrt{7}}{4}$$

$$= -\frac{6\sqrt{7}}{16}$$

$$= -\frac{3\sqrt{7}}{8}$$

$$\cos 2x = \left(\frac{\sqrt{7}}{4}\right)^2 - \left(-\frac{3}{4}\right)^2$$

$$= \frac{7}{16} - \frac{9}{16}$$

$$= -\frac{2}{16}$$

$$= -\frac{1}{8}$$

$$\sin \frac{x}{2} = \sqrt{\frac{1 - \frac{\sqrt{7}}{4}}{2}} \qquad \cos \frac{x}{2} = \sqrt{\frac{1 + \frac{\sqrt{7}}{4}}{2}}$$

$$= \sqrt{\frac{4 - \sqrt{7}}{8}} \cdot \frac{\sqrt{8}}{\sqrt{8}} \qquad = \sqrt{\frac{4 + \sqrt{7}}{8}} \cdot \frac{\sqrt{8}}{\sqrt{8}}$$

$$= \frac{\sqrt{32 - 8\sqrt{7}}}{8} \qquad = \frac{\sqrt{32 + 8\sqrt{7}}}{8}$$

$$= \frac{2\sqrt{8 - 2\sqrt{7}}}{8} \qquad = \frac{2\sqrt{8 + 2\sqrt{7}}}{8}$$

$$= \frac{\sqrt{8 - 2\sqrt{7}}}{4} \qquad = \frac{\sqrt{8 + 2\sqrt{7}}}{4}$$

17. $\left(-\frac{3}{5}\right)^2 + \cos^2 x = 1$

$$\cos^2 x = 1 - \frac{9}{25}$$

$$\cos^2 x = \frac{16}{25}$$

$$\cos x = -\sqrt{\frac{16}{25}}$$

$$\cos x = -\frac{4}{5}$$

$$\sin 2x = 2 \cdot \left(-\frac{3}{5}\right) \cdot \left(-\frac{4}{5}\right) \qquad \cos 2x = 1 - 2 \cdot \left(-\frac{3}{5}\right)^2$$

$$= \frac{24}{25} \qquad = 1 - 2 \cdot \frac{9}{25}$$

$$= 1 - \frac{18}{25}$$

$$= \frac{7}{25}$$

$$\sin \frac{x}{2} = \sqrt{\frac{1 - \left(-\frac{4}{5}\right)}{2}} \qquad \cos \frac{x}{2} = -\sqrt{\frac{1 + \left(-\frac{4}{5}\right)}{2}}$$

$$= \sqrt{\frac{\frac{9}{5}}{2}} \qquad = -\sqrt{\frac{\frac{1}{5}}{2}}$$

$$= \sqrt{\frac{9}{10}} \cdot \frac{\sqrt{10}}{\sqrt{10}} \qquad = -\sqrt{\frac{1}{10}} \cdot \frac{\sqrt{10}}{\sqrt{10}}$$

$$= \frac{3\sqrt{10}}{10} \qquad = -\frac{\sqrt{10}}{10}$$

18. $\left(-\frac{1}{4}\right)^2 + \cos^2 x = 1$

$$\cos^2 x = 1 - \frac{1}{16}$$

$$\cos^2 x = \frac{15}{16}$$

$$\cos x = -\sqrt{\frac{15}{16}}$$

$$= -\frac{\sqrt{15}}{4}$$

$$\sin 2x = 2 \cdot \left(-\frac{1}{4}\right) \cdot \left(-\frac{\sqrt{15}}{4}\right)$$

$$= \frac{2\sqrt{15}}{16}$$

$$= \frac{\sqrt{15}}{8}$$

$$\cos 2x = 1 - 2\left(-\frac{1}{4}\right)^2$$

$$= 1 - 2 \cdot \frac{1}{16}$$

$$= \frac{7}{8}$$

$$\sin \frac{x}{2} = \sqrt{\frac{1 - \left(-\frac{\sqrt{15}}{4}\right)}{2}}$$

$$= \sqrt{\frac{4 + \sqrt{15}}{8}} \cdot \frac{\sqrt{8}}{\sqrt{8}}$$

$$= \frac{\sqrt{32 + 8\sqrt{15}}}{8}$$

$$= \frac{2\sqrt{8 + 2\sqrt{15}}}{8}$$

$$= \frac{\sqrt{8 + 2\sqrt{15}}}{4}$$

$$\cos \frac{x}{2} = \sqrt{\frac{1 + \left(-\frac{\sqrt{15}}{4}\right)}{2}}$$

$$= \sqrt{\frac{4 - \sqrt{15}}{8}} \cdot \frac{\sqrt{8}}{\sqrt{8}}$$

$$= \sqrt{\frac{32 - 8\sqrt{15}}{8}}$$

$$= \frac{2\sqrt{8 - 2\sqrt{15}}}{8}$$

$$= \frac{\sqrt{8 - 2\sqrt{15}}}{4}$$

19. $\sin^2 x + \left(-\frac{1}{3}\right)^2 = 1$

$\sin^2 x = 1 - \frac{1}{9}$

$\sin^2 x = \frac{8}{9}$

$\sin x = \sqrt{\frac{8}{9}}$

$\quad = \frac{2\sqrt{2}}{3}$

$\sin 2x = 2 \cdot \frac{2\sqrt{2}}{3} \cdot \left(-\frac{1}{3}\right) \qquad \cos 2x = 2 \cdot \left(-\frac{1}{3}\right)^2 - 1$

$\quad\quad = -\frac{4\sqrt{2}}{9} \qquad\qquad\qquad\quad = \frac{2}{9} - 1$

$\qquad\qquad\qquad\qquad\qquad\qquad\qquad = -\frac{7}{9}$

$\sin \frac{x}{2} = \sqrt{\frac{1 - \left(-\frac{1}{3}\right)}{2}} \qquad \cos \frac{x}{2} = \sqrt{\frac{1 + \left(-\frac{1}{3}\right)}{2}}$

$\quad = \sqrt{\frac{\frac{4}{3}}{2}} \qquad\qquad\qquad = \sqrt{\frac{\frac{2}{3}}{2}}$

$\quad = \frac{\sqrt{4}}{\sqrt{6}} \cdot \frac{\sqrt{6}}{\sqrt{6}} \qquad\qquad = \frac{\sqrt{2}}{\sqrt{6}} \cdot \frac{\sqrt{6}}{\sqrt{6}}$

$\quad = \frac{2\sqrt{6}}{6} \qquad\qquad\qquad = \frac{2\sqrt{3}}{6}$

$\quad = \frac{\sqrt{6}}{3} \qquad\qquad\qquad = \frac{\sqrt{3}}{3}$

20. $\sin 105° = \sin \frac{210°}{2}$

$\quad = \pm\sqrt{\frac{1 - \cos 210°}{2}}$

$\quad = \pm\sqrt{\frac{1 - \left(-\frac{\sqrt{3}}{2}\right)}{2}}$

$\quad = \pm\sqrt{\frac{\frac{2 + \sqrt{3}}{2}}{2}}$

$\quad = \frac{\sqrt{2 + \sqrt{3}}}{2}$

21. $\cos \frac{\pi}{8} = \cos 22.5° = \cos \frac{45°}{2}$

$\quad = \pm\sqrt{\frac{1 + \cos 45°}{2}}$

$\quad = \pm\sqrt{\frac{1 + \frac{\sqrt{2}}{2}}{2}}$

$\quad = \pm\sqrt{\frac{\frac{2 + \sqrt{2}}{2}}{2}}$

$\quad = \frac{\sqrt{2 + \sqrt{2}}}{2}$

22. $\sin 22\frac{1}{2}° = \sin \frac{45°}{2}$

$\quad = \pm\sqrt{\frac{1 - \cos 45°}{2}}$

$\quad = \pm\sqrt{\frac{1 - \frac{\sqrt{2}}{2}}{2}}$

$\quad = \frac{\sqrt{2 - \sqrt{2}}}{2}$

23. $\sin 195° = \sin \frac{390°}{2}$

$\quad = \pm\sqrt{\frac{1 - \cos 390°}{2}}$

$\quad = \pm\sqrt{\frac{1 - \frac{\sqrt{3}}{2}}{2}}$

$\quad = \frac{\sqrt{2 - \sqrt{3}}}{2}$

24. $\cos \frac{19\pi}{12} = \cos 285° = \cos \frac{570°}{2}$

$\quad = \pm\sqrt{\frac{1 + \cos 570°}{2}}$

$\quad = \pm\sqrt{\frac{1 + \left(-\frac{\sqrt{3}}{2}\right)}{2}}$

$\quad = \frac{\sqrt{2 - \sqrt{3}}}{2}$

25. $\sin \frac{7\pi}{8} = \sin 157.5° = \sin \frac{315°}{2}$

$\quad = \pm\sqrt{\frac{1 - \cos 315°}{2}}$

$\quad = \pm\sqrt{\frac{1 - \frac{\sqrt{2}}{2}}{2}}$

$\quad = \frac{\sqrt{2 - \sqrt{2}}}{2}$

26.

$(\sin x + \cos x)^2 \overset{?}{=} 1 + \sin 2x$

$\sin^2 x + 2 \sin x \cos x + \cos^2 x \overset{?}{=} 1 + \sin 2x$

$\sin^2 x + \cos^2 x + 2 \sin x \cos x \overset{?}{=} 1 + \sin 2x$

$1 + 2 \sin x \cos x \overset{?}{=} 1 + \sin 2x$

$1 + \sin 2x = 1 + \sin 2x$

27. $\cos^2 2x + 4 \sin^2 x \cos^2 x \overset{?}{=} 1$

$\cos^2 2x + \sin^2 2x \overset{?}{=} 1$

$1 = 1$

28. $\sin 2x \overset{?}{=} 2 \cot x \sin^2 x$

$2 \sin x \cos x \overset{?}{=} 2 \frac{\cos x}{\sin x} \cdot \sin^2 x$

$2 \sin x \cos x = 2 \sin x \cos x$

29. $\sin^2 \theta \overset{?}{=} \frac{1}{2}(1 - \cos 2\theta)$

$\sin^2 \theta \overset{?}{=} \frac{1}{2}[1 - (1 - 2\sin^2 \theta)]$

$\sin^2 \theta \overset{?}{=} \frac{1}{2}(2\sin^2 \theta)$

$\sin^2 \theta = \sin^2 \theta$

30. $\dfrac{1}{\sin x \cos x} - \dfrac{\cos x}{\sin x} \overset{?}{=} \tan x$

$\dfrac{1 - \cos^2 x}{\sin x \cos x} \overset{?}{=} \tan x$

$\dfrac{\sin^2 x}{\sin x \cos x} \overset{?}{=} \tan x$

$\tan x = \tan x$

31. $\sin^4 x - \cos^4 x \overset{?}{=} 2\sin^2 x - 1$

$(\sin^2 x - \cos^2 x)(\sin^2 x + \cos^2 x) \overset{?}{=} 2\sin^2 x - 1$

$(\sin^2 x - \cos^2 x) \cdot 1 \overset{?}{=} 2\sin^2 x - 1$

$[\sin^2 x - (1 - \sin^2 x)] \cdot 1 \overset{?}{=} 2\sin^2 x - 1$

$\sin^2 x - 1 + \sin^2 x \overset{?}{=} 2\sin^2 x - 1$

$2\sin^2 x - 1 = 2\sin^2 x - 1$

32. $\tan^2 \dfrac{x}{2} \overset{?}{=} \dfrac{1 - \cos x}{1 + \cos x}$

$\dfrac{\sin^2 \frac{x}{2}}{\cos^2 \frac{x}{2}} \overset{?}{=} \dfrac{1 - \cos x}{1 + \cos x}$

$\dfrac{\left(\pm\sqrt{\dfrac{1 - \cos x}{2}}\right)^2}{\left(\pm\sqrt{\dfrac{1 + \cos x}{2}}\right)^2} \overset{?}{=} \dfrac{1 - \cos x}{1 + \cos x}$

$\dfrac{1 - \cos x}{1 + \cos x} = \dfrac{1 - \cos x}{1 + \cos x}$

33. $2\cos^2 \dfrac{x}{2} \overset{?}{=} 1 + \cos x$

$2\left(\pm\sqrt{\dfrac{1 + \cos x}{2}}\right)^2 \overset{?}{=} 1 + \cos x$

$2\left(\dfrac{1 + \cos x}{2}\right) \overset{?}{=} 1 + \cos x$

$1 + \cos x = 1 + \cos x$

34. Use the half-angle formula to first find $\sin 2x$ and then to find $\sin x$.

$\left(\dfrac{2}{3}\right)^2 + \cos^2 4x = 1$

$\cos^2 4x = 1 - \dfrac{4}{9}$

$\cos^2 4x = \dfrac{5}{9}$

$\cos 4x = \dfrac{-\sqrt{5}}{3}$

$\sin 2x = \sin \dfrac{4x}{2} = \sqrt{\dfrac{1 - \left(-\dfrac{\sqrt{5}}{3}\right)}{2}}$

$= \sqrt{\dfrac{3 + \sqrt{5}}{6}} \cdot \dfrac{\sqrt{6}}{\sqrt{6}}$

$= \dfrac{\sqrt{18 + 6\sqrt{5}}}{6}$

$\left(\dfrac{\sqrt{18 + 6\sqrt{5}}}{6}\right)^2 + \cos^2 2x = 1$

$\cos^2 2x = 1 - \dfrac{18 + 6\sqrt{5}}{36}$

$\cos^2 2x = \dfrac{18 - 6\sqrt{5}}{36}$

$\cos 2x = \dfrac{\sqrt{18 - 6\sqrt{5}}}{6}$

$\sin x = \sin \dfrac{2x}{2} = \sqrt{\dfrac{1 - \dfrac{\sqrt{18 - 6\sqrt{5}}}{6}}{2}}$

$= \sqrt{\dfrac{\dfrac{6 - \sqrt{18 - 6\sqrt{5}}}{6}}{2}}$

$= \sqrt{\dfrac{6 - \sqrt{18 - 6\sqrt{5}}}{12} \cdot \dfrac{\sqrt{12}}{\sqrt{12}}}$

$= \dfrac{\sqrt{72 - 12\sqrt{18 - 6\sqrt{5}}}}{12}$

$= \dfrac{2\sqrt{18 - 3\sqrt{18 - 6\sqrt{5}}}}{12}$

$= \dfrac{\sqrt{18 - 3\sqrt{18 - 6\sqrt{5}}}}{6}$

35. **a.** $\sin 60° = \dfrac{\sqrt{3}}{2}$, $\cos 60° = \dfrac{1}{2}$

$\sin 2\theta = \sin 2 \cdot 60° = 2 \cdot \dfrac{\sqrt{3}}{2} \cdot \dfrac{1}{2}$

$= \dfrac{\sqrt{3}}{2}$

$d = \dfrac{100^2}{32} \cdot \dfrac{\sqrt{3}}{2}$

≈ 270.6 feet

b. $\sin 30° = \dfrac{1}{2}$, $\cos 30° = \dfrac{\sqrt{3}}{2}$

$\sin 2 \cdot 30° = 2 \cdot \dfrac{1}{2} \cdot \dfrac{\sqrt{3}}{2}$

$= \dfrac{\sqrt{3}}{2}$

$d = \dfrac{100^2}{32} \cdot \dfrac{\sqrt{3}}{2}$

≈ 270.6 feet

c. $45°$; The greatest value of the sine function is 1 and $\sin 2\theta = 1$ when $\theta = 45°$.

36. $90°$

37.
```
Stem | Leaf
 4   |
  •  | 6 6
 5   | 2
  •  | 5 5 5 8 8 9 9
 6   | 0 0 0 2
  •  | 5 5 9 9
 7   | 0 0
  •  | 6 8
```
6 | 0 represents $60.

38. $26 = 6 + (6 - 1)d$

$26 = 6 + 5d$

$5d = 20$

$d = 4$

10, 14, 18, 22

39. $9^{\log_9 5} = 5$

40. $y = \dfrac{10}{x}$

$xy = 10$ inverse; 10

Graphing Calculator Exploration: Solving Trigonometric Equations

PAGE 821   EXERCISES

1. $0, 180°$

2. $0, 120°, 240°$

3. $-360°, -300°, -180°, -60°, 0°, 60°, 180°, 300°$

4. $-333.5°, -290.8°, -270°, -249.2°, -200.8°, -90°,$
   $16.5°, 69.2°, 90°, 110.8°, 163.5°, 270°$

5. $30°, 150°, 270°$

6. $-342.8°, -197.2°, 17.2°, 162.8°$

7. $-244.8°, -115.2°, 115.2°, 244.8°$

8. $281.3°, 308.7°$

17-7   Solving Trigonometric Equations

PAGE 825   CHECKING FOR UNDERSTANDING

1. infinitely many

2. $4; 30°, 150°, 210°, 330°$

3. none   **4.** $2; 30°, 150°$

5. $2; 150°, 210°$ **6.** $2; 45°, 225°$

7. $2; 0°, 180°$ **8.** 0

9. $2;$ about $108°26'$, about $288°26'$

10. $4; 15°, 75°, 195°, 255°$

11. 0

12. $8; 22°30', 67°30', 112°30', 157°30', 202°30',$
    $247°30', 292°30', 337°30'$

13. 0

14. $4; 120°, 150°, 300°, 330°$

15. $8; 0°, 45°, 90°, 135°, 180°, 225°, 270°, 315°$

PAGES 826-827   EXERCISES

16. $2 \sin^2 x - 1 = 0$

$\sin^2 x = \dfrac{1}{2}$

$\sin x = \pm \dfrac{\sqrt{2}}{2}$

$x = 45°, 135°, 225°, 315°$

17. $4 \cos^2 x = 1$

$\cos^2 x = \dfrac{1}{4}$

$\cos x = \pm \dfrac{1}{2}$

$x = 60°, 120°, 240°, 300°$

18. $2 \cos^2 x = \sin x + 1$

$2(1 - \sin^2 x) - \sin x - 1 = 0$

$2 - 2 \sin^2 x - \sin x - 1 = 0$

$2 \sin^2 x - \sin x - 1 = 0$

$(2 \sin x - 1)(\sin x + 1) = 0$

$\sin x = \dfrac{1}{2}$ or $\sin x = -1$

$x = 30°, 150°, 270°$

19. $\sin 2x = 2 \cos x$

$2 \sin x \cos x - 2 \cos x = 0$

$2 \cos x (\sin x - 1) = 0$

$\cos x = 0$ or $\sin x = 1$

$x = 90°, 270°$

20. $\sin 2x = \cos x$

$2 \sin x \cos x - \cos x = 0$

$\cos x (2 \sin x - 1) = 0$

$\cos x = 0$ or $\sin x = \dfrac{1}{2}$

$x = 90°, 270°, 30°, 150°$

21. $4 \sin^2 x - 4 \sin x + 1 = 0$

$(2 \sin x - 1)^2 = 0$

$\sin x = \dfrac{1}{2}$

$x = 30°, 150°$

22. $2 \cos \theta - 1 = 0$

$2 \cos \theta = 1$

$\cos \theta = \dfrac{1}{2}$

$\theta = \dfrac{\pi}{3}, \dfrac{5\pi}{3}$

23. $2 \sin \theta = -1$

$\sin \theta = -\dfrac{1}{2}$

$\theta = \dfrac{7\pi}{6}, \dfrac{11\pi}{6}$

24. $4 \sin^2 \theta = 1$

$\sin^2 \theta = \frac{1}{4}$

$\sin \theta = \pm \frac{1}{2}$

$\theta = \frac{\pi}{6}, \frac{5\pi}{6}, \frac{7\pi}{6}, \frac{11\pi}{6}$

25. $2 \sin \theta = -\sqrt{3}$

$\sin \theta = -\frac{\sqrt{3}}{2}$

$\theta = \frac{4\pi}{3}, \frac{5\pi}{3}$

26. $2 \sin^2 \theta = -\sin \theta$

$2 \sin^2 \theta + \sin \theta = 0$

$\sin \theta (2 \sin \theta + 1) = 0$

$\sin \theta = 0$ or $\sin \theta = -\frac{1}{2}$

$\theta = 0, \pi, \frac{7\pi}{6}, \frac{11\pi}{6}$

27. $2 \sin^2 \theta - \sin \theta = 1$

$2 \sin^2 \theta - \sin \theta - 1 = 0$

$(2 \sin \theta + 1)(\sin \theta - 1) = 0$

$\sin \theta = \frac{-1}{2}$ or $\sin \theta = 1$

$\theta = \frac{7\pi}{6}, \frac{11\pi}{6}, \frac{\pi}{2}$

28. $\sin^2 x - 2 \sin x - 3 = 0$

$(\sin x - 3)(\sin x + 1) = 0$

$\sin x = 3$ or $\sin x = -1$

The equation $\sin x = 3$ does not have any solutions.

Thus, $x = 270° + n \cdot 360°$.

29. $\sin x = \cos x$

$\frac{\sin x}{\cos x} = 1$

$\tan x = 1$

$x = 45° + n \cdot 180°$

30. $\tan x = \sin x$

$\frac{\tan x}{\sin x} = 1$

$\frac{\sin x}{\cos x} \cdot \frac{1}{\sin x} = 1$

$\sec x = 1$

$x = 0° + n \cdot 180°$

31. $\cos 2x = \cos x$

$(2 \cos^2 x - 1) - \cos x = 0$

$2 \cos^2 x - \cos x - 1 = 0$

$(2 \cos x + 1)(\cos x - 1) = 0$

$\cos x = -\frac{1}{2}$ or $\cos x = 1$

$x = 0° + n \cdot 120°$

32. $3 \cos 2x - 5 \cos x = 1$

$3(2 \cos^2 x - 1) - 5 \cos x = 1$

$6 \cos^2 x - 5 \cos x - 4 = 0$

$(3 \cos x - 4)(2 \cos x + 1) = 0$

$\cos x = \frac{4}{3}$ or $\cos x = -\frac{1}{2}$

The equation $\cos x = \frac{4}{3}$ does not have any solutions.

Thus, $x = 120° + n \cdot 360°$ or $x = 240° + n \cdot 360°$.

33. $\sin x = 1 + \cos x$

$\sin^2 x = 1 + 2 \cos x + \cos^2 x$

$1 - \cos^2 x = 1 + 2 \cos x + \cos^2 x$

$2 \cos^2 x + 2 \cos x = 0$

$2 \cos x (\cos x + 1) = 0$

$2 \cos x = 0$ or $\cos x = -1$

$x = 90° + n \cdot 360°$ or $x = 180° + n \cdot 360°$

34. $\tan^2 x - \sqrt{3} \tan x = 0$

$\tan x (\tan x - \sqrt{3}) = 0$

$\tan x = 0$ or $\tan x = \sqrt{3}$

$x = 0° + n \cdot 180°$ or $x = 60° + n \cdot 180°$

35. $\cos 2x + \cos x + 1 = 0$

$(2 \cos^2 x - 1) + \cos x + 1 = 0$

$2 \cos^2 x + \cos x = 0$

$\cos x(2 \cos x + 1) = 0$

$\cos x = 0$ or $\cos x = -\frac{1}{2}$

$x = 90° + n \cdot 180°$ or $x = 120° + n \cdot 360°$

or $x = 240° + n \cdot 360°$

36. $\cos x \tan x - \sin^2 x = 0$

$\cos x \cdot \frac{\sin x}{\cos x} - \sin^2 x = 0$

$\sin x - \sin^2 x = 0$

$\sin x (1 - \sin x) = 0$

$\sin x = 0$ or $\sin x = 1$

$x = 0° + n \cdot 180°$ or $x = 90° + n \cdot 360°$

37. $\sin^2 x - \sin x = 0$

$\sin x (\sin x - 1) = 0$

$\sin x = 0$ or $\sin x = 1$

$x = 0° + n \cdot 180°$ or $x = 90° + n \cdot 360°$

38. $\cos 2\theta + 3 \cos \theta - 1 = 0$

$2 \cos^2 \theta - 1 + 3 \cos \theta - 1 = 0$

$2 \cos^2 \theta + 3 \cos \theta - 2 = 0$

$(2 \cos \theta - 1)(\cos \theta + 2) = 0$

$\cos \theta = \frac{1}{2}$ or $\cos \theta = -2$

The equation $\cos \theta = -2$ does not have any solutions.

Thus $\theta = \frac{\pi}{3} + 2n\pi$ or $\theta = \frac{5\pi}{3} + 2n\pi$.

39. $2 \sin^2 \theta - 3 \sin \theta - 2 = 0$

$(2 \sin \theta + 1)(\sin \theta - 2) = 0$

$\sin \theta = -\frac{1}{2}$ or $\sin \theta = 2$

The equation $\sin \theta = 2$ does not have any solutions.

Thus, $\theta = \frac{7\pi}{6} + 2n\pi$ or $\theta = \frac{11\pi}{6} + 2n\pi$.

40. $2 \sin^2 \theta - \cos \theta - 1 = 0$

$-\cos \theta = 1 - 2 \sin^2 \theta$

$-\cos \theta = 2 \cos^2 \theta - 1$

$2 \cos^2 \theta + \cos \theta - 1 = 0$

$(2 \cos \theta - 1)(\cos \theta + 1) = 0$

$\cos \theta = \frac{1}{2}$ or $\cos \theta = -1$

$\theta = \frac{\pi}{3} + 2n\pi$ or $\theta = \frac{5\pi}{3} + 2n\pi$ or $\theta = \pi + 2n\pi$

41. $3 \sin^2 \theta - \cos^2 \theta = 0$

$3 \sin^2 \theta - (1 - \sin^2 \theta) = 0$

$3 \sin^2 \theta + \sin^2 \theta - 1 = 0$

$4 \sin^2 \theta = 1$

$\sin^2 \theta = \frac{1}{4}$

$\sin \theta = \pm \frac{1}{2}$

$\theta = \frac{\pi}{6} + n \cdot \pi$ or $\theta = \frac{5\pi}{6} + n \cdot \pi$

42. $\cos^2 \theta - \frac{7}{2} \cos \theta - 2 = 0$

$2 \cos^2 \theta - 7 \cos \theta - 4 = 0$

$(2 \cos \theta + 1)(\cos \theta - 4) = 0$

$\cos \theta = -\frac{1}{2}$ or $\cos \theta = 4$

The equation $\cos \theta = 4$ does not have any solutions.

Thus $\theta = \frac{2\pi}{3} + 2n\pi$ or $\theta = \frac{4\pi}{3} + 2n\pi$.

43. $\cos^2 \theta - \frac{5}{2} \cos \theta - \frac{3}{2} = 0$

$2 \cos^2 \theta - 5 \cos \theta - 3 = 0$

$(2 \cos \theta + 1)(\cos \theta - 3) = 0$

$\cos \theta = -\frac{1}{2}$ or $\cos \theta = 3$

The equation $\cos \theta = 3$ does not have any solutions.

Thus $\theta = \frac{2\pi}{3} + 2n\pi$ or $\theta = \frac{4\pi}{3} + 2n\pi$

44. $2 \cos^2 \theta + 3 \sin \theta - 3 = 0$

$(2 \cos^2 \theta - 1) + 3 \sin \theta - 2 = 0$

$1 - \sin^2 \theta + 3 \sin \theta - 2 = 0$

$-2 \sin^2 \theta + 3 \sin \theta - 1 = 0$

$2 \sin^2 \theta - 3 \sin \theta + 1 = 0$

$(2 \sin \theta - 1)(\sin \theta - 1) = 0$

$\sin \theta = \frac{1}{2}$ or $\sin \theta = 1$

$\theta = \frac{\pi}{6} + 2n\pi$ or $\theta = \frac{5\pi}{6} + 2n\pi$ or $\theta = \frac{\pi}{2} + 2n\pi$

45. $4 \cos^2 \theta - 4 \cos \theta + 1 = 0$

$(2 \cos \theta - 1)^2 = 0$

$2 \cos \theta = 1$

$\cos \theta = \frac{1}{2}$

$\theta = \frac{\pi}{3} + 2n\pi$ or $\theta = \frac{5\pi}{3} + 2n\pi$

46. $\cos \theta = 3 \cos \theta - 2$

$-2 \cos \theta = -2$

$\cos \theta = 1$

$\theta = 0 + 2n\pi$

47. $\cos 2\theta = 1 - \sin \theta$

$1 - 2 \sin^2 \theta = 1 - \sin \theta$

$1 - 2 \sin^2 \theta - 1 + \sin \theta = 0$

$-2 \sin^2 \theta + \sin \theta = 0$

$\sin \theta (-2 \sin \theta + 1) = 0$

$\sin \theta = 0$ or $\sin \theta = \frac{1}{2}$

$\theta = 0 + n \cdot \pi$ or $\theta = \frac{\pi}{6} + 2n\pi$ or $\theta = \frac{5\pi}{6} + 2n\pi$

48. $(\tan x - \sin x)(\sec x + 1)$

$= (\tan x + \sin x)(\sec x - 1)$

$\tan x \sec x + \tan x - \sin x \sec x - \sin x$

$= \tan x \sec x - \tan x + \sin x \sec x - \sin x$

$1 = 1$

all reals except $0 + \frac{n\pi}{2}$, where n is any integer.

49. a. $y = 2 \sin\left(2\pi - \dfrac{\pi}{2}\right)$

$\qquad = 2 \sin\left(\dfrac{3\pi}{2}\right)$

$\qquad = 2 \cdot -1$

$\qquad = -2$ ft from equilibrium point

b. $0 = 2 \sin\left(\pi t - \dfrac{\pi}{2}\right)$

$\qquad t = \dfrac{1}{2}$

$\qquad 0.5 + n$ seconds, where n is any integer

c. 2 seconds

50. $n = \dfrac{\sin 60^\circ}{\sin 30^\circ}$

$\qquad = \dfrac{\frac{\sqrt{3}}{2}}{\frac{1}{2}}$

$\qquad = \sqrt{3}$

$\qquad \approx 1.732$

51. a. 60°

b. $90^\circ, 270^\circ$

c. no solution

d. $-360^\circ, -225^\circ, -180^\circ, -45^\circ, 0$

e. $0^\circ, 30^\circ, 150^\circ, 180^\circ, 360^\circ, 390^\circ, 510^\circ, 540^\circ,$
$\qquad 720^\circ$

52. $\cos 300^\circ = \dfrac{1}{2}$

53. $\dfrac{5}{12} \cdot \dfrac{5}{12} = \dfrac{25}{144} \approx 0.174$

54. median: 6.5

mode: 0

mean: 7.4

55. $S_n = \dfrac{n}{2}\left(a_1 + a_n\right)$

$\qquad = \dfrac{19}{2}(5 + 95)$

$\qquad = 950$

56. $\log_3 27 + \log_3 3 \overset{?}{=} \log_3 81$

$\qquad\qquad 3 + 1 \overset{?}{=} 4$

$\qquad\qquad\qquad 4 = 4$

57. $x = 0$

Technology: Trigonometric Equations

1. 60° **2.** 22.5°

3. 63.4349° **4.** $0^\circ, 20.9052^\circ$

5. 16.6015° **6.** $-54.7356^\circ, 54.7356^\circ$

17-8	**Trigonometric Notation for Complex Numbers**

1. $r = \sqrt{a^2 + b^2}$; $\theta = \text{Arctan } \dfrac{b}{a}$ if $a > 0$ and

$\qquad \theta = \text{Arctan } \dfrac{b}{a} + \pi$ if $a < 0$.

2. $x = 1, y = -1$

$r = \sqrt{x^2 + y^2}$ $\theta = \text{Arctan } \dfrac{y}{x}$

$r = \sqrt{1^2 + (-1)^2}$ $= \text{Arctan } (-1)$

$r = \sqrt{2}$ $= \dfrac{7\pi}{4}$

$1 - i = \sqrt{2}\left(\cos \dfrac{7\pi}{4} + i \sin \dfrac{7\pi}{4}\right)$

3. $12\left[\cos\left(\dfrac{\pi}{6} + \dfrac{2\pi}{3}\right) + i \sin\left(\dfrac{\pi}{6} + \dfrac{2\pi}{3}\right)\right]$

$\qquad = 12\left(\cos \dfrac{5\pi}{6} + i \sin \dfrac{5\pi}{6}\right)$

4. $x = 1, y = -1$

$r = \sqrt{x^2 + y^2}$ $\theta = \text{Arctan } \dfrac{y}{x}$

$\qquad = \sqrt{1^2 + (-1)^2}$ $= \text{Arctan } (-1)$

$\qquad = \sqrt{2}$ $= -\dfrac{\pi}{4}$

$1 - i = \sqrt{2}\left(\cos\left(-\dfrac{\pi}{4}\right) + i \sin\left(-\dfrac{\pi}{4}\right)\right)$

5. $x = 0, y = 7$

$r = \sqrt{0 + 7^2}$ $\theta = \text{Arctan } \dfrac{y}{x}$

$\qquad = 7$ $= \text{Arctan } \dfrac{7}{0}$

$\qquad\qquad\qquad\qquad\qquad\quad = \dfrac{\pi}{2}$

$7i = 7\left(\cos \dfrac{\pi}{2} + i \sin \dfrac{\pi}{2}\right)$

6. $x = -2, y = 2$

$r = \sqrt{2^2 + (-2)^2}$ $\theta = \text{Arctan } \dfrac{2}{-2} + \pi$

$\qquad = \sqrt{8}$ $= \text{Arctan } (-1) + \pi$

$\qquad = 2\sqrt{2}$ $= -\dfrac{\pi}{4} + \pi = \dfrac{3\pi}{4}$

$-2 + 2i = 2\sqrt{2}\left(\cos \dfrac{3\pi}{4} + i \sin \dfrac{3\pi}{4}\right)$

7. $r = 2$

$x = r \cos \theta, \ y = r \sin \theta$

$\quad = 2 \cdot 1 \qquad = 0$

$\quad = 2$

2

8. $r = 3$

$x = 3 \cos \pi, \ y = 3 \sin \pi$

$\quad = 3(-1) \qquad = 3 \cdot 0$

$\quad = -3 \qquad\quad = 0$

-3

9. $r = 1$

$x = 1 \cdot \cos \frac{\pi}{2}, \quad y = 1 \cdot \sin \frac{\pi}{2}$

$\quad = 0 \qquad\qquad = 1$

i

10. $4\left(\cos \frac{\pi}{3} + i \sin \frac{\pi}{3}\right)$

11. $3\left(\cos \frac{5\pi}{4} + i \sin \frac{5\pi}{4}\right)$

12. $\sqrt{2}\left(\cos \left(-\frac{\pi}{6}\right) + i \sin \left(-\frac{\pi}{6}\right)\right)$

PAGES 832-833   EXERCISES

13. $x = 1, \; y = 1$

$r = \sqrt{1^2 + 1^2} \qquad\qquad \theta = \text{Arctan } 1$

$\quad = \sqrt{2} \qquad\qquad\qquad\quad = \frac{\pi}{4}$

$1 + i = \sqrt{2}\left(\cos \frac{\pi}{4} + i \sin \frac{\pi}{4}\right)$

14. $x = -3, \; y = -3$

$r = \sqrt{(-3)^2 + (-3)^2} \qquad \theta = \text{Arctan } 1 + \pi$

$\quad = \sqrt{18} \qquad\qquad\qquad\quad = \frac{\pi}{4} + \pi$

$\quad = 3\sqrt{2} \qquad\qquad\qquad\quad = \frac{5\pi}{4}$

$-3 - 3i = 3\sqrt{2}\left(\cos \frac{5\pi}{4} + i \sin \frac{5\pi}{4}\right)$

15. $x = 0, \; y = 3$

$r = \sqrt{0^2 + 3^2} \qquad\qquad \theta = \text{Arctan } \frac{3}{0}$

$\quad = 3 \qquad\qquad\qquad\qquad = \frac{\pi}{2}$

$3i = 3\left(\cos \frac{\pi}{2} + i \sin \frac{\pi}{2}\right)$

16. $x = -5, \; y = -1$

$r = \sqrt{(-5)^2 + (-1)^2} \qquad \theta = \text{Arctan } \frac{1}{5} + \pi$

$\quad = \sqrt{26} \qquad\qquad\qquad\quad = 3.34$

$-5 - i = \sqrt{26}(\cos 3.34 + i \sin 3.34)$

17. $x = -2, \; y = 5$

$r = \sqrt{(-2)^2 + 5^2} \qquad \theta = \text{Arctan } -\frac{5}{2} + \pi$

$\quad = \sqrt{29} \qquad\qquad\qquad\quad = 1.95$

$-2 + 5i = \sqrt{29}(\cos 1.95 + i \sin 1.95)$

18. $x = 2\sqrt{3}, \; y = -3$

$r = \sqrt{(2\sqrt{3})^2 + (-3)^2} \qquad \theta = \text{Arctan } \frac{-3}{2\sqrt{3}}$

$\quad = \sqrt{21} \qquad\qquad\qquad\quad = -0.71$

$2\sqrt{3} - 3i = \sqrt{21}(\cos (-0.71) + i \sin (-0.71))$

19. $r = \sqrt{2}$

$x = \sqrt{2} \cos \frac{5\pi}{4} = -1$

$y = \sqrt{2} \sin \frac{5\pi}{4} = -1$

$-1 - i$

20. $r = 6$

$x = 6 \cos \frac{3\pi}{2} = 0$

$y = 6 \sin \frac{3\pi}{2} = -6$

$-6i$

21. $r = 12$

$x = 12 \cos \frac{5\pi}{3} = 6$

$y = 12 \sin \frac{5\pi}{3} = -6\sqrt{3}$

$6 - 6\sqrt{3}i$

22. $r = 2$

$x = 2 \cos 3 = -1.98$

$y = 2 \sin 3 = 0.28$

$-1.98 + 0.28i$

23. $8 \cdot 2\left[\cos \left(\frac{3\pi}{4} + \frac{5\pi}{4}\right) + i \sin \left(\frac{3\pi}{4} + \frac{5\pi}{4}\right)\right]$

$\quad = 16(\cos 2\pi + i \sin 2\pi)$

$r = 16$

$x = 16 \cos 2\pi = 1$

$y = 16 \sin 2\pi = 0$

16

24. $3 \cdot 6\left[\cos \left(\frac{7\pi}{6} + \frac{\pi}{6}\right) + i \sin \left(\frac{7\pi}{6} + \frac{\pi}{6}\right)\right]$

$\quad = 18\left(\cos \frac{4\pi}{3} + i \sin \frac{4\pi}{3}\right)$

$r = 18$

$x = 18 \cos \frac{4\pi}{3} = -9$

$y = 18 \sin \frac{4\pi}{3} = \frac{-\sqrt{3}}{2} \cdot 18 = -9\sqrt{3}$

$-9 - 9i\sqrt{3}$

25. $5 \cdot 2\left[\cos \left(\frac{3\pi}{4} + \frac{2\pi}{3}\right) + i \sin \left(\frac{3\pi}{4} + \frac{2\pi}{3}\right)\right]$

$\quad = 10\left(\cos \frac{17\pi}{12} + i \sin \frac{17\pi}{12}\right)$

$r = 10$

$x = 10 \cos \frac{17\pi}{12} = -2.59$

$y = 10 \sin \frac{17\pi}{12} = -9.66$

$-2.59 - 9.66i$

26. $\frac{1}{3} \cdot 3\sqrt{3}\left[\cos \left(\frac{7\pi}{8} - \frac{\pi}{4}\right) + i \sin \left(\frac{7\pi}{8} - \frac{\pi}{4}\right)\right]$

$\quad = \sqrt{3}\left(\cos \frac{5\pi}{8} + i \sin \frac{5\pi}{8}\right)$

$r = \sqrt{3}$

$x = \sqrt{3} \cos \frac{5\pi}{8} = -0.66$

$y = \sqrt{3} \sin \frac{5\pi}{8} = 1.6$

$-0.66 + 1.6i$

27. $-1 - i - i - i^2 = -2i$

28. $-2\sqrt{3} + 2i\sqrt{3} - 2i + 2i^2 = -2 - 2\sqrt{3} + 2i\sqrt{3} - 2i$

$\qquad\qquad\qquad\qquad\qquad = -5.46 + 1.46i$

29. $2 - 2i - 2i + 2i^2 = -4i$

30. $24 + 40i - 6i - 10i^2$

$34 + 34i$

31. $3^3(\cos 3\pi + i \sin 3\pi)$

$= 27(\cos 3\pi + i \sin 3\pi)$

$r = 27$

$x = 27 \cos 3\pi = -27$

$y = 27 \sin 3\pi = 0$

-27

32. $2^5\left(\cos \frac{5\pi}{2} + i \sin \frac{5\pi}{2}\right)$

$= 32\left(\cos \frac{5\pi}{2} + i \sin \frac{5\pi}{2}\right)$

$r = 32$

$x = 32 \cos \frac{5\pi}{2} = 0$

$y = 32 \sin \frac{5\pi}{2} = 32$

$32i$

33. $2^5\left(\cos \frac{5\pi}{4} + i \sin \frac{5\pi}{4}\right)$

$= 32\left(\cos \frac{5\pi}{4} + i \sin \frac{5\pi}{4}\right)$

$r = 32$

$x = 32 \cos \frac{5\pi}{4} = -16\sqrt{2}$

$y = 32 \sin \frac{5\pi}{4} = -16\sqrt{2}$

$-16\sqrt{2} - 16i\sqrt{2}$

34. $\cos \frac{7\pi}{2} + i \sin \frac{7\pi}{2}$

$r = 1$

$x = \cos \frac{7\pi}{2} = 0$

$y = \sin \frac{7\pi}{2} = -1$

$-i$

35. $(-3)^3 + 3(-3)^2(3i) + 3(-3)(3i)^2 + (3i)^3$

$-27 + 3(9)(3i) + (-9)(-9) - 27i$

$-27 + 81i + 81 - 27i$

$54 + 54i$

36. $3^4 + 4(3^3)(4i) + 6(3^2)(4i)^2 + 4 \cdot 3(4i)^3 + (4i)^4$

$= 81 + 432i - 864 - 768i + 256$

$= -527 - 336i$

37. $x = 0, \ y = 1$

$r = \sqrt{0^2 + 1^2}$ $\theta = \text{Arctan } \frac{1}{0}$

$\quad = 1$ $= \frac{\pi}{2}$

$\left(\cos \frac{\pi}{2} + i \sin \frac{\pi}{2}\right)^{\frac{1}{2}}$

$= \cos \left(\frac{1}{2} \cdot \frac{\pi}{2}\right) + i \sin \left(\frac{1}{2} \cdot \frac{\pi}{2}\right)$

$= \cos \frac{\pi}{4} + i \sin \frac{\pi}{4}$

$r = 1$

$x = \cos \frac{\pi}{4} = \frac{\sqrt{2}}{2}$

$y = \sin \frac{\pi}{4} = \frac{\sqrt{2}}{2}$

$\frac{\sqrt{2}}{2} + \frac{i\sqrt{2}}{2}$

38.

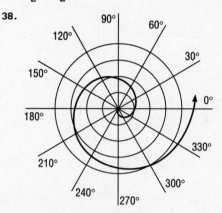

39. The needle travels slower as it approaches the center of the record.

40. $\cos 56.45° = \frac{10}{x}$

$x = \frac{10}{\cos 56.45°}$

$x \approx 18.09$ ft or 18 feet 1 in.

41. $\left(\frac{1}{2}\right)^5 = \frac{1}{32}$ 42. $3^4 = 81$

$\qquad = 0.03125$

43. median: 8

mode: 8

mean: 6.94

44. $a_1 = 15,000(1.03) = 15,450$

$r = 0.03$

$s = \frac{15,450(1 + 0.03)^{10}}{1 + 0.03}$

$\approx 20,159$ people

45. $\log_{12} 50 = \frac{\log 50}{\log 12}$

$\qquad \approx 1.5743$

46. $(\pm 2, 0); \ (\pm\sqrt{29}, 0)$

Chapter 17 Summary and Review

PAGES 834-836 SKILLS AND CONCEPTS

1. 2π 1

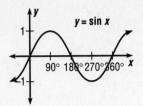

$y = \sin x$

2. 2π $\frac{1}{2}$

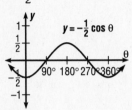

$y = -\frac{1}{2}\cos\theta$

3. π 4

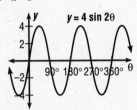

$y = 4\sin 2\theta$

4. 4π 1

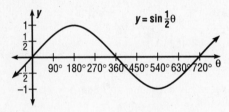

$y = \sin\frac{1}{2}\theta$

5. 2π

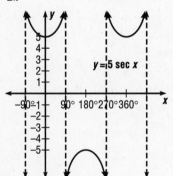

$y = 5\sec x$

6. $\frac{\pi}{4}$

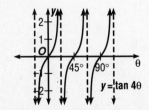

$y = \tan 4\theta$

7. $\frac{\pi}{6}$

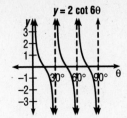

$y = 2\cot 6\theta$

8. 3π

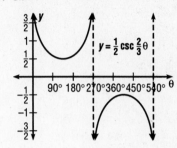

$y = \frac{1}{2}\csc\frac{2}{3}\theta$

9. $\left(\frac{1}{2}\right)^2 + \cos^2\theta = 1$

$\cos^2\theta = 1 - \frac{1}{4}$

$\cos^2\theta = \frac{3}{4}$

$\cos\theta = -\sqrt{\frac{3}{4}}$

$\cos\theta = -\frac{\sqrt{3}}{2}$

10. $\left(-\frac{1}{4}\right)^2 + 1 = \csc^2\theta$

$\csc^2\theta = 1 + \frac{1}{16}$

$\csc^2\theta = \frac{17}{16}$

$\csc\theta = \sqrt{\frac{17}{16}}$

$\csc\theta = \frac{\sqrt{17}}{4}$

11. $\cot^2\theta + 1 = \left(-\frac{5}{3}\right)^2$

$\cot^2\theta = -1 + \frac{25}{9}$

$\cot^2\theta = \frac{16}{9}$

$\cot\theta = -\sqrt{\frac{16}{9}}$

$\cot\theta = -\frac{4}{3}$

12. $\left(-\frac{1}{2}\right)^2 + \cos^2 \theta = 1$

$\cos^2 \theta = 1 - \frac{1}{4}$

$\cos \theta = \frac{3}{4}$

$\cos \theta = \sqrt{\frac{3}{4}}$

$\cos \theta = \frac{\sqrt{3}}{2}$

$\sec \theta = \frac{1}{\cos \theta} = \frac{2}{\sqrt{3}} \cdot \frac{\sqrt{3}}{\sqrt{3}}$

$\sec \theta = \frac{2\sqrt{3}}{3}$

13. $\sin^4 x - \cos^4 x$

$= (\sin^2 x - \cos^2 x)(\sin^2 x + \cos^2 x)$

$= 1 \cdot (\sin^2 x - \cos^2 x)$

$= \sin^2 x - \cos^2 x$

14. $\frac{\sin \theta}{\tan \theta} + \frac{\cos \theta}{\cot \theta} \stackrel{?}{=} \cos \theta + \sin \theta$

$\sin \theta \cdot \frac{\cos \theta}{\sin \theta} + \cos \theta \cdot \frac{\sin \theta}{\cos \theta} = \cos \theta + \sin \theta$

15. $\frac{\sin \theta}{1 - \cos \theta} \stackrel{?}{=} \frac{1}{\sin \theta} + \frac{\cos \theta}{\sin \theta}$

$\frac{\sin \theta}{1 - \cos \theta} \stackrel{?}{=} \frac{1 + \cos \theta}{\sin \theta} \cdot \frac{1 - \cos \theta}{1 - \cos \theta}$

$\frac{\sin \theta}{1 - \cos \theta} \stackrel{?}{=} \frac{1 - \cos^2 \theta}{\sin \theta (1 - \cos \theta)}$

$\frac{\sin \theta}{1 - \cos \theta} \stackrel{?}{=} \frac{\sin^2 \theta}{\sin \theta (1 - \cos \theta)}$

$\frac{\sin \theta}{1 - \cos \theta} = \frac{\sin \theta}{1 - \cos \theta}$

16. $\cot^2 \theta \sec^2 \theta \stackrel{?}{=} 1 + \cot^2 \theta$

$\frac{\cos^2 \theta}{\sin^2 \theta} \cdot \frac{1}{\cos^2 \theta} \stackrel{?}{=} \csc^2 \theta$

$\frac{1}{\sin^2 \theta} \stackrel{?}{=} \csc^2 \theta$

$\csc^2 \theta = \csc^2 \theta$

17. $\sec x (\sec x - \cos x) \stackrel{?}{=} \tan^2 x$

$\sec^2 x - \sec x \cos x \stackrel{?}{=} \tan^2 x$

$\sec^2 x - 1 \stackrel{?}{=} \tan^2 x$

$\tan^2 x = \tan^2 x$

18. $\frac{\cos x}{\csc x} - \frac{\sin x}{\cos x} \stackrel{?}{=} -\sin^2 x \tan x$

$\frac{\cos^2 x \sin x}{\cos x} - \frac{\sin x}{\cos x} \stackrel{?}{=} -\sin^2 x \tan x$

$\frac{\sin x(\cos^2 x - 1)}{\cos x} \stackrel{?}{=} -\sin^2 x \tan x$

$-\sin^2 x \cdot \frac{\sin x}{\cos x} \stackrel{?}{=} -\sin^2 x \tan x$

$-\sin^2 x \tan x = -\sin^2 x \tan x$

19. $\frac{\csc \theta + 1}{\cot \theta} \stackrel{?}{=} \frac{\cot \theta}{\csc \theta - 1} \cdot \frac{\csc \theta + 1}{\csc \theta + 1}$

$\frac{\csc \theta + 1}{\cot \theta} \stackrel{?}{=} \frac{\cot \theta (\csc \theta + 1)}{\csc^2 \theta - 1}$

$\frac{\csc \theta + 1}{\cot \theta} \stackrel{?}{=} \frac{\cot \theta (\csc \theta + 1)}{\cot^2 \theta}$

$\frac{\csc \theta + 1}{\cot \theta} = \frac{\csc \theta + 1}{\cot \theta}$

20. $\sin (60° + 45°)$

$= \sin 60° \cos 45° + \cos 60° \sin 45°$

$= \frac{\sqrt{3}}{2} \cdot \frac{\sqrt{2}}{2} + \frac{1}{2} \cdot \frac{\sqrt{2}}{2}$

$= \frac{\sqrt{6} + \sqrt{2}}{4}$

21. $\cos (45° - 30°)$

$= \cos 45° \cos 30° + \sin 45° \sin 30°$

$= \frac{\sqrt{2}}{2} \cdot \frac{\sqrt{3}}{2} + \frac{\sqrt{2}}{2} \cdot \frac{1}{2}$

$= \frac{\sqrt{6} + \sqrt{2}}{4}$

22. $\cos (225° + 60°)$

$= \cos 225° \cos 60° - \sin 225° \sin 60°$

$= -\frac{\sqrt{2}}{2} \cdot \frac{1}{2} - \left(-\frac{\sqrt{2}}{2}\right) \cdot \frac{\sqrt{3}}{2}$

$= \frac{-\sqrt{2} + \sqrt{6}}{4}$

23. $\sin (135° + 60°)$

$= \sin 135° \cos 60° + \cos 135° \sin 60°$

$= \frac{\sqrt{2}}{2} \cdot \frac{1}{2} + \left(-\frac{\sqrt{2}}{2}\right) \cdot \frac{\sqrt{3}}{2}$

$= \frac{\sqrt{2} - \sqrt{6}}{4}$

24. $\cos (90° - \theta) = \cos 90° \cos \theta + \sin 90° \sin \theta$

$= \sin \theta$

25. $\cos (x + y) + \cos (x - y)$

$= \cos x \cos y - \sin x \sin y + \cos x \cos y$

$+ \sin x \sin y$

$= 2 \cos x \cos y$

26. $\cos (60° + \theta) + \cos (60° - \theta)$

$= \cos 60° \cos \theta - \sin 60° \sin \theta + \cos 60° \cos \theta$

$+ \sin 60° \sin \theta$

$= 2 \cos 60° \cos \theta$

$= \cos \theta$

27. $\left(-\frac{3}{5}\right)^2 + \cos^2 x = 1$

$\cos^2 x = 1 - \frac{9}{25}$

$\cos^2 x = \frac{16}{25}$

$\cos x = -\frac{4}{5}$

$\sin 2x = 2\left(-\frac{3}{5}\right)\left(-\frac{4}{5}\right)$

$= \frac{24}{25}$

28. $\cos 2x = 1 - 2\left(\frac{1}{4}\right)^2$

$\qquad = 1 - \frac{1}{8}$

$\qquad = \frac{7}{8}$

29. $\qquad -\frac{17}{25} = 1 - 2\sin^2 x$

$\qquad 2\sin^2 x = 1 + \frac{17}{25}$

$\qquad \sin^2 x = \frac{42}{25} \cdot \frac{1}{2}$

$\qquad \sin^2 x = \frac{42}{50}$

$\qquad\qquad = \frac{21}{25}$

$\qquad \sin x = \frac{\sqrt{21}}{5}$

30. $\sin \frac{x}{2} = \sqrt{\dfrac{1 - \frac{1}{6}}{2}}$

$\qquad = \sqrt{\frac{5}{6} \cdot \frac{1}{2}}$

$\qquad = \sqrt{\frac{5}{12} \cdot \frac{\sqrt{12}}{\sqrt{12}}}$

$\qquad = \frac{\sqrt{60}}{12}$

$\qquad = \frac{2\sqrt{15}}{12}$

$\qquad = \frac{\sqrt{15}}{6}$

31. $(\sin x - \cos x)^2$

$\qquad = \sin^2 x - 2\sin x \cos x + \cos^2 x$

$\qquad = 1 - \sin 2x$

32. $\cos^2 x + \sin^2 x + \cos^2 x - 2\cos x = 0$

$\qquad\qquad 1 + \cos^2 x - 2\cos x = 0$

$\qquad\qquad \cos^2 x - 2\cos x + 1 = 0$

$\qquad\qquad\qquad (\cos x - 1)^2 = 0$

$\qquad\qquad\qquad\qquad \cos x = 1$

$\qquad\qquad\qquad\qquad\quad x = 0°$

33. $\sin x + \cos x = 1$

$\qquad x = 0°, \ 90°$

34. $\sin 2x = \frac{1}{2}$

$\qquad x = 15°, \ 75°, \ 195°, \ 255°$

35. $(3\sin \theta - 4)(2\sin \theta + 1) = 0$

$\qquad \sin \theta = -\frac{4}{3}$ or $\sin \theta = -\frac{1}{2}$

$\qquad \theta = \frac{7\pi}{6} + 2n\pi$ or $\theta = \frac{11\pi}{6} + 2n\pi$

36. $\cos 2\theta \sin \theta = 1$

$\qquad \theta = \frac{3\pi}{2} + 2n\pi$

37. $\dfrac{\sqrt{1 + \cos \theta} + \sqrt{1 - \cos \theta}}{\sqrt{2}} = \sqrt{2}$

$\qquad \dfrac{\sqrt{1 + \cos \theta} + \sqrt{1 - \cos \theta}}{2} = 1$

$\qquad \theta = \frac{\pi}{2} + 2n\pi$

38. $x = 0, \ y = -6$

$\qquad r = \sqrt{0^2 + (-6)^2} \qquad\qquad \theta = \text{Arctan } \frac{-6}{0}$

$\qquad r = 6 \qquad\qquad\qquad\qquad\quad \theta = \frac{3\pi}{2}$

$\qquad 6\left(\cos \frac{3\pi}{2} + i \sin \frac{3\pi}{2}\right)$

39. $x = -2, \ y = 2\sqrt{3}$

$\qquad r = \sqrt{(-2)^2 + (2\sqrt{3})^2} \qquad \theta = \text{Arctan } -\sqrt{3}$

$\qquad = \sqrt{16} \qquad\qquad\qquad\qquad = \frac{2\pi}{3}$

$\qquad = 4$

$\qquad 4\left(\cos \frac{2\pi}{3} + i \sin \frac{2\pi}{3}\right)$

40. $r = 4$

$\qquad x = 4\cos \frac{5\pi}{6} = -2\sqrt{3}$

$\qquad y = 4\sin \frac{5\pi}{6} = 2$

$\qquad -2\sqrt{3} + 2i$

41. $r = 8$

$\qquad x = 8\cos \frac{7\pi}{4} = 4\sqrt{2}$

$\qquad y = 8\sin \frac{7\pi}{4} = -4\sqrt{2}$

$\qquad 4\sqrt{2} - 4i\sqrt{2}$

42. $2 \cdot 4\left[\cos \frac{2\pi}{3} + i \sin \frac{2\pi}{3}\right]$

$\qquad = 8\left(\cos \frac{2\pi}{3} + i \sin \frac{2\pi}{3}\right)$

$\qquad r = 8$

$\qquad x = 8\cos \frac{2\pi}{3} = -4$

$\qquad y = 8\sin \frac{2\pi}{3} = 4\sqrt{3}$

$\qquad -4 + 4i\sqrt{3}$

43. $x = 2, \ y = 2$

$\qquad r = \sqrt{4 + 4} \qquad\qquad \theta = \text{Arctan } 1$

$\qquad = 2\sqrt{2} \qquad\qquad\qquad = \frac{\pi}{4}$

$\qquad \left[2\sqrt{2}\left(\cos \frac{\pi}{4} + i \sin \frac{\pi}{4}\right)\right]^8$

$\qquad = (2\sqrt{2})^8 (\cos 2\pi + i \sin 2\pi)$

$\qquad = 4096$

44. $x = -2$, $y = -2\sqrt{3}$

$r = \sqrt{(-2)^2 + (-2\sqrt{3})^2}$ $\theta = \text{Arctan } \sqrt{3} + \pi$

$\qquad = \sqrt{16}$ $= \dfrac{4\pi}{3}$

$\qquad = 4$

$\left[4\left(\cos \dfrac{4\pi}{3} + i \sin \dfrac{4\pi}{3} \right) \right]^3$

$= 4^3 (\cos 4\pi + i \sin 4\pi)$

$= 64$

PAGE 836   **APPLICATIONS AND CONNECTIONS**

45. $\left(\dfrac{4}{5}\right)^2 + \cos^2 \theta = 1$

$\qquad\qquad \cos^2 \theta = 1 - \dfrac{16}{25}$

$\qquad\qquad \cos^2 \theta = \dfrac{9}{25}$

$\qquad\qquad \cos \theta = \dfrac{3}{5}$

$\qquad\qquad \cot \theta = \dfrac{\cos \theta}{\sin \theta}$

$\qquad\qquad\qquad = \dfrac{\frac{3}{5}}{\frac{4}{5}}$

$\qquad\qquad\qquad = \dfrac{3}{4}$

46. $12 + 4 + 10 + 12 + 4 + 10 = \$52$

Chapter 17 Test

PAGE 837

1. 2, π

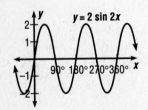

2. 2, 10π

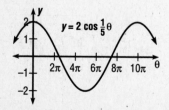

3. $\dfrac{3}{4}$, 3π

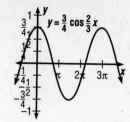

4. $\dfrac{\pi}{3}$

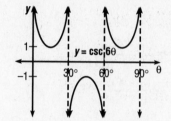

5. 3π

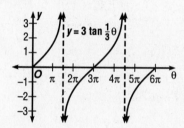

6. 2π

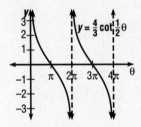

7. $\left(-\dfrac{1}{2}\right)^2 + \cos^2 \theta = 1$

$\qquad\qquad \cos^2 \theta = 1 - \dfrac{1}{4}$

$\qquad\qquad \cos^2 \theta = \dfrac{3}{4}$

$\qquad\qquad \cos \theta = -\dfrac{\sqrt{3}}{2}$

$\qquad\qquad \tan \theta = \dfrac{\sin \theta}{\cos \theta}$

$\qquad\qquad\qquad = \dfrac{-\frac{1}{2}}{-\frac{\sqrt{3}}{2}}$

$\qquad\qquad\qquad = \dfrac{1}{\sqrt{3}}$

$\qquad\qquad\qquad = \dfrac{\sqrt{3}}{3}$

8. $1 + \tan^2 \theta = \sec^2 \theta$

$$1 + \left(\frac{4}{3}\right)^2 = \sec^2 \theta$$

$$\frac{25}{9} = \sec^2 \theta$$

$$\sec \theta = -\frac{5}{3}$$

9. $\dfrac{\cos x}{1 - \sin^2 x} \stackrel{?}{=} \sec x$

$$\frac{\cos x}{\cos^2 x} \stackrel{?}{=} \sec x$$

$$\sec x = \sec x$$

10.
$$\frac{\sec x}{\sin x} - \frac{\sin x}{\cos x} \stackrel{?}{=} \cot x$$

$$\frac{1}{\sin x \cos x} - \frac{\sin^2 x}{\sin x \cos x} \stackrel{?}{=} \cot x$$

$$\frac{1 - \sin^2 x}{\sin x \cos x} \stackrel{?}{=} \cot x$$

$$\frac{\cos^2 x}{\sin x \cos x} \stackrel{?}{=} \cot x$$

$$\frac{\cos x}{\sin x} \stackrel{?}{=} \cot x$$

$$\cot x = \cot x$$

11. $\dfrac{1 + \tan^2 \theta}{\cos^2 \theta} \stackrel{?}{=} \sec^4 \theta$

$$\frac{\sec^2 \theta}{\cos^2 \theta} \stackrel{?}{=} \sec^4 \theta$$

$$\sec^4 \theta = \sec^4 \theta$$

12. $2(x + 80 - 100) = 460$

$$2x - 40 = 460$$

$$2x = 500$$

$$x = 250 \text{ points}$$

13. $\cos (135° + 30°)$

$= \cos 135° \cos 30° - \sin 135° \sin 30°$

$= \dfrac{\sqrt{2}}{2} \cdot \dfrac{\sqrt{3}}{2} - \dfrac{\sqrt{2}}{2} \cdot \dfrac{1}{2}$

$= \dfrac{-\sqrt{6} - \sqrt{2}}{4}$

14. $\sin (120° + 135°)$

$= \sin 120° \cos 135° + \cos 120° \sin 135°$

$= \dfrac{\sqrt{3}}{2} \cdot \left(-\dfrac{\sqrt{2}}{2}\right) + \left(-\dfrac{1}{2}\right) \cdot \dfrac{\sqrt{2}}{2}$

$= \dfrac{-\sqrt{6} - \sqrt{2}}{4}$

15. $\sin 150° = \dfrac{1}{2}$

16. $\sin \dfrac{x}{2} = \sqrt{\dfrac{1 - \dfrac{3}{4}}{2}}$

$$= \sqrt{\frac{1}{4} \cdot \frac{1}{2}}$$

$$= \sqrt{\frac{1}{8}}$$

$$= \frac{1}{2\sqrt{2}} \cdot \frac{\sqrt{2}}{\sqrt{2}}$$

$$= \frac{\sqrt{2}}{4}$$

17. $\dfrac{7}{9} = \cos^2 x - \left(\dfrac{1}{3}\right)^2$

$$\frac{7}{9} = \cos^2 x - \frac{1}{9}$$

$$\cos^2 x = \frac{8}{9}$$

$$\cos x = \sqrt{\frac{8}{9}}$$

$$\cos x = \frac{2\sqrt{2}}{3}$$

18. $\sec x - \tan x = 1$

$$\sec^2 x = 1 + 2 \tan x + \tan^2 x$$

$$1 + \tan^2 x = 1 + 2 \tan x + \tan^2 x$$

$$2 \tan x = 0$$

$$\tan x = 0$$

$$x = 0°$$

19. $\cos 2x + \sin x = 1$

$$(1 - 2 \sin^2 x) + \sin x = 1$$

$$2 \sin^2 x - \sin x = 0$$

$$\sin x (2 \sin x - 1) = 0$$

$$\sin x = 0 \text{ or } \sin x = \frac{1}{2}$$

$$x = 0°, 30°, 150°, 180°$$

20. $2 \sin x \cos x - \sin x = 0$

$$\sin x (2 \cos x - 1) = 0$$

$$\sin x = 0 \text{ or } \cos x = \frac{1}{2}$$

$$x = 0°, 60°, 180°, 300°$$

21. $\sin \dfrac{\theta}{2} + \cos \theta = 1$

$$\sqrt{\frac{1 - \cos \theta}{2}} + \cos \theta = 1$$

$$\frac{1 - \cos \theta}{2} = 1 - 2 \cos \theta + \cos^2 \theta$$

$$1 - \cos \theta = 2 - 4 \cos \theta + \cos^2 \theta$$

$$2 \cos^2 \theta - 3 \cos \theta + 1 = 0$$

$$(\cos \theta - 1)(2 \cos \theta - 1) = 0$$

$$\cos \theta = 1 \text{ or } \cos \theta = \frac{1}{2}$$

$$\theta = 0 + 2n\pi \text{ or } \theta = \frac{\pi}{3} + 2\pi n \text{ or } \theta = \frac{5\pi}{3} + 2n\pi$$

22. $3 \tan^2 \theta - \sqrt{3} \tan \theta = 0$

$\tan \theta (3 \tan \theta - \sqrt{3}) = 0$

$\tan \theta = 0$ or $\tan \theta = \dfrac{\sqrt{3}}{3}$

$\theta = 0 + n \cdot \pi$ or $\theta = \dfrac{\pi}{6} + n\pi$

23. $x = -4, \ y = 4$

$r = \sqrt{(-4)^2 + 4^2}$ $\qquad \theta = \text{Arctan} -1 + \pi$

$= \sqrt{32}$ $\qquad\qquad\qquad = \dfrac{3\pi}{4}$

$= 4\sqrt{2}$

$4\sqrt{2}\left(\cos \dfrac{3\pi}{4} + i \sin \dfrac{3\pi}{4}\right)$

24. $r = 2$

$x = 2 \cos \dfrac{\pi}{3} = 1$

$y = 2 \sin \dfrac{\pi}{3} = \sqrt{3}$

$1 + i\sqrt{3}$

25. $4 \cdot 3\left[\cos \left(\dfrac{3\pi}{2} + \dfrac{\pi}{4}\right) + i \sin \left(\dfrac{3\pi}{2} + \dfrac{\pi}{4}\right)\right]$

$= 12\left(\cos \dfrac{7\pi}{4} + i \sin \dfrac{7\pi}{4}\right)$

$r = 12$

$x = 12 \cos \dfrac{7\pi}{4} = 6\sqrt{2}$

$y = 12 \sin \dfrac{7\pi}{4} = -6\sqrt{2}$

$6\sqrt{2} - 6i\sqrt{2}$

PAGE 837   BONUS

$x = 1, \ y = -1$

$r = \sqrt{1^2 + (-1)^2}$ $\qquad \theta = \text{Arctan} -1$

$= \sqrt{2}$ $\qquad\qquad\qquad = -\dfrac{\pi}{4}$

$\left[\sqrt{2}\left(\cos -\dfrac{\pi}{4} + i \sin -\dfrac{\pi}{4}\right)\right]^8$

$= \sqrt{2}^8[\cos (-2\pi) + i \sin (-2\pi)]$

$= 16$